CALCULUS ∪ Analytic Geometry ∪ Vectors

CALCULUS ∪ Analytic Geometry ∪ Vectors

John F. Randolph

The University of Rochester

DICKENSON PUBLISHING COMPANY, INC.

Belmont, California

Preface

The physical sciences have deep roots in mathematics, and mathematics is now permeating such traditionally qualitative subjects as business, economics, linguistics, medicine, and psychology. These applications, moreover, increasingly depend upon basic principles rather than handbook recipes. Even so, an early display of rigor may be viewed as exalting the beauty of mathematics over its utility. Until the need for the epsilon-delta method is felt, there is danger of stifling interest by force-feeding this powerful technique too soon. This book, therefore, begins on a descriptive level and proceeds in a gradually tightening atmosphere of rigor consistent with the student's development. After an intuitive discussion, for example, limits are defined, but how a delta depends on an epsilon is subtly worked in later. Limit theorems are stated in Chapter 2 and the simplest proofs given, but the other proofs are more likely to be honored in their setting of Chapter 13, after repeated evidence that intuition cannot always be relied upon even in applications.

Geometric vectors are natural models for directed quantities, and a novice forced to jump this visual aid may be lost in a morass of ordered triples, dots, and crosses. With the background of vectors in this book, however, later progress should be eased when the student sees that the founders of linear spaces transcribed the same pictures into symbols. The vector notion is also the catalyst unifying rectangular and polar coordinates, rotation of axes, parametric equations, curvilinear motion, and complex numbers. Isaac Newton (1642–1727) leaned heavily on vector concepts in formulating his ideas leading to organized calculus. The present interest in artificial satellites, incidentally, makes the spark of Newton's genius shine brighter than ever, as shown in the section on space travel. Even though vectors appear in the first chapter and repeatedly thereafter, they are considered to be tools, as are algebra and set notation. In particular, currently fashionable Boolean algebra is not included since the needs of calculus and analytic geometry are satisfied, and greatly aided, by a bare minimum of unions and intersections.

There is ample evidence that upper and lower Darboux sums squeeze in too much, and the step-function ladder reaches too high, for initial exposure of most students to definite integrals. Also, an attenuated version of measure theoretic methods using Jordan content fosters a delusion, hard to counteract, that definite integrals are primarily for finding areas. The definite integral is defined in this book as the limit, when it exists, of finite sums, its role in defining

v

continuous quantities as extensions of discrete ones is featured, and it is used early and frequently. The more sophisticated methods are excellent for a later course, but prior to a sharp awareness of the potency of definite integrals, a detailed development would consume time and energy out of proportion with the benefits.

So many persons have contributed to this book that I dare not name any for fear of missing some. I have, however, personally thanked all I can remember.

John F. Randolph

Contents

Vectors

Chapter 1

1-1. Geometric Vectors and Vector Algebra

Vector analysis originated in the desire of nineteenth-century physicists and mathematicians to deal with such quantities as forces and velocities whose properties are not specified in terms of numbers alone. Directed line segments furnished a natural geometrical model for such quantities. Both the directions and magnitudes of forces F_1 and F_2 applied at a point of a body were modeled by directed line segments $\overrightarrow{OP}$ and $\overrightarrow{OQ}$ with the same initial point O. The single force F producing the same effect on the body is represented by the directed diagonal $\overrightarrow{OR}$ of a parallelogram as in Fig.

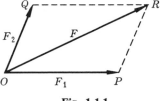

Fig. 1-1.1

1-1.1. Thus, the (geometric) parallelogram law for adding vectors emerged to give

$$\overrightarrow{OP} + \overrightarrow{OQ} = \overrightarrow{OR}.$$

Physical concepts may then be interpreted in terms of geometrical properties.

The physical counterpart of the geometrical operation of moving $\overrightarrow{OQ}$ to $\overrightarrow{PR}$ would apply the force F_2 at a different point of the body and produce a different effect on the body. The same directed line segment $\overrightarrow{OR}$ is obtained, however, by the triangle law illustrated in Fig. 1-1.2. The algebraic expression

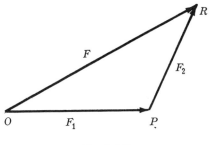

Fig. 1-1.2

$$\overrightarrow{OP} + \overrightarrow{PR} = \overrightarrow{OR}$$

of the triangle law then furnishes a "cancellation" technique not evident in $\overrightarrow{OP} + \overrightarrow{OQ} = \overrightarrow{OR}$. Hence, the concept arose of a vector being free to move parallel to its original position. Although $\overrightarrow{OQ}$ is geometrically distinct from $\overrightarrow{PR}$, the substitution of $\overrightarrow{PR}$ for $\overrightarrow{OQ}$ in

1

$$\overrightarrow{OP} + \overrightarrow{OQ} = \overrightarrow{OP} + \overrightarrow{PR} = \overrightarrow{OR}$$

has a meaningful interpretation, and thus algebraically $\overrightarrow{PR} = \overrightarrow{OQ}$.

The concepts of bound and free vectors then developed. A bound vector $\vec{v}$ having O as its initial point is merely a directed line segment $\overrightarrow{OP}$. A bound vector is completely determined by specifying its initial and terminal points. The length (in terms of some preassigned unit) of the line segment joining O and P is called the **norm** of $\vec{v}$ and is denoted by $|\vec{v}| = |\overrightarrow{OP}|$. A vector $\vec{v}$ having $|\vec{v}| = 1$ is called a **unit vector**.

In contrast, a free vector $\vec{v}$ was conceived as a whole collection of directed line segments, any one of which is a parallel translation of any other. Thus, if $\overrightarrow{PR}$ and $\overrightarrow{OQ}$ are specific bound vectors of a free vector $\vec{v}$, then $\overrightarrow{PR}$ and $\overrightarrow{OQ}$ have the same norm and the same direction but different initial points. Even though $\overrightarrow{PR}$ and $\overrightarrow{OQ}$ are geometrically distinct, either may be substituted for the other in the algebra associated with free vectors, as developed below. Hence, the free vector $\vec{v}$ is represented by either $\overrightarrow{PR}$ or $\overrightarrow{OQ}$. It is customary to set

$$\vec{v} = \overrightarrow{PR} \text{ or } \vec{v} = \overrightarrow{OQ}$$

and to interpret these as specifying the norm and direction common to all those directed line segments (Fig. 1-1.3) constituting the free vector $\vec{v}$.

Fig. 1-1.3

The word "vector" without an adjective will generally mean "free vector." Whenever a specific bound vector is used to represent a free vector, this will be indicated by context. Thus, the norm $|\vec{v}|$ of a vector $\vec{v}$ is the norm of any (and all) of the representatives of $\vec{v}$.

Given two vectors $\vec{u}$ and $\vec{v}$, take any representative $\overrightarrow{OP}$ of $\vec{u}$ and represent $\vec{v}$ by $\overrightarrow{PQ}$. Then $\overrightarrow{OQ}$ represents a vector called the **sum** (or resultant) of $\vec{u}$ and $\vec{v}$ and denoted by $\vec{u} + \vec{v}$. But $\vec{v}$ could have been represented first by $\overrightarrow{OP_1}$ and then P_1 used as the initial point of a representative $\overrightarrow{P_1Q_1}$ of $\vec{u}$ to obtain $\vec{v} + \vec{u}$ represented by $\overrightarrow{OQ_1}$. By similar triangles, Q_1 and Q are at the same point, so that

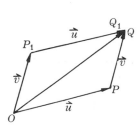

Fig. 1-1.4

(1) $$\vec{u} + \vec{v} = \vec{v} + \vec{u}.$$

With $\vec{w}$ a third vector, Fig. 1-1.5a gives $\overrightarrow{OR}$ as a representative of $(\vec{u} + \vec{v}) + \vec{w}$. The superposition of Fig. 1-1.5b upon Fig. 1-1.5a shows that $\overrightarrow{OR}$ also represents $\vec{u} + (\vec{v} + \vec{w})$, so that

(2) $$(\vec{u} + \vec{v}) + \vec{w} = \vec{u} + (\vec{v} + \vec{w}).$$

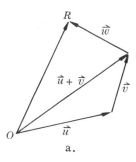

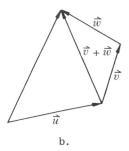

a.   b.

Fig. 1-1.5

Hence, in forming the sum of three vectors it is not necessary to associate two of them before adding the third, and thus the sum may be written

$$\vec{u} + \vec{v} + \vec{w}.$$

By reversing the direction of each representative of a vector $\vec{v}$, an associated vector denoted by $-\vec{v}$ is obtained. The actual distance between the endpoints of any representative of $-\vec{v}$ is the same as for $\vec{v}$, so that

$$|-\vec{v}| = |\vec{v}|.$$

Then, with $\vec{u}$ a vector, the subtraction of $\vec{v}$ from $\vec{u}$ is defined by

(3) $$\vec{u} - \vec{v} = \vec{u} + (-\vec{v}).$$

Hence, if the representations $\vec{u} = \overrightarrow{OP}$ and $\vec{v} = \overrightarrow{OQ}$ are used, the directed segment $\overrightarrow{QP}$ represents $\vec{u} - \vec{v}$, as shown in Fig. 1-1.6. Algebraically, $-\vec{v} = \overrightarrow{QO}$ and

$$\vec{u} + (-\vec{v}) = \overrightarrow{OP} + \overrightarrow{QO} = \overrightarrow{QO} + \overrightarrow{OP} = \overrightarrow{QP}.$$

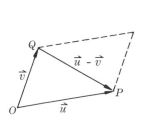

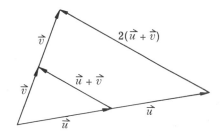

Fig. 1-1.6   Fig. 1-1.7

If each representative of a vector $\vec{v}$ is doubled in length, without change of direction, the result is a vector denoted by $2\vec{v}$. Thus,

$$2\vec{u} + 2\vec{v} = 2(\vec{u} + \vec{v})$$

follows, since the lengths of corresponding sides of two similar triangles are in the same ratio (Fig. 1-1.7).

Whenever numbers and vectors are used together, the numbers are referred to as **scalars**. Thus, each scalar a has an absolute value denoted by $|a|$, where, by definition,

$$|a| = \begin{cases} a \text{ if } a \geq 0 \\ -a \text{ if } a < 0. \end{cases}$$

For example, $|-2| = |2| = 2$ and $|x| = 0$ if and only if $x = 0$.

With a a nonzero scalar and $\vec{v}$ a vector, then a vector denoted by $a\vec{v}$ is obtained by:

(a) multiplying the length of each representative of $\vec{v}$ by $|a|$ and then

(b) reversing the direction if and only if a is negative. In particular, $-\vec{v} = (-1)\vec{v}$ and $-(2\vec{v}) = (-2)\vec{v} = 2(-\vec{v})$.

It is now convenient to extend the vector notion to include the so-called **null** (or zero) vector $\vec{0}$ as having zero norm but with no direction assigned. The null vector is not represented geometrically, but is used algebraically with any vector $\vec{v}$ as:

(4) $$\vec{v} + \vec{0} = \vec{v},$$

(5) $$\vec{v} - \vec{v} = \vec{0}, \text{ and}$$

(6) $$a\vec{v} = \vec{0} \text{ if either } a = 0 \text{ or } \vec{v} = \vec{0}.$$

The following laws then hold even if null vectors or zero scalars appear:

(7) $$a\vec{v} + b\vec{v} = (a + b)\vec{v},$$

(8) $$a\vec{u} + a\vec{v} = a(\vec{u} + \vec{v}),$$

(9) $$\text{if } a\vec{v} = b\vec{v} \text{ and } \vec{v} \neq \vec{0}, \text{ then } a = b, \text{ and}$$

(10) $$\text{if } a\vec{u} = a\vec{v} \text{ and } a \neq 0, \text{ then } \vec{u} = \vec{v}.$$

1-2. Basic Unit Vectors

Let O be a given point. A standard notation is $\vec{i}$ and $\vec{j}$ for two vectors perpendicular to one another, each one unit long and each with initial end at O. The vectors are called **basic unit vectors** of the plane in which they lie. It is usual to have $\vec{i}$ horizontal pointing right and $\vec{j}$ vertical pointing up (toward the top of the page).

Given a vector $\vec{v}$ in the plane of $\vec{i}$ and $\vec{j}$ and also with initial end at O, there are scalars x and y such that

(1) $$\vec{v} = x\vec{i} + y\vec{j}.$$

To see this, let $\overrightarrow{OP_1}$ be the vector projection of $\vec{v}$ on the line containing $\vec{i}$. Then $\overrightarrow{OP_1}$ is a multiple of $\vec{i}$; that is, there is a scalar x such that $\overrightarrow{OP_1} = x\vec{i}$. This scalar x may be positive, negative, or zero. In the same way, a vector $\overrightarrow{OP_2} = y\vec{j}$ is determined by projecting $\vec{v}$ onto the line containing $\vec{j}$. Then

$$\vec{v} = \overrightarrow{OP_1} + \overrightarrow{OP_2} = x\vec{i} + y\vec{j}.$$

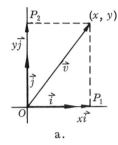 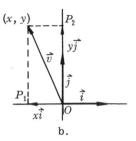

a.   b.

Fig. 1-2.1

The terminal end of $\vec{v}$ such that (1) holds is labeled (x, y). Hence, a one-to-one correspondence is established between vectors $\vec{v}$ with initial ends at O and ordered pairs (x, y) of scalars. It is then unambiguous to speak of "the vector (x, y)" instead of "the vector $x\vec{i} + y\vec{j}$ with initial end at O." For example, $(2, -1) + (1, 5) = (3, 4)$ is another way of indicating the vector addition

$$(2\vec{i} - \vec{j}) + (\vec{i} + 5\vec{j}) = (2 + 1)\vec{i} + (-1 + 5)\vec{j} = 3\vec{i} + 4\vec{j}.$$

As defined earlier, the actual length of a vector $\vec{v}$, denoted by $|\vec{v}|$, is called the **norm** (or absolute value) of $\vec{v}$. With $\vec{v} = x\vec{i} + y\vec{j}$, then, by the Pythagorean theorem,

(2) $$|\vec{v}| = \sqrt{x^2 + y^2}.$$

Hence, if $\vec{v} \neq \vec{0}$, then $|\vec{v}| \neq 0$, or, equivalently, if $|\vec{v}| = 0$, then $\vec{v} = \vec{0}$.

With basic unit vectors $\vec{i}$ and $\vec{j}$ selected, then a label (x, y) for each point of the plane is determined. It is then said that a **plane coordinate system** has been established. "The point labeled (x, y)" is shortened to "the point (x, y)." Also, x is called the **abscissa** and y the **ordinate** of the point. The whole line containing $\vec{i}$ is called the **axis of abscissas** (or x-axis), while the half of this line with endpoint O and containing $\vec{i}$ is called the **positive x-axis**, with the other half called the **negative x-axis**. Similar definitions are given for the **axis of ordinates**. The point O is called the **origin**.

Saying "the vector (x, y)" or "the point (x, y)" establishes the context as primarily concerned with vectors or coordinates, respectively. The interplay between vectors and coordinate geometry is an aid to both.

With points (x_1, y_1) and (x_2, y_2) given, the vectors

$$\vec{v_1} = x_1\vec{i} + y_1\vec{j} \text{ and } \vec{v_2} = x_2\vec{i} + y_2\vec{j},$$

with initial ends at the origin, terminate at the points (x_1, y_1) and (x_2, y_2). The vector difference

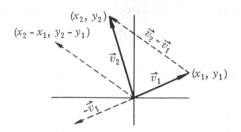

Fig. 1-2.2

$$\vec{v}_2 - \vec{v}_1 = (x_2\vec{i} + y_2\vec{j}) - (x_1\vec{i} + y_1\vec{j}) = (x_2 - x_1)\vec{i} + (y_2 - y_1)\vec{j}$$

may be pictured as the vector from the point (x_1, y_1) to the point (x_2, y_2) or else as the vector from the origin to the point $(x_2 - x_1, y_2 - y_1)$. Hence, by (2), the norm of this vector,

$$|v_2 - v_1| = \sqrt{(x_2 - x_1)^2 + (y_2 - y_1)^2},$$

may be visualized as the distance between the points (x_1, y_1) and (x_2, y_2).

The vector from the origin to the point two-fifths of the way from the point (x_1, y_1) to (x_2, y_2) is

$$\vec{v} = \vec{v}_1 + \tfrac{2}{5}(\vec{v}_2 - \vec{v}_1) = \tfrac{3}{5}\vec{v}_1 + \tfrac{2}{5}\vec{v}_2$$
$$= \tfrac{3}{5}(x_1\vec{i} + y_1\vec{j}) + \tfrac{2}{5}(x_2\vec{i} + y_2\vec{j})$$
$$= \frac{3x_1 + 2x_2}{5}\vec{i} + \frac{3y_1 + 2y_2}{5}\vec{j}.$$

The terminal end of this vector is therefore the point

$$\left(\frac{3x_1 + 2x_2}{5}, \frac{3y_1 + 2y_2}{5}\right).$$

By a similar method, show: *The line segment joining the points (x_1, y_1) and (x_2, y_2) has midpoint*

$$\left(\frac{x_1 + x_2}{2}, \frac{y_1 + y_2}{2}\right).$$

Problem 1. Show that each of the vectors has unit norm:

a. $\dfrac{\sqrt{3}}{2}\vec{i} + \dfrac{1}{2}\vec{j}.$ c. $-\dfrac{1}{\sqrt{2}}\vec{i} + \dfrac{1}{\sqrt{2}}\vec{j}.$ e. $\dfrac{5}{13}\vec{i} + \dfrac{12}{13}\vec{j}.$

b. $\dfrac{\sqrt{3}}{2}\vec{i} - \dfrac{1}{2}\vec{j}.$ d. $-\dfrac{3}{5}\vec{i} - \dfrac{4}{5}\vec{j}.$ f. $0.8\vec{i} - 0.6\vec{j}.$

Problem 2. Draw the vector and find its norm:

a. $3\vec{i} + 4\vec{j}.$ c. $3\vec{i} - 3\vec{j}.$ e. $-\sqrt{2}\,\vec{i} + 0\vec{j}.$
b. $5\vec{i} - 12\vec{j}.$ d. $\vec{i} + \vec{j}.$ f. $0\vec{i} - 5\vec{j}.$

Problem 3. Given any vector $\vec{v} \neq \vec{0}$, show that the vector

$$\vec{u} = \frac{1}{|\vec{v}|}\vec{v}$$

is a unit vector; that is, has norm 1.

Problem 4. Show that if $x^2 + y^2 = 4$, then the terminal end of $\vec{v} = x\vec{i} + y\vec{j}$ is on the circle of radius 2 with center at the origin.

Problem 5. Find the distance between the pairs of points:

a. (2, 4), (5,8).   d. (0, 1), (1, 0).   g. (2, −2), (−2, 2).

b. (−2, 4), (−5, 8).   e. (−2, 0), (3, 0).   h. (4, −4), (−1, 8).

c. (2, 3), (−1, −7).   f. (5, −1), (6, −1).   i. (0.4, −0.4), (−0.1, 0.8).

Problem 6. Show that the three points are vertices of an isosceles triangle:

a. (−2, 2), (3, −3), (4, 3).   b. (−1, 1), (2, 2), (1, 5).

Problem 7. Find the points which divide the segment joining the points $(-1, 0)$ and $(4, 10)$ into five equal parts.

Problem 8. Replace the points of Prob. 7 by $(-1, 2)$ and $(6, -3)$, respectively.

Problem 9. Draw $\vec{v}_1 = 4\vec{i} + \vec{j}$, $\vec{v}_2 = -3\vec{i} + 5\vec{j}$ and $\vec{v}$ (as given below) each with initial end at the origin. Also find the coordinates of the terminal end of $\vec{v}$, where:

a. $\vec{v} = \vec{v}_1 + \frac{1}{2}\vec{v}_2$.   c. $\vec{v} = \vec{v}_1 - 2\vec{v}_2$.   e. $2\vec{v} = \vec{v}_1 + \vec{v}_2$.

b. $\vec{v} = 2\vec{v}_1 + \vec{v}_2$.   d. $\vec{v} = 3\vec{v}_1 + 4\vec{v}_2$.   f. $2\vec{v} = 4\vec{v}_1 + \frac{1}{2}\vec{v}_2$.

Problem 10. The vertices of a triangle are $(-3, 1)$, $(4, 2)$, and $(1, 8)$. Let $\vec{u}_1, \vec{u}_2$, and $\vec{u}_3$ be the vectors from the origin to these vertices. Let $\vec{v}_1, \vec{v}_2$, and $\vec{v}_3$ be the vectors from the origin to the midpoints of the sides of the triangle. Express each of these six vectors in terms of $\vec{i}$ and $\vec{j}$. Check algebraically that

$$\vec{u}_1 + \vec{u}_2 + \vec{u}_3 = \vec{v}_1 + \vec{v}_2 + \vec{v}_3.$$

Problem 11. Consider the vector $\vec{v} = (-3, 4)$; that is, $\vec{v} = -3\vec{i} + 4\vec{j}$. Find the vector obtained by rotating $\vec{v}$ about O through the angle:

a. 90°,   b. −90°,   c. 180°,   d. −180°,

and also by reflecting $\vec{v}$ in the:

e. *x*-axis,   f. *y*-axis.

1-3. Trigonometric Functions

Previous experience with trigonometry is assumed. This section and the following two are, therefore, in the nature of a quick review, coupled with additional work with vectors.

An angle is positive or negative according to whether it was generated by counterclockwise or clockwise rotation. An angle with its initial side on the positive *x*-axis and vertex at the origin is said to be in **standard position**.

Given a vector $\vec{v} \neq \vec{0}$ with its initial end at the origin, then any angle θ in standard position having $\vec{v}$ as terminal side is said to be an **amplitude** of $\vec{v}$.

DEFINITIONS. With $\vec{v} = x\vec{i} + y\vec{j} \neq \vec{0}$ and θ any amplitude of $\vec{v}$, then by definition

$$\sin \theta = \frac{y}{|\vec{v}|} \qquad\qquad \cot \theta = \frac{x}{y} \text{ if } y \neq 0$$

$$\cos \theta = \frac{x}{|\vec{v}|} \qquad\qquad \sec \theta = \frac{|\vec{v}|}{x} \text{ if } x \neq 0$$

$$\tan \theta = \frac{y}{x} \text{ if } x \neq 0 \qquad \csc \theta = \frac{|\vec{v}|}{y} \text{ if } y \neq 0.$$

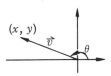   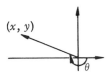

Fig. 1-3.1   **Fig. 1-3.2**

In particular, if $\vec{v} = -2\vec{i} + 0\vec{j}$, then $\vec{v}$ has amplitudes $180°$, $-180°$, $540°$, etc. Also, $\vec{v}$ has $|\vec{v}| = \sqrt{(-2)^2 + 0^2} = \sqrt{4} = 2$. Hence,

$$\sin 180° = \sin(-180°) = \sin 540° = \frac{0}{2} = 0;$$

$$\cos 180° = \cos(-180°) = \cos 540° = \frac{-2}{2} = -1;$$

$$\tan 180° = \tan(-180°) = \tan 540° = \frac{0}{-2} = 0;$$

$$\cot 180°, \ \cot(-180°), \ \cot 540°, \text{ and } \frac{-2}{0} \text{ are undefined;}$$

$$\sec 180° = \sec(-180°) = \sec 540° = \frac{2}{-2} = -1;$$

$$\csc 180°, \ \csc(-180°), \ \csc 540°, \text{ and } \frac{2}{0} \text{ are undefined.}$$

As another example, the vector $\vec{v} = -\vec{i} + \vec{j}$ has $135°$ and $-225°$ as two amplitudes. Also, $|\vec{v}| = \sqrt{(-1)^2 + 1^2} = \sqrt{2}$, so that

$$\sin 135° = \sin(-225°) = \frac{1}{\sqrt{2}},$$

$$\cos 135° = \cos(-225°) = \frac{-1}{\sqrt{2}},$$

$$\tan 135° = \tan(-225°) = \frac{1}{-1} = -1, \text{ etc.}$$

Given a number $c > 0$ and an angle θ, then there is one and only one vector $\vec{v}$ having norm $|\vec{v}| = c$ and θ as an amplitude. This vector is

$$\vec{v} = c(\vec{i} \cos \theta + \vec{j} \sin \theta).$$

For let (x, y) be the terminal end of $\vec{v}$, so that

$$\vec{v} = x\vec{i} + y\vec{j}.$$

Then $|\vec{v}| = \sqrt{x^2 + y^2} = c$ and, by definition of $\sin \theta$ and $\cos \theta$,

$$\sin \theta = \frac{y}{c} \quad \text{and} \quad \cos \theta = \frac{x}{c};$$

so that $x = c \cos \theta$ and $y = c \sin \theta$. Consequently,

$$\vec{v} = x\vec{i} + y\vec{j} = (c \cos \theta)\vec{i} + (c \sin \theta)\vec{j} = c(\vec{i} \cos \theta + \vec{j} \sin \theta).$$

Example. Find the smallest positive amplitude of $\vec{v} = 3\vec{i} - 4\vec{j}$ to the nearest $10'$.

Solution. Draw the vector $\vec{v}$, its reflection $\vec{u}$ in the x-axis, and see that $\vec{u} = 3\vec{i} + 4\vec{j}$ has an amplitude α between $0°$ and $90°$. Hence, $-\alpha$ is an amplitude of $\vec{v}$ and $\theta = 360° - \alpha$ is the smallest positive amplitude of $\vec{v}$.

Since $\vec{u} = 3\vec{i} + 4\vec{j}$, then $\tan \alpha = \frac{4}{3} = 1.3333$. In the tan-cot columns of Table I in the back of the book is found 1.3351 as the entry closest to 1.3333, so that $\alpha = 53°10'$ to the nearest $10'$. Hence,

$$\theta = 360° - 53°10' = 306°50'.$$

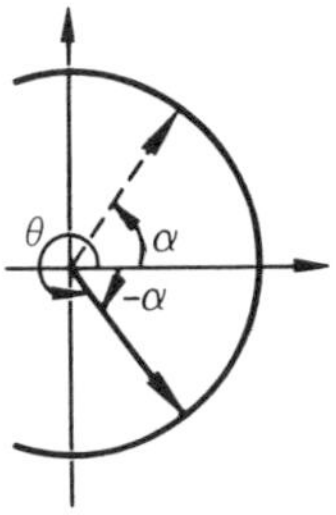

Fig. 1-3.3

If a vector $\vec{v}$ does not have amplitude between $0°$ and $90°$, then by reflecting $\vec{v}$ through the x-axis, or the y-axis, or by rotating $\vec{v}$ through $180°$, a vector $\vec{u}$ may be obtained with an amplitude α between $0°$ and $90°$. By finding this amplitude α of $\vec{u}$, then the amplitudes of $\vec{v}$ itself may be obtained.

Problem 1. Find the four-place approximation of x and y if the vector $\vec{v} = x\vec{i} + y\vec{j}$ has norm c and θ as an amplitude.

a. $c = 5$, $\theta = 25°10'$.

b. $c = 5$, $\theta = -25°10'$.

c. $c = 2$, $\theta = 72°10'$.

d. $c = 3$, $\theta = 150°$.

e. $c = 3$, $\theta = 147°20'$.

f. $c = 4$, $\theta = -130°$.

Problem 2. Given the vector $\vec{v} = 1.5\vec{i} + 3.7\vec{j}$, write the vector $\vec{u}$ obtained by rotating $\vec{v}$ through:

a. $180°$,   b. $90°$,   c. $-90°$,   d. $-180°$,

and also by reflecting $\vec{v}$ in:

e. the x-axis,   f. the y-axis,   g. the origin.

Problem 3. Replace $\vec{v}$ of Prob. 2 by $\vec{v} = -5.6\vec{i} + 1.2\vec{j}$.

Problem 4. Replace $\vec{v}$ of Prob. 2 by

$$\vec{v} = 2(\vec{i} \cos 225° + \vec{j} \sin 225°).$$

Problem 5. Work the example of the text for:

a. $\vec{v} = -3\vec{i} + 4\vec{j}$.　　　c. $\vec{v} = \vec{i} - 0.4040\vec{j}$.　　　e. $\vec{v} = -1.212\vec{i} - 3\vec{j}$.

b. $\vec{v} = -3\vec{i} - 4\vec{j}$.　　　d. $\vec{v} = -3\vec{i} + 1.212\vec{j}$.　　　f. $\vec{v} = -\sqrt{3}\,\vec{i} + \vec{j}$.

1-4.　Identities

From $\vec{v} = \vec{i}x + \vec{j}y = |\vec{v}|(\vec{i} \cos \theta + \vec{j} \sin \theta) \neq \vec{0}$, it follows that

1.　$\csc \theta \equiv \dfrac{1}{\sin \theta}$　since　$\dfrac{|\vec{v}|}{y} = 1 \div \dfrac{y}{|\vec{v}|}$ if $y \neq 0$,

2.　$\sec \theta \equiv \dfrac{1}{\cos \theta}$　since　$\dfrac{|\vec{v}|}{x} = 1 \div \dfrac{x}{|\vec{v}|}$ if $x \neq 0$,

3.　$\cot \theta \equiv \dfrac{1}{\tan \theta}$　since　$\dfrac{x}{y} = 1 \div \dfrac{y}{x}$ if $x \neq 0$ and $y \neq 0$,

4.　$\tan \theta \equiv \dfrac{\sin \theta}{\cos \theta}$　since　$\dfrac{y}{x} = \dfrac{y}{|\vec{v}|} \div \dfrac{x}{|\vec{v}|}$ if $x \neq 0$,

5.　$\cot \theta \equiv \dfrac{\cos \theta}{\sin \theta}$　since　$\dfrac{x}{y} = \dfrac{x}{|\vec{v}|} \div \dfrac{y}{|\vec{v}|}$ if $y \neq 0$,

6.　$\sin^2 \theta + \cos^2 \theta \equiv 1$　since　$\left(\dfrac{y}{|\vec{v}|}\right)^2 + \left(\dfrac{x}{|\vec{v}|}\right)^2 = \dfrac{y^2 + x^2}{|\vec{v}|^2} = \dfrac{|\vec{v}|^2}{|\vec{v}|^2} = 1$,

7.　$\tan^2 \theta + 1 \equiv \sec^2 \theta$　since　$\left(\dfrac{y}{x}\right)^2 + 1 = \dfrac{y^2 + x^2}{x^2} = \dfrac{|\vec{v}|^2}{x^2} = \left(\dfrac{|\vec{v}|}{x}\right)^2$,

8.　$1 + \cot^2 \theta \equiv \csc^2 \theta$　since　$1 + \left(\dfrac{x}{y}\right)^2 = \dfrac{y^2 + x^2}{y^2} = \dfrac{|\vec{v}|^2}{y^2} = \left(\dfrac{|\vec{v}|}{y}\right)^2$.

From these eight fundamental identities many other identities may be established without returning to the definitions of the trigonometric functions.

Example 1. Show that $2 \csc \theta - \cot \theta \cos \theta \equiv \csc \theta + \sin \theta$.

Solution. From the left side, but keeping an eye on the right side,

$$2 \csc \theta - \cot \theta \cos \theta \equiv \csc \theta + (\csc \theta - \cot \theta \cos \theta)$$

$$\equiv \csc \theta + \left(\dfrac{1}{\sin \theta} - \dfrac{\cos \theta}{\sin \theta} \cos \theta\right) \text{ from 1. and 5.}$$

$$\equiv \csc \theta + \dfrac{1 - \cos^2 \theta}{\sin \theta}$$

$$\equiv \csc \theta + \dfrac{\sin^2 \theta}{\sin \theta} \text{ from 6.}$$

$$\equiv \csc \theta + \sin \theta.$$

Some trigonometric expressions may be simplified by using the eight fundamental identities.

Example 2. Simplify $\cot \theta \sec \theta - \cos \theta \cot \theta$.

Solution. The expression has $\cot \theta$ as a factor, so is identical to

$$\cot \theta \,(\sec \theta - \cos \theta) \equiv \cot \theta \left(\frac{1}{\cos \theta} - \cos \theta\right) \equiv \cot \theta \left(\frac{1 - \cos^2 \theta}{\cos \theta}\right)$$

$$\equiv \cot \theta \,\frac{\sin^2 \theta}{\cos \theta} \equiv \frac{\cos \theta}{\sin \theta} \frac{\sin^2 \theta}{\cos \theta} \equiv \sin \theta.$$

Problem 1. Establish the identities:

a. $\dfrac{\tan \theta + \cot \theta}{\sec \theta \csc \theta} \equiv 1.$

b. $\sin^2 \theta + \tan^2 \theta + \cos^2 \theta \equiv \sec^2 \theta.$

c. $\cos^2 \theta - \sin^2 \theta \equiv 2\cos^2 \theta - 1.$

d. $\dfrac{\sec \theta + \csc \theta}{\sec \theta - \csc \theta} \equiv \dfrac{\sin \theta + \cos \theta}{\sin \theta - \cos \theta}.$

e. $\dfrac{\sec \theta \sin^3 \theta}{1 + \cos \theta} \equiv \tan \theta - \sin \theta.$

f. $\dfrac{2 + \tan^2 \theta}{\sec^2 \theta} \equiv 1 + \cos^2 \theta.$

g. $\sec^2 \theta + \csc^2 \theta \equiv \sec^2 \theta \csc^2 \theta.$

h. $\cot \theta + \tan \theta \equiv \sec \theta \csc \theta.$

i. $(\sec \theta - \tan \theta)^2 \equiv \dfrac{1 - \sin \theta}{1 + \sin \theta}.$

j. $\dfrac{1 + \sin \theta}{1 - \csc^2 \theta} \equiv \dfrac{\sin \theta}{1 - \csc \theta}.$

k. $\cos^3 \theta \sin \theta + \sin^3 \theta \cos \theta \equiv \sin \theta \cos \theta.$

l. $\sin^4 \theta + \cos^4 \theta \equiv 1 - 2(\sin \theta \cos \theta)^2.$

m. $\sin^4 \theta - \cos^4 \theta \equiv \sin^2 \theta - \cos^2 \theta.$

n. $\dfrac{1}{1 - \cos \theta} - \dfrac{1}{1 + \cos \theta} \equiv 2 \cot \theta \csc \theta.$

Problem 2. Each of the following may be simplified considerably:

a. $(1 + \tan \theta)^2 - \sec^2 \theta.$

b. $\dfrac{\tan \theta + \cot \theta}{\sec \theta \csc \theta}.$

c. $\dfrac{1 - \sin \theta}{\cos \theta} - \dfrac{\cos \theta}{1 + \sin \theta}.$

d. $\cot^2 \theta \sec^2 \theta - \dfrac{1}{\tan^2 \theta}.$

e. $\sin \theta + \cot \theta \cos \theta.$

f. $\dfrac{\cos^2 \theta \csc \theta}{1 + \csc \theta} + \sin \theta.$

g. $\dfrac{\sin \theta + \tan \theta}{1 + \cos \theta}.$

h. $\dfrac{\sin^4 \theta - \cos^4 \theta}{\sin^2 \theta - \cos^2 \theta}.$

i. $\dfrac{\sec^2 \theta - \tan^2 \theta}{1 + \tan^2 \theta} + \tan^2 \theta \cos^2 \theta.$

j. $\dfrac{\sec^2 \theta - 1}{\sin^2 \theta \sec^2 \theta} + \dfrac{\csc^2 \theta - 1}{\cos^2 \theta \csc^2 \theta}.$

k. $\sin^2 \theta + \dfrac{1 - \tan^2 \theta}{\sec^2 \theta}.$

Problem 3.

a. With $a > 0$ and $b > 0$, show that

$$\sqrt{a^2 + b^2} = \frac{a}{\cos \theta}, \text{ where } 0° < \theta < 90° \text{ and } \tan \theta = \frac{b}{a}.$$

b. With $0 < a < c$, show that

$$\sqrt{c^2 - a^2} = c \sin \theta, \text{ where } 0° < \theta < 90° \text{ and } \cos \theta = \frac{a}{c}.$$

1-5. Addition Formulas

Let α and β be any angles whatever. Consider two vectors $\vec{u}$ and $\vec{v}$, each with unit norm; $\vec{u}$ with amplitude α and $\vec{v}$ with amplitude β. Hence,

(1) $\qquad \vec{u} = \vec{i} \cos \alpha + \vec{j} \sin \alpha \text{ and } \vec{v} = \vec{i} \cos \beta + \vec{j} \sin \beta.$

Then $\vec{u} - \vec{v} = \vec{i}(\cos \alpha - \cos \beta) + \vec{j}(\sin \alpha - \sin \beta)$ is such that

$$
\begin{aligned}
(2) \quad |\vec{u} - \vec{v}|^2 &= (\cos \alpha - \cos \beta)^2 + (\sin \alpha - \sin \beta)^2 \\
&= (\cos^2 \alpha - 2 \cos \alpha \cos \beta + \cos^2 \beta) \\
&\quad + (\sin^2 \alpha - 2 \sin \alpha \sin \beta + \sin^2 \beta) \\
&= (\cos^2 \alpha + \sin^2 \alpha) + (\cos^2 \beta + \sin^2 \beta) \\
&\quad - 2(\cos \alpha \cos \beta + \sin \alpha \sin \beta) \\
&= 2 - 2(\cos \alpha \cos \beta + \sin \alpha \sin \beta).
\end{aligned}
$$

Also, let γ be any angle whatever. Rotate each of the vectors $\vec{u}$ and $\vec{v}$ through the angle γ. The results are two vectors $\vec{u}_1$ and $\vec{v}_1$, each with unit norm; $\vec{u}_1$ having amplitude $\alpha + \gamma$ and $\vec{v}_1$ having amplitude $\beta + \gamma$. Thus,

$$
\begin{aligned}
(3) \quad \vec{u}_1 &= \vec{i} \cos(\alpha + \gamma) + \vec{j} \sin(\alpha + \gamma), \\
\vec{v}_1 &= \vec{i} \cos(\beta + \gamma) + \vec{j} \sin(\beta + \gamma).
\end{aligned}
$$

Hence, the difference

$$\vec{u}_1 - \vec{v}_1 = \vec{i}[\cos(\alpha + \gamma) - \cos(\beta + \gamma)] + \vec{j}[\sin(\alpha + \gamma) - \sin(\beta + \gamma)]$$

has the square of its norm given by

(4) $\quad |\vec{u}_1 - \vec{v}_1|^2 = 2 - 2[\cos(\alpha + \gamma) \cos(\beta + \gamma) + \sin(\alpha + \gamma) \sin(\beta + \gamma)],$

as may be seen by computations similar to (2).

Since $\vec{u}_1$ and $\vec{v}_1$ are rotations of $\vec{u}$ and $\vec{v}$, it follows that $\vec{u}_1 - \vec{v}_1$ is a rotation of $\vec{u} - \vec{v}$ and hence $|\vec{u}_1 - \vec{v}_1| = |\vec{u} - \vec{v}|$. By equating (4) with (2) and simplifying, the identity

$$
\begin{aligned}
(5) \quad \cos(\alpha + \gamma) &\cos(\beta + \gamma) + \sin(\alpha + \gamma) \sin(\beta + \gamma) \\
&\equiv \cos \alpha \cos \beta + \sin \alpha \sin \beta
\end{aligned}
$$

is obtained for α, β, and γ *any angles whatever.*

Formula (5) is a basic formula which may be specialized and modified in various ways, some of which will be considered now.

The first special form of (5) is obtained by setting $\gamma = -\beta$. Under this substitution,

$$\cos(\beta + \gamma) = \cos(\beta - \beta) = \cos 0 = 1,$$

$$\sin(\beta + \gamma) = \sin(\beta - \beta) = \sin 0 = 0,$$

and hence (5) reduces to

$$[\cos(\alpha - \beta)] \cdot 1 + [\sin(\alpha - \beta)] \cdot 0 \equiv \cos \alpha \cos \beta + \sin \alpha \sin \beta;$$

that is,

(6) $$\cos(\alpha - \beta) \equiv \cos\alpha\cos\beta + \sin\alpha\sin\beta.$$

This is the first of the so-called subtraction formulas for any angles α and β. In particular, for $\alpha = 0$, the identity (6) reduces to

$$\cos(0 - \beta) \equiv \cos 0 \cos\beta + \sin 0 \sin\beta; \text{ so}$$

(7) $$\cos(-\beta) \equiv \cos\beta.$$

Also, from (6) with $\alpha = 90°$,

$$\cos(90° - \beta) \equiv \cos 90° \cos\beta + \sin 90° \sin\beta;$$

that is,

(8) $$\cos(90° - \beta) \equiv \sin\beta \qquad (\text{since } \cos 90° = 0 \text{ and } \sin 90° = 1).$$

In (8), replace β by $90° - \beta$ to obtain

$$\cos[90° - (90° - \beta)] \equiv \sin(90° - \beta),$$

and hence

(9) $$\cos\beta \equiv \sin(90° - \beta).$$

Now $\sin(-\alpha) \equiv \sin(360° - \alpha) \equiv \sin[90° - (\alpha - 270°)]$

$$\equiv \cos(\alpha - 270°) \qquad\qquad\qquad \text{by (9)}$$

$$\equiv \cos\alpha\cos 270° + \sin\alpha\sin 270°$$

from (6), so that

(10) $$\sin(-\alpha) \equiv -\sin\alpha \qquad (\text{since } \cos 270° = 0 \text{ and } \sin 270° = -1).$$

Hence, $\cos(\alpha + \beta) \equiv \cos[\alpha - (-\beta)] \equiv \cos\alpha\cos(-\beta) + \sin\alpha\sin(-\beta)$ from (6). Thus, from (7) and (10),

(11) $$\cos(\alpha + \beta) \equiv \cos\alpha\cos\beta - \sin\alpha\sin\beta.$$

Companion formulas for $\sin(\alpha + \beta)$ and $\sin(\alpha - \beta)$ may be obtained as follows:

$$\sin(\alpha + \beta) \equiv \cos[90° - (\alpha + \beta)] \qquad\qquad \text{from (8)}$$

$$\equiv \cos[(90° - \alpha) - \beta]$$

$$\equiv \cos(90° - \alpha)\cos\beta + \sin(90° - \alpha)\sin\beta \qquad \text{from (6)}$$

(12) $$\equiv \sin\alpha\cos\beta + \cos\alpha\sin\beta \qquad\qquad \text{from (8) and (9),}$$

$$\sin(\alpha - \beta) \equiv \sin[\alpha + (-\beta)]$$

$$\equiv \sin\alpha\cos(-\beta) + \cos\alpha\sin(-\beta) \qquad\qquad \text{from (12)}$$

$$\equiv \sin\alpha\cos\beta - \cos\alpha\sin\beta \qquad\qquad \text{from (7) and (10).}$$

It should be noticed in particular that the above formulas have no restrictions whatever on the angles involved.

Problem 1. For n an integer and α any angle, show that:

a. $\sin (2n \, 90° + \alpha) \equiv (-1)^n \sin \alpha.$ c. $\sin [(2n + 1)90° + \alpha] \equiv (-1)^n \cos \alpha.$

b. $\cos (2n \, 90° + \alpha) \equiv (-1)^n \cos \alpha.$ d. $\cos [(2n + 1)90° + \alpha] \equiv (-1)^{n+1} \sin \alpha.$

Problem 2. Establish the identities:

a. $\cos 3\theta \cos 2\theta - \sin 3\theta \sin 2\theta \equiv \cos 5\theta.$

b. $\sin 3\theta \cos \theta - \cos 3\theta \sin \theta \equiv \sin 2\theta.$

c. $\sin (\alpha + \beta) \sin (\alpha - \beta) \equiv \sin^2 \alpha - \sin^2 \beta.$

d. $\sin (\alpha + 15°) \cos (\alpha - 15°) + \cos (\alpha + 15°) \sin (\alpha - 15°) \equiv \sin 2\alpha.$

e. $\cos (\alpha + 15°) \cos (\alpha + 15°) + \sin (\alpha + 15°) \sin (\alpha + 15°) \equiv 1.$

f. $\cos (15° + \alpha) \cos (30° + \alpha) + \sin (15° + \alpha) \sin (30° + \alpha) \equiv \cos 15°.$

g. $\dfrac{\sin (\alpha + \beta) + \sin (\alpha - \beta)}{\cos (\alpha + \beta) + \cos (\alpha - \beta)} \equiv \tan \alpha.$

Problem 3. Establish the following identities, which are usually given as formulas:

a. $\tan (\alpha + \beta) \equiv \dfrac{\tan \alpha + \tan \beta}{1 - \tan \alpha \tan \beta}.$ c. $\cot (\alpha + \beta) \equiv \dfrac{\cot \alpha \cot \beta - 1}{\cot \alpha + \cot \beta}.$

b. $\tan (\alpha - \beta) \equiv \dfrac{\tan \alpha - \tan \beta}{1 + \tan \alpha \tan \beta}.$ d. $\cot (\alpha - \beta) \equiv \dfrac{\cot \alpha \cot \beta + 1}{\cot \beta - \cot \alpha}.$

Problem 4. Establish each of the following "double" or "half angle" formulas:

a. $\sin 2\theta \equiv 2 \sin \theta \cos \theta.$

b. $\cos 2\theta \equiv \cos^2 \theta - \sin^2 \theta$

   $\equiv 2 \cos^2 \theta - 1$

   $\equiv 1 - 2 \sin^2 \theta.$

c. $2 \sin^2 \dfrac{\theta}{2} \equiv 1 - \cos \theta, \quad 2 \cos^2 \dfrac{\theta}{2} \equiv 1 + \cos \theta.$

d. $2 \sin \dfrac{\theta}{2} \cos \dfrac{\theta}{2} \equiv \sin \theta.$

e. $\tan \dfrac{\theta}{2} \equiv \dfrac{1 - \cos \theta}{\sin \theta} \equiv \dfrac{\sin \theta}{1 + \cos \theta}.$

Problem 5. The following identities will be used later on:

a. $\sin^2 \alpha \equiv \tfrac{1}{2}(1 - \cos 2\alpha).$ c. $\sin^3 \alpha \equiv \tfrac{1}{4}(3 \sin \alpha - \sin 3\alpha).$

b. $\cos^2 \alpha \equiv \tfrac{1}{2}(1 + \cos 2\alpha).$ d. $\cos^3 \alpha \equiv \tfrac{1}{4}(3 \cos \alpha + \cos 3\alpha).$

1-6. Forces

A force is represented by a vector with initial end at the point of action and length proportional to the magnitude of force.

Example 1. Forces $\vec{F}_1$ and $\vec{F}_2$ of 25.6 lb and 42.3 lb both act at a point in directions separated by a 34° angle. Find the direction and magnitude of the resultant force $\vec{v}$.

Solution. Select basic unit vectors $\vec{i}$ and $\vec{j}$ so $\vec{F}_1 = 25.6\vec{i}$ and

$$\vec{F}_2 = 42.3(\vec{i}\cos 34° + \vec{j}\sin 34°).$$

Then

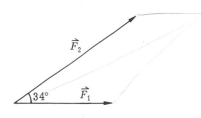

$$\vec{v} = (25.6 + 42.3\cos 34°)\vec{i} + (42.3\sin 34°)\vec{j}$$
$$= (25.6 + 42.3 \times 0.8290)\vec{i}$$
$$+ (42.3 \times 0.5592)\vec{j} \text{ from Table I}$$
$$= (25.6 + 35.07)\vec{i} + 23.65\vec{j} = 60.67\vec{i}$$
$$+ 23.65\vec{j}.$$

Hence, the direction θ and norm of $\vec{v}$ are such that

(1) $$\tan\theta = \frac{23.65}{60.67} \text{ and}$$

Fig. 1-6.1

(2) $$|\vec{v}| = \sqrt{(60.67)^2 + (23.65)^2} = 60.67\sqrt{1 + \left(\frac{23.65}{60.67}\right)^2} = 60.67\sqrt{1 + \tan^2\theta}$$

$$= 60.67\sqrt{\sec^2\theta} = 60.67\sec\theta = \frac{60.67}{\cos\theta}.$$

The logarithmic work for finding θ from (1) and $|\vec{v}|$ from (2) may be arranged as follows:

log 23.65	11.3738 − 10
(−) log 60.67	1.7830
log tan θ	9.5908 − 10
θ	21°18′

log 60.67	11.7830 − 10
(−) log cos θ	9.9722 − 10
log $|\vec{v}|$	1.8108
$|\vec{v}|$	64.7

Example 2. Replace the 34° angle of Example 1 by 146°.

Solution. With $\vec{F}_1 = 25.6\vec{i}$ and

$$\vec{F}_2 = 42.3(\vec{i}\cos 146° + \vec{j}\sin 146°) = 42.3[\vec{i}\cos(180° - 34°) + \vec{j}\sin(180° - 34°)]$$
$$= 42.3(-\vec{i}\cos 34° + \vec{j}\sin 34°),$$

then $$\vec{v} = (25.6 - 42.3\cos 34°)\vec{i} + (42.3\sin 34°)\vec{j}$$
$$= (25.6 - 42.3 \times 0.8290)\vec{i} + 42.3 \times 0.5592\vec{j}$$
$$= (25.6 - 35.07)\vec{i} + 23.65\vec{j} = -9.47\vec{i} + 23.65\vec{j},$$

$$\tan\theta = \frac{23.65}{-9.47}, \quad \tan(180° - \theta) = -\tan\theta = \frac{23.65}{9.47},$$

$$|\vec{v}| = \sqrt{(-9.47)^2 + (23.65)^2} = 9.47\sqrt{1 + \left(\frac{23.65}{9.47}\right)^2}$$

$$= 9.47\sqrt{1 + \tan^2(180° - \theta)} = \frac{9.47}{\cos(180° - \theta)}.$$

log 23.65	1.3738
(−) log 9.47	0.9763
log tan (180° − θ)	0.3975
180° − θ	68°11′
θ	111°49′

log 9.47	10.9763 − 10
(−) log cos (180° − θ)	9.5701 − 10
log $|\vec{v}|$	1.4062
$|\vec{v}|$	25.5

Problem 1. Two forces $\vec{F}_1$ and $\vec{F}_2$ acting on the same point have magnitude as given, and the angle between the forces is given. Find the magnitude of the resultant force $\vec{v}$ and the angle θ from $\vec{F}_1$ to $\vec{v}$.

a. 14.7, 21.3, 25°.   c. 126, 324, 154°.

b. 7.89, 10.4, 15°20′.   d. 87.3, 16.1, 137°.

Problem 2. Find the magnitude and amplitude of the resultant of the three forces:

a. $\vec{F}_1 = 5.7\vec{i} + 2.3\vec{j}$,
$\vec{F}_2 = 3.8\vec{i} - 1.7\vec{j}$,
$\vec{F}_3 = -4.5\vec{i} + 6.9\vec{j}$.

b. $\vec{F}_1 = -27.8\vec{i} - 15.2\vec{j}$,
$\vec{F}_2 = -13.7\vec{i} + 34.2\vec{j}$,
$\vec{F}_3 = 10.7\vec{i} + 22.0\vec{j}$.

c. $\vec{F}_1 = 15.4(\vec{i} \cos 57° + \vec{j} \sin 57°)$,
$\vec{F}_2 = 11.7(\vec{i} \cos 105° + \vec{j} \sin 105°)$,
$\vec{F}_3 = 13.2\vec{i} \cos (-15°) + \vec{j} \sin (-15°)$.

d. $\vec{F}_1 = 23.2(\vec{i} \cos 116° + \vec{j} \sin 116°)$,
$\vec{F}_2 = 15.8(\vec{i} \cos 25° + \vec{j} \sin 25°)$,
$\vec{F}_3 = 34.8[\vec{i} \cos (-25°) + \vec{j} \sin (-25°)]$.

1-7. Scalar Product

The **scalar**, or **dot**, product of vectors $\vec{u}$ and $\vec{v}$ is denoted by $\vec{u} \cdot \vec{v}$, and is defined by the equation

$$(1) \qquad \vec{u} \cdot \vec{v} = |\vec{u}| |\vec{v}| \cos \theta,$$

where θ is the smallest positive angle between $\vec{u}$ and $\vec{v}$ when their initial ends are placed in coincidence. Thus, $\vec{u} \cdot \vec{v}$ is a scalar which is positive if $0° \leq \theta < 90°$, is zero if $\theta = 90°$, and is negative if $90° < \theta \leq 180°$. Also,

$$(2) \qquad \vec{u} \cdot \vec{v} = \vec{v} \cdot \vec{u}$$

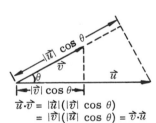

$\vec{u} \cdot \vec{v} = |\vec{u}|(|\vec{v}| \cos \theta)$
$= |\vec{v}|(|\vec{u}| \cos \theta) = \vec{v} \cdot \vec{u}$

Fig. 1-7.1

since θ is measured either from $\vec{u}$ to $\vec{v}$ or from $\vec{v}$ to $\vec{u}$, whichever is positive and less than or equal to 180°. Hence, the order of writing the factors of a scalar product is immaterial.

If either $\vec{u} = \vec{0}$ or $\vec{v} = \vec{0}$, then θ has no meaning, but the definition of $\vec{u} \cdot \vec{v}$ and $\vec{v} \cdot \vec{u}$ is extended by setting these equal to zero. Hence,

$$(3) \quad \vec{u} \cdot \vec{v} = 0 \text{ if } \vec{u} = \vec{0}, \text{ or } \vec{v} = \vec{0}, \text{ or } \theta = 90°.$$

If $\vec{u} \neq \vec{0}$ and $\vec{v} \neq \vec{0}$, then $|\vec{v}| \cos \theta$ is the length of the projection of $\vec{v}$ on the line containing $\vec{u}$ whenever $0° \leq \theta < 90°$, is the negative of this length if $90° < \theta \leq 180°$, and is zero if $\theta = 90°$. The scalar

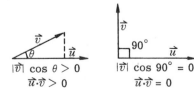

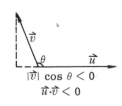

$|\vec{v}| \cos \theta > 0$ $|\vec{v}| \cos 90° = 0$ $|\vec{v}| \cos \theta < 0$
$\vec{u} \cdot \vec{v} > 0$ $\vec{u} \cdot \vec{v} = 0$ $\vec{u} \cdot \vec{v} < 0$

Fig. 1-7.2

$$|\vec{v}| \cos \theta$$

is called the **signed projection** of $\vec{v}$ on $\vec{u}$. Hence, the scalar product of $\vec{u}$ and $\vec{v}$ is

$$\vec{u} \cdot \vec{v} = (|\vec{u}| \text{ times the signed projection of } \vec{v} \text{ on } \vec{u}), \quad \text{or}$$
$$= (|\vec{v}| \text{ times the signed projection of } \vec{u} \text{ on } \vec{v}).$$

Both $k\vec{v}$ and $\vec{v}$, with k a scalar, have their signed projections on $\vec{u}$ of the same sign if $k > 0$, opposite signs if $k < 0$, and in either case

$$(\text{signed projection of } k\vec{v} \text{ on } \vec{u}) = k(\text{signed projection of } \vec{v} \text{ on } \vec{u}).$$

Hence, upon multiplying by $|\vec{u}|$, it follows that

(4) $$\vec{u} \cdot (k\vec{v}) = k(\vec{u} \cdot \vec{v}).$$

Now $(k\vec{u}) \cdot \vec{v} = \vec{v} \cdot (k\vec{u}) = k(\vec{v} \cdot \vec{u}) = k(\vec{u} \cdot \vec{v})$, so that "a scalar may be factored from either factor of a scalar product." In particular,

(5) $$\vec{u} \cdot (-\vec{v}) = -(\vec{u} \cdot \vec{v}) = (-\vec{u}) \cdot \vec{v}.$$

A third vector $\vec{w}$ and the vector sum $(\vec{v} + \vec{w})$ have signed projections on $\vec{u}$, where

$$[\text{signed projection of } (\vec{v} + \vec{w})]$$
$$= (\text{signed projection of } \vec{v} + \text{signed projection of } \vec{w}).$$

On multiplying both sides by $|\vec{u}|$, the result is

(6) $$\vec{u} \cdot (\vec{v} + \vec{w}) = \vec{u} \cdot \vec{v} + \vec{u} \cdot \vec{w}.$$

Since the factors may be written in either order, then

(7) $$(\vec{v} + \vec{w}) \cdot \vec{u} = \vec{v} \cdot \vec{u} + \vec{w} \cdot \vec{u}.$$

The basic unit vectors $\vec{i}$ and $\vec{j}$ are perpendicular to one another, so that

$$\vec{i} \cdot \vec{j} = \vec{j} \cdot \vec{i} = |\vec{i}||\vec{j}| \cos 90° = 0 \quad \text{since } \cos 90° = 0.$$

Also, $\vec{i} \cdot \vec{i} = |\vec{i}||\vec{i}| \cos 0° = 1$, and likewise $\vec{j} \cdot \vec{j} = 1$. The equalities

(8) $$\vec{i} \cdot \vec{j} = \vec{j} \cdot \vec{i} = 0 \quad \text{and} \quad \vec{i} \cdot \vec{i} = \vec{j} \cdot \vec{j} = 1,$$

together with the above facts about factoring out scalars and removing parentheses, show that

$$(a_1\vec{i} + b_1\vec{j}) \cdot (a_2\vec{i} + b_2\vec{j}) = a_1\vec{i} \cdot (a_2\vec{i} + b_2\vec{j}) + b_1\vec{j} \cdot (a_2\vec{i} + b_2\vec{j})$$
$$= a_1a_2\vec{i} \cdot \vec{i} + a_1b_2\vec{i} \cdot \vec{j} + b_1a_2\vec{j} \cdot \vec{i} + b_1b_2\vec{j} \cdot \vec{j}$$
$$= (a_1a_2)1 + (a_1b_2)0 + (b_1a_2)0 + (b_1b_2)1.$$

Consequently,

(9) $$(a_1\vec{i} + b_1\vec{j}) \cdot (a_2\vec{i} + b_2\vec{j}) = a_1a_2 + b_1b_2.$$

Since $\vec{u} \cdot \vec{v} = |\vec{u}||\vec{v}| \cos \theta$, it follows that

(10) $$\cos \theta = \frac{\vec{u} \cdot \vec{v}}{|\vec{u}||\vec{v}|}.$$

Example 1. Vectors are drawn from the origin to the points $A(4,1)$ and $B(-2,3)$. Find the angle AOB.

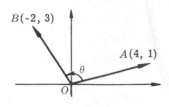

B(-2, 3)

A(4, 1)

θ

O

Fig. 1-7.3

Solution. $\overrightarrow{OA} = 4\vec{i} + \vec{j}$, $\overrightarrow{OB} = -2\vec{i} + 3\vec{j}$, so that, with $\theta = $ angle AOB,

$$\cos \theta = \frac{\overrightarrow{OA}\cdot\overrightarrow{OB}}{|\overrightarrow{OA}||\overrightarrow{OB}|} = \frac{(4\vec{i} + \vec{j})\cdot(-2\vec{i} + 3\vec{j})}{\sqrt{4^2 + 1^2}\sqrt{(-2)^2 + 3^2}}$$

$$= \frac{4(-2) + 1(3)}{\sqrt{17}\sqrt{13}} = \frac{-5}{\sqrt{(17)(13)}}.$$

From the negative sign it follows that $90° < \theta < 180°$. But then

$$\cos(180° - \theta) = -\cos\theta = \frac{5}{\sqrt{(17)(13)}}.$$

Hence, $180° - \theta = 70°20'$ and $\theta = 109°40'$ to the nearest $10'$.

Example 2. Find the interior angles of the triangle having vertices $A(3, 1)$, $B(1, 5)$, and $C(-2,2)$.

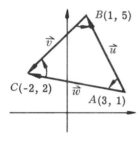

B(1, 5)

$\vec{v}$

$\vec{u}$

C(-2, 2)

$\vec{w}$

A(3, 1)

Fig. 1-7.4

Solution. To save notation, let A, B, and C also denote the angles within the triangle at the respective vertices. Make the sides into vectors as shown in Fig. 1-7.4, so that

$$\vec{u} = \overrightarrow{AB} = (1 - 3)\vec{i} + (5 - 1)\vec{j} = -2\vec{i} + 4\vec{j},$$

$$\vec{v} = \overrightarrow{BC} = (-2 - 1)\vec{i} + (2 - 5)\vec{j}$$
$$= -3\vec{i} - 3\vec{j},$$

$$\vec{w} = \overrightarrow{AC} = (-2 - 3)\vec{i} + (2 - 1)\vec{j} = -5\vec{i} + \vec{j}$$

(check that $\vec{w} = \vec{u} + \vec{v}$).

Since both $\vec{u}$ and $\vec{w}$ have initial ends at A, then

$$\cos A = \frac{\vec{u}\cdot\vec{w}}{|\vec{u}||\vec{w}|} = \frac{(-2)(-5) + 4(1)}{\sqrt{(-2)^2 + 4^2}\sqrt{(-5)^2 + 1^2}} = \frac{14}{\sqrt{(20)(26)}}.$$

To obtain angle B, note that $\vec{v}$ and $-\vec{u}$ have initial end at point B, so that

$$\cos B = \frac{(-\vec{u})\cdot\vec{v}}{|-\vec{u}||\vec{v}|} = -\frac{\vec{u}\cdot\vec{v}}{|\vec{u}||\vec{v}|} = -\frac{(-2\vec{i} + 4\vec{j})\cdot(-3\vec{i} - 3\vec{j})}{\sqrt{2^2 + 4^2}\sqrt{3^2 + 3^2}}$$

$$= -\frac{(-2)(-3) + 4(-3)}{\sqrt{20}\sqrt{18}} = \frac{6}{\sqrt{20}\sqrt{18}}.$$

Both $\vec{v}$ and $\vec{w}$ may be moved along their respective lines until both have point C as initial end, so that angle C is such that

$$\cos C = \frac{\vec{v}\cdot\vec{w}}{|\vec{v}||\vec{w}|} = \frac{(-3)(-5) + (-3)1}{\sqrt{18}\sqrt{26}} = \frac{12}{\sqrt{18}\sqrt{26}}.$$

Logarithmic (or slide rule) computation shows that, to the nearest $10'$,

$$A = 52°10', \quad B = 71°30', \quad C = 56°20'.$$

Vectors $\vec{u} \neq \vec{0}$ and $\vec{v} \neq \vec{0}$ are perpendicular if and only if $\vec{u} \cdot \vec{v} = 0$. Hence, the condition of perpendicularity of

(11) $\vec{u} = a_1 \vec{i} + b_1 \vec{j}$ and $\vec{v} = a_2 \vec{i} + b_2 \vec{j}$ is $a_1 a_2 + b_1 b_2 = 0$.

Example 3. Show that the line containing $(3, -1)$ and $(2, 4)$ is perpendicular to the line containing $(-5, 4)$ and $(5, 6)$.

Solution. The lines are perpendicular if a vector on one line is perpendicular to a vector on the other line. The vector

$\vec{u} = (2 - 3)\vec{i} + [4 - (-1)]\vec{j} = -\vec{i} + 5\vec{j}$

joins the given points on the first line, while

$\vec{v} = [5 - (-5)]\vec{i} + (6 - 4)\vec{j} = 10\vec{i} + 2\vec{j}$

is on the second line. Since

$\vec{u} \cdot \vec{v} = (-1)10 + 5(2) = -10 + 10 = 0,$

the vectors (and hence the lines) are perpendicular.

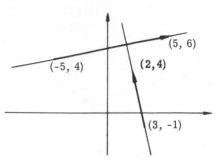

Fig. 1-7.5

Problem 1. Find $\vec{u} \cdot \vec{v}$ for:

a. $\vec{u} = 4\vec{i} - 3\vec{j}, \vec{v} = \vec{i} + 2\vec{j}.$

b. $\vec{u} = 3\vec{i} + 2\vec{j}, \vec{v} = -2\vec{i} + \vec{j}.$

c. $\vec{u} = \vec{i} + \vec{j}, \vec{v} = \vec{i} - \vec{j}.$

d. $\vec{u} = \vec{i}, \vec{v} = 2\vec{i} - 400\vec{j}.$

e. $\vec{u} = 25\vec{i} - 3\vec{j}, \vec{v} = \vec{i} + 8\vec{j}.$

f. $\vec{u} = 25(\vec{i} + \vec{j}), \vec{v} = 3(2\vec{i} - \vec{j}).$

Problem 2. Find the smallest positive angle between the vectors:

a. $\vec{u} = \vec{i}, \vec{v} = \vec{i} + \sqrt{3}\,\vec{j}.$

b. $\vec{u} = \vec{i}, \vec{v} = \sqrt{3}\,\vec{i} - \vec{j}.$

c. $\vec{u} = \sqrt{3}\,\vec{i} + \vec{j}, \vec{v} = \vec{i} + \sqrt{3}\,\vec{j}.$

d. $\vec{u} = 3\vec{i} - 2\vec{j}, \vec{v} = 6\vec{i} - 4\vec{j}.$

e. $\vec{u} = 3\vec{i} - 2\vec{j}, \vec{v} = -6\vec{i} + 4\vec{j}.$

f. $\vec{u} = 3\vec{i} - 2\vec{j}, \vec{v} = \vec{i} + 4\vec{j}.$

Problem 3. Find the interior angles of the triangle having vertices:

a. $(3, 1), (1, 5), (8, 2).$

b. $(3, -1), (1, 3), (-2, 0).$

c. $(0, 0), (5, -1), (3, 3).$

d. $(4, 1), (2, 5), (-2, 3).$

e. $(4, 1), (2, 5), (6, 7).$

f. $(2, -3), (4, 5), (2, -6).$

Problem 4. Show that the vector joining the first pair of points is perpendicular to the vector joining the second pair of points:

a. $(1, 4), (-2, 3); (5, 7), (7, 1).$

b. $(0, 0), (1, 4); (0, 0), (-8, 2).$

c. $(-1, 1), (0, 5); (1, 0), (-3, 1).$

d. $(250, 340), (255, 342); (-1, 2), (-5, 12).$

Problem 5. Find x or y such that a vector joining the first pair of points will be perpendicular to the line joining the second pair of points:

a. $(1, -3), (4, 2); (1, 7), (x, 5).$

b. $(1, -3), (4, 2); (1, 7), (3, y).$

c. $(-3, y), (4, 1); (2, 6), (4, 3).$

d. $(0, 0), (1, 0); (0, 0), (x, 2).$

1-8.   Lines

From plane geometry, through a given point there is one and only one line perpendicular to a given line.

Let (x_0, y_0) be a given point and $\vec{u} = A\vec{i} + B\vec{j}$ a given vector with initial end at the origin and having A and B not both zero. Through (x_0, y_0) there is one and only one line perpendicular to the line of $\vec{u}$. A variable point (x, y) will be on this line if and only if the variable vector

$$\vec{v} = (x - x_0)\vec{i} + (y - y_0)\vec{j}$$

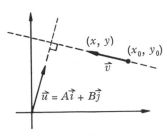

Fig. 1-8.1

from the fixed point (x_0, y_0) to the variable point (x, y) is always perpendicular to $\vec{u}$. The condition of perpendicularity of $\vec{u}$ and $\vec{v}$ in terms of the scalar product (see Sec. 1-7) is

$$\vec{u} \cdot \vec{v} = 0,$$

$$(A\vec{i} + B\vec{j}) \cdot [(x - x_0)\vec{i} + (y - y_0)\vec{j}] = 0;$$

that is,

$$(1) \qquad A(x - x_0) + B(y - y_0) = 0.$$

The line through (x_0, y_0) perpendicular to $\vec{u} = A\vec{i} + B\vec{j}$ is said to have (1) as an equation.

Equation (1) may be written $Ax + By - (Ax_0 + By_0) = 0$ and then the constant $-(Ax_0 + By_0)$ set equal to C. The result is

$$(2) \qquad Ax + By + C = 0.$$

Conversely, given constants A and B not both zero and given a constant C, the graph of Eq. (2) is a straight line. If $B \neq 0$, let x_0 be an arbitrary constant and $y_0 = -(Ax_0 + C)/B$. If $B = 0$, then $A \neq 0$, so choose $x_0 = -C/A$ and let $y_0 = 0$. Note that in either case $Ax_0 + By_0 + C = 0$. Also, let x and y be variables but related by having $Ax + By + C = 0$. Hence,

$$Ax + By + C - (Ax_0 + By_0 + C) = 0; \quad \text{i.e.,} \quad A(x - x_0) + B(y - y_0) = 0.$$

Interpreted geometrically, this last equation says that the vector

$$\vec{v} = (x - x_0)\vec{i} + (y - y_0)\vec{j}$$

from the fixed point (x_0, y_0) to the variable point (x, y) is always perpendicular to the vector $\vec{u} = A\vec{i} + B\vec{j}$. The variable point (x, y) is thus restricted to a line and the graph of (2) is this line. Equation (2) is called the **general form** of the equation of a line.

If $B = 0$, then $A \neq 0$, $\vec{u}$ reduces to $\vec{u} = A\vec{i}$ along the x-axis, and (1) reduces to $A(x - x_0) = 0$, which means that

$$(3) \qquad x = x_0.$$

Thus, (3) is the equation of the line perpendicular to the x-axis through the point (x_0, y_0).

If $B \neq 0$, then $\vec{u} = A\vec{i} + B\vec{j}$ is not along the x-axis and (1) may be written as

(4) $$\frac{y - y_0}{x - x_0} = -\frac{A}{B} \quad \text{for } x \neq x_0.$$

Also, for any variable point (x, y) on the line, any amplitude θ of the vector $\vec{v} = (x - x_0)\vec{i} + (y - y_0)\vec{j}$ is such that

(5) $$\tan \theta = \frac{y - y_0}{x - x_0} = -\frac{A}{B} \quad \text{for } x \neq x_0.$$

This value is called the **slope** m of the line:

(6) $$m = \frac{y - y_0}{x - x_0} = -\frac{A}{B} \quad \text{for } x \neq x_0.$$

Note that "slope" is defined only for lines not perpendicular to the x-axis. Upon replacing $-A/B$ in (4) by m, the result may be written as

(7) $$y - y_0 = m(x - x_0).$$

The line is said to have (7) as its **point-slope** equation.

Example 1. The line through the point $(-2, 3)$ with slope $\frac{5}{4}$ has point-slope equation

$$y - 3 = \tfrac{5}{4}(x + 2).$$

This equation may be written in the forms

$$4y - 12 = 5x + 10, \quad 4y - 5x - 22 = 0,$$

or $$5x - 4y + 22 = 0,$$

the last of which is the general equation of the line. From this general equation, it follows that the line is perpendicular to the vector $\vec{u} = 5\vec{i} - 4\vec{j}$.

A line of slope m and cutting the y-axis at the point $(0, b)$ has equation

(8) $$y = mx + b.$$

This equation is obtained by setting $x_0 = 0$ and $y_0 = b$ in (7). The line is said to have y-intercept b, and (8) is called its **slope-intercept** equation.

Example 2. Find the slope and y-intercept of the line whose general equation is $3x + 4y - 6 = 0$.

Solution. Upon solving for y, the result is

$$y = -\tfrac{3}{4}x + \tfrac{3}{2},$$

which is in the form (8). Hence, the slope is $m = -\frac{3}{4}$ and the y-intercept is $b = \frac{3}{2}$.

Two points also determine a unique line. Let (x_0, y_0) and (x_1, y_1) be two fixed points, draw the line containing them, and let (x, y) be a variable point on the line. If $x_1 = x_0$, the line is perpendicular to the x-axis, so its equation is given by (3). If $x_1 \neq x_0$, the line is not perpendicular to the x-axis and has slope m given both by

$$m = \frac{y - y_0}{x - x_0} \quad \text{if } x \neq x_0 \quad \text{and} \quad m = \frac{y_1 - y_0}{x_1 - x_0}$$

from (6), since (x, y) and (x_1, y_1) are both points on the line. Thus,

$$\frac{y - y_0}{x - x_0} = \frac{y_1 - y_0}{x_1 - x_0} \quad \text{if } x \neq x_0,$$

which may be written as

(9) $$y - y_0 = \frac{y_1 - y_0}{x_1 - x_0}(x - x_0), \quad \text{even if } x = x_0.$$

Equation (9) is called the **two-point equation** of the line.

Example 3. The line through the points $(-1, 2)$ and $(3, -4)$ has the two-point equation

$$y - 2 = \frac{(-4 - 2)}{3 + 1}(x + 1).$$

This equation may be written in any of the forms:

$$y - 2 = -\tfrac{3}{2}(x + 1), \quad \text{point-slope form;}$$

$$y = -\tfrac{3}{2}x + \tfrac{1}{2}, \quad \text{slope-intercept form;}$$

$$3x + 2y - 1 = 0, \quad \text{general form.}$$

Two lines are parallel if and only if they are both perpendicular to a third line. Let two lines have equations

(10) $$y = m_1 x + b_1 \quad \text{and} \quad y = m_2 x + b_2.$$

These equations, written as $-m_1 x + y - b_1 = 0$ and $-m_2 x + y - b_2 = 0$, show that the lines are perpendicular to the vectors

$$\vec{u}_1 = -m_1 \vec{i} + \vec{j} \quad \text{and} \quad \vec{u}_2 = -m_2 \vec{i} + \vec{j},$$

respectively. Thus, the lines will be parallel provided only that $\vec{u}_1$ and $\vec{u}_2$ lie along a common line and hence are such that

$$\vec{u}_1 = k\vec{u}_2; \quad \text{that is,} \quad -m_1 \vec{i} + \vec{j} = k(-m_2 \vec{i} + \vec{j})$$

for some constant $k \neq 0$. Upon equating coefficients of $\vec{i}$ and $\vec{j}$:

$$-m_1 = k(-m_2), \quad 1 = k,$$

it follows that the lines having equations (10) are parallel if and only if $m_1 = m_2$.

Thus, two lines are parallel if and only if either:

(a)   they both have the same slope, or else
(b)   neither has a slope (so both are perpendicular to the x-axis).

Example 4. Find an equation of the line through the point $(3, -5)$ parallel to the line $2x - y = 6$.

Solution. The given equation in slope-intercept form is

$$y = 2x - 6,$$

showing that $m = 2$ is the desired slope. Hence, the desired equation is

$$(y + 5) = 2(x - 3).$$

Problem 1. Find the equation of the line perpendicular to the given vector $\vec{u}$ and passing through the given point:

a. $\vec{u} = \vec{i} - 3\vec{j}, (2, 4)$.

b. $\vec{u} = 2\vec{i} + 3\vec{j}, (2, 3)$.

c. $\vec{u} = \vec{i}, (4, -3)$.

d. $\vec{u} = \vec{j}, (4, -3)$.

e. $\vec{u} = 1.5\vec{i} + \vec{j}, (-2, 5)$.

f. $\vec{u} = 2\vec{i} - 3\vec{j}, (0, 0)$.

Problem 2. Write the equation of the line determined by the two points:

a. $(1, -2), (3, 4)$.

b. $(0, 0), (3, 4)$.

c. $(6, -5), (1, 0)$.

d. $(2, 0), (0, 3)$.

e. $(3, 4), (3, -6)$.

f. $(3, 4), (-3, 4)$.

Problem 3. Find the equation of the line having:

a. Slope 2, y-intercept 3.

b. Slope -2, y-intercept 3.

c. Slope undefined, through $(3, -5)$.

d. Slope zero, through $(3, -5)$.

Problem 4. Find the equation of the line passing through the given point and satisfying the given condition:

a. $(-2, 4)$, parallel to line $3x - 7y = 4$.

b. $(3, -5)$, parallel to segment joining $(-1, 6)$ and $(4, 5)$.

c. $(4, 1)$, parallel to segment joining $(0, 0)$ and $(3, -2)$.

d. $(5, -2)$, parallel to vector $3\vec{i} - 2\vec{j}$.

e. End of $4\vec{i} - 3\vec{j}$ and perpendicular to this vector.

1-9. Perpendicular Lines

Two lines L_1 and L_2 having slopes m_1 and m_2 are perpendicular if and only if

(1) $$1 + m_1 m_2 = 0.$$

To see this, let (x_0, y_0) be the intersection of L_1 and L_2, and select points (x_1, y_1) on L_1 and (x_2, y_2) on L_2. The vectors

$$\vec{v}_1 = (x_1 - x_0)\vec{i} + (y_1 - y_0)\vec{j} \quad \text{and} \quad \vec{v}_2 = (x_2 - x_0)\vec{i} + (y_2 - y_0)\vec{j}$$

are perpendicular, provided that $\vec{v}_1 \cdot \vec{v}_2 = 0$; that is,

$$(x_1 - x_0)(x_2 - x_0) + (y_1 - y_0)(y_2 - y_0) = 0.$$

This equation written as

$$1 + \frac{y_1 - y_0}{x_1 - x_0} \frac{y_2 - y_0}{x_2 - x_0} = 0$$

is (1), since

$$m_1 = \frac{y_1 - y_0}{x_1 - x_0} \quad \text{and} \quad m_2 = \frac{y_2 - y_0}{x_2 - x_0}.$$

Equation (1) may be written as

$$m_2 = -\frac{1}{m_1} \quad \text{or} \quad m_1 = -\frac{1}{m_2}$$

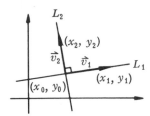

*L*₂

(x_2, y_2)

$\vec{v}_2$ $\vec{v}_1$ *L*₁

(x_1, y_1)

(x_0, y_0)

and the result stated as: *Two lines, neither perpendicular to the x-axis, are perpendicular to each other if and only if their slopes are negative reciprocals of each other.*

If a line is perpendicular to the *x*-axis, then this line has no slope, while any line perpendicular to it has slope 0.

Fig. 1-9.1

Example. Find equations of the line through $(-1, 2)$ and perpendicular to the line $4x + 3y - 7 = 0$.

Solution. The equation $4x + 3y - 7 = 0$ written in slope-intercept form is

$$y = -\tfrac{4}{3}x + \tfrac{7}{3},$$

showing that this line has slope $-\tfrac{4}{3}$. Thus, the desired line has slope

$$m = -\frac{1}{-\frac{4}{3}} = \frac{3}{4},$$

and hence has point-slope equation $y - 2 = \tfrac{3}{4}(x + 1)$. The general equation is

$$3x - 4y + 11 = 0.$$

1-10. Distance from a Point to a Line

The vector $\vec{u} = A\vec{i} + B\vec{j}$ is perpendicular to the line $L: Ax + By + C = 0$, and hence so is $k\vec{u}$ for any constant $k \neq 0$. The terminal end of $k\vec{u}$ is the point (kA, kB). This point is on L if $A(kA) + B(kB) + C = 0$, and hence if

$$k = -\frac{C}{A^2 + B^2}.$$

On setting $\vec{U} = k\vec{u}$ with this value of k, the vector

(1) $$\vec{U} = \frac{-C}{A^2 + B^2}(A\vec{i} + B\vec{j}),$$

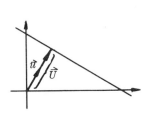

$\vec{u}$ $\vec{U}$

Fig. 1-10.1

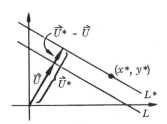

$\vec{U}* - \vec{U}$

$\vec{U}$ $\vec{U}*$

$(x*, y*)$

*L**

L

Fig. 1-10.2

with initial end at the origin, has terminal end on L and $\vec{U}$ is perpendicular to L.

A corollary of this result is: *The perpendicular distance d from a fixed point (x^*, y^*) to the line L: $Ax + By + C = 0$ is*

$$(2) \qquad\qquad d = \pm \frac{Ax^* + By^* + C}{\sqrt{A^2 + B^2}}.$$

To see this, note first that the line L^* through (x^*, y^*) parallel to L is distance d from L, and L^* has equation

$$A(x - x^*) + B(y - y^*) = 0 \quad \text{or} \quad Ax + By - (Ax^* + By^*) = 0.$$

The constant term is $-(Ax^* + By^*)$. Hence, by (1), the vector

$$\vec{U}^* = -\frac{-(Ax^* + By^*)}{A^2 + B^2}(A\vec{i} + B\vec{j}) = \frac{Ax^* + By^*}{A^2 + B^2}(A\vec{i} + B\vec{j})$$

has terminal end on L^*. The vector

$$(3) \qquad \vec{U}^* - \vec{U} = \frac{Ax^* + By^*}{A^2 + B^2}(A\vec{i} + B\vec{j}) - \frac{-C}{A^2 + B^2}(A\vec{i} + B\vec{j})$$

$$= \frac{Ax^* + By^* + C}{A^2 + B^2}(A\vec{i} + B\vec{j})$$

is perpendicular to both L and L^*, and may be pictured with initial end on L and terminal end on L^*. Hence, the norm $|\vec{U}^* - \vec{U}|$ is the distance d, so that

$$(4) \qquad d = \left| \frac{Ax^* + By^* + C}{A^2 + B^2} \right| \sqrt{A^2 + B^2} = \pm \frac{Ax^* + By^* + C}{\sqrt{A^2 + B^2}}.$$

In a specific problem, the plus or minus sign is chosen so as to make d positive.

Example. For the point $(-6, 5)$ and line $4x - 3y + 19 = 0$,

$$\frac{Ax^* + By^* + C}{\sqrt{A^2 + B^2}} = \frac{4(-6) + (-3)5 + 19}{\sqrt{4^2 + 3^2}} = \frac{-20}{5} = -4,$$

showing that the point $(-6, 5)$ and origin are on opposite sides of the line with the point 4 units from the line.

Problem 1. Find the equation of the line through the given point and perpendicular to the given line:

a. $(1, -3)$, $2x - 3y + 4 = 0$.   d. $(3, -4)$, $y = 6$.

b. $(2, 5)$, $x + y - 47 = 0$.   e. $(-3, -6)$, $x = 2y + 8$.

c. $(3, -4)$, $x = 10$.   f. $(-8, 10)$, $16x + 4y - 13 = 0$.

Problem 2. For A and B not both zero and C_1 and C_2 any constants, show that the lines $Ax + By + C_1 = 0$ and $Bx - Ay + C_2 = 0$ are perpendicular.

Problem 3. Find the distance from the given point to the given line:

a. $(2, 6)$, $3x + 4y - 25 = 0$.   c. $(1, 0)$, $5x - 12y = 2$.

b. $(-2, -6)$, $3x + 4y - 25 = 0$.   d. $(4, 5)$, $x - 2y = 4$.

Problem 4. Find the distance between the pair of parallel lines:

a. $3x + 4y = 5, 6x + 8y = -7$.   c. $y = 3x - 4, 3x - y = 5$.

b. $x - 2y = 4, 3x - 6y = 5$.   d. $2x = 7, 3x - 4 = 0$.

Problem 5. Find the radius of the circle that is tangent to the line $7x + 24y = 6$ and has center at $(4, -3)$.

Problem 6. Find the equations of the lines parallel to $12x - 5y = 23$ and tangent to the circle with center $(2, -3)$ and radius 4.

1-11.   Radian Measure

This section is included for those who are either unfamiliar with radians or else need a review of them (also see Sec. 2-11).

Along the circumference of a circle, lay off an arc whose length is the same as the length r of the radius. This arc subtends a central angle which, by definition, is **one radian**.

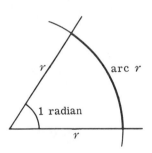

A central angle of 2 radians thus subtends an arc of length $2r$, a central angle of $\frac{1}{2}$ radian subtends an arc of length $\frac{1}{2}r$, and a central angle of x radians subtends an arc of length s, where

(1) $s = rx$, x in radians.

Central angles of $1°$ and $2°$ subtend arcs with the second twice the length of the first. In general, angles of $x°$ and $y°$ subtend arcs of lengths s_1 and s_2, which satisfy the proportion

Fig. 1-11.1

$$\frac{s_1}{s_2} = \frac{x}{y}.$$

By considering s_2 the whole circumference, and thus $y° = 360°$, it follows that a central angle of $x°$ subtends an arc of length s, where

$$\frac{s}{2\pi r} = \frac{x}{360}.$$

Thus,

(2) $$s = \left(\frac{\pi}{180} r\right) x,$$ x in degrees.

The fact that (1) is simpler than (2) is one of the reasons radian measure is used instead of degree measure.

An angle expressed in degrees may be converted to radians and vice versa. To obtain the conversion factors, replace the s of (1) by the circumference $2\pi r$:

$$2\pi r = rx,$$ x is 1 revolution in radians.

Since 1 revolution in degrees is $360°$, then 2π radians $= 360°$. Consequently,

(3) π radians $= 180°$,

(4)
$$1 \text{ radian} = \left(\frac{180}{\pi}\right)^{\circ},$$

(5)
$$1^{\circ} = \frac{\pi}{180} \text{ radians.}$$

The irrational number π is approximately 3.1416. Thus, an angle of 1 radian is approximately

$$\left(\frac{180}{3.1416}\right)^{\circ} = 57.2956^{\circ} = 57^{\circ} + (0.2956)60'$$
$$= 57^{\circ}17.736' = 57^{\circ}17' + (0.736)60''$$
$$= 57^{\circ}17'44.16''.$$

An angle of 1° is approximately

$$\frac{3.1416}{180} = 0.01745 \text{ radians.}$$

Also, areas of sectors are proportional to the central angles of the sectors. By considering the area of the whole circle as the area of a sector with central angle 2π radians, then the area A of a sector with central angle x radians is such that

(6)
$$\frac{A}{\pi r^{2}} = \frac{x}{2\pi} \quad \text{and} \quad A = (\tfrac{1}{2}r^{2})x \quad \text{for radian measure.}$$

In contrast, if the central angle is x°, then

(7)
$$\frac{A}{\pi r^{2}} = \frac{x}{360} \quad \text{and} \quad A = \left(\frac{\pi}{360}r^{2}\right)x \quad \text{for degree measure.}$$

Again, (6) is simpler than (7)—another reason for using radian measure.

Unfortunately, there is no established symbolism for indicating radian measure similar to the small superscript zero for degree measure. It is well accepted, however, that in a context where radian measure is being used no decoration whatever appears. Thus,

$$y = \sin x$$

means "with x a given number, form an angle of x radians and take the sine of that angle." If only a trigonometric table listing angles in degree measure is available, then the conversion

$$\sin 0.5 = \sin \left(\frac{1}{2}\frac{180}{\pi}\right)^{\circ}$$

would have to be made. Hence, approximately

$$\sin 0.5 = \sin \tfrac{1}{2} \, (57^{\circ}17'44.16'')$$
$$= \sin (28^{\circ}38'52.08''),$$

with interpolation to whatever accuracy is desired.

Chapter 2

Functions, Limits, and Derivatives

2-1. Sets

A few notions of naïve set theory are reviewed here in order to be specific about notation. The word "set" as used here is synonymous with "collection" or "aggregate." The set of dishes in a home or a man's set of golf clubs are examples. A set could consist of three specific boys who happen to be playing together. This set may be designated by

$$\{\text{Tom, Bob, George}\}.$$

The set whose only elements are the numbers 0, 1, 2, and 5 is designated by

$$\{0, 1, 2, 5\} \quad \text{or} \quad \{1, 0, 2, 5\} \quad \text{or} \quad \{5, 2, 1, 0\}$$

or any order of listing the elements.

The braces $\{\ \}$ are not merely fences to confine the elements but, by convention, are also flags to signal that set notation is being used.* In case the elements are too numerous to list individually, another bracket-bar notation is used. Thus,

$$\{x \mid 0 < x < 1\}$$

is the set of all positive numbers actually less than 1, or, isomorphically, the open unit interval of a coordinate line. Then

$$\{x \mid 0 \leq x \leq 1\}$$

is the above set of numbers augmented by the numbers 0 and 1 (or the origin and unit point to form the closed unit interval). In a similar way, if $a < b$, then

$$\{x \mid a < x < b\} \text{ and } \{x \mid a \leq x \leq b\}$$

are sets of numbers, or intervals, or both, according to the context or the inclination of the reader.

It is common practice to designate sets by capital letters A, B, X, Y, etc., and elements of sets by lower-case letters a, b, x, y, etc. The statement "x is

*This does not preclude the use of braces for grouping symbols such as
$$\{[(a + b)^2 + c]^3\}^4 + d.$$

28

an element of the set X" is replaced by

$$x \in X.$$

If A and B are sets such that, whenever $a \in A$ then also $a \in B$, the notation

$$A \subset B$$

is used and read "A is a subset of B." For example,

$$\{x \mid -1 \leq x \leq 1\} \subset \{x \mid -1 \leq x \leq 2\}.$$

In a house, the set D of dishes and the set C of cups are such that $C \subset D$.

Notice that, if A is any set, then $A \subset A$.

If A and B are sets, then $\{x \mid x \in A$ and $y \in B\}$ is called the **intersection** of A and B, and is denoted by $A \cap B$:

$$A \cap B = \{x \mid x \in A \text{ and } y \in B\}.$$

Thus,

$$\{x \mid -1 \leq x \leq 1\} \cap \{x \mid 0 < x \leq 2\} = \{x \mid 0 < x \leq 1\}.$$

There is no number (element) in the "set"

$$\{x \mid 0 \leq x < 1\} \cap \{x \mid 1 \leq x \leq 2\}.$$

Even though sets were originally conceived as consisting of "objects," mathematicians admit a special **empty set** as a convenience. The empty set will be denoted by $\emptyset$. Thus,

$$A \cap B = \emptyset$$

states that this set A and this set B have no element in common.

If A and B are sets, then $\{x \mid x \in A$ or $x \in B\}$ is called the **union** of A and B, and is denoted by $A \cup B$:

$$A \cup B = \{x \mid x \in A \text{ or } x \in B\}.$$

Thus,

$$\{x \mid -1 \leq x \leq 1\} \cup \{x \mid 0 < x < 2\} = \{x \mid -1 \leq x < 2\}.$$

The "or" appearing here is the "inclusive or"; it means that an element x is put in $A \cup B$, provided x satisfies at least one of*

$$x \in A, \ x \in B, \ x \in A \cap B.$$

Another concept is that of an **ordered pair**. The sets

$$\{a, b\} \text{ and } \{b, a\}$$

are identical, since the order of listing elements is immaterial. However, the ordered pairs

$$(a, b) \text{ and } (b, a)$$

are quite distinct if $a \neq b$, since ordering is all-important here. On an ordinary

---

*The "exclusive or" is used by the father who tells his son, "You may either go to college or go to work."

coordinate plane, the points designated by (1, 2) and (2,1) are plotted at different places. Logicians define "ordered" pair in a most formal manner, but the naïve notion that the "*first member* is named first and the *second member* is named second" is sufficient here.

Since sets may consist of any kind of elements whatever, sets of ordered pairs may be considered. For example,

$$R = \{(x, y) \,|\, 0 \leq x \leq 2 \text{ and } 0 \leq y \leq 1\}$$

may be represented on a coordinate plane by a rectangle and its interior, as in Fig. 2-1.1. The set

$$\{(1, 1), (-1, 1), (1, 2), (3, 1)\}$$

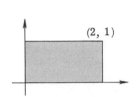

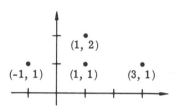

Fig. 2-1.1   Fig. 2-1.2

is represented graphically in Fig. 2-1.2.

The set

$$A = \{(x, y) \,|\, 0 \leq x \leq 1 \text{ and } 2x \leq y \leq 2\}$$

is represented by the shaded triangle of Fig. 2-1.3*A*. A convenient way of thinking about this is first to pick a number arbitrarily between 0 and 1, inclusive, and call it x. Whatever number x stands for, there is a number $2x$, and the points representing the ordered pairs

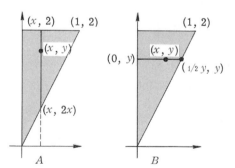

Fig. 2-1.3

$$(x, 2x) \text{ and } (x, 2)$$

may be visualized. Each point on the segment joining these points has a first coordinate x and a second coordinate y such that $2x \leq y \leq 2$. Then A is the set of all such points for all possible choices of x, $0 \leq x \leq 1$, and y, $2x \leq y \leq 2$.

A set B of ordered pairs of numbers is described by

$$B = \{(x, y) \,|\, 0 \leq y \leq 2 \text{ and } 0 \leq x \leq \tfrac{1}{2}y\}.$$

The notation means that a number y is to be selected first such that $0 \leq y \leq 2$. Then a number x such that $0 \leq x \leq \tfrac{1}{2}y$ is selected and the point (x, y) plotted as in Fig. 2-1.3*B*. Finally, the set of all points determined in this way represents the set *B*.

It is thus seen that $A = B$.

The equal sign has been used between symbols representing sets under the tacit assumption that anyone would consider sets to be equal provided both sets consist of exactly the same elements. Thus, sets *S* and *T* are equal, $S = T$, if and only if both $S \subset T$ and $T \subset S$, even if the descriptions of *S* and *T* are quite different.

The set notation and terminology given above are sufficient for the supporting role sets will play in the remainder of this book. Whether

$$\{(x, y) \,|\, y = x^2\}$$

is thought of as a set of ordered pairs of real numbers or as the representation of this set in a coordinate plane is immaterial.

2-2. Real Numbers

To the layman the number system of ordinary arithmetic is a finality, although he might be hard put if pressed for an unambiguous definition of what a real number is. The purpose of this section is *not* to push the development of the real number "field" to an axiomatic basis but rather to review the laws of real numbers in a vocabulary that students should become familiar with. Also, further experience with inequalities using the symbols $<$ and $>$ is preparatory for later work.

The system of real numbers is called a "field" because its operations of addition (taking a sum) and multiplication (taking a product) on any of its elements *a*, *b*, *c* and special elements 0 and 1 obey laws that define a **field** in modern terminology:

F_1. *Closure Laws.* The sum and product of two elements are elements.

F_2. *Associative Laws.* $a + (b + c) = (a + b) + c,$ $\qquad\qquad a(bc) = (ab)c.$

F_3. *Commutative Laws.* $\qquad a + b = b + a,$ $\qquad\qquad ab = ba.$

F_4. *Distributive Laws.* $\qquad\qquad a(b + c) = ab + ac.$

F_5. *Identity Elements.* $\qquad a + 0 = a,$ $\qquad\qquad a \cdot 1 = a.$

F_6. *Inverse Elements.* $\quad a + (-a) = 0,$ $\qquad\qquad a(1/a) = 1$ if $a \neq 0.$

Also, the *Cancellation Laws* hold:

(i) For *addition.* $a + c = b + c$ if and only if $a = b$.

(ii) For *multiplication.* For $c \neq 0$, then $ac = bc$ if and only if $a = b$.

Notice that $a \cdot 0 = 0$ is not included. However, $a + 0 = a$ by F_5, then $a \cdot a + a \cdot 0 = a \cdot a$ by F_4, and

$$a \cdot a + a \cdot 0 = a \cdot a + 0 \text{ again by } F_5.$$

Hence, cancellation of $a \cdot a$ by (i) gives $a \cdot 0 = 0$.

Subtraction and division are defined in terms of addition and multiplication. In particular,

$$b - c \text{ means } b + (-c),$$

$$a(b - c) = ab - ac, \text{ and}$$

$$\frac{a}{b} = a\left(\frac{1}{b}\right), \ b \neq 0.$$

The following theorem is an illustration of what can be proved on the basis of F_1 through F_6 (and intuitive properties of equality).

THEOREM. *$ab = 0$ if and only if $a = 0$ or $b = 0$.*

This theorem is assumed in elementary algebra when the factors in an equation such as $(x - 3)(x + 4) = 0$ are set equal to zero. A proof of the theorem, and other detailed deductions in abstract number fields, is reserved for a course on modern algebra. In this book, properties of the real number field will simply be accepted and statements will be made dogmatically.

The first equation of F_6 means that corresponding to each number a there is a number $(-a)$ such that $a + (-a) = 0$. This does not imply that a is a positive number or that $(-a)$ is a negative number. The terminology "let x be (or represent) a number" does not mean that the number is positive, and any tendency to think of x as positive should be curbed. Thus, $-x$ might be positive and certainly is positive if x is negative.

The set of nonzero real numbers is partitioned into the set of positive numbers and the set of negative numbers. By agreement,

"$0 < a$" is synonymous with "a is positive," and

"$a < 0$" is synonymous with "a is negative."

Hence, if x is a real number, then one and only one of

$$x < 0, \ x = 0, \ 0 < x$$

holds.

The following facts are stated for possible reference:

(1)   If $a < 0$, then $1/a < 0$; if $0 < a$, then $0 < 1/a$.

(2)   If $0 < a$ and $0 < b$, then $0 < ab$.

(3)   If $a < 0$ and $b < 0$, then $0 < ab$.

(4)   If $a < 0$ and $0 < b$, then $ab < 0$.

The applicability of $<$ is extended in the definition below.

DEFINITION. *For a and b real numbers, then*

$$a < b \text{ if and only if } 0 < b - a; \text{ or, equivalently,}$$

(5)   *if and only if $a - b < 0$.*

It is also agreed that $a > b$ may be used instead of $b < a$ and read as "a is greater than b" or as "b is less than a." Thus,

(6) $\qquad\qquad a > b$ if and only if $a - b > 0.$

It follows that, if a and b are real numbers, then one and only one of

$$a < b, \ a > b, \ a = b$$

holds; that is, there is an "order" in the real number system. This ordering of the real numbers has the properties:

0_1. *Transitive.* If $a < b$ and $b < c$, then $a < c$.

0_2. *Additive Cancellation.* $a + c < b + c$ if and only if $a < b$.

0_3. *Multiplicative Cancellation.*

  (i) For $c > 0$, then $ac < bc$ if and only if $a < b$.

  (ii) For $c < 0$, then $ac < bc$ if and only if $a > b$.

As an illustration, 0_3(ii) will be proved:

Case 1: $c < 0$ and $ac < bc$. Then $ac - bc < 0$ by (5), $c(a - b) < 0$ by F_4, and now (1) and "minus times minus is plus" as condensed in (3) give

$$\frac{1}{c}c(a - b) > 0.$$

Hence, by F_6 and F_3, $a - b > 0$, so that $a > b$ by (6).

Case 2: $c < 0$ and $a > b$. Mentally check, with reasons, that

$$a - b > 0, \ c(a - b) < 0, \ ca - cb < 0, \ ac < bc.$$

Hence, operations cryptically described by "transpose," "cross multiply," etc., may be performed using $<$ or $>$ instead of $=$. Care must be taken, however, to change the direction of the inequality whenever both sides are multiplied or divided by a negative number. For example, if x is a number such that $-2x + 1 < 6$, then

$$-2x + 1 + (-1) < 6 - 1 \qquad\qquad \text{by } 0_2,$$

$$-2x < 5,$$

$$x > -\tfrac{5}{2} \text{ by } 0_3 \text{ (ii), with } c = -\tfrac{1}{2}.$$

Another situation in which the inequality is reversed is:

$$\text{if } 0 < a < b, \text{ then } \frac{1}{a} > \frac{1}{b} > 0.$$

The symbols used in mathematical formulas may be classified as constants, variables, and auxiliary symbols. In

$$(3 + x)^2,$$

there is no question about 3 and 2 being constants. The formula leaves open what number x stands for, and more about this will be discussed presently.

The parentheses act somewhat as punctuation marks in that their omission yields $3 + x^2$, which has a different meaning from $(3 + x)^2$.

As one author observes, "in mathematics, a variable is a shadowy, ill-defined entity,"* and the word "variable" is avoided by some mathematicians. Nevertheless, the word is used,† but should be shorn of its historical implication that in some vague way "a number can vary." As usually understood today, *a **variable** is a symbol used to represent an arbitrary element of a set.* The set may either be specified in advance or understood by context.

A statement in which one or more variables occur is called an **open statement**. Thus,

(7) $$x^2 + x - 12 = 0$$

is an open statement. The variable x may take any number as a value, and for some values the assertion of the statement is true, but for others it is false.

The set of values of the variables for which the assertion of an open statement is true is called the **truth set** of the statement. Hence, $\{-4, 3\}$ is the truth set for (7). The open statement $-2x < 1$ has truth set $\{x \mid x > -\frac{1}{2}\}$.

The **conjunction** of two open statements involving a single variable x has as truth set the intersection of the truth sets of the separate statements.

Example 1. Find the truth set of the conjunction

(8) $$x + 4 > 0 \text{ and } 3 - x > 0.$$

Solution. The separate truth sets are

$$T_1 = \{x \mid x > -4\} \text{ and } T_2 = \{x \mid 3 > x\}.$$

Hence, the truth set of the conjunction (8) is

$$\{x \mid x > -4\} \cap \{x \mid 3 > x\} = \{x \mid -4 < x < 3\}.$$

It is natural to represent the situation as in Fig. 2–2.1.

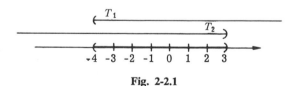

Fig. 2-2.1

Example 2. Find the truth set of the conjunction

$$x + 4 < 0 \text{ and } 3 - x < 0.$$

Solution. The separate truth sets are $\{x \mid x < -4\}$ and $\{x \mid 3 < x\}$, so that (see Fig. 2–2.2)

---

*J. Barkley Rosser, *Logic for Mathematicians* (New York: McGraw-Hill Book Company, Inc., 1953), p. 87.

†Some departments of mathematics, for example, offer courses entitled "Functions of a Real Variable" and "Functions of Complex Variables."

$$\{x \mid x < -4\} \cap \{x \mid 3 < x\} = \emptyset.$$

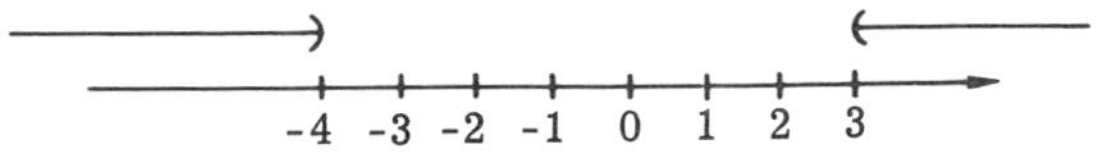

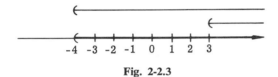

Fig. 2-2.2

The truth set being empty merely means that no number satisfies both inequalities.

The **disjunction** of two open statements of a single variable x is the union of the separate truth sets.

Example 3. Find the truth set of the disjunction*

$$x + 4 > 0 \text{ or } 3 - x < 0.$$

Solution. $T_1 = \{x \mid x > -4\}$, $T_2 = \{x \mid 3 < x\}$, so that (see Fig. 2–2.3)

$$T_1 \cup T_2 = \{x \mid x > -4\} \cup \{x \mid 3 < x\} = \{x \mid x > -4\}.$$

Fig. 2-2.3

Even though the equal sign is used in both

$$x^2 + x - 12 = (x - 3)(x + 4) \text{ and } x^2 + x - 12 = 0,$$

distinct meanings are conveyed. The first open statement has the whole number field as its truth set, whereas the second has truth set $\{3, -4\}$. In the first situation the equal sign is sometimes replaced by $\equiv$ for emphasis, and the statement is called an identity. An **identity** is an open statement in a variable x in which the truth set of the statement is the whole possibility set for x. "Possibility set for x" is inserted to take care of such situations as

$$\tan x \equiv \frac{\sin x}{\cos x},$$

in which the definition of $\tan x$ excludes the possibility of x being $\pi/2 + m\pi$, with m an integer.

The following example illustrates the analysis of an open statement by considerations of conjunctions and disjunctions of simpler open statements.

Example 4. Find the truth set of the open statement

(9) $$x^2 + x - 12 > 0.$$

*The "or" is the "inclusive or"; see p. 29.

Solution. From the identity $x^2 + x - 12 \equiv (x - 3)(x + 4)$, the open statement
$$(x - 3)(x + 4) > 0$$
has the same truth set as (9). Now

(10) $$x - 3 > 0 \quad \text{and} \quad x + 4 > 0$$

is one conjunction, while

(11) $$x - 3 < 0 \quad \text{and} \quad x + 4 < 0$$

is another, and the disjunction of these two is a statement with the same truth set as (9). Since the truth sets of (10) and (11) are, respectively,

$$T_1 = \{x \mid x > 3\} \cap \{x \mid x > -4\} = \{x \mid x > 3\},$$
$$T_2 = \{x \mid x < 3\} \cap \{x \mid x < -4\} = \{x \mid x < -4\},$$

then the truth set T of (9) is the union of T_1 with T_2:

$$T = T_1 \cup T_2 = \{x \mid x < -4\} \cup \{x \mid x > 3\}.$$

Two open statements are said to be **equivalent** if they have the same truth set. Thus, the following open statements are equivalent:

$$-1 < 1 - 3x < 4,$$
$$-1 - 1 < -3x < -1 + 4 \qquad (\text{-1 added to each term}),$$
$$-2 < -3x < 3,$$
$$\tfrac{2}{3} > x > -1 \qquad (\text{each term divided by } -3),$$
$$-1 < x < \tfrac{2}{3}.$$

The last of these is said to be the **solution** of the first. In this terminology, Example 4 is restated and reworked as:

Example 4′. Solve the inequality $x^2 + x - 12 > 0$.

Solution. $(x - 3)(x + 4) \equiv x^2 + x - 12 > 0$ holds whenever both factors are positive or else both factors are negative.

Case 1: $x - 3 > 0$ and $x + 4 > 0$.	*Case 2:* $x - 3 < 0$ and $x + 4 < 0$.
$x > 3$ and $x > -4$,	$x < 3$ and $x < -4$,
$\therefore x > 3$	$\therefore x < -4$

Answer: Either $x > 3$ or else $x < -4$.

As another approach, the graph of $y = (x - 3)(x + 4)$ crosses the x-axis when $x = 3$ and $x = -4$, and there is no break in the graph (as established later). It is then easy to check where the graph is above the x-axis and thus visualize all values of x for which $(x - 3)(x + 4) > 0$ (see Fig. 2-2.4). The interplay between geometry and algebra is the heart and soul of analytic geometry.

Real numbers are endowed with a further property that is not pointed out specifically in most discussions of arithmetic and algebra but that is fundamental in calculus. A concise statement requires clarification of some terminology.

A set A of real numbers is said to be **bounded above** if there is at least one

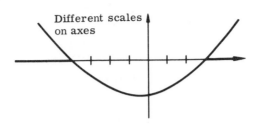

Different scales
on axes

Fig. 2-2.4

number b such that $a \le b$ for every $a \in A$. Such a number b is said to be an
upper bound of A. If b is an upper bound of A, then any number greater than b
is an upper bound of A, but it is possible that there is no upper bound of A
which is less than b. In fact, a number b_0 is said to be a **least upper bound** of
A if both:

(i) b_0 is an upper bound of A, and

(ii) there is no upper bound of A less than b_0.

Hence, if b_0 is a least upper bound of A and $b' < b_0$, then b' is not an upper
bound of A; that is, a set can have at most one least upper bound. Of course,
a set need not have any upper bound at all, in which case the set is said to be
unbounded above. For example, the set of all integers is unbounded above.

   The property of real numbers alluded to above may now be stated.

   THE COMPLETION AXIOM.* *If a set A of real numbers is nonempty and bounded
above, then there is a unique number b_0 which is the least upper bound of A.*

   This is an axiom, and as such neither calls for, nor admits of, a proof. The
Completion Axiom is given now so as not to interrupt later expositions, but
an appreciation of its significance is not expected until its utility has been
demonstrated by actual use. This axiom plays a basic role in mathematical
analysis.

   Problem 1. Let a and b be numbers. Justify each step in the following:

$$(-a)(-b) = (-a)(-b) + 0$$
$$= (-a)(-b) + a \cdot 0$$
$$= (-a)(-b) + a[b + (-b)]$$
$$= (-a)(-b) + ab + a(-b)$$
$$= (-a)(-b) + a(-b) + ab$$
$$= [(-a) + a](-b) + ab$$
$$= 0 \cdot (-b) + ab$$
$$= 0 + ab$$
$$= ab.$$

*Sometimes called "The Continuity Axiom."

Problem 2. Establish the following set equalities:

a. $\{(x, y)\,|\,0 \leq x \leq 2,\ 0 \leq y \leq x\} = \{(x, y)\,|\,0 \leq y \leq 2,\ y \leq x \leq 2\}$.

b. $\{(x, y)\,|\,1 \leq x \leq 2,\ 1 \leq y \leq x\} = \{(x, y)\,|\,1 \leq y \leq 2,\ y \leq x \leq 2\}$.

c. $\{(x, y)\,|\,-1 \leq x \leq 0,\ 0 \leq y \leq -x\} = \{(x, y)\,|\,0 \leq y \leq 1,\ -1 \leq x \leq -y\}$.

d. $\{(x, y)\,|\,0 \leq x \leq 1,\ 1 \leq y \leq 1 + x\} = \{(x, y)\,|\,1 \leq y \leq 2,\ y - 1 \leq x \leq 1\}$.

e. $\{(x, y)\,|\,0 \leq x \leq 1,\ \frac{1}{2}x \leq y \leq x\} \cup \{(x, y)\,|\,1 \leq x \leq 2,\ \frac{1}{2}x \leq y \leq 1\}$
$$= \{(x, y)\,|\,0 \leq y \leq 1, y \leq x \leq 2y\}.$$

Problem 3. Find the truth set of each of the conjunctions:

a. $2x - 1 > 0$ and $x - 3 \leq 0$.   c. $x > 2$ and $-x > -3$.

b. $x - 1 \geq 1$ and $1 - x < 0$.   d. $3x - 3 \leq 3$ and $-3x - 3 \leq -3$.

Problem 4. Find the truth set of each of the disjunctions:

a. $2x - 1 > 0$ or $x - 3 \leq 0$.   c. $x > 2$ or $-x < -3$.

b. $2x - 1 < 0$ or $x - 3 \geq 0$.   d. $1/(1 + x) < 0$ or $-x \geq 2$.

Problem 5. Solve the inequalities:

a. $-2 < 3x + 1 < 4$.   e. $x^2 + x - 2 > 0$

b. $3x > 2 > x$.   f. $2x^2 - x - 6 < 0$.

c. $-2 - x < 3x + 1 < 4 - x$.   g. $x^2 + 3x + 2 < 0$.

d. $2x + 1 < 2 < 3x$.   h. $(x - 1)(x + 1)(x - 3) < 0$.

2-3. Functions

A function, as used in mathematics, has a set D called the **domain** (of definition) and a **rule** f for assigning to each element of the domain an element of a second set Y. The sets D and Y may consist of any type of elements whatever, as illustrated in the following examples.

Example 1. D is the set of human beings now living in Greater New York City, Y is the set of nonnegative integers, and the rule f is:

> Assign to each person his age
> in years to the nearest integer.

Example 2. *Rule:* Each person is assigned his first name. D is the set of all persons living in San Francisco.

Example 3. $D = Y = $ set of all real numbers. *Rule:* Whatever number is given, cube it.

Example 4. $D = \{x\,|\,-1 \leq x \leq 1\}$, $Y = \{y\,|\,y \geq 0\}$. *Rule:* For $x \in D$, assign the solution of $x^2 + y^2 = 1$, which is in Y.

Example 5. Sets $D = \{0, 1, 3, 5\}$, $Y = \{2, 3, 4, 6, 8\}$, and

(1) $\{(0, 2),\ (1, 2),\ (3, 4),\ (5, 6),\ (7, 8),\ (10, 2),\ (5, 10)\}$

are given. *Rule:* In the given set of ordered pairs, if an ordered pair has first member in D and second member in Y, then assign that second member to that first member.

Example 6. The table

x	2	-1	1	3
y	3	-4	3	7

gives D as the set of x values, Y as the set of y values and the rule: To each x value assign the y value immediately below it.

The rule in Example 1 could be applied to any person whatever, whether he lived in Greater New York City or not. Thus, if the rule in Example 1 is applied to the domain of Example 2, then a function is obtained which, however, is different from both of the original functions.

In Example 1, the specification of Y was much too generous in that nowhere near all of its elements were used. In fact, it would be safe to replace Y by

$$Y_1 = \{y \mid y \text{ is an integer and } 0 \le y \le 150\}.$$

The function so obtained would be the same as before. If, however, Y were replaced by

$$Y_2 = \{y \mid y \text{ is an integer and } 0 \le y \le 50\}$$

then there would be no function in that there would be at least one element of D which could not be assigned a value by the rule.

It is possible that the age of some person in Greater New York City is not known to himself or to anyone else. This would not destroy the function of Example 1. In the same way with

D = set of positive integers, Y = set of nonnegative integers, and
the rule: Assign to $n \in D$ the nth digit in the decimal expansion of π

a function is defined even though no one knows what integer to assign to $10^{10} \in D$.

Mathematicians rely upon conventions about notation to subdue verbosity. If f stands for the rule characterizing a function, then

$$y = f(x)$$

is used to specify the $y \in Y$ assigned to $x \in D$. Thus,

(2) $$y = x^3$$

is sufficiently descriptive for reasonable communication about the function of Example 3. The description of the function of Example 4 is distilled to*

(3) $$y = \sqrt{1 - x^2}, \quad -1 \le x \le 1.$$

The statement "let g be the function defined by

*The use of the square root symbol is discussed later.

$$g(0) = 2, \; g(1) = 2, \; g(3) = 4, \; g(5) = 6 \text{ "}$$

is preferable to the full description of the function given in Example 5. Note that if the set (1) were augmented by the element (0, 3), then there would be no function; that is, $g(0)$ would not be defined uniquely by the rule.

It is permissible to let the rule imply a usable set for Y. This was done in Example 2 and could have been done in other examples as well. The equations (2) and (3) leave little doubt that the functions indicated have values in the set of real numbers. In fact, the set Y is usually of little importance, provided only that it is extensive enough to include all assignments the rule (applied to D) calls for. Of more significance is the range of a function (as defined below).

A terse summary of the above discussion is given in the following definition.

DEFINITION. *A function f is a set of ordered pairs such that, if $(a, b) \in f$ and $(a, c) \in f$, then $b = c$. The set of all first members of elements of f is called the **domain** D_f of f. The set of all second members of elements of f is called the **range** R_f of f. If $x \in D_f$, then the $y \in R_f$ such that $(x, y) \in f$ is called the **value** of f at x, and is represented by*

$$y = f(x).$$

For example,

$$f = \{(0, 1), (2, 3), (3, 1)\}$$

is a function that could be given by listing

$$f(0) = f(3) = 1, \; f(2) = 3.$$

Another perfectly good set of ordered pairs is

$$g = \{(1, 0), (3, 2), (1, 3)\}.$$

Here both $(1, 0) \in g$ and $(1, 3) \in g$, but $0 \neq 3$. Hence, this set g is not a function.

Precision is desirable, but sometimes it is too austere. In any case, mathematicians do not agree on how to define a function.* The proliferation of notation and terminology may be illustrated by the following example:

Let D and Y both be the set of all real numbers and for $x \in D$ assign $y \in Y$ by the rule $y = x^2$.

Among the ways appearing in the literature of describing this function (call it f) are the following:

(a) $y = f(x) = x^2$ is a function of x, or

     y is a function of the independent variable x, or

     the dependent variable y is a function of the independent variable x.

(b) f is the function defined by $f(x) = x^2$, or

     f is the function whose value at x is $f(x) = x^2$.

(c) $f: D \longrightarrow Y$ is the function on D **into** Y given by $f(x) = x^2$;

     $f: D \longrightarrow R_f$ is the function on D **onto** R_f given by $f(x) = x^2$.

*I do not know of two books, even revisions by the same author, with identical definitions.

(d) f: (x, y) is the function whose ordered pairs are (x, x^2).
(e) $f = \{(x, y) \mid y = x^2\}$.

For any of these, there are situations in which one method seems to have advantages (or preferences) over the others. For example, (c) is indigenous to any situation in which the transformation or mapping feature of the function is predominent: f "carries" each element of D to its correspondent in Y or "represents" D on R_f. It is fairly common to replace "function" in (c) by "transformation" or "map" or "mapping." In this book, neither (c) nor (d) is used.

The mass of pre-World War II mathematical textbooks, together with current literature on applications, are replete with (a), and it is doubtful if this method will ever fade out completely.

Present fashion apparently favors (e) slightly over (b) and both of these over the others in most situations.

Since students are preparing for the future, but cannot ignore either the past or allied fields, all three of (a), (b), and (e) will be used in this book.

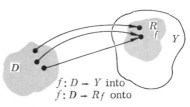

$f: D \rightarrow Y$ into
$f: D \rightarrow R_f$ onto

Fig. 2-3.1

2-4.　Functional Notation

The use of functional notation is illustrated in the following examples.

Example 1. Let f be the function defined for each real x by

$$f(x) = x^2 - 3.$$

Then $f(0) = 0^2 - 3 = -3$,
$f(1) = 1^2 - 3 = -2$, $f(2) = 1$, and

$$f(2.1) = (2.1)^2 - 3 = 4.41 - 3 = 1.41.$$

Such ratios as

$$\frac{f(2.1) - f(2)}{2.1 - 2} = \frac{1.41 - 1}{0.1} = \frac{0.41}{0.1} = 4.1$$

will come into play shortly. Since the points $(2, 1)$ and $(2.1, 1.41)$ are on the graph of f, this ratio shows that the line joining these points has slope $m = 4.1$. For x any number and $h \neq 0$,

$$\frac{f(x + h) - f(x)}{h}$$

is the slope of the line joining the points

$$(x, f(x)) \text{ and } (x + h, f(x + h))$$

of the graph of f.

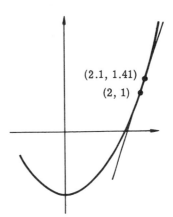

(2.1, 1.41)
(2, 1)

Fig. 2-4.1

For any numbers a and b, then $f(a) = a^2 - 3$, $f(b) = b^2 - 3$, and

$$f(a + b) = (a + b)^2 - 3 = a^2 + 2ab + b^2 - 3.$$

It therefore follows that the inequality

$$f(a + b) \neq f(a) + f(b)$$

is more to be expected than to have equality hold. Thus, $f(x)$ must not be thought of as "f times x."

Special symbols are often used in defining functions, such as $|x|$ and $\sqrt{x}$.

The absolute value symbol $|x|$ is easily interpreted for any specific value of x. Thus, $|-2| = 2$. It should be understood (to repeat the definition given on page 4) that, by definition,

(1)
$$|x| = \begin{cases} x & \text{if } x \geq 0, \\ -x & \text{if } x < 0. \end{cases}$$

Example 2. Let f and g be the functions defined by

$$f = \{(x, y) \,|\, y = |x|\} \quad \text{and} \quad g = \left\{(x, y) \,\middle|\, y = \frac{x + |x|}{2}\right\}.$$

Then $f(-1) = |-1| = 1$ and $g(-1) = \frac{1}{2}(-1 + |-1|) = \frac{1}{2}(-1 + 1) = 0$. Moreover, $g(x)$ may be expressed in two parts, corresponding to the way $|x|$ was defined:

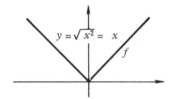

$y = \sqrt{x^2} = x$ f

Fig. 2-4.2

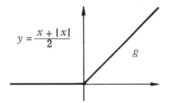

$y = \dfrac{x + |x|}{2}$ g

Fig. 2-4.3

$$g(x) = \begin{cases} \frac{1}{2}(x + x) = x & \text{if } x \geq 0, \\ \frac{1}{2}(x - x) = 0 & \text{if } x < 0. \end{cases}$$

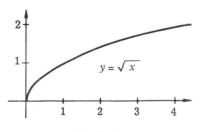

$y = \sqrt{x}$

Fig. 2-4.4

The accompanying graphs of f and g should be examined. Note that neither has a break, but each has a corner.

Many mistakes have been made in mathematics and its applications because of a prevalent misunderstanding about the square root symbol, $\sqrt{}$. The following definition is labeled as such to emphasize that, in calculus and beyond, an unambiguous meaning is attached to $\sqrt{x}$ for $x \geq 0$.

DEFINITION. *If x is any nonnegative number, then $\sqrt{x}$ is that **nonnegative number** whose square is x.*

Thus, $\sqrt{4} = 2$, not ± 2. Also, $\sqrt{(-2)^2} = 2 = |-2|$.

The mistakes mentioned above occur by the careless replacement of $\sqrt{x^2}$ by x. It follows from the above definition that, if x is any number, then

$$\sqrt{x^2} = \begin{cases} x \text{ if } x \geq 0, \\ -x \text{ if } x < 0, \end{cases} \quad \text{or briefly,} \quad \sqrt{x^2} = |x|.$$

Hence, the graphs of $y = \sqrt{x^2}$ and $y = |x|$ are identical, as shown in Fig. 2-4.2. Also note that

$$\sqrt{1 - \sin^2 x} = \begin{cases} \cos x \text{ if } 0 \leq x \leq \pi/2 \text{ or } 3\pi/2 \leq x \leq 2\pi \\ -\cos x \text{ if } \pi/2 \leq x \leq 3\pi/2. \end{cases}$$

Example 3. If a particle moves in the (x, y)-plane in such a way that its distance from the origin is always exactly three units, then the coordinates (x, y) of the particle at any time are such that $\sqrt{x^2 + y^2} = 3$. Hence, the open statement (of two variables)

(2) $$x^2 + y^2 = 9$$

has its truth set represented by a circle. With (x, y) confined to this truth set, the variables x and y are restricted by

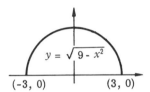 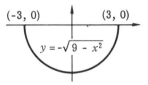

Fig. 2-4.5

$-3 \leq x \leq 3$ and $-3 \leq y \leq 3$.

If x is selected as the independent variable, then y is given by either

$$y = \sqrt{9 - x^2} \text{ or } y = -\sqrt{9 - x^2}, \quad -3 \leq x \leq 3.$$

In further analysis of these functional relationships, possible confusion caused by the dual use of y could be avoided by defining functions f_1 and f_2 by

$$f_1(x) = \sqrt{9 - x^2} \text{ and } f_2(x) = -\sqrt{9 - x^2},$$
$$-3 \leq x \leq 3.$$

Example 4. The equation $y^2 = x$ may be dealt with either by:
1. Defining two functions $f_1(x) = \sqrt{x}$ and $f_2(x) = -\sqrt{x}$, $0 \leq x$; or else
2. Considering x as a function of y and defining a function g by setting $g(y) = y^2$.

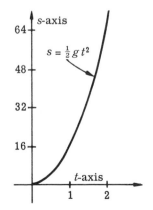

Fig. 2-4.6
(for Ex. 5, p. 44)

Example 5. The distance s a body falls in a vacuum is a function of the time $t \geq 0$ given by

$$s = \tfrac{1}{2}gt^2.$$

Note that g is not used here in the functional sense but represents the constant of gravitation whose value in the foot-pound-second system is approximately 32.2 ft-lb/sec. The graph on a (t, s)-coordinate system is given in Fig. 2–4.6.

Example 6. The equations

$$y = \sin x \text{ and } y = \cos x$$

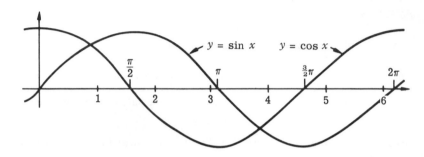

Fig. 2-4.7

designate the sine and cosine functions. *Throughout all of the calculus of trigonometric functions, angles are measured in radians.** Thus, sin 2 means "The sine of an angle of 2 radians."

Example 7. The equation

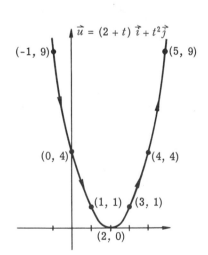

Fig. 2-4.8

(3) $\vec{u} = (2 + t)\vec{i} + t^2\vec{j}$

denotes a vector-valued function of the real variable t. As defined earlier, a function is a set of ordered pairs such that, if (a, b) and (a, c) are in the set, then $b = c$. However, the nature of the members of the ordered pairs was not specified. Hence, the above indicated function could have been given as

$$\vec{F} = \{(t, \vec{u}) \mid \vec{u} = (2 + t)\vec{i} + t^2\vec{j}\}.$$

A vector-valued function $\vec{u} = \vec{F}(t)$ is used in studying motion of a particle and is called a **law of motion**. The particle is visualized at time t as being at the terminal end of the vector $\vec{F}(t)$ having initial end at the origin. The following table was constructed from (3):

*Reasons for using radian measure are given in Sec. 2–11.

t	-3	-2	-1	0	1	2	3
$\vec{u}$	$-\vec{i}+9\vec{j}$	$0\vec{i}+4\vec{j}$	$\vec{i}+\vec{j}$	$2\vec{i}+0\vec{j}$	$3\vec{i}+\vec{j}$	$4\vec{i}+4\vec{j}$	$5\vec{i}+9\vec{j}$

The terminal ends of these specific vectors are plotted and then joined by a smooth curve in Fig. 2-4.8. Arrowheads are placed on the curve to show direction of motion of the particle along the curve.

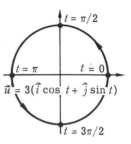

Recall that (2) was introduced as giving variable locations of a particle moving, but always staying three units from the origin. From equation (2) alone, the location of the particle at any time cannot be predicted. The graph of the vector-valued function

$$(4) \qquad \vec{u} = 3(\vec{i}\ \cos t + \vec{j}\ \sin t)$$

Fig. 2-4.9

is also a circle, since at any specified time t the terminal end of $\vec{u}$ is at the point $(3 \cos t, 3 \sin t)$ whose distance to the origin is

$$|\vec{u}| = \sqrt{(3 \cos t)^2 + (3 \sin t)^2} = \sqrt{9(\cos^2 t + \sin^2 t)} = \sqrt{9} = 3.$$

The particle starts (when $t = 0$) at the point $(3, 0)$ and moves counterclockwise around and around the circle at uniform speed.

A particle with law of motion

$$\vec{u} = 3(\vec{i}\ \cos 2t + \vec{j}\ \sin 2t)$$

starts at the same point $(3, 0)$, moves on the same circle, but at twice the speed of the particle following the law (4).

Problem 1. Given:

a. $f = \{(x,y) \mid y = x^2 - x + 2\}$, compute $f(2), f(-2), f(2.1) - f(2), f(2 + h) - f(2)$.

b. $g(x) = \dfrac{3x - 1}{x}$, $x \neq 0$, compute $g(4), g(-3), g(3.2) - g(3), g(3 + h) - g(3)$.

c. S is the function defined by $S(x) = \sin(\pi x)$, compute $S(\tfrac{1}{2}), S(\tfrac{1}{3}), S(\tfrac{2}{3}), S(-\tfrac{1}{3})$, $S(\tfrac{1}{2}) - S(\tfrac{1}{3})$.

d. $y = L(x) = \log_{10} x$, $x > 0$, find $L(1), L(2), L(\tfrac{1}{2}), L(3)$.
Is $L(x_1 + x_2)$ equal to $L(x_1) + L(x_2)$?
Is $L(x_1 x_2)$ equal to $L(x_1)L(x_2)$?
Is $L(x_1 + x_2)$ equal to $L(x_1)L(x_2)$?

Problem 2. Write out and simplify $\dfrac{f(a + h) - f(a)}{h}$ if:

a. f is the function defined by $f(x) = x^2$.

b. $f = \{(x, y) \mid y = x^2 - x + 2\}$.

c. $f = \{(t, s) \mid s = \tfrac{1}{3}t^3\}$.

d. $f(u) = \log_{10} u$, $u > 0$.

e. $y = f(x) = x + \dfrac{1}{x}$ for $x \neq 0$.

f. $s = f(t) = \dfrac{3t^2 + 1}{t}$, $t \neq 0$.

Problem 3. Sketch a graph of each of the following functions of x:

a. $y = x^2 - 4$.

b. $y = x + \dfrac{1}{x}$.

c. $y = 2 \sin x$.

d. $y = \sin(2x)$.

e. $y = \sin(x + 2)$.

f. $y = \cos(x - \pi)$.

Problem 4. Sketch the graphs of the vector-valued functions:

a. $\vec{u} = (2 - t)\vec{i} + t^2\vec{j}$.

b. $\vec{u} = t^2\vec{i} + (2 + t)\vec{j}$.

c. $\vec{u} = t(2\vec{i} + 3\vec{j})$.

d. $\vec{u} = (\sin t)(2\vec{i} + 3\vec{j})$.

e. $\vec{u} = 2\vec{i} \cos t + 3\vec{j} \sin t$.

f. $\vec{u} = 2\vec{i} \cos t - 3\vec{j} \sin t$.

Problem 5. Establish the following set equalities:

a. $\{(x, y) \,|\, 0 \le x \le 1,\ 0 \le y \le x^2\} = \{(x, y) \,|\, 0 \le y \le 1,\ \sqrt{y} \le x \le 1\}$.

b. $\{(x, y) \,|\, 0 \le x \le 1,\ x^2 \le y \le 1\} = \{(x, y) \,|\, 0 \le y \le 1,\ 0 \le x \le \sqrt{y}\}$.

c. $\{(x, y) \,|\, 0 \le x \le 1,\ x^2 \le y \le \sqrt{x}\} = \{(x, y) \,|\, 0 \le y \le 1,\ y^2 \le x \le \sqrt{y}\}$.

d. $\{(x, y) \,|\, -1 \le x \le 1,\ x^2 \le y \le 1\} = \{(x, y) \,|\, 0 \le y \le 1,\ -\sqrt{y} \le x \le \sqrt{y}\}$.

e. $\{(x, y) \,|\, -1 \le x \le 1,\ |x| \le y \le 1\} = \{(x, y) \,|\, 0 \le y \le 1,\ -y \le x \le y\}$.

2-5. Tangent Lines, Velocities

On a curve select a point $P(x_1, y_1)$ and a nearby point $Q(x_2, y_2)$ also on the curve. The line segment joining P and Q is a chord of the curve. This chord has slope m_{PQ} given by

(1)
$$m_{PQ} = \frac{y_2 - y_1}{x_2 - x_1}, \quad x_1 \ne x_2.$$

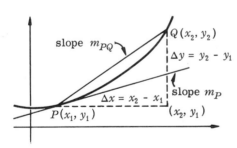

Fig. 2-5.1

As Q slides along the curve and approaches P, then y_2 approaches y_1, x_2 approaches x_1, and m_{PQ} may or may not approach some definite number. If m_{PQ} approaches a definite number, this number is denoted by m_P, and the line through $P(x_1, y_1)$ with slope m_P is said to be the **tangent line** of the curve at $P(x_1, y_1)$.

In the algebraic determination of tangent lines it is convenient to use the standard notation

$$\Delta x = x_2 - x_1 \quad \text{and} \quad \Delta y = y_2 - y_1.$$

The variables Δx and Δy are called **increments** of x and y, respectively. Thus, (1) written in increment notation is

$$m_{PQ} = \frac{\Delta y}{\Delta x}.$$

Also, the accepted notation for the above verbal description of "m_{PQ} approaching m_P" is

$$m_P = \lim_{Q \to P} m_{PQ} = \lim_{\Delta x \to 0} \frac{\Delta y}{\Delta x}.$$

Example 1. Find the slope of the tangent to the graph of

$$y = f(x) = 4 - x^2$$

at the point P of the curve having $x_1 = 1$.

Solution. Since $f(1) = 4 - 1^2 = 3$, then $y_1 = 3$ and hence $P(1, 3)$ is the desired point. Since $x_2 = x_1 + \Delta x = 1 + \Delta x$, then

$$y_2 = f(1 + \Delta x) = 4 - (1 + \Delta x)^2$$
$$= 4 - (1 + 2\,\Delta x + \overline{\Delta x}^2) = 3 - 2\,\Delta x - \overline{\Delta x}^2$$

and the point Q is $(1 + \Delta x, 3 - 2\,\Delta x - \overline{\Delta x}^2)$. Therefore,

$$m_{PQ} = \frac{\Delta y}{\Delta x} = \frac{y_2 - y_1}{x_2 - x_1} = \frac{(3 - 2\,\Delta x - \overline{\Delta x}^2) - 3}{(1 + \Delta x) - 1}$$

$$= \frac{-2\,\Delta x - \overline{\Delta x}^2}{\Delta x} = -2 - \Delta x.$$

The increment Δx is never assigned the value zero (for, if $\Delta x = 0$, then P and Q would coincide). Note, however, that $m_{PQ} = -2 - \Delta x$ may be made as close to $m_P = -2$ as desired merely by choosing Δx close enough to zero. As Q approaches P, then $\Delta x \to 0$ and

$$m_P = \lim_{Q \to P} m_{PQ} = \lim_{\Delta x \to 0} (-2 - \Delta x) = -2.$$

Thus, at the point $P(1, 3)$ of the graph of $y = f(x) = 4 - x^2$, the tangent to the graph has slope $m_P = -2$. The point-slope equation of this tangent is therefore

$$y - 3 = -2(x - 1).$$

Example 2. Find m_P for the graph of $y = f(x) = 4 - x^2$ and $P(x_1, y_1)$ a point of this graph.

Solution. First, $y_1 = f(x_1) = 4 - x_1^2$. For $x_2 = x_1 + \Delta x$, then

$$y_2 = f(x_2) = f(x_1 + \Delta x) = 4 - (x_1 + \Delta x)^2$$
$$= 4 - x_1^2 - 2x_1\,\Delta x - \overline{\Delta x}^2,$$

and

$$\Delta y = y_2 - y_1 = f(x_1 + \Delta x) - f(x_1)$$
$$= (4 - x_1^2 - 2x_1\,\Delta x - \overline{\Delta x}^2) - (4 - x_1^2)$$
$$= -2x_1\,\Delta x - \overline{\Delta x}^2.$$

Upon dividing Δy by Δx, the result is

$$m_{PQ} = \frac{\Delta y}{\Delta x} = \frac{f(x_1 + \Delta x) - f(x_1)}{\Delta x} = \frac{-2x_1\,\Delta x - \overline{\Delta x}^2}{\Delta x} = -2x_1 - \Delta x.$$

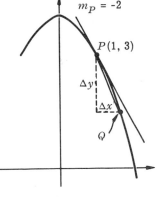

$m_P = -2$

$P(1, 3)$

Δy

Δx

Q

Fig. 2-5.2

Now x_1 is a constant but $\Delta x \neq 0$ is a variable. So as $\Delta x \to 0$, then $-2x_1 - \Delta x$ approaches the constant $-2x_1$ as a limit. In notation,

$$\dot{m}_P = \lim_{Q \to P} m_{PQ} = \lim_{\Delta x \to 0} \frac{\Delta y}{\Delta x} = \lim_{\Delta x \to 0} \frac{f(x_1 + \Delta x) - f(x_1)}{\Delta x}$$

$$= \lim_{\Delta x \to 0} (-2x_1 - \Delta x) = -2x_1.$$

For velocity considerations, first take a particle moving on the x-axis according to the law

$$\vec{u} = \vec{F}(t) = (t^2 - 4t)\vec{i}.$$

At any constant time t_1, the position of the particle is given by

$$\vec{u}_1 = \vec{F}(t_1) = (t_1^2 - 4t_1)\vec{i}.$$

With Δt an increment of time, then at $t_2 = t_1 + \Delta t$ the position of the particle is given by

$$\vec{u}_2 = \vec{F}(t_2) = [(t_1 + \Delta t)^2 - 4(t_1 + \Delta t)]\vec{i}.$$

During the time interval from t_1 to $t_2 = t_1 + \Delta t$, the change in position of the particle is given by the vector

$$\Delta \vec{u} = \vec{u}_2 - \vec{u}_1 = [(t_1 + \Delta t)^2 - 4(t_1 + \Delta t)]\vec{i} - (t_1^2 - 4t_1)\vec{i}$$

$$= (t_1^2 + 2t_1\, \Delta t + \overline{\Delta t}^2 - 4t_1 - 4\, \Delta t - t_1^2 + 4t_1)\vec{i}$$

$$= (2t_1\, \Delta t + \overline{\Delta t}^2 - 4\, \Delta t)\vec{i}.$$

Hence, during this time interval Δt from t_1 to $t_1 + \Delta t$, the average velocity is

$$\frac{\Delta \vec{u}}{\Delta t} = \frac{(2t_1\, \Delta t + \overline{\Delta t}^2 - 4\, \Delta t)\vec{i}}{\Delta t} = (2t_1 + \Delta t - 4)\vec{i}.$$

As this time interval is made to approach zero by making $\Delta t \to 0$, these average velocities approach a limit called the **instantaneous velocity** $\vec{V}(t_1)$ at time t_1; that is,

$$\vec{V}(t_1) = \lim_{\Delta t \to 0} \frac{\Delta \vec{u}}{\Delta t} = \lim_{\Delta t \to 0} (2t_1 + \Delta t - 4)\vec{i} = (2t_1 - 4)\vec{i}.$$

For example, if $t_1 = 1$, then

$$\vec{F}(1) = (1^2 - 4 \cdot 1)\vec{i} = -3\vec{i} \quad \text{and} \quad \vec{V}(1) = (2 \cdot 1 - 4)\vec{i} = -2\vec{i},$$

which means the particle is three units to the left of the origin and moving to the left at the instantaneous rate of two x units per time unit. Also, if $t_1 = 3$, then

$$\vec{F}(3) = (3^2 - 4 \cdot 3)\vec{i} = -3\vec{i} \quad \text{and} \quad \vec{V}(3) = (2 \cdot 3 - 4)\vec{i} = 2\vec{i},$$

and the particle is again three units to the left of the origin but this time is moving to the right at the rate of two x units per time unit.

For general considerations, let the plane motion of a particle be governed by a vector function

$$\vec{u} = \vec{F}(t).$$

For t_1 a constant and Δt an increment of time, at times t_1 and $t_1 + \Delta t$ the particle will be at the terminal ends of the vectors $\vec{F}(t_1)$ and $\vec{F}(t_1 + \Delta t)$. The difference $\Delta \vec{u} = \vec{F}(t_1 + \Delta t) - \vec{F}(t_1)$ is a vector chord of the particle's path, and

$$\frac{\Delta \vec{u}}{\Delta t} = \frac{\vec{F}(t_1 + \Delta t) - \vec{F}(t_1)}{\Delta t}$$

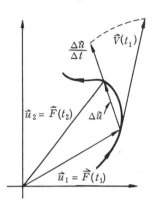

is called the **average velocity vector**. Notice that, if Δt is numerically less than 1, then the average velocity vector $\dfrac{\Delta \vec{u}}{\Delta t}$ is longer than the vector chord $\Delta \vec{u}$. As $\Delta t \to 0$, this average velocity vector will, for most motions, approach a vector $\vec{V}(t_1)$ with initial end at the terminal end of $\vec{F}(t_1)$:

$$\vec{V}(t_1) = \lim_{\Delta t \to 0} \frac{\Delta \vec{u}}{\Delta t} = \lim_{\Delta t \to 0} \frac{\vec{F}(t_1 + \Delta t) - \vec{F}(t_1)}{\Delta t}.$$

Then $\vec{V}(t_1)$ is called the **instantaneous velocity vector** at time $t = t_1$, and the norm $|\vec{V}(t_1)| = S(t_1)$ is a nonnegative scalar called the **instantaneous speed** at time $t = t_1$.

Fig. 2-5.3

Example 3. Find the velocity and speed at $t = t_1$ if

$$\vec{u} = \vec{F}(t) = (2 - t)\vec{i} + t^2\vec{j}.$$

Solution.

$$\Delta \vec{u} = \vec{F}(t_1 + \Delta t) - \vec{F}(t_1)$$
$$= [(2 - t_1 - \Delta t)\vec{i} + (t_1 + \Delta t)^2 \vec{j}] - [(2 - t_1)\vec{i} + t_1^2 \vec{j}]$$
$$= [(2 - t_1 - \Delta t)\vec{i} + (t_1^2 + 2t_1 \Delta t + \overline{\Delta t}^2)\vec{j}] - [(2 - t_1)\vec{i} + t_1^2 \vec{j}]$$
$$= (-\Delta t)\vec{i} + (2t_1 \Delta t + \overline{\Delta t}^2)\vec{j},$$
$$\frac{\Delta \vec{u}}{\Delta t} = -\vec{i} + (2t_1 + \Delta t)\vec{j},$$
$$\vec{V}(t_1) = \lim_{\Delta t \to 0} \frac{\Delta \vec{u}}{\Delta t} = \lim_{\Delta t \to 0} [-\vec{i} + (2t_1 + \Delta t)\vec{j}]$$
$$= -\vec{i} + 2t_1 \vec{j},$$
$$S(t_1) = |\vec{V}(t_1)| = \sqrt{(-1)^2 + (2t_1)^2} = \sqrt{1 + 4t_1^2}.$$

In Fig. 2–5.4, the particle's path is shown together with

$$\vec{F}(-2) = 4\vec{i} + 4\vec{j}, \qquad \vec{V}(-2) = -\vec{i} - 4\vec{j};$$
$$\vec{F}(-1) = 3\vec{i} + \vec{j}, \qquad \vec{V}(-1) = -\vec{i} - 2\vec{j};$$
$$\vec{F}(0) = 2\vec{i}, \qquad \vec{V}(0) = -\vec{i};$$
$$\vec{F}(1) = \vec{i} + \vec{j}, \qquad \vec{V}(1) = -\vec{i} + 2\vec{j};$$
$$\vec{F}(2) = 4\vec{j}, \qquad \vec{V}(2) = -\vec{i} + 4\vec{j}.$$

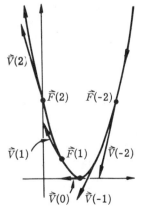

Fig. 2-5.4

Problem 1. Find the slope of the tangent to the graph of the given function at the given point P:

a. f is defined by $f(x) = x^2 - 1$ and the point is $P(2, 3)$.

b. f is defined by $f(x) = \frac{1}{2}x^2 - 3x$, $P(-2, 8)$.

c. $f = \{(x, y)\,|\,y = x^3\}$, $P(1, 1)$.

d. $f = \{(x, y)\,|\,y = 2x - x^3\}$, $P(2, -4)$.

e. $f(x) = 2x - x^3$, $P(1, 1)$.

f. $y = x^2 - x^3$, $P(-1, 2)$.

Problem 2. Find the slope of the tangent to the graph of the given function at the point of the graph having $x = x_1$:

a. $y = f(x) = x - 2x^2$.

b. $y = (x - 1)(x + 2)$.

c. $f = \{(x, y)\,|\,y = x^2(x - 1)\}$.

d. f is defined by $f(x) = x^4$.

Problem 3. Show that the tangent to the curve $y = f(x) = x^2 - 6x + 10$ at the point $P(3, 1)$ has slope zero.

Problem 4. Replace the function and point of Prob. 3 by

$$f = \{(x, y)\,|\,y = x^3 - 3x + 5\}, \quad P(-1, 7).$$

Problem 5. For the following laws of motion, find the velocity vector at $t = t_1$. Then sketch the velocity vectors for $t_1 = 0, 1, 2,$ and 3.

a. $\vec{u} = \vec{F}(t) = (2 - t^2)\vec{i} + t\vec{j}$.   c. $\vec{u} = \vec{F}(t) = t^2\vec{i} - t^2\vec{j}$.

b. $\vec{u} = \vec{F}(t) = (2 + t^2)\vec{i} - t\vec{j}$.   d. $\vec{u} = \vec{F}(t) = \frac{1}{3}t^3\vec{i} + \vec{j}$.

2-6. Derivatives

In Sec. 2-5, the determination of tangents to curves, and of velocity vectors, depended mainly upon evaluating the limits

$$\lim_{\Delta x \to 0} \frac{\Delta y}{\Delta x} = \lim_{\Delta x \to 0} \frac{f(x_1 + \Delta x) - f(x_1)}{\Delta x} \quad \text{and}$$

$$\lim_{\Delta t \to 0} \frac{\Delta \vec{u}}{\Delta t} = \lim_{\Delta t \to 0} \frac{\vec{F}(t_1 + \Delta t) - \vec{F}(t_1)}{\Delta t}$$

for given functions $y = f(x)$ and $\vec{u} = \vec{F}(t)$. Here x_1 and t_1 are arbitrary, but fixed, values of the independent variables x and t.

The **limit** of the ratio of the increment of a function to the increment of the independent variable, as the increment of the independent variable approaches zero, is given a special name; it is *the* **derivative** *of the function with respect to the independent variable.* A notation used is

$$D_x y = \lim_{\Delta x \to 0} \frac{\Delta y}{\Delta x} = \lim_{\Delta x \to 0} \frac{f(x + \Delta x) - f(x)}{\Delta x},$$

where $D_x y$ is read "the derivative of y with respect to x." The subscript has been dropped from x, but during the process of taking the limit, the variable x is to be held constant as the variable Δx is made to approach 0. Also,

$$D_t \vec{u} = \lim_{\Delta t \to 0} \frac{\Delta \vec{u}}{\Delta t} = \lim_{\Delta t \to 0} \frac{\vec{F}(t + \Delta t) - \vec{F}(t)}{\Delta t},$$

and $D_t \vec{u}$ is read "the derivative of $\vec{u}$ with respect to t."

Example 1. Find $D_x y$ given that

$$y = f(x) = \frac{1}{x}.$$

Solution. First. Hold x fixed and compute Δy:

$$\Delta y = f(x + \Delta x) - f(x) = \frac{1}{x + \Delta x} - \frac{1}{x}.$$

Second. Divide by Δx $\left(\text{or multiply by } \frac{1}{\Delta x}\right)$:

(1)
$$\frac{\Delta y}{\Delta x} = \frac{f(x + \Delta x) - f(x)}{\Delta x} = \left(\frac{1}{x + \Delta x} - \frac{1}{x}\right)\frac{1}{\Delta x}.$$

Third. Try to let $\Delta x \to 0$. From the right side of (1) this would formally lead to

$$\left(\frac{1}{x + 0} - \frac{1}{x}\right)\frac{1}{0}, \ \left(\frac{1}{x} - \frac{1}{x}\right)\frac{1}{0}, \ 0 \cdot \frac{1}{0},$$

which are all undefined and tell nothing about whether the limit exists or what it is if it does exist. Hence, simplify the right side of (1) by algebra:.

$$\left(\frac{1}{x + \Delta x} - \frac{1}{x}\right)\frac{1}{\Delta x} = \frac{x - (x + \Delta x)}{(x + \Delta x)x} \cdot \frac{1}{\Delta x} = \frac{-\Delta x}{(x + \Delta x)x} \cdot \frac{1}{\Delta x}$$

$$= \frac{-1}{(x + \Delta x)x} \cdot \frac{\Delta x}{\Delta x} = \frac{-1}{(x + \Delta x)x}.$$

Try again to let $\Delta x \to 0$. Since x is being held fixed, then

$$x + \Delta x \to x \text{ as } \Delta x \to 0.$$

Fourth. Write out the full result of the whole process:

$$D_x y = \lim_{\Delta x \to 0} \frac{\Delta y}{\Delta x} = \lim_{\Delta x \to 0} \frac{f(x + \Delta x) - f(x)}{\Delta x} = \lim_{\Delta x \to 0} \frac{-1}{(x + \Delta x)x} = \frac{-1}{x^2}.$$

These four steps, if accomplished, will produce the derivative of a given function. The first, second, and fourth steps are quite formal and definite, but the third step usually calls for some ingenuity. In the third step, it is generally advisable to simplify the right side algebraically by establishing a common denominator (as in Example 1 above) or by rationalizing the numerator (as in Example 2 below) and simplifying until the Δx in the denominator cancels out with a Δx from the numerator.

Example 2. Find $D_x y$ if $y = f(x) = \sqrt{x}$.

Solution.

1) $$y = f(x + \Delta x) - f(x) = \sqrt{x + \Delta x} - \sqrt{x}.$$

2) $$\frac{\Delta y}{\Delta x} = \frac{\sqrt{x + \Delta x} - \sqrt{x}}{\Delta x}.$$

3) As $\Delta x \to 0$, this would take the form $\dfrac{\sqrt{x + 0} - \sqrt{x}}{0} = \dfrac{0}{0}$; so, in this case, rationalize the numerator:

$$\frac{\Delta y}{\Delta x} = \frac{\sqrt{x + \Delta x} - \sqrt{x}}{\Delta x} \cdot \frac{\sqrt{x + \Delta x} + \sqrt{x}}{\sqrt{x + \Delta x} + \sqrt{x}} = \frac{(x + \Delta x) - x}{\Delta x(\sqrt{x + \Delta x} + \sqrt{x})}$$

$$= \frac{\Delta x}{\Delta x(\sqrt{x + \Delta x} + \sqrt{x})} = \frac{1}{\sqrt{x + \Delta x} + \sqrt{x}}, \qquad \text{since } \frac{\Delta x}{\Delta x} = 1.$$

4) $$D_x y = \lim_{\Delta x \to 0} \frac{\Delta y}{\Delta x} = \lim_{\Delta x \to 0} \frac{f(x - \Delta x) - f(x)}{\Delta x}$$

$$= \lim_{\Delta x \to 0} \frac{1}{\sqrt{x + \Delta x} + \sqrt{x}}$$

$$= \frac{1}{\sqrt{x} + \sqrt{x}} = \frac{1}{2\sqrt{x}}.$$

When $y = f(x) = \dfrac{1}{x}$, then $D_x y = -\dfrac{1}{x^2}$, as shown in Example 1. Instead of this long statement, the shorter designation

$$D_x\!\left(\frac{1}{x}\right) = -\frac{1}{x^2}$$

is often used. Also, the result of Example 2 is given as

$$D_x\sqrt{x} = \frac{1}{2\sqrt{x}}.$$

These two results may also be expressed, respectively, as

$$D_x x^{-1} = -1 \cdot x^{-2} \quad \text{and} \quad D_x x^{1/2} = \tfrac{1}{2}x^{-1/2}.$$

Example 3. Find $D_t \vec{u}$, given that $\vec{u} = \vec{F}(t) = t^{-1}\vec{i} + \sqrt{t}\,\vec{j}$.

Solution. From Examples 1 and 2, it is merely a change of notation to obtain $D_t t^{-1} = -t^{-2}$ and $D_t \sqrt{t} = \tfrac{1}{2}t^{-1/2}$, and hence to see that

$$D_t \vec{u} = -t^{-2}\vec{i} + \tfrac{1}{2}t^{-1/2}\vec{j}.$$

In fact, vector functions given in terms of the basic unit vectors $\vec{i}$ and $\vec{j}$ may be written in terms of component functions $x = x(t)$ and $y = y(t)$ of the independent variable t:

$$\vec{u} = \vec{F}(t) = \vec{i}\,x(t) + \vec{j}\,y(t).$$

Then $D_t \vec{u} = \vec{i}\,D_t x(t) + \vec{j}\,D_t y(t)$, so the determination of velocity vectors

$\vec{V}(t) = D_t\vec{u}$ depends only on obtaining the two ordinary derivatives $D_tx(t)$ and $D_ty(t)$.

Problem 1. Find the derivative D_xy, given that:

a. $y = \dfrac{1}{x+1}$.

b. $y = \sqrt{x+1}$.

c. $y = \dfrac{3}{x^2+1}$.

d. $y = \dfrac{3}{\sqrt{2x+1}}$.

e. $y = \sqrt{x^2+1}$.

f. $y = x + \dfrac{1}{x}$.

g. $y = x^2 + \dfrac{1}{x}$.

h. $y = x^2 + \sqrt{x+3}$.

i. $y = \dfrac{x}{x+1}$.

Problem 2. Establish each of the following:

a. $D_xx^2 = 2x$.

b. $D_xx^3 = 3x^2$.

c. $D_xx^4 = 4x^3$.

d. $D_xx^5 = 5x^4$.

e. $D_xx^{-2} = -2x^{-3}$.

f. $D_xx^{-3} = -3x^{-4}$.

Problem 3. Find each of the following derivatives:

a. $D_x(x^2 - x + 1)$.

b. $D_x\left(\dfrac{x+1}{x}\right)$.

c. $D_x\sqrt{x^2 - x + 1}$.

d. $D_t t^3$.

e. $D_t\dfrac{3}{\sqrt{10-t}}$.

f. $D_t(t - t^3)$.

g. $D_s(s^2 - 3s + 1)$.

h. $D_u\left(\dfrac{u+1}{2u}\right)$.

i. $D_v(v^2 + \sqrt{v})$.

Problem 4. Find $D_t\vec{u}$, given:

a. $\vec{u} = \left(t^2 + \dfrac{1}{t}\right)\vec{i} + t^2\vec{j}$.

b. $\vec{u} = (t^2 - t + 1)\vec{i} + (t+1)(t-2)\vec{j}$.

c. $\vec{u} = \sqrt{t^2 + 1}\,\vec{i} + \sqrt{t^2 + 5}\,\vec{j}$.

d. $\vec{u} = \dfrac{1}{t^2+1}\vec{i} + (t^2 + 1)\vec{j}$.

2-7. Limits

As used in previous sections, the variable Δx is never assigned the value 0 since Δx appeared in the denominator until the latter stages in the determination of D_xy. Thus, if $y = f(x) = 3x^2$, then

$$\frac{\Delta y}{\Delta x} = \frac{f(x + \Delta x) - f(x)}{\Delta x} = \frac{3(x + \Delta x)^2 - 3x^2}{\Delta x}$$

$$= \frac{3(x^2 + 2x\,\Delta x + \overline{\Delta x}^2) - 3x^2}{\Delta x} = \frac{6x\,\Delta x + 3\,\overline{\Delta x}^2}{\Delta x}$$

$$= (6x + 3\,\Delta x)\frac{\Delta x}{\Delta x},$$

all of which has meaning for Δx different from zero but has no meaning for $\Delta x = 0$. Moreover,

$$(6x + 3\,\Delta x)\frac{\Delta x}{\Delta x} \text{ is equal to } 6x + 3\,\Delta x$$

because $\Delta x \neq 0$, and hence no matter how else Δx varies it is always true that $\frac{\Delta x}{\Delta x} = 1$. Then, with x held fixed, the limit

$$\lim_{\Delta x \to 0} (6x + 3\,\Delta x) = 6x$$

means there is no doubt about $6x + 3\,\Delta x$ differing from $6x$ by less than any given amount for all values of Δx which are close enough to (but different from) zero. Precisely (with x held constant),

$6x + 3\,\Delta x$ differs from $6x$ by less than $\frac{1}{2}$ if $0 < |\Delta x| < \frac{1}{6}$,

$6x + 3\,\Delta x$ differs from $6x$ by less than $\frac{1}{10}$ if $0 < |\Delta x| < \frac{1}{30}$;

and for any given number $\epsilon > 0$, then

$6x + 3\,\Delta x$ differs from $6x$ by less than ϵ if $0 < |\Delta x| < \frac{\epsilon}{3}$;

that is,

$$6x - \epsilon < 6x + 3\,\Delta x < 6x + \epsilon, \text{ provided}$$

$$\text{either } -\frac{\epsilon}{3} < \Delta x < 0 \text{ or } 0 < \Delta x < \frac{\epsilon}{3}.$$

This does not mean that $6x + 3\,\Delta x$ always differs from $6x$ by less than ϵ, but does mean that $6x + 3\,\Delta x$ will certainly differ from $6x$ by less than ϵ for all values of Δx within the stated bounds.

All of calculus is based on the concept of a limit. This concept will be presented in a manner general enough for wide use by employing functions of an independent variable other than x, Δx, t, or Δt. The independent variable will be denoted by h, and for geometric considerations an (h, y) coordinate system will be used. Another step in generality will be to let $h \to c$, where c is a constant (rather than always having the independent variable approach zero).

Let $y = f(h)$ be a function of h, let c be a constant, and let L be a constant. Then, by definition:

$$\lim_{h \to c} f(h) = L,$$

provided that for each arbitrary number $\epsilon > 0$ there is a number $\delta > 0$ depending upon ϵ such that

(1) *$L - \epsilon < f(h) < L + \epsilon$ if either*

$c - \delta < h < c$ or $c < h < c + \delta$.

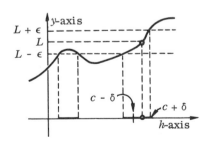

Fig. 2-7.1

A geometric interpretation of this definition is to represent $y = f(h)$ as a graph on an (h, y)-coordinate system, to represent c by the point $(c, 0)$ on the h-

axis, and to represent L by the point $(0, L)$ on the y-axis. With $(0, L)$ as center, take the interval of length 2ϵ on the y-axis and note the portion or portions of the graph lying strictly between the levels of the lower and upper ends of this interval. Project such portion or portions onto the h-axis. If this projection contains two intervals, one with upper endpoint $(c, 0)$ and the other with lower endpoint also $(c, 0)$, then the length of the shorter of these intervals may be taken for δ. For then all those h values either restricted to the domain $c - \delta < h < c$ or to the domain $c < h < c + \delta$ are such that

$$L - \epsilon < f(h) < L + \epsilon.$$

A set-oriented definition of a limit is:

DEFINITION. *For f a function, c and L numbers, then*

$$\lim_{h \to c} f(h) = L,$$

if corresponding to each number $\epsilon > 0$ there is a number δ such that (see Fig. 2-7.2)

(2) $\quad \{(h, y) \,|\, c - \delta < h < c + \delta, \ h \neq c, \ y = f(h)\}$

$$\subset \{(h, y) \,|\, c - \delta < h < c + \delta, \ h \neq c, \ L - \epsilon < y < L + \epsilon\}.$$

Note carefully that $h = c$ is excluded from consideration by the inequalities $c - \delta < h < c$ and $c < h < c + \delta$ in (1) and by $h \neq c$ in (2). It is immaterial whether $f(c)$ is defined or not; even if it is defined, this value is not used in deciding whether $f(h) \to L$ as $h \to c$.

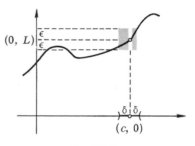

Fig. 2-7.2

In fact, if $\lim_{h \to c} f(h) = L$, if $f(c)$ is defined, and if $L = f(c)$, then the function f is said to be **continuous** at $h = c$. This essentially means that, if f is continuous at c, then the graph of $y = f(h)$ passes through the point $(c, f(c))$ without a break. Most of calculus is concerned with functions which are continuous at points where the functions are defined. (Continuous functions are discussed in more detail in Sec. 2-15.)

The above definition of a limit is not intended as a direct aid to discovering what a limit of any specified function is. The main purpose of the definition is to furnish a solid basis on which to establish limit theorems. One of the uses of limit theorems is to ease the task of finding limits of specific functions and to establish derivative formulas. Derivative formulas will then be used (in Sec. 2-8 et seq.) to obtain derivatives of complicated functions without returning to the four steps given in the previous section.

THEOREM 1. *If $f(h)$ and $F(h)$ are functions of h and are such that both approach the same limit L as $h \to c$, that is,*

$$\lim_{h \to c} f(h) = \lim_{h \to c} F(h) = L,$$

and if $g(h)$ is a third function such that $f(h) < g(h) < F(h)$, then also

$$\lim_{h \to c} g(h) = L.$$

PROOF. Let ϵ be an arbitrary positive number. Since $f(h)$ has the limit L as $h \to c$, determine a number $\delta_1 > 0$ such that

(1) $L - \epsilon < f(h) < L + \epsilon$ if $c - \delta_1 < h < c$ or $c < h < c + \delta_1$.

Since $F(h)$ also approaches the same limit L as $h \to c$, let $\delta_2 > 0$ be such that

(2) $L - \epsilon < F(h) < L + \epsilon$ if $c - \delta_2 < h < c$ or $c < h < c + \delta_2$.

There is no way of telling which of δ_1 and δ_2 is the smaller or in fact whether they differ at all. To be on the safe side, do the following:

If $\delta_1 \leq \delta_2$, set $\delta = \delta_1$; but if $\delta_2 \leq \delta_1$, set $\delta = \delta_2$.

In either case, it then follows that $\delta > 0$ and that both

$$L - \epsilon < f(h) < L + \epsilon \text{ and } L - \epsilon < F(h) < L + \epsilon$$
$$\text{if } c - \delta < h < c \text{ or } c < h < c + \delta.$$

Since $f(h) < g(h) < F(h)$ for all h, then certainly

$$L - \epsilon < f(h) < g(h) < F(h) < L + \epsilon$$
$$\text{if } c - \delta < h < c \text{ or } c < h < c + \delta.$$

It thus follows that

$$L - \epsilon < g(h) < L + \epsilon \text{ if } c - \delta < h < c \text{ or } c < h < c + \delta,$$

which, by the definition of a limit, means the existence of

$$\lim_{h \to c} g(h) = L,$$

which is the conclusion stated in the theorem.

THEOREM 2. *If $f(h)$ and $g(h)$ are functions of h such that the limits*

$$\lim_{h \to c} f(h) = a \text{ and } \lim_{h \to c} g(h) = b$$

both exist, then the following limits exist and the equalities hold:

(i) $\lim_{h \to c} [f(h) \pm g(h)] = \lim_{h \to c} f(h) \pm \lim_{h \to c} g(h) = a \pm b;$

(ii) $\lim_{h \to c} [f(h)g(h)] = [\lim_{h \to c} f(h)][\lim_{h \to c} g(h)] = ab;$

(iii) *In case $b \neq 0$,*

$$\lim_{h \to c} [f(h) \div g(h)] = [\lim_{h \to c} f(h)] \div [\lim_{h \to c} g(h)] = \frac{a}{b}.$$

PROOF OF (i). Let $\epsilon > 0$ be arbitrary. Corresponding to $\epsilon/2$, let $\delta_1 > 0$ and $\delta_2 > 0$ be such that

$$a - \frac{\epsilon}{2} < f(h) < a + \frac{\epsilon}{2}$$

if $c - \delta_1 < h < c$ or $c < h < c + \delta_1$

and

$$b - \frac{\epsilon}{2} < g(h) < b + \frac{\epsilon}{2}$$

if $c - \delta_2 < h < c$ or $c < h < c + \delta_2$.

Next, if $\delta_1 \le \delta_2$ set $\delta = \delta_1$, but if $\delta_2 \le \delta_1$ set $\delta = \delta_2$. In either case, $\delta < 0$ and

$$\left(a - \frac{\epsilon}{2}\right) + \left(b - \frac{\epsilon}{2}\right) < f(h) + g(h) < \left(a + \frac{\epsilon}{2}\right) + \left(b + \frac{\epsilon}{2}\right)$$

if $c - \delta < h < c$ or $c < h < c + \delta$.

Consequently,

$$(a + b) - \epsilon < f(b) + g(b) < (a + b) + \epsilon$$
$$\text{if } c - \delta < h < c \text{ or } c < h < c + \delta,$$

and this, from the definition of a limit, means that (i) holds with "$+$" throughout. The proof with "$-$" is similar.

Proofs of (ii) and (iii) are similar to the proof of (i), but the details are more complicated. These proofs are included later* after gaining more experience in abstract thinking.

Make careful note of the condition $b \ne 0$ in (iii). Thus,

$$\lim_{\Delta x \to 0} \frac{6x\,\Delta x + \overline{\Delta x}^2}{\Delta x} \text{ is not } \frac{\lim_{\Delta x \to 0} [6x\,\Delta x + \overline{\Delta x}^2]}{\lim_{\Delta x \to 0} \Delta x},$$

although the first limit exists and is $6x$, but by a method not using (iii).

Another theorem not proved here is the following.

THEOREM 3. If $\lim_{h \to c} f(h) = a > 0$, and p and q are integers, then

$$\lim_{h \to c} [f(h)]^{p/q} = [\lim_{h \to c} f(h)]^{p/q} = a^{p/q}.$$

It may seem tautological to state

$$\lim_{h \to c} h = c \text{ and } \lim_{h \to c} a = a,$$

where a is a constant, but these facts together with the above theorems lead to practically all determinations of limits that are required.

Example 1. Find

$$\lim_{h \to 3} \frac{h^4 - 2h + 5}{\sqrt{h^2 + 16}}.$$

*Problem 8 of Sec. 13–2.

Solution.

$$\lim_{h\to 3} h^2 = (\lim_{h\to 3} h)(\lim_{h\to 3} h) = 3\cdot 3 = 9 \qquad \text{by Theorem 2(ii);}$$

$$\lim_{h\to 3} h^4 = (\lim_{h\to 3} h^2)(\lim_{h\to 3} h^2) = 9\cdot 9 = 81 \qquad \text{by 2(ii) and the above;}$$

$$\lim_{h\to 3}(h^4 - 2h + 5) = \lim_{h\to 3} h^4 - \lim_{h\to 3} 2h + \lim_{h\to 3} 5 \qquad \text{by 2(i) used twice}$$

$$= 81 - (\lim_{h\to 3} 2)(\lim_{h\to 3} h) + 5$$

$$= 81 - 2\cdot 3 + 5 = 80.$$

For the denominator,

$$\lim_{h\to 3}(h^2 + 16) = \lim_{h\to 3} h^2 + \lim_{h\to 3} 16 = 9 + 16 = 25, \text{ so that}$$

$$\lim_{h\to 3}\sqrt{h^2 + 16} = \sqrt{\lim_{h\to 3}(h^2 + 16)} = \sqrt{25} = 5$$

by Theorem 3, with $p/q = \frac{1}{2}$.

Hence, the desired limit is $80/5 = 16$ by 2(iii).

Example 2.

$$\lim_{x\to 4}\frac{x - 4}{\sqrt{x} - 2} = \frac{\lim_{x\to 4}(x - 4)}{\lim_{x\to 4}(\sqrt{x} - 2)} = \frac{4 - 4}{\sqrt{4} - 2} = \frac{0}{0}$$

is a false start in trying to use 2(iii). Hence, another method, such as rationalizing the denominator, must be used:

$$\frac{x - 4}{\sqrt{x} - 2} = \frac{x - 4}{\sqrt{x} - 2}\cdot\frac{\sqrt{x} + 2}{\sqrt{x} + 2} = \frac{(x - 4)(\sqrt{x} + 2)}{x - 4} = \sqrt{x} + 2 \text{ for } x \neq 4,$$

and

$$\lim_{x\to 4}\frac{x - 4}{\sqrt{x} - 2} = \lim_{x\to 4}(\sqrt{x} + 2) = \sqrt{4} + 2 = 2 + 2 = 4.$$

Problem 1. Find each of the following limits, being sure to justify (in your own mind at least) every step taken:

a. $\lim_{h\to 2}\dfrac{h^2 - 2h + 1}{\sqrt{h^4 + 9}}$.

b. $\lim_{x\to -1}\dfrac{\sqrt{x^2 - 1}}{x^3 + 5}$.

c. $\lim_{t\to -6}\dfrac{t^2 + 3}{t}$.

d. $\lim_{y\to 0}\dfrac{3y + 4y^2 - 6}{y - 2}$.

e. $\lim_{h\to 3}\dfrac{\sqrt{h} - \sqrt{3}}{h - 3}$.

f. $\lim_{h\to -1}\dfrac{h + 1}{1 - \sqrt{h + 2}}$.

Problem 2. Find the limits as:

a. $h \to 2$ and $h \to 0$ of $\dfrac{1}{h}\left(\dfrac{1}{3 + h} - \dfrac{1}{3}\right)$.

b. $x \to 1$ and $x \to 0$ of $\dfrac{\sqrt{2 + 2x} - \sqrt{2}}{x}$.

c. $h \to 1$ and $h \to -1$ of $\dfrac{1}{h + 1}\left(\dfrac{1}{4 + h} - \dfrac{1}{3}\right)$.

d. $h \to 4$ and $h \to -4$ of $\dfrac{1}{h - 4}\left(\dfrac{1}{h^2} - \dfrac{1}{16}\right)$.

Problem 3. Find $\lim\limits_{h \to c} f(h)$, given that:

a. $f(h) = \dfrac{1 - h}{1 - \sqrt{h}}$ and $c = 1$.

b. $f(h) = \dfrac{h^2 + 9}{(h - 2)^2}$ and $c = 0$.

c. $f(h) = \dfrac{|h| - 1}{h^2 - 1}$ and $c = 1$.

d. $f(h) = \dfrac{\sqrt{-h} - 2}{h + 4}$ and $c = -4$.

e. $f(h) = 4h - \sqrt{h^2 - 4}$ and $c = 2$.

f. $f(h) = \dfrac{h^2 - 4}{h^4 - 16}$ and $c = 2$.

g. $f(h) = \dfrac{\sqrt{h^2 - 1}}{h + 1}$ and $c = -1$.

h. $f(h) = \dfrac{h - 0.25}{\sqrt{h} - 0.5}$ and $c = 0.25$.

2-8. Derivative Formulas

The derivative of a function

$$y = f(x)$$

was defined (see Sec. 2-6) by

$$D_x y = \lim_{\Delta x \to 0} \frac{\Delta y}{\Delta x} = \lim_{\Delta x \to 0} \frac{f(x + \Delta x) - f(x)}{\Delta x}.$$

While taking the limit as $\Delta x \to 0$, the variable x is held to a constant value.

By using this definition, it has been established in examples or problems that

$$D_x x^2 = 2x, \quad D_x x^3 = 3x^2, \quad \text{and} \quad D_x x^4 = 4x^3.$$

These are special cases of the first derivative formula to be derived:

(1) $\qquad\qquad D_x x^n = nx^{n-1}$ for n a positive integer.

The derivation is effected by starting with

$$y = x^n$$

and then performing the following:

First. Add an increment Δx to x and let Δy be the corresponding increment of y, so that

$$\Delta y = (x + \Delta x)^n - x^n.$$

Second. Divide by Δx:

$$\frac{\Delta y}{\Delta x} = \frac{(x + \Delta x)^n - x^n}{\Delta x}.$$

Third. Use the binomial expansion formula on $(x + \Delta x)^n$ to obtain

$$\frac{\Delta y}{\Delta x} = \frac{1}{\Delta x}\left[\left(x^n + nx^{n-1}\,\Delta x + \frac{n(n-1)}{1\cdot 2}x^{n-2}\,\overline{\Delta x}^2 + \cdots + \overline{\Delta x}^n\right) - x^n\right]$$

$$= \frac{1}{\Delta x}\left[nx^{n-1}\,\Delta x + \frac{n(n-1)}{1\cdot 2}x^{n-2}\,\overline{\Delta x}^2 + \cdots + \overline{\Delta x}^n\right]$$

since x^n cancels

$$= nx^{n-1} + \frac{n(n-1)}{1\cdot 2}x^{n-2}\,\Delta x + \cdots + \overline{\Delta x}^{\,n-1}$$

Note that all terms except the first have Δx as a factor.

Fourth. Since the limit of a sum is the sum of the individual limits [Sec. 2-7, Theorem 2(i)], then

$$D_x y = \lim_{\Delta x\to 0} nx^{n-1} + \lim_{\Delta x\to 0}\frac{n(n-1)}{1\cdot 2}x^{n-2}\,\Delta x + \cdots + \lim_{\Delta x\to 0}\overline{\Delta x}^{\,n-1}$$

$$= nx^{n-1}$$

since all terms are constant as far as x is concerned and all except the first approach 0 as $\Delta x \to 0$.

Hence, $D_x y = nx^{n-1}$ when $y = x^n$, so (1) has been established.

It was also shown (Example 2 of Sec. 2–6) that

$$D_x x^{1/2} = \tfrac{1}{2}x^{-1/2}, \text{ which may be written as } D_x x^{1/2} = \tfrac{1}{2}x^{(1/2)-1}$$

to make it look like (1) with n replaced by $\tfrac{1}{2}$. Formula (1) was derived only for n a positive integer, but the formula

(2) $$D_x x^a = ax^{a-1}$$

holds for any constant a, as will be shown later.

Example 1.
$$D_x x^{4/3} = \tfrac{4}{3}x^{(4/3)-1} = \tfrac{4}{3}x^{1/3}.$$

Even though (2) has not now been proved, this formula will be used.

The next fact is not a derivative formula but is used in deriving derivative formulas. If $y = f(x)$ has a derivative, then

(3) $$\lim_{\Delta x\to 0}\Delta y = \lim_{\Delta x\to 0}[f(x + \Delta x) - f(x)] = 0.$$

To see this, note that

$$\lim_{\Delta x\to 0}\Delta y = \lim_{\Delta x\to 0}\frac{\Delta y}{\Delta x}\cdot \Delta x = \lim_{\Delta x\to 0}\frac{\Delta y}{\Delta x}\cdot \lim_{\Delta x\to 0}\Delta x$$

since the limit of a product
is the product of the limits

$$= (D_x y)\cdot 0 = 0.$$

When two functions $f(x)$ and $g(x)$ are involved, (3) for each of them is written

(3′) $$\lim_{\Delta x\to 0}\Delta f(x) = 0 \text{ and } \lim_{\Delta x\to 0}\Delta g(x) = 0.$$

The next three derivative formulas,

(4) $$D_x[f(x) + g(x)] = D_x f(x) + D_x g(x),$$

(5) $$D_x[f(x)g(x)] = f(x)D_x g(x) + g(x)D_x f(x), \text{ and}$$

(6) $$D_x \frac{f(x)}{g(x)} = \frac{g(x)D_x f(x) - f(x)D_x g(x)}{g^2(x)} \text{ if } g(x) \neq 0,$$

are written together to emphasize that the derivative of a sum is the sum of the derivatives but the derivative of a product is **not** the product of the derivatives and also the derivative of a quotient is **not** the quotient of the derivatives.

PROOF OF (4). Let $y = f(x) + g(x)$, so that
First.
$$\Delta y = [f(x + \Delta x) + g(x + \Delta x)] - [f(x) + g(x)]$$
$$= [f(x + \Delta x) - f(x)] + [g(x + \Delta x) - g(x)]$$
$$= \Delta f(x) + \Delta g(x).$$

Second.
$$\frac{\Delta y}{\Delta x} = \frac{\Delta f(x) + \Delta g(x)}{\Delta x}.$$

Third.
$$\frac{\Delta y}{\Delta x} = \frac{\Delta f(x)}{\Delta x} + \frac{\Delta g(x)}{\Delta x}.$$

Fourth.
$$D_x y = \lim_{\Delta x \to 0} \frac{\Delta y}{\Delta x} = \lim_{\Delta x \to 0} \left[\frac{\Delta f(x)}{\Delta x} + \frac{\Delta g(x)}{\Delta x} \right]$$
$$= \lim_{\Delta x \to 0} \frac{\Delta f(x)}{\Delta x} + \lim_{\Delta x \to 0} \frac{\Delta g(x)}{\Delta x} \qquad \binom{\text{limit of sum}}{= \text{ sum of limits}}$$
$$= D_x f(x) + D_x g(x).$$

Since $y = f(x) + g(x)$, this is the formula (4).

PROOF OF (5). Let $y = f(x) \cdot g(x)$, so that:
First.
$$\Delta y = f(x + \Delta x)g(x + \Delta x) - f(x)g(x).$$

Second.
$$\frac{\Delta y}{\Delta x} = \frac{f(x + \Delta x)g(x + \Delta x) - f(x)g(x)}{\Delta x}.$$

Third. Since $\Delta f(x) = f(x + \Delta x) - f(x)$, then
$$f(x + \Delta x) = \Delta f(x) + f(x) \text{ and also } g(x + \Delta x) = \Delta g(x) + g(x),$$
so that
$$\frac{\Delta y}{\Delta x} = \frac{[\Delta f(x) + f(x)][\Delta g(x) + g(x)] - f(x)g(x)}{\Delta x}$$
$$= \frac{\Delta f(x)\,\Delta g(x) + f(x)\,\Delta g(x) + g(x)\,\Delta f(x) + f(x)g(x) - f(x)g(x)}{\Delta x}$$
$$= \frac{\Delta f(x)\,\Delta g(x)}{\Delta x} + \frac{f(x)\,\Delta g(x)}{\Delta x} + \frac{g(x)\,\Delta f(x)}{\Delta}$$
$$= \frac{\Delta f(x)}{\Delta x} \cdot \Delta g(x) + f(x)\frac{\Delta g(x)}{\Delta x} + g(x)\frac{\Delta f(x)}{\Delta x}.$$

Fourth.

$$D_x y = \lim_{\Delta x \to 0} \frac{\Delta y}{\Delta x}$$

$$= \lim_{\Delta x \to 0} \frac{\Delta f(x)}{\Delta x} \lim_{\Delta x \to 0} \Delta g(x) + f(x) \lim_{\Delta x \to 0} \frac{\Delta g(x)}{\Delta x} + g(x) \lim_{\Delta x \to 0} \frac{\Delta f(x)}{\Delta x}$$

$$= [D_x f(x)] \cdot 0 + f(x) D_x g(x) + g(x) D_x f(x),$$

where the zero in the first term comes from (3'). Hence, the first term drops out and the remaining is the same as in (5).

The establishing of (6) is left as a problem.

One more formula will be derived in this section; it is

(7) $D_x c = 0$ for c a constant.

This means that the function f having range $\{y \mid y = c\}$ is considered. Then $f(x) = c$ and also $f(x + \Delta x) = c$. Thus,

$$\lim_{\Delta x \to 0} \frac{f(x + \Delta x) - f(x)}{\Delta x} = \lim_{\Delta x \to 0} \frac{c - c}{\Delta x} = \lim_{\Delta x \to 0} 0 = 0,$$

which is the sense in which (7) is understood.

Hence, $D_x cg(x) = cD_x g(x) + g(x)D_x c$, from (5) with $f(x) = c$, and therefore, from (7),

(5, 7) $D_x cg(x) = cD_x g(x).$

This formula is then a combination of (5) and (7), but it should be used whenever applicable to save time and effort. A similar combination of (6) and (7) yields

(6, 7) $D_x \dfrac{c}{g(x)} = -c \dfrac{D_x g(x)}{g^2(x)}.$

Example 2.

$$D_x \frac{3x^2 - 5}{x^3 + x - 6} = \frac{(x^3 + x - 6)D_x(3x^2 - 5) - (3x^2 - 5)D_x(x^3 + x - 6)}{(x^3 + x - 6)^2}$$

by (6)

$$= \frac{(x^3 + x - 6)[D_x 3x^2 - D_x 5] - (3x^2 - 5)[D_x x^3 + D_x x - D_x 6]}{(x^3 + x - 6)^2}$$

by (4)

$$= \frac{(x^3 + x - 6)[3D_x x^2 - 0] - (3x^2 - 5)[3x^2 + 1 - 0]}{(x^3 + x - 6)^2}$$

by (5), (7), and (1)

$$= \frac{(x^3 + x - 6)6x - (3x^2 - 5)(3x^2 + 1)}{(x^3 + x - 6)^2}$$

by (1)

$$= \frac{-3x^4 + 18x^2 - 36x + 5}{(x^3 + x - 6)^2}.$$

Problem 1. Use whatever combination of formulas is necessary to find:

a. $D_x(4x^5 - 3x^2 + 2).$ g. $D_x(x + 2)(x - 3)^{-1}.$

b. $D_x(\frac{1}{5}x^5 - \frac{1}{2}x^2 + 2).$

h. $D_x\frac{x^2 + 4x - 5}{x}.$

c. $D_x(2x^{3/2} - 4x - 10).$

i. $D_x\frac{x}{x^2 + 4x - 5}.$

d. $D_x\left(\frac{2}{x^2} - \frac{x^2}{2}\right).$

j. $D_x\frac{x + 4\sqrt{x} - 5}{\sqrt{x}}.$

e. $D_x(x^2 + 2x - 3)(x^3 - 6x + 2).$

k. $D_x\left[\frac{16 - x}{x} + \frac{25}{x^2 + 1}\right].$

f. $D_x(x - \sqrt[3]{x})(2x^5 - 5).$

l. $D_x(x^2 + 1)^2.$

Problem 2. Find:

a. $D_x y$, given $y = (x - 1)(x^2 - 3x + 42).$

b. $D_x u$, given $u = \frac{x + 4}{x + 6}.$

c. $D_x h$, given $h = \sqrt{x} - x + 5.$

d. $D_h x$, given $x = \sqrt{h} - h + 5.$

e. $D_t s$, given $s = 16.1t^2.$

f. $D_s t$, given $t = \frac{3s + 2}{s^2 + 1}.$

Problem 3. Find the slope of the graph of the given equation at the point on the graph having the given value of x.

a. $y = x^4 - 28x + 2; \; x = 2.$

[*Hint:* First find $D_x y$ and then substitute $x = 2$.]

b. $y = \frac{x - 1}{x + 1}; \; x = 1.$

e. $y = \frac{\sqrt{x} - 1}{\sqrt{x} + 1}; \; x = 4.$

c. $y = \frac{9}{x}; \; x = 3.$

f. $y = \frac{x}{x^2 + 5}; \; x = 5.$

d. $y = \frac{x}{9}; \; x = 3.$

g. $y = \frac{x^2 + 5}{x}; \; x = 5.$

Problem 4. Find the equation of the tangent to the graph of the given function at the point on the graph having the given value of x.

a. $y = x^2 + \frac{1}{x}; \; x = 2.$

[*Hint:* Substitute x in this equation: $y = 4 + \frac{1}{2} = 4.5$, so the point on the curve is $(2, 4.5)$. Now find the slope as in Prob. 3, then use the point-slope form of the equation of a line.]

b. $y = \frac{x^3 + 1}{x}; \; x = 2.$

d. $y = (x - 6)(x^2 + 1); \; x = 6.$

c. $y = \frac{x}{x^3 + 1}; \; x = 2.$

e. $y = \frac{x - 6}{x^2 + 1}; \; x = 6.$

Problem 5. Find $D_t \vec{u}$, given:

a. $\vec{u} = (3t^2 - 1)\vec{i} + (t^3 - 6t + 1)\vec{j}$.   c. $\vec{u} = (t^2 + 1)(5\vec{i} - 2t\vec{j})$.

b. $\vec{u} = \dfrac{\vec{i}}{t^2 + 1} + \vec{j}(16t^2)$.   d. $\vec{u} = \dfrac{1}{t^2 + 1}(5\vec{i} - 2t\vec{j})$.

2-9. Function of a Function

Let f, g, and F be the functions defined by

(1) $f(x) = x^3,\ g(x) = x^2 + 1,\ \text{and}\ F(x) = (x^2 + 1)^3$.

One way of thinking about the function f is to write

$$f(\ ) = (\ )^3$$

and understand that whatever number, or symbol representing a number, is placed between either pair of parentheses, the same must also be placed between the other pair. Then $f(2) = 2^3, f(-1) = (-1)^3, f(h) = h^3$, and

$$f(x^2 + 1) = (x^2 + 1)^3 = F(x).$$

But $x^2 + 1 = g(x)$, so that

$$f(g(x)) = F(x).$$

For functions f and g (not necessarily the ones above), the function F defined by

$$F(x) = f(g(x)),$$

for all $x \in \mathcal{D}_g$ such that also $g(x) \in \mathcal{D}_f$, is called the **composition** of f and g.

The "empty parentheses" idea is carried further. For f as in (1), the derivative $D_x f(x) = 3x^2$ is represented by

$$D_{(\ )} f(\ ) = 3(\ )^2.$$

Now fill the parentheses with $g(x)$:

(2) $D_{g(x)} f(g(x)) = 3(g(x))^2$

          $= 3(x^2 + 1)^2$ for g as in (1).

At first it may seem strange to "take the derivative with respect to $g(x)$," but this is interpreted to mean:

First. Take the derivative with respect to x, and then
Second. Replace x by $g(x)$.

But the derivative of $f(g(x))$ with respect to x [not $g(x)$] is usually wanted. A formula expressing $D_x f(g(x))$ is

(3) $D_x f(g(x)) = D_{g(x)} f(g(x)) \cdot D_x g(x)$.

This is called the **Chain Rule**; it links $D_{g(x)} f(g(x))$ and $D_x g(x)$ to form $D_x f(g(x))$.

Formula (3) says, by using (2), that

$$D_x(x^2 + 1)^3 = 3(x^2 + 1)^2 D_x(x^2 + 1)$$
$$= 3(x^2 + 1)^2 \cdot 2x$$
$$= 6x(x^2 + 1)^2.$$

The correctness of this result should be checked by first expanding $(x^2 + 1)^3$ by the binomial theorem and then taking the derivative.

An intuitive discussion of formula (3) will now be given. First set

$$y = f(h) \quad \text{and} \quad h = g(x) \quad \text{so that} \quad y = f(g(x)).$$

With $\Delta x \neq 0$, then from $h = g(x)$,

$$\Delta h = g(x + \Delta x) - g(x), \quad \lim_{\Delta x \to 0} \Delta h = 0, \quad \text{and} \quad D_x h = \lim_{\Delta x \to 0} \frac{\Delta h}{\Delta x}.$$

The increment Δh and $y = f(h)$ give

$$\Delta y = f(h + \Delta h) - f(h) \quad \text{and} \quad D_h y = \lim_{\Delta h \to 0} \frac{\Delta y}{\Delta h}.$$

The increment Δx, of the ultimate independent variable, is not equal to zero, so that

$$\frac{\Delta y}{\Delta x} = \frac{\Delta y}{\Delta h} \cdot \frac{\Delta h}{\Delta x}, \quad \text{provided} \quad \Delta h \neq 0.$$

Now the limit as $\Delta x \to 0$ (and hence also $\Delta h \to 0$) leads to

(4) $$D_x y = D_h y \cdot D_x h.$$

Since y is a stand-in for $f(g(x))$ and h for $g(x)$, then (3) is (4) in different notation. *The proviso, $\Delta h \neq 0$, is the main reason that this discussion is not a proof.*

A proof of the validity of (3) under appropriate conditions will be given in Sec. 2-13 after further notation more suitable to this type of reasoning is introduced; in the meantime, these formulas will be used.

In case $y = h^n$, with n a positive integer, $D_x y = nh^{n-1} D_x h$, and formulas (3, 4) reduce to

(5) $$D_x[g(x)]^n = n[g(x)]^{n-1} D_x g(x), \quad n \text{ a positive integer.}$$

Recall that, by definition,

$$D_x x^{1/n} = \lim_{\Delta x \to 0} \frac{(x + \Delta x)^{1/n} - x^{1/n}}{\Delta x}$$

A proof of the existence, and value, of this limit is involved. A slick way of hiding the fact that nothing is actually proved is to set $g(x) = x^{1/n}$ in (5):

$$D_x x = D_x(x^{1/n})^n = n[x^{1/n}]^{n-1} D_x x^{1/n},$$

$$1 = n(x^{1-(1/n)}) D_x x^{1/n},$$

(6) $$D_x x^{1/n} = \frac{1}{n} x^{(1/n)-1}.$$

This formula is correct, for n a positive integer, and will be used. Combining (6) and (4) yields

$$D_x(x^m)^{1/n} = \frac{1}{n}(x^m)^{(1/n)-1}D_x x^m$$

$$= \frac{1}{n}x^{(m/n)-m}mx^{m-1}$$

(7) $$D_x x^{m/n} = \frac{m}{n}x^{(m/n)-1}.$$

This heuristic discussion shows at least how these formulas could have been discovered.

As $\sin^2 x$ is used for $(\sin x)^2$ to avoid using parentheses, so will $f^{m/n}(x)$ be used for $[f(x)]^{m/n}$.

The formula

$$D_x f^{m/n}(x) = \frac{m}{n}f^{(m/n)-1}(x)D_x f(x)$$

is left for the student to think about.

Example 1.

$$D_x(\sqrt{x^2+1})^3 = \tfrac{3}{2}(x^2+1)^{(3/2)-1}D_x(x^2+1)$$
$$= \tfrac{3}{2}(x^2+1)^{1/2}2x = 3x\sqrt{x^2+1}.$$

Example 2.

$$D_x[x\sqrt{x^2+1}]^4 = 4[x\sqrt{x^2+1}]^3 D_x[x\sqrt{x^2+1}]$$
$$= 4[x\sqrt{x^2+1}]^3[xD_x\sqrt{x^2+1} + \sqrt{x^2+1}D_x x]$$
$$= 4[x\sqrt{x^2+1}]^3[x\cdot\tfrac{1}{2}(x^2+1)^{-1/2}D_x(x^2+1) + \sqrt{x^2+1}]$$
$$= 4[x\sqrt{x^2+1}]^3\left[\frac{x^2}{\sqrt{x^2+1}} + \sqrt{x^2+1}\right].$$

It is simpler to first write $[x\sqrt{x^2+1}]^4 = x^4(x^2+1)^2 = x^8 + 2x^6 + x^4$ and then take the derivative and obtain $8x^7 + 12x^5 + 4x^3$, which the above expression simplifies to.

Problem 1. Find each of the derivatives:

a. $D_x(x^2+1)^4$.

b. $D_x(x^2+3x+1)^4$.

c. $D_x\left(\dfrac{x}{\sqrt[3]{x^2+1}}\right)$.

d. $D_x[x^2\sqrt{x^2+1}]$.

e. $D_x[x+\sqrt{x^2+1}]^3$.

f. $D_x\left[\dfrac{\sqrt[3]{x^2+x+1}}{1+\sqrt{x}}\right]$.

g. $D_x\{x + [1 + (2+x)^2]^3\}^4$.

Problem 2. Find $D_x F(x)$ if $F(x) = f(g(x))$ and:

a. $f(x) = x^4$, $g(x) = x^3 + 1$.

b. $f(x) = \sqrt{x^2+x}$, $g(x) = 1 - x$.

c. $f(x) = \dfrac{x}{1+x}$, $g(x) = \sqrt{x}$.

d. $f(h) = 3h^3$, $g(x) = x^2 + 1$.

e. $f(s) = s^2 + 1$, $g(t) = t + 1$.

f. $f(s) = \dfrac{1-s}{1+s}$, $g(t) = \dfrac{1-t}{1+t}$.

Problem 3. Find the equation of the tangent to the graph of $y = f(x)$ at the point of the graph having $x = x_0$:

a. $f(x) = \sqrt{x^2 + 9}$, $x_0 = 4$.

c. $f(x) = \sqrt{9 + \sqrt{x}}$, $x_0 = 256$.

b. $f(x) = \sqrt{x^2 + 9}$, $x_0 = -4$.

d. $f(x) = \dfrac{x}{\sqrt{3x + 1}}$, $x_0 = 3$.

2-10.   Implicit Functions

The function f defined by $f(x) = \sqrt{25 - x^2}$, $-5 \le x \le 5$, is expressed explicitly in terms of x. For this function,

$$D_x f(x) = \frac{1}{2}(25 - x^2)^{-1/2}(-2x) = \frac{-x}{\sqrt{25 - x^2}} = -\frac{x}{f(x)}, \quad -5 < x < 5.$$

Also, $g(x) = -\sqrt{25 - x^2}$ is given explicitly in terms of x and

$$D_x g(x) = -\frac{1}{2}(25 - x^2)^{-1/2}(-2x) = \frac{x}{\sqrt{25 - x^2}} = -\frac{x}{g(x)}, \quad -5 < x < 5.$$

Let a point P move on the circle of radius 5 and center at the origin. In any position, the coordinates (x, y) of P are restricted by

(1) $$x^2 + y^2 = 25.$$

This equation then implies a relation between the variables x and y. By choosing x as the independent variable and thinking of y as either the above $f(x)$ or $g(x)$, then the left side of (1) is a function of x and formally

$$D_x(x^2 + y^2) = D_x 25 \quad \text{and} \quad D_x x^2 + D_x y^2 = 0.$$

Since y is a function of x, the Chain Rule may be used to give the expression $D_x y^2 = 2y D_x y$. It thus follows that $2x + 2y D_x y = 0$ and then

(2) $$D_x y = -\frac{x}{y}.$$

Example. Find the equation of the tangent to the circle (1) at the point $(3, 4)$.

Solution. Since $(3, 4)$ is on the upper half of the circle, y stands for $f(x)$ as given above. The desired slope may be obtained by setting $x = 3$ and $y = 4$ in (2), so that $m = -\frac{3}{4}$. Thus, the tangent has equation

$$y - 4 = -\tfrac{3}{4}(x - 3).$$

The equation

(3) $$xy^3 = x^3 + 6y - 4$$

cannot be solved readily for either y in terms of x or for x in terms of y. Nevertheless, there may be a function such that, for some domain of x-values,

$$xf^3(x) = x^3 + 6f(x) - 4.$$

Such a function is said to be defined *implicitly* by (3). If $f(x)$ has a derivative, then the derivatives

$$D_x[xf^3(x)] \text{ and } D_x[x^3 + 6f(x) - 4]$$

not only exist but are equal. The process of finding the derivatives of any function defined implicitly by (3) is first to set

$$D_x(xy^3) = D_x(x^3 + 6y - 4),$$
$$xD_xy^3 + y^3D_xx = D_xx^3 + 6D_xy - D_x4.$$

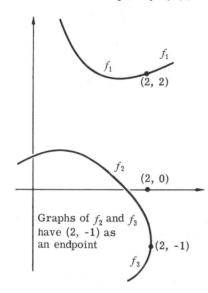

The Chain Rule then gives $D_xy^3 = 3y^2D_xy$, so that

$$3xy^2D_xy + y^3 = 3x^2 + 6D_xy.$$

Now D_xy may be solved for

$$(3xy^2 - 6)D_xy = 3x^2 - y^3,$$

(4) $$D_xy = \frac{3x^2 - y^3}{3xy^2 - 6}.$$

Figure 2–10.1 is a portion of the graph of (3); it indicates three functions, $f_1, f_2,$ and f_3, defined implicitly by (3) and each having $x = 2$ in its domain. The function f_1 has (2, 2) on its graph. At $x = 2$, the function f_1 has a derivative whose value is obtained by substituting $x = 2$ and $y = 2$ into the right side of (4):

Graphs of f_2 and f_3 have (2, -1) as an endpoint

Fig. 2-10.1

$$\frac{12 - 8}{24 - 6} = \frac{2}{9}.$$

The point $(2, -1)$ is on the graph of both f_2 and f_3, but the formal substitution of $(2, -1)$ into (4) shows that neither f_2 nor f_3 has a derivative when $x = 2$.

Let r be a positive rational number. This means that r is the ratio of positive integers p and q:

$$r = \frac{p}{q}.$$

It will now be shown that, if the function defined by $y = x^r$ is differentiable, then $D_xy = rx^{r-1}$; that is,

$$D_xx^r = rx^{r-1},$$

which extends the power formula $D_xx^n = nx^{n-1}$ from integers to rational numbers r. Since

$$y = x^r = x^{p/q}, \text{ then } y^q = x^p,$$

and hence $D_xy^q = D_xx^p$. But p and q are positive integers, so that

$$qy^{q-1}D_xy = px^{p-1},$$

$$D_xy = \frac{p}{q}\frac{x^p}{y^q}x^{-1}y = \frac{p}{q}x^{-1}x^r = rx^{r-1}.$$

Problem 1. Find $D_x y$, given that:

a. $y = h^2$ and $h = 5x - 3$.

c. $y = \sqrt{h}$ and $h = x^3 + 6x$.

b. $y = \dfrac{1}{h^2}$ and $h = 4x^2 - 3x + 2$.

d. $y = h\sqrt{h}$ and $h = x^4 + 6$.

Problem 2. Find:

a. $D_x \sqrt{20 - x^2}$.

d. $D_x(6x\sqrt{x^2 + 2})$.

b. $D_x \sqrt{\dfrac{x + 4}{x - 4}}$.

e. $D_x \dfrac{4x}{\sqrt{x^2 + 2}}$.

c. $D_x \sqrt{(x + 4)(x - 4)}$.

f. $D_x(4x^2 - 2\sqrt{x + 10} - 25)$.

Problem 3. By using procedures for implicit derivatives, find:

a. $D_x y$, given $xy^2 - 4x = x^3 - 3$.

c. $D_x y$, given $\sqrt{x} + \sqrt{y} = 2$.

b. $D_x y$, given $x^2 + xy + y^2 = 1$.

d. $D_t s$, given $(t - 1)^2 + (s + 2)^2 = 16$.

e. $D_y x$, given $x^2 - xy - 3y^2 = 0$.

Problem 4. Find $D_x y$ and $D_y x$ if:

a. $2xy + y^2 = x + y$.

c. $y^3 + 4x^3 y - 3x^5 = 2$.

b. $\dfrac{1}{x} + \dfrac{1}{y} = 1$.

d. $\dfrac{xy + 2}{xy - 2} = 2$.

Problem 5. Check that the graph of the equation passes through the point P, then find the equation of the tangent to the curve at P.

a. $x^2 - xy + 2y^2 + x = 8$; $P(1, 2)$.

c. $\sqrt{x} + \sqrt{y} = 5$; $P(4, 9)$.

b. $xy^2 + x^2 y + 6 = 0$; $P(-2, 3)$.

d. $y^2 = 4x^3$; $P(1, -2)$.

2-11. Sine-Cosine Derivatives

Here is a place where it is easy to get into a logically vicious circle; that is, to use one thing to prove something else and then use the second to prove the first. This is elaborated on below.

The sectors of a circle in Fig. 2–11.1 seem to have areas. It might reasonably be assumed that if the central angle of a sector is doubled, the area should be doubled; if halved, the area should be cut in two, etc. More generally, it might be expected that the ratio of the areas of two sectors is equal to the ratio of the subtended angles:

(1) $$\frac{A}{B} = \frac{\alpha}{\beta}.$$

This is under the assumption that some square unit was selected to measure areas and that A and B are numbers such that A units^2 and B units^2 are the areas of the sectors in terms of this unit of area.

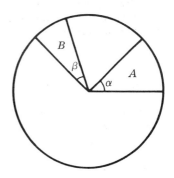

Fig. 2-11.1

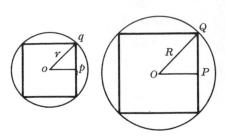

Fig. 2-11.2

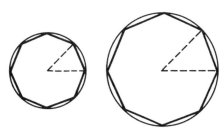

Fig. 2-11.3

Also, α and β are numbers measuring the angles in terms of some angular unit (such as degrees, radians, or hours).

But what is meant by the "area of a sector" or, even more basic, the "area of a circle"? History records how Archimedes (c. 250 B.C.) inscribed squares within two circles. In Fig. 2–11.2, triangles *opq* and *OPQ* are similar; their areas are proportional to the squares of the radii r and R, respectively; and thus the areas of the squares are also proportional to the squares of the radii. Now if the arcs between consecutive vertices of squares (ruler and compass construction) are bisected and the inscribed octagons are drawn as shown in Fig. 2–11.3, then, according to Archimedes' reasoning, the areas of the octagons are proportional to the squares of the radii. Archimedes visualized an indefinitely continuing process of doubling the number of sides of inscribed regular polygons which would, he thought, "exhaust" the interiors of the circles. Since, at each stage, the areas of the inscribed polygons were to each other as their radii squared, Archimedes thought that if k and K are the areas of circles of radii r and R, then

$$\frac{k}{r^2} = \frac{K}{R^2}.$$

Because the ratio of the area of a circle to the square of the radius is the same for all circles, Archimedes denoted this ratio by π. He also obtained the approximation

$$\frac{\text{XXII}}{\text{VII}}$$

of the number represented by π, which is no mean accomplishment considering the difficulty of computation with Roman numerals.*

It can be shown, on the intuitive level of Archimedes' work, that if c and C are the circumferences of circles of radii r and R, then

$$\frac{c}{2r} = \frac{C}{2R} = \pi$$

for the same number π.

---

*Archimedes even obtained the approximation 223/71, though it is now known that π cannot be written as the ratio of two integers; that is, π is an irrational number. In particular, π cannot be written in finite decimal notation, no matter how many places are used. In 1949, the electronic computer ENIAC computed the approximation of π to 2034 decimal places, and in 1962, computation was continued to 100,265 decimal places in order to test some hypotheses proposed by the late mathematical genius John von Neumann.

The so-called "method of exhaustion"* is the genesis of the concept of definite integrals, as will be discussed in Chapter 7. Both arc length and area will be defined in terms of definite integrals. By means of definite integrals it can be shown that, in a circle, two sectors with central angles α_1 and α_2 have arc lengths c_1 and c_2 and areas A_1 and A_2 such that

(2)
$$\frac{c_1}{\alpha_1} = \frac{c_2}{\alpha_2} \quad \text{and} \quad \frac{A_1}{\alpha_1} = \frac{A_2}{\alpha_2}$$

in terms of any unit for measuring lengths and areas, and any angular unit. Then a sector having arc the length of the radius is said to have central angle 1 **radian**, thus establishing the radian as a unit for measuring angles. Since, from (2), a circle of radius r has circumference $c = 2\pi r$, there are 2π radians in one revolution.

A circle of radius r may be considered as a sector of central angle 2π radians. In this circle, a sector with central angle h radians, $0 \le h \le 2\pi$, has area K units^2 such that, from the second part of (2),

$$\frac{K}{h} = \frac{\pi r^2}{2\pi},$$

so that

(3)
$$K = \tfrac{1}{2}r^2 h.$$

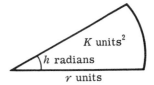

Fig. 2-11.4

The property of areas of circular sectors as expressed in (2) led to (3). Equation (3) will be used presently to obtain a limit formula which leads to the formula for $D_x \sin x$, which in turn will be used later on to derive a formula for the area of a sector. This is not the logically vicious circle that it may seem, since the intermediate theoretical work will not depend on a formula by means of which areas of sectors of circles can be computed. Notice throughout the theory that the only property of π which is used is its representation of the constant ratio of circumference to diameter and area to radius squared. Any numerical approximation of π is used to give a feeling of magnitude in problems illustrating, but not part of, the theoretical work. The only reason for not following a strictly logical approach is that such a program delays too long the introduction of the calculus of trigonometric functions.

Some trigonometric limits are necessary in order to derive formulas for $D_x \sin x$ and $D_x \cos x$. These limits depend directly on the fact that, in a circle of radius r units, a sector with central angle of h radians has area K units^2, where

(1)
$$K = \tfrac{1}{2}r^2 h.$$

This is formula (3) (in small print above) and will be used as if it had been proved.

Figure 2-11.5 is a sector OAB of a circle of radius 1, the central angle being h radians. C is the foot of the perpendicular from B, so that

(2)
$$\sin h = \frac{CB}{OB} = \frac{CB}{1} = CB \quad \text{and} \quad \cos h = \frac{OC}{OB} = OC.$$

Arc CD is on the circle with center O and radius OC, and hence

*Used even before Archimedes by Eudoxus (408–355 b.c.).

area sector $OCD = (\tfrac{1}{2})(OC)^2 h$ by (1).

Since area sector $OCD <$ area triangle $OAB <$ area sector OAB, then

$$\tfrac{1}{2}(OC)^2 h < \tfrac{1}{2}(OA)(CB) < \tfrac{1}{2}(OA)^2 h.$$

Upon multiplying by 2, using both equations in (2) and remembering $OA = 1$, it follows that

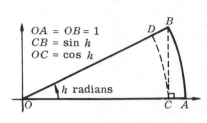

$OA = OB = 1$
$CB = \sin h$
$OC = \cos h$

h radians

Fig. 2-11.5

(3) $(\cos^2 h)h < \sin h < h.$

Now divide by the positive number h to obtain

(4) $$\cos^2 h < \frac{\sin h}{h} < 1.$$

Since the cosine curve passes smoothly through the point $(0, 1)$, then

$$\lim_{h \to 0} \cos h = 1 \quad \text{so} \quad \lim_{h \to 0} \cos^2 h = 1.$$

Insert $\lim\limits_{h \to 0}$ before each term of (4) which involves h:

$$1 = \lim_{h \to 0} \cos^2 h \le \lim_{h \to 0} \frac{\sin h}{h} \le 1,$$

where $<$ in (4) had to be changed to $\le$ in taking the limit.* This is justified by Theorem 1 of Sec. 2-7, and it may be concluded that

(5) $$\lim_{h \to 0} \frac{\sin h}{h} = 1.$$

A more exacting method of going from (3) to (5) is to note first, from the right side of (3), that $\sin^2 h < h^2$. Hence,

$$1 - \cos^2 h < h^2, \quad \text{so} \quad 1 - h^2 < \cos^2 h,$$

which, upon substitution into (4), yields

(6) $$1 - h^2 < \frac{\sin h}{h} < 1.$$

These inequalities hold even if h is negative, since

$$1 - (-h)^2 = 1 - h^2 \quad \text{and} \quad \frac{\sin(-h)}{-h} = \frac{-\sin h}{-h} = \frac{\sin h}{h}.$$

As $h \to 0$, then $1 - h^2 \to 1$; thus, by choosing h sufficiently small in (6), the ratio $\dfrac{\sin h}{h}$ may be made as near to 1 as desired, and this is all that (5) means.

The limit equation (5) is the basis of all calculus of trigonometric functions, as should be noted in the following exposition (and in Chapter 6). Note also that (5) does not hold if h is not measured in radians, as may be seen by going

*For example, $1 - h^2 < 1$ for all $h \ne 0$, but $\lim\limits_{h \to 0} (1 - h^2) = 1$.

back to (1) and deriving a corresponding formula for h measured, say, in degrees.

The trigonometric limit (5) will be used to show that

(7) $$\lim_{h \to 0} \frac{1 - \cos h}{h} = 0.$$

First, $1 - \cos^2 h = \sin^2 h$ and hence $(1 - \cos h)(1 + \cos h) = \sin^2 h$.

Thus, since

$$1 - \cos h = \frac{\sin^2 h}{1 + \cos h}, \quad \text{then} \quad \frac{1 - \cos h}{h} = \frac{\sin h}{h} \cdot \frac{\sin h}{1 + \cos h}, \quad \text{and}$$

$$\lim_{h \to 0} \frac{1 - \cos h}{h} = \lim_{h \to 0} \frac{\sin h}{h} \lim_{h \to 0} \frac{\sin h}{1 + \cos h} = 1 \cdot \frac{0}{1 + 1} = 0.$$

Now (5) and (7) will be used to derive the first trigonometric derivative formula; namely,

(8) $$D_x \sin x = \cos x.$$

This formula is derived by carrying out the usual four steps:

First. Set $y = \sin x$ so that $\Delta y = \sin(x + \Delta x) - \sin x$.

Second.

$$\frac{\Delta y}{\Delta x} = \frac{\sin(x + \Delta x) - \sin x}{\Delta x}.$$

Third. From $\sin (A + B) = \sin A \cos B + \cos A \sin B$,

$$\frac{\Delta y}{\Delta x} = \frac{\sin x \cos \Delta x + \cos x \sin \Delta x - \sin x}{\Delta x}$$

$$= \frac{\cos x \sin \Delta x - \sin x(1 - \cos \Delta x)}{\Delta x}$$

$$= \cos x \frac{\sin \Delta x}{\Delta x} - \sin x \frac{1 - \cos \Delta x}{\Delta x}.$$

Fourth. This specific form was obtained so (5) and (7) could be used (with h replaced by Δx) to show that

$$D_x y = \lim_{\Delta x \to 0} \frac{\Delta y}{\Delta x} = \cos x \lim_{\Delta x \to 0} \frac{\sin \Delta x}{\Delta x} - \sin x \lim_{\Delta x \to 0} \frac{1 - \cos \Delta x}{\Delta x}$$

$$= (\cos x)(1) - (\sin x)(0) = \cos x.$$

Since $y = \sin x$, this is the desired formula (8).

As with all formulas, the variable x may be replaced in (8) by any other variable whatever, provided, of course, that the replacement is made throughout the whole formula. Thus,

(9) $$D_h \sin h = \cos h.$$

Now if h is really a function of x and the derivative with respect to x of $\sin h$ is desired, then the Chain Rule may be used:

$$D_x \sin h = D_h \sin h \, D_x h$$
$$= \cos h \, D_x h.$$

This formula is important enough for boldface display:

(10) $D_x \sin h = \cos h \, D_x h.$

Example 1. $D_x \sin (3x^2 - 4x + 5) = \cos (3x^2 - 4x + 5) D_x (3x^2 - 4x + 5)$
$$= [\cos (3x^2 - 4x + 5)](6x - 4)$$
$$= (6x - 4) \cos (3x^2 - 4x + 5).$$

Since $\cos x = \sin \left(\dfrac{\pi}{2} - x \right)$, then

$$D_x \cos x = D_x \sin \left(\frac{\pi}{2} - x \right) = \cos \left(\frac{\pi}{2} - x \right) D_x \left(\frac{\pi}{2} - x \right) \qquad \text{from (10)}$$

$$= \cos \left(\frac{\pi}{2} - x \right)(-1) = -\cos \left(\frac{\pi}{2} - x \right).$$

But also $\cos \left(\dfrac{\pi}{2} - x \right) = \sin x$, and therefore

(11) $D_x \cos x = -\sin x.$

Again using the Chain Rule,

(12) $D_x \cos h = -\sin h \, D_x h.$

Example 2. $D_x \cos x^2 = -\sin x^2 \, D_x x^2 = -2x \sin x^2.$

Example 3. $D_x \cos^2 x = 2 \cos x \, D_x \cos x$
$$= 2 \cos x (-\sin x)$$
$$= -2 \sin x \cos x = -\sin 2x.$$

Example 4. A wheel of radius 3 ft revolves on its axis at the rate of 200 rev/min. Find the velocity vector and the speed of a point on the rim of the wheel as functions of t.

Solution. Select basic vectors $\vec{i}$ and $\vec{j}$ at the center of the wheel. Then t min after the point is at a horizontal position, the vector from the origin to the point has amplitude $400\pi t$ radians and the vector itself is

$$\vec{u} = 3(\vec{i} \cos 400\pi t + \vec{j} \sin 400\pi t).$$

Hence, the velocity vector $\vec{V}(t)$ is

$$\vec{V}(t) = D_t \vec{u} = 3[\vec{i} \, D_t \cos 400\pi t + \vec{j} \, D_t \sin 400\pi t]$$
$$= 3[\vec{i}(-\sin 400\pi t)D_t 400\pi t + \vec{j}(\cos 400\pi t)D_t(400\pi t)]$$
$$= 3[-\vec{i}(\sin 400\pi t)400\pi + \vec{j}(\cos 400\pi t)400\pi]$$
$$= 1200\pi[-\vec{i} \sin 400\pi t + \vec{j} \cos 400\pi t].$$

Thus, the speed $S(t)$ of the point is given by

$$S(t) = |\vec{V}(t)| = 1200\pi \sqrt{(-\sin 400\pi t)^2 + (\cos 400\pi t)^2}$$
$$= 1200\pi \text{ ft/min.}$$

Hence, the velocity vector function varies with t, but the speed is a constant.

Problem 1. With all angles measured in radians, evaluate the limits:

a. $\lim\limits_{\theta \to 0} \dfrac{\sin 2\theta}{\theta}$.

[*Hint:* Write $\dfrac{\sin 2\theta}{\theta} = 2\dfrac{\sin 2\theta}{2\theta}$ and use (5) with $h = 2\theta$.]

b. $\lim\limits_{\theta \to 0} \dfrac{\sin \theta}{2\theta}$.

d. $\lim\limits_{h \to 0} \dfrac{\sin^2 h}{h^2}$.

c. $\lim\limits_{h \to 0} \dfrac{\tan h}{h}$.

e. $\lim\limits_{h \to 0} \dfrac{\sin^3 h}{h^2}$.

f. $\lim\limits_{\theta \to 0} \dfrac{1 - \cos \theta}{\theta^2}$.

[*Hint:* $1 - \cos \theta \equiv 2 \sin^2(\theta/2)$.]

g. $\lim\limits_{\theta \to 0} \dfrac{1 - \cos \theta}{\sin^2 \theta}$.

h. $\lim\limits_{x \to 0} \dfrac{\sin 5x}{\sin 3x}$.

Problem 2. Find $D_x y$ if:

a. $y = \sin(2x - 3)$.

d. $y = \cos(2x - 3)$.

g. $y = x^2 + \sin 3x$.

b. $y = x \sin x$.

e. $y = x \cos x$.

h. $y = \sqrt{2 - \sin^2 x}$.

c. $y = \dfrac{\sin x}{x}$.

f. $y = \sin x \cos x$.

i. $y = \sqrt{3 - \cos 3x}$.

Problem 3. Find the velocity vector function of t and the speed function of t for a particle whose law of motion is:

a. $\vec{u} = \vec{i}\, 3 \cos 2\pi t + \vec{j}\, 4 \sin 2\pi t$.

c. $\vec{u} = \vec{i}(1 + \cos 3t) + \vec{j}(2 + \sin 3t)$.

b. $\vec{u} = \vec{i} \cos t + \vec{j} \cos 2t$.

d. $\vec{u} = \vec{i} \cos 2t + \vec{j} \sin t$.

2-12. Differentials

For y a function x:

(1) $$y = f(x)$$

and Δx an increment of the independent variable x, then the corresponding increment Δy of the dependent variable y is given by

(2) $$\Delta y = f(x + \Delta x) - f(x).$$

The increments Δx and Δy were used to define $D_x y$:

(3) $$D_x y = \lim_{\Delta x \to 0} \frac{\Delta y}{\Delta x}.$$

With the definition of $D_x y$ already accomplished, another way of denoting a change in the independent variable x is by using dx instead of Δx. This change dx is called a **differential of** x, and dx is read "differential x." The corresponding differential of y is denoted by dy, and is defined by

(4) $$dy = D_x y\, dx.$$

There is little, if any, conceptual distinction between the increment Δx and the differential dx of the independent variable x. The big distinction be-

tween increments and differentials is in the quite different manner in which the
dependent variable y is assigned an increment Δy by (2) or a differential dy
by (4).

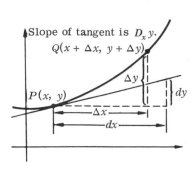

Fig. 2-12.1

A graphical representation of increments
and differentials is shown in Fig. 2-12.1. Since
Δx and dx are both independent of each other
(or of anything else), they may on occasion be
the same, but they need not be the same as
shown on the figure. Even if $dx = \Delta x$, it is
generally true that $dy \neq \Delta y$, since Δy reaches
from the level of $P(x, y)$ up to the curve at
$Q(x + \Delta x, y + \Delta y)$, while the extent of dy is
to the tangent instead of to the curve.

At this time, no attempt will be made
to enumerate reasons for introducing differentials, but practice in using the notation may
be gained from the following examples and problems.

Example 1. Find dy if $y = \sin x^2$.

Solution. It is already known, or may be worked out, that

$$D_x y = 2x \cos x^2.$$

Thus, by definition (4), $dy = D_x y \, dx = 2x \sin x^2 \, dx$.

Finding the differential of a function is merely finding the derivative of the
function and then multiplying by the differential of the independent variable.

Since $y = f(x)$, definition (4) may be written as

(5) $df(x) = D_x f(x) \, dx.$

Some economy is then gained when $f(x)$ is given explicitly. As examples,

$$dx^2 = 2x \, dx, \quad d(x^2 + 5) = dx^2 + d5 = 2x \, dx + 0 \, dx = 2x \, dx.$$

Thus, the result of Example 1, starting with $y = \sin x^2$, may be written
formally as

$$dy = d \sin x^2 = \cos x^2 \, dx^2 = (\cos x^2)2x \, dx = 2x \cos x^2 \, dx.$$

Many mathematicians prefer to find implicit derivatives by using differentials, as illustrated in Example 2.

Example 2. Find $D_x y$ if $x^2 - xy + y^2 = 4$.

Solution.
$$d(x^2 - xy + y^2) = d4,$$
$$dx^2 - d(xy) + dy^2 = 0,$$
$$2x \, dx - (x \, dy + y \, dx) + 2y \, dy = 0,$$
$$dy(2y - x) = dx(y - 2x),$$
$$\frac{dy}{dx} = \frac{y - 2x}{2y - x}.$$

Both sides of (4) may be divided by dx to obtain

$$\frac{dy}{dx} = D_x y.$$

Thus, in this example, the answer is

$$D_x y = \frac{y - 2x}{2y - x}.$$

In fact, it is a universal custom to use $\frac{dy}{dx}$ and $D_x y$ interchangeably.

Problem 1. Find dy if:

a. $y = \cos x^2$.   c. $y = \sin x^3$.   e. $y = \sin(x^{-3})$.

b. $y = (x^2 + 3)^3$.   d. $y = (x^3 + 3)^2$.   f. $y = \cos(x^{-3})$.

Problem 2. Obtain:

a. $d(x^2 - 3x + 4)$.   g. $d(x^3 - 10)$.

b. $d\sqrt{x^2 - 3x + 4}$.   h. $d(x^3 - 125)$.

c. $d \sin(x^2 - 3x + 4)$.   i. $d\sqrt{x^4 + 5}$.

d. $d \cos(x^2 - 3x + 4)$.   j. $d \sin(x^4 + 5)$.

e. $d(x^3 + 5)$.   k. $d(x^4 + 5)^{3/2}$.

f. $d(x^3 + 6)$.   l. $d(x^4 + 5)^{5/2}$.

Problem 3. Use differentials to find $D_x y$:

a. $x^4 - x^2 y + y^3 = 4$.   c. $x \sin y + y = 4$.

b. $x^3 - xy^2 = xy + 3$.   d. $2 \sin x + \cos y = 1$.

2-13. Another Derivative Notation

Isaac Newton (1642–1727) and Gottfried Wilhelm Leibniz (1646–1716) are considered as the founders of the body of knowledge now classified as calculus. Although these men were contemporaries, they seem to have worked independently (Newton in England, Leibniz in Germany) and each used his own notation and terminology. As calculus developed further, still other notations were introduced. Among the various notations for the derivative with respect to x of a function $y = f(x)$, there are three which are so ingrained in the literature of mathematics and its applications that all three must be learned. Two of these are

$$D_x f(x) \quad \text{and} \quad \frac{df(x)}{dx}$$

and the third is $f'(x)$. For example, if $f(x) = 3x^2$, then the derivative with respect to x may be indicated by

$$D_x f(x) = 6x, \quad \frac{df(x)}{dx} = 6x, \quad \text{or} \quad f'(x) = 6x.$$

It should be emphasized that the process of taking a derivative, namely,

$$\lim_{\Delta x \to 0} \frac{f(x + \Delta x) - f(x)}{\Delta x},$$

has one and only one meaning, and it is only the notations used to indicate this process that are different.

The *D*-notation and the *d*-notation are in one sense more complete than the prime notation. Either

$$D_x y \quad \text{or} \quad \frac{dy}{dx}$$

indicates clearly (by the subscript *x* in the first and the denominator *dx* in the second) that the derivative is "with respect to *x* as the independent variable," whereas

$$y'$$

has no *x*, or any other independent variable, in evidence. For example, either

$$D_s \cos s = -\sin s \quad \text{or} \quad \frac{d \cos s}{ds} = -\sin s$$

is compact and complete, whereas in the prime notation it would have to be stated (or known by context) that if $y = \cos s$ with *s* the independent variable, then

$$y' = -\sin s.$$

There are, furthermore, conventions that have been established by repeated use. For example, given the function of *x*:

$$y = f(x) = \sqrt{x - 1},$$

it is almost universal usage to have

$$D_x f(5) = 0, \quad \frac{df(5)}{dx} = 0, \quad \text{but } f'(5) = \tfrac{1}{4}.$$

For some inexplicable reason, the first two are interpreted as "substituting $x = 5$ first and then taking the derivative of the resulting constant," whereas the third is interpreted as "taking the derivative first:

$$f'(x) = \frac{1}{2\sqrt{x - 1}}$$

and then substituting $x = 5$."

If $y = f(x)$ is a function of *x* and it is desired to indicate the derivative with respect to *x* evaluated at $x = a$, then the cumbersome notations

$$D_x f(x)]_{x=a} \quad \text{or} \quad \frac{df(x)}{dx}\bigg]_{x=a}$$

are used, but the same result in the prime notation is

$$f'(a).$$

Why such an arbitrary convention has arisen no one seems to know, but its use is so universal that the student must become accustomed to it and consistently write what will not be misinterpreted.

The student should also resist the temptation of further complicating the situation. For example,

$$d_x f(x), \quad \frac{Df(x)}{Dx}, \quad f'_x(x), \quad \frac{f'(x)}{dx}$$

should *not* be used; they are analogous to misspelled words in an English theme.

Given that u and v are functions of x, and that the prime indicates the derivative with respect to x, then the sum, product, and quotient formulas may be written

$$(u + v)' = u' + v',$$
$$(uv)' = uv' + vu',$$
$$\left(\frac{u}{v}\right)' = \frac{vu' - uv'}{v^2}.$$

Note that alternate ways of writing the definition of $f'(x)$ are

(1) $\lim\limits_{\Delta x \to 0} \dfrac{f(x + \Delta x) - f(x)}{(x + \Delta x) - x} = f'(x)$ and $\lim\limits_{t \to x} \dfrac{f(t) - f(x)}{t - x} = f'(x).$

The prime notation for derivatives is well adapted to stating and proving the Chain Rule theorem, which was introduced heuristically in Sec. 2-9.

THE CHAIN RULE THEOREM. *Let f and g be functions, denote*

$$\{x \,|\, g(x) \text{ and } f(g(x)) \text{ both exist}\} \text{ by } \mathscr{D}_F,$$

and let F be the composition of f and g so that

(2) $F(x) = f(g(x)) \text{ for each } x \in \mathscr{D}_F.$

If x_0 is such that $g'(x_0)$ and $f'(g(x_0))$ both exist, then $F'(x_0)$ also exists and the Chain Rule

(3) $F'(x_0) = f'(g(x_0))\, g'(x_0)$

holds.

PROOF. Define an auxiliary function G with domain $\mathscr{D}_F$ by setting

(4) $G(t) = \dfrac{f(t) - f(g(x_0))}{t - g(x_0)} \text{ if } t \neq g(x_0) \text{ and } t \in \mathscr{D}_F, \text{ but}$

(5) $G(g(x_0)) = f'(g(x_0)).$

By keeping $t \neq g(x_0)$, while letting $t \to g(x_0)$ in (4),

$$\lim_{t \to g(x_0)} G(t) = \lim_{t \to g(x_0)} \frac{f(t) - f(g(x_0))}{t - g(x_0)} = f'(g(x_0))$$

from the second form in (1) for the definition of f' evaluated at $g(x_0)$. Thus, from (5),

(6) $$\lim_{t \to g(x_0)} G(t) = G(g(x_0)).$$

Now $g'(x_0)$ exists so that $\lim_{\Delta x \to 0} g(x_0 + \Delta x) = g(x_0)$ and hence, from (6),

(7) $$\lim_{\Delta x \to 0} G(g(x_0 + \Delta x)) = G(g(x_0)).$$

Next, go back to (4) again and write it in the form

$$G(t)[t - g(x_0)] = f(t) - f(g(x_0)).$$

Now check that this equality also holds if $t = g(x_0)$, since both sides are then equal to zero. Hence, whether $g(x_0 + \Delta x)$ is equal to $g(x_0)$ or not,

$$G(g(x_0 + \Delta x))[g(x_0 + \Delta x) - g(x_0)] = f(g(x_0 + \Delta x)) - f(g(x_0))$$
$$= F(x_0 + \Delta x) - F(x_0).$$

The second equation follows from the definition (2) of F. Thus, upon dividing by $\Delta x \neq 0$,

$$G(g(x_0 + \Delta x))\frac{g(x_0 + \Delta x) - g(x_0)}{\Delta x} = \frac{F(x_0 + \Delta x) - F(x_0)}{\Delta x}$$

As $\Delta x \to 0$, the first factor on the left approaches $G(g(x_0))$ by (7), the second factor approaches $g'(x_0)$, and thus the limit of the right side exists. Hence, from the definition of $F'(x_0)$.

$$G(g(x_0))g'(x_0) = F'(x_0).$$

Finally, use (5) to replace $G(g(x_0))$ by $f'(g(x_0))$ and thus obtain the desired conclusion (3).

Note: A special notation is often used for the composition of functions f and g; it is $f \circ g$. Thus, for $x \in \mathcal{D}_F$, where $\mathcal{D}_F$ was defined in the Chain Rule theorem,

$$(f \circ g)(x) = f(g(x)).$$

In this notation, the Chain Rule formula (3) appears as

$$(f \circ g)'(x) = (f' \circ g)(x)\, g'(x).$$

The circle notation for the composition of two functions is not used in this book.

Problem 1. For each of the following functions, find $f'(x)$:

a. $f(x) = (x - 2)^2$.

b. $f(x) = \dfrac{x}{\sqrt{x^2 + 1}}$.

c. $f(x) = \sin^2 x \cos 2x$.

d. $f(x) = \sqrt{1 + \sin^2 x}$.

e. $f(x) = \dfrac{x}{\sin x}$.

f. $f(x) = (x + \sin x)^2$.

Problem 2. Given:

a. $f(x) = 2 \sin x$, find $D_x f\left(\frac{\pi}{4}\right)$, $\frac{df(\pi/4)}{dx}$, $f'\left(\frac{\pi}{4}\right)$.

b. $f(x) = \frac{x \sin x}{x + 1}$, find $D_x f(\pi)$, $\frac{df(\pi)}{dx}$, $f'(\pi)$.

c. $f(x) = x + \sqrt{x - 1}$, show that $D_x f(1)$ exists but $f'(1)$ does not exist.

d. $f(x) = \sin x + \cos x$, find $D_x f(\pi/4)$ and $f'(\pi/4)$.

Problem 3. For $f(x)$ as given, sketch the graph of $y = f(x)$ and the graphs of the following equations:

a. $f(x) = x^2$, $y - f(1) = f'(1)(x - 1)$, $y - f(1) = f'(x)(x - 1)$.

b. $f(x) = \frac{1}{x}$, $y - f(2) = f'(2)(x - 2)$, $y - f(2) = f'(x)(x - 2)$.

c. $f(x) = \sin x$, $y - f\left(\frac{\pi}{6}\right) = f'\left(\frac{\pi}{6}\right)\left(x - \frac{\pi}{6}\right)$.

d. $f(x) = \sqrt{x - 1}$, $y - f(5) = f'(5)(x - 5)$.

Problem 4. For the function $f(x)$ with independent variable x, find $f'(2t)$ and $D_t f(2t)$:

a. $f(x) = \sin x$.   b. $f(x) = \frac{x}{x - 1}$.   c. $f(x) = \frac{x - 1}{x}$.

Problem 5. With the function $f(x)$ and the constants a and b as given, solve $f(b) - f(a) = f'(x)(b - a)$ for x:

a. $f(x) = x^2$, $a = 1$, $b = 5$.   c. $f(x) = \frac{1}{x}$, $a = 2$, $b = 8$.

b. $f(x) = x^3$, $a = 1$, $b = 5$.   d. $f(x) = \frac{1}{x - 1}$, $a = 3$, $b = 9$.

Problem 6. For the given function $f(x)$ of x, find $D_x[f'(x)]$.

a. $f(x) = \frac{\sin x}{x}$.   c. $f(x) = x^3 + 5x^2 - 4x + 1$.

b. $f(x) = \frac{x}{\sin x}$.   d. $f(x) = \frac{1}{x^3} + \frac{5}{x^2} - \frac{4}{x} + 1$.

Problem 7. With time t the independent variable and with $\vec{F}'(t)$ denoting the time derivative, find $\vec{F}'(t)$ if:

a. $\vec{F}(t) = \vec{i} \sin t + \vec{j} \cos 2t$.   b. $\vec{F}(t) = 2\vec{i} t^3 + 3\vec{j} t^2$.

2-14. Acceleration

A moving car will sometimes speed up, sometimes slow down, and sometimes its speed will not change. Also, at times the car may be stopped and at other times it may go backward, either at a constant rate or at an increasing or decreasing rate. Consider forward motion as the positive (or natural) direction and backward motion as the negative direction. Let

$$\vec{i}\, x(t)$$

be the car's vector position at time t along a straight road (the x-axis) measured from some predetermined origin. Then the velocity is the vector function $\vec{v}(t)$ given by

$$\vec{v}(t) = \vec{i}\,\frac{dx(t)}{dt} = \vec{i}\,x'(t) \text{ mi/hr.}$$

The actual change in the velocity from time t to time $t + \Delta t$ is given by

$$\Delta\vec{v}(t) = \vec{v}(t + \Delta t) - \vec{v}(t)$$
$$= \vec{i}\,x'(t + \Delta t) - \vec{i}\,x'(t)$$
$$= \vec{i}[x'(t + \Delta t) - x'(t)] \text{ mi/hr.}$$

Thus, the ratio

$$\frac{\Delta\vec{v}(t)}{\Delta t}\frac{\text{mi/hr}}{\text{hr}} = \vec{i}\,\frac{x'(t + \Delta t) - x'(t)}{\Delta t}\frac{\text{mi}}{(\text{hr})^2}$$

is a measure of the average rate at which the velocity changed between time t and time $t + \Delta t$, and is called the **average acceleration** for this time interval. The limit as $\Delta t \to 0$ of the average acceleration,

$$\lim_{\Delta t \to 0}\frac{\Delta\vec{v}(t)}{\Delta t} = \lim_{\Delta t \to 0}\vec{i}\,\frac{x'(t + \Delta t) - x'(t)}{\Delta t} = \vec{i}\,\frac{dx'(t)}{dt}\frac{\text{mi}}{(\text{hr})^2},$$

is defined as the **acceleration** at time t, often called the **instantaneous acceleration** at time t.

Since $\vec{v}(t)$ is a function, then by definition the derivative of $\vec{v}(t)$ with respect to t is given by

(1) $$\frac{d\vec{v}(t)}{dt} = \lim_{\Delta t \to 0}\frac{\Delta\vec{v}(t)}{\Delta t}.$$

Upon letting $\vec{\alpha}(t)$ denote the acceleration at time t, then

(2) $$\vec{\alpha}(t) = \frac{d\vec{v}(t)}{dt} = \vec{i}\,\frac{dx'(t)}{dt}.$$

Since the function $x'(t)$ is already a derivative, it is natural to call its derivative the **second derivative** of the function $x(t)$ and to set

$$\frac{dx'(t)}{dt} = x''(t).$$

As noted, there are three commonly used notations for the ordinary derivative, now called the **first derivative** of $x(t)$; namely,

$$D_t x(t), \quad x'(t), \quad \text{and} \quad \frac{dx(t)}{dt}.$$

Hence, there are also three corresponding notations for the second derivative of $x(t)$ with respect to t:

$$D_t^2 x(t), \quad x''(t), \quad \text{and} \quad \frac{d^2 x(t)}{dt^2}.$$

Example 1. Given $x(t) = \sin 3t$, find the second derivative $x''(t)$.

Solution. The first derivative is first computed:

$$x'(t) = \frac{d \sin 3t}{dt} = \cos 3t \frac{d3t}{dt} = 3 \cos 3t.$$

Then the second derivative is merely the derivative of this derivative:

$$x''(t) = \frac{d3 \cos 3t}{dt} = 3 \frac{d \cos 3t}{dt} = 3 \left[-\sin 3t \frac{d3t}{dt} \right] = -9 \sin 3t.$$

It is not necessary to list formulas for second derivatives. *To find a second derivative of a function, merely take the ordinary derivative and then take the derivative of the result.*

Acceleration is also defined for motions that are not necessarily rectilinear (that is, are not necessarily motions along a straight line). Thus, if a motion is represented by

$$\vec{u}(t) = \vec{i} x(t) + \vec{j} y(t),$$

then the velocity $\vec{v}(t)$ is defined by

$$\vec{v}(t) = \frac{d\vec{u}(t)}{dt} = \vec{i} x'(t) + \vec{j} y'(t)$$

and the acceleration $\vec{\alpha}(t)$ by

$$\vec{\alpha}(t) = \frac{d\vec{v}(t)}{dt} = \vec{i} x''(t) + \vec{j} y''(t).$$

The acceleration vector $\vec{\alpha}(t)$, as well as the velocity vector $\vec{v}(t)$, is usually drawn with initial end at the terminal end of $\vec{u}(t)$.

Example 2. A particle moving according to the law

$$\vec{u} = (2 - t)\vec{i} + t^2\vec{j}$$

has vector velocity $\vec{v} = \dfrac{d\vec{u}}{dt} = -\vec{i} + 2t\vec{j}$. Hence, the acceleration vector

$$\vec{\alpha} = \frac{d\vec{v}}{dt} = 0 \cdot \vec{i} + 2\vec{j}$$

is constant and is shown at each of the times $t = -2$, $-1, 0, 1,$ and 2 in Fig. 2–14.1 (which is Fig. 2–5.4 with the acceleration vectors appended).

In Example 2 the acceleration vector is a constant. In the following example, the acceleration vector is not constant but has constant absolute value.

Example 3. A particle following the law

(3) $$\vec{u} = 2(\vec{i} \cos \tfrac{1}{2}t + \vec{j} \sin \tfrac{1}{2}t)$$

moves on a circle of radius 2 and center at the origin, since

$$|\vec{u}| = 2\sqrt{\cos^2 \tfrac{1}{2}t + \sin^2 \tfrac{1}{2}t} = 2.$$

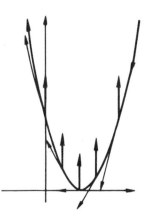

Fig. 2-14.1

The velocity vector

$$\vec{v} = \frac{d\vec{u}}{dt} = 2\left[\vec{i}\left(-\frac{1}{2}\sin\frac{1}{2}t\right) + \vec{j}\,\frac{1}{2}\cos\frac{1}{2}t\right] = -\vec{i}\,\sin\frac{1}{2}t + \vec{j}\,\cos\frac{1}{2}t$$

is variable with time, but has constant length 1. The acceleration vector

(4) $$\vec{\alpha} = \frac{d\vec{v}}{dt} = -\frac{1}{2}\left[\vec{i}\,\cos\frac{1}{2}t + \vec{j}\,\sin\frac{1}{2}t\right]$$

is variable, but with constant length $\frac{1}{2}$. Note also from (3) that

$$\vec{i}\,\cos\tfrac{1}{2}t + \vec{j}\,\sin\tfrac{1}{2}t = \tfrac{1}{2}\vec{u},$$

and upon substitution into (4) the result may be expressed as

$$\vec{\alpha} = -\frac{1}{4}\vec{u}; \text{ that is, } \frac{d^2\vec{u}}{dt^2} = -\frac{1}{4}\vec{u}.$$

Hence, in this example, at any time, the acceleration vector is directed oppositely from the position vector, with length one-fourth the length of the position vector.

As shown in this section, the discussion of accelerated motion depends on second derivatives taken with respect to time. Given a function $y = f(x)$ of x, the second derivative of y with respect to x is denoted by

$$\frac{d^2y}{dx^2}, \quad y'', \quad \text{or} \quad D_x^2 y;$$

a geometric interpretation of this second derivative is given later. Third, fourth, and higher order derivatives will be used in Chapter 13.

Problem 1. Find $\dfrac{d^2y}{dx^2}$ for each of the functions:

a. $y = \sin 2x$.

b. $y = x \sin x$.

c. $y = x^4 + x^2$.

d. $y = x^{-4} + x^{-2}$.

e. $y = \sqrt[4]{x} + \sqrt{x}$.

f. $y = \sin^2 x$.

g. $y = \cos^2 x$.

h. $y = x\sqrt{x+1}$.

i. $y = \dfrac{\sin x}{x}$.

Problem 2.

a. Given $y = 3\cos 2x + 5\sin 2x$, show that $y'' + 4y = 0$.

b. Given $y = 4\sin\frac{1}{3}x - 6\cos\frac{1}{3}x$, show that $9y'' + y = 0$.

Problem 3. For the law of motion given by (3) of Example 3, show that $\vec{u}\cdot\vec{v} = 0$ and $\vec{v}\cdot\vec{\alpha} = 0$ and interpret each of these equations.

Problem 4. For each of the following motions, find the position of the particle when $t = 0, 1, 2,$ and 3. Also draw the velocity and acceleration vectors at these points.

a. $\vec{u} = \vec{i}\,t^2 + \vec{j}\,\frac{1}{3}t^3$.

b. $\vec{u} = \vec{i}\,t + \vec{j}(t^2 - 3t + 2)$.

c. $\vec{u} = \vec{i}\,t + \vec{j}\,\sin\frac{\pi}{4}t$.

d. $\vec{u} = \vec{i}\,3\cos\frac{\pi}{4}t + \vec{j}\,2\sin\frac{\pi}{4}t$.

Problem 5. Sketch the path of a particle following the law

$$\vec{u} = \vec{i}\,t + \vec{j}\,\frac{1}{t}.$$

Also sketch the velocity and acceleration vectors at $t = \frac{1}{2}, 1$, and 2.

2-15. Law of the Mean

This section is mostly theoretical, whereas the rest of the chapter is more concerned with formalistic and manipulative work. The Law of the Mean at the end of the section is, however, very important for understanding some of the significant developments that follow.

For intuitive background, draw an (x, y)-coordinate system. Place a pencil point on the paper. Without letting the pencil point leave the paper, sketch a curve, always moving to the right. The curve need not have a tangent at each point; that is, it is all right to stop at some point and abruptly change direction. Now locate a point on the curve whose y-coordinate seems to be greater than or equal to the y-coordinates of all other points of the curve. That there is indeed such a point under the conditions stated in Theorem 2-15.2 is the principle on which the Law of the Mean rests.

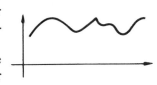

Fig. 2-15.1

To explain this, some previous work will be reviewed and then extended. The results that appear incidental here are also important.

The conditions, on p. 55, under which a function $y = f(x)$ is said to be **continuous** at $x = c$ are displayed more vividly as:

(i) $f(c)$ is defined,
(ii) $\lim\limits_{x \to c} f(x)$ exists, and
(iii) $\lim\limits_{x \to c} f(x) = f(c)$.

In slightly different notation, the function f is continuous at a specific value x_0 if

$$(1) \qquad \lim_{\Delta x \to 0} f(x_0 + \Delta x) = f(x_0).$$

This equation implies that $f(x_0)$ is defined, that $\lim\limits_{\Delta x \to 0} f(x_0 + \Delta x)$ exists, and that (1) holds. Moreover, (1) holds if and only if

$$\lim_{\Delta x \to 0} [f(x_0 + \Delta x) - f(x_0)] = 0$$

and thus if and only if

$$(2) \qquad \lim_{\Delta x \to 0} \Delta y = 0.$$

Hence, the result "if a function $y = f(x)$ has a derivative at a point $x = x_0$, then (2) holds" (as shown on p. 60) may be recast as:

If $f'(x_0)$ exists, then $y = f(x)$ is continuous at $x = x_0$.

The converse is not so, and it takes only one example to disprove the converse.* All that is needed is a function that is continuous at a point where the function fails to have a derivative. An easy example is

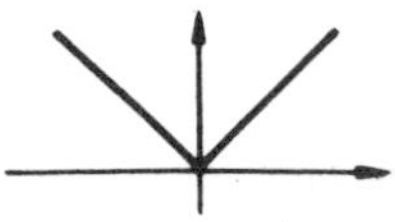

$$y = f(x) = |x|$$

considered at $x_0 = 0$. For, $f(0) = |0| = 0$ and $\lim\limits_{x \to 0} |x| = 0$,

so that all three of (i), (ii), and (iii) hold for this function at $x_0 = c = 0$. This function fails, however, to have a deri-

Fig. 2-15.2

vative at $x_0 = 0$. To see this, note that

$$\frac{\Delta y}{\Delta x} = \frac{f(0 + \Delta x) - f(0)}{\Delta x}$$

$$= \frac{|\Delta x| - |0|}{\Delta x} = \frac{|\Delta x|}{\Delta x} = \begin{cases} 1 & \text{if } \Delta x > 0, \\ -1 & \text{if } \Delta x < 0. \end{cases}$$

Thus, as Δx approaches 0 through positive values, the difference quotient remains at the value 1; but if Δx approaches 0 through negative values, the difference quotient is equal to -1. Hence, this difference quotient does not have the limit 1, nor -1, nor any other number as $\Delta x \to 0$; that is, $f'(0)$ does not exist.

This brings up the subject of one-sided limits.

DEFINITION. *Let a function* $y = f(x)$ *be defined at least for* $c < x < b$, *and let* L_r *be a number. If corresponding to each positive number* ϵ *there is a number* $\delta > 0$ *such that*

whenever $c < x < c + \delta$, *then* $|f(x) - L_r| < \epsilon$,

the function is said to have L_r *as* **right-hand limit** (*or limit from the right*) *at* $x = c$ *and the notation*

$$\lim_{x \to c+} f(x) = L_r$$

is used.

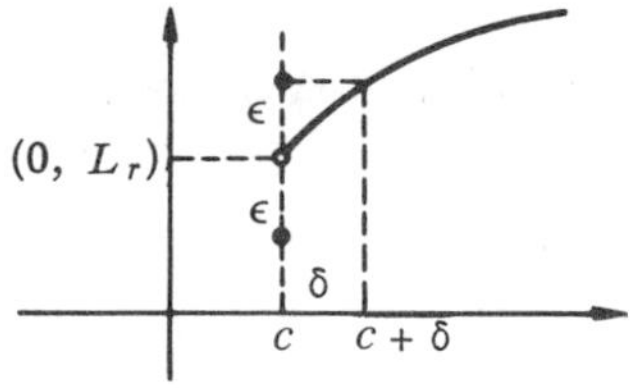

A definition of the left-hand limit L_l at $x = c$,

$$\lim_{x \to c-} f(x) = L_l,$$

should be thought through by making appropriate changes in the above definition.

Fig. 2-15.3

THEOREM 2-15.1. *A function* $y = f(x)$ *has a limit* L *at* $x = c$ *if and only if the right-hand*

---

*The converse is the (false) statement, "if $y = f(x)$ is continuous at $x = x_0$, then $f'(x_0)$ exists."

limit L_r and left-hand limit L_l both exist and are equal, and then $L_r = L_l = L$.

PROOF. *Case 1.* The limit L exists. Let $\epsilon > 0$ be arbitrary and choose $\delta > 0$ such that

whenever $c - \delta < x < c$ or $c < x < c + \delta$, then $|f(x) - L| < \epsilon$.

Now block out $c - \delta < x < c$ and what is left is the condition that L be the right-hand limit L_r. Removing $c < x < c + \delta$ shows that $L = L_l$. Thus, $L = L_r = L_l$.

Case 2. L_r and L_l exist and $L_r = L_l$. Let $\epsilon > 0$ be arbitrary and $\delta_1 > 0$ and $\delta_2 > 0$ be such that

whenever $c < x < c + \delta_1$, then $|f(x) - L_r| < \epsilon$, and

whenever $c - \delta_2 < x < c$, then $|f(x) - L_l| < \epsilon$.

Erase the subscripts from L_r and L_l, since $L_r = L_l$ in this case. Now let δ be the smaller of δ_1 and δ_2. Hence,

whenever $c < x < c + \delta$ or $c - \delta < x < c$, then $|f(x) - L| < \epsilon$.

But this is exactly the definition of this L (the common value of L_r and L_l) being the limit at $x = c$.

The **right-hand derivative** $f'(x +)$ and the **left-hand derivative** $f'(x -)$ are defined by

$$f'(x +) = \lim_{\Delta x \to 0+} \frac{f(x + \Delta x) - f(x)}{\Delta x} \text{ and } f'(x -) = \lim_{\Delta x \to 0-} \frac{f(x + \Delta x) - f(x)}{\Delta x},$$

provided these right-hand and left-hand limits exist.

Hence, a corollary of Theorem 2–15.1 is:

COROLLARY. *A function $y = f(x)$ has a derivative at $x = x_0$ if and only if $f'(x_0 +)$ and $f'(x_0 -)$ both exist and are equal, and then $f'(x_0) = f'(x_0 +) = f'(x_0 -)$.*

It is now natural to say that a function $y = f(x)$ is **right-hand continuous** at $x = c$ if all three of the following hold:

$$f(c) \text{ is defined,}$$

$$\lim_{x \to c+} f(x) \text{ exists,}$$

$$\lim_{x \to c+} f(x) = f(c).$$

Similarly, left-hand continuity is defined.

Continuity, left- and right-hand continuity at a point have thus been defined and will now be extended to continuity relative to a closed interval.

DEFINITION. *A function $y = f(x)$ is said to be continuous relative to the closed interval $a \leq x \leq b$ if it is right-hand continuous at $x = a$, left-hand continuous at $x = b$, and continuous at $x = x_0$ for every x_0 satisfying $a < x_0 < b$.*

Figure 2-15.4 shows how a function can be discontinuous at $x = a$ and still be continuous relative to $a \leq x \leq b$.

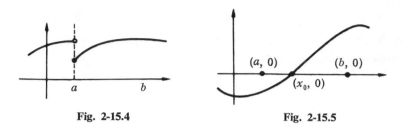

Fig. 2-15.4   Fig. 2-15.5

If a curve that is the graph of a continuous function $y = f(x)$ is below the x-axis at $x = a$ and above the x-axis at $x = b$, then it seems that there must be at least one point $(x_0, 0)$ with $a < x_0 < b$ where the curve crosses the x-axis (as in Fig. 2-15.5). A proof that there is such an x_0 may be made by using the Completion Axiom, but the details will not be presented here. This "intermediate value property of continuous functions" is stated here for later reference.

THEOREM 2-15.2. *If a function $f(x)$ is continuous on the closed interval $a \leq x \leq b$, and if $f(a)$ and $f(b)$ have opposite signs, then there is a number x_0 such that $a < x_0 < b$ and $f(x_0) = 0$.*

All this discussion of continuity was needed so that the meaning of the following theorem would be perfectly clear.

THEOREM 2-15.3. *If a function $y = f(x)$ is continuous relative to a closed interval $a \leq x \leq b$, then there is at least one number $\bar{x}$ such that $a \leq \bar{x} \leq b$ and*

$$f(\bar{x}) \geq f(x) \text{ for every } x \text{ satisfying } a \leq x \leq b.$$

Also, there is at least one $\underline{x}$, $a \leq \underline{x} \leq b$, such that

$$f(\underline{x}) \leq f(x) \text{ for } a \leq x \leq b.$$

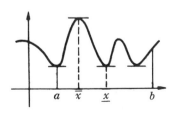

Fig. 2-15.6

Figure 2-15.6 shows a curve for which there is only one possibility for $\bar{x}$, but three possibilities for $\underline{x}$ on $a \leq x \leq b$.

Although the theorem may seem intuitively obvious, the proof involves deeper and more basic notions and therefore will not be given here.

Nevertheless, the facts stated in the theorem will be used in the proof of other theorems.

ROLLE'S THEOREM. *If a function $y = g(x)$ is continuous relative to the closed interval $a \leq x \leq b$, if*

(3) $\qquad$ $g'(x)$ *exists for each* x *such that* $a < x < b$,

and if

(4) $\qquad\qquad\qquad g(a) = g(b) = 0,$

then there is an x_1 *such that*

(5) $\qquad\qquad a < x_1 < b \quad and \quad g'(x_1) = 0.$

PROOF. *Case 1.* $g(x) = 0$ for $a \leq x \leq b$. In this (trivial) case,

$$g'(x) = 0 \text{ for all } x \text{ such that } a \leq x \leq b.$$

Hence, choose any x_1 such that $a < x_1 < b$ and (5) holds for this x_1.

Case 2. $g(x)$ is positive for some x (not necessarily all x) between a and b. By Theorem 2–15.3, let $\bar{x}$ be such that $a \leq \bar{x} \leq b$ and

(6) $\qquad g(\bar{x}) \geq g(x)$ for every x satisfying $a \leq x \leq b$.

Since $g(x) > 0$ for some x between a and b, then $g(\bar{x}) > 0$. The only thing this is used for is to be certain that

$$a < \bar{x} < b,$$

which must hold since $g(a) = g(b) = 0$. Now for $\Delta x \neq 0$ but so small that $a < \bar{x} + \Delta x < b$ also, it follows from (6) that

$$g(\bar{x}) \geq g(\bar{x} + \Delta x).$$

Hence, $g(\bar{x} + \Delta x) - g(\bar{x}) \leq 0$, so that

(7) $\qquad \dfrac{g(\bar{x} + \Delta x) - g(\bar{x})}{\Delta x} \begin{cases} \leq 0 \text{ if } \Delta x > 0, \\ \geq 0 \text{ if } \Delta x < 0. \end{cases}$

Since $a < \bar{x} < b$, the existence of $g'(\bar{x})$ is assured by (3). Thus, the existence of $g'(\bar{x} +)$ and $g'(\bar{x} -)$ and the equality

$$g'(\bar{x}) = g'(\bar{x} +) = g'(\bar{x} -)$$

follows from the corollary of Theorem 2–15.1. Now $g'(\bar{x} +) \leq 0$ from the upper part of (7), and the lower part shows that $g'(\bar{x} -) \geq 0$. Hence, the conclusion $g'(\bar{x}) = 0$ is reached. Thus, the identification $x_1 = \bar{x}$ yields both parts of (5).

Case 3. $g(x)$ is negative for some x such that $a < x < b$. The proof in this case is left as an exercise. These three cases being exhaustive, Rolle's Theorem is established.

A geometric analog of Rolle's Theorem is:

If a curve is smooth (meaning it has a tangent at each point on it) and touches or crosses the x-axis at two points, then the arc between these points has at least one horizontal tangent (see Fig. 2-15.7).

The curve of Fig. 2-15.8 also crosses the x-axis at two points, but the arc between these points has no horizontal tangent. This illustrates that if a function fails to have a derivative at a single point, then Rolle's Theorem may not be applied.

Fig. 2-15.7   Fig. 2-15.8

The next theorem relaxes the condition (4) of Rolle's Theorem and has a different conclusion.

LAW OF THE MEAN. *If a function* $y = f(x)$ *is continuous relative to the closed interval* $a \leq x \leq b$ *and if*

$$f'(x) \text{ exists for each } x \text{ such that } a < x < b,$$

then there is a number x_1 *such that*

(8) $f(b) = f(a) + f'(x_1)(b - a)$ *and* $a < x_1 < b.$

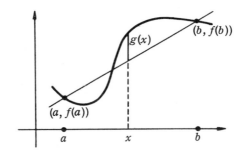

Fig. 2-15.9

PROOF. The equation of the line passing through the two points $(a, f(a))$ and $(b, f(b))$ may be written as

$$y = \frac{f(b) - f(a)}{b - a}(x - a) + f(a).$$

Subtract the expression on the right from $f(x)$ to define a function $g(x)$ by

(9) $g(x) = f(x) - \dfrac{f(b) - f(a)}{b - a}(x - a) - f(a)$ for $a \leq x \leq b.$

Geometrically, $g(x)$ is, for $a \leq x \leq b$, the length (or its negative) of a vertical segment between the arc and its chord joining $(a, f(a))$ and $(b, f(b))$ (see Fig. 2–15.9).

The function $g(x)$ is continuous relative to $a \le x \le b$, since $f(x)$ is continuous relative to $a \le x \le b$. Also, $g'(x)$ exists for $a < x < b$, and

(10)
$$g'(x) = f'(x) - \frac{f(b) - f(a)}{b - a}.$$

Furthermore, $g(a) = g(b) = 0$ by substitution into (9). Thus, $g(x)$ satisfies all of the conditions of Rolle's Theorem. Hence, let x_1 be a number such that

$$a < x_1 < b \text{ and } g'(x_1) = 0.$$

Then, from (10),

$$f'(x_1) - \frac{f(b) - f(a)}{b - a} = 0 ;$$

that is, $f(b) = f(a) + f'(x_1)(b - a)$, which, with $a < x_1 < b$, is the desired conclusion.

Example. Show that $|\sin \alpha - \sin \beta| \le |\alpha - \beta|$ for any numbers α and β.

Solution. The equality holds if $\alpha = \beta$. Consider $\alpha < \beta$. Let

$$f(x) = \sin x, \text{ so that } f'(x) = \cos x.$$

By the Law of the Mean, let x_1 be a number such that

$$\sin \beta = \sin \alpha + (\cos x_1)(\beta - \alpha) \text{ and } \alpha < x_1 < \beta.$$

Then $\sin \beta - \sin \alpha = (\cos x_1)(\beta - \alpha)$, and

$$|\sin \beta - \sin \alpha| = |\cos x_1||\beta - \alpha| \le |\beta - \alpha|,$$

since $|\cos x_1| \le 1$.

In case $\beta < \alpha$, apply the Law of the Mean to $f(x) = \sin x$ on $\beta \le x \le \alpha$ and see that the same conclusion follows.

Let $f(x)$ be defined at least for $a \le x \le b$. Even if $f(x)$ is defined for some value of x less than a or greater than b, it is said that:

$f'(x)$ exists **relative** to $a \le x \le b$ if $f'(a+)$, $f'(b-)$, and $f'(x_0)$ exists for each x_0 such that $a < x_0 < b$.

Figure 2-15.10 illustrates how a function can fail to have a derivative at $x = a$ and still have the qualified existence of the derivative relative to $a \le x \le b$.

It should be seen that:

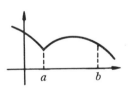

If $f'(x)$ exists relative to $a \le x \le b$, then $f(x)$ is continuous relative to $a \le x \le b$.

Fig. 2-15.10

Hence, the Law of the Mean may be applied to any function whose derivative exists relative to $a \le x \le b$; that is,

If $f'(x)$ exists relative to $a \leq x \leq b$, then $f(b) = f(a) + f'(x_1)(b - a)$ for some x_1, $a < x_1 < b$.

The following problems are corollaries of the above results and thus extend the theory. These problems are different from those in most sections, since the results will be referred to later as if they were part of the regular text. In fact, Prob. 4 is used in the first section of the next chapter.

Problem 1. If $f'(x)$ exists and $f'(x) > 0$ for $a < x < b$, then $f(x)$ is increasing on $a < x < b$; that is,

$$\text{if } a < x_1 < x_2 < b, \text{ then } f(x_1) < f(x_2).$$

[*Hint:* Apply the Law of the Mean to $x_1 \leq x \leq x_2$.]

Problem 2. If $f'(x)$ exists and $f'(x) < 0$ for $a < x < b$, then $f(x)$ is decreasing on $a < x < b$.

Problem 3. If $f'(x)$ exists and $f'(x) = 0$ for $a \leq x \leq b$, then $f(x)$ is a constant on $a \leq x \leq b$.

[*Note:* This is the converse of: If $y = f(x)$ is a constant, then $f'(x) = 0$.]

Problem 4. If $F(x)$ and $G(x)$ are functions such that the existence of the derivatives and the equality

$$F'(x) = G'(x)$$

hold for $a \leq x \leq b$, then there is a constant c such that

$$G(x) = F(x) + c \text{ on } a \leq x \leq b.$$

[*Hint:* Set $f(x) = F(x) - G(x)$.]

Integration

Chapter 3

3-1. Antiderivatives

After children learn to add integers, they are introduced to subtraction by such "antiaddition" problems as "find the number which added to 3 yields 5." The problem of finding $D_x x^2$ is a derivative problem, and now such antiderivative problems as "find y if $D_x y = 2x$" will be considered. One solution of this particular problem is

$$y = x^2.$$

But it is also known that $D_x(x^2 + c) = 2x$ for any constant c, so another answer for $D_x y = 2x$ is

$$y = x^2 + c.$$

So far, no function other than one of the form $y = x^2 + c$ has been met whose derivative is $2x$. "Is there a function $y = F(x)$ other than one of the form $x^2 + c$ such that $D_x F(x) = 2x$?" may well be asked.

In more general terms it will be shown that:

If $f(x)$ is a given function, if the equation

$$D_x y = f(x)$$

is to be solved for y as a function of x, and if $y = F(x)$ is a solution found by any means whatever, then any other solution $y = G(x)$ is such that

(1) $$G(x) = F(x) + c$$

for some constant c.

In fact, this is essentially what the statement in Problem 4, Sec. 2–15, says. For let $a \leq x \leq b$ be an interval on which $f(x)$ is defined. Then the assumption that $y = F(x)$ and $y = G(x)$ are both solutions of $D_x y = f(x)$ means that

$$F'(x) = G'(x) = f(x) \quad \text{for} \quad a \leq x \leq b.$$

Then (see Prob. 4) there is a constant c for which (1) holds, at least for $a \leq x \leq b$.

Thus, since $y = x^2$ is one solution of $D_x y = 2x$, any solution is of the form $y = x^2 + c$ for c a constant.

Example 1. Solve $D_x y = \sin 2x$ for y as a function of x.

Solution. Since $D_x(a \cos 2x) = -a \sin 2x$ $D_x 2x = -2a \sin 2x$, it is seen by choosing $a = -\frac{1}{2}$ that

$$D_x(-\tfrac{1}{2} \cos 2x) = \sin 2x.$$

Thus, one answer is $y = -\frac{1}{2} \cos 2x$ and then, from the above statement, all solutions are of the form

$$y = -\tfrac{1}{2} \cos 2x + c.$$

In differential notation, $dy = D_x y \, dx$, and thus the problem of Example 1 may be posed in differential notation as:

"Solve $dy = \sin 2x \, dx$ for y as a function of x."

In either form the problem is an "antiderivative" problem and could be stated either as:

"Find the most general antiderivative of $\sin 2x$," or as

"Find the most general antidifferential of $\sin 2x \, dx$."

In either case, the answer is $y = -\frac{1}{2} \cos 2x + c$. Actually neither of these forms of stating the problem is used (except to introduce the idea), but new notation and terminology are in common use. The notation is

(2)
$$\int \sin 2x \, dx,$$

which is read "the indefinite integral of $\sin 2x \, dx$," and means "find the most general function whose derivative with respect to x is $\sin 2x$, or whose differential is $\sin 2x \, dx$." Thus,

(3)
$$\int \sin 2x \, dx = -\tfrac{1}{2} \cos 2x + c.$$

The process of starting with the left-hand member of (3) as given and finding the right-hand member is referred to as "indefinite integration." The adjective "indefinite" refers to the fact that the additive constant c is arbitrary and, in the absence of further information, is not assigned a definite value.

With $f(x)$ a given function of x, appearing in the indefinite integral

$$\int f(x) \, dx,$$

the differential $f(x) \, dx$ is referred to as the **integrand.**

The usual power formula $dx^p = px^{p-1} \, dx$ leads directly to

$$d \frac{1}{p+1} x^{p+1} = \frac{1}{p+1} (p+1) x^p \, dx = x^p \, dx \text{ if } p \neq -1.$$

Hence, upon using the last term as the integrand, it follows that

1. $$\int x^p \, dx = \frac{1}{p+1} x^{p+1} + c \quad \text{if } p \neq -1.$$

This is the first of several integration formulas.

With a and b constants, the integration formula

2. $$\int [af(x) + bg(x)] \, dx = a \int f(x) \, dx + b \int g(x) \, dx$$

follows directly from the derivative formula

$$D_x[af(x) + bg(x)] = aD_x f(x) + bD_x g(x).$$

Note that the special case of **2** in which $b = 0$ is

2'. $$\int af(x) \, dx = a \int f(x) \, dx.$$

Example 2.

$$\int \left(3x^4 - 5x^2 + \frac{2}{x^3}\right) dx = 3\int x^4 \, dx - 5\int x^2 \, dx + 2\int x^{-3} \, dx \qquad \text{from 2}$$

$$= 3\left(\frac{1}{5}x^5 + c_1\right) - 5\left(\frac{1}{3}x^3 + c_2\right) + 2\left(\frac{1}{-2}x^{-2} + c_3\right)$$

$$\text{from 1}$$

$$= \frac{3}{5}x^5 - \frac{5}{3}x^3 - \frac{1}{x^2} + (3c_1 - 5c_2 + 2c_3).$$

Note, however, that the three constants c_1, c_2, and c_3 are arbitrary, so $3c_1 - 5c_2 + 2c_3$ is merely an arbitrary constant. Thus, the result is usually given as

$$\int \left(3x^4 - 5x^2 + \frac{2}{x^3}\right) dx = \frac{3}{5}x^5 - \frac{5}{3}x^3 - \frac{1}{x^2} + c.$$

Another way of thinking of it is to note that

$$y = \frac{3}{5}x^5 - \frac{5}{3}x^3 - \frac{1}{x^2}$$

is the simplest function such that $D_x y = 3x^4 - 5x^2 + 2/x^3$, and hence the general answer for the whole problem is to add an arbitrary constant to this simplest answer.

The differential formulas

$$d \sin ax = \cos ax \, d(ax) = a \cos ax \, dx \quad \text{and}$$

$$d \cos ax = -\sin ax \, d(ax) = -a \sin ax \, dx$$

may be written in the form

$$d\left(\frac{1}{a} \sin ax\right) = \cos ax \, dx \quad \text{and} \quad d\left(-\frac{1}{a} \cos ax\right) = \sin ax \, dx.$$

By using the right-hand members as integrands (and using the second one first), the following two integration formulas are obtained:

3.
$$\int \sin ax \, dx = -\frac{1}{a} \cos ax + c \quad \text{and}$$

4.
$$\int \cos ax \, dx = \frac{1}{a} \sin ax + c.$$

Example 3.

$$\int \left(2 \sin 3x - 4 \cos \frac{1}{2}x\right) dx = 2 \int \sin 3x \, dx - 4 \int \cos \frac{1}{2}x \, dx \qquad \text{from 2}$$

$$= 2\left(-\frac{1}{3} \cos 3x\right) - 4\left(\frac{1}{\frac{1}{2}} \sin \frac{1}{2}x\right) + c \qquad \text{from 3 and 4}$$

$$= -\frac{2}{3} \cos 3x - 8 \sin \frac{1}{2}x + c.$$

Problem 1. Establish each of the following by two methods; first by starting with the left-hand member and integrating, second by starting with the right-hand member and differentiating.

a. $\int \left(x^2 - 4 + \frac{1}{x^2}\right) dx = \frac{1}{3}x^3 - 4x - \frac{1}{x} + c.$

b. $\int (8x^3 + 7x^2 - 2) \, dx = 2x^4 + \frac{7}{3}x^3 - 2x + c.$

c. $\int (3 \sin x - \sin 3x) \, dx = -3 \cos x + \frac{1}{3} \cos 3x + c.$

d. $\int (\cos x + 4 \sin 4x) \, dx = \sin x - \cos 4x + c.$

Problem 2. Integrate each of the following, and check by differentiating the answer to recover the integrand:

a. $\int (\frac{5}{2}x^{3/2} - x) \, dx.$

d. $\int (x + 1)^2 \, dx.$

b. $\int (\sqrt{x} - 3x^2) \, dx.$

e. $\int (x^2 + 2)^2 \, dx.$

c. $\int (x^2 - \sin x) \, dx.$

f. $\int (1 + \cos 2x) \, dx.$

Problem 3. First find the indicated derivative, and then use the result to perform the integration:

a. $D_x(x^3 + 1)^{3/2}, \quad \int \sqrt{x^3 + 1} \, x^2 \, dx.$

b. $D_x(x^2 + 1)^{4/3}, \quad \int \sqrt[3]{x^2 + 1} \, x \, dx.$

c. $D_x \sin^3 x, \quad \int \sin^2 x \cos x \, dx.$

d. $D_x \cos^4 x, \quad \int \cos^3 x \sin x \, dx.$

e. $D_x \dfrac{x}{\sqrt{x^2+4}}, \quad \displaystyle\int \dfrac{1}{(x^2+4)^{3/2}}\,dx.$

f. $D_x \dfrac{x}{(x^2+1)^{3/2}}, \quad \displaystyle\int \dfrac{1-2x^2}{(x^2+1)^{5/2}}\,dx.$

g. $D_x(x\sin x + \cos x), \quad \displaystyle\int x\cos x\,dx.$

h. $D_x(x^2\sin x + 2x\cos x - 2\sin x), \quad \displaystyle\int x^2\cos x\,dx.$

3-2. Substitutions

As derivatives may be taken with respect to variables other than x, so integration may be done in terms of any variable whatever. Thus, the formulas

1. $$\int u^p\,du = \frac{1}{p+1}u^{p+1} + c \quad \text{for } p \ne -1,$$

2. $$\int [af(u) + bg(u)]\,du = a\int f(u)\,du + b\int g(u)\,du,$$

3, 4. $$\int \sin u\,du = -\cos u + c, \quad \text{and} \quad \int \cos u\,du = \sin u + c$$

are neither more general nor more particular than the corresponding formulas of Sec. 3–1.

Sometimes, however, a change of variable makes an integral more easily recognized as fitting one of the standard forms.

Example 1. Find $\displaystyle\int (x^3+1)^{3/2}x^2\,dx.$

Solution. Upon setting $u = x^3 + 1$, then $du = 3x^2\,dx$ and hence

$$x^2\,dx = \tfrac{1}{3}\,du.$$

Thus, by replacing $x^3 + 1$ by u and $x^2\,dx$ by $\tfrac{1}{3}\,du$, then

$$\int (x^3+1)^{3/2}\,x^2\,dx = \int u^{3/2}\left(\frac{1}{3}\,du\right)$$

$$= \frac{1}{3}\int u^{3/2}\,du$$

$$= \frac{1}{3}\frac{u^{5/2}}{\frac{5}{2}} + c \qquad\qquad \text{by 1 with } p = \tfrac{3}{2}$$

$$= \frac{2}{15}(x^3+1)^{5/2} + c \qquad\qquad \text{by resubstitution.}$$

Check:

$$d\frac{2}{15}(x^3 + 1)^{5/2} = \frac{2}{15} \cdot \frac{5}{2}(x^3 + 1)^{3/2} \, d(x^3 + 1)$$

$$= \frac{1}{3}(x^3 + 1)^{3/2} \, 3x^2 \, dx = (x^3 + 1)^{3/2} \, x^2 \, dx,$$

which is the given integrand.

The student is strongly advised to check each integration answer by differentiating this answer to recover the integrand. This not only has the obvious advantages of avoiding errors and reviewing differentiation, but has the more important attribute of confirming the fact that integration by substitution is the integral analog of the differentiation of a function of a function

$$\frac{dy}{dx} = \frac{dy}{du} \cdot \frac{du}{dx},$$

where y is a function of u and u is a function of x.

Familiarity with differentiation formulas is the best aid to making a suitable substitution.

Example 2. Find $\int \sin^2 3x \cos 3x \, dx$ and $\int x \sin x^2 \, dx$.

Solution. In the first integral, the substitution

$$u = \sin 3x$$

is made, since it is recognized in advance that then

$$du = \cos 3x \, d \, 3x = 3 \cos 3x \, dx,$$

which is the latter part of the integrand except for the multiplicative constant 3. Thus,

$$\int \sin^2 3x \cos 3x \, dx = \int u^2(\tfrac{1}{3} \, du) = \tfrac{1}{3} \int u^2 \, du$$

$$= \tfrac{1}{3}\frac{u^3}{3} + c = \tfrac{1}{9} \sin^3 3x + c.$$

Check:

$$d\tfrac{1}{9} \sin^3 3x = \tfrac{1}{9} \, 3 \sin^2 3x \, d \sin 3x = \tfrac{1}{3} \sin^2 3x \cos 3x \, d(3x)$$

$$= \tfrac{1}{3} \sin^3 3x \cos 3x \, (3 \, dx) = \sin^2 3x \cos 3x \, dx.$$

In the second integral set $u = x^2$, then $du = 2x \, dx$, and

$$\int x \sin x^2 \, dx = \int \sin x^2(x \, dx) = \int \sin u(\tfrac{1}{2} \, du) = \tfrac{1}{2} \int \sin u \, du$$

$$= \tfrac{1}{2}(-\cos u) + c = -\tfrac{1}{2} \cos x^2 + c.$$

Check:

$$d(-\tfrac{1}{2} \cos x^2) = -\tfrac{1}{2} d \cos x^2 = -\tfrac{1}{2}(-\sin x^2 \, dx^2)$$

$$= \tfrac{1}{2} \sin x^2(2x \, dx) = x \sin x^2 \, dx.$$

Problem 1. Integrate each of the following by making the suggested substitution:

a. $\int (x^2 + 1)^3 x \, dx$, $u = x^2 + 1$.

b. $\int x \sin(x^2 + 1) \, dx$, $u = x^2 + 1$.

c. $\int (x^2 + 1)(x^3 + 3x + 5)^4 \, dx$, $u = x^3 + 3x + 5$.

d. $\int \sqrt{x}\,(x^{3/2} + 1)^4 \, dx$, $u = x^{3/2} + 1$.

e. $\int \dfrac{x^2}{\sqrt{4 + x^3}} \, dx$, $u = 4 + x^3$.

f. $\int \sqrt{4 + \sin^3 x}\, \sin^2 x \cos x \, dx$, $u = 4 + \sin^3 x$.

g. $\int \sin x \cos x \, dx$, once using $u = \sin x$, again using $u = \cos x$, and again using the identity $2 \sin x \cos x \equiv \sin 2x$.

Problem 2. Integrate:

a. $\int x^3 \sqrt{4 + x^4} \, dx$.

b. $\int x^3 \sin x^4 \, dx$.

c. $\int (x - 1) \sin(x^2 - 2x + 5) \, dx$.

d. $\int (x - 1) \sqrt{x^2 - 2x + 5} \, dx$.

e. $\int \sqrt{2 + \cos x}\, \sin x \, dx$.

f. $\int \dfrac{\sin x}{\sqrt{2 + \cos x}} \, dx$.

g. $\int (4 + \sin^3 x) \cos x \, dx$.

h. $\int \dfrac{\sin x}{\cos^2 x} \, dx$.

Problem 3. Each of the following may be solved very easily if looked at properly:

a. $\int \dfrac{4x^2 + 12x + 9}{(2x + 3)^2} \, dx$.

b. $\int (\cos^2 x + \sin^2 x) \, dx$.

c. $\int D_x (x^4 \sin^3 x^2) \, dx$.

d. $\int D_x [(x - 4)^5 \cos^3 (2x - 3)] \, dx$.

e. $D_x \int (x^2 - 2x \sin x + \cos^2 x) \, dx$.

f. $\int \cos^4 x \, dx + \int \sin^2 x(2 - \sin^2 x) \, dx$.

3-3. Differential Equations

The indefinite integration symbolism

(1) $$\int f(x) \, dx = F(x) + c$$

means, by definition, that the functions $f(x)$ and $F(x)$ are related by the equation $D_x F(x) = f(x)$ or, in differential notation,

(2) $$dF(x) = f(x) \, dx.$$

Thus, by replacing $f(x) \, dx$ in (1) by $dF(x)$, then

$$(3) \qquad \int dF(x) = F(x) + c.$$

Also, (3) may be thought of as "integrating both sides of (2)":

$$\int dF(x) = \int f(x) \, dx$$
$$= F(x) + c.$$

If therefore y is a function of x, then $\int dy = y + c$. As a particular example, if $dy = (x^3 + 2) \, dx$, then, by integrating both sides,

$$\int dy = \int (x^3 + 2) \, dx,$$
$$y + c_1 = \tfrac{1}{4}x^4 + 2x + c_2,$$

where an arbitrary constant appears on both sides. It now follows that $y = \tfrac{1}{4}x^4 + 2x + (c_2 - c_1)$, where $c_2 - c_1$ may be replaced by a single arbitrary constant to obtain

$$(4) \qquad y = \tfrac{1}{4}x^4 + 2x + c.$$

Example 1. A curve passes through the point $(2, 1)$, and at the variable point (x, y) on the curve, the tangent to the curve has slope $x^3 + 2$. Find the equation of the curve.

Solution. The slope condition may be expressed as

$$(5) \qquad \frac{dy}{dx} = x^3 + 2, \quad \text{so that} \quad dy = (x^3 + 2) \, dx.$$

Thus, as above, the slope condition alone yields (4). But c must be determined so that the equation is satisfied by $x = 2$ and $y = 1$. Hence, c must be such that

$$1 = \tfrac{1}{4}(2^4) + 2 \cdot 2 + c, \quad \text{so} \quad c = -7.$$

Therefore,

$$(6) \qquad y = \tfrac{1}{4}x^4 + 2x - 7$$

satisfies both the slope condition and the point condition.

Example 2. At each point (x, y) of a curve, the tangent to the curve has slope $-x/y$ and the curve passes through the point $(3, 4)$. Find the equation of the curve.

Solution. Here,

$$(7) \qquad \frac{dy}{dx} = -\frac{x}{y} \quad \text{or} \quad y \, dy = -x \, dx,$$

so $\int y \, dy = -\int x \, dx$, $\tfrac{1}{2}y^2 = -\tfrac{1}{2}x^2 + c$, and therefore

$$(8) \qquad x^2 + y^2 = 2c.$$

From the point condition, $3^2 + 4^2 = 2c$, so $2c = 25$ and

(9) $$x^2 + y^2 = 25$$

is the desired equation.

Either form of the equation in (7) is an example of a differential equation; that is, an equation involving two variables and their differentials. Because of the arbitrary constant in (8), the equation in (8) is called the **general solution** of the differential equation in (7). Also, (9) is called the **particular solution** satisfying the supplementary condition $y = 4$ when $x = 3$.

Differential equations abound in applied mathematics, and there is a great deal of current mathematical research being done on differential equations.

The only differential equations to be considered now are of the type which may be written in the form

(10) $$g(y)\, dy = f(x)\, dx,$$

where $g(y)$ is a function of y alone and $f(x)$ is a function of x alone. Thus, (5) is of this form, with $g(y) = 1$ and $f(x) = x^3 + 2$. Also, (7) is of this form, with $g(y) = y$ and $f(x) = -x$.

Example 3. Find the particular solution of

$$dy = (x + 1)^2 \sqrt{y}\, dx \quad \text{subject to } y = 4 \text{ when } x = 0.$$

Solution. First write the equation in the form (10), integrate both sides, and obtain the general solution:

$$y^{-1/2}\, dy = (x + 1)^2\, dx, \quad \int y^{-1/2}\, dy = \int (x + 1)^2\, dx,$$

$$2\sqrt{y} = \tfrac{1}{3}(x + 1)^3 + c.$$

In this general solution, substitute $y = 4$ and $x = 0$ to obtain c.

$$2\sqrt{4} = \frac{1}{3}(0 + 1)^3 + c, \quad c = 4 - \frac{1}{3} = \frac{11}{3}.$$

Thus, the desired particular solution is

$$2\sqrt{y} = \frac{1}{3}(x + 1)^3 + \frac{11}{3}.$$

Problem 1. A curve passes through the given fixed point, and at the variable point (x, y) on the curve, the slope of the tangent to the curve is given. Find the equation of the curve:

a. $(1, 4)$, slope $= (x + 1)y^2$.

b. $(0, 0)$, slope $= 2x$.

c. $(0, 0)$, slope $= 1$.

d. $(0, 4)$, slope $= x/y$.

e. $(\pi/4, 1)$, slope $= \sin x$.

f. $(1, 2)$, slope $= (y + 1)^2(x - 1)$.

Problem 2. Find the general solution of the differential equation:

a. $dy = (x + 1)\sqrt{y + 1}\, dx$.

b. $\sqrt{x^2 + 1}\, dy = xy^2\, dx$.

c. $\cos y\, dy + x^2\, dx = dx$.

d. $\sin^2 x^2\, dy = x \cos x^2\, dx$.

Problem 3. Solve for the particular solution:

a. $dy = \sqrt{xy}\, dx$; $y = 4$ when $x = 0$.

b. $y\, dy = \sin x\, dx$; $y = 0$ when $x = \pi/2$.

c. $x^2 D_x y = 2$; $y = 5$ when $x = 2$.

d. $y\, dy = \sqrt{(2 + y^2)^3}\, dx$; $y = 1$ when $x = 0$.

3-4. Physical Applications

In some types of physical problems, the velocity law of a moving body is first discovered. If the position of the body is then known at a single instant, its position at any time may be predicted.

Example 1. Find the vector law of motion $\vec{u} = \vec{F}(t)$ given the initial condition $\vec{F}(0) = 4\vec{i} - 3\vec{j}$ and the velocity law

(1) $$\vec{v}(t) = -\vec{i} + 2t\vec{j}.$$

Solution. The law of motion is $\vec{F}(t) = \vec{i}x + \vec{j}y$, with x and y functions (as yet unknown) of t. Since the velocity is

(2) $$\vec{v}(t) = D_t\vec{F}(t) = \vec{i}D_t x + \vec{j}D_t y,$$

then, by matching (1) and (2), it follows for this motion that

$$D_t x = -1 \quad \text{and} \quad D_t y = 2t.$$

These equations, together with the given initial condition, lead to a pair of differential equations with side conditions

$$dx = -dt; \quad x = 4 \text{ when } t = 0 \quad \text{and}$$
$$dy = 2t\, dt; \quad y = -3 \text{ when } t = 0.$$

Hence,

$$x = -t + c_1 \quad \text{and} \quad y = t^2 + c_2$$

are the general solutions. From the initial conditions, c_1 and c_2 are determined:

$$4 = -0 + c_1 \quad \text{and} \quad -3 = 0^2 + c_2.$$

The particular solutions are $x = -t + 4$ and $y = t^2 - 3$, and the law of motion (which gives the position of the particle at a variable time t) is

$$\vec{u} = \vec{F}(t) = (-t + 4)\vec{i} + (t^2 - 3)\vec{j}.$$

Also, if the acceleration law is known as a vector function of t and if the velocity and position are known at a single instant, then the vector position function of t may be obtained. The most notable example is the flight of a projectile in vacuum. Saying that the projectile moves in vacuum means that the only forces acting on the projectile are the force which gives it the initial velocity and, thereafter, the force of gravity only. By experiment, the force of gravity causes a constant acceleration toward the earth. This constant of gravitation is denoted by g and in the foot-pound-second (FPS) system is approximately

$$g = 32.2 \text{ ft/sec}^2.$$

Example 2. Let the projectile be shot from the origin into the first quadrant, the initial speed being v_0 ft/sec and the angle of elevation being α, where $0 \leq \alpha \leq 90°$. Find the vector position function

(3) $$\vec{u} = \vec{F}(t) = \vec{i}x + \vec{j}y.$$

Solution. The acceleration is

(4) $$\frac{d^2\vec{u}}{dt^2} = \vec{F}''(t) = \vec{i}x'' + \vec{j}y'' = \vec{i} \cdot 0 + \vec{j}(-g),$$

where $-g$ is used since the y-axis points upward while the force of gravity is downward. The coefficient of $\vec{i}$ is zero, since no other force (such as air resistance) acts to hinder or aid horizontal motion.

Since the initial (scalar) speed is the constant v_0, and this initial speed is imparted at an angle α with the horizontal, then the initial velocity is

(5) $$\vec{F}'(0) = \vec{i}x'(0) + \vec{j}y'(0) = \vec{i}v_0 \cos \alpha + \vec{j}v_0 \sin \alpha.$$

The fact that the particle is shot (at time $t = 0$) from the origin is expressed by

(6) $$\vec{F}(0) = \vec{i}x(0) + \vec{j}y(0) = \vec{i} \cdot 0 + \vec{j} \cdot 0.$$

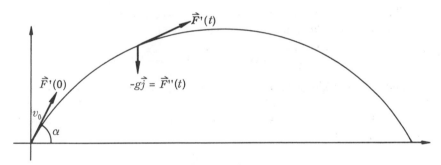

Fig. 3-4.1

Equations (4), (5), and (6) yield the two differential equations,

(7) $$\frac{d^2x}{dt^2} = 0 \quad \text{and} \quad \frac{d^2y}{dt^2} = -g,$$

subject to the conditions

(8) $$x = 0, \ y = 0; \ \frac{dx}{dt} = v_0 \cos \alpha, \ \frac{dy}{dt} = v_0 \sin \alpha, \text{ when } t = 0.$$

Since a second derivative is merely a derivative of a derivative, it follows from (7) alone that

(9) $$\frac{dx}{dt} = c_1 \quad \text{and} \quad \frac{dy}{dt} = -gt + c_2.$$

Now set $t = 0$ in these and use the second two equations of (8):

$$v_0 \cos \alpha = c_1 \quad \text{and} \quad v_0 \sin \alpha = -g \cdot 0 + c_2.$$

Thus, the differential equations (without arbitrary constants)

(10) $$\frac{dx}{dt} = v_0 \cos \alpha \quad \text{and} \quad \frac{dy}{dt} = -gt + v_0 \sin \alpha$$

are obtained. The general solutions of these are

$$x = (v_0 \cos \alpha)t + c_3 \quad \text{and} \quad y = -\tfrac{1}{2}gt^2 + (v_0 \sin \alpha)t + c_4.$$

Thus, the particular solutions (obtained by setting $t = 0$ and using the first two equations of (8) to see that $c_3 = c_4 = 0$) are

(11) $$x = tv_0 \cos \alpha \quad \text{and} \quad y = tv_0 \sin \alpha - \tfrac{1}{2}gt^2.$$

The vector law of motion is therefore

(12) $$\vec{u} = \vec{F}(t) = \vec{i}(tv_0 \cos \alpha) + \vec{j}(tv_0 \sin \alpha - \tfrac{1}{2}gt^2).$$

When will the projectile return to the x-axis? Answer: At the time $t \neq 0$, making the coefficient of $\vec{j}$ equal to 0; that is,

$$tv_0 \sin \alpha - \tfrac{1}{2}gt^2 = 0 \quad \text{or} \quad t(v_0 \sin \alpha - \tfrac{1}{2}gt) = 0,$$

$$t = 0 \quad \text{(when at the origin), so when} \quad t = \frac{2v_0 \sin \alpha}{g}.$$

Where will the projectile return to the x-axis? Answer: At the place it reaches when t has the above value, and thus at

(13) $$\vec{i}\frac{2v_0 \sin \alpha}{g}v_0 \cos \alpha + \vec{j} \cdot 0 = \vec{i}\frac{v_0^2}{g}\sin 2\alpha.$$

What is the highest point reached by the projectile? The projectile is on its way up as long as $dy/dt > 0$, is on its way down whenever $dy/dt < 0$, so reaches its highest point when $dy/dt = 0$, and thus [from the second equation of (10)] when

$$t = \frac{v_0 \sin \alpha}{g}.$$

This value substituted into (12) gives the vector position of the highest point as

$$\vec{i}\frac{v_0 \sin \alpha}{g}v_0 \cos \alpha + \vec{j}\left(\frac{v_0 \sin \alpha}{g}v_0 \sin \alpha - \frac{1}{2}g\frac{v_0^2 \sin^2 \alpha}{g^2}\right)$$

$$= \vec{i}\frac{v_0^2}{2g}\sin 2\alpha + \vec{j}\frac{1}{2}\frac{v_0^2}{g}\sin^2 \alpha$$

$$= \frac{v_0^2}{2g}(\vec{i}\sin 2\alpha + \vec{j}\sin^2 \alpha).$$

The **range** R of the projectile is defined to be the distance from its starting point to the point where the projectile returns to the same horizontal. Thus, from (13),

$$R = \frac{v_0^2}{g} \sin 2\alpha.$$

For a given initial speed v_0, the range is a function of the angle of elevation α. Note that the maximum range is obtained when $\sin 2\alpha$ has its maximum value, namely 1, and thus for $2\alpha = 90°$ so for $\alpha = 45°$.

Projectile flight in vacuum is only a first approximation of the real situation, but is a fairly good approximation for heavy projectiles at low velocities. "Exterior ballistics" is the name applied to the attempt to predict trajectories, taking into consideration such things as projectile shape and spin, air densities at various levels, and the earth's curvature, rotation, and revolution. The impetus for the construction of the first electronic computers was furnished by the desire for more rapid and accurate computation of approximations of solutions of differential equations arising in the exterior ballistics. "Interior ballistics" is the study of propellants and their action on a projectile before it leaves the gun.

In the following problems use $g = 32$.

Problem 1. A projectile is fired from the origin with initial velocity 1024 ft/sec. Find the time of flight, range, and greatest height, if the angle of elevation α is:

a. $\alpha = 30°$.   b. $\alpha = 45°$.   c. $\alpha = 60°$.

Problem 2. Change Prob. 1 so the firing is from a 64-ft tower and replace the range by the distance from the foot of the tower to the point where the projectile hits the earth.

Problem 3. From the top of a 100-ft tower a stone is tossed upward at a $45°$ angle with the horizontal and hits the ground 3 sec later. Show that the stone would have hit the ground farther from the tower if it had been tossed horizontally with the same velocity.

Problem 4. Two bullets are fired with velocity 3000 ft/sec both at $45°$ to the horizontal, but one from the foot and the other from the top of a 100-ft tower. How much farther along the ground will the second one hit than the first?

3-5. Area

In the previous work on differential equations, a differential equation was given to start with (or was essentially given) and its solution sought. In this section and the next, it is shown how some questions may be analyzed in such a way that a differential equation is first derived and then solved to yield the answer.

The number of square units in a rectangle is the number of linear units in its base times the number of linear units in its altitude. The area of a circle is π times the square of the number of linear units in its radius. Upon seeing a region in the plane, there is a natural feeling that its area should be equal to some number of square units. For example, consider the region bounded by the graph of

(1) $y = \tfrac{1}{2}x^2$,

the x-axis, and the lines $x = 1$ and $x = 3$ (see Fig. 3-5.2). How many square units are there in this region; that is, what is the area of this region?

Upon making two rather natural assumptions, this question may be answered. These assumptions are that:

1. If one region is part of another region, then the smaller region has area less than (or at most equal to) the area of the larger region.

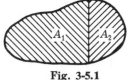

Fig. 3-5.1

2. If a region of area A is divided into two subregions by a straight-line segment, and the area of one of the subregions is A_1, then the area A_2 of the other subregion is given by

(2) $A_2 = A - A_1$;   that is, $A = A_1 + A_2$.

Toward answering the question posed above, hold x constant for the moment with $1 \leq x$. Draw the line segment from the point $(x, 0)$ up to the curve as in Fig. 3-5.2. This line segment has length $\tfrac{1}{2}x^2$ because of equation (1). Using functional notation, let $A(x)$ be the area of the region under the graph and above the interval of the x-axis joining the points $(1, 0)$ and $(x, 0)$. Now let x vary (but only such that $1 \leq x$) and $A(x)$ be a function of x such that the constant

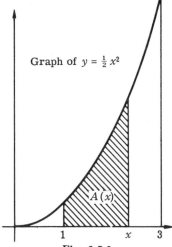

Graph of $y = \tfrac{1}{2}x^2$

$A(x)$

1   x 3

Fig. 3-5.2

(3) $A(3)$ is the desired answer to the question,

but this constant is not known at the moment.

Note that $A(1)$ means "the area under the graph of (1) and above the interval from $(1, 0)$ to $(1, 0)$," and thus

(4) $A(1) = 0$.

Even though $A(1) = 0$ is the only presently known value of the function $A(x)$, it is possible (as shown below) to find the derivative $D_x A(x)$.

Again, hold x fixed at a value such that $1 \leq x$. Choose another constant $\Delta x > 0$. Now $1 \leq x < (x + \Delta x)$, and $A(x + \Delta x)$ is the area under the graph of (1) and above the interval from $(1, 0)$ to $(x + \Delta x, 0)$. Thus, by assumption 2,

$$A(x + \Delta x) - A(x)$$

is the area under the graph of (1) and above the interval from $(x, 0)$ to $(x + \Delta x, 0)$. The left side of this strip has altitude $\frac{1}{2}x^2$, the right side has altitude $\frac{1}{2}(x + \Delta x)^2$, so the strip (with a curved top) includes a rectangle of area $\frac{1}{2}x^2(\Delta x)$ but is included in a rectangle of area $\frac{1}{2}(x + \Delta x)^2 \Delta x$. Thus, by assumption 1,

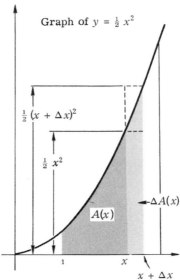

Fig. 3-5.3

$$\tfrac{1}{2}x^2 \Delta x \le A(x + \Delta x) - A(x) \le \tfrac{1}{2}(x + \Delta x)^2 \Delta x.$$

Next, divide by Δx and, since $\Delta x > 0$, see that

$$\frac{1}{2}x^2 \le \frac{A(x + \Delta x) - A(x)}{\Delta x} \le \frac{1}{2}(x + \Delta x)^2.$$

Still holding x fixed, let $\Delta x \to 0+$ and obtain

$$\frac{1}{2}x^2 \le \lim_{\Delta x \to 0+} \frac{A(x + \Delta x) - A(x)}{\Delta x} \le \lim_{\Delta x \to 0+} \frac{1}{2}(x + \Delta x)^2 = \frac{1}{2}x^2.$$

Now upon recalling the definition of a derivative,* it follows that

$$\frac{1}{2}x^2 \le \frac{dA(x)}{dx} \le \frac{1}{2}x^2, \quad \text{so} \quad \frac{dA(x)}{dx} = \frac{1}{2}x^2.$$

This equation together with (4) is the differential equation

(5) $dA(x) = \frac{1}{2}x^2 \, dx$ with side condition $A(1) = 0$.

---

*If $f(x)$ is a function of x, then $df(x)/dx = \lim_{\Delta x \to 0} [f(x + \Delta x) - f(x)]/\Delta x$, by definition. This emphasizes why it is important to remember the definition of a derivative; remembering only formulas for taking derivatives is not sufficient.

The general solution is

$$A(x) = \int \tfrac{1}{2}x^2 \, dx = \tfrac{1}{6}x^3 + c.$$

But the side condition now shows that $A(1) = \tfrac{1}{6}1^3 + c = 0$, so $c = -\tfrac{1}{6}$, and the particular solution is

$$A(x) = \tfrac{1}{6}x^3 - \tfrac{1}{6}.$$

Finally, it follows [see (3) above] that

$$A(3) = \tfrac{1}{6}3^3 - \tfrac{1}{6} = \tfrac{26}{6} = \tfrac{13}{3} \text{ sq units}$$

is the area of the region under the graph of (1) and above the interval $1 \le x \le 3$.

All of the above analysis was for the special function $y = \tfrac{1}{2}x^2$ and the region below the graph and above the interval $1 \le x \le 3$. The student should now consider a general function $y = f(x)$ with graph above an interval $a \le x \le b$, define $A(x)$ to be the area of the region between the graph and the interval from $(a, 0)$ to $(x, 0)$, and see that this area function $A(x)$ is the solution of the differential equation comparable to (5):

(6) $\qquad dA(x) = f(x)\, dx \quad$ with side condition $\quad A(a) = 0.$

Hence,

(7) $$A(x) = \int f(x)\, dx + c,$$

wherein c may be determined by the side condition.

Example 1. Find the area between the x-axis and the first arch of the sine curve.

Solution. The sine curve has equation $y = \sin x$, and the first arch has $0 \le x \le \pi$, so the a of (6) is $a = 0$ and $b = \pi$. From (7),

$$A(x) = \int \sin x \, dx = -\cos x + c.$$

From the side condition, $A(0) = -\cos 0 + c = -1 + c = 0$, so $c = 1$. Thus,

$$A(x) = -\cos x + 1$$

and the answer is $A(\pi) = -\cos \pi + 1 = -(-1) + 1 = 2$ sq units.

In the above general discussion, either or both of the constants a and b may be negative, provided only that $a < b$. Also, the graph of $y = f(x)$ lay above the interval $a \le x \le b$.

Now keeping $a < b$, but letting $y = f(x)$ be a function whose graph may cross the interval $a \le x \le b$ (as in Fig. 3-5.4), consider the differential equation [similar to (6)]

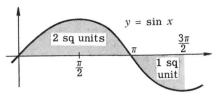

Fig 3-5.4.

(8) $dF(x) = f(x)\,dx$ with side condition $F(a) = 0.$

Since $f(x)$ is assumed given, then

$$F(x) = \int f(x)\,dx + c.$$

c may be determined by the side condition, and then $F(b)$ computed. It should be seen that $F(b)$ is the number of square units in the region under the portion of the graph of $y = f(x)$ which is above the interval $a \le x \le b$ minus the number (positive) of square units in the region below the interval and above the graph.

Example 2. Find $F(3\pi/2)$, given that
$$dF(x) = \sin x\,dx \quad \text{and} \quad F(0) = 0.$$

Solution. As in Example 1, $F(x) = -\cos x + 1.$ Thus,

$$F\left(\frac{3\pi}{2}\right) = -\cos\frac{3\pi}{2} + 1 = -0 + 1 = 1,$$

which is the area (namely, 2 sq units) under the graph of $y = \sin x$ above the interval $0 \le x \le \pi$ **minus** the area having $+1$ sq unit of the region above the graph and below the interval $\pi \le x \le \frac{3}{2}\pi$.

Problem 1. For the given interval, show that the graph of the function lies above the interval and find the area of the region below the graph and above the interval:

a. $1 \le x \le 9,\ y = \sqrt{x}.$

b. $-1 \le x \le 2,\ y = \frac{1}{2}x^2.$

c. $-1 \le x \le 1,\ y = 1 - x^2.$

d. $-1 \le x \le 1,\ y = \sqrt{1 - x^3}\,x^2.$

e. $-\pi \le x \le \pi,\ y = \cos\frac{1}{2}x.$

f. $-\pi \le x \le \pi,\ y = \sin^2\frac{1}{2}x\cos\frac{1}{2}x.$

Problem 2. Check that the above procedure for finding the area under a curve gives the correct answer for a right triangle of altitude h and base b. Do this by using the equation of a straight line through:

a. The origin and the point (h, b).

b. The origin and the point (b, h).

c. The points $(0, b)$ and $(h, 0)$.

Problem 3. Find $F(b)$ for each of the following, and give a geometric interpretation of the result.

   a. $dF(x) = x^3 \, dx$, $F(-2) = 0$, and $b = 2$.
   b. $dF(x) = (x - 1)^3 \, dx$, $F(-1) = 0$, and $b = 3$.
   c. $dF(x) = \sin 2x \, dx$, $F(0) = 0$, and $b = \pi$.
   d. $dF(x) = \sin x \cos x \, dx$, $F(0) = 0$, and $b = \pi$.
   e. $dF(x) = (\sin x + \cos x) \, dx$, $F(0) = 0$, and $b = \pi$.
   f. $dF(x) = (x^3 + x^2) \, dx$, $F(-2) = 0$, and $b = 2$.

3-6. Work

Discussions of physical phenomena are facilitated by agreeing upon a technical meaning for concepts of general experience. Such agreements usually amount to assigning quantitative measurements, since it is easier to compare numbers than expressions of opinion. It is a matter of opinion whether calculus problems are harder to work than physics problems. However, by defining the work done in raising a w-lb weight h ft as $w \cdot h$ ft·lb, it is possible to say whether raising a 12-lb weight 100 ft is more or less "work" than raising a ton 6 in.

In the definitions below, "work" has technical, rather than opinionated, meaning.

DEFINITION 1. *If a body is moved along a coordinate line (unit 1 ft) from a to b by a* **constant** *force of f lb acting in the line of motion, then the* **work** *W done on the body is*

(1)
$$W = f \cdot (b - a) \text{ ft·lb.}$$

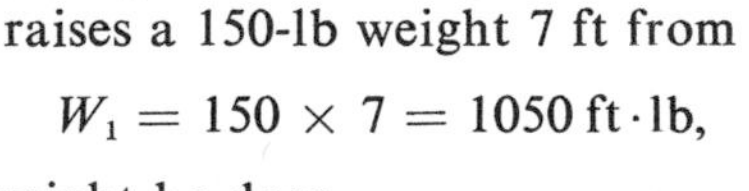

Fig. 3-6.1

Note that f may be positive or negative, $b - a$ may be positive or negative, and hence W may be positive or negative. Thus, considering "up" as positive, if an athlete raises a 150-lb weight 7 ft from the floor, he does

$$W_1 = 150 \times 7 = 1050 \text{ ft·lb,}$$

but as he lowers the weight he does

$$W_2 = 150 \times (-7) = -1050 \text{ ft·lb}$$

of work, so his total work is $W_1 + W_2 = 0$ ft·lb (but try to convince the athlete who uses a nontechnical idea of work).

If motion is linear, but the force is not in the line of motion, then only the component of force in the line of motion is considered (motion may be constrained as, for example, when a railroad car on a track is pulled by a cable attached to a locomotive on a parallel track). Hence, a more practical definition is in terms of vectors.

DEFINITION 2. *Having selected a positive direction on the line of motion, let $\vec{u}$ be the motion vector and $\vec{f}$ the constant force vector (which need not be in the line of motion). Then, by definition, the work W is defined by*

(2)
$$W = \vec{f} \cdot \vec{u},$$

$$|\vec{f}| \cos \theta > 0 \qquad |\vec{f}| \cos \theta < 0$$
$$W = |\vec{u}| \, |\vec{f}| \cos \theta > 0 \qquad W = |\vec{u}| \, |\vec{f}| \cos \theta < 0$$

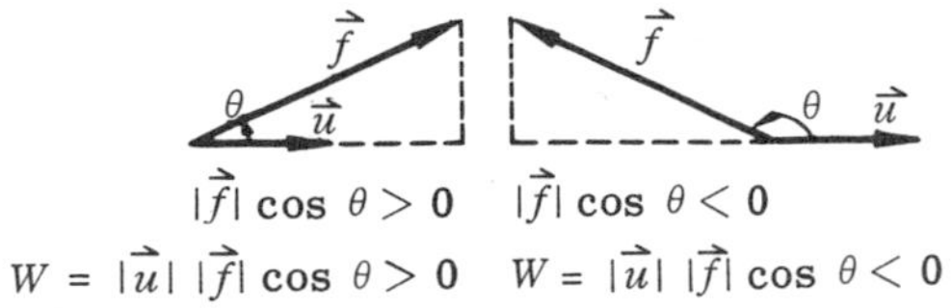

Fig. 3-6.2

*where $\vec{f} \cdot \vec{u}$ is the scalar product.**

Thus, if motion is along the vector $\vec{u} = 3\vec{i} - 2\vec{j}$ (the unit being 1 ft) and the force is $\vec{f} = 6\vec{i} + 8\vec{j}$ (unit of force being 1 lb), then the work is

$$W = (6\vec{i} + 8\vec{j}) \cdot (3\vec{i} - 2\vec{j}) = 6 \cdot 3 + 8(-2) = 2 \text{ ft} \cdot \text{lb}.$$

Notice that work is always a scalar even though $\vec{f}$ and $\vec{u}$ are vectors.

Definition 2 was included here for the sake of completeness, but for the immediately following development only Definition 1 is necessary.

Consider now a motion caused by a force in the line of motion but with the force variable instead of constant. A natural assumption to make is:

If a variable force moves an object h ft, then the work is between h times the smallest and h times the largest force during the motion.

Thus, if a leaking bucket of water weighs 60 lb to start but 40 lb after being raised 10 ft, then the work is between 400 and 600 ft·lb.

A method of attack is illustrated in the following example.

Example 1. A bucket plus its water weighs 60 lb at the water level 10 ft down a well. As the bucket is steadily raised, it leaks water at the steady rate of 2 lb /ft. Find the work done in raising the bucket (with whatever water is left) to the surface of the ground.

Solution. When the bucket is x ft up the well it weighs $(60 - 2x)$ lb; that is, the force function is

$$f(x) = (60 - 2x) \text{ lb}.$$

Saying "x ft up the well" means $x = 0$ at water level and $x = 10$ at ground level.

Now let $W(x)$ be the work done in raising the bucket to level x. Then with $\Delta x > 0$, the work done in raising the bucket to level $x + \Delta x$ is $W(x + \Delta x)$. Hence, the work in raising the bucket from level x to level $x + \Delta x$ is

$$W(x + \Delta x) - W(x).$$

---

*Actually the scalar (dot) product of vectors was first introduced for this particular use and it was later that its use in geometry was developed.

Here is where the above assumption comes in. The force at level x is $60 - 2x$ lb, but at level $x + \Delta x$ is the smaller force $60 - 2(x + \Delta x)$ lb. Hence,

$$[60 - 2(x + \Delta x)]\, \Delta x \leq W(x + \Delta x) - W(x) \leq [60 - 2x]\, \Delta x.$$

Thus,

$$60 - 2(x + \Delta x) \leq \frac{W(x + \Delta x) - W(x)}{\Delta x} \leq 60 - 2x$$

and

$$\lim_{\Delta x \to 0} [60 - 2(x + \Delta x)] \leq \lim_{\Delta x \to 0} \frac{W(x + \Delta x) - W(x)}{\Delta x} \leq 60 - 2x.$$

Since the limit on the left is $60 - 2x$ and the limit in the middle is $dW(x)/dx$, it follows that

$$\frac{dW(x)}{dx} = 60 - 2x.$$

No work is done until motion is started, so $W(0) = 0$. Hence, the differential equation

$$dW(x) = (60 - 2x)\, dx \quad \text{subject to} \quad W(0) = 0$$

is obtained. The particular solution (since $c = 0$ in this case) is

$$W(x) = 60x - x^2.$$

Hence, the total work in raising the leaky bucket is

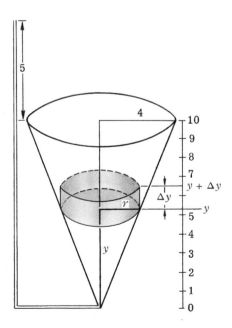

Fig. 3-6.3

$$W(10) = 600 - 100 = 500 \text{ ft·lb.}$$

The distance, as well as the force, may be variable, as shown in the following example.

Example 2. A conical tank having radius of base 4 ft, altitude 10 ft, and vertex down is full of water (weight 62.5 lb/ft³). Find the work required to pump all of the water to a level 5 ft above the top of the tank.

Solution. No coordinate system is present, so one must be provided. To do so, stand a scale (unit 1 ft) beside the tank with $y = 0$ at the bottom and $y = 10$ at the top. An x-axis need not be considered.

Hold y fixed, such that $0 \leq y \leq 10$, and consider the situation where the surface of the water is at level y. Let $W(y)$ be the work already accomplished in pumping the water that was above this level to 5 ft above the top of the tank. With $\Delta y > 0$, then $W(y + \Delta y)$ is the work required to lower the water to level $y + \Delta y$, and [since $W(y + \Delta y)$ is less than $W(y)$]

$$(3) \qquad\qquad W(y) - W(y + \Delta y)$$

is the work done in raising the thin layer that was between the levels y to $y + \Delta y$ to 5 ft above the top of the tank. This layer weighed a certain amount, and each molecule of water in this layer was raised at least $15 - (y + \Delta y)$ ft and at most $15 - y$ ft.

An estimate of the weight of this layer will now be obtained. Let r be the radius of the surface of water at level y. By similar triangles,

$$(4) \qquad\qquad \frac{r}{y} = \frac{4}{10}, \quad \text{so} \quad r = \frac{2}{5}y.$$

The water flares out above this level, so the volume of the layer between levels y and $y + \Delta y$ is more than the volume of a cylinder of radius $r = \frac{2}{5}y$ and altitude Δy; that is, more than

$$\pi(\tfrac{2}{5}y)^2 \, \Delta y \text{ ft}^3.$$

Thus, the weight of this layer is more than

$$62.5 \, \pi \, \frac{4}{25} \, y^2 \, \Delta y \text{ lb.}$$

By considering the radius of the upper surface of the layer, etc., it should be seen that the weight of the layer is less than

$$62.5\pi[\tfrac{2}{5}(y + \Delta y)]^2 \, \Delta y \text{ lb.}$$

The work $W(y) - W(y + \Delta y)$ in moving the layer is between

(smallest force)×(smallest distance) and (largest force) × (largest distance):

$$62.5\pi\frac{4}{25} \, y^2 \, \Delta y \, [15 - (y + \Delta y)] \leq W(y) - W(y + \Delta y)$$

$$\leq 62.5\pi\frac{4}{25} \, (y + \Delta y)^2 \, [15 - y] \, \Delta y,$$

$$62.5\pi\frac{4}{25} \, y^2 \, [15 - y - \Delta y] \leq \frac{W(y) - W(y + \Delta y)}{\Delta y}$$

$$\leq 62.5\pi\frac{4}{25}(y + \Delta y)^2 \, [15 - y].$$

As $\Delta y \to 0$, both left and right sides approach the same value, so*

(5) $$-\frac{dW(y)}{dy} = 62.5\pi\frac{4}{25} y^2 (15 - y) = 10\pi(15y^2 - y^3).$$

"No work has been done when the tank is full" is translated into $W(10) = 0$. Thus, with y the independent variable, the differential equation

(6) $$dW(y) = -10\pi(15y^2 - y^3) \, dy \text{ subject to } W(10) = 0$$

is obtained. The general solution is

$$W(y) = -10\pi(5y^3 - \tfrac{1}{4}y^4) + c$$

and, since $W(10) = 0$, the constant $c = 10^4\pi\frac{5}{2}$, so

$$W(y) = -10\pi(5y^3 - \tfrac{1}{4}y^4) + 10^4 \pi\frac{5}{2}.$$

When all the water has been pumped out, then $y = 0$ and

(7) $$W(0) = 10^4\pi\tfrac{5}{2} = 7.85 \times 10^4 \text{ ft} \cdot \text{lb}$$

is the answer to this problem.

Many actual problems arise, or are stated, without any coordinate system in evidence (such as Example 2). It is then up to the solver to select a coordinate system of his own; this may usually be done in a variety of ways. An important thing to realize, however, is that once a coordinate system has been selected, then this coordinate system must be strictly adhered to throughout the remainder of the problem.

Problem 1. Consider the problem stated in Example 2. This time, however, place the 10-ft scale next to the tank with $y = 0$ at the top and $y = 10$ at the bottom (instead of as in Fig. 3-6.3):

a. Note that the level $y + \Delta y$ is below (instead of above) the level y. (The student should draw another figure.)
b. Instead of (3), obtain $W(y + \Delta y) - W(y)$ ft·lb.
c. See that each molecule of water in the layer between y and $y + \Delta y$ is moved at least $5 + y$ ft and at most $5 + y + \Delta y$ ft.
d. Instead of (4), obtain $r/(10 - y) = 4/10$, so $r = \tfrac{2}{5}(10 - y)$.
e. Instead of (6), obtain

$$dW(y) = 62.5\pi\frac{4}{25}(10 - y)^2(5 + y) \, dy$$

$$= 62.5\pi\frac{4}{25}(y^3 - 15y^2 + 500)$$

---

*The minus sign occurs on the left in (5) since, by definition,

$$\frac{dW(y)}{dx} = \lim_{\Delta y \to 0} \frac{W(y + \Delta y) - W(y)}{\Delta y}, \text{ and thus}$$

$$\lim_{\Delta y \to 0} \frac{W(y) - W(y + \Delta y)}{\Delta y} = -\lim_{\Delta y \to 0} \frac{W(y + \Delta y) - W(y)}{\Delta y} = -\frac{dW(y)}{dy}.$$

subject, however, to $W(0) = 0$.
f. Solve this system, and then see that the answer is

$$W(10) = 7.85 \times 10^4 \text{ ft} \cdot \text{lb}.$$

Problem 2. Again consider the problem of Example 2, but this time place a 15-ft scale with $y = 0$ five ft above the top of the tank and $y = 15$ at the level of the vertex. (Be sure to draw the figure.) Go through the analysis to obtain, instead of (6), the differential equation

$$dW(y) = 62.5\pi \frac{4}{25} (15 - y)^2 \, y \, dy \quad \text{subject to} \quad W(5) = 0$$

but valid only for $5 \leq y \leq 15$. Now solve and obtain the final answer

$$W(15) = 7.85 \times 10^4 \text{ ft} \cdot \text{lb}.$$

Problem 3. Find the work done in pumping the water to h ft above the top of the tank described:
a. Conical, vertex down, altitude 5 ft, radius of base 4 ft; $h = 10$.
b. Same as part a but vertex up.
c. Hemispherical bowl, radius 5 ft; $h = 8$.
d. Trough of length 10 ft, vertical-ends isosceles triangles of base 3 ft and altitude 2 ft; $h = 5$.
e. Trough of length 10 ft, vertical-ends isosceles trapezoids of altitude 4 ft, upper base 3 ft, lower base 2 ft; $h = 5$.

Problem 4. A bucket plus its water weighs 50 lb at the bottom of a well 30 ft deep. The bucket is drawn up at a steady rate to ground level in 2 min. Water leaks from the bucket at the steady rate of 5 lb/min. Find the work done.

3-7. Sigma Notation

The material in this section may not seem to have any connection with that of the preceding sections, but there is an intimate connection, as will be shown in Sec. 3–9.

With a and d constants, then the sequence

(1) $\qquad\qquad a, a + d, a + 2d, a + 3d, \ldots$

is called an **arithmetic progression.** The three dots are used to indicate that succeeding terms follow the same law. The kth term is

$$a + (k - 1)d.$$

This means that the substitution of $k = 1$ yields the first term $a + (1 - 1)d = a$, that $k = 2$ yields the second term $a + (2 - 1)d = a + d$, etc. The tenth term, for example, is $a + (10 - 1)d = a + 9d$.

The sum of n terms of (1) is

(2) $\qquad\qquad a + (a + d) + (a + 2d) + \cdots + a + (n - 1)d.$

A standard notation for this sum is

(3)
$$\sum_{k=1}^{n} [a + (k - 1)d]$$

and is read "the sum from $k = 1$ to $k = n$ of $a + (k - 1)d$" or, more simply, as "sigma $k = 1$ to n of $a + (k - 1)d$." The symbol Σ is the Greek capital letter sigma.

If a is a constant as far as k is concerned, then

(4)
$$\sum_{k=1}^{n} a \text{ means to add } \underbrace{a + a + \cdots + a}_{n \text{ terms}} = na.$$

Thus, (2) written as

$$\underbrace{a + a + \cdots + a}_{n \text{ terms}} + d[0 + 1 + 2 + \cdots + (n - 1)] = na + d \sum_{k=1}^{n} (k - 1)$$

shows that

(5)
$$\sum_{k=1}^{n} [a + (k - 1)d] = \sum_{k=1}^{n} a + d \sum_{k=1}^{n} (k - 1).$$

From $(k - 1)^2 = k^2 - 2k + 1$, it follows that

$$k^2 - (k - 1)^2 = 2k - 1.$$

Now by summing both sides from $k = 1$ to n, the result may be written as

$$\sum_{k=1}^{n} k^2 - \sum_{k=1}^{n} (k - 1)^2 = 2 \sum_{k=1}^{n} k - \sum_{k=1}^{n} 1.$$

Think of the two sums on the left written out. Then all except the single term n^2 cancel, leaving

$$n^2 = 2 \sum_{k=1}^{n} k - n.$$

The last n follows from (4), with $a = 1$. Hence,

(6)
$$\sum_{k=1}^{n} k = \frac{n^2 + n}{2}$$

is a formula for finding the sum of the first n integers.

Next, note that $(k - 1)^3 = k^3 - 3k^2 + 3k - 1$, so that

$$k^3 - (k - 1)^3 = 3k^2 - 3k + 1 \quad \text{and}$$

$$\sum_{k=1}^{n} k^3 - \sum_{k=1}^{n} (k - 1)^3 = 3 \sum_{k=1}^{n} k^2 - 3 \sum_{k=1}^{n} k + \sum_{k=1}^{n} 1$$

$$= 3 \sum_{k=1}^{n} k^2 - 3 \frac{n^2 + n}{2} + n.$$

Again, the left side cancels down to a single term—namely, n^3—and upon solving for $\sum_{k=1}^{n} k^2$, the result is

(7)
$$\sum_{k=1}^{n} k^2 = \frac{1}{3}\left[n^3 + 3\frac{n^2+n}{2} - n\right]$$
$$= \frac{1}{6}(2n^3 + 3n^2 + n),$$

which is a formula for finding the sum of the squares of the first n integers.

Example. The curve of Fig. 3-7.1 is the graph of

$$y = f(x) = \tfrac{1}{2}x^2$$

and there are 10 rectangles with bases on the interval $1 \leq x \leq 3$. This interval is of length $3 - 1 = 2$, so each base has length $2/10$. The kth base (counting from the left) has upper end at the point whose x-value is called x_k, where

$$x_k = 1 + k\frac{2}{10}.$$

Thus, the altitude of the kth rectangle is

$$f(x_k) = \frac{1}{2}x_k^2 = \frac{1}{2}\left(1 + k\frac{2}{10}\right)^2$$

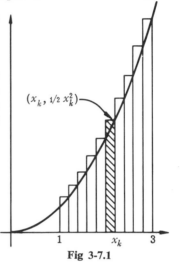

Fig 3-7.1

and the area of this kth rectangle is

$$f(x_k)\frac{2}{10} = \frac{1}{2}\left(1 + k\frac{2}{10}\right)^2 \frac{2}{10}.$$

Hence, the sum of the areas of the 10 rectangles is

$$\sum_{k=1}^{10} f(x_k)\frac{2}{10} = \sum_{k=1}^{10} \frac{1}{2}\left(1 + k\frac{2}{10}\right)^2 \frac{2}{10}$$

$$= \frac{1}{2}\left(\frac{2}{10}\right)\sum_{k=1}^{10}\left[1 + 2 \cdot \frac{2}{10}k + \left(\frac{2}{10}\right)^2 k^2\right]$$

$$= \frac{1}{2}\left(\frac{2}{10}\right)\left\{\sum_{k=1}^{10}1 + 2\left(\frac{2}{10}\right)\sum_{k=1}^{10}k + \left(\frac{2}{10}\right)^2 \sum_{k=1}^{10}k^2\right\}$$

$$= \frac{1}{2}\left(\frac{2}{10}\right)\left\{10 + 2\left(\frac{2}{10}\right)\frac{10^2 + 10}{2} + \left(\frac{2}{10}\right)^2\frac{1}{6}(2\cdot 10^3 + 3\cdot 10^2 + 10)\right\}$$

by using (6) and (7).

The obvious cancellations have not been made, so it will be easier for the student to check that by dividing the interval $1 \leq x \leq 3$ into n (instead of 10) subintervals and proceeding as above, then the sum of the resulting n rectangles is

(8) $$\sum_{k=1}^{n} f(x_k)\frac{2}{n} = \frac{1}{2}\frac{2}{n}\left\{n + 2\left(\frac{2}{n}\right)\frac{n^2+n}{2} + \left(\frac{2}{n}\right)^2\frac{1}{6}(2n^3 + 3n^2 + n)\right\}.$$

For practice the student should carefully make the suggested derivation of (8) and then do the algebra on the right of (8) to see that

$$\sum_{k=1}^{n} f(x_k) \frac{2}{n} = \frac{13}{3} + \frac{4}{n} + \frac{2}{3} \frac{1}{n^2}.$$

Now if n is very large, then $4/n$ and $\frac{2}{3}(1/n^2)$ are very small and, as defined in the next section,

$$\lim_{n \to \infty} \sum_{k=1}^{n} f(x_k) \frac{2}{n} = \frac{13}{3}.$$

A visualization of Fig. 3-7.1 with a large number n of rectangles (instead of only 10 rectangles) should now be fairly convincing evidence that the area under the graph of

$$y = \tfrac{1}{2}x^2 \text{ for } 1 \le x \le 3$$

is 13/3 sq units. Recall that this same number 13/3 was obtained for the same area in Sec. 3-5 by the differential equations method. The fact that these two quite distinct methods lead to the same result portends a fundamental property to be established in Sec. 3-9.

3-8. Limit as n → ∞

DEFINITION. *For $S(n)$ a function of n, then*

$$\lim_{n \to \infty} S(n) = L,$$

provided that for each arbitrary positive number ϵ there is an integer N depending upon ϵ such that

$$L - \epsilon < S(n) < L + \epsilon \text{ for all } n > N.$$

This definition does not imply that n will ever be ∞, but only that $S(n)$ will be within any prescribed tolerance of L for all n which are finite but sufficiently large. For the specific function $S(n) = 1/n$, the limit as $n \to \infty$ is $L = 0$; that is,

(1) $$\lim_{n \to \infty} \frac{1}{n} = 0.$$

For upon naming any tolerance $\epsilon > 0$, then $1/\epsilon$ need not be an integer but there is an integer $N > 1/\epsilon$. Now

$$0 - \epsilon < \frac{1}{n} < 0 + \epsilon \text{ for all } n > N.$$

If c is a constant as far as n is concerned, then

(2) $$\lim_{n \to \infty} c = c.$$

A theorem similar to the one (Theorem 2 of Sec. 2-7) for $h \to c$ also holds for $n \to \infty$:

THEOREM. *If $S_1(n)$ and $S_2(n)$ are functions of n such that the limits*

$$\lim_{n\to\infty} S_1(n) = L_1 \quad \text{and} \quad \lim_{n\to\infty} S_2(n) = L_2$$

both exist, then the following limits exist as $n \to \infty$:
  (i) $\lim [S_1(n) \pm S_2(n)] = \lim S_1(n) \pm \lim S_2(n) = L_1 \pm L_2$,
  (ii) $\lim [S_1(n) \cdot S_2(n)] = [\lim S_1(n)][\lim S_2(n)] = L_1 \cdot L_2$,
  (iii) $\lim \dfrac{S_1(n)}{S_2(n)} = \dfrac{\lim S_1(n)}{\lim S_2(n)} = \dfrac{L_1}{L_2}$ *if $L_2 \neq 0$.*

This theorem will be accepted without proof at this time but will be proved in Sec. 13-2.

Example 1. Show that

$$\lim_{n\to\infty} \frac{3n^2 + 50n}{253 - 2n^2} = -\frac{3}{2}.$$

Solution. Upon dividing both numerator and denominator by n^2, then

$$\lim_{n\to\infty} \frac{3n^2 + 50n}{253 - 2n^2} = \lim_{n\to\infty} \frac{\dfrac{3n^2 + 50n}{n^2}}{\dfrac{253 - 2n^2}{n^2}} = \lim_{n\to\infty} \frac{3 + \dfrac{50}{n}}{\dfrac{253}{n^2} - 2}$$

$$= \frac{\lim\limits_{n\to\infty}\left(3 + \dfrac{50}{n}\right)}{\lim\limits_{n\to\infty}\left(\dfrac{253}{n^2} - 2\right)} \qquad \text{by (iii)}$$

$$= \frac{\lim\limits_{n\to\infty} 3 + \lim\limits_{n\to\infty}\dfrac{50}{n}}{\lim\limits_{n\to\infty}\dfrac{253}{n^2} - \lim\limits_{n\to\infty} 2} \qquad \text{by (i)}$$

$$= \frac{3 + \lim\limits_{n\to\infty} 50 \cdot \lim\limits_{n\to\infty}\dfrac{1}{n}}{\lim\limits_{n\to\infty} 253 \cdot \lim\limits_{n\to\infty}\dfrac{1}{n} \cdot \lim\limits_{n\to\infty}\dfrac{1}{n} - 2} \qquad \text{by (2) and (ii)}$$

$$= \frac{3 + 50 \cdot 0}{253 \cdot 0 \cdot 0 - 2} = -\frac{3}{2} \qquad \text{by (1).}$$

If a function involves the two variables x and n, then as $n \to \infty$ the variable x is held constant.

Example 2.

$$\lim_{n\to\infty} \left[\left(\frac{x}{n}\right)^3 \frac{1}{6}(2n^3 + 3n^2 + n)\right] = \frac{x^3}{6} \lim_{n\to\infty} \frac{2n^3 + 2n^2 + n}{n^3}$$

$$= \frac{x^3}{6} \lim_{n\to\infty}\left(2 + \frac{3}{n} + \frac{1}{n^2}\right)$$

$$= \frac{x^3}{6} \cdot 2 = \frac{1}{3}x^3.$$

Problem 1. Use formulas (6) and (7) of Sec. 3-7 to obtain each of the following sums. Check each sum for $n = 1$, $n = 2$, and $n = 3$:

a. $\sum\limits_{k=1}^{n} (2k - 1) = n^2$; that is, the sum of the first n odd integers is equal to n^2.

b. $\sum\limits_{k=1}^{n} (2k) = n^2 + n$.

c. $\sum\limits_{k=1}^{n} (2k - 1)^2 = \dfrac{1}{3} (4n^3 - n)$.

d. $\sum\limits_{k=1}^{n} (2k)^2 = \dfrac{2}{3}(2n^3 + 3n^2 + n)$.

e. $\sum\limits_{k=1}^{n} k(k + 1) = \dfrac{1}{3}n(n + 1)(n + 2)$.

Problem 2.
a. Check that $k^4 - (k - 1)^4 = 4k^3 - 6k^2 + 4k - 1$.
b. Sum both sides, then use (6) and (7) of Sec. 3-7 to establish

$$\sum_{k=1}^{n} k^3 = \frac{1}{4}(n^4 + 2n^3 + n^2).$$

c. Derive the formula

$$\sum_{k=1}^{n} k^4 = \frac{1}{30}(6n^5 + 15n^4 + 10n^3 - n).$$

Problem 3. Establish each of the limits:

a. $\lim\limits_{n\to\infty} \dfrac{n - 20}{3n + 40} = \dfrac{1}{3}$.

b. $\lim\limits_{n\to\infty} \dfrac{2 + 4n - 5n^2}{n^2 + 3n - 4} = -5$.

c. $\lim\limits_{n\to\infty} \dfrac{(2n - 1)(3n + 5)}{(n + 4)(2n - 7)} = 3$.

d. $\lim\limits_{n\to\infty} \dfrac{(1 - n)(2n + 3)^2}{n^3} = -4$.

Problem 4. First reduce the summation to an algebraic function of n and then let $n \to \infty$ to show that:

a. $\lim\limits_{n\to\infty} \sum\limits_{k=1}^{n} \left(1 + \dfrac{k}{n}\right) \dfrac{1}{n} = \dfrac{3}{2}$.

b. $\lim\limits_{n\to\infty} \sum\limits_{k=1}^{n} \left(1 + \dfrac{k}{n}\right)^2 \dfrac{1}{n} = \dfrac{7}{3}$.

c. $\lim\limits_{n\to\infty} \sum\limits_{k=1}^{n} \left(1 + \dfrac{k}{n}\right)^3 \dfrac{1}{n} = \dfrac{15}{4}$.

Problem 5. A student who can carry out each step in proper order to establish each part of this problem has a good foundation for understanding the work of the next section. With a and b numbers and n a positive integer, let $(b - a)/n = \Delta x$ and

$$x_k = a + k \Delta x \quad \text{for } k = 1, 2, 3, \ldots, n.$$

For each of the given functions $f(x)$, show that

$$\lim_{n\to\infty} \sum_{k=1}^{n} f(x_k) \Delta x = F(b) - F(a), \quad \text{where } F(x) = \int f(x)\, dx:$$

a. $f(x) = x$.   b. $f(x) = x^2$.   c. $f(x) = x(x - 1)$.

3-9. The Definite Integral

The two preceding sections were groundwork for the definition of "the definite integral from a constant a to a constant b of a function

$$y = f(x)$$

of the variable x." At this time, a purely mathematical definition will be given, but it should be emphasized that there are many practical applications of this notion in physics, chemistry, engineering, and, in fact, in most fields where mathematics is applied.

DEFINITION. *A function $y = f(x)$ of x and an interval $a \leq x \leq b$ with constant endpoints are given.*

FIRST. *With n a positive integer, divide the interval $a \leq x \leq b$ into n subintervals by the points*

$$x_0 = a, \, x_1, \, x_2, \ldots, x_{n-1}, \, x_n = b.$$

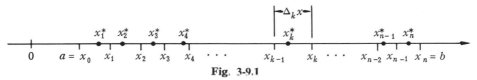

Fig. 3-9.1

SECOND. *For each integer $k = 1, 2, 3, \ldots, n$ let $\Delta_k x$ be the length of the interval $x_{k-1} \leq x \leq x_k$, so that*

$$\Delta_k x = x_k - x_{k-1}.$$

THIRD. *On the interval $x_{k-1} \leq x \leq x_k$, choose any point and call it x_k^*. Hence,*

$$x_{k-1} \leq x_k^* \leq x_k.$$

FOURTH. *Form the sum*

$$(1) \qquad f(x_1^*) \, \Delta_1 x + f(x_2^*) \, \Delta_2 x + \cdots + f(x_n^*) \, \Delta_n x = \sum_{k=1}^{n} f(x_k^*) \, \Delta_k x.$$

FIFTH. *As $n \to \infty$ in such a way that each $\Delta_k x \to 0$, the sums (1) will approach a limit for a large class of functions $f(x)$ and in particular will do so if $f(x)$ is a continuous function.* Assuming such a limit of (1) exists, this limit is denoted by*

$$(2) \qquad \lim_{\substack{n \to \infty \\ \Delta_k x \to 0}} \sum_{k=1}^{n} f(x_k^*) \, \Delta_k x = \int_a^b f(x) \, dx.$$

The symbolism

$$(3) \qquad \int_a^b f(x) \, dx$$

---

*The fact that such limits exist cannot be proved in a first course of calculus.

is read "the definite integral from a to b of $f(x)\,dx$." It should be understood that (3) stands for a constant; namely, that constant which is obtained by executing the five steps of the definition. It is, however, seldom that a definite integral is evaluated directly from the definition, but the definition establishes a basis on which to build a pattern of thinking into the essential ingredients sufficient for the analysis of many practical problems.

In the next section it will be shown that

(4) $$\int_a^b f(x)\,dx = F(b) - F(a), \quad \text{where} \quad F(x) = \int f(x)\,dx.$$

Thus, the definite integral [which is the limit as $n \to \infty$ of sums of the form (2)] is related to the indefinite integral (which is merely an antiderivative) and (4) is the statement of this relation.

Example 1. Show that $\int_0^\pi \sin x\,dx = 2$.

Solution. Here $f(x) = \sin x$ and thus

$$F(x) = \int \sin x\,dx = -\cos x + c.$$

Hence, from (4) with $a = 0$ and $b = \pi$,

$$\int_0^\pi \sin x\,dx = [-\cos \pi + c] - [-\cos 0 + c]$$

$$= -\cos \pi + \cos 0 + c - c$$

$$= -(-1) + 1 = 2.$$

As the above example shows, it is not necessary to add the arbitrary constant when finding $F(x) = \int f(x)\,dx$; it cancels out anyway when computing $F(b) - F(a)$.

The notation is condensed slightly by setting

$$F(b) - F(a) = F(x)]_a^b.$$

Example 2.

$$\int_1^3 \frac{1}{2}x^2\,dx = \frac{1}{6}x^3\Big]_1^3 = \frac{1}{6}\,3^3 - \frac{1}{6}\,1^3 = \frac{27 - 1}{6} = \frac{13}{3}.$$

The following problem furnishes an opportunity to review indefinite integration.

Problem. Evaluate each of the definite integrals:

a. $\displaystyle\int_{-1}^3 x^2\,dx.$

b. $\displaystyle\int_{-3}^{-2} x^3\,dx.$

c. $\displaystyle\int_0^3 \sqrt{4^2 + x^2}\,x\,dx.$

f. $\displaystyle\int_1^3 (3x^2 - 4x + 5)\,dx.$

g. $\displaystyle\int_0^\pi (2\cos x - 3\sin x)\,dx.$

h. $\displaystyle\int_{-\pi}^\pi (2\cos 2x - 3\sin 2x)\,dx.$

d. $\int_0^{12} \sqrt{5^2 + x^2}\, x\, dx.$

i. $\int_{\pi/2}^{\pi} \sin^2 x \cos x\, dx.$

e. $\int_{-\pi/2}^{\pi} \sin x\, dx.$

j. $\int_0^{\pi} \cos^2 2x \sin 2x\, dx.$

3-10. Fundamental Theorem of Calculus

Throughout this section it will be assumed that

$$y = f(x)$$

is a continuous function of x.

The five steps given in Sec. 3-9 in the definition of

(1) $$\int_a^b f(x)\, dx$$

should be reviewed. Let m be the minimum value and M the maximum value of $y = f(x)$ for $a \le x \le b$. Hence, in the notation of the definition, it follows that

$$m \le f(x_k^*) \le M, \quad \text{so} \quad m\, \Delta_k x \le f(x_k^*)\, \Delta_k x \le M\, \Delta_k x \quad \text{and}$$

$$\sum_{k=1}^{n} m\, \Delta_k x \le \sum_{k=1}^{n} f(x_k^*)\, \Delta_k x \le \sum_{k=1}^{n} M\, \Delta_k x.$$

Since m and M are constants, they may be factored out of the left and right sums. Also the interval $a \le x \le b$ was divided into subintervals of lengths $\Delta_1 x, \Delta_2 x, \ldots, \Delta_n x$, so the sum of these is the length of the interval $a \le x \le b$; that is,

$$m(b - a) \le \sum_{k=1}^{n} f(x_k^*)\, \Delta_k x \le M(b - a).$$

Now by letting $n \to \infty$ in such a way that each $\Delta_k x \to 0$, the middle term approaches the expression in (1) by definition, and thus:

If m is the minimum and M the maximum of $y = f(x)$ on $a \le x \le b$, then

(2) $$m(b - a) \le \int_a^b f(x)\, dx \le M(b - a).$$

Another property of definite integrals is:

If $a < c < b$, then

(3) $$\int_a^b f(x)\, dx = \int_a^c f(x)\, dx + \int_c^b f(x)\, dx.$$

A proof of (3) is quite long and detailed, but the truth of (3) was undoubtedly anticipated by noting that the definition of a definite integral applied first to $a \le x \le c$ and then to $c \le x \le b$ is essentially the same as applying the definition to the whole interval $a \le x \le b$.

Recall that the derivative of $f(x)$ with respect to x was defined by

$$D_x f(x) = \lim_{\Delta x \to 0} \frac{f(x + \Delta x) - f(x)}{\Delta x}.$$

Also, the indefinite integral was defined by setting

$$F(x) = \int f(x)\,dx \text{ if and only if } D_x F(x) = f(x);$$

that is, a function $F(x)$ is an indefinite integral of $f(x)\,dx$ merely means that $F(x)$ is an antiderivative of $f(x)$. Finally, the definite integral, from a to b of a function $f(x)$ of the variable x, is a constant that is determined by going through the five steps of the definition in Sec. 3-9. Different as the processes of definite integration and differentiation seem, they are intimately related. The statement of this relationship is the following theorem.

FUNDAMENTAL THEOREM OF CALCULUS. *If $y = f(x)$ is a continuous function of x for $a \leq x \leq b$, then*

$$(4) \qquad \int_a^b f(x)\,dx = F(x)\Big]_a^b, \quad \text{where} \quad F(x) = \int f(x)\,dx$$

or, equivalently,

$$(4') \qquad \int_a^b f(x)\,dx = F(x)\Big]_a^b, \quad \text{where} \quad D_x F(x) = f(x).$$

PROOF. The form $(4')$ will be established. It is necessary to use two separate independent variables. A convenient way to think of this is first to take an ordinary (x, y)-coordinate system and then superimpose upon it an (h, y)-coordinate system with the x-axis and the h-axis coinciding, the y-axis being the same for both systems.

First fix the variable x at some constant value such that

$$a \leq x.$$

Now with a and x constants, the definition of a definite integral may be completely restated in terms of the variable h and the interval $a \leq h \leq x$. Hence, the definite integral of $f(h)$ from $h = a$ to $h = x$ depends on x, and for convenience set

$$(5) \qquad\qquad G(x) = \int_a^x f(h)\,dh.$$

In particular, if x were chosen as $x = a$, then the "interval" $a \leq h \leq a$ consists of one point, so

$$(6) \qquad\qquad G(a) = \int_a^a f(h)\,dh = 0.$$

For later use, note also that

$$(7) \qquad\qquad \int_a^b f(h)\,dh = G(b).$$

Next, with $\Delta x > 0$, apply the definite integral definition to the interval $a \le h \le x + \Delta x$ and obtain

$$G(x + \Delta x) = \int_{a}^{x+\Delta x} f(h)\, dh.$$

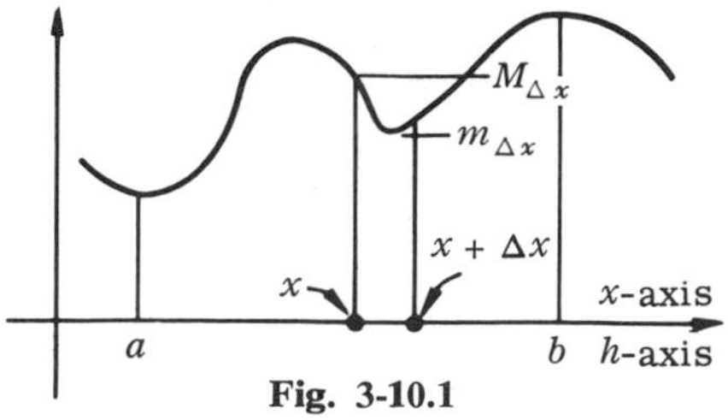

Fig. 3-10.1

Since x is between a and $x + \Delta x$, then [from (3)]

$$G(x + \Delta x) = \int_{a}^{x+\Delta x} f(h)\, dh = \int_{a}^{x} f(h)\, dh + \int_{x}^{x+\Delta x} f(h)\, dh$$

$$= G(x) + \int_{x}^{x+\Delta x} f(h)\, dh,$$

$$G(x + \Delta x) - G(x) = \int_{x}^{x+\Delta x} f(h)\, dh.$$

Let $m_{\Delta x}$ and $M_{\Delta x}$ be the minimum and maximum of $f(h)$ on the interval $x \le h \le x + \Delta x$. Hence, (2), with appropriate changes in notation of variables and constants, shows that

$$m_{\Delta x} \cdot \Delta x \le \int_{x}^{x+\Delta x} f(h)\, dh \le M_{\Delta x} \cdot \Delta x; \quad \text{that is,}$$

$$m_{\Delta x} \cdot \Delta x \le G(x + \Delta x) - G(x) \le M_{\Delta x} \cdot \Delta x, \quad \text{so that}$$

$$m_{\Delta x} \le \frac{G(x + \Delta x) - G(x)}{\Delta x} \le M_{\Delta x}.$$

Hence,

$$\lim_{\Delta x \to 0} m_{\Delta x} \le \lim_{\Delta x \to 0} \frac{G(x + \Delta x) - G(x)}{\Delta x} \le \lim_{\Delta x \to 0} M_{\Delta x}.$$

But as $\Delta x \to 0$, both $m_{\Delta x}$ and $M_{\Delta x}$ approach the same value, namely, the value of $f(h)$ when $h = x$ from the continuity of the function f. Thus, $m_{\Delta x}$ and $M_{\Delta x}$ both approach $f(x)$. Therefore, $f(x) \le D_x G(x) \le f(x)$, so that

(8) $$D_x G(x) = f(x).$$

The equations (6), (7), and (8) assembled on one line for further analysis are

$$\int_{a}^{b} f(h)\, dh = G(b), \quad G(a) = 0, \quad \text{and} \quad D_x G(x) = f(x).$$

The variable h may now be replaced by x to yield

(9) $\int_a^b f(x)\,dx = G(b)$, $G(a) = 0$,   and $D_x G(x) = f(x)$.

Finally, note that if $F(x)$ is any function of x such that
$$D_x F(x) = f(x),$$
then $F(x)$ and $G(x)$ differ at most by a constant (see Prob. 4, Sec. 2-15):
$$G(x) = F(x) + c.$$
Then $0 = G(a) = F(a) + c, c = -F(a)$, $G(x) = F(x) - F(a)$, and in partic-ular for $x = b$,
$$G(b) = F(b) - F(a).$$

Hence, (9) becomes
$$\int_a^b f(x)\,dx = F(b) - F(a), \quad \text{where} \quad D_x F(x) = f(x),$$
and this is (4′), whose proof is now established.

The definite integral of $f(x)\,dx$ from a to b (with $a < b$),
$$\int_a^b f(x)\,dx,$$
was defined. The definite integral from b to a is defined by setting
$$\int_b^a f(x)\,dx = -\int_a^b f(x)\,dx$$
$$= -[F(b) - F(a)], \quad \text{where} \quad F(x) = \int f(x)\,dx$$
$$= F(a) - F(b)$$
$$= F(x)\Big]_b^a.$$

Thus, without paying any attention to which of c or d is the larger,
$$\int_c^d f(x)\,dx = F(x)\Big]_c^d, \quad \text{where} \quad F(x) = \int f(x)\,dx.$$

Problem 1. Give arguments in terms of limits of sums to indicate the truth of each of the following:

a. If $f(x) \geq 0$ for $a \leq x \leq b$, then $\int_a^b f(x)\,dx \geq 0$.

b. $\int_a^b [f(x) + g(x)]\,dx = \int_a^b f(x)\,dx + \int_a^b g(x)\,dx$.

c. $\int_a^b [f(x) - g(x)]\,dx = \int_a^b f(x)\,dx - \int_a^b g(x)\,dx$.

d. If c is a constant, then $\int_a^b cf(x)\,dx = c\int_a^b f(x)\,dx$.

Problem 2. Given $f(x) = x^3$ and $g(x) = x - 1$, compute the four definite integrals,

$$\int_1^2 f(x)\,dx, \quad \int_1^2 g(x)\,dx, \quad \int_1^2 f(x)g(x)\,dx, \quad \text{and} \quad \int_1^2 \frac{g(x)}{f(x)}\,dx.$$

Now check that

$$\int_1^2 f(x)g(x)\,dx \neq \int_1^2 f(x)\,dx \cdot \int_1^2 g(x)\,dx, \quad \text{and}$$

$$\int_1^2 \frac{g(x)}{f(x)}\,dx \neq \frac{\displaystyle\int_1^2 g(x)\,dx}{\displaystyle\int_1^2 f(x)\,dx}.$$

3-11.   Area Between Curves

One of the reasons for introducing area and work problems before definite integrals was to establish a pattern of thinking necessary for the proof of the Fundamental Theorem of Calculus. Now with an introduction to definite integrals in the background, an alternate approach to area and work problems via definite integrals is at hand.

For example, if a region of the plane has x-extent $a \leq x \leq b$ and $l(x)$ is the length of the vertical segment across the region, then the area A of the region is given by

(1)

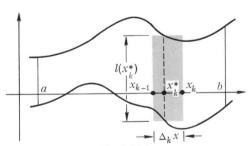

Fig 3-11.1

For, with $a = x_0 < x_1 < \cdots < x_n = b$ and for each $k = 1, 2, \cdots, n$, a point x_k^* is chosen such that $x_{k-1} \leq x_k^* \leq x_k$ and $\Delta_k x = x_k - x_{k-1}$. Then $l(x_k^*)\,\Delta_k x$ approximates a strip across the region,

$$\sum_{k=1}^{n} l(x_k^*)\,\Delta_k x$$

approximates the whole region, and the limit of sums as $n \to \infty$ and $\Delta_k x \to 0$ is (by definition) the definite integral and the area A. Further information about the upper and lower boundaries of the region is necessary in order to determine the function $l(x)$.

Example 1. Find the area bounded by the graphs of

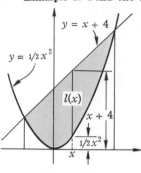

$$y = \tfrac{1}{2}x^2 \quad \text{and} \quad y = x + 4.$$

Solution. Solve the equations simultaneously:

$$\tfrac{1}{2}x^2 = x + 4, \quad x^2 - 2x - 8 = 0,$$

$$(x + 2)(x - 4) = 0;$$

$$x = -2 \quad \text{or} \quad x = 4.$$

So the x-extent is $-2 \leq x \leq 4$. Hence, in (1), $a = -2$ and $b = 4$. From Fig. 3-11.2,

$$l(x) = x + 4 - \tfrac{1}{2}x^2, \text{ so}$$

Fig. 3-11.2

$$A = \int_{-2}^{4} \left(x + 4 - \frac{1}{2}x^2\right) dx = \left[\frac{1}{2}x^2 + 4x - \frac{1}{6}x^3\right]_{-2}^{4}$$

$$= \left[\frac{1}{2}4^2 + 4\cdot 4 - \frac{1}{6}4^3\right] - \left[\frac{1}{2}(-2)^2 + 4(-2) - \frac{1}{6}(-2)^3\right] = 18.$$

If the x-extent of a region is $a \leq x \leq b$ and if the upper and lower boundaries of the region have equations

$$y = f(x) \quad \text{and} \quad y = g(x), \quad \text{respectively,}$$

then $l(x) = f(x) - g(x)$ and (1) may be written more precisely as

(2) $$A = \int_{a}^{b} [f(x) - g(x)]\, dx.$$

Either curve may be above or below the x-axis, or have portions above or below the x-axis, but it is absolutely necessary to have

$$g(x) \leq f(x) \quad \text{for} \quad a \leq x \leq b.$$

With this condition satisfied, be sure to subtract the actual expression for the lower curve from that of the upper curve.

Example 2. Find the area bounded by

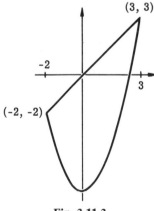

$$y = x^2 - 6 \quad \text{and} \quad y = x.$$

Solution. The curves intersect when $x = -2$ and when $x = 3$, and for $-2 \leq x \leq 3$ the second graph is above the first (Fig. 3-11.3). Hence, in (2) set $f(x) = x$ and $g(x) = x^2 - 6$:

$$A = \int_{-2}^{3} (x - x^2 + 6)\, dx = \frac{125}{6}.$$

Sometimes the function $l(x)$ in (1) changes form someplace between a and b. Two ways of handling such a situation are illustrated in the next example.

Example 3. Find the area bounded by the graphs

Fig. 3-11.3   of

$$y^2 = 2x \quad \text{and} \quad y = x - 4.$$

Solution 1. By simultaneous solution of these equations, the graphs intersect at

(2, −2)   and   (8, 4).

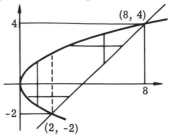

Figure 3-11.4 shows, however, that the x-extent is not $2 \leq x \leq 8$ but is

$$0 \leq x \leq 8.$$

Note also that if $0 \leq x \leq 2$, then a vertical line segment across the region has both upper and lower ends on the first graph, whereas if $2 \leq x \leq 8$, the upper end is on the first graph but the lower end is on the second graph. The first equation solved for y is

Fig. 3-11.4

$$y = \pm\sqrt{2x}.$$

Thus, the function $l(x)$ in (1) must be expressed in two parts as

$$l(x) = \begin{cases} \sqrt{2x} - (-\sqrt{2x}) = 2\sqrt{2x} \text{ if } 0 \leq x \leq 2, \\ \sqrt{2x} - (x - 4) = \sqrt{2x} - x + 4 \text{ if } 2 \leq x \leq 8. \end{cases}$$

Thus,

$$A = \int_0^2 2\sqrt{2x}\, dx + \int_2^8 (\sqrt{2x} - x + 4)\, dx$$

$$= 2\sqrt{2} \int_0^2 x^{1/2}\, dx + \int_2^8 (\sqrt{2}\, x^{1/2} - x + 4)\, dx$$

$$= \frac{4}{3}\sqrt{2}\, x^{3/2}\Big]_0^2 + \left[\frac{2}{3}\sqrt{2}\, x^{3/2} - \frac{1}{2}x^2 + 4x\right]_2^8 = \text{etc.}$$

A lot of arithmetic is necessary to evaluate this to find $A = 18$.

Solution 2. All developments of definite integrals have been for functions $y = f(x)$ of the independent variable x and limits $x = a$ and $x = b$. The roles of x and y may be interchanged throughout and

$$\int_a^b f(y)\, dy$$

could have been developed entirely in terms of y as the independent variable.

Thus, in analogy to (2), a region having y-extent $a \leq y \leq b$, bounded on the right (instead of above) by $x = f(y)$ and on the left (instead of below) by $x = g(y)$, has area A, where

$$A = \int_a^b [f(y) - g(y)]\, dy.$$

In the present example, the y-extent is $-2 \leq y \leq 4$ throughout, while the entire right boundary is $x = f(y) = y + 4$ and the entire left boundary is $x = g(y) = \frac{1}{2}y^2$. Thus,

$$A = \int_{-2}^4 [y + 4 - \tfrac{1}{2}y^2]\, dy = 18$$

(which need not even be worked out since the same integral appears in Example 1 with x in place of y throughout).

From the above discussion, it should be seen that:

The area of the portion (or portions) of the plane that lies between continuous graphs $y = f(x)$ and $y = g(x)$ and between lines $x = a$ and $x = b$ with $a < b$ is

$$area = \int_a^b |f(x) - g(x)|\ dx.$$

Such an area, therefore, is positive regardless of its position relative to the axes—even if all of it lies below the x-axis. In any specific case the integral is evaluated by dividing the interval $a \leq x \leq b$ into subintervals on which $f(x) \geq g(x)$ and subintervals on which $f(x) \leq g(x)$.

Example 4. The area between the graphs of $y = \cos x$, $y = -1 + \sin x$, the y-axis, and the line $y = 3\pi/2$ (Fig. 3-11.5) is

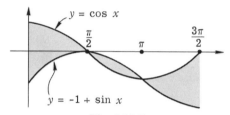

Fig. 3-11.5

$$area = \int_0^{3\pi/2} |\cos x - (-1 + \sin x)|dx$$

$$= \int_0^{\pi/2} (\cos x + 1 - \sin x)\ dx + \int_{\pi/2}^{\pi} (-1 + \sin x - \cos)\ dx$$

$$+ \int_{\pi}^{3\pi/2} (\cos x + 1 - \sin x)\ dx = 2 + \frac{\pi}{2}.$$

Problem 1. Find the area of the region bounded by the graphs of:

a. $y = x^2$, $y = -x$.
b. $y = x^2$, $y = -x + 2$.
c. $y = x^2 - 6$, $y = -x$.
d. $y = (x - 1)^2$, $y = x + 1$.
e. $y^2 = 4x$, $x^2 = 4y$.
f. $y^2 = 4x$, $2x - y = 4$.
g. $y^2 = 4x$, $x = 12 + 2y - y^2$.
h. $y = \sin x$, $y = \cos x$, $-\frac{3}{4}\pi \leq x \leq \pi/4$.
i. $y = \sin x$, $y = x$, $0 \leq x \leq \pi$.
j. $y = 3 \sin 2x$, $y = \sin x$, $0 \leq x \leq \pi/4$.
k. $x = \sin y$, $x = \cos y$, $0 \leq y \leq \pi/4$.
l. $y = \cos 2x$, $y = -2 \sin^2 x$, $-\pi \leq x \leq \pi$.

m. $y = x^2 - 4, \quad y = 0.$
n. $y = x^4 - 8x^2, \quad y = -16.$

Problem 2. Each of the following pairs of graphs bound more than one region; find the areas of the regions:

a. $y = x^3, \quad y = x.$

b. $y = x^3, \quad y = x^2 + 4x - 4.$

c. $y = (x - 2)^3, \quad 7x - y = 8.$

d. $y = x^3 - 3x^2 + 2x - 4, \quad y = -4.$

e. $y = x(x - 1)(x - 2), \quad y = x(x - 1)(x - 2)(x - 3).$

3-12.   Review and Preview

There are two central themes in calculus: differentiation,

$$D_x f(x) = \lim_{\Delta x \to 0} \frac{\Delta f(x)}{\Delta x} = \lim_{\Delta x \to 0} \frac{f(x + \Delta x) - f(x)}{\Delta x},$$

and integration,

$$\int_a^b f(x)\, dx = \lim_{n \to \infty} \sum_{k=1}^n f(x_k)\, \Delta x, \quad \text{where} \quad \Delta x = \frac{b - a}{n}, \quad x_k = a + k\, \Delta x.$$

All other topics in this book are preliminary to these, depend on them, or are applications of one or both. Moreover, differentiation and integration are themselves related by

$$\int_a^b f(x)\, dx = F(x) \Big]_a^b, \quad \text{where} \quad D_x F(x) = f(x), \quad \text{so} \quad F(x) = \int f(x)\, dx,$$

as stated by the Fundamental Theorem of Calculus.

These first three chapters should be considered as a survey of the bare essentials of vectors, analytic geometry, and differential and integral calculus—a sort of inspection tour to get the lay of the land. A more thorough study of each phase will now be started, as the next four chapter headings show. On this second trip, the whole organization and its interrelations should be kept in mind; for example, the possibility of each new derivative formula reappearing later on as an integral formula should be an incentive to master and retain whatever is presented. Also, each new fact should not be memorized as an isolated item but should be mentally catalogued relative to the whole scheme.

The second trip, like the first, is concerned mainly with plane analytic geometry and functions of a single independent variable. After this is completed with Chapter 9, then a third trip is made, this time bringing in the third dimension, for solid analytic geometry, and functions of more than one independent variable. Even three times over the same terrain leaves gaps, a few of which are filled in the later chapters by topics whose utility has assured them a permanent place in a first course on calculus.

The following set of problems serves as a review of the first three chapters.

Anyone who can work these problems without looking back for a formula or idea should be ready to proceed in the book.

Problem 1. a. Show that if vectors

$$\vec{v}_1 = \overrightarrow{P_0 P_1}, \ \vec{v}_2 = \overrightarrow{P_1 P_2}, \ \cdots, \ \vec{v}_n = \overrightarrow{P_{n-1} P_n}$$

are such that $\vec{v}_1 + \vec{v}_2 + \cdots + \vec{v}_n = \vec{0}$, then $P_n = P_0$.

b. Given $\vec{u}_1 = \vec{i} + 4\vec{j}, \ \vec{u}_2 = \vec{i} - 7\vec{j}, \ \vec{v}_1 = 4\vec{i} + \vec{j}, \ \vec{v}_2 = 2\vec{i} + 3\vec{j}$, show that $\vec{u}_1 + \vec{u}_2$ is perpendicular to $\vec{v}_1 + \vec{v}_2$.

c. Find the coordinate of the midpoint of $P_1(-2, 5)$, $P_2(4, -1)$ by using the vector $\vec{u} = \overrightarrow{OP_1} + \frac{1}{2}\overrightarrow{P_1 P_2}$ and again by using the vector $\vec{v} = \overrightarrow{OP_2} + \frac{1}{2}\overrightarrow{P_2 P_1}$.

d. Find the coordinate of the point one third of the way from $P_1(-2, 5)$ to $P_2(4, -1)$ by using the vector $\vec{u} = \overrightarrow{OP_1} + \frac{1}{3}\overrightarrow{P_1 P_2}$.

e. Solve $3\vec{i} + 4\vec{j} + \vec{x} = 7\vec{i} - \vec{j}$ both algebraically and geometrically.

f. Given $\vec{u} = \vec{i} \cos \alpha + \vec{j} \sin \alpha$ and $\vec{v} = \vec{i} \cos \beta + \vec{j} \sin \beta$, show that

$$\vec{u} \cdot \vec{v} = \cos(\alpha - \beta).$$

Problem 2. On a horizontal c-axis and vertical f-axis, find the equation of the line passing through the points $(0, 32)$ and $(100, 212)$. Note that the resulting equation is the centigrade-Fahrenheit conversion law.

Problem 3. Find the equation of the line which:

a. Passes through $(4, -3)$ with slope 2.

b. Passes through $(3, -2)$ and $(4, 5)$.

c. Is the perpendicular bisector of the segment joining $(-1, 3)$ and $(5, 6)$.

Problem 4. With θ a constant angle and p a constant, find the value of k if the vector $k(\vec{i} \cos \theta + \vec{j} \sin \theta)$ with initial end at the origin has terminal end on the line $x \cos \theta + y \sin \theta + p = 0$.

Problem 5. Given the function $f(x) = 3 + x - x^2$:

a. Find $f(0)$, $f(3)$, $f(-3)$, and $-f(3)$.

b. Find $10[f(3.1) - f(3)]$.

c. Without using derivative formulas, find $D_x f(x)$.

Problem 6. Use derivative formulas to find:

a. $D_x y$ if $y = x\sqrt{x^2 + 1}$.

b. $D_x y$ if $y = x \sin^2 x$.

c. $\dfrac{dy}{dx}$ if $x^2 + 2xy + 3y^2 = 16$.

d. $\dfrac{dy}{dx}$ if $y = \cos u$ and $u = x^2$.

e. $\dfrac{ds}{dt}$ if $s = \sin h^2 + 2 \cos h$ and $h = 3 - t^2$.

f. $D_t \vec{u}$ if $\vec{u} = \vec{i}t \sin t + \vec{j} \cos t$.

Problem 7. Find the equation of the tangent to the graph of:

a. $y = \dfrac{x+1}{x-1}$ at the point on the graph with $x = 3$.

b. $x^2 - 3xy + y^2 = 5$ at the point $(4, 1)$.

Problem 8. A particle follows the law $\vec{u} = \vec{F}(t) = 2t\vec{i} + (t^2 - 1)\vec{j}$. Sketch the path together with the velocity vectors at the times $t = 0, 1, 2$, and 3.

Problem 9. Let $y = f(t) = t^2$ be a function of t and let a and x be constants. By using summation and limit formulas, show that

$$\lim_{n \to \infty} \sum_{k=1}^{n} f\left(a + k\frac{x-a}{n}\right) \frac{x-a}{n} = \frac{x^3 - a^3}{3}.$$

Now let x be a variable and show that

$$D_x\left(\frac{x^3 - a^3}{3}\right) = f(x).$$

Interpret the above results in terms of integrals.

Problem 10. A tank is the frustum of a right circular cone with radius of lower base 2 ft, radius of upper base 5 ft, and altitude 6 ft. The tank has oil (weight 50 lb/ft^3) 4 ft deep in the tank. Find the work in pumping the oil to a level 7 ft above the top of the tank.

Problem 11. Find the indefinite integrals:

a. $\displaystyle\int \left(x + 1 + \frac{1}{x^2}\right) dx.$

c. $\displaystyle\int x^2 \sin x^3 \, dx.$

b. $\displaystyle\int (x + \sin x) \, dx.$

d. $\displaystyle\int t\sqrt{1 + t^2} \, dt.$

Problem 12. Solve the differential equations:

a. $yD_x y = x^2 + 2$.

c. $(x + 3)\, dx + x^3 \, dy = 0$.

b. $x^2 y \sin y^2 \, dy = dx$.

d. $D_x y = 1$.

Problem 13. Prove the following theorem:

Second Law of the Mean for Integrals. If $f(x)$ and $g(x)$ are continuous functions and $g(x) > 0$ on $a \le x \le b$, then there is a number ξ such that $a < \xi < b$ and

$$\int_a^b f(x)g(x) \, dx = f(\xi) \int_a^b g(x) \, dx.$$

[Note: The First Law of the Mean is the special case in which $g(x) = 1$ for $a \le x \le b$. The formula is then

$$\int_a^b f(x) \, dx = f(\xi)(b - a).]$$

Chapter 4

Plane Analytic Geometry

4-1. Graphs of Equations

Analytic geometry combines algebra and geometry. Thus

(1)
$$y = (x - 1)^3$$

is an algebraic equation, but its graph is a geometric object. The elementary method of obtaining a graph is first to form a table of related values of x and y:

x	-2	-1	0	1	2	3	4
y	-27	-8	-1	0	1	8	27

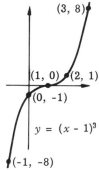

(3, 8)

(1, 0) (2, 1)

(0, -1)

$y = (x - 1)^3$

(-1, -8)

Fig. 4-1.1

Then plot the points with these coordinates and join the points by a smooth curve. This method works fairly well with simple equations, but more complicated ones, such as

(2)
$$y^2(1 - x^2) = 1,$$

are better analyzed according to the following suggestions about symmetry, extent, and asymptotes.

For general discussions, an equation in x and y will be written as

(3)
$$F(x, y) = 0.$$

For example, (1) written as $y - (x - 1)^3 = 0$ and (2) as $y^2(1 - x^2) - 1 = 0$ are in this form. By the graph (or curve) of (3) is meant the collection of points $P(x, y)$ whose coordinates satisfy (2). Thus,

(i) Every point whose coordinates satisfy (2) is on the graph, and
(ii) Every point on the graph has coordinates satisfying (2).

Symmetry. Two points P and Q are said to be **symmetric to a line** l if l is the perpendicular bisector of the segment PQ. Thus, (x, y) and $(x, -y)$ are symmetric to the x-axis, while (x, y) and $(-x, y)$ are symmetric to the y-axis. Also, P and Q are **symmetric to a third point** 0, if 0 is the midpoint of segment PQ. Hence, (x, y) and $(-x, -y)$ are symmetric to the origin.

134

A graph is symmetric to a line *l* (or point 0) if the graph can be divided into two halves so that every point *P* on either half has a point *Q* on the other half, with *P* and *Q* symmetric to *l* (or 0). Thus, the graph of (3) is symmetric to:

1. The *x*-axis if $F(x, -y) = \pm F(x, y)$, since if (x, y) is on the graph then $F(x, y) = 0$ by (ii) and then $F(x, -y) = \pm F(x, y) = 0$ so $(x, -y)$ is on the graph by (i).
2. The *y*-axis if $F(-x, y) = \pm F(x, y)$.
3. The origin if $F(-x, -y) = \pm F(x, y)$.

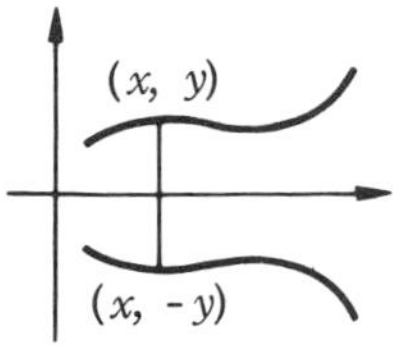

Fig. 4-1.2

Example 1. For $F(x, y) = 25x^2 - 16y^2 - 400$, then

$$F(x, -y) = 25x^2 - 16(-y)^2 - 400 = 25x^2 - 16y^2 - 400 = F(x, y).$$

Thus, the graph of $25x^2 - 16y^2 - 400 = 0$; that is, the graph of

(4) $$\frac{x^2}{16} - \frac{y^2}{25} = 1$$

is symmetric to the *x*-axis. Also, $F(-x, y) = F(x, y)$ and $F(-x, -y) = F(x, y)$, so the graph is symmetric to the *y*-axis and the origin.

Example 2. For $F(x, y) = xy - 1$, then

$$F(x, -y) = x(-y) - 1 = -xy - 1 \neq \pm(xy - 1) = \pm F(x, y),$$

so the curve of $xy - 1 = 0$ is not symmetric to the *x*-axis. Also,

$$F(-x, y) \neq \pm F(x, y), \quad \text{but} \quad F(-x, -y) \equiv F(x, y),$$

so the curve is not symmetric to the *y*-axis but is symmetric to the origin.

Example 3. Since $\cos(-x) = \cos x$, the graph of

$$y = \cos x$$

is symmetric to the *y*-axis. Since $\sin(-x) = -\sin x$, then

$$y = \sin x$$

has its graph symmetric to the origin.

Extent. Negative numbers may not appear under square roots (or even roots), since only points with real coordinates are plotted. Also, only non-zero denominators may occur. The extent, or limitations on the ranges of the variables, in

$$F(x, y) = 0$$

may be determined by first solving for *y* to find the extent of *x* and then solving for *x* to find the extent of *y*.

Example 4. Equation (4) solved first for *y* and then *x* is

$$y = \pm\tfrac{5}{4}\sqrt{x^2 - 16} \quad \text{and} \quad x = \pm\tfrac{4}{5}\sqrt{25 + y^2}.$$

Thus, the graph of (4) must have either $x \geq 4$ or else $x \leq -4$, but (from the second equation) *y* has no limitation.

Known properties of functions also yield information about extent. For example, since $-1 \leq \sin A \leq 1$, then for

$$y = 2 \sin \left(\tfrac{1}{2}x\right)$$

it follows that $-2 \leq y \leq 2$.

Asymptotes. Upon solving $xy - y - 1 = 0$ for y, the result is

$$y = \frac{1}{x - 1}.$$

Hence, for this graph, $x \neq 1$ is the only limitation on the x-extent. However, if x is a little more than 1, then y is a large positive number and may be made as large as desired by choosing x close enough to 1. If x is less than 1, then y is negative with magnitude increasing without bound as x is given values less than 1 but closer and closer to 1. These verbal descriptions are symbolized by

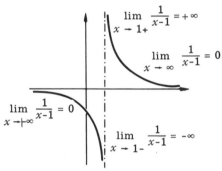

Fig. 4-1.3

$$\lim_{x \to 1+} \frac{1}{x - 1} = +\infty \quad \text{and} \quad \lim_{x \to 1-} \frac{1}{x - 1} = -\infty.$$

Also, the graph of $xy - y - 1 = 0$ is said to have the line $x = 1$ as a **vertical asymptote** in both the positive and negative y-directions.

If $y = f(x)$ is a function and c is a constant, and if for each number $G > 0$, no matter how great, there is a number $\delta > 0$ such that

$$\text{whenever} \quad c < x < c + \delta \quad \text{it follows that} \quad f(x) > G,$$

then it is customary to use the symbolism

$$\lim_{x \to c+} f(x) = \infty.$$

Also, under these circumstances the curve $y = f(x)$ is said to have the line $x = c$ as a **vertical asymptote** in the positive direction.

Similar general definitions are given for

$$\lim_{x \to c-} f(x) = \infty, \quad \lim_{x \to c+} f(x) = -\infty, \quad \text{and} \quad \lim_{x \to c-} f(x) = -\infty.$$

Moreover, the roles of x and y may be interchanged to obtain definitions of horizontal asymptotes.

The solution of $xy - y - 1 = 0$ for x is

$$x = \frac{y+1}{y} = 1 + \frac{1}{y} \quad \text{and} \quad \lim_{y \to 0\pm} x = \pm\infty.$$

Hence, the line $y = 0$ (that is, the x-axis) is a horizontal asymptote in both directions for the curve.

Previous use was made of

$$\lim_{n \to \infty} f(n) \quad \text{and} \quad \lim_{n \to -\infty} f(n),$$

when $f(n)$ was a function of n. These will now be extended to $f(x)$ as a function of the continuous variable x and to $f(y)$ as a function of y.

The same asymptotes $x = 1$ and $y = 0$ for the curve $xy - y - 1 = 0$ may be obtained by solving for x:

$$x = \frac{y+1}{y} = 1 + \frac{1}{y} \quad \text{and taking} \quad \lim_{y \to \pm\infty} \left(1 + \frac{1}{y}\right) = 1$$

or by solving for y:

$$y = \frac{1}{x-1} \quad \text{and taking} \quad \lim_{x \to \pm\infty} \left(\frac{1}{x-1}\right) = 0.$$

If $F(x, y) = 0$ has a solution for y as $y = f(x)$, where

$$\lim_{x \to \pm\infty} f(x) = c,$$

then $y = c$ is a horizontal asymptote of the curve. If $x = g(y)$ is the solution for x and

$$\lim_{y \to \pm\infty} g(y) = d,$$

then $x = d$ is a vertical asymptote of the curve.

After the discussion of this section, the attack on drawing a curve of an equation $F(x, y) = 0$ should be:

1. Examine for possible symmetry. If there is symmetry to either axis or the origin, then only half of the curve needs further analysis, only one fourth if there is symmetry to both axes.
2. Solve for x in terms of y and for y in terms of x.
   a. Examine each equation for extent.
   b. Take limits to determine possible horizontal or vertical asymptotes.
3. Find a sufficient number of specific points on the curve to place the curve relative to the axes. This may require only one or two points if 1 and 2 have given enough information.
4. Only after 1, 2, and 3 have been completed, sketch the curve.

Example 5. Sketch the graph of $y^2(1 - x^2) = 1$.

Solution 1.

$$(-y)^2(1 - x^2) = y^2(1 - x^2) \quad \text{and} \quad y^2[1 - (-x)^2] = y^2(1 - x^2),$$

so the graph is symmetric to both axes (and hence also to the origin). Hence, only one fourth of the curve needs further analysis. This further analysis is made for the first quadrant.

Solution 2a. The positive solution for y is

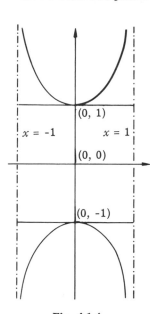

Fig. 4-1.4

(5)
$$y = \frac{1}{\sqrt{1 - x^2}},$$

showing that in the first quadrant

$$0 \le x < 1 \quad \text{is the } x\text{-extent.}$$

Thus, the first quadrant portion of the curve is confined to the vertical strip between the lines $x = 0$ (that is, the y-axis) and $x = 1$.

The solution for positive x is

(6)
$$x = \frac{\sqrt{y^2 - 1}}{y}, \quad \text{so} \quad y \ge 1,$$

showing that the first quadrant portion of the curve is above the line $y = 1$.

Solution 2b. Since

$$\lim_{x \to 1-} \frac{1}{\sqrt{1 - x^2}} = \infty,$$

the line $x = 1$ is a vertical asymptote. From the y in the denominator of (6), it might be thought that

$$\lim_{y \to 0+} \frac{\sqrt{y^2 - 1}}{y} \quad \text{would be} \quad +\infty$$

and lead to $y = 0$ being an asymptote, *but this is not so* since y cannot approach 0 because of the y-extent $y \ge 1$.

Solution 3. The positive y-intercept (obtained by setting $x = 0$ in $y^2(1 - x^2) = 1$) is the point $(0, 1)$. From this point and information in 2.a and 2.b the first quadrant portion is sketched, then the other quadrant portions filled in by the symmetry discovered in 1. Also, by symmetry: x-extent is $-1 < x < 1$, y-extent is either $y \ge 1$ or else $y \le -1$, asymptotes $x = \pm 1$.

The fact that the curve has a horizontal tangent at $(1, 0)$ may be checked by using (5) and the derivative

$$D_x y = D_x \frac{1}{\sqrt{1 - x^2}} = D_x(1 - x^2)^{-1/2} = -\frac{1}{2}(1 - x^2)^{-3/2} D_x(1 - x^2)$$

$$= +\frac{1}{2} \frac{1}{\sqrt{(1 - x^2)^3}} 2x,$$

which has value 0 when $x = 0$.

Problem 1. Without drawing the curve, check whether the curve whose equation is given is symmetric to either axis or to the origin:

a. $x^2y - 4 = 0$.   c. $x^2y^2 - 4 = 0$.   e. $xy - \sin x = 0$.

b. $xy^2 - 4 = 0$.   d. $xy - 4 = 0$.   f. $xy - \cos x = 0$.

Problem 2. Without drawing the curve, determine the x- and y-extents:

a. $x^2 + 4y^2 = 16$.   c. $(x - 2)^2 + 4y^2 = 16$.   e. $y = -3 \sin \dfrac{x}{2}$.

b. $x^2 - 4y^2 = 16$.   d. $(x - 2)^2 - 4y^2 = 16$.   f. $y^2 = -(x - 2)(x + 4)$.

Problem 3. Without drawing the curve, determine its vertical and horizontal asymptotes:

a. $x(y - 1) = 2$.   c. $(x^2 + 1)(y - 1) = 2$.   e. $xy + 2x - 3y = 0$.

b. $(x + 1)(y - 1) = 2$.   d. $(x + 1)(y^2 - 1) = 2$.   f. $xy = x + y$.

Problem 4. Discuss and sketch the graph of:

a. $y(x^2 - 1) = 1$.   c. $y(x^2 + 1) = 1$.   e. $x^2(1 - y^2) = 1$.

b. $x(y^2 - 4) = 1$.   d. $x^4 + y^4 = 1$.   f. $y^2(1 - x^2) = 1$.

4-2. Composition of Graphs

In Fig. 4-2.1 the dashed line and dotted curve are the graphs of

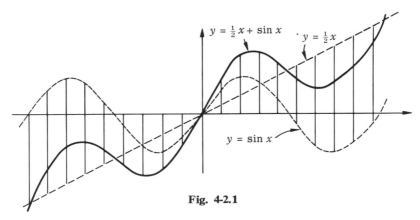

Fig. 4-2.1

(1) $$y = \tfrac{1}{2}x \quad \text{and} \quad y = \sin x$$

(with x in radians for the sine curve) and the composition of these is the solid curve for

(2) $$y = \tfrac{1}{2}x + \sin x.$$

A way of thinking of such a composition* is to visualize the graphs of the equations in (1) as being traced by the terminal ends of the variable vectors

*Not to be confused with the composition of functions as defined in Sec. 2-9.

$$\vec{u} = \vec{i}x + \vec{j}\tfrac{1}{2}x \quad \text{and} \quad \vec{v} = \vec{i}x + \vec{j}\sin x$$

and at each position keep the common x-component but add the y-components to obtain the tracing vector

$$\vec{w} = \vec{i}x + \vec{j}\tfrac{1}{2}x + \vec{j}\sin x$$

of (2). A draftsman's compasses are convenient for translating distances of the sine curve above or below the x-axis to distances above or below the line $y = \tfrac{1}{2}x$.

Notice $D_x \sin x = \cos x = 0$ if $x = \pm\pi/2,\ \pm3\pi/2$, etc., whereas

$$D_x(\tfrac{1}{2}x + \sin x) = \tfrac{1}{2} + \cos x = 0 \quad \text{if} \quad \cos x = -\tfrac{1}{2},$$

$$\text{so} \quad x = \pm\frac{2\pi}{3},\ \pm\frac{8\pi}{3},\ \text{etc.}$$

Thus, the relative high and low points of the curve (2) do not occur directly above or below those of the curve $y = \sin x$.

Example 1. Sketch the graph of $xy - x^2 = 1$.

Solution. This equation may be written

$$y = \frac{x^2 + 1}{x} = x + \frac{1}{x}$$

and the curve (Fig. 4-2.2) drawn as the composition of the simpler graphs of

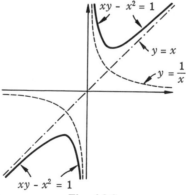

Fig. 4-2.2

$$y = x \quad \text{and} \quad y = \frac{1}{x}.$$

DEFINITION. *If an equation $F(x, y) = 0$ can be solved for y in the form*

$$(3) \qquad y = mx + b + f(x), \quad \text{where} \quad \lim_{x \to \pm\infty} f(x) = 0$$

with m and b constants, then the graph of $F(x, y) = 0$ is said to have the line $y = mx + b$ as an asymptote.

By considering the graph of $y = mx + b + f(x)$ as the composition of the graphs of

$$y = mx + b \quad \text{and} \quad y = f(x), \quad \text{where} \quad \lim_{x \to \pm\infty} f(x) = 0,$$

the remote portions of the graph of $F(x, y) = 0$ approach the line

$$y = mx + b.$$

Example 2. Show that the curve $x^2 - xy + x + y = 5$ has two asymptotes.

Solution. Write the equation as $y(-x + 1) = -x^2 - x + 5$, change all signs, and then divide by $x - 1$:

$$y = \frac{x^2 + x - 5}{x - 1}, \qquad \begin{array}{r} x + 2 \\ x - 1 \overline{)x^2 + x - 5} \\ \underline{x^2 - x} \\ 2x \\ \underline{2x - 2} \\ -3. \end{array}$$

By dividing $x^2 + x - 5$ by $x - 1$, as shown, then

$$y = x + 2 - \frac{3}{x - 1}, \quad \text{where} \quad \lim_{x \to \pm\infty} \frac{-3}{x - 1} = 0.$$

This is in the form (3) with $m = 1$ and $b = 2$, so the line $y = x + 2$ is an asymptote. The curve (Fig. 4-2.3) is the composition of the curves

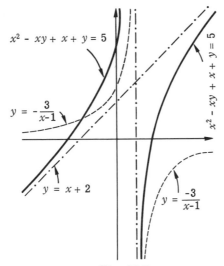

$x^2 - xy + x + y = 5$

$y = -\dfrac{3}{x-1}$

$y = x + 2$

$y = \dfrac{-3}{x-1}$

$x^2 - xy + x + y = 5$

Fig. 4-2.3

$$y = x + 2 \quad \text{and} \quad y = \frac{-3}{x - 1}.$$

Also $\lim_{x \to 1\pm} \{x + 2 - [3/(x - 1)]\} = \mp\infty$ so the line $x = 1$ is also an asymptote.

The results of the following example will be used later on, so this example should be studied carefully.

Example 3. With $a > 0$ and $b > 0$ constants, discuss the graph of

(4)
$$\frac{x^2}{a^2} - \frac{y^2}{b^2} = 1.$$

Solution. Since $(-x)^2 = x^2$ and $(-y)^2 = y^2$, the curve is symmetric to both axes, so only the first quadrant portion is studied carefully. The equation is

$$-\frac{y^2}{b^2} = -\frac{x^2}{a^2} + 1, \quad \frac{y^2}{b^2} = \frac{x^2 - a^2}{a^2},$$

so the positive solution for y is

(5)
$$y = \frac{b}{a}\sqrt{x^2 - a^2},$$

showing first quadrant x-extent $x \geq a$. The positive x-solution

$$x = \frac{a}{b}\sqrt{y^2 + a^2}$$

shows there is no limitation on the y-extent. There are no horizontal or vertical asymptotes, but there are oblique asymptotes, as will now be shown. Equation (5) will be put in form (3) by adding and subtracting $(b/a)x$ to the right side of (5):

$$y = \frac{b}{a}x + \frac{b}{a}(-x + \sqrt{x^2 - a^2}),$$

and it remains to show that $\lim_{x \to \infty} f(x) = 0$, where $f(x) = (b/a)(-x + \sqrt{x^2 - a^2})$. To do so, rationalize the numerator:

$$f(x) = \frac{b}{a}(-x + \sqrt{x^2 - a^2})\frac{x + \sqrt{x^2 - a^2}}{x + \sqrt{x^2 - a^2}}$$

$$= \frac{b}{a}\frac{-x^2 + (x^2 - a^2)}{x + \sqrt{x^2 - a^2}} = \frac{-ab}{x + \sqrt{x^2 - a^2}},$$

$$\lim_{x \to \infty} f(x) = \lim_{x \to \infty} \frac{-ab}{x + \sqrt{x^2 - a^2}} = 0.$$

Thus, the graph of (4) has the line $y = (b/a)x$ as an asymptote in the first quadrant. By symmetry, the lines

$$y = \pm \frac{b}{a}x$$

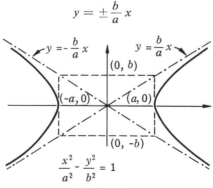

$$\frac{x^2}{a^2} - \frac{y^2}{b^2} = 1$$

Fig. 4-2.4

are asymptotes in both directions, as shown in Fig. 4-2.4. Also, the overall x-extent is either $x \geq a$ or else $x \leq -a$.

Problem 1. Use composition of graphs to sketch:

a. $y = \frac{1}{2}x + \cos x$.

b. $y = \sin x + \cos x$.

c. $y = -\frac{1}{2}x + \sin x$.

d. $y = x - 1 + \sin x$.

e. $y = x^2 + \dfrac{1}{x}$.

f. $y = x^2 - \dfrac{1}{x}$.

g. $x = y + \dfrac{1}{y}$.

h. $x = y + \sin y$.

Problem 2. Find the asymptotes and sketch:

a. $x^2 - xy + 2x - y + 2 = 0$.

b. $x^2 - 2xy + 2x + 2 = 0$.

c. $2x^2 + x(y + 1) = 1$.

d. $xy - x \sin x = 1$.

Problem 3. Put each of the following in the form (4), draw the asymptotes, and then sketch the curve:

a. $9x^2 - 4y^2 = 36$.

b. $x^2 - y^2 = 1$.

c. $(2x - 3y)(2x + 3y) = 36$.

d. $4x^2 - 9y^2 = 1$.

Problem 4. First draw the circle whose equation is given and use this to sketch the graph of the next equation:

a. $x^2 + y^2 = 4$, $y = x \pm \sqrt{4 - x^2}$.

b. $x^2 + y^2 = 9$, $y = x + 10 \pm \sqrt{9 - x^2}$.

c. $x^2 + y^2 = 4^2$, $y = 5 \pm \sqrt{4^2 - x^2}$.

d. $x^2 + y^2 = 25$, $y^2 - 4xy + 5x^2 - 25 = 0$.

e. $x^2 + y^2 = 25$, $2x^2 + 2xy + y^2 - 4x - 4y = 21$.

4-3. Equation of a Locus

In some books the words "graph," "curve," and "locus" are used almost interchangeably, but in others the word "locus" is used when a set of points is described initially by some means other than an equation. For example, "the set of points each of which is twice as far from $(-1, 2)$ as from $(3, 5)$" is described as "the locus of points twice as far from $(-1, 2)$ as from $(3, 5)$." A verbal description of a locus may be translated into an equation whose graph is the locus. For the locus just described, let (x, y) be a variable point on the locus. Then the distance requirement is

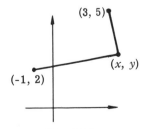

(1)
$$\sqrt{[x - (-1)]^2 + (y - 2)^2}$$
$$= 2\sqrt{(x - 3)^2 + (y - 5)^2},$$

so this is an equation of the locus. It is, however, usually desirable to have an equation without radicals and all x- and y-terms collected. By squaring

Fig. 4-3.1

both sides of (1), the result is

$$x^2 + 2x + 1 + y^2 - 4y + 4 = 4(x^2 - 6x + 9 + y^2 - 10y + 25),$$

and the terms collect into

$$3x^2 + 3y^2 - 26x - 36y + 131 = 0,$$

which is also an equation of the locus. Later on it will be shown that this locus is a circle, but for the time being only equations for loci will be sought.

Example 1. Find an equation of the locus of points equidistant from the point $(-1, 2)$ and the line $x = -2$.

Solution. Let (x, y) be a variable point on the locus. The distance between (x, y) and $(-1, 2)$ is

$$\sqrt{(x + 1)^2 + (y - 2)^2}.$$

The other distance in question is the length of the perpendicular from the point (x, y) to the line $x = -2$. For each value of y, this is the distance between the points (x, y) and $(-2, y)$, so is

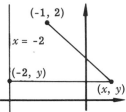

$$\sqrt{(x + 2)^2 + (y - y)^2} = \sqrt{(x + 2)^2} = |x + 2|.$$

Note that the variable x in the point (x, y) must not be confused with the constant x in $x = -2$.

Thus, an equation of the locus is

$$\sqrt{(x + 1)^2 + (y - 2)^2} = |x + 2|,$$

which, by squaring and collecting terms, simplifies to

Fig. 4-3.2

$$y^2 - 4y - 2x + 1 = 0.$$

In finding an equation of a locus, a sequence of steps to follow is:
1. On a coordinate system, plot any constant points or lines occurring in the description.
2. Label some point as (x, y) to represent a typical point of the locus. Whether or not the labeled point (x, y) is actually on the locus is quite immaterial.
3. Express the described conditions by an equation involving x, y, and any constants appearing in step 1.
4. Simplify the resulting equation.

Example 2. A point moves so the line from it to $(2, -1)$ has slope twice the slope of the line from it to $(3, 1)$. Find an equation of the locus of this point and sketch this locus.

Solution. Plot the points $(2, -1)$ and $(3, 1)$. Place a point (x, y) arbitrarily and join this point to $(2, -1)$ and to $(3, 1)$. Then

$$\text{first slope} = \frac{y + 1}{x - 2}, \quad \text{second slope} = \frac{y - 1}{x - 3},$$

so an equation of the locus is

$$\frac{y+1}{x-2} = 2\frac{y-1}{x-3},$$

which algebraically simplifies to

$$xy - 3x - y + 7 = 0.$$

It is easier to graph this equation than to try to visualize the locus from its description. Solve for y:

$$y = \frac{3x-7}{x-1} = 3 - \frac{4}{x-1}$$

and then sketch the graph (Fig. 4-3.3) as the composition of

$$y = 3 \quad \text{and} \quad y = \frac{-4}{x-1}.$$

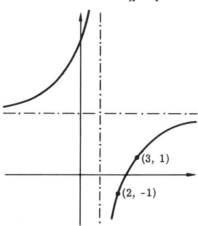

Fig. 4-3.3

Problem 1. Find an equation of the locus of points:

a. Equidistant from $(5, -2)$ and $(3, 4)$.
b. Equidistant from $(4, 4)$ and $(-2, -8)$.
c. Twice as far from $(4, 0)$ as from $(1, 0)$.
d. With distance to $(4, 0)$ two thirds the distance to $(9, 0)$.
e. Equidistant from line $x = 4$ and point $(-4, 0)$.
f. Equidistant from line $y + 3 = 0$ and point $(1, 2)$.
g. Sum of squares of distances from $(2, 0)$ and $(-2, 0)$ is 10.
h. Sum of squares of distances from $(0, 3)$ and $(0, -3)$ is 54.
i. Sum of distances from $(4, 0)$ and $(-4, 0)$ is 10.
j. Sum of distances from $(1, 0)$ and $(-1, 0)$ is $2\sqrt{2}$.

Problem 2. A point moves as described; find an equation of its locus and sketch this locus:

a. From it the lines to $(-2, 3)$ and $(4, 5)$ have equal slopes.
b. Of the lines from it to $(-2, 3)$ and $(4, 5)$, the first has slope twice the slope of the second.
c. It and the points $(-2, 3)$ and $(4, 5)$ form an isosceles triangle.

d. It and the points $(-2, 3)$ and $(4, 5)$ form a right triangle with the right angle at $(4, 5)$.

e. It is at the right angle of a right triangle with the other vertices at $(-2, 0)$ and $(2, 0)$.

f. The vectors from $(-4, 0)$ and $(4, 0)$ to it have scalar product zero.

4-4. Circle

A circle is the locus of points at a given distance from a fixed point. If the distance (radius) is $r > 0$ and the fixed point is (h, k), then an equation of the circle is

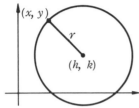

Fig. 4-4.1

$$\sqrt{(x - h)^2 + (y - k)^2} = r; \quad \text{that is,}$$

$$(1) \qquad (x - h)^2 + (y - k)^2 = r^2.$$

Example 1. Show that the graph of

$$(2) \qquad 3x^2 + 3y^2 - 6x + 4y = 5$$

is a circle and find its center and radius.

Solution. To put this equation in the form (1), first divide by 3 and collect x and y terms.

$$(x^2 - 2x \qquad) + \left(y^2 + \frac{4}{3}y \qquad\right) = \frac{5}{3},$$

leaving space to "complete the squares." Since each of the squared terms has coefficient 1, the square is completed by taking half the coefficient of the first-degree term and squaring the result:

$$(x^2 - 2x + 1) + \left(y^2 + \frac{4}{3}y + \left(\frac{2}{3}\right)^2\right) = \frac{5}{3} + 1 + \frac{4}{9},$$

where the terms on the right are added to balance the equation. Now this equation is written as

$$(x - 1)^2 + \left(y + \frac{2}{3}\right)^2 = \frac{28}{9} = \left(\frac{2\sqrt{7}}{3}\right)^2,$$

which is in the form (1) with $h = 1$, $k = -\frac{2}{3}$, and $r = (2\sqrt{7})/3$. Hence, (2) is an equation of the circle with

$$\text{center } \left(1, -\frac{2}{3}\right) \text{ and radius } r = \frac{2\sqrt{7}}{3}.$$

Equation (1) may be written

$$x^2 + y^2 - 2hx - 2ky + h^2 + k^2 - r^2 = 0$$

and then new constants introduced by setting

$$(3) \qquad D = -2h, \quad E = -2k, \quad F = h^2 + k^2 - r^2$$

to obtain the general equation of the circle*

(4) $$x^2 + y^2 + Dx + Ey + F = 0.$$

Three noncollinear points $P(x_1, y_1)$, $Q(x_2, y_2)$, and $R(x_3, y_3)$ determine a circle, as may be seen geometrically by drawing the perpendicular bisectors of PQ and QR and noting that their intersection S (being equidistant from P, Q, and R) is the center. Algebraically, the circle is determined by substituting the coordinates of P, Q, and R into (4) and solving the three simultaneous equations for D, E, and F.

Example 2. Find the equation of the circle passing through the three, points $P(3, -2)$, $Q(-1, -4)$, and $R(2, -5)$.

Solution. Respective substitutions into (4) yield

$$\left.\begin{array}{l} 9 + 4 + 3D - 2E + F = 0 \\ 1 + 16 - D - 4E + F = 0 \\ 4 + 25 + 2D - 5E + F = 0 \end{array}\right\} \quad \text{or} \quad \left\{\begin{array}{l} 3D - 2E + F = -13 \\ -D - 4E + F = -17 \\ 2D - 5E + F = -29. \end{array}\right.$$

Eliminate F by subtracting the middle equation from the top and bottom ones:

$$\left.\begin{array}{l} 4D + 2E = 4 \\ 3D - E = -12 \end{array}\right\} \quad \begin{array}{l} \text{with simultaneous solutions} \\ D = -2, E = 6. \end{array}$$

$D = -2$ and $E = 6$ substituted into any of the original equations yield $F - 5$ and hence the equation

$$x^2 + y^2 - 2x + 6y + 5 = 0.$$

At a point (x_0, y_0) on a circle, the tangent to the circle is perpendicular to the radius at (x_0, y_0). Let the circle have center (h, k), radius r, let (x, y) be a point on the tangent, and note that

$$\vec{u} = (x - h)\vec{i} + (y - k)\vec{j}$$

is the vector from the center to this point. Also,

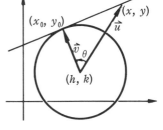

Fig. 4-4.2

$$\vec{v} = (x_0 - h)\vec{i} + (y_0 - k)\vec{j}$$

is the vector radius to the point (x_0, y_0). Hence, $|\vec{v}| = r$ and

(5) $$\vec{u} \cdot \vec{v} = (x - h)(x_0 - h) + (y - k)(y_0 - k),$$

since $\vec{i} \cdot \vec{i} = \vec{j} \cdot \vec{j} = 1$, while $\vec{i} \cdot \vec{j} = \vec{j} \cdot \vec{i} = 0$, But, by definition,

(6) $$\vec{u} \cdot \vec{v} = |\vec{u}||\vec{v}| \cos \theta,$$

*The constants D, E, and F are used since the general second-degree equation will be written $Ax^2 + Bxy + Cy^2 + Dx + Ey + F = 0$.

where θ is the smallest positive angle between $\vec{u}$ and $\vec{v}$. In the right triangle formed by $\vec{u}$, $\vec{v}$, and the tangent

$$\cos\theta = \frac{|\vec{v}|}{|\vec{u}|}, \quad \text{so (6) becomes} \quad \vec{u}\cdot\vec{v} = |\vec{u}||\vec{v}|\frac{|\vec{v}|}{|\vec{u}|} = |\vec{v}|^2 = r^2.$$

Hence, substituting $\vec{u}\cdot\vec{v} = r^2$ into (5) yields

(7) $$(x - h)(x_0 - h) + (y - k)(y_0 - k) = r^2$$

as the *equation of the tangent to the circle, with center (h, k) and radius r, at a point (x_0, y_0) on this circle.*

The tangent equation (7) may be expanded and collected as

$$xx_0 + yy_0 - h(x + x_0) - k(y + y_0) + h^2 + k^2 - r^2 = 0.$$

By making the substitutions (3), the result is that

(8) $$xx_0 + yy_0 + \frac{D}{2}(x + x_0) + \frac{E}{2}(y + y_0) + F = 0$$

is the equation of the tangent to the circle

$$x^2 + y^2 + Dx + Ey + F = 0$$

at the point (x_0, y_0) on this circle.

Example 3. Find the equations of the tangents to the circle

$$x^2 + y^2 - 4x + 6y - 12 = 0$$

at the points of the circle where $x = 5$.

Solution. By substituting $x = 5$, the result is

$$25 + y^2 - 20 + 6y - 12 = 0, \quad \text{so} \quad y^2 + 6y - 7 = 0,$$

which factors into $(y + 7)(y - 1) = 0$. Hence, the desired points are $(5, -7)$ and $(5, 1)$.

Now write the equation of the circle as

$$xx + yy - 2(x + x) + 3(y + y) - 12 = 0.$$

Wherever a pair of x's occurs, replace one of them by 5 and similarly replace one of a pair of y's by -7 to obtain

$$5x - 7y - 2(x + 5) + 3(y - 7) - 12 = 0,$$

which collects as $3x - 4y = 43$ for one of the tangents. The other tangent is $3x + 4y = 19$.

Problem 1. Find the general equation of the circle:

a. Center $(-4, 3)$, radius 5.   c. Center $(-1, -2)$, tangent to x-axis.
b. Center $(1, 5)$, radius 4.   d. Center $(3, -2)$, passing through $(0, 0)$.
     e. Center $(1, -2)$, tangent to line $3x + 4y - 10 = 0$.
     f. Center $(2, 3)$, tangent to line $x - 4y = 3$.

g. Passing through $(0, 4)$, $(-4, 6)$, $(-3, 5)$.
h. Passing through $(5, 2)$, $(4, 0)$, $(-3, -2)$.
i. Center on $x - 2y + 2 = 0$ and passing through $(-1, -3)$, $(-5, 3)$.
j. Center on $x - 2y + 7 = 0$ and passing through $(-2, -1)$, $(-6, 5)$.

Problem 2. Find the center and radius of the circle:
a. $x^2 + y^2 - 2x + 4y + 1 = 0$.   c. $4x^2 + 4y^2 - 4x + 8y = 3$.
b. $x^2 + y^2 + 6x - 8y + 9 = 0$.   d. $9x^2 + 9y^2 = 24y + 20$.
e. Tangent to $4x - 3y = 26$ at $(5, -2)$ and passing through $(-2, -3)$.
f. Tangent to $2x + y = 7$ at $(3, 1)$ and passing through $(6, 4)$.

Problem 3. A point moves as described; show that the locus is a circle:
a. It is always at the right angle of a right triangle, with the other vertices $(-1, 2)$, $(5, 4)$.
b. The vectors from it to $(1, 5)$ and $(3, -3)$ have scalar product zero.
c. The vectors from it to $(2, 3)$ and $(-2, 1)$ have scalar product equal to 4.
d. It is twice as far from $(4, 3)$ as from $(-1, -2)$.
e. The sum of the squares of its distances to $(0, 0)$ and $(3, 4)$ is 2.
f. The sum of the squares of its distances to $(0, 0)$, $(0, 1)$, $(1, 0)$, and $(1, 1)$ is equal to 3.

Problem 4. Show that there is no point (x, y) having:
a. $x^2 + y^2 - 2x - 4y + 6 = 0$.
b. $4x^2 + 4y^2 - 4x + 16y + 21 = 0$.
c. The sum of the squares of its distances to $(0, 0)$, $(0, 1)$, $(1, 0)$, and $(1, 1)$ equal to 1.

Problem 5. First check that the point is on the circle and then find the equation of the tangent to the circle at this point both by using the formulas of this section and by using calculus.
a. $(x - 2)^2 + (y - 1)^2 = 25$, $(6, -2)$.
b. $x^2 + y^2 - 6x - 2y = 15$, $(-1, 4)$.
c. $x^2 + y^2 - 6x + 2y = 15$, $(3, -6)$.
d. $x^2 + y^2 - 6x - 2y = 15$, $(-2, 1)$.

4-5.   Parabola

Let F be a fixed point and l a fixed line. The locus of points equidistant from F and l is, by definition, a **parabola** with **focus** F and **directrix** l. The midpoint V of the segment from F perpendicular to l is equidistant from F and l, so it is a point of the parabola. This point V is called the **vertex** of the parabola. The line through F perpendicular to l is called the **axis** of the parabola. Through F draw the segment $P_1 P_2$ parallel to l, with

$$FP_1 = FP_2 = \text{distance from } F \text{ to } l.$$

Hence, P_1 and P_2 are both equidistant from F and l so P_1

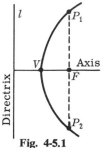

Fig. 4-5.1

and P_2 are also points of the parabola. The segment P_1P_2 is called the **latus rectum** of the parabola.

The equation of a parabola appears in a simple form if the vertex is placed at the origin and the focus is placed on one of the axes. With $V(0, 0)$ and $F(p, 0)$, then the directrix has equation $x = -p$. Hence, a point (x, y) on the locus is equidistant from $F(p, 0)$ and the point $(-p, y)$ on l, so that

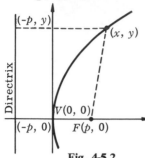

Fig. 4-5.2

$$\sqrt{(x - p)^2 + (y - 0)^2}$$
$$= \sqrt{(x + p)^2 + (y - y)^2}.$$

Upon squaring both sides, the result is

$$x^2 - 2px + p^2 + y^2 = x^2 + 2px + p^2,$$

which simplifies to the standard form

(1) $$y^2 = 4px$$

of the equation of the parabola, with vertex $V(0, 0)$ and focus $F(p, 0)$.

From (1), by taking differentials the result is $2y\,dy = 4p\,dx$, so

$$\frac{dy}{dx} = \frac{2p}{y},$$

which is undefined if $y = 0$, as it is at the vertex $V(0, 0)$. However,

$$\frac{dx}{dy} = \frac{y}{2p} \quad \text{is 0 if } y = 0,$$

showing this parabola to have a vertical tangent at $V(0, 0)$.

Example 1. Find the focus, directrix, ends of the latus rectum, and sketch the parabola

$$y^2 = 6x.$$

Solution. The standard form (1) has a factor 4 on the right, so this specific equation is written as

$$y^2 = 4(\tfrac{6}{4})x = 4(\tfrac{3}{2})x,$$

showing that $p = \tfrac{3}{2}$. Hence, $F(\tfrac{3}{2}, 0)$ is the focus. Also, the distance from the vertex $V(0, 0)$ to the directrix is $\tfrac{3}{2}$, so the directrix has equation $x = -\tfrac{3}{2}$. The distance from the focus to the directrix is thus 3, so the ends P_1 and P_2 of the latus rectum are 3 units from $F(\tfrac{3}{2}, 0)$ on the vertical through F. Hence, the ends of the latus rectum are $P_1(\tfrac{3}{2}, 3)$ and $P_2(\tfrac{3}{2}, -3)$. With V, P_1, and P_2 determined, a portion of the parabola is easily sketched.

The number p may be either positive or negative. If $p > 0$, the parabola is illustrated in Fig. 4–5.2, but the reflection of this curve in the y-axis is obtained if $p < 0$.

Example 2. Work Example 1 with the equation replaced by

$$y^2 + 6x = 0.$$

Solution. First write this equation as

$$y^2 = -6x = 4(-\tfrac{3}{2})x.$$

Hence, $p = -\tfrac{3}{2}$, so that $F(-\tfrac{3}{2}, 0)$, directrix equation $x = \tfrac{3}{2}$, and the two points $P_1(-\tfrac{3}{2}, 3)$, $P_2(-\tfrac{3}{2}, -3)$ are obtained.

An important property of a parabola is revealed by the result of the following example; namely, from a light source at the focus of a parabolic mirror, all rays are reflected parallel to the axis. Conversely, incoming light rays parallel to the axis of a parabolic mirror are all gathered at the focus.

Example 3. On the parabola $y^2 = 4px$, with $p > 0$, take a point (x, y). Let $\vec{T}$ be a tangent vector to the parabola at (x, y), let $\vec{u}$ be the vector from the focus $F(p, 0)$ to (x, y), and draw the unit vector $\vec{i}$ at (x, y) (see Fig. 4-5.3). With α the

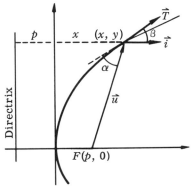

Fig. 4-5.3

angle between $\vec{u}$ and $\vec{T}$, and with β the angle between $\vec{i}$ and $\vec{T}$, check that $\alpha = \beta$.

Solution. First $2y\dfrac{dy}{dx} = 4p$, so that $\dfrac{dy}{dx} = \dfrac{2p}{y}$. Thus,

$$\vec{T} = \vec{i} + \vec{j}\frac{2p}{y}$$

is tangent to the parabola at (x, y). The vector $\vec{u}$ is

$$\vec{u} = \vec{i}(x - p) + \vec{j}y.$$

The angles α and β, therefore, have their cosines given by

$$\cos\alpha = \frac{\vec{u} \cdot \vec{T}}{|\vec{u}||\vec{T}|} = \frac{(x - p) + 2p}{|\vec{u}||\vec{T}|} = \frac{x + p}{|\vec{u}|}\frac{1}{|\vec{T}|} \quad \text{and}$$

$$\cos\beta = \frac{\vec{i} \cdot \vec{T}}{|\vec{i}||\vec{T}|} = \frac{\vec{i} \cdot (\vec{i} + \vec{j}\,2p/y)}{(1)|\vec{T}|} = \frac{1}{|\vec{T}|}.$$

These two cosines may not appear to be equal, but they are. To see this, remember that (x, y) is on the parabola, so its distance to F (namely, $|\vec{u}|$) is equal to its distance $x + p$ to the directrix

$$|u| = x + p \quad \text{and*} \quad \frac{x + p}{|\vec{u}|} = 1.$$

Hence, $\cos \alpha = \cos \beta$ and therefore $\alpha = \beta$, since both angles are less than a right angle.

By interchanging the roles x and y in the derivation of (1), it follows that

(2) $$x^2 = 4py$$

is the standard form of the parabola with vertex $V(0, 0)$, focus $F(0, p)$, directrix $y = -p$, and ends of latus rectum $P_1(2p, p)$, $P_2(-2p, p)$.

Problem 1. Find the focus, directrix and ends of the latus rectum, and sketch parabola:

a. $y^2 = 8x$.   d. $x^2 = -16y$.   g. $9x^2 + 4y = 0$.
b. $y^2 = 5x$.   e. $4x^2 + 5y = 0$.   h. $(x - 1)(x + 1) = y - 1$.
c. $x^2 = -3y$.   f. $2x + 7y^2 = 0$.   i. $24x + 5y^2 = 0$.

Problem 2. Find the equation of the parabola satisfying the conditions:

a. Directrix $x = -5$, focus $(5, 0)$.
b. Directrix $y = 2$, focus $(-2, 0)$.
c. Vertex $(0, 0)$, directrix $y = 6$.
d. Vertex $(0, 0)$, focus $(-5, 0)$.
e. Vertex $(0, 0)$, focus on x-axis, passing through $(5, 1)$.
f. Vertex $(0, 0)$, ends of latus rectum $(-4, 2)$, $(4, 2)$.
g. Vertex $(0, 0)$, directrix perpendicular to y-axis, passing through $(5, -10)$.
h. Symmetric to the x-axis, vertex $(0, 0)$, each end of latus rectum having abscissa -3.

Problem 3. Check that the point is on the parabola, then find the equation of the tangent to the parabola at the point:

a. $y^2 = 3x$, $(3, -3)$.   c. $5y^2 - 2x = 0$, $(10, -2)$.
b. $2x^2 + 4y = 0$, $(4, -8)$.   d. $3x = 4y^2$, $(12, 3)$.

Problem 4. With (x_0, y_0) a point on the parabola $y^2 = 4px$, show that the tangent to the parabola at this point has equation

$$yy_0 = 2p(x + x_0).$$

Problem 5. Show that the tangents to a parabola at the ends of its latus rectum are:

a. Perpendicular to one another.
b. Intersect at the point where the directrix meets the axis.

*Algebraically,

$$|\vec{u}| = \sqrt{(x - p)^2 + y^2} = \sqrt{(x^2 - 2px + p^2) + 4px}$$
$$= \sqrt{x^2 + 2px + p^2} = \sqrt{(x + p)^2} = x + p.$$

Problem 6. Show that the terminal end of the variable vector (having initial end at the origin) traces out a parabola with vertex at the origin:

a. $\vec{F}(x) = \vec{i}x + \vec{j}x^2$.

b. $\vec{F}(x) = \vec{i}x - \vec{j}x^2$.

c. $\vec{F}(t) = \vec{i}\,2t + \vec{j}\,t^2$.

d. $\vec{F}(t) = \vec{i}2t^2 + \vec{j}3t$.

e. $\vec{F}(y) = \vec{i}\,y^2 + \vec{j}\,y$.

f. $\vec{F}(y) = -4\vec{i}\,y^2 + \vec{j}\,y$.

Problem 7. Find the area bounded by a parabola and its latus rectum.

Problem 8. A parabola with vertex at the origin passes through the two points $Q_1(h, b/2)$ and $Q_2(h, -b/2)$. Show that the area bounded by this parabola and the chord $Q_1 Q_2$ is $(\frac{2}{3})hb$.

Problem 9. Obtain the same reflexive property of parabolic mirrors as in Example 3, but use the parabola $x^2 = 4py$, $p > 0$.

4-6. Central Conics

The sum of two sides of a triangle is greater than the third side. Thus, if F_1, F_2, and P are vertices of a triangle (as in Fig. 4–6.1), then

(1) $$PF_1 + PF_2 > F_1F_2$$

and $PF_1 < PF_2 + F_1F_2$ so that also

(2) $$PF_1 - PF_2 < F_1F_2.$$

The following definitions involve fixed points F_1 and F_2 and a moving point P.

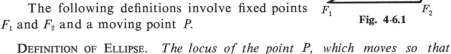

Fig. 4-6.1

DEFINITION OF ELLIPSE. *The locus of the point P, which moves so that the sum of its distances to F_1 and F_2 remains constant, is called an* **ellipse**.

DEFINITION OF HYPERBOLA. *The locus of the point P, which moves so that the difference of its distances to F_1 and F_2 remains constant, is called a* **hyperbola**.

The points F_1 and F_2 are called **foci** for both the ellipse and hyperbola, and the constant distance between them is represented by $2c$, so that $F_1F_2 = 2c$. For the ellipse, the constant sum of the distances from P to F_1 and F_2 is represented by $2a$, that is, $PF_1 + PF_2 = 2a$; so for the ellipse, $a > c$ from inequality (1). For the hyperbola, the constant difference between the longer and shorter distances from P to F_1 and F_2 is also represented by $2a$, that is, $|PF_1 - PF_2| = 2a$; so for the hyperbola, $0 < a < c$ from inequality (2).

With $F_1(-c, 0)$ and $F_2(c, 0)$, the equation of both the ellipse 'and hyperbola is

(3) $$\frac{x^2}{a^2} + \frac{y^2}{a^2 - c^2} = 1, \quad \begin{cases} \textit{where } a > c \textit{ for the ellipse, but} \\ 0 < a < c \textit{ for the hyperbola.} \end{cases}$$

Case 1. Ellipse $(a > c)$. A point $P(x, y)$ is on the ellipse if

1. $\sqrt{(x + c)^2 + y^2} + \sqrt{(x - c)^2 + y^2} = 2a.$

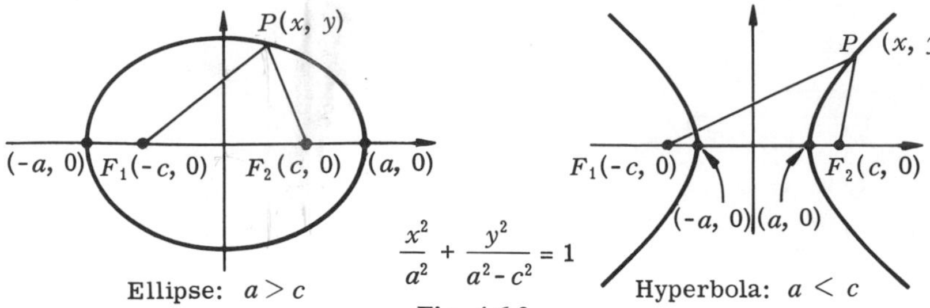

$$\frac{x^2}{a^2} + \frac{y^2}{a^2 - c^2} = 1$$

Ellipse: $a > c$ Hyperbola: $a < c$

Fig. 4-6.2

To obtain an equation without radicals, transpose one radical,

2. $\sqrt{(x + c)^2 + y^2} = 2a - \sqrt{(x - c)^2 + y^2};$

square both sides,

3. $x^2 + 2cx + c^2 + y^2$
                    $= 4a^2 - 4a\sqrt{(x - c)^2 + y^2} + x^2 - 2cx + c^2 + y^2;$

cancel and collect terms with the radical on one side,

4. $a\sqrt{(x - c)^2 + y^2} = a^2 - cx;$

square again,

5. $a^2(x^2 - 2cx + c^2 + y^2) = a^4 - 2a^2cx + c^2x^2;$

cancel again and collect in the form,

6. $(a^2 - c^2)x^2 + a^2y^2 = a^2(a^2 - c^2);$

and finally divide both sides by $a^2(a^2 - c^2)$; and the result is (3).

Case 2. Hyperbola $(0 < a < c)$. A point $P(x, y)$ is on the hyperbola if

1'. $\sqrt{(x + c)^2 + y^2} - \sqrt{(x - c)^2 + y^2} = \pm 2a,$

where the plus or minus sign is used according to which radical is larger. Transpose one of the radicals,

2'. $\sqrt{(x + c)^2 + y^2} = \pm 2a + \sqrt{(x - c)^2 + y^2};$

square both sides,

3'. $x^2 + 2cx + c^2 + y^2$
                    $= 4a^2 \pm 4a\sqrt{(x - c)^2 + y^2} + x^2 - 2cx + c^2 + y^2;$

cancel and collect,

4'. $\pm a\sqrt{(x - c)^2 + y^2} = a^2 - cx;$

square again,

5'. $$a^2(x^2 - 2cx + c^2 + y^2) = a^4 - 2a^2 cx + c^2x^2;$$

which is the same as 5 in Case 1, so there is no need to repeat the above step (6) to obtain (3) in this case also.

Whether $a > c$ or $0 < a < c$, the graph of (1) is symmetric to both axes (and hence also to the origin) and intersects the x-axis at the points $V_1(-a, 0)$ and $V_2(a, 0)$, which are called the **vertices** of the ellipse or hyperbola, as the case may be. Parabolas, ellipses, and hyperbolas are called **conics**, with ellipses and hyperbolas called **central conics** since they have a point of symmetry (naturally thought of as the "center").

Example 1. Find the foci and vertices of the central conics

$$\frac{x^2}{25} + \frac{y^2}{16} = 1 \quad \text{and} \quad \frac{x^2}{16} - \frac{y^2}{9} = 1.$$

Name and sketch each of these conics.

Solution. The first equation has $a^2 = 25$ and $a^2 - c^2 = 16$. Since a is positive, $a = 5$ and $c^2 = 25 - 16 = 9$ and hence $c = 3$. Since $c < a$ in this equation, the graph is an ellipse with foci and vertices

$$F_1(-3, 0), \quad F_2(3, 0), \quad V_1(-5, 0), \quad V_2(5, 0).$$

By setting $x = 0$ in the first equation, the graph intersects the y-axis at the points

$$(0, -4) \quad \text{and} \quad (0, 4).$$

Continuing with the first equation and taking differentials,

$$\frac{2x}{25} dx + \frac{2y}{16} dy = 0 \quad \text{so}$$

$$\frac{dy}{dx} = -\frac{16}{25} \frac{x}{y} \quad \text{and} \quad \frac{dx}{dy} = -\frac{25}{16} \frac{y}{x}.$$

By substituting $x = 0$ and $y = \pm 4$ in dy/dx, the result

$$-\frac{16}{25} \cdot \frac{0}{\pm 4} = 0$$

shows the ellipse has horizontal tangents at the intercepts with the y-axis. Also,

$$\frac{dx}{dy} = -\frac{25}{16} \frac{0}{\pm 5} = 0 \quad \text{at} \quad V_1(-5, 0) \quad \text{and} \quad V_2(5, 0),$$

so at the vertices the tangents are vertical. With this information, the ellipse is easily drawn.

In fitting the second equation into the form (1), the second equation is written (with the + sign between the terms) as

$$\frac{x^2}{16} + \frac{y^2}{(-9)} = 1,$$

showing that $a^2 = 16$ and $a^2 - c^2 = -9$. Thus, $a = 4$ and

$$c^2 = a^2 + 9 = 16 + 9 = 25 \quad \text{and} \quad c = 5.$$

Thus, $0 < a < c$ and the locus is a hyperbola with

$$F_1(-5, 0), \quad F_2(5, 0), \quad V_1(-4, 0), \quad V_2(4, 0).$$

Upon solving the second equation for y and x, the results are

$$y = \pm \frac{3}{4}\sqrt{x^2 - 16} \quad \text{and} \quad x = \pm \frac{4}{3}\sqrt{y^2 + 9},$$

showing x-extent $x \geq 4$ or $x \leq -4$ but no limitation on y-extent. Recall from Example 3, p. 142, the second locus has asymptotes

$$y = \pm \frac{3}{4}x.$$

With this information, the hyperbola is easily drawn.

Let (x_0, y_0) be a fixed point on the conic (3) so the constants x_0 and y_0 are related by

$$(4) \qquad \frac{x_0^2}{a^2} + \frac{y_0^2}{a^2 - c^2} = 1.$$

The equation of the tangent to (3) at (x_0, y_0) is sought. To find it, use (3) and take differentials

$$\frac{2x\,dx}{a^2} + \frac{2y\,dy}{a^2 - c^2} = 0, \quad \text{so} \quad \frac{dy}{dx} = -\frac{a^2 - c^2}{a^2}\frac{x}{y}.$$

Hence, at (x_0, y_0) the slope m and the equation of the tangent are

$$m = -\frac{a^2 - c^2}{a^2}\frac{x_0}{y_0} \quad \text{and} \quad y - y_0 = -\frac{a^2 - c^2}{a^2}\frac{x_0}{y_0}(x - x_0).$$

The equation of the tangent may be written as

$$\frac{yy_0 - y_0^2}{a^2 - c^2} = -\frac{xx_0 - x_0^2}{a^2} \quad \text{and then as}$$

$$\frac{xx_0}{a^2} + \frac{yy_0}{a^2 - c^2} = \frac{x_0^2}{a^2} + \frac{y_0^2}{a^2 - c^2}.$$

Now the right side is equal to 1 by equation (4) and hence, *at (x_0, y_0) on the conic*

$$(5) \qquad \frac{x^2}{a^2} + \frac{y^2}{a^2 - c^2} = 1, \quad \text{the tangent is} \quad \frac{xx_0}{a^2} + \frac{yy_0}{a^2 - c^2} = 1.$$

Example 2. The point $(5, 3)$ is on the conic $x^2 - 2y^2 = 7$, and the equation of the tangent at this point is $5x - 6y = 7$.

By interchanging the roles of x and y, it follows that central conics with foci $F_1(0, -c)$, $F_2(0, c)$ on the y-axis have equations in the form

$$(6) \qquad \frac{y^2}{a^2} + \frac{x^2}{a^2 - c^2} = 1, \quad \begin{cases} \text{where } a > c \text{ for ellipses but} \\ 0 < a < c \text{ for hyperbolas.} \end{cases}$$

Problem 1. Find the vertices, foci, intersections with the axes, possible asymptotes, and sketch the central conics:

a. $\dfrac{x^2}{25} + \dfrac{y^2}{9} = 1.$ e. $\dfrac{x^2}{9} - \dfrac{y^2}{16} = \dfrac{1}{4}.$ i. $x^2 - y^2 = 1.$

b. $\dfrac{y^2}{9} + \dfrac{x^2}{25} = 1.$ f. $\dfrac{x^2}{25} + \dfrac{y^2}{9} = \dfrac{1}{4}.$ j. $4x^2 - y^2 = 2.$

c. $\dfrac{y^2}{9} - \dfrac{x^2}{16} = 1.$ g. $16x^2 + 25y^2 = 400.$ k. $(3x - 4y)(3x + 4y) = 1.$

d. $\dfrac{x^2}{9} - \dfrac{y^2}{16} = 1.$ h. $16x^2 - 25y^2 = 400.$ l. $(3y - 4x)(3y + 4x) = 12^2.$

Problem 2. Find an equation of the central conic with center at the origin which also satisfies:

a. Vertices $(\pm 6, 0)$, foci $(\pm 4, 0)$.   c. Vertices $(0, \pm 3)$, foci $(0, \pm 7)$.
b. Vertices $(\pm 4, 0)$, foci $(\pm 6, 0)$.   d. Vertices $(0, \pm 7)$, foci $(0, \pm 3)$.
   e. Vertices $(\pm 2, 0)$, asymptotes $4y = \pm 3x$.
   f. Vertices $(0, \pm 5)$, asymptotes $3y = \pm 2x$.
   g. Foci $(0, \pm 6)$, intercepts on x-axis $(\pm 3, 0)$.
   h. Vertices $(\pm 5, 0)$, passing through $(4, 1.8)$.
   i. Vertices $(\pm 5, 0)$, passing through $(-10, 4\sqrt{3})$.
   j. Foci $(\pm 10, 0)$, asymptotes $y = \pm 2x$.

Problem 3. Show that the terminal end of the variable vector (with initial end at the origin) traces out a conic.

a. $\vec{F}(t) = \vec{i}\, 5 \cos t + \vec{j}\, 4 \sin t.$ d. $\vec{F}(t) = \vec{i} \sec t + \vec{j} \tan t.$

b. $\vec{F}(t) = \vec{i}\, 4 \sin t + \vec{j}\, 5 \cos t.$ e. $\vec{F}(t) = \vec{i}\, 2 \sec t + \vec{j}\, 3 \tan t.$

c. $\vec{F}(t) = \vec{i} \sin t \cos t + \vec{j} \cos 2t.$ f. $\vec{F}(t) = \vec{i}\, 3 \tan t - \vec{j}\, 2 \sec t.$

Problem 4. A point moves as described; show that the locus is a central conic:

   a. Its distance to the line $x = 8$ is twice its distance to $(2, 0)$.
   b. Its distance to $(8, 0)$ is twice its distance to the line $x = 2$.
   c. Its distance to $(6, 0)$ divided by its distance to the line $3x = 8$ is 1.5.
   d. Its distance to $(0, -4)$ divided by its distance to the line $y = -9$ is $\frac{2}{3}$.
   e. It is on a 9-in. segment $E_1 E_2$ and 5 in. from E_1, where $E_1 E_2$ moves with E_1 always on the x-axis and E_2 always on the y-axis.

4-7. Eccentricity

For an ellipse, the distance c between the center and a focus is less than the distance a between the center and a vertex, so $a^2 - c^2$ is positive and a new constant $b > 0$ is introduced by setting

(1) $$b^2 = a^2 - c^2 \quad \text{for ellipses.}$$

Hence, the equation of an ellipse with $V_1(-a, 0)$ and $V_2(a, 0)$ becomes

(2) $$\frac{x^2}{a^2} + \frac{y^2}{b^2} = 1, \quad \text{with} \quad 0 < b < a.$$

The segment between $V_1(-a, 0)$ and $V_2(a, 0)$ is called the **major axis,** while the distance between $(0, -b)$ and $(0, b)$ is called the **minor axis.**

For a hyperbola, the distance c between the center and a focus is greater than the distance a between the center and a vertex, so $a^2 - c^2$ is negative and a new constant $b > 0$ is introduced by setting

(3) $$b^2 = -(a^2 - c^2) = c^2 - a^2 \quad \text{for hyperbolas.}$$

The equation of a hyperbola with $V_1(-a, 0)$ and $V_2(a, 0)$ becomes

(4) $$\frac{x^2}{a^2} - \frac{y^2}{b^2} = 1, \quad \text{with} \quad 0 < b < c.$$

The segment between $V_1(-a, 0)$ and $V_2(a, 0)$ is called the **transverse axis,** while the segment between $(0, -b)$ and $(0, b)$ is called the **conjugate axis.**

Note carefully that $c^2 = b^2 - a^2$ from (1), but $c^2 = a^2 + b^2$ from (3). Thus, the distance from

(5) $$\text{center to focus} = \begin{cases} c = \sqrt{a^2 - b^2} & \text{for ellipses,} \\ c = \sqrt{a^2 + b^2} & \text{for hyperbolas.} \end{cases}$$

The roles of x and y may be interchanged in (2) and (4), but for ellipses the larger denominator is called a^2, whereas for hyperbolas the denominator of the positive term is called a^2 regardless of size.

Example 1. Find the vertices and foci of the central conics

$$\frac{x^2}{16} + \frac{y^2}{25} = 1 \quad \text{and} \quad \frac{x^2}{9} - \frac{y^2}{16} = 1.$$

Solution. The first is an ellipse and should be written

$$\frac{y^2}{5^2} + \frac{x^2}{4^2} = 1$$

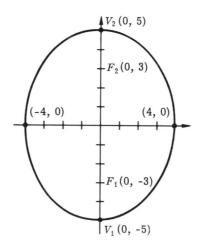

Fig 4-7.1.

to reveal clearly that $a = 5$ and $b = 4$. Hence, $c = \sqrt{5^2 - 4^2} = 3$ from the upper part of (5). Since the larger denominator is in the y-term, the vertices and foci are on the y-axis. Hence,

$$V_1(0, -5), \quad V_2(0, 5), \quad F_1(0, -3), \quad F_2(0, 3).$$

The ends of the minor axis are $(-4, 0)$ and $(4, 0)$ and, since the ellipse passes through these two points and the vertices, the ellipse is easily sketched.

In the second equation, the positive term is the x-term, so $a^2 = 9$ even though the other denominator is larger. Hence, the vertices and foci are on the x-axis. In this equation, $b^2 = 16$ and $c = \sqrt{9 + 16} = 5$ from the lower part of (5). For this hyperbola,

$$V_1(-3, 0), \quad V_2(3, 0), \quad F_1(-5, 0), \quad F_2(5, 0).$$

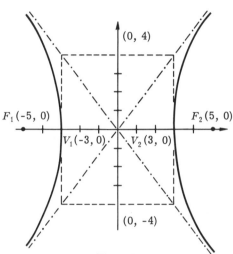

Fig. 4-7.2

The ends of the conjugate axis are $(0, -4)$ and $(0, 4)$, and although the hyperbola does not pass through these points they are helpful in drawing the asymptotes. In fact, the verticals through the vertices and horizontals through the ends of the conjugate axis form a rectangle whose diagonals extended are the asymptotes.

For both the hyperbola and the ellipse a number e, called the **eccentricity**, is introduced by setting

$$(6) \qquad\qquad\qquad e = \frac{c}{a}.$$

In terms of a and b, it then follows from (5) that

$$(7) \quad e = \frac{\sqrt{a^2 - b^2}}{a} \quad \text{for the ellipse, but} \quad e = \frac{\sqrt{a^2 + b^2}}{a} \quad \text{for the hyperbola.}$$

Notice therefore that $0 < e < 1$ for the ellipse, but $e > 1$ for the hyperbola.

However, from **(6)**, *the distance from the center to a focus is* $c = ae$ *for both the ellipse and the hyperbola.*

Recall that parabolas were defined in terms of a focus F and a directrix l. Central conics also have directrices, as shown in the next example.

Example 2. With $a > 0$ and e also positive but $e \neq 1$, let the point $F_2(ae, 0)$ and a line l_2 having equation $x = a/e$ be given. Show that the locus of points $P(x, y)$ such that

(8) $$\frac{PF_2}{Pl_2} = e$$

is a central conic.

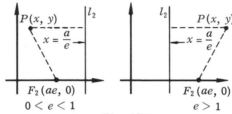

Fig. 4-7.3

Solution. PF_2 is the distance between $P(x, y)$ and $F_2(ae, 0)$, while Pl_2 is the distance between $P(x, y)$ and $(a/e, y)$, so that (8) written as $PF_2 = ePl_2$ becomes

$$\sqrt{(x - ae)^2 + y^2} = e\sqrt{\left(x - \frac{a}{e}\right)^2 + (y - y)^2},$$

$$x^2 - 2aex + a^2 e^2 + y^2 = e^2\left(x^2 - 2\frac{a}{e}x + \frac{a^2}{e^2}\right)$$

$$= e^2 x^2 - 2aex + a^2.$$

By cancellation and collection this equation may be written as

$$x^2(1 - e^2) + y^2 = a^2(1 - e^2)$$

and hence, upon dividing by $a^2(1 - e^2)$, as

(9) $$\frac{x^2}{a^2} + \frac{y^2}{a^2(1 - e^2)} = 1,$$

which is a central conic. By using the first or second part of (7), according to whether $e < 1$ or $e > 1$, check that (9) is

$$\frac{x^2}{a^2} + \frac{y^2}{b^2} = 1 \quad \text{if} \quad e < 1 \quad \text{but is} \quad \frac{x^2}{a^2} - \frac{y^2}{b^2} = 1 \quad \text{if} \quad e > 1.$$

Upon setting $e = 0$ in (9) [this would not be valid in (8)], then (9) may be written $x^2 + y^2 = a^2$, which is a circle. Upon setting $e = 1$ in (8) [this would not be valid in (9)], then the definition of a parabola is obtained. By extending eccentricity e to $e = 0$ and $e = 1$, as above, then:

a circle has $e = 0$,

an ellipse has $0 < e < 1$,

a parabola has $e = 1$,

a hyperbola has $e > 1$.

Problem 1. With $a > 0$ and e positive but $e \neq 1$, let $F_1(-ae, 0)$ and a line l_1 having equation $x = -a/e$ be given. Show that the locus of points $P(x, y)$ such that $PF_1 = ePl_1$ has (9) as its equation. [Note: This problem and Example 2 show that each central conic (circle excluded) has two directrices as well as two foci.]

Problem 2. Find the vertices, eccentricity, foci, equations of directrices, ends of the minor or conjugate axis, as the case may be, and sketch the central conic:

a. $\dfrac{x^2}{169} + \dfrac{y^2}{144} = 1$.   c. $\dfrac{x^2}{49} - \dfrac{y^2}{16} + 1 = 0$.   e. $\dfrac{x^2}{8} + \dfrac{y^2}{12} = 1$.

b. $4x^2 - 45y^2 = 180$.   d. $9x^2 - 5y^2 + 36 = 0$.   f. $64y^2 + 100x^2 = 6400$.

Problem 3. Find the equation of the central conic having:

a. Foci $(\pm 4, 0)$, $e = 0.8$.   d. Vertices $(0, \pm\sqrt{5})$, minor axis 4.

b. Foci $(\pm 5, 0)$, $e = 1.25$.   e. Vertices $\left(\pm\dfrac{1}{2}, 0\right)$, $e = \dfrac{1}{\sqrt{5}}$.

c. Vertices $(0, \pm 12)$, $e = 2.6$.   f. Foci $(0, \pm 5)$,   conjugate axis 3.

Problem 4. Given the hyperbolas

$$\frac{x^2}{p^2} - \frac{y^2}{q^2} = 1 \quad \text{and} \quad \frac{y^2}{q^2} - \frac{x^2}{p^2} = 1,$$

show:

a. They have the same asymptotes.

b. If e_1 and e_2 are the eccentricities, respectively, then

$$e_1^2 + e_2^2 = e_1^2 e_2^2.$$

Problem 5. Let δ be the angle between the asymptotes of a hyperbola and bisected by the transverse axis. Show that $e = \sec(\delta/2)$.

4-8.   Translation of Axes

In the plane having an (x, y)-coordinate system with origin O, select a fixed point $Q(h, k)$; then

$$\overrightarrow{OQ} = \vec{i}h + \vec{j}k$$

and any point $P(x, y)$ is such that

$$\overrightarrow{OP} = \vec{i}x + \vec{j}y$$

With Q as new origin, draw a new X-axis parallel to the old x-axis and a new Y-axis parallel to the old y-axis. Then $P(x, y)$ referred to the old system is $P(X, Y)$ referred to the new system, where

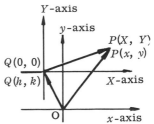

Fig. 4-8.1

$$\overrightarrow{QP} = \vec{i}X + \vec{j}Y.$$

Since $\overrightarrow{OP} = \overrightarrow{OQ} + \overrightarrow{QP}$, then

$$\vec{i}x + \vec{j}y = (\vec{i}h + \vec{j}k) + (\vec{i}X + \vec{j}Y)$$
$$= \vec{i}(h + X) + \vec{j}(k + Y).$$

By equating the coefficients of $\vec{i}$ and of $\vec{j}$ on both sides, *the equations*

(1) $$x = h + X \quad and \quad y = k + Y$$

of translation of axes are obtained.

A curve in the plane has both an (x, y)-equation and an (X, Y)-equation. In some cases, the new origin may be selected to make the (X, Y)-equation simpler than the given (x, y)-equation.

Example 1. Show that the graph of

$$9x^2 - 16y^2 - 36x - 32y = 124$$

is a central conic. Find the usual information about this conic and sketch it.

Solution. First write the equation as

$$9(x^2 - 4x \quad) - 16(y^2 + 2y \quad) = 124,$$

leaving space to complete the squares:

$$9(x^2 - 4x + 4) - 16(y^2 + 2y + 1) = 124 + 36 - 16,$$

where $9 \cdot 4$ (not merely 4) and $-16 \cdot 1$ (not merely 1) were used on the left so must also be inserted on the right to balance the equation. Thus,

$$9(x - 2)^2 - 16(y + 1)^2 = 144$$

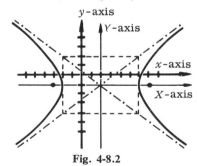

Fig. 4-8.2

is obtained. By making the substitutions

(2) $$X = x - 2, \quad Y = y + 1,$$

the result is $9X^2 - 16Y^2 = 144$ or, in standard form,

$$\frac{X^2}{16} - \frac{Y^2}{9} = 1,$$

so the curve is a hyperbola with $a = 4$, $b = 3$, $c = \sqrt{16 + 9} = 5$, and $e = \frac{5}{4}$.

The equations (2) are put in the form (1) by writing (2) as

(2') $$x = 2 + X \quad \text{and} \quad y = -1 + Y,$$

showing that $h = 2$ and $k = -1$. Coordinates of foci, equations of asymptotes, etc., are now found in (X, Y)-coordinates and then translated by means of (2) or (2') to (x, y)-coordinates:

	(X, Y)-System	(x, y)-System
Center	$(0, 0)$	$(2, -1)$
Vertices	$(\pm 4, 0)$	$(6, -1), (-2, -1)$
Foci	$(\pm 5, 0)$	$(7, -1), (-3, -1)$
Ends of Conjugate Axis	$(0, \pm 3)$	$(2, 2), (2, -4)$
Asymptotes	$4Y = \pm 3X$	$4(y + 1) = \pm 3(x - 2)$

The use of completing squares, as in the above example, is one method of determining a simplifying translation; another method is illustrated in the following example.

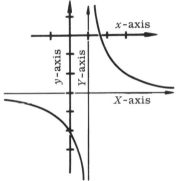

Example 2. Discuss and sketch the graph of

(3) $$xy + 3x - y = 5.$$

Solution. With h and k constants to be determined later, make the substitutions (1) into (3):

$$(h + X)(k + Y) + 3(h + X) - (k + Y) = 5.$$

Expand and collect terms in the form

(3') $$XY + X(k + 3) + Y(h - 1)$$
$$+ hk + 3h - k = 5.$$

This equation will be simplified by setting the coefficients of X and Y equal to zero; that is, set

Fig. 4-8.3

$$k + 3 = 0 \quad \text{and} \quad h - 1 = 0, \quad \text{so that} \quad k = -3 \quad \text{and} \quad h = 1.$$

Hence, the transformation equations (1) are

$$x = 1 + X \quad \text{and} \quad y = -3 + Y$$

and (3') becomes $XY + X \cdot 0 + Y \cdot 0 + 1(-3) + 3(1) - (-3) = 5$, so that

(3'') $$XY = 2.$$

Relative to the new axes, the graph of (3'') is symmetric to the origin and has the lines $X = 0$ and $Y = 0$ as asymptotes. Thus, relative to the old axes, the graph is symmetric to $(1, -3)$ and has the lines $x = 1$ and $y = -3$ as asymptotes.

First completing the square and then using judgment may lead to a simplifying translation.

Example 3. Simplify $x^2 + 4x - 3y + 13 = 0$ by a translation and discuss the curve.

Solution. Write $x^2 + 4x = 3y - 13$ and complete the square

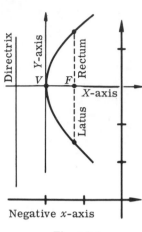

Fig. 4-8.4

$$x^2 + 4x + 4 = 3y - 13 + 4,$$

so that $(x + 2)^2 = 3y - 9$. First set

$$x + 2 = X \quad \text{so} \quad x = -2 + X,$$

giving $h = -2$ and the half-translated equation

$$X^2 = 3y - 9.$$

Write this as $X^2 = 3(y - 3)$ and see that $y - 3 = Y$
or

$$y = 3 + Y$$

gives $k = 3$ and the translated equation

$$X^2 = 3Y.$$

This may be written in the typical form of a parabola
as

$$X^2 = 4(\tfrac{3}{4})Y.$$

Information in X, Y is then obtained and translated into x, y by

$$x = -2 + X \quad \text{and} \quad y = 3 + Y:$$

	(X, Y)-System	(x, y)-System
Vertex	$(0, 0)$	$(-2, 3)$
Focus	$(\tfrac{3}{4}, 0)$	$(-\tfrac{5}{4}, 3)$
Equation of Directrix	$X = -\tfrac{3}{4}$	$x = -\tfrac{11}{4}$
Ends of Latus Rectum	$(\tfrac{3}{4}, \tfrac{3}{2}), \ (\tfrac{3}{4}, -\tfrac{3}{2})$	$(-\tfrac{5}{4}, \tfrac{9}{2}), \ (-\tfrac{5}{4}, \tfrac{3}{2}).$

Problem 1. By using translation of axes, identify the curve and find the usual information about it:

a. $16x^2 - 9y^2 + 64x + 18y = 89.$

b. $16x^2 - 9y^2 - 32x + 36y = 164.$

c. $25x^2 + 16y^2 + 50x - 64y = 311.$

d. $x^2 + 4y^2 - 4x - 8y = 92.$

e. $x^2 + y^2 + 8y + 11 = 0.$

f. $(x - 2)^2 + (y + 4)^2 - 4x + 8y + 24 = 0.$

g. $y^2 = 4(x + y) + 8.$

h. $x(x - 2) = y + 2.$

Problem 2. Find the (x, y)-equation of the:

a. Hyperbola having vertices $(-5, 2)$, $(3, 2)$, and foci $(-6, 2)$, $(4, 2)$.

b. Conic having foci $(-3, 1)$, $(7, 1)$, and $e = \tfrac{5}{4}$.

c. Conic having vertices $(-3, 1)$, $(7, 1)$, and $e = 0.6$.

d. Parabola having vertex $(-1, 2)$ and focus $(1, 2)$.

e. Parabola having focus $(4, 5)$ and directrix $y = 2$.

f. Circle with ends of a diameter $(6, 1)$ and $(-4, -1)$.

Problem 3. Show that each of the following equations has a pair of lines as a graph, a single point as graph, or no graph at all:

a. $x^2 - y^2 - x + 5y - 6 = 0.$

b. $x^2 - y^2 + 6x - 2y + 8 = 0.$

c. $x^2 + y^2 + 4x - 6y + 13 = 0.$

d. $4x^2 + 4y^2 - 4x + 8y + 5 = 0.$

e. $2x^2 + y^2 - 4x + 2y + 4 = 0.$

f. $x^2 + 3y^2 - 4x + 4y + 8 = 0.$

4-9. Rotation of Axes

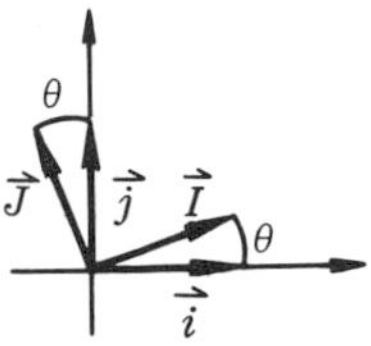

A vector $\vec{i}\cos\alpha + \vec{j}\sin\alpha$, with initial end at the origin, when rotated through an angle θ becomes

$$\vec{i}\cos(\alpha+\theta) + \vec{j}\sin(\alpha+\theta).$$

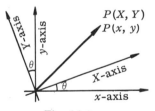

Fig. 4-9.1

In particular,

$$\vec{i} = \vec{i}\cos 0 + \vec{j}\sin 0 \quad \text{becomes} \quad \vec{I} = \vec{i}\cos\theta + \vec{j}\sin\theta,$$

$$\vec{j} = \vec{i}\cos 90° + \vec{j}\sin 90° \quad \text{becomes} \quad \vec{J} = \vec{i}\cos(90° + \theta) + \vec{j}\sin(90 + \theta)$$

$$= -\vec{i}\sin\theta + \vec{j}\cos\theta.$$

With $\vec{I}$ and $\vec{J}$ the unit vectors of a new (X, Y)-coordinate system, a point $P(x, y)$ in the old system is $P(X, Y)$ in the new system; that is,

$$\overrightarrow{OP} = \vec{i}x + \vec{j}y \quad \text{in the } (x, y)\text{-system, but}$$

$$\overrightarrow{OP} = \vec{I}X + \vec{J}Y \quad \text{in the } (X, Y)\text{-system.}$$

Thus,

$$\vec{i}x + \vec{j}y = \vec{I}X + \vec{J}Y$$

$$= (\vec{i}\cos\theta + \vec{j}\sin\theta)X + (-\vec{i}\sin\theta + \vec{j}\cos\theta)Y$$

$$= \vec{i}(X\cos\theta - Y\sin\theta) + \vec{j}(X\sin\theta + Y\cos\theta).$$

By equating the coefficients of $\vec{i}$ and of $\vec{j}$, then

(1)
$$x = X\cos\theta - Y\sin\theta$$
$$y = X\sin\theta + Y\cos\theta$$

are equations of rotation. The (x, y)-system may be considered as the (inverse) rotation of the (X, Y)-system through the angle $-\theta$, so that

Fig. 4-9.2

$$X = x\cos(-\theta) - y\sin(-\theta) = x\cos\theta + y\sin\theta$$

(2)
$$Y = x\sin(-\theta) + y\cos(-\theta) = -x\sin\theta + y\cos\theta.$$

A curve in the plane has both an (x, y)-equation and an (X, Y)-equation and θ may often be selected so that the second is simpler than the first.

Example 1. Sketch the graph of

$$x^2 + 4xy + y^2 = 1$$

by first rotating the axes through the angle $\theta = 45°$.

Solution. Since $\sin 45° = \cos 45° = 1/\sqrt{2}$, the equations (1) for $\theta = 45°$ are

$$(3) \qquad x = \frac{1}{\sqrt{2}}(X - Y), \quad y = \frac{1}{\sqrt{2}}(X + Y).$$

Upon substituting these into the given equation, then

$$\frac{1}{2}(X - Y)^2 + 4\frac{1}{\sqrt{2}}(X - Y)\frac{1}{\sqrt{2}}(X + Y) + \frac{1}{2}(X + Y)^2 = 1,$$

$$\tfrac{1}{2}(X^2 - 2XY + Y^2) + \tfrac{4}{2}(X^2 - Y^2) + \tfrac{1}{2}(X^2 + 2XY + Y^2) = 1,$$

and this simplifies to $3X^2 - Y^2 = 1$ or, in standard form,

$$\frac{X^2}{\frac{1}{3}} - \frac{Y^2}{1} = 1.$$

Thus, the graph is a hyperbola with $a = 1/\sqrt{3}$, $b = 1$, $c = \sqrt{a^2 + b^2} = 2/\sqrt{3}$, and $e = 2$. Analysis of the graph is made in the (X, Y)-system and then transformed to the (x, y)-system by means of (3) and (4) below, which comes from (2) with $\theta = 45°$:

$$(4) \qquad X = \frac{1}{\sqrt{2}}(x + y), \quad Y = \frac{1}{\sqrt{2}}(-x + y).$$

	(X, Y)-System	(x, y)-System
Center	$(0, 0)$	$(0, 0)$
Vertices	$(\pm 1/\sqrt{3}, 0)$	$(\pm 1/\sqrt{6}, \pm 1/\sqrt{6})$
Foci	$(\pm 2/\sqrt{3}, 0)$	$(\pm\sqrt{2/3}, \pm\sqrt{2/3})$
Conjugate Axis Ends	$(0, \pm 1)$	$(\mp 1/\sqrt{2}, \pm 1/\sqrt{2})$
Asymptotes	$Y = \pm\sqrt{3}\,X$	$-x + y = \pm\sqrt{3}\,(x + y)$.

Problem 1. Show that the solutions of equations (1) for X and Y are (2).

Problem 2. Sketch each of the curves after making the rotation of axes through the given angle θ:

    a. $2x^2 - 2xy + 2y^2 = 1$, $\theta = 45°$.
    b. $2x^2 + 2\sqrt{3}\,xy = 1$, $\theta = 30°$.
    c. $\sqrt{3}\,(x^2 - y^2) + 2xy = 0$, $\theta = 60°$.
    d. $(x + y)^2 - 2(x - y) = 0$, $\theta = -45°$.
    e. $7x^2 - 2\sqrt{3}\,xy + 5y^2 + 4 = 0$, $\theta = -30°$.
    f. $x^2 - 2\sqrt{3}\,xy - y^2 = 4$, $\theta = 60°$.
    g. $16x^2 - 24xy + 9y^2 = 25$, $\cot\theta = -\tfrac{4}{3}$.

Problem 3. Obtain the equation resulting from $\theta = 45°$ and also from $\theta = -45°$:

    a. $x^2 - y^2 = 1$.   c. $(x + y)^2 = 1$.   e. $x^2 + y^2 = 4$.
    b. $xy = 1$.   d. $(x + y)^2 = x - y$.   f. $x^2 + 2y^2 = 4$.

4-10. Second-Degree Curves

The most general equation of second degree in x and y is of the form

(1) $$Ax^2 + Bxy + Cy^2 + Dx + Ey + F = 0.$$

With the term Bxy present, the type of conic represented cannot be predicted directly from previous typical forms. It is, however, always possible to rotate axes through an angle θ in the first quadrant so the resulting (X, Y)-equation will not have an XY-term. To see this, substitute the rotation equations (1) of Sec. 4-9 into (1) above:

$$A(X \cos \theta - Y \sin \theta)^2 + B(X \cos \theta - Y \sin \theta)(X \sin \theta + Y \cos \theta)$$
$$+ C(X \cos \theta + Y \sin \theta)^2 + D(X \cos \theta - Y \sin \theta)$$
$$+ E(X \sin \theta + Y \cos \theta) + F = 0.$$

Visualize the result of expanding this expression. There will be an X^2, an XY, a Y^2, an X, a Y, and a constant term. The angle θ is to be chosen so that no XY-term will be present; that is, so the coefficient of XY will be zero. Thus, collect only the coefficient of XY and set this coefficient equal to zero; the result is

$$-2A \sin \theta \cos \theta + B \cos^2 \theta - B \sin^2 \theta + 2C \sin \theta \cos \theta = 0, \quad \text{so that}$$
$$B(\cos^2 \theta - \sin^2 \theta) - (A - C) 2 \sin \theta \cos \theta = 0.$$

Recalling $\cos^2 \theta - \sin^2 \theta = \cos 2\theta$ and $2 \sin \theta \cos \theta = \sin 2\theta$, then

$$B \cos 2\theta - (A - C) \sin 2\theta = 0, \quad \text{and hence}$$

(2) $$\cot 2\theta = \frac{A - C}{B}.$$

The use of this formula is illustrated in the next example.

Example. Rotate axes so the graph of

(3) $$2x^2 - 3xy - 2y^2 = 5$$

will have (X, Y)-equation with no XY-term.

Solution. Since $A = 2$, $B = -3$, and $C = -2$, the angle θ to use is such that, from (2),

(4) $$\cot 2\theta = \frac{2 - (-2)}{-3} = -\frac{4}{3}.$$

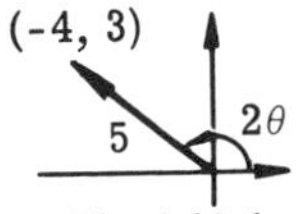

Fig 4-10.1

The vector from the origin to the point $(-4, 3)$ has an amplitude 2θ satisfying (4) with 2θ in the second quadrant. Since $\sqrt{(-4)^2 + 3^2} = 5$, then $\cos 2\theta = -\frac{4}{5}$. Angle θ itself is in the first quadrant, so both $\sin \theta$ and $\cos \theta$ are positive. By the use of trigonometric formulas,

$$\cos \theta \equiv \sqrt{\frac{1 + \cos 2\theta}{2}} = \sqrt{\frac{1 - \frac{4}{5}}{2}} = \frac{1}{\sqrt{10}},$$

$$\sin \theta \equiv \sqrt{\frac{1 - \cos 2\theta}{2}} = \sqrt{\frac{1 + \frac{4}{5}}{2}} = \frac{3}{\sqrt{10}}.$$

In particular, the new X-axis will pass through the (x, y)-point $(1, 3)$, so the angle θ itself need never be found. Equations (1) of Sec. 4-9 then become

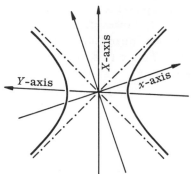

$$x = \frac{1}{\sqrt{10}} (X - 3Y)$$

and $\quad y = \dfrac{1}{\sqrt{10}} (3X + Y).$

When these are substituted into (3) (as practice the student should do this), the result simplifies to

$$Y^2 - X^2 = 1,$$

which, according to design, has no XY-term. This, being the standard form of a hyperbola, shows that the curve (3) is a hyperbola.

Fig. 4-10.2

Problem 1. Rotate axes so the resulting equation has no XY-term, draw both sets of axes, and sketch the graph:

a. $8x^2 - 4xy + 5y^2 = 36.$

b. $11x^2 + 24xy + 4y^2 = 20.$

c. $x^2 - 3xy + y^2 = 5.$

d. $12xy - 5y^2 = 1.$

e. $12xy + 5y^2 = 1.$

f. $x^2 + xy + y^2 = 1.$

Problem 2. First rotate axes to eliminate the product term, then for the resulting equation translate to eliminate the first-degree terms.

     a. $4x^2 + 24xy + 11y^2 + 8x - 6y = 15.$

     b. $5x^2 + 4xy + 8y^2 - 16x + 8y = 16.$

Chapter 5

Applications of Derivatives

5-1. Concavity

In Sec. 2–5 it was shown that the graph of $y = f(x)$ has a tangent at a point (x_0, y_0), where $y_0 = f(x_0)$, if the derivative $f'(x_0)$ exists. The slope of this tangent is $m_1 = f'(x_0)$, and the equation of this tangent is

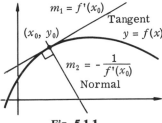

Fig. 5-1.1

(1) $$y - y_0 = f'(x_0)(x - x_0).$$

The line perpendicular to this tangent at (x_0, y_0) is called the **normal** to the curve $y = f(x)$ at the point (x_0, y_0). The slope m_2 of this normal is the negative reciprocal of $m_1 = f'(x_0)$; that is, $m_2 = -1/f'(x_0)$ (see Sec. 1–9). Hence, the normal has equation

(2) $$y - y_0 = -\frac{1}{f'(x_0)}(x - x_0).$$

Example 1. Find equations of the tangent and normal to the graph of $y^2 = 16x$ at the point having $y_0 = 3$.

Solution. When $y = y_0 = 3$, then $3^2 = 16x$ so $x = x_0 = 9/16$ and the desired point is $(9/16, 3)$. Since this point is on the upper half of the curve, only the positive solution $y = 4\sqrt{x} = f(x)$ of $y^2 = 16x$ need be considered. Hence,

$$f'(x) = 4\frac{d\sqrt{x}}{dx} = \frac{2}{\sqrt{x}} \quad \text{so} \quad f'\left(\frac{9}{16}\right) = \frac{2}{\sqrt{9/16}} = \frac{8}{3}.$$

Equations of the desired tangent and normal are, therefore,

$$y - 3 = \frac{8}{3}\left(x - \frac{9}{16}\right) \quad \text{and} \quad y - 3 = -\frac{3}{8}\left(x - \frac{9}{16}\right),$$

respectively. These equations may be written, respectively, as

$$16x - 6y + 9 = 0 \quad \text{and} \quad 48x + 128y = 411.$$

If only a point on a curve and the tangent at this point are given (but the curve has not been drawn), then from this information alone it cannot

169

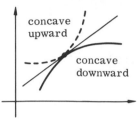

Fig. 5-1.2

be told whether, in the vicinity of this point, the curve is **concave downward** (as the solid curve of Fig. 5-1.2) or **concave upward** (as the dotted curve of Fig. 5-1.2).

The second derivative gives information (as shown below) about concavity properties of a curve.

The curve $y = f(x)$ may also be thought of as being traced by the variable terminal end of the vector

$$\vec{F}(x) = \vec{i}x + \vec{j}f(x)$$

having (fixed) initial end at the origin. Then the vector

$$\vec{F}'(x) = \frac{d\vec{F}(x)}{dx} = \vec{i}\frac{dx}{dx} + \vec{j}\frac{df(x)}{dx}$$

$$= \vec{i} + \vec{j}f'(x),$$

if drawn with initial end at the point $(x, f(x))$, lies along the tangent to the curve and indicates the instantaneous direction of motion of the point tracing the curve (see Fig. 5-1.3).

With x held fixed for the moment, the vector

$$(4) \qquad \vec{F}'(x + \Delta x) = \vec{i} + \vec{j}f'(x + \Delta x)$$

indicates the direction of the curve at a neighboring point. If, however, $\vec{F}'(x)$ and $\vec{F}'(x + \Delta x)$ are both drawn with initial ends at the point $(x, f(x))$, the difference

$$(5) \qquad \Delta\vec{F}'(x) = \vec{F}'(x + \Delta x) - \vec{F}'(x)$$

$$= [\vec{i} + \vec{j}f'(x + \Delta x)] - [\vec{i} + \vec{j}f'(x)]$$

$$= \vec{j}[f'(x + \Delta x) - f'(x)] = \vec{j}\Delta f'(x)$$

is a vector pointing downward if the curve is concave downward (as in Fig.

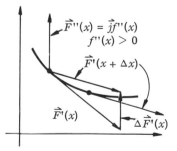

Fig. 5-1.3

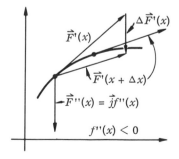

Fig. 5-1.4   **Fig. 5-1.5**

5-1.4), but a vector pointing upward if the curve is concave upward (as in Fig. 5-1.5).

Since

$$\vec{F}''(x) = \lim_{\Delta x \to 0} \frac{\Delta \vec{F}'(x)}{\Delta x}$$

$$= \lim_{\Delta x \to 0} \vec{j} \frac{\Delta f'(x)}{\Delta x}$$

$$= \vec{j} f''(x),$$

it follows that *if $f''(x) < 0$, the curve is concave downward, but if $f''(x) > 0$, the curve is concave upward.*

Thus, the vector $\vec{j} f''(x)$ can be thought of as "pulling the curve in its direction."

Example 2. Sketch a portion of the curve $x \cos y + 2 \sin x = 1$ in the vicinity of the point $(\pi/6, \pi/2)$.

Solution. First check that the point is on the curve:

$$\frac{\pi}{6} \cos \frac{\pi}{2} + 2 \sin \frac{\pi}{6} = \frac{\pi}{6} \cdot 0 + 2 \left(\frac{1}{2} \right) = 1.$$

Next, find y' by implicit differentiation

$$x(- \sin y)\, dy + \cos y\, dx + 2 \cos x\, dx = 0,$$

$$y' = \frac{dy}{dx} = \frac{\cos y + 2 \cos x}{x \sin y}.$$

Hence, the desired slope m of the tangent is

$$m = y'|_{(\pi/6, \pi/2)} = \frac{0 + 2(\sqrt{3}/2)}{(\pi/6) \cdot 1} = \frac{6\sqrt{3}}{\pi} = 3.3.$$

Next,

$$y'' = \frac{d^2 y}{dx^2} = \frac{x \sin y(-\sin y\, y' - 2 \sin x) - (\cos y + 2 \cos x)(x \cos y\, y' + \sin y)}{(x \sin y)^2}.$$

Only the sign of y'' at $(\pi/6, \pi/2)$ is desired. Since $y'|_{(\pi/6, \pi/2)}$ is positive, while the sines and cosines of $\pi/6$ and $\pi/2$ are not negative, it follows that $y''|_{(\pi/6, \pi/2)}$ is negative, and the desired portion of the curve is concave downward as shown in Fig. 5-1.6.

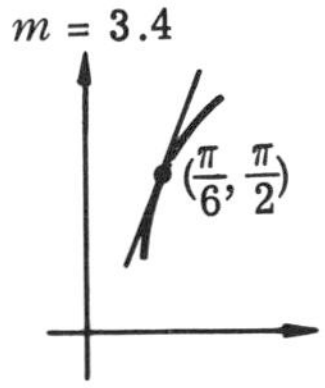

$m = 3.4$

Fig. 5-1.6

Example 3. Sketch the curve $y = x^4/12 - x^3/3 + 1$, showing concave-upward and concave-downward portions, together with tangents at the points dividing these portions.

Solution. First,

$$y' = \frac{x^3}{3} - x^2 \quad \text{and} \quad y'' = x^2 - 2x = x(x - 2).$$

Consequently, $y'' > 0$ if either $x < 0$ or $x > 2$, whereas $y'' < 0$ if $0 < x < 2$.

When $x = 0$, then $y = 1$, and when $x = 2$, then $y = -\frac{1}{3}$. Thus, the points $(0, 1)$ and $(2, -\frac{1}{3})$ divide the concave-upward portions from the concave-downward portions. By substituting $x = 0$ and $x = 2$ into y', the slopes at these points are $m_1 = 0$ and $m_2 = -\frac{4}{3}$.

Notice that $y' = 0$ if

$$\frac{x^3}{3} - x^2 = x^2\left(\frac{x}{3} - 1\right) = 0$$

and thus when $x = 0$ or $x = 3$. Also, when $x = 3$, then $y = -\frac{5}{4}$. Hence, the point $(3, -\frac{5}{4})$ is on a concave-upward portion of the curve, at this point the tangent is horizontal, and thus this point is the lowest point of this concave-upward portion.

If a curve has a point [such as $(0, 1)$ or $(2, -\frac{1}{3})$ of Fig. 5-1.7] where a tangent to the curve exists and which separates concave-upward and concave-downward portions, then this point is called an **inflection point** of the curve.

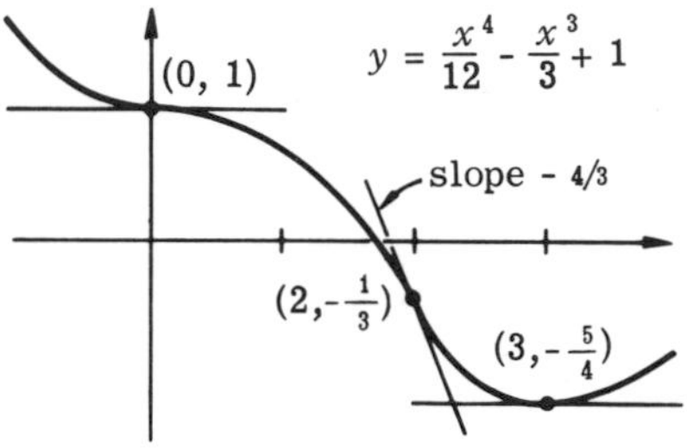

If a curve $y = f(x)$ has a point of inflection when $x = x_0$ and if $f''(x_0)$ exists, then $f''(x_0)$ can be neither positive nor negative, and hence it must follow that $f''(x_0) = 0$.

In summary, notice that if throughout a portion of the curve $y = f(x)$:

(1) $y' > 0$, the portion is ascending to the right.

(2) $y' < 0$, the portion is descending to the right.

Fig. 5-1.7

(3) $y'' > 0$, the portion is concave upward.

(4) $y'' < 0$, the portion is concave downward.

Problem 1. Find equations of the tangent and normal to the curve at the point indicated:

a. $y = x^2$, $x_0 = 2$.

c. $y = \cos x$, $x_0 = \dfrac{\pi}{3}$.

b. $y = \dfrac{1}{x}$, $x_0 = -2$.

d. $y = x + \sin x$, $x_0 = \dfrac{5\pi}{6}$.

Problem 2. Find the portions of the following curves which are (1) ascending to the right, (2) descending to the right, (3) concave upward, (4) concave downward:

a. $y = x^4 - 6x^2$.

c. $y = \dfrac{x}{x + 1}$.

e. $y = x + \dfrac{4}{x}$.

b. $y = x^3 - 3x$.

d. $y = \dfrac{x + 1}{x}$.

f. $y = x - \dfrac{4}{x}$.

Problem 3. a. Sketch a continuous curve $y = f(x)$ having all of the characteristics:

$$f(-3) = 4, \quad f'(-3) = 1, \quad f''(x) < 0 \text{ if } x < -1;$$
$$f(0) = 2, \quad f'(0) = -1, \quad f''(x) > 0 \text{ if } x > -1;$$

$$f(2) = 1, \qquad f'(2) = 0.$$

b. Show that if all these characteristics are as prescribed except that $f(2) = 1$ is changed to $f(2) = 0$, then no such curve exists.

Problem 4. Find all points on the curve where the tangent is horizontal and for each such point determine whether it is on a concave-upward or concave-downward portion of the curve.

a. $y = x^2 - 2x - 4$.

b. $y = 1 + 4x - x^2$.

c. $y = x + \dfrac{1}{x}$.

d. $y = \frac{1}{6}(2x^3 + 3x^2 - 12x + 6)$.

e. $y = \frac{1}{6}(18 + 12x + 3x^2 - 2x^3)$.

f. $y = \dfrac{x^2}{2} - \dfrac{1}{x}$.

Problem 5. Show that the curve $y = x^4$ is concave-upward throughout its whole length and hence has no point of inflection even though $y'' = 0$ when $x = 0$.

Problem 6. a. Sketch the graph of $y = f(x)$ given that

$$f(x) = \begin{cases} x^2 \text{ if } x \geq 0, \\ x^3 \text{ if } x \leq 0. \end{cases}$$

b. Show that the x-axis is tangent to the curve at the origin.

c. Show that the origin is a point of inflection.

d. Show that $f''(0)$ does not exist.

5-2. Maxima and Minima

A function $y = f(x)$ is said to have a **local maximum** at $x = x_1$, and $f(x_1)$ is said to be a **local maximum value**, if

(1) $$f(x_1) \geq f(x)$$

for all values of x sufficiently close to x_1. If (1) holds for all x for which $f(x)$ is defined, then $f(x_1)$ is said to have an **absolute maximum** of $y = f(x)$.

In a similar way, $f(x_2)$ is a **local minimum** or an **absolute minimum** of $y = f(x)$ if

(2) $$f(x_2) \leq f(x)$$

for all x sufficiently close to x_2 or for all x, respectively.

The test below follows from Sec. 5-1.

TEST 1. *If* $f'(x_0) = 0$, *then* $f(x_0)$ *is a:*
1. *Local maximum if* $f''(x_0) < 0$,
2. *Local minimum if* $f''(x_0) > 0$.

Fig. 5-2.1

Notice that even if $f'(x_0) = 0$ it may be that $f(x_0)$ is neither a local maximum nor a local minimum. For example, if also $f''(x_0) = 0$, then the point $(x_0, f(x_0))$ could be an inflection point of the curve $y = f(x)$. Thus, if $f''(x_0) = 0$, the above test is not applicable.

The following examples illustrate how some geometric and physical problems may be turned into equations defining functions whose maximum or minimum values are significant.

Example 1. Of all isosceles triangles having equal sides of constant length a, does the equilateral triangle have largest area?

Solution. Consider such an isosceles triangle with base of length $2x$. Here $2x$ (rather than x) is chosen for the length of base, so the altitude takes the simple form $\sqrt{a^2 - x^2}$ and the area the simple form

$$A = x\sqrt{a^2 - x^2}.$$

With A a function of x (of course, with x positive and less than a), the maximum of A is sought. First,

$$\frac{dA}{dx} = x\frac{d\sqrt{a^2 - x^2}}{dx} + \sqrt{a^2 - x^2}\frac{dx}{dx}$$

$$= x\frac{1}{2}\cdot\frac{-2x}{\sqrt{a^2 - x^2}} + \sqrt{a^2 - x^2} = \frac{-x^2 + a^2 - x^2}{\sqrt{a^2 - x^2}} = \frac{a^2 - 2x^2}{\sqrt{a^2 - x^2}}.$$

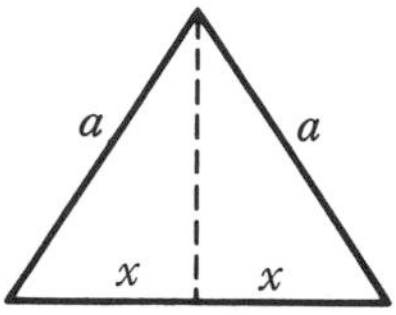

Next, according to the above test, solve $A' = 0$:

$$\frac{a^2 - 2x^2}{\sqrt{a^2 - x^2}} = 0, \quad a^2 - 2x^2 = 0, \quad x = x_0 = \frac{a}{\sqrt{2}}.$$

In order to apply Test 1 to see if $x_0 = a/\sqrt{2}$ furnishes a maximum value of A, it is necessary to compute

Fig. 5-2.2

$$A'' = \left[\sqrt{a^2 - x^2}(-4x) - (a^2 - 2x^2)\frac{-x}{\sqrt{a^2 - x^2}}\right]\frac{1}{(\sqrt{a^2 - x^2})^2}$$

and substitute $x = x_0 = a/\sqrt{2}$ into this expression. The result is

$$\left[\sqrt{a^2 - \frac{a^2}{2}}\left(-4\frac{a}{\sqrt{2}}\right) - 0\right]\frac{1}{+},$$

which is negative. Thus, the only point on the curve $y = A = x\sqrt{a^2 - x^2}$ where $A' = 0$ occurs is on a concave-downward portion, so the whole curve is concave-downward (remember $0 < x < a$). Hence, $x = x_0 = a/\sqrt{2}$ furnishes the maximum area, which is

$$A_{\max} = \frac{a}{\sqrt{2}}\sqrt{a^2 - \frac{a^2}{2}} = \frac{a^2}{2}.$$

The equilateral triangle, therefore, is not the triangle of maximum area. In fact, the isosceles triangle with all three sides equal to a is an equilateral triangle of

$$\text{area} = \frac{a^2}{4}\sqrt{3} = \text{approximately } 0.433a^2 < \frac{a^2}{2}.$$

Example 2. According to engineering tests, the strength of a rectangular beam is proportional to the width and the square of the depth. Find the dimensions of the rectangular cross-section of the strongest beam which may be cut from a log 12 in. in diameter.

Solution. With w in. the width and h in. the depth, the strength is given by

$$S = kwh^2,$$

where k is a positive constant depending on the variety of wood. Here S is a function of two variables (w and h), so one of these must be eliminated by further conditions of the problem. Since the diameter of the log is 12 in., it follows that $w^2 + h^2 = 12^2$, so that $h^2 = 12^2 - w^2$ and

$$S = kw(12^2 - w^2) = k(12^2 w - w^3)$$

is now a function of the single variable w. The derivative of S with respect to w is

$$S' = k(12^2 - 3w^2),$$

so $S' = 0$ when $w = w_0 = 4\sqrt{3}$. Only the positive square root is used, since w must be positive. Also,

$$S'' = k(-6w)$$

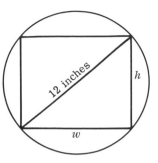

Fig. 5-2.3

is always negative (since $w > 0$) and thus $w = w_0 = 4\sqrt{3}$ in. is the width to use for the strongest beam. Hence.

$$h = h_0 = \sqrt{12^2 - w_0^2} = \sqrt{12^2 - (4\sqrt{3})^2} = 4\sqrt{6} \text{ in.}$$

is the depth to use.

Notice that this problem did not ask for the strength of the strongest beam but merely for the cross-section dimensions of the strongest beam.

A suggested procedure in solving such maximum-minimum problems is:

(1) Read the problem very carefully.
(2) Determine the quantity to be maximized or minimized. Select a suggestive letter to represent this quantity as a function.
(3) Use letters to label other variable quantities and express the function of step (2) in terms of these variables.
(4) If the function in step (3) is expressed by more than one variable, then reread the problem and determine enough relations between these variables so all except one variable may be eliminated.
(5) Now with the quantity to be maximized or minimized expressed as a function of a single variable, take first and second derivatives with respect to this variable.
(6) Apply Test 1 and put down the answer.
(7) Reread the problem again to be sure the answer contains those things and only those things called for.

Problem 1. Of all isosceles triangles having perimeter 18 in., what are the dimensions of the triangle of greatest area?

Problem 2. A pan is to be made from a flat 9 in. × 24 in. rectangle of tin by cutting equal squares from the corners and turning up the sides. Find the dimensions and volume of the pan of greatest volume that can be so made.

Problem 3. In Prob. 2 use a rectangle 12 in. × 18 in.

Problem 4. Figure 5-2.4 represents a 12 in. × 12 in. sheet

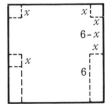

Fig. 5-2.4

of tin with squares x in. $\times$ x in. cut from two corners and rectangles x in. $\times$ 6 in. cut from the other corners. The sides may be turned up and then the flap turned down to form a box and lid. Find the dimensions and volume of the box of largest volume that can be so made.

Problem 5. Replace the square of Prob. 4 by a 9 in. $\times$ 24 in. rectangle, cut the squares from a 9 in. side and the rectangles of proper dimensions from the 24 in. sides.

Problem 6. A box with square base and no lid is to be made to have volume 32 in³. Find the dimensions which will make the surface area the smallest. Neglect the thickness of material.

Problem 7. Change Prob. 6 to a box with lid and volume 64 in³.

Problem 8. Change Prob. 6 so that the dimensions are for the minimum cost desired, given that material for the sides costs 10¢ per sq in. and for the bottom 15¢ per sq in.

Problem 9. A right circular cylindrical can of volume 54 in³. is to be made. Find the dimensions for minimum surface area. The can has both top and bottom.

Problem 10. Rectangular posters of 12 sq ft are to be made with side margins of 3 in. and top and bottom margins of 4 in. Find the dimensions for greatest area of printing. [Hint: Note the different units.]

Problem 11. Rectangular posters of 16-ft perimeter are to be made, etc., as in Prob. 10.

Problem 12. A V-shaped trough of maximum capacity is to be made by bending a long rectangular piece of tin 12 in. wide down its center line. How wide should the top of the trough be?

Problem 13. Answer Prob. 12 if the cross section of the trough is to be rectangular.

Problem 14. Answer Prob. 13 if the cross section is a trapezoid with sides making angles of 120° with the base.

Problem 15. A farmer put up a half mile of straight fence and had 100 ft of fencing left over. With this extra fencing he wants to enclose as much area as possible in a rectangular plot, using part of his already erected fence for one side. What dimension plot should he plan?

Problem 16. What dimensions should the farmer of Prob. 15 use if he wants to have two equal plots abutting each other and the existing fence if the plots are:
a. On the same side of the existing fence?
b. On opposite sides of the existing fence?

Problem 17. Find the dimensions of the rectangle of greatest area that can be inscribed in the given figure with its base along the base of the given figure:
a. Semicircle of radius 4.
b. Isosceles triangle with base 10 and altitude 10.

Problem 18. A right circular cylindrical can with both top and bottom is to be designed. Find the dimensions if:

    a. The total area is 24π sq in. and the volume is maximum.

    b. The volume is 54 cu in. and the area is minimum.

Problem 19. A wire of length l is cut into two pieces, one of which is bent into a square and the other into another figure. Find the dimensions of the square if the sum of the areas of the square and the other figure is a minimum, given that the other figure is:

    a. A circle.

    b. An equilateral triangle.

Problem 20. A trapezoid has one base 4 in. longer that the other, and the sum of the two bases and altitude is 28 in. Find the altitude and bases if the area is a maximum.

5-3.   Critical Values

A number c is said to be a **critical argument** for a function $y = f(x)$ if $f(c)$ is defined and either $f'(c) = 0$ or else $f'(c)$ does not exist. Also, if $y = f(x)$ is defined only on a closed interval $a \le x \le b$, then a and b are also called critical arguments for $y = f(x)$. If c is a critical argument for $y = f(x)$, then $f(c)$ is said to be a **critical value** of this function.

For example, the function $y = (x - 1)^{2/3}$ has $c = 1$ as a critical argument since

$$y' = \frac{2}{3} \frac{1}{(x - 1)^{1/3}}$$

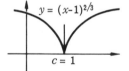

$y = (x-1)^{2/3}$

$c = 1$

Fig. 5-3.1

is not defined if $x = c = 1$.

From earlier discussions it follows that, if x_1 is a constant such that $f'(x_1) > 0$, then $y = f(x)$ is increasing at $x = x_1$ and if $f'(x_2) < 0$, then $y = f(x)$ is decreasing at $x = x_2$. Thus, if $x = c$ is such that $f(c)$ is a local maximum or a local minimum of $y = f(x)$, then either $f'(c) = 0$ or else $f'(c)$ does not exist and in either case $x = c$ is a critical argument.

Also, if $y = f(x)$ is defined only on the closed interval $a \le x \le b$, it may be that $f(a)$ or $f(b)$ is the (absolute) maximum or minimum of the function.

It thus follows that if a function $y = f(x)$ defined on a closed interval $a \le x \le b$ has a maximum or minimum value, then these values are taken on at critical arguments of the function. For such a function, the following test is sometimes easier to apply than Test 1 of Sec. 5–2, and sometimes Test 1 is not applicable (as in Example 1 below).

TEST 2. *Determine all critical arguments for* $y = f(x)$, *where* $a \le x \le b$ *[that is, find all solutions of* $f'(x) = 0$, *find all values of* x *where* $f'(x)$ *does not* *exist, and also record $x = a$ and $x = b$]. Compute the value of $f(x)$ at all of these critical arguments (there will generally be only a few of them). Among these values the largest is the maximum and the smallest is the minimum of $y = f(x)$ on the whole interval $a \leq x \leq b$.*

Example 1. Find the points on the ellipse

(1)
$$\frac{x^2}{5^2} + \frac{y^2}{4^2} = 1$$

which are closest to and farthest from the point (2, 0).

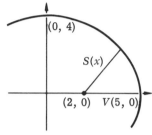

Fig. 5-3.2

Solution. Select a point (x, y) on the ellipse and note that its distance to the point (2, 0) is

$$\sqrt{(x - 2)^2 + y^2}.$$

But since (x, y) must satisfy (1), this distance as a function of x is

(2)
$$S(x) = \sqrt{(x - 2)^2 + 4^2\left(1 - \frac{x^2}{5^2}\right)},$$

where, because of (1), x is restricted to $-5 \leq x \leq 5$. Now

$$S'(x) = \frac{(x - 2) - 16x/25}{S(x)} = \frac{9x - 50}{25S(x)}.$$

The formal solution of $S'(x) = 0$ is $x = 50/9 = 5.5+$, which is not allowable since $-5 \leq x \leq 5$. This merely means that $S'(x)$ is never zero for $-5 \leq x \leq 5$, so there are no critical arguments of this type. Since $S'(x)$ exists for $-5 \leq x \leq 5$, the only critical arguments are the end values $x = -5$ and $x = 5$. Upon substituting these values into (2), the results are

$$S(-5) = \sqrt{(-5 - 2)^2} = 7 \quad \text{and} \quad S(5) = \sqrt{(5 - 2)^2} = 3.$$

Thus, the vertex $(-5, 0)$ is the point of the ellipse farthest from the point (2, 0), and the vertex (5, 0) is closest.

Neither Test 1 nor Test 2 should be relied upon to the exclusion of the other. The following example illustrates a situation in which Test 2, though applicable, would be difficult to apply.

Example 2. Light travels through a homogeneous medium in a straight line at a constant velocity, depending on the medium. Denote the velocity of light in air by the constant v_1 and in water by the constant v_2. Show that a light ray will travel from a point A in air to a point B in water in the shortest time if

(3)
$$\frac{\sin \alpha}{v_1} = \frac{\sin \beta}{v_2},$$

where the ray in air and in water makes angles α and β , respectively, with the normal to the surface. [Note: The fact stated here is a fundamental law of optics known as Snells' Law.]

Solution. In the notation of Fig. 5-3.3 let $T(x)$ be the time a light ray would

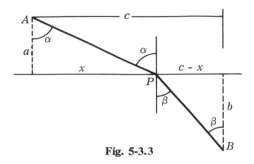

Fig. 5-3.3

travel from A to B via P, so that (distance divided by constant velocity equals time)

$$T(x) = \frac{\sqrt{a^2 + x^2}}{v_1} + \frac{\sqrt{b^2 + (c - x)^2}}{v_2},$$

wherein a, b, c, v_1, and v_2 are constants but x is a variable restricted by $0 \le x \le c$. Then

$$T'(x) = \frac{1}{v_1} \frac{x}{\sqrt{a^2 + x^2}} - \frac{1}{v_2} \frac{(c - x)}{\sqrt{b^2 + (c - x)^2}}.$$

This derivative will be zero if $x = x_0$ is such that

(4) $$\frac{1}{v_1} \frac{x_0}{\sqrt{a^2 + x_0^2}} = \frac{1}{v_2} \frac{c - x_0}{\sqrt{b^2 + (c - x_0)^2}}.$$

But (4) is the same as (3), since

$$\sin \alpha = \frac{x_0}{\sqrt{a^2 + x_0^2}} \quad \text{and} \quad \sin \beta = \frac{c - x_0}{\sqrt{b^2 + (c - x_0)^2}}.$$

If Test 2 were to be used to see if $x = x_0$ satisfying (4) does, in fact, furnish a minimum of $T(x)$, it would be necessary to solve (4) for x_0 and this would be tedious. To apply Test 1, the second derivative $T''(x)$ is computed and is (after some simplification)

$$T''(x) = \frac{1}{v_1} \frac{a^2}{(\sqrt{a^2 + x^2})^3} + \frac{1}{v_2} \frac{b^2}{(\sqrt{b^2 + (c - x)^2})^3},$$

which is always positive. Thus, the graph of $y = T(x)$ is concave upward throughout its entirety, so the argument $x = x_0$ making $T'(x) = 0$ does, in fact, furnish an absolute minimum, and there is no doubt that (3) is the condition for the shortest time path from A to B.

    Problem 1. Find the points on the ellipse $x^2/5^2 + y^2/4^2 = 1$ which are closest to and farthest from:

a. Point (1, 0).   c. Point (0, 2).
b. Focus (3, 0).   d. Point (0, 4).

Problem 2. A man in a rowboat 3 mi from the nearest point A of a straight shore wishes to reach a point B on the shore in the shortest time. If he can row 4 mi/hr and walk 5 mi/hr, find the point C (see Fig. 5-3.4) he should row toward if:
a. $AB = 6$ mi.   b. $AB = 5$ mi.   c. $AB = 4$ mi.   d. $AB = 3$ mi.

Problem 3. In Fig. 5-3.5 find the value of x which minimizes the given expres-

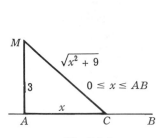

Fig. 5-3.4

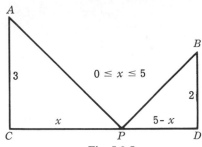

Fig. 5-3.5

sion and find this minimum value:
a. $AP + BP$.   c. $2(AP)^2 + (BP)^2$.   e. Area ACP + area BDP.
b. $(AP)^2 + (BP)^2$.   d. $(BP)^2 - (AP)^2$.   f. Area APB.

Problem 4. In Prob. 3, change "minimizes" and "minimum" to "maximizes" and "maximum."

Problem 5. For each of the following functions $F(t)$ of t, find the maximum and minimum values for the associated interval for t:

a. $F(t) = \int_t^{t+1} x^2 \, dx, \quad -1 \le t \le 1$.

b. $F(t) = \int_{-1}^1 (t + x)^2 \, dx, \quad -1 \le t \le 1$.

c. $F(t) = \int_0^\pi t \sin(tx) \, dx, \quad 0 \le t \le 2$.

d. $F(t) = \int_0^\pi (t + \sin x) \, dx, \quad 0 \le t \le 2$.

Problem 6. Given that x_1, x_2, x_3 are constants and m_1, m_2, and m_3 are positive constants, show that the function of x,

$$f(x) = m_1(x - x_1)^2 + m_2(x - x_2)^2 + m_3(x - x_3)^2,$$

assumes its minimum value when

$$x = \frac{m_1 x_1 + m_2 x_2 + m_3 x_3}{m_1 + m_2 + m_3}.$$

Problem 7. Find the dimensions of a rectangle of perimeter 36 which will sweep out as large a volume as possible when revolved about:
    a. A side.
    b. A line parallel to, and one unit from, a side.

Problem 8. Find the dimensions of a right circular cylinder of maximum volume inscribed in a sphere of radius r.

Problem 9. In Prob. 8, change "cylinder" to "cone."

Problem 10. On the parabola $y^2 = 4x$, find the point nearest to (2, 1).

Problem 11. a. The line of Fig. 5-3.6 has equation $y = x$. Find the value of x, subject to $0 \le x \le 3$, for which the shaded area is maximum.

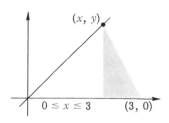

Also solve the problem with the line $y = x$ replaced by:

Fig. 5-3.6

    b. The line $y = mx$, $m > 0$.
    c. The parabola $y^2 = 4x$.
    d. The parabola $y^2 = 4px$, $p > 0$.
    e. The parabola $x^2 = 4py$, $p > 0$.
    f. The curve $y = 1/(3 - x)$.

5-4. Related Rates

If a function $s(t)$ of time t is given, then the derivative $s'(t)$ of $s(t)$ with respect to t gives the rate at which $s(t)$ is changing at any time t. In Sec. 2–5, it was shown how this time rate of change gave pertinent information in some physical or geometric problems. In Sec. 2–5, the method used was to express $s(t)$ explicitly in terms of t before taking the derivative.

It frequently happens that two or more quantities are related, but the relationship may be expressed implicitly rather than explicitly. Each of these quantities may depend on time, but again this dependence may not be expressed explicitly. If, however, the time derivatives of all except one of these quantities are known, then a relation between all time derivatives may be obtained from which the one remaining derivative (that is, rate) may be discovered. The central idea is to find relations between the rates.

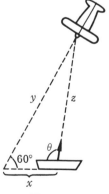

Example 1. A cruiser is being attacked by a dive bomber that will pass overhead and toward a point directly astern of the cruiser. This straight dive path extended makes a 60° angle with the cruiser track. A radar-controlled gun is kept pointed toward the bomber at a changing angle θ, as illustrated in Fig. 5-4.1. The speed of the ship is 20 knots and the bomber is going 200 knots in its path. (a) Find how the rate of change of θ and the speeds of cruiser and bomber are related. (b) Given that when the bomber passes directly overhead it will be $\frac{1}{2}$ mi up, find the rate of change of θ at this instant.

Fig. 5-4.1

Solution a. In the notation of the figure, the sine laws for triangles give

(1)
$$\frac{\sin \theta}{y} = \frac{\sin (120° - \theta)}{x}.$$

The ship and bomber speeds are expressed by

(2)
$$\frac{dx}{dt} = 20 \quad \text{and} \quad \frac{dy}{dt} = -200.$$

Now (1) may be thought of as defining θ as an implicit function of x and y and, for purposes of taking derivatives, is expressed better as

$$x \sin \theta = y \sin \left(\frac{2\pi}{3} - \theta\right).$$

Hence,

$$x \cos \theta \frac{d\theta}{dt} + \sin \theta \frac{dx}{dt} = -y \cos \left(\frac{2\pi}{3} - \theta\right) \frac{d\theta}{dt} + \sin \left(\frac{2\pi}{3} - \theta\right) \frac{dy}{dt}$$

is an equation, relating the rates, into which (2) may be substituted:

$$x \cos \theta \frac{d\theta}{dt} + 20 \sin \theta = -y \cos \left(\frac{2\pi}{3} - \theta\right) \frac{d\theta}{dt} - 200 \sin \left(\frac{2\pi}{3} - \theta\right),$$

$$\frac{d\theta}{dt} = \frac{-200 \sin \left(\frac{2\pi}{3} - \theta\right) - 20 \sin \theta}{x \cos \theta + y \cos \left(\frac{2\pi}{3} - \theta\right)}.$$

Solution b. In order to answer this part of the question, note that, at the instant the bomber is directly overhead, $z = \frac{1}{2}$ and $\theta = 90°$. Hence, at this instant, the triangle is a 30°, 60°, 90° triangle, with $x = 1/(2\sqrt{3})$, $y = 1/\sqrt{3}$, and

$$\frac{d\theta}{dt}\bigg]_{\theta = \pi/2} = \frac{-200 \sin 30° - 20 \sin 90°}{\frac{1}{2\sqrt{3}} \cos 90° + \frac{1}{\sqrt{3}} \cos 30°}$$

$$= -240 \text{ radians/hr} = -4 \text{ radians/min}.$$

In some situations, the rates may be related by separate equations rather than by a single equation or implicit function.

Example 2. The volume of a sphere is increasing 3 in³./min. At the instant the radius is 4 in., find the rate at which the surface is changing.

Solution. The volume and surface are $V = (4/3)\pi r^3$ and $S = 4\pi r^2$. Thus,

$$\frac{dV}{dt} = 4\pi r^2 \frac{dr}{dt} \quad \text{and} \quad \frac{dS}{dt} = 8\pi r \frac{dr}{dt}$$

show that the rates of change of volume and surface are related to the radius and its rate of change, and hence are related to each other and the radius by

$$\frac{dS}{dt} = \frac{2}{r} \frac{dV}{dt}.$$

Hence, the desired answer is that at the indicated instant, and at this instant only,

$$\frac{dS}{dt} = \frac{2}{4 \text{ in.}} \left(\frac{3 \text{ in}^3.}{\text{min}}\right) = \frac{3}{2} \text{ in}^2./\text{min}.$$

Warning: In working rate-time problems, always represent any variable quantity by a letter (thought of as a function of time) and never substitute a constant for this letter until **after** the time derivative has been taken.

Example 3. A radar station observes an airplane 5 airline mi away approaching the station at 6 mi/min. If the plane is flying at 4 mi elevation on a level course that will take the plane directly over the station, find the speed of the plane.

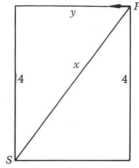

Solution. Even though the plane is observed when it is 5 mi away, Fig. 5-4.2 does not represent this distance by 5 but by x, since the distance is variable. It should also be recorded that

$$x' = \frac{dx}{dt} = -6 \text{ when } x = 5$$

and perhaps at no other time.

On the other hand, the elevation is denoted by 4 and not by a letter, since "the course is level." Also, the

Fig. 5-4.2

distance from the airplane to the point above the station is variable, denoted in the figure by y, and $y' = dy/dt$ is sought.

First, $4^2 + y^2 = x^2$, so $2yy' = 2xx'$ and thus

$$y' = \frac{x}{y} x'.$$

When (and only when) $x = 5$, $x' = -6$, and at this instant $y = \sqrt{5^2 - 4^2} = 3$.

Thus, at this instant,

$$y' = \frac{5}{3} \frac{\text{mi}}{\text{mi}} (-6) \frac{\text{mi}}{\text{min}} = \frac{5}{3} (-6) 60 \frac{\text{mi}}{\text{hr}} = -600 \frac{\text{mi}}{\text{hr}}.$$

Both x' and y' are negative since both x and y are decreasing, but the airplane is traveling 600 mi/hr at the given instant. Further information would be necessary to tell whether it maintains this speed.

Problem 1. A 20-ft ladder leans against a vertical wall. If the foot of the ladder is being pulled along the horizontal floor away from the wall at 4 ft/sec, find how fast the top is sliding down the wall when:

    a. The foot is 5 ft from the wall.
    b. The foot is 16 ft from the wall.
    c. The upper end is 16 ft above the floor.
    d. The upper end is 1 ft above the floor.

Problem 2. A tank is in the form of a right circular cone, with vertex down. The radius of the base is 5 ft and the altitude is 10 ft. Water is running into the tank at the rate of 2 ft³/min. Find how fast the surface of the water is rising when the depth of the water is:

a. 2 ft.   b. 5 ft.   c. 8 ft.   d. 10 ft.

Problem 3. Sand is pouring from a spout at 5 ft³/min and forms a conical pile with radius always 1.5 times the altitude. When the altitude is 3 ft find how fast:
a. The altitude is increasing.   b. The radius is increasing.

Problem 4. A man 6 ft tall walks at 5 ft/sec directly away from a lamp post holding the lamp 16 ft up. How fast is his shadow lengthening? How fast is the tip of his shadow moving?

Problem 5. A spherical iron ball of 5-in. radius is covered by a uniform thickness of ice. When the ice is 2 in. thick and melting at the rate of 10 in.³/min, how fast is the outer surface decreasing?

Problem 6. At noon a ship S_1 is 30 mi due north of a ship S_2. If S_1 is steaming due east at 20 mi/hr while S_2 is steaming north at 15 mi/hr, both rates being uniform, find how the distance between the ship is changing at 1 P. M.

Problem 7. A conical filter is 18 in. deep and 12 in. across the top. A solution is being filtered and collected in a cylindrical vessel 10 in. in diameter. When the solution in the filter is 12 in. deep the surface is falling at $\frac{1}{2}$ in./min. At this instant, what is the rate at which the level in the cylinder is rising?

Problem 8. A 10-ft long trough has vertical equilateral triangular cross sections. If water is flowing into the trough at 15 ft³/min, how fast is the surface rising when the water is 18 in. deep?

Problem 9. Replace the trough of Prob. 8 by one whose vertical cross section is a semicircle of radius 2 ft. [Hint: Either work out, or take for granted, that the shaded area of Fig. 5-4.3 is

$$r^2(\theta - \sin\theta\cos\theta).]$$

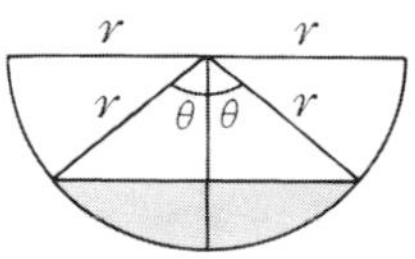

Fig. 5-4.3

Problem 10. A circular plate is expanding but remaining circular.
a. With 1 in. the unit of length and 1 min the unit of time, how long is the radius when the rate in (length)²/time of increase of area is twice the rate in length/time of increase of radius?
b. Change the time unit to 1 sec and answer the question.
c. Change the linear unit to 1 ft and answer the question.

Problem 11. From a balloon remaining spherical, gas is escaping at 2 ft³/min. How is the radius and surface area decreasing when the radius is 10 ft?

Problem 12. From a weight resting on the ground, a rope goes straight up 45 ft to a pulley, then 40 ft straight down where a man grasps the end. Keeping his hand 5 ft above the floor, the man walks away at the constant rate of 2 ft/sec.
a. How fast is the weight rising when the man has walked 9 ft?
b. If the weight weighs 25 lb, with what force will it hit the pulley? [Recall that force equals mass times acceleration.]

Problem 13. Figure 5-4.4 represents a 25-ft crane hinged at *H*. A cable fastened at *F* passes over pulley *P* and to a winch *W* where *HP* is a rigid 10-ft upright. *LF* is a 6-ft cable dangling a load *L*. If the winch pulls in the cable at 4 ft/sec, find

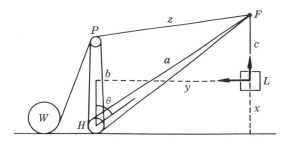

Fig. 5-4.4

the rates at which the load L is rising and moving horizontally, respectively, when $\theta = 60°$. [Hint: First apply the law of cosines to a triangle *HFP*.]

Problem 14. An observer watches a balloon start from the ground 90 ft away and rise vertically at 12 ft/sec and zero acceleration. When the balloon is 120 ft up, at what rate and acceleration is it leaving the observer?

5-5. Expansions of Polynomials

The usual textbook problems are generally designed with care to keep the arithmetic and algebra simple so as not to distract from the underlying theory. In actual practice, however, a polynomial may not factor exactly, but still the roots, or approximations of them, may be the key in an important practical situation. Also, simple-looking equations, such as $2 \sin x = x$, may arise in an engineering problem which do not yield to ordinary methods taught in trigonometry courses.

The purpose of the next three sections is to give background and experience with methods of approximating solutions when it may not be possible to find exact solutions. These sections are therefore computational in nature and may be highly useful to a practical man met with the necessity of solving an equation to the accuracy justified by his measuring instruments or scales.

It may seem at first that the algebraic work of this section is not related to analytic geometry or calculus, but connections to both subjects are made in succeeding sections. All discussions in this section are confined to the specific polynomial

(1) $$P(x) = 2x^4 - 7x^3 + 8x^2 - 19x + 6,$$

but are general enough to indicate techniques applicable to any polynomial.

The coefficients 2, -7, 8, -19, and 6 form the top line of the display, which, as explained below, is a schematic way for finding $P(3)$:

(2)
$$
\begin{array}{rrrrr|l}
2 & -7 & 8 & -19 & 6 & \underline{3} \\
  & 6 & -3 & 15 & -12 & \\
\hline
2 & -1 & 5 & -4 & -6 &
\end{array}
$$

Here 2 is brought below the line, multiplied by 3 to obtain the 6 of the second line, 6 is added to -7 to obtain -1 in the bottom line, -1 is multiplied by 3 to obtain the second entry in the second line, etc. It will now be shown how (2) may be interpreted to show that

(3) $$P(x) = (2x^3 - x^2 + 5x - 4)(x - 3) - 6.$$

In order to show this, let $b_3, b_2, b_1, b_0,$ and R be numbers such that

$$P(x) \equiv (b_3 x^3 + b_2 x^2 + b_1 x + b_0)(x - 3) + R$$
$$\equiv b_3 x^4 + (-3b_3 + b_2)\, x^3 + (-3b_2 + b_1)\, x^2$$
$$+ (-3b_1 + b_2)\, x + (-3b_0 + R).$$

In this form, the coefficients of like powers of x must agree with the corresponding coefficients of powers of x in (1); that is,

$$b_3 = 2$$
$$-3b_3 + b_2 = -7, \quad b_2 = 3b_3 - 7 = 6 - 7 = -1$$
$$-3b_2 + b_1 = 8, \quad b_1 = 3b_2 + 8 = -3 + 8 = 5$$
$$-3b_1 + b_0 = -19, \quad b_0 = 3b_1 - 19 = 15 - 19 = -4$$
$$-3b_0 + R = 6, \quad R = 3b_0 + 6 = -12 + 6 = -6.$$

Note that at each stage "the previous result is multiplied by 3 and this product added to the corresponding coefficient in $P(x)$," exactly as in the display (2).

An incidental but important result is obtained by substituting $x = 3$ into (3) to obtain at a glance that

(4) $$P(3) = -6.$$

Thus, (2) shows that

(5) $$P(x) = 2x^4 - 7x^3 + 8x^2 - 19x + 6$$
$$= (2x^3 - x^2 + 5x - 4)(x - 3) - 6.$$

Upon starting with the new polynomial $2x^2 - x^2 + 5x - 4$, the display

(6)

$$
\begin{array}{rrrr|l}
2 & -1 & 5 & -4 & \underline{3} \\
  & 6 & 15 & 60 & \\
\hline
2 & 5 & 20 & 56 &
\end{array}
$$

shows that $2x^3 - x^2 + 5x - 4 = (2x^2 + 5x + 20)(x - 3) + 56$. Next, upon substituting this result into (5), the result is

(7) $$P(x) = (2x^2 + 5x + 20)(x - 3)^2 + 56(x - 3) - 6.$$

The student should now apply the same technique to the new polynomial $2x^2 + 5x + 20$ to obtain

$$2x^2 + 5x + 20 = (2x + 11)(x - 3) + 53,$$

and then substitute into (7) to obtain

(8) $P(x) = (2x + 11)(x - 3)^3 + 53(x - 3)^2 + 56(x - 3) - 6.$

Since the top line of display (6) is the bottom line of display (2), these two displays may be telescoped and then extended two more steps:

$$
\begin{array}{c}
(2) \\
(6)
\end{array}
\left\{
\begin{array}{rrrrrl}
2 & -7 & 8 & -19 & 6 & \underline{|3} \\
 & 6 & -3 & 15 & -12 & \\
\hline
2 & -1 & 5 & -4 & -6 & = P(3) \\
 & 6 & 15 & 60 & & \\
\hline
2 & 5 & 20 & 56 & & \\
 & 6 & 33 & & & \\
\hline
2 & 11 & 53 & & & \\
 & 6 & & & & \\
\hline
2 & 17 & & & &
\end{array}
\right.
$$

to obtain the coefficients 2, 17, 53, 56, and −6 in

(9) $P(x) = 2(x - 3)^4 + 17(x - 3)^3 + 53(x - 3)^2 + 56(x - 3) - 6.$

This latter form is said to be "the expansion of $P(x)$ in powers of $x - 3$."
Notice that, upon using $x = 4$ (instead of $x = 3$), then

$$
\begin{array}{rrrrrl}
2 & -7 & 8 & -19 & 6 & \underline{|4} \\
 & 8 & 4 & 48 & 116 & \\
\hline
2 & 1 & 12 & 29 & 122 & = P(4)
\end{array}
$$

Since $P(3) = -6$ while $P(4) = 122$ have opposite signs, there is a solution of $P(x) = 0$ between $x = 3$ and $x = 4$. A method of approximating this solution is the topic of the next section.

5-6. Horner's Method

Attention will again be restricted to the specific polynomial

(1) $y = P(x) = 2x^4 - 7x^3 + 8x^2 - 19x + 6$

for illustrative development of theory leading to a systematic method, known as Horner's Method, for approximating solutions of polynomial equations such as

(2) $2x^4 - 7x^3 + 8x^2 - 19x + 6 = 0.$

As in Sec. 5–5 the expansion of $P(x)$ in powers of $x - 3$ is

(3) $y = P(x) = 2(x-3)^4 + 17(x-3)^3 + 53(x-3)^2 + 56(x-3) - 6,$

and the method of Sec. 5–5 is an easy way of obtaining this expansion.

Since (3) is merely an alternative form of (1), the graphs of (1) and (3) are identical. As seen in Sec. 5–5, this graph crosses the x-axis between $x = 3$ and $x = 4$.

A new coordinate system will now be chosen with the new origin at the

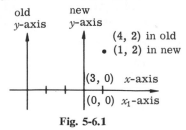

Fig. 5-6.1

old point (3, 0). The formulas for this translation of axes (see Sec. 4–8) will be denoted by

$$x_1 = x - 3, \quad y_1 = y,$$

where x_1 is not a constant (as usually denoted by a subscript) but is a new variable related to the old variable x. The equation $y_1 = y$ means that any point has the same y-value in both coordinate systems; that is, the x_1-axis is the same as the x-axis except for a different origin. Hence, (3) becomes

(4) $$y = 2x_1^4 + 17x_1^3 + 53x_1^2 + 56x_1 - 6,$$

whose graph relative to the new coordinate system is exactly the same as the graph of (1) and (3) relative to the old coordinate system. Thus, the graph of (4) crosses the horizontal axis the same amount greater than $x_1 = 0$ that (1) crosses greater than $x = 3$. It is customary to say "the root has been **reduced by 3.**"

Hence, the polynomial in (4) set equal to zero has a solution between $x_1 = 0$ and $x_1 = 1$. Since the square, cube, and fourth power of a number between 0 and 1 is smaller than the number itself, a first guess for this solution is obtained by neglecting higher powers of x_1 in (4) and setting

$$56x_1 - 6 = 0, \quad x_1 = \frac{6}{56} = \text{about } 0.1.$$

The next step is to consider writing (4) in powers of $(x_1 - 0.1)$ preparatory to using a second new variable $x_2 = x_1 - 0.1$. The relevant display starts as

2	17.0	53.00	56.000	−6.0000	0.1
	0.2	1.72	5.472	6.1472	
2	17.2	54.72	61.472	0.1472	

but this is not continued since the constant term of (4) is negative (namely, −6), whereas the constant term of the polynomial in $x_2 = x_1 - 0.1$ is the positive term 0.1472. This means that the desired solution has been "overshot."

Thus, divide by the next hundredth less than 0.1. This leads to the translation

(5) $$x_2 = x_1 - 0.09,$$

and is obtained from the display

2	17.00	53.00 00	56.00 00 00	−6.00 00 00 00	0.09
	0.18	1.54 62	4.90 91 58	5.48 18 24 22	
2	17.18	54.54 62	60.90 91 58	−0.51 81 75 78	
	0.18	1.56 24	5.04 97 74		
2	17.36	56.10 86	65.95 89 32		
	0.18	1.57 86			
2	17.54	57.68 72			
	0.18				
2	17.72				

Hence, the graph of

(6) $$y = 2x_2^4 + 17.72x_2^3 + 57.6872x_2^2 + 65.958932x_2 - 0.51817578$$

crosses the x_2-axis between $x_2 = 0$ and $x_2 = 0.01$ and close to the solution of $65.958932x_2 - 0.51817578$ or (by rounding off numbers) close to

$$\frac{0.52}{66} = \text{about } 0.008.$$

Since $x_1 = x - 3$ and $x_2 = x_1 - 0.09$, then

$$x = 3 + x_1 = 3 + (0.09 + x_2) = 3.09 + x_2.$$

But (6) set equal to zero has solution close to $x_2 = 0.008$, and hence the solution of (2) is close to

(7) $$x = 3.09 + 0.008 = 3.098.$$

If even more accuracy is desired, then (6) would be expanded in powers of $x_3 = x_2 - 0.008$, etc.

Now that the theory has been developed, the following example illustrates all of the numerical computation, except for a small amount of scratch work, needed to find an approximate solution of a polynomial equation.

Example. Given that the polynomial equation

$$2x^3 - 11x^2 + 22x - 17 = 0$$

has a root between $x = 2$ and $x = 3$, find the approximation of this root accurate to two decimal places and estimate the third decimal place. Note: If the integer values between which a root lies had not been given, then some trial-and-error scratch work would have been necessary to so locate a root. Hints about this phase are given in the next section.

Solution.

```
2   −11     22    −17   | 2
     4    −14     16
    ────────────────────
2    −7      8    −1        ½ = 0.5 is probably too large since all other terms are
     4     −6               positive, so try 0.4
    ───────────
2    −3      2
     4
    ──────
2    1.0    2.00  −1.000  | 0.4
     0.8    0.72   1.088
    ─────────────────────
2    1.8    2.72   0.088      sign changed, so overshot solution, try 0.3
```

```
2    1.0    2.00  −1.000  | 0.3
     0.6    0.48   0.744
    ─────────────────────
2    1.6    2.48  −0.256      0.256
     0.6    0.66              ─────  = about 0.08
    ───────────              3.14
2    2.2    3.14
     0.6
    ──────
2    2.80   3.1400  −0.256000  | 0.08
     0.16   0.2368   0.270144
    ──────────────────────────
2    2.96   3.3768   +   so overshot, try 0.07
```

```
2    2.80   3.1400  −0.256000  | 0.07
     0.14   0.2058   0.234206
    ──────────────────────────
2    2.94   3.3458  −0.021794     0.021794            0.022
     0.14   0.2156                ────────  = about   ─────  = about  0.006.
    ───────────                    3.5614             3.56
2    3.08   3.5614
```

Note that the root was first reduced by 2, then by 0.3, then by 0.07. Answer.
$2 + 0.3 + 0.07 + 0.006^+ = 2.376^+$.

Problem 1. Expand $P(x) = 2x^3 - 4x^2 + x - 5$ in powers of:

a. $x - 3$.   b. $x - 2$.   c. $x + 3$.   d. $x + 2$.

Problem 2. Check that the given number is an approximation of a root of the given equation:

    a. 2.178, $x^3 + x^2 - 6x - 2 = 0$.
    b. 4.102, $x^3 + x^2 + x - 90 = 0$.
    c. 1.838, $4x^3 - 12x^2 + 8x + 1 = 0$.
    d. 1.428, $2x^3 - 5x^2 - x + 5 = 0$.

Problem 3. Note that, for $f(x) = 2x^3 - 4x^2 + x - 5$, the accompanying display gives $f(1.23) = -6.100$ rounded off to three decimal places:

$$
\begin{array}{rrrr|r}
2 & -4 & 1 & -5 & \underline{|1} \\
  & 2 & -2 & -1 & \\
\hline
2 & -2 & -1 & -6 & \\
  & 2 & 0 & & \\
\hline
2 & 0 & -1 & & \\
  & 2 & & & \\
\hline
2 & 2.0 & -1.00 & -6.000 & \underline{|0.2} \\
  & 0.4 & 0.48 & -0.104 & \\
\hline
2 & 2.4 & -0.52 & -6.104 & \\
  & 0.4 & 0.56 & & \\
\hline
2 & 2.8 & 0.04 & & \\
  & 0.4 & & & \\
\hline
2 & 3.20 & 0.0400 & -6.104000 & \underline{|0.03} \\
  & 0.06 & 0.0978 & 0.004134 & \\
\hline
2 & 3.26 & 0.1378 & -6.099866 & \\
\end{array}
$$

Use the above scheme to find to three decimal places:

a. $f(1.23)$ if $f(x) = 3x^3 - 4x^2 + 2x + 4$.

b. $f(2.15)$ if $f(x) = -2x^3 + 5x^2 - x + 3$.

Problem 4. Find the root indicated to two decimal places and estimate the third:

a. $x^3 - 3x^2 - 2x + 5 = 0$, root between 3 and 4.

b. $x^3 - 3x^2 - 2x + 5 = 0$, root between 2 and 3.

c. $2x^3 - 26x^2 + 0 \cdot x + 143 = 0$, root between 2 and 3.

d. $3x^3 - 5x^2 - 3x - 4 = 0$, root between 2 and 3.

e. $2x^3 + 4x^2 - 35x - 95 = 0$, root between 4 and 5.

f. $x^3 + 3x^2 - 4x + 1 = 0$, root between 0.3 and 0.4.

g. $x^3 + 3x^2 - 4x + 1 = 0$, root between 0.6 and 0.7.

h. $3x^4 + 0 \cdot x^3 - 30x^2 + x + 30 = 0$, root between 2 and 3.

i. $x^3 - 65x^2 + 2x - 560$, root between 65 and 66. [Hint: First use 60, then 5.]

Problem 5. A box without a lid is to be made from a sheet of tin 8 in. × 10 in. by cutting squares x in. on a side and turning up the tin to form the sides. Show that the volume V of the box is

$$V = 4x^3 - 36x^2 + 80x.$$

Find x accurate to 0.01 in. if:

a. $V = 44$ in^3.   b. V is maximum.

c. Also, find V for the value of x found in part b.

5-7. Derivative Coefficients

For a function $f(x)$ the first and second derivatives are denoted in the "prime notation" by $f'(x)$ and $f''(x)$. The derivative of the second derivative

—that is, the third derivative—is denoted by $f'''(x)$. The prime notation is, however, too cumbersome for the fourth and higher derivatives and these are denoted by $f^4(x)$, $f^5(x)$, etc. Note that $f^4(x)$ *does not* mean $f(x)$ raised to the fourth power.

Again the specific polynomial

(1) $$y = P(x) = 2x^4 - 7x^3 + 8x^2 - 19x + 6$$

and the value $x = 3$ will be used for illustrative purposes.

Let a_4, a_3, a_2, a_1, and a_0 be constants such that

(2) $$P(x) = a_4(x-3)^4 + a_3(x-3)^3 + a_2(x-3)^2 + a_1(x-3) + a_0.$$

is the expansion of $P(x)$ in powers of $x - 3$. First by substituting $x = 3$,

$$P(3) = a_0.$$

The other coefficients may be expressed in terms of the derivatives of $P(x)$ by first noting that

$$P'(x) = 4a_4(x - 3)^3 + 3a_3(x - 3)^2 + 2a_2(x-3) + a_1,$$
$$P''(x) = 4 \cdot 3a_4(x - 3)^2 + 3 \cdot 2a_3(x-3) + 2a_2,$$
$$P'''(x) = 4 \cdot 3 \cdot 2a_4(x - 3) + 3 \cdot 2a_3,$$
$$P^4(x) = 4 \cdot 3 \cdot 2a_4.$$

Now in each of these substitute $x = 3$ and obtain, respectively,

$$P'(3) = a_1, \quad P''(3) = 2a_2, \quad P'''(3) = 3 \cdot 2a_3 = 3!a_3, \quad P^4(3) = 4!a_4$$

so that

$$a_1 = P'(3), \quad a_2 = \frac{P''(3)}{2}, \quad a_3 = \frac{P'''(3)}{3!}, \quad a_4 = \frac{P^4(3)}{4!}.$$

Upon combining these new facts with the method in Sec. 5-5 of determining the coefficients, note that

$$
\begin{array}{rrrrr|l}
2 & -7 & 8 & -19 & 6 & 3 \\
 & 6 & -3 & 15 & -12 & \\
\hline
2 & -1 & 5 & -4 & -6 = P(3) \\
 & 6 & 15 & 60 & \\
\hline
2 & 5 & 20 & 56 = P'(3) \\
 & 6 & 33 & \\
\hline
2 & 11 & 53 = \dfrac{P''(3)}{2} \\
 & 6 & \\
\hline
2 & 17 = \dfrac{P'''(3)}{3!} \\
\hline
2 = \dfrac{P^4(3)}{4!}
\end{array}
$$

This new information (especially about the first derivative) is useful in the trial-and-error stage of locating a root between two successive integers.* For example, $P(3) = -6$ says the graph of $y = P(x)$ is below the x-axis when $x = 3$ while $P'(3) = 56$ says the graph is sloping steeply upward and will undoubtedly cross the x-axis between $x = 3$ and $x = 4$; a check then shows that it does.

From

$$
\begin{array}{rrrrr|l}
2 & -7 & 8 & -19 & 6 & \underline{2} \\
 & 4 & -6 & 4 & -30 & \\
\hline
2 & -3 & 2 & -15 & -24 = P(2) \\
 & 4 & 2 & 8 & \\
\hline
2 & 1 & 4 & -7 = P'(2) \\
\end{array}
$$

the graph is below the axis when $x = 2$ and sloping downward [since $P'(2) = -7$] so will be unlikely to cross the x-axis betweem $x = 2$ and $x = 3$. Going back toward $x = 1$, the curve is so far down (-24) that the slope -7 would probably not bring it up to the x-axis between $x = 1$ and $x = 2$.

Note that the expansion of $P(x)$ in powers of $x - 3$ may be expressed as

$$P(x) = P(3) + P'(3)(x - 3) + \frac{P''(3)}{2}(x - 3)^2$$

$$+ \frac{P'''(3)}{3!}(x - 3)^3 + \frac{P^4(3)}{4!}(x - 3)^4.$$

Later on (Chapter 13) it will be seen that, under proper conditions, $P(x)$ may be replaced by a more general function $f(x)$ and the expansion extended endlessly.

At the trial-and-error stage of locating roots between integers, evidence of upper and lower bounds of roots should be watched for, as now illustrated. The value of $P(4)$ is obtained as follows:

$$
\begin{array}{rrrrr|l}
2 & -7 & 8 & -19 & 6 & \underline{4} \\
 & 8 & 4 & 48 & 116 & \\
\hline
2 & 1 & 12 & 29 & 122 = P(4) \\
\end{array}
$$

But each number in the bottom row is positive. Hence if a number larger than $x = 4$ were used, then each number in the bottom row would be even larger, and, in particular, P of that number would be even larger than $P(4) = 122$. Thus, $P(x) = 0$ has no root larger than $x = 4$.

Now try a negative number, say, $x = -1$:

---

*Notice also that the estimate of the nearest tenth to try for a root is 6/56. This fraction is now seen to be $-P(3)/P'(3)$ and hence the root is probably close to $3 - P(3)/P'(3)$. This footnote will be referred to later.

$$
\begin{array}{rrrrr|l}
2 & -7 & 8 & -19 & 6 & \underline{-1} \\
  & -1 & 8 & -16 & 35 & \\
\hline
2 & -8 & 16 & -35 & 41 & = P(-1)
\end{array}
$$

The signs in the bottom row alternate. Hence any number more negative than $x = -1$ would produce a display with lower line alternating in sign and ending up with a positive number even greater than $P(-1) = 41$. Thus, a number more negative than -1 cannot be a root of $P(x) = 0$. In fact, $P(x)$ itself has coefficients $2, -7, 8, -19$, and 6 alternating in sign, so no negative number whatever can be a root of $P(x) = 0$.

Example 1. Isolate the roots of $Q(x) = 0$ between consecutive integers, where $Q(x) = 2x^3 - 26x^2 + 143$.

Solution. Note the missing x term, which means that x has coefficient 0, so write

$$Q(x) = 2x^3 - 26x^2 + 0 \cdot x + 143.$$

First, $Q(0) = 143$. Next,

$$
\begin{array}{rrrr|l}
2 & -26 & 0 & 143 & \underline{1} \\
  & 2 & -24 & -24 & \\
\hline
2 & -24 & -24 & 119 & = Q(1) \\
  & 2 & -22 & & \\
\hline
2 & -22 & -46 & = Q'(1) &
\end{array}
$$

The curve is way up since $Q(1) = 119$ and not coming down fast enough, even though $Q'(1) = -46$, to cross before $x = 2$. Thus, try $x = 3$:

$$
\begin{array}{rrrr|l}
2 & -26 & 0 & 143 & \underline{3} \\
  & 6 & -60 & -180 & \\
\hline
2 & -20 & -60 & -37 & = Q(3) \\
  & 6 & -42 & & \\
\hline
2 & -14 & -102 & = Q'(3) &
\end{array}
$$

Hence, there is a root between $x = 1$ and $x = 3$, so go back to $x = 2$:

$$
\begin{array}{rrrr|l}
2 & -26 & 0 & 143 & \underline{2} \\
  & 4 & -44 & -88 & \\
\hline
2 & -22 & -44 & + & = Q(2)
\end{array}
$$

Since $Q(2)$ is positive and $Q(3)$ is negative, there is a root between $x = 2$ and $x = 3$.

Since (two steps above) $Q'(3) = -102$, the curve is on its way down at $x = 3$ and will continue going down until after the derivative turns positive. This will not be until x is considerably larger than $x = 3$ (because the second coefficient -26 is negative, but so much larger in absolute value than the first coefficient 2). In fact, it is natural to try $x = 13$:

$$
\begin{array}{rrrr|l}
2 & -26 & 0 & 143 & \underline{13} \\
  & 26 & 0 & 0 & \\
\hline
2 & 0 & 0 & 143 & = Q(13)
\end{array}
$$

and there is no root larger than $x = 13$. Now move back to $x = 12$:

$$
\begin{array}{rrrr|l}
2 & -26 & 0 & 143 & \underline{12} \\
  & 24 & -24 & -288 & \\
\hline
2 & -2 & -24 & -145 = Q(12)
\end{array}
$$

so a second root is between $x = 12$ and $x = 13$.

Having exhausted reasonable positive roots, try for a negative root:

$$
\begin{array}{rrrr|l}
2 & -26 & 0 & 148 & \underline{-1} \\
  & -2 & 28 & -28 & \\
\hline
2 & -28 & 28 & + = Q(-1) & \text{same sign as } Q(0) = 143
\end{array}
$$

$$
\begin{array}{rrrr|l}
2 & -26 & 0 & 143 & \underline{-2} \\
  & -4 & 60 & -120 & \\
\hline
2 & -30 & 60 & 23 = Q(-2) & \text{same sign as } Q(-1),
\end{array}
$$

$$
\begin{array}{rrrr|l}
2 & -26 & 0 & 143 & \underline{-3} \\
  & -6 & 96 & -288 & \\
\hline
2 & -32 & 96 & -145 = Q(-3) & \text{change of sign}
\end{array}
$$

so there is a root between $x = -3$ and $x = -2$.

The three roots of the third-degree polynomial equation have thus been isolated between consecutive integers.

Example 2. Find the nearest two-decimal approximation of the root between $x = -3$ and $x = -2$.

Solution. For negative roots, it is usually better to first go to the negative integer just below the root and then work up toward the root.

$$
\begin{array}{rrrr|l}
2 & -26 & 0 & 143 & \underline{-3} \\
  & -6 & 96 & -288 & \\
\hline
2 & -32 & 96 & -145 & \\
  & -6 & 114 & & \\
\hline
2 & -38 & 210 & & \\
  & -6 & & & \\
\hline
2 & -44.0 & 210.00 & -145.000 & \underline{0.8} \\
  & 1.6 & -33.92 & 140.864 & \\
\hline
2 & -42.4 & 176.08 & -4.136 & \\
  & 1.6 & -32.64 & & \\
\hline
2 & -40.8 & 143.44 & & \\
  & 1.6 & & & \\
\hline
2 & -39.20 & 143.4400 & -4.136000 & \underline{0.03} \\
  & 0.06 & -1.1742 & 4.267974 & \\
\hline
2 & -39.14 & 142.2658 & 0.131974 & \\
\end{array}
$$

$\dfrac{145}{210}$ = about 0.7, but because of the large negative number -145 try 0.8

$\dfrac{4.136}{143.44}$ or $\dfrac{4}{143}$ is less than 0.03, so try 0.03

is positive, so try 0.02

$$
\begin{array}{rrrr|l}
2 & -39.20 & 143.4400 & -4.136000 & \underline{0.02} \\
  & 0.04 & -0.7832 & 2.853136 & \\
\hline
2 & -39.16 & 142.6568 & -1.282864 & \\
\end{array}
$$

which is farther from zero than 0.131974, so 0.03 is closer than 0.02 to the correct value. Hence, the nearest two-decimal approximation is

$$x = -3 + 0.8 + 0.03 = -3 + 0.83 = -2.17.$$

Here the root was first increased by 3, then reduced by 0.8.

Note that even though long numbers are involved in Horner's Method it is never necessary to multiply a long number by more than one digit and this can be done without scratch work.

Problem 1. Given $f(x) = 2x^3 - 4x^2 + 6x - 4$, compute the values of $f(x)$ and its first three derivatives for the values:

a. $x = 3$,   b. $x = -3$,   c. $x = -4$,   d. $x = 4$,

both by the method of this section and by direct substitution.

Problem 2. Isolate the roots of $P(x) = 0$ between consecutive integers:

a. $P(x) = x^2 - 41$.   c. $P(x) = 8x^3 - 3x^2 - 18x + 9$.
b. $P(x) = x^2 + x - 1$.   d. $P(x) = x^3 - 8.1x^2 - 2.4x + 19.7$.

Problem 3. For each of the polynomials of Prob. 2, approximate each of the roots accurate to two decimal places and estimate the third decimal place.

Problem 4. Find the positive square root of each of the numbers:

a. 74,565.123.   b. 475.324.   c. 626.143.   d. 10,500.

[Hint: The answer to part a, for example, is the positive root of $x^2 + 0 \cdot x - 74{,}565.123 = 0$. First, $(2 \cdot 10^2)^2 = 40{,}000$ while $(3 \cdot 10)^2 = 90{,}000$, the first less but the second greater than 74,565.123, so first reduce the root by $2 \cdot 10^2 = 200$. From the resulting display, locate the root between consecutive multiples of 10 and reduce the root by the smaller of these. Next reduce the roots by an integer, then by a multiple of $10^{-1} = 0.1$, etc.]

Problem 5. For $y = f(x) = 2x^3 + 15x^2 + 36x + 29$, show that the local maximum and minimum are on the same side of the x-axis. Sketch a rough graph to show that this means $f(x) = 0$ has only one real root. Approximate this root.

Problem 6. Work Prob. 5 for
$$y = f(x) = x^3 - 3x - 3.$$

[Note: In a course on theory of equations a great deal more can be learned about the roots of a polynomial, such as the number of real and the number of complex roots, whether there are rational roots, etc. If a polynomial arises in an engineering problem, however, the engineer will have supplementary information to give him a feeling for a fairly narrrow range within which the root significant to the situation lies, and other roots (if there are any) would be extraneous for his purposes.]

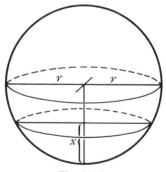

Fig. 5-7.1

Problem 7. A body of volume V is said to have **specific gravity** s, where $0 < s$

< 1, if, as the body floats in water, the water it displaces has volume sV. For example, a solid sphere of specific gravity $s = \frac{1}{2}$ will sink to an equator.

In a sphere of radius r, a section of altitude x (see Fig. 5-7.1) has volume $\pi(rx^2 - \frac{1}{3}x^2)$. This formula is derived later.

   a. Show that a sphere of radius 2 ft and specific gravity $s = \frac{1}{4}$ will float with its lowest point x ft below the surface, where x is the solution between **0** and 2 of $x^3 - 6x^2 + 8 = 0$.

   b. Find to the nearest 0.01 ft how deep the sphere of part a sinks into water.

   c. Work parts a and b if $s = \frac{3}{4}$.

Problem 8. Let $P(x) = a_4x^4 + a_3x^3 + a_2x^2 + a_1x + a_0$ and let r be a constant. Find the expression for $P(r)$ and then by using calculus also find $P'(r)$, $P''(r)$, $P'''(r)$ and $P^4(r)$. The following display is the start of one similar to that of p. 192, but with letters instead of numbers. Finish this display and note how the expressions for $P(r)$, $P'(r)$, $\ldots$, $P^4(r)/4!$ appear:

$$
\begin{array}{cccccc}
a_4 & a_3 & a_2 & a_1 & a_0 & \underline{\;r} \\
 & a_4r & a_4r^2 + a_3r & & & \\
\hline
a_4 & a_4r + a_3 & a_4r^2 + a_3r + a_2 & \ldots & &
\end{array}
$$

5-8. Newton's Method

In a trigonometry course, the equation $2 \sin x = 1$ was solved by writing it as

$$\sin x = \tfrac{1}{2}$$

and then noting that $x = 30°, 150°$, etc. if answers in degree measure are desired, or

$$x = \frac{\pi}{6}, \frac{5}{6}\pi, \text{ etc,}$$

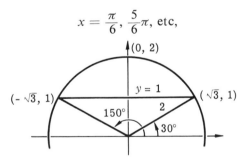

Fig. 5-8.1

if radian measure is used. If, however, a solution is sought of an equation such as

(1) $$2 \sin x = x,$$

the situation is more complicated.

Newton's Method is a systematic way of attacking such equations. Equation(1) is first written as $2 \sin x - x = 0$, and then the function

(2) $$f(x) = 2 \sin x - x$$

is introduced. The theory of Newton's Method will be developed using a general function,

(3) $$y = f(x),$$

of which (2) is a typical example.

First. By trial and error, locate two constants $x = x_0$ and $x = \bar{x}$ fairly close together such that $f(x_0)$ and $f(\bar{x})$ have opposite signs and with $|f(x_0)| < |f(\bar{x})|$. Hints to use at this stage are given later.

Second. Find the point on the curve $y = f(x)$ having $x = x_0$. At this point, draw the tangent to the curve and obtain the equation of this tangent:

(4) $$y - f(x_0) = f'(x_0)(x - x_0).$$

Find where this tangent crosses the x-axis; that is, set $y = 0$ in (4) and solve for x. Let $x = x_1$ be this solution:

(5) $$x_1 = x_0 - \frac{f(x_0)}{f'(x_0)}.$$

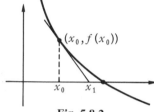

Fig. 5-8.2

Here x_1 is a constant and for most curves (see Fig. 5-8.2) $x = x_1$ will be closer to the solution of $f(x) = 0$ than $x = x_0$ was.*

Third. Think of repeating the second step with x_0 replaced by x_1, and thus obtain

(6) $$x_2 = x_1 - \frac{f(x_1)}{f'(x_1)}.$$

as an even better approximation of the desired solution.

Fourth. Repeat this iterative process, obtaining x_3, x_4, ..., until two successive approximations agree to the desired number of places.† Use this agreement as an approximation of the root.

The first example is kept simple so the essential features of the procedure will not be lost.

Example 1. Use Newton's Method to find the three-decimal-place approximation of $\sqrt{3}$.

Solution. The desired number is the positive solution of $x^2 - 3 = 0$, so define the function $f(x)$ by

$$f(x) = x^2 - 3, \quad \text{and note} \quad f'(x) = 2x.$$

---

*Sometimes x_1 will not be a better approximation than x_0, as shown in Prob. 1.

†There are rare cases where even though two successive approximations agree to a certain number of decimal places, they may still differ from the root by more than this amount. Conditions for determining the reliability of the approximations x_1, x_2, $\cdots$ are discussed in a course on numerical analysis, but the rule of thumb given above is usually sufficient in practical situations.

By trial and error, $f(1) = 1 - 3 = -2$ and $f(2) = 4 - 3 = 1$ have opposite signs, with $x = 2$ closer than $x = 1$ to the solution. Hence, set $x_0 = 2$. By direct substitution into (5),

$$x_1 = 2 - \frac{2^2 - 3}{2 \cdot 2} = 2 - \frac{1}{4} = 1.75.$$

Next, by direct substitution of $x_1 = 1.75$ into (6),

$$x_2 = 1.75 - \frac{(1.75)^2 - 3}{2(1.75)} = 1.75 - \frac{3.0625 - 3}{3.5}$$

$$= 1.75 - \frac{0.0625}{3.5} = 1.75 - 0.018 = 1.732^+.$$

Now add one to the subscripts to obtain

$$x_3 = 1.732 - \frac{(1.732)^2 - 3}{2(1.732)} = 1.732 - \frac{2.9998^+ - 3}{3.464}$$

$$= 1.732 - \frac{(-0.0002^+)}{3.464},$$

which to three decimal places is 1.732, and this is the desired approximation.

The form of (5) and (6) together with the footnote of p. 193 show that Horner's Method is really Newton's Method applied to polynomial equations.

Before starting the next example, it may be well to review some pertinent trigonometry.

The degree column of Table 2 is given at $10'$ intervals. Thus, in order to find $\sin 56° \, 43'$, it is necessary to use interpolation:

$$\begin{aligned} \sin 56° \, 40' &= 0.8355 \\ \sin 56° \, 43' &= 0.83?? \\ \sin 56° \, 50' &= 0.8371 \end{aligned} \qquad \frac{03}{10} = \frac{x}{71 - 55}, \qquad x = \frac{(03)(16)}{10} = \frac{48}{10} = 4.8,$$

so use $x = 5$ to obtain $\sin 56° \, 43' = 0.8355 + 0.0005 = 0.8360$.

In Table 2 there is also a radian column. If, for example, $\sin 1.2283$ is sought, then a search for 1.2283 in the radian column is made. Since no such entry occurs, interpolation is again necessary. In the radian column are found 1.2275 and 1.2305 spanning the desired radian measure 1.2283. Hence, a similar arrangement is made as above:

$$\begin{aligned} \sin 1.2275 &= 0.9417 \\ \sin 1.2283 &= 0.94?? \\ \sin 1.2305 &= 0.9426 \end{aligned} \qquad \frac{283 - 275}{305 - 275} = \frac{x}{26 - 17}, \qquad x = \frac{(8)(9)}{30} = \frac{72}{30},$$

so that $x = 2$ is used to obtain

(7) $$\sin 1.2283 = 0.9417 + 0.00(02) = 0.9419.$$

The degree measures of Table 2 are from $0°$ to $90°$. Thus, if $\sin 134° 18'$ is sought, then the trigonometric identities

$$\sin A = \sin(180° - A) \quad \text{and} \quad \cos A = -\cos(180° - A)$$

are first used to bring the angles within the range of the table.

In the same way, the radian columns of Table 2 are from 0.0000 to $\pi/2$ = 1.5708. Thus, if sin 1.9133 and cos 1.9133 are sought, then

$$\sin x = \sin(\pi - x) \quad \text{and} \quad \cos x = -\cos(\pi - x)$$

are used to give

(8) $\sin 1.9133 = \sin(3.1416 - 1.9133) = \sin 1.2283 = 0.9419$ by (7)

(9) $\cos(1.9133) = -\cos(1.2283) = -0.3358,$

where this cosine value should be checked for practice.

Example 2. Find the three-decimal approximation of the positive root of $2 \sin x = x$. (Here the angle must be measured in radians.)

Solution. As suggested above, set

$$f(x) = 2 \sin x - x \quad \text{and then obtain} \quad f'(x) = 2 \cos x - 1.$$

Now a hint about the trial and error stage. The value of x where the curve $y = 2 \sin x - x$ crosses the x-axis is same as the value of x where the two curves

$$y = 2 \sin x \quad \text{and} \quad y = x$$

intersect one another, and these curves are easy to sketch fairly accurately (see

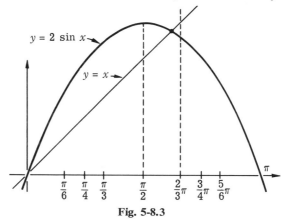

Fig. 5-8.3

Fig. 5-8.3). These curves intersect between $x = \pi/2$ and $x = 2\pi/3$, seemingly closer to the latter, so choose $x_0 = 2\pi/3 = \pi - \pi/3 = 3.1416 - 1.0472 = 2.0944$. Hence, from (5),

$$x_1 = 2.0944 - \frac{2\sin(2\pi/3) - 2.0944}{2\cos(2\pi/3) - 1} = 2.0944 - \frac{2(\sqrt{3}/2) - 2.0944}{2(-\tfrac{1}{2}) - 1}$$

$$= 2.0944 - \frac{1.7321 - 2.0944}{-2} = 2.0944 - \frac{0.3623}{2}$$

$$= 2.0944 - 0.1811 = 1.9133.$$

This value is now substituted into (6):

$$x_2 = 1.9133 - \frac{2 \sin (1.9133) - 1.9133}{2 \cos (1.9133) - 1}$$

$$= 1.9133 - \frac{2(0.9419) - 1.9133}{2(-0.3358) - 1} \quad \text{by (8) and (9)}$$

$$= 1.9133 - \frac{0.0295}{1.6716} = 1.9133 - 0.0176 = 1.8957.$$

The student should check the following computations:

$$x_3 = 1.8957 - \frac{2 \sin (1.8957) - 1.8957}{2 \cos (1.8957) - 1}$$

$$= 1.8957 - \frac{2(0.9477) - 1.8957}{2(-0.3192) - 1} = 1.8957 - \frac{0.0003}{1.6384}.$$

Since x_2 and x_3 agree to three decimal places, the number 1.8957 is rounded off to 1.896 as the desired approximation.

Problem 1. Figure. 5-8.4 illustrates a graphical determination of x_1, x_2, and x_3. Make a similar graphical determination in:

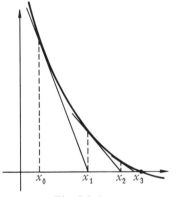

Fig. 5-8.4

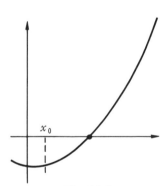

Fig. 5-8.5

    a. Figure. 5-8.5, and note that x_1 is on the other side of the solution from x_0, but then x_2 is a better approximation than x_1, x_3 is better than x_2, etc.

    b. Figure 5-8.6, and note that x_3 is out of range.

[Note: The concavity of the curve of Fig. 5-8.4 is away from $(x_0, 0)$. In Fig. 5-8.5, the concavity is toward $(x_0, 0)$, but then away from $(x_1, 0)$, while in Fig. 5-8.6 the concavity changes direction. Such observations indicate that the behavior of the second derivative $f''(x)$ near a solution is important. If a solution is programmed for an electronic computer, such considerations are important,

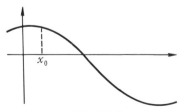

Fig. 5-8.6

and this is one reason why well-trained mathematicians are necessary in a computing center. If, however, computation is being done by hand or on a desk calculator, then the solver can watch $x_1, x_2, \ldots$ and can tell whether $f(x_1), f(x_2)$, etc., are getting closer and closer to zero; if not, he returns to trial and error to find a better starting value, x_0.]

Problem 2. Work Example 2, starting with $x_0 = \pi/2$.

Problem 3. For each of the following, determine a starting value x_0, then compute $x_1, x_2 \ldots$ until two successive values agree to three decimal places:

a. $\sin 2x = x$.   d. $\sin x = 1 - 2x$.

b. $\cos x = x$.   e. $2 \cos x = x^2$, $x > 0$.

c. $\sin x = 2x \cos x$.   f. $2 \sin x = x^2$, $x > 0$.

Problem 4. Let a be a positive constant, and sketch the graph of $y = x^2 - a$. Show graphically that if $x_0 > \sqrt{a}$, then Newton's Method gives $x_1, x_2, \ldots$, decreasing toward $\sqrt{a}$, but if $0 < x_0 < \sqrt{a}$, then x_1 may be far from $\sqrt{a}$.

  a. Expand $(\sqrt{a} - 1)^2 \geq 0$ and rearrange to show that

$$\sqrt{a} < \tfrac{1}{2}(a + 1).$$

Hence, in finding $\sqrt{a}$, a safe, and usually fairly good, starting value is

$$x_0 = (0.5)a + 0.5.$$

  b. Show that

$$x_1 = \frac{1}{2}\left(x_0 + \frac{a}{x_0}\right) = 0.5x_0 + 0.5\frac{a}{x_0}, \quad x_2 = 0.5x_1 + 0.5\frac{a}{x_1}, \quad \text{etc.}$$

  c. Use the above to recompute $\sqrt{3}$.

[Note: For some electronic computers, all problems must be scaled, so all numbers have absolute value less than 1. Note that with $0 < a < 1$ and $\sqrt{a} < x_n$, then $a < x_n\sqrt{a}$, so $a/x_n < \sqrt{a} < 1$. Thus, if $0 < a < 1$, the above arrangement of Newton's Method for computing $\sqrt{a}$ uses only numbers between 0 and 1, even in intermediate stages.]

Problem 5. With c a constant, $f(x) = (1/x) - c$ and x_0 an approximation of $1/c$ show that Newton's Method gives

$$x_1 = x_0(2 - x_0c), \quad x_2 = x_1(2 - x_1c), \quad \text{etc.}$$

for approximating $1/c$. Approximate $1/3$ by starting with $x_0 = 0.3$.

Problem 6. With $c > 0$ and x_0 an approximation of $1/\sqrt{c}$, obtain

$$x_1 = \frac{x_0}{2}(3 - x_0^2c), \quad x_2 = \frac{x_1}{2}(3 - x_1^2c), \quad \text{etc.},$$

for approximating $1/\sqrt{c}$. Approximate $1/\sqrt{3}$ by using $x_0 = 0.5$.

[Note: Problems 5 and 6 show that the reciprocal and the reciprocal square root may be approximated by using only multiplications and additions. Once $1/\sqrt{c}$ is approximated, then c times this approximation approximates $\sqrt{c}$ without using division. Also, by multiplying the approximations of $1/c$ and $1/\sqrt{c}$, an approximation of $1/c^{3/2}$ is obtained without using division.]

Transcendental Functions

Chapter 6

6-1. Trigonometric Derivatives

Recall that the derivative with respect to x of the function $y = f(x)$ was defined by

$$\frac{dy}{dx} = \frac{df(x)}{dx} = \lim_{\Delta x \to 0} \frac{f(x + \Delta x) - f(x)}{\Delta x},$$

wherein x was held fixed during the process of letting $\Delta x \to 0$. Thus, if $y = \tan x$, then

$$\frac{d \tan x}{dx} = \lim_{\Delta x \to 0} \frac{\tan (x + \Delta x) - \tan x}{\Delta x}.$$

It is not necessary, however, to go through the limiting process to find the derivative of the function $y = \tan x$ since the formulas

(1)(2)
$$\frac{d \sin x}{dx} = \cos x, \quad \frac{d \cos x}{dx} = -\sin x,$$

$$\frac{d}{dx} \frac{u}{v} = \frac{v\frac{du}{dx} - u\frac{dv}{dx}}{v^2} \quad \text{and} \quad \tan x = \frac{\sin x}{\cos x}$$

are already known. Hence

$$\frac{d}{dx} \tan x = \frac{d}{dx} \frac{\sin x}{\cos x} = \frac{\cos x \dfrac{d \sin x}{dx} - \sin x \dfrac{d \cos x}{dx}}{\cos^2 x}$$

$$= \frac{\cos x(\cos x) - \sin x(-\sin x)}{\cos^2 x}$$

$$= \frac{\cos^2 x + \sin^2 x}{\cos^2 x} = \frac{1}{\cos^2 x} = \sec^2 x.$$

The derivative with respect to x of the other trigonometric functions may be obtained in a similar way. The student should check each of the following formulas:

(3)
$$\frac{d \tan x}{dx} = \sec^2 x,$$

203

(4)
$$\frac{d \cot x}{dx} = -\csc^2 x,$$

(5)
$$\frac{d \sec x}{dx} = \sec x \tan x,$$

(6)
$$\frac{d \csc x}{dx} = -\csc x \cot x.$$

Recall also that if y is a function of u while u is a function of x, then y as a function of x has its derivative with respect to x given by

(7)
$$\frac{dy}{dx} = \frac{dy}{du}\frac{du}{dx}.$$

Even though the above formulas (1) through (6) use x as the independent variable, any other variable could be used. For example, (4) could just as well have been written

(4')
$$\frac{d \cot u}{du} = -\csc^2 u.$$

Hence, in order to find the derivative with respect to x of the function $y = \cot(3x^2 - 4x + 1)$, formulas (4') and (7) are used with $u = 3x^2 - 4x + 1$:

$$\frac{d}{dx}\cot(3x^2 - 4x + 1) = -\csc^2(3x^2 - 4x + 1)\frac{d}{dx}(3x^2 - 4x + 1)$$

$$= -(6x - 4)\csc^2(3x^2 - 4x + 1).$$

As another example:

$$\frac{d \cot^3 x^2}{dx} = 3 \cot^2 x^2 \frac{d \cot x^2}{dx}, \quad \text{since} \quad \frac{du^3}{dx} = 3u^2\frac{du}{dx}$$

$$= 3 \cot^2 x^2 [-\csc^2 x^2]\frac{dx^2}{dx}, \quad \text{since} \quad \frac{d \cot u}{dx} = -\csc^2 u\frac{du}{dx}$$

$$= 3 \cot^2 x^2 [-\csc^2 x^2] 2x$$

$$= -6x[\cot x^2 \csc x^2]^2.$$

Example 1. *A bomber B is flying a level course to pass over a target T (Fig. 6-1.1) and the bombardier keeps T in the sights of his instruments as determined*

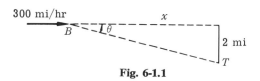

Fig. 6-1.1

by the angle θ. If the elevation is 2 mi and the speed 300 mi/hr, find how fast θ is changing when $\theta = \pi/6$.

Solution. In terms of the lettering on the figure,

$$x = 2 \cot \theta, \quad \text{where} \quad D_t x = -300 \text{ mi/hr},$$

and the question is to find $d\theta/dt$ when $\theta = \pi/6$. Hence,

(8) $$-300 = \frac{dx}{dt} = 2 \frac{d}{dt} \cot \theta = 2(-\csc^2 \theta) \frac{d\theta}{dt}, \quad \text{so that}$$

$$\frac{d\theta}{dt}\bigg]_{\theta=\pi/6} = \frac{300}{2 \csc^2 (\pi/6)} = 150 \sin^2 \frac{\pi}{6} = 150 \left(\frac{1}{2}\right)^2 = 37.5.$$

But 37.5 what? If the dimensions of the quantities in (8) are kept, it being understood that a trigonometric function is a dimensionless quantity, then (8) would be written

$$-300 \text{ mi} = 2 \text{ mi}(-\csc^2 \theta) \frac{d\theta}{dt} \frac{\text{rad}}{\text{hr}}, \quad \text{so that}$$

$$\frac{d\theta}{dt} = \frac{300 \text{ mi}}{2 \text{ mi}(\csc^2 \theta)} \frac{\text{rad}}{\text{hr}} = 150 \sin^2 \theta \frac{\text{rad}}{\text{hr}}.$$

Then the answer to the problem may be given in any of the dimensions:

$$37.5 \frac{\text{rad}}{\text{hr}} = \frac{37.5}{60} \frac{\text{rad}}{\text{min}} = \frac{37.5}{60 \cdot 60} \frac{\text{rad}}{\text{sec}} = \frac{37.5}{60 \cdot 60} \frac{180}{\pi} \frac{\text{deg}}{\text{sec}}$$

$$= \frac{37.5}{60 \cdot 60} \cdot \frac{180}{\pi} 60' \text{ per sec} = \left(\frac{3}{\pi} 37.5\right)' \text{ per sec}$$

$$= 35.8' + \text{ per sec to slide-rule accuracy.}$$

Example 2. An architect for a factory building is told:

    1. A certain hallway is to be 5 ft wide.
    2. A second hallway is to meet this one at right angles.
    3. A thin 30-ft inflexible rod must go around the corner horizontally.

How narrow may the second hallway be?

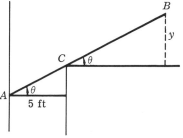

Fig. 6-1.2

Solution. Referring to Fig. 6-1.2 (in which $AB = 30$), as A slides along the wall and the rod always touches the corner C, then B traces a curve on the floor of the second hallway. Thus, the minimum width of the second hallway is the maximum value of y as a a function of θ. Since

$$30 = AC + CB = 5 \sec \theta + y \csc \theta, \quad 0 < \theta < \pi/2, \quad \text{then}$$

(9) $$y = 30 \sin \theta - 5 \tan \theta,$$

$$\frac{dy}{d\theta} = 30 \cos \theta - 5 \sec^2 \theta = \frac{5}{\cos \theta}(6 \cos^3 \theta - 1), \quad \text{and}$$

$$\frac{d^2 y}{d\theta^2} = -30 \sin \theta - 10 \sec^2 \theta \tan \theta.$$

Since the second derivative is negative ($0 < \theta < \pi/2$), the curve is concave down-

Fig. 6-1.3

ward. Hence the maximum value of y occurs where the first derivative is zero; that is, where

$$\cos \theta = \frac{1}{\sqrt[3]{6}}, \quad 0 < \theta < \frac{\pi}{2}.$$

The value of θ need not be found since the desired values of $\sin \theta$ and $\tan \theta$ to be substituted into (9) may be read from Fig. 6-1.3. Hence,

$$y = 5(6^{2/3} - 1)^{3/2} = 17.46 \text{ ft}$$

is the minimum width of the second hallway for an "ideal rod of no thickness."

Problem 1. Find each of the following derivatives:

a. $\dfrac{d \tan (2x^2 + 1)}{dx}$.

b. $\dfrac{d}{dx} \csc \sqrt{x}$.

c. $\dfrac{d}{dx}(\sin x + \tan x)$.

d. $\dfrac{d}{dx}(x \cot x)$.

e. $\dfrac{d}{dx}\left(x \tan \dfrac{1}{x}\right)$.

f. $\dfrac{d \tan^2 x}{dx}$.

g. $\dfrac{d}{dx} \sec^3 x$.

h. $\dfrac{d}{dx} \csc^4 x$.

i. $\dfrac{d}{dx}\left(\dfrac{x}{\tan x}\right)$.

j. $\dfrac{d}{dx}\left(\dfrac{\tan x}{x}\right)$.

Problem 2. Establish each of the following:

a. $\dfrac{d}{dx}\left(\dfrac{1}{n} \sec^n x\right) = \sec^n x \tan x$.

b. $\dfrac{d}{dx}\left(\dfrac{-\cot^{n+1} x}{n + 1}\right) = \cot^n x \csc^2 x$.

c. $D_x (c + \tan^2 x) = D_x \sec^2 x$ for any constant c.

d. $D_x (\cot^2 x - \csc^2) = 0$.

e. $D_x (\tfrac{1}{3} \tan^3 x - \tan x + x) = \tan^4 x$.

Problem 3. Find y' and y'' if:

a. $y = \tan^2 x$.
b. $y = \tan (x^2)$.
c. $y = \sec (1/x)$.
d. $y = 1/\sec x$.

e. $y = \sin 2x \tan x$.
f. $y = \sin x \tan 2x$.
g. $y = x^2 \tan x$.
h. $y = x \tan^2 x$.

Problem 4. Use implicit differentiation to find dy/dx if:

a. $x = \cot (x + y)$.
b. $\sin x + \tan y = y^2$.

c. $x^2 + \tan^2 y = 4$.
d. $y = \csc (xy)$.

Problem 5. Show that:

a. If $\quad x = \tan y$, $\quad$ then $\quad \dfrac{dy}{dx} = \dfrac{1}{1 + x^2}$.

b. If $\quad x = \cot y$, $\quad$ then $\quad \dfrac{dy}{dx} = \dfrac{-1}{1 + x^2}$.

Problem 6. A tower $\tfrac{3}{4}$ mi from a straight section of highway has a beacon sending out a beam of light that sweeps out one revolution every 3 sec. Find how fast the lighted spot of the highway is traveling along the highway when the spot is $\frac{1}{2}$ mi from the foot of the perpendicular from the tower to the highway.

Problem 7. Two corridors, one 5 ft wide and the other 8 ft wide, meet at right angles. Find the length of the longest thin rod that will go around the corner horizontally.

Problem 8. The solid lines of Fig. 6-1.4 represent an existing structure to which is to be added the dotted support. Find the shortest inside length *AB* for this support.

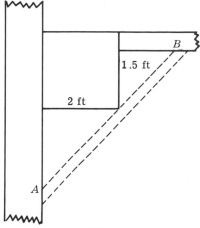

Fig. 6-1.4

6-2. Inverse Trigonometric Functions

In a trigonometry course, the solutions of the equation cos $x = 0.5$ were found and listed as $x = 60°$, $-60°$, or either of these plus or minus any integer multiple of $360°$, with $60°$ called the **principal value**. Any of these angles has its cosine equal to 0.5 and (according to the trigonometry book used) this was denoted by

$$\cos^{-1} 0.5 = 60° + m360°, \quad -60° + m360°, \quad \text{or}$$
$$\arccos 0.5 = 60° + m360°, \quad -60° + m360°.$$

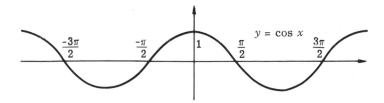

Fig. 6-2.1

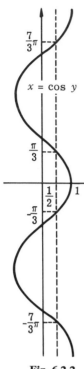

x = cos y

Fig. 6-2.2

The graphs of $y = \cos x$ and $x = \cos y$ were also drawn (Figs. 6-2.1 and 6-2.2, respectively) and the second was said to be the graph of $y = \cos^{-1} x$ or $y = \arccos x$. This inverse (or arc) cosine function is thus multiple-valued, as defined in a trigonometry course.

In calculus, the inverse trigonometric functions are made to be single-valued functions by the restriction that only principal values are used. In this book, the notation $\sin^{-1} x$, $\cos^{-1} x$, etc. (rather than arcsin x, arccos x,etc.), will be used. In particular, the functions $y = \sin^{-1} x$ and $y = \cos^{-1} x$ must have $-1 \leq x \leq 1$, but in addition

(1) $y = \sin^{-1} x$ if $-\pi/2 \leq y \leq \pi/2$ and $\sin y = x$,

(2) $y = \cos^{-1} x$ if $0 \leq y \leq \pi$ and $\cos y = x$.

Note carefully that these two functions have different ranges for y (see Figs. 6-2.3 and 6-2.4). Also, $\sin^{-1} x$ must not be confused with $(\sin x)^{-1}$. The first of these, $\sin^{-1} x$, means the radian measure of the angle whose sine is x, while

$$(\sin x)^{-1} = \frac{1}{\sin x} = \csc x.$$

The derivative with respect to x of the function $\sin^{-1} x$ is obtained by writing $y = \sin^{-1} x$ in the alternate form $\sin y = x$ and then using implicit derivatives:

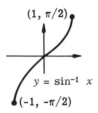

Fig. 6-2.3

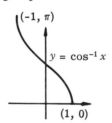

Fig. 6-2.4

$$\frac{d \sin y}{dx} = \frac{dx}{dx},$$

$$\cos y \frac{dy}{dx} = 1,$$

$$\frac{dy}{dx} = \frac{1}{\cos y}.$$

Since $\sin^2 y + \cos^2 y = 1$, then $\cos^2 y = 1 - \sin^2 y = 1 - x^2$, so that $\cos y = \pm\sqrt{1 - x^2}$. At this point, the restriction $-\pi/2 \leq y \leq \pi/2$, as given in (1), is used to see that $\cos y$ is positive and thus the minus sign of $\pm\sqrt{1 - x^2}$ is extraneous in this situation. Hence,

$$\frac{dy}{dx} = \frac{1}{\sqrt{1-x^2}} \quad \text{and not} \quad \frac{1}{-\sqrt{1-x^2}}.$$

Since, in this derivation, $y = \sin^{-1} x$ it follows that

1. $$\frac{d}{dx} \sin^{-1} x = \frac{1}{\sqrt{1-x^2}}.$$

The student should now derive the formula

2. $$\frac{d}{dx} \cos^{-1} x = \frac{-1}{\sqrt{1-x^2}},$$

and note carefully where the restriction $0 \le y \le \pi$ of (2) is used.

Also, the student should heed the earlier suggestion that each derivative formula be remembered both forward and backward since it will reappear later as an integral formula.

Again, these formulas could be written by using any variable in place of x. Hence, by using the Chain Rule:

$$\frac{d}{dx} \sin^{-1}(3x^2 - 2) = \frac{1}{\sqrt{1-(3x^2-2)^2}} \frac{d}{dx}(3x^2 - 2)$$

$$= \frac{6x}{\sqrt{-9x^2 + 12x - 3}}.$$

The curves $y = \tan x$ and $y = \cot x$ are made up of infinitely many separate branches. By interchanging the roles of x and y, the same is true of the curves $x = \tan y$ and $x = \cot y$. After an examination of these multiple branches, it should seem natural to restrict the inverse tangent and cotangent functions as follows:

(3) $y = \tan^{-1} x$ if $-\pi/2 < y < \pi/2$ and $\tan y = x$,

(4) $y = \cot^{-1} x$ if $0 < y < \pi$ and $\cot y = x$.

Each curve consists of a single branch as shown in Figs. 6-2.5 and 6-2.6.

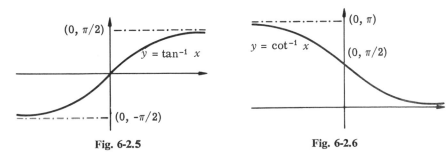

Fig. 6-2.5   Fig. 6-2.6

Hence, if $y = \tan^{-1} x$, then $\tan y = x$, so that

$$\frac{d}{dx} \tan y = \frac{dx}{dx},$$

$$\sec^2 y \frac{dy}{dx} = 1, \quad \frac{dy}{dx} = \frac{1}{\sec^2 y} = \frac{1}{1 + \tan^2 y} = \frac{1}{1 + x^2},$$

3.
$$\frac{d}{dx} \tan^{-1} x = \frac{1}{1 + x^2},$$

In a similar way,

4.
$$\frac{d}{dx} \cot^{-1} x = \frac{-1}{1 + x^2}.$$

The inverse secant and cosecant functions are somewhat more complicated than the other inverse trigonometric functions.

If either $x < -1$ or $x > 1$, then $-1 < 1/x < 1$ and hence $\cos^{-1} 1/x$ is defined and $0 \leq \cos^{-1} 1/x \leq \pi$ from (2). Hence, upon setting $y = \cos^{-1} 1/x$, then $0 \leq y \leq \pi$ and $\cos y = 1/x$, so that

$$x = \frac{1}{\cos y} = \sec y, \quad \text{provided} \quad \cos y \neq 0; \quad \text{that is,} \quad y \neq \frac{\pi}{2}.$$

This discussion gives the clue for defining $\sec^{-1} x$ and $\csc^{-1} x$ for $|x| > 1$ by

(5) $y = \sec^{-1} x = \cos^{-1} 1/x$,   where $0 \leq y < \pi/2$ or $\pi/2 < y \leq \pi$;

(6) $y = \csc^{-1} x = \sin^{-1} 1/x$,   where $-\pi/2 \leq y < 0$ or $0 < y \leq \pi/2$.

Note carefully that the ranges of y coincide (except for midpoints) with those of $y = \cos^{-1} x$ and $y = \sin^{-1} x$, respectively.*

The curve $y = \sec^{-1} x$ is seen (Fig. 6-2.7) to have two separate branches and at each point of each branch the slope is positive. Also, the curve $y = \csc^{-1} x$ (Fig. 6-2.8) has two branches, but the slope is negative throughout.

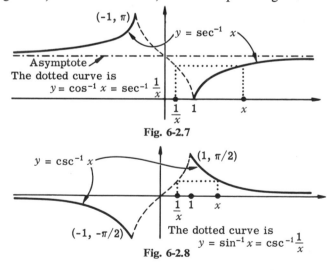

Fig. 6-2.7

Fig. 6-2.8

*Some books give y ranges different from these. Whenever a different book is consulted, the ranges of $y = \sec^{-1} x$ and $y = \csc^{-1} x$ should be carefully checked.

From (5),

$$\frac{d}{dx}\sec^{-1}x = \frac{d}{dx}\cos^{-1}\frac{1}{x} = \frac{1}{\sqrt{1-\left(\frac{1}{x}\right)^2}}\frac{d}{dx}\left(\frac{1}{x}\right)$$

$$= \frac{\sqrt{x^2}}{\sqrt{x^2-1}}\left(-\frac{1}{x^2}\right) = \frac{\sqrt{x^2}}{x^2}\frac{1}{\sqrt{x^2-1}}.$$

Recall now that $\sqrt{a^2}$ must be positive for $a \neq 0$ and hence

$$\sqrt{x^2} = |x| = \begin{cases} x & \text{if } x \geq 0, \\ -x & \text{if } x < 0. \end{cases}$$

Since $|x| \geq 1$ for $\sec^{-1}x$, then if $x > 0$ it follows that $x \geq 1$, but if $x < 0$ then $x \leq -1$. Hence,

5. $$\frac{d}{dx}\sec^{-1}x = \frac{1}{|x|\sqrt{x^2-1}} = \begin{cases} \dfrac{+1}{x\sqrt{x^2-1}} & \text{if } x > 1, \\[3mm] \dfrac{-1}{x\sqrt{x^2-1}} & \text{if } x < -1. \end{cases}$$

In particular, note that this derivative is always positive. Also, even though $y = \sec^{-1}x$ is defined if $x = \pm 1$, its derivative is not defined if $x = \pm 1$ because of the zero denominator.

In a similar way,

6. $$\frac{d}{dx}\csc^{-1}x = \frac{-1}{|x|\sqrt{x^2-1}} = \begin{cases} \dfrac{-1}{x\sqrt{x^2-1}} & \text{if } x > 1, \\[3mm] \dfrac{1}{x\sqrt{x^2-1}} & \text{if } x < -1. \end{cases}$$

Example. A picture that is 6 ft from lower to upper edge hangs with its lower edge 2 ft above the eye of an observer. How far away should the observer stand to make the picture subtend the greatest angle at his eye?

Solution. From Fig. 6-2.9, the problem is to determine x so that θ will be maximum, where $\theta = \alpha - \beta$:

$$\tan\alpha = \frac{8}{x} \quad \text{or} \quad \cot\alpha = \frac{x}{8},$$

and $$\tan\beta = \frac{2}{x} \quad \text{or} \quad \cot\beta = \frac{x}{2}.$$

Since derivatives are easier when the variable is in the numerator, it is better to use the cotangent form of α and β. Hence,

$$\theta = \cot^{-1}\frac{x}{8} - \cot^{-1}\frac{x}{2},$$

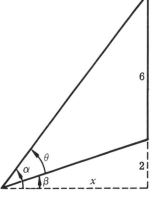

Fig. 6-2.9

$$\frac{d\theta}{dx} = \frac{-1}{1 + (x/8)^2}\frac{1}{8} - \frac{-1}{1 + (x/2)^2}\frac{1}{2}$$

$$= \frac{-8}{64 + x^2} + \frac{2}{4 + x^2} = \frac{96 - 6x^2}{(64 + x^2)(4 + x^2)}.$$

The positive solution of $d\theta/dx = 0$ is $x = 4$. Thus, θ is largest when $x = 4$, since $d\theta/dx$ is positive or negative according to whether x takes a smaller or larger value than $x = 4$.

Problem 1. Find the derivative with respect to x of each of the functions:

a. $\sin^{-1}(x/2)$.

e. $\cos^{-1}(1 - x)$.

b. $\frac{1}{3}\tan^{-1}(x/3)$.

f. $\tan^{-1}\dfrac{x - 1}{x + 1}$.

c. $\sqrt{1 - x^2} + x\sin^{-1}x$.

g. $\cot^{-1}\sqrt{x}$.

d. $\frac{1}{2}(x\sqrt{1 - x^2} + x\sin^{-1}x)$.

h. $\cos^{-1}(x^{-2})$.

Problem 2. In obtaining the derivative with respect to x of each of the following functions, be careful to note that $\sqrt{a^2}$ is not necessarily equal to a but always $\sqrt{a^2} = |a|$.

a. $\sin^{-1}\sqrt{1 - x^2}$.

d. $-\dfrac{1}{3}\sin^{-1}(x^{-3})$.

b. $\dfrac{1}{2}\sin^{-1}\dfrac{2}{x}$.

e. $\dfrac{1}{2}\cos^{-1}\dfrac{2}{x}$.

$\dfrac{1}{2}\cos^{-1}\dfrac{1 - x^2}{1 + x^2}$.

f. $\sec^{-1}\dfrac{1}{x}$.

Problem 3. One of the important uses of inverse trigonometric functions is in providing integral formulas. For example, part a below will reappear later in the form

$$\int\frac{1}{\sqrt{a^2 - x^2}}dx = \sin^{-1}\frac{x}{a} + c.$$

Find each of the following derivatives and mentally visualize the associated integral form of the result:

a. $\dfrac{d}{dx}\sin^{-1}\dfrac{x}{a} = \dfrac{1}{\sqrt{a^2 - x^2}}$, $a > 0$.

b. $\dfrac{d}{dx}\dfrac{1}{a}\tan^{-1}\dfrac{x}{a} = \dfrac{1}{a^2 + x^2}$.

c. $\dfrac{d}{dx}\dfrac{1}{\sqrt{ac}}\tan^{-1}\left(x\sqrt{\dfrac{a}{c}}\right) = \dfrac{1}{ax^2 + c}$, $ac > 0$.

d. $\dfrac{d}{dx}\dfrac{1}{\sqrt{a}}\sin^{-1}\left(x\sqrt{\dfrac{a}{c}}\right) = \dfrac{1}{\sqrt{-ax^2 + c}}$, $a > 0,\ \ c > 0,\ \ -ax^2 + c > 0$.

e. $\dfrac{d}{dx}\dfrac{1}{2}\left\{x\sqrt{a^2 - x^2} + a^2\sin^{-1}\dfrac{x}{a}\right\} = \sqrt{a^2 - x^2}$, $a > 0$.

f. $\dfrac{d}{dx}\left\{\dfrac{1}{a}\sqrt{1 - a^2x^2} + x\sin^{-1}ax\right\} = \sin^{-1}ax$.

g. $\dfrac{d}{dx}\dfrac{2}{\sqrt{4ac - b^2}}\tan^{-1}\dfrac{2ax + b}{\sqrt{4ac - b^2}} = \dfrac{1}{ax^2 + bx + c}$, $4ac - b^2 > 0$.

Problem 4. A 10-ft high billboard has lower edge 13 ft above ground. How far back should a man, whose eyes are 5 ft above ground, stand for the best view?

Problem 5. At what point $(x, 0)$ does the segment joining $(2, 4)$ and $(8, 8)$ subtend the maximum angle?

Problem 6. A ship is 4 mi from the closest point of a straight shore and a car is 3 mi from this point traveling away from it along the shore at 30 mi/hr. How fast is a searchlight on the ship trained on the car rotating at this instant if:

    a. The ship is stationary?

    b. The ship is headed straight for the shore at 10 mi/hr?

6-3. Logarithms

Common logarithms (that is, logarithms to the base 10) were used in high school to aid in computation, mainly in the trigonometry course. Logarithms are, however, useful in many situations other than as aids to numerical computation. To understand and appreciate these other uses of logarithms it is necessary to be thoroughly familiar with the definition of logarithms to a general base b. The mere ability to determine characteristics and to look up mantissas of common logarithms is not sufficient for the applications to be made of logarithms.

The general situation will be discussed after considering four functions in which the usual roles of x and y are interchanged so that y is the independent variable. These special functions, together with tables for a few related values, are:

$x = 2^y$		$x = (\tfrac{1}{2})^y$		$x = 1^y$		$x = (-1)^y$	
y	x	y	x	y	x	y	x
-2	$\tfrac{1}{4}$	-2	4	-2	1	-2	1
-1	$\tfrac{1}{2}$	-1	2	-1	1	-1	-1
0	1	0	1	0	1	0	1
1	2	1	$\tfrac{1}{2}$	1	1	1	-1
2	4	2	$\tfrac{1}{4}$	2	1	2	1

The graphs of the first three are in Fig. 6-3.1 and indicate, by being solid, that for each real value of y (whether positive, negative, rational, or irrational) there is a real and positive value of x. The fourth function $x = (-1)^y$ is, however, more complicated. For example, if $y = \tfrac{1}{2}$, then $x = \sqrt{-1} = i$, and if y is any fraction with even denominator and odd numerator the corresponding value of x is imaginary. Thus, a graph for $x = (-1)^y$ cannot be drawn.

The curve $x = 2^y$ is always rising to the right and indicates (and is proved in a more advanced course) that for any positive value of x there is one and only one value of y. Thus, if $x = 2^y$ and x is considered the inde-

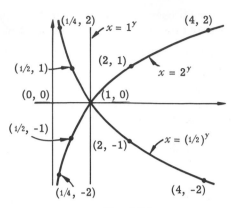

Fig. 6-3.1

pendent variable (restricted to $x > 0$), then y is a function of x which is written $y = \log_2 x$.

In a similar way, $x = (\frac{1}{2})^y$ and $y = \log_{1/2} x$ are two functions with identical graphs, the first with y independent but the second with x independent.

If, however, $x = 1^y$, then a value of x does not determine a value of y; that is, y is not a function of x.

These considerations indicate why b is taken positive but not equal to 1 in the following definition.

DEFINITION. *Given a positive number b but $b \neq 1$, then*

$$(1) \qquad\qquad x = b^y$$

determines y as a function of x and this function is defined by

$$(2) \qquad\qquad y = \log_b x,$$

which is read "y is the logarithm to the base b of x."

Thus, a property of logarithms is obtained by substituting y from (2) into (1) to obtain

$$(3) \qquad\qquad x = b^{\log_b x}$$

for any positive number x. The property (3) is used in proving the usual laws of logarithms. For example, if M and N are positive numbers, then MN is also positive. Upon replacing x in (3) first by M, then by N, and finally by MN, it follows that

$$(4) \qquad M = b^{\log_b M}, \quad N = b^{\log_b N}, \quad \text{and} \quad MN = b^{\log_b MN}.$$

Next, multiply the first two of these:

$$MN = b^{\log_b M} \, b^{\log_b N} = b^{(\log_b M + \log_b N)}.$$

The law of exponents $b^a \cdot b^c = b^{a+c}$ was used in obtaining the second equality.

Now this expression for MN substituted into the left side of the third equation of (4) yields

$$b^{(\log_b M + \log_b N)} = b^{\log_b MN}.$$

Since b raised to the exponent $\log_b M + \log_b N$ is equal to b raised to the exponent $\log_b MN$, these exponents must be equal; that is,

$$(5) \qquad \log_b MN = \log_b M + \log_b N.$$

In a similar way,

$$(6) \qquad \log_b (M/N) = \log_b M - \log_b N.$$

Also, if p is any number, then upon raising both sides of the first equation of (4) to the power p the result is

$$M^p = (b^{\log_b M})^p = b^{p \log_b M},$$

where the law of exponents $(b^a)^p = b^{p \cdot a}$ was used to obtain the second equality. But also, by replacing x in (3) by M^p, then

$$M^p = b^{\log_b M^p}.$$

These two expressions for M^p mean that the exponents on the right are equal:

$$(7) \qquad \log_b M^p = p \log_b M.$$

In (3), replace x by b to obtain $b = b^{\log_b b}$, which shows that

$$(8) \qquad \log_b b = 1.$$

In (3), replace x by 1 to obtain $1 = b^{\log_b 1}$, then write $1 = b^0$, and hence see that the exponents $\log_b 1$ and 0 are equal:

$$(9) \qquad \log_b 1 = 0.$$

The following example and problems furnish experience in handling logarithms and the above logarithmic formulas. The base b is omitted since all properties hold for any positive base not equal to 1.

Example. Show that $\log (\sqrt{2} - 1) = -\log (\sqrt{2} + 1)$.

Solution.

$$\log (\sqrt{2} - 1) = \log \left[(\sqrt{2} - 1) \frac{\sqrt{2} + 1}{\sqrt{2} + 1} \right]$$

$$= \log \frac{(\sqrt{2} - 1)(\sqrt{2} + 1)}{\sqrt{2} + 1} = \log \frac{2 - 1}{\sqrt{2} + 1}$$

$$= \log \frac{1}{\sqrt{2} + 1} = \log 1 - \log (\sqrt{2} + 1) \quad \text{by (6)}$$

$$= -\log (\sqrt{2} + 1) \quad \text{by (9).}$$

Problem 1. Establish each of following

a. $\log (2 - \sqrt{3}) = -\log (2 + \sqrt{3})$.

b. $\log(\sqrt{3} - 1) = \log 2 - \log(\sqrt{3} + 1)$.

c. $\log(\sqrt{x^2 + 1} - x) = -\log(\sqrt{x^2 + 1} + x)$.

d. $\log(x - \sqrt{x^2 - 1}) = -\log(x + \sqrt{x^2 - 1})$ if $x \geq 1$.

e. $\log(\sqrt{x^2 - 1} - x) = -\log(-x - \sqrt{x^2 - 1})$ if $x \leq -1$.

f. $2 \log \sin x = \log(1 - \cos x) + \log(1 + \cos x)$ if $0 < x < \pi$.

g. $\log \tan \dfrac{x}{2} = \log \sin x - \log(1 + \cos x)$ if $0 < x < \pi$.

Problem 2. First change each of the following to exponential form and then by inspection solve for x:

a. $x = \log_2 16$.

b. $x = \log_{1/2} 16$.

c. $x = \log_{1/3} 81$.

d. $x = \log_3 81$.

e. $x = \log_3 (1/81)$.

f. $x = \log_4 (1/64)$.

g. $x = \log_9 27$.

h. $x = \log_{27} 9$.

Problem 3. a. With $a > 0$ and $a \neq 1$, derive the formula

(1) $$\log_b x = \log_a x \log_b a.$$

[Note: This is called the formula for change of base.] [Hint: Start with $x = a^{\log_a x}$ and take the logarithm to the base b of both sides.]

b. Show that

(2) $$\log_a b = \frac{1}{\log_b a}.$$

Use Table 1 (for logarithms to the base 10) to find the approximations to four decimal places of:

c. $\log_2 4.31$.

d. $\log_{6.31} 4.31$.

Problem 4. a. Show that if x and $x + h$ are positive, then

$$\frac{\log(x + h) - \log x}{h} = \frac{1}{x} \log \left(1 + \frac{h}{x}\right)^{x/h}.$$

b. Show that if $x \neq 0$, $h \neq 0$, and $|h| < |x|$, then

$$\frac{\log |x + h| - \log |x|}{h} = \frac{1}{x} \log \left(1 + \frac{h}{x}\right)^{x/h}.$$

6-4. Derivatives of Logarithmic Functions

If $b > 0$ and $b \neq 1$, then $\log_b |x|$ is defined for each $x \neq 0$. It is natural to ask if the function $\log_b |x|$ has a derivative, and if it does what the formula is. The usual four steps lead to seeing if the limit as $\Delta x \to 0$ exists for any of the expressions

$$\frac{\log_b |x + \Delta x| - \log_b |x|}{\Delta x} = \frac{1}{\Delta x} \log_b \frac{|x + \Delta x|}{|x|}$$

$$= \frac{1}{\Delta x} \log_b \left|1 + \frac{\Delta x}{x}\right|$$

$$= \frac{1}{\Delta x} \log_b \left(1 + \frac{\Delta x}{x}\right).$$

The absolute value was not used in the last expression since, as $\Delta x \to 0$, eventually $1 + (\Delta x)/x$ will be positive. All of these take the form $0/0$ as $\Delta x \to 0$. Upon multiplying the last expression by x/x, the expressions

$$\frac{1}{x}\frac{x}{\Delta x}\log_b\left(1 + \frac{\Delta x}{x}\right) = \frac{1}{x}\log_b\left(1 + \frac{\Delta x}{x}\right)^{x/\Delta x}$$

are obtained. This raises two questions:

(i) Does $\displaystyle\lim_{\Delta x \to 0}\left(1 + \frac{\Delta x}{x}\right)^{x/\Delta x}$ exist?

If so:

(ii) Is $\displaystyle\frac{1}{x}\lim_{\Delta x \to 0}\log_b\left(1 + \frac{\Delta x}{x}\right)^{x/\Delta x} = \frac{1}{x}\log_b\left[\lim_{\Delta x \to 0}\left(1 + \frac{\Delta x}{x}\right)^{x/\Delta x}\right]$?

It was found that not only does the limit in (i) exist but it is a number e which in no way depends upon the value of x. The answer to (ii) is also in the affirmative, so that

$$\frac{d}{dx}\log_b |x| = \frac{1}{x}\log_b e.$$

In (i), $\Delta x/x \to 0$ and $|x/\Delta x| \to \infty$ as $\Delta x \to 0$. The question in (i) was attacked by first noting that

$$\left(1 + \frac{1}{2}\right)^2 = 1 + 2\left(\frac{1}{2}\right) + \left(\frac{1}{2}\right)^2 = 2 + \frac{1}{4},$$

$$\left(1 + \frac{1}{3}\right)^3 = 1 + 3\left(\frac{1}{3}\right) + 3\left(\frac{1}{3}\right)^2 + \left(\frac{1}{3}\right)^3 = 2 + \frac{10}{27},$$

and, for any positive integer n, by the binomial theorem,

$$\left(1 + \frac{1}{n}\right)^n = 1 + n\left(\frac{1}{n}\right) + \frac{n(n-1)}{1\cdot 2}\frac{1}{n^2}$$

$$+ \frac{n(n-1)(n-2)}{3!}\frac{1}{n^3} + \cdots + \frac{n!}{n!}\frac{1}{n^n}$$

$$= 2 + \frac{1}{2}\left(1 - \frac{1}{n}\right) + \frac{1}{3!}\left(1 - \frac{1}{n}\right)\left(1 - \frac{2}{n}\right)$$

$$+ \cdots + \frac{1}{n!}\left(1 - \frac{1}{n}\right)\left(1 - \frac{2}{n}\right)\cdots\left(\frac{1}{n}\right)$$

$$< 2 + \frac{1}{2} + \frac{1}{3!} + \cdots + \frac{1}{n!}$$

$$< 2 + \frac{1}{2} + \frac{1}{2^2} + \cdots + \frac{1}{2^{n-1}} < 2 + 1.$$

Even though $(1 + 1/n)^n$ is between 2 and 3, this does not prove that the limit as $n \to \infty$ exists, but this limit does exist and is denoted by e:

(1) $$\lim_{n\to\infty}\left(1 + \frac{1}{n}\right)^n = e.$$

The full details in answering questions (i) and (ii) are many and complicated. As more knowledge was gained, it was found that direct attacks on these questions could be avoided. In fact, the proof of (1) and then

$$(2) \qquad \lim_{h \to 0} \frac{e^h - 1}{h} = 1$$

will become so easy that they are given as Prob. 8, Sec. 13-2. The number e is irrational (Prob. 13, Sec. 13-13) and is approximated by

$$2.718281828459045,$$

as methods in Chapter 13 will show.

The fact expressed in (2) will now be used, as if it had been established, to find $D_x e^x$. It should be noted that no circular reasoning will be involved; this procedure merely delays the proofs of (1) and (2) until further exprience in finding limits is gained and in the meantime allows the use of some important formulas.

From the four-step rule for finding a derivative,

$$(3) \qquad \frac{de^x}{dx} = \lim_{\Delta x \to 0} \frac{e^{x + \Delta x} - e^x}{\Delta x} = \lim_{\Delta x \to 0} \frac{e^x e^{\Delta x} - e^x}{\Delta x}$$

$$= e^x \lim_{\Delta x \to 0} \frac{e^{\Delta x} - 1}{\Delta x} = e^x \quad \text{by (2)}.$$

A formula that says neither more nor less than (3) is

$$(4) \qquad \frac{de^u}{du} = e^u.$$

The number e defined by (1) occurs frequently in mathematics and applications. Logarithms to the base e are called **natural logarithms.** Logarithms to the base 10 are called **common logarithms.** If "log" is written without indicating a base, it is assumed the base is 10. Also, "ln" is used instead or "$\log_e$." Any base b other than 10 or e is usually written in, as $\log_b$.

Formula (4) will now be used to prove that $D_x \ln |x|$ exists and

$$(5) \qquad \frac{d}{dx} \ln |x| = \frac{1}{x} \quad \text{for} \quad x \neq 0.$$

Before starting this proof, check that

$$(6) \qquad \frac{d|x|}{dx} = \left\{ \begin{array}{l} 1 \text{ if } x > 0 \\ -1 \text{ if } x < 0 \end{array} \right\} = \frac{|x|}{x} \text{ for } x \neq 0.$$

First, let $F(s)$ be the function defined by

$$(7) \qquad F(s) = \int_1^s \frac{1}{t}\, dt \quad \text{for } s > 0,$$

and note that $F(1) = 0$. By the Fundamental Theorem of Calculus, not only does $D_s F(s)$ exist but the formula

(8)
$$\frac{d}{ds} F(s) = \frac{1}{s}$$

holds.* Hence, by the Chain Rule,

(9)
$$\frac{d}{dx} F(|x|) = \frac{1}{|x|} \frac{d|x|}{dx} = \frac{1}{|x|} \frac{|x|}{x} = \frac{1}{x} \quad \text{for } x \neq 0.$$

It will next be shown that $F(|x|) = \ln |x|$, $x \neq 0$, and as soon as this is done the existence of $D_x \ln |x|$ is established, and formula (5) is formula (9). In (8), set $s = e^u$, then use the Chain Rule and (4) to obtain

$$\frac{d}{du} F(e^u) = \frac{1}{e^u} \frac{de^u}{du} = \frac{1}{e^u} e^u = 1, \quad \text{since } e^u > 0.$$

Consequently, $F(e^u) = u + c$ for some constant c and all values of the variable u. By setting $u = 0$, then $F(e^0) = 0 + c$. But $F(e^0) = F(1) = 0$, as noted above, so that $c = 0$ and hence

$$F(e^u) = u.$$

Finally, set $u = \ln |x|$, $x \neq 0$, and from $e^{\ln |x|} = |x|$ obtain

$$F(|x|) = \ln |x|.$$

From the above comments, formula (5) is proved.

Again, from the Chain Rule, if $u(x)$ is a function of x, then

(10)
$$\frac{d}{dx} \ln |u(x)| = \frac{u'(x)}{u(x)}$$

for each value of x at which $u'(x)$ exists and $u(x) \neq 0$.

Example.

$$\frac{d \ln |\sin x|}{dx} = \frac{1}{\sin x} \frac{d \sin x}{dx} = \frac{\cos x}{\sin x} = \cot x, \quad x \neq m\pi.$$

Recall the change of base formula [(10) of Prob. 3, Sec. 6-3],

$$\log_b x = \log_a x \log_b a,$$

with proper restrictions on a, b, and x. Set $a = e$ and see that

$$\log_b |x| = \ln |x| \log_b e, \quad x \neq 0, \quad b > 0, \quad b \neq 1.$$

Since $\log_b e$ is a constant, then

(11)
$$\frac{d \log_b |x|}{dx} = \frac{1}{x} \log_b e, \quad x \neq 0, \quad \text{and}$$

(12)
$$\frac{d \log_b |u(x)|}{dx} = \frac{u'(x)}{u(x)} \log_b e$$

for each x such that $u'(x)$ exists and $u(x) \neq 0$.

*Recall that if $f(x)$ is continuous, then
$$\frac{d}{dx} \int_a^x f(t)\, dt = f(x).$$

The existence of the derivative $D_x \ln |x|$ and formula (5) were obtained without actually using the four-step rule on the function $\ln |x|$ itself. It is therefore known that the function $\ln|x|$ is continuous (since its derivative exists) and that

$$\lim_{h \to 0} \frac{\ln |x + h| - \ln |x|}{h} \quad \text{exists and is equal to} \quad \frac{1}{x}$$

for any $x \neq 0$. In particular, for $x = 1$ it follows that

$$\lim_{h \to 0} \frac{\ln |1 + h| - \ln 1}{h} = \lim_{h \to 0} \left[\frac{1}{h} \ln |1 + h| \right] = \frac{1}{1} = 1,$$

since $\ln 1 = 0$. By considering only values of $h \neq 0$ so near to zero that $1 + h > 0$, then $|1 + h| = 1 + h$ and

$$1 = \lim_{h \to 0} \left[\frac{1}{h} \ln (1 + h) \right] = \lim_{h \to 0} \ln (1 + h)^{1/h}.$$

Since $\ln e = 1$ and $\ln |x|$ is continuous, it must be that

(13) $$\lim_{h \to 0} (1 + h)^{1/h} = e.$$

In some situations, this formula and the others obtained below are more useful than the definition (1) of e. By setting $h = 1/t$, then $|t| \to \infty$ as $h \to 0$, and the additional formula

(14) $$\lim_{|t| \to \infty} \left(1 + \frac{1}{t} \right)^t = e$$

is obtained. Now, with $r \neq 0$, then by setting $t = n/r$,

(15) $$\lim_{n \to \infty} \left(1 + \frac{r}{n} \right)^n = \lim_{n \to \infty} \left[\left(1 + \frac{r}{n} \right)^{n/r} \right]^r = e^r.$$

Upon setting $b = 10$ and $a = e$ in the change of base formulas, it follows that

$$\log x = \ln x \log e \quad \text{and} \quad \ln x = \frac{\log x}{\log e}.$$

From the approximation $e = 2.7182818$ and a six-place table of common logarithms,

$$\log e = 0.434294 \quad \text{and} \quad \frac{1}{\log e} = \frac{1}{0.434294} = 2.302585.$$

Thus, the special formulas for interchanging bases 10 and e are the approximations

(16) $$\log x = 0.434294 \ln x \quad \text{and} \quad \ln x = 2.302585 \log x.$$

Problem 1. Find y' and y'' for each of the following:

a. $y = 5 \ln (x^2 + 4)$.

b. $y = 5 \ln |x^2 - 4|$.

e. $y = \ln |x + \sqrt{x^2 - 4}|$.

f. $y = \ln |\cos x|$.

c. $y = x \ln (x^2 + 1)$.
d. $y = \ln (x + \sqrt{x^2 + 4})$.

g. $y = \ln |\tan 3x|$.
h. $y = (\ln x^2)^2$.

Problem 2. Establish each of the following and mentally visualize how an associated integral formula would appear:

a. $\dfrac{d}{dx} \dfrac{1}{b} \ln \left| \dfrac{x}{ax + b} \right| = \dfrac{1}{x(ax + b)}$.

b. $\dfrac{d}{dx} \left\{ -\dfrac{1}{bx} + \dfrac{a}{b^2} \ln \left| \dfrac{ax + b}{x} \right| \right\} = \dfrac{1}{x^2(ax + b)}$.

c. $\dfrac{d}{dx} \left\{ \dfrac{1}{b(ax + b)} + \dfrac{1}{b^2} \ln \left| \dfrac{x}{ax + b} \right| \right\} = \dfrac{1}{x(ax + b)^2}$.

d. $\dfrac{d}{dx} \ln |x + \sqrt{x^2 \pm a^2}| = \dfrac{1}{\sqrt{x^2 \pm a^2}}$.

e. $\dfrac{1}{2} \dfrac{d}{dx} \{ x \sqrt{x^2 \pm a^2} \pm a^2 \ln |x + \sqrt{x^2 \pm a^2}| \} = \sqrt{x^2 \pm a^2}$.

f. $D_x(x \tan^{-1} x - \ln \sqrt{1 + x^2}) = \tan^{-1} x$.

g. $D_x \ln |\sec x + \tan x| = \sec x$.

Problem 3. Find the slope of each of the curves at the point indicated:

a. $y = x^2 \ln |x|$, at $x = -3$.
b. $y = x^2 \ln |x|$, at $x = 3$.
c. $y = x^{-1} \ln |x|$, at $x = 2$.

d. $y = x^{-1} \ln |x|$, at $x = -2$.
e. $y = \ln |\cos x|$, at $x = 5\pi/6$.
f. $y = \ln |x + \sqrt{x^2 + 16}|$, at $x = 3$.

Problem 4. Establish each of the following equations.

a. $D_x \ln |3x| = D_x \ln |x|$.

b. $\dfrac{d}{dx} \ln \dfrac{2}{|x|} = -\dfrac{d}{dx} \ln |x|$.

c. $\dfrac{d}{dx} \ln \left(\dfrac{x + \sqrt{x^2 + a^2}}{a^2} \right) = \dfrac{d}{dx} \ln (x + \sqrt{x^2 + a^2}) = -\dfrac{d}{dx} \ln |x - \sqrt{a^2 + x^2}|$.

Problem 5. Show that

a. $\ln (1 + x) \le x$ for $x > -1$.
   [Hint: Find maximum of $f(x) = -x + \ln (1 + x)$.]

b. $x - \dfrac{x^2}{2} < \ln (1 + x)$ for $x > 0$.

c. $\ln \dfrac{1 - x}{1 + x} \le -2 \left(x + \dfrac{x^3}{3} \right)$ for $0 \le x < 1$.

d. Show that $\ln \dfrac{1 - x}{1 + x}$ is less than or equal to the polynomial

$$-2 \left(x + \dfrac{x^3}{3} + \dfrac{x^5}{5} + \cdots + \dfrac{x^{2n+1}}{2n + 1} \right) \text{ if } 0 \le x < 1$$

but is greater than or equal to the polynomial if $-1 < x \le 0$.

Problem 6. Let r be the annual interest a bank pays. Thus, $\$P$ earns $\$Pr$ in a year if interest is compounded annually and the new principal for the next year is $\$P(1 + r)$. Show that the new principal is:

a. $\$P \left(1 + \dfrac{r}{2} \right)^2$ if interest is compounded semiannually.

b. $\$P \left(1 + \dfrac{r}{4} \right)^4$ if interest is compounded quarterly.

c. $\$P\left(1 + \dfrac{r}{n}\right)^n$ if interest is compounded at n equally spaced times in the year.

d. Is $\$Pe^r$ a natural value to define for the new principal if "interest is compounded continuously"?

6-5. Logarithmic Differentiation

The following example illustrates a situation in which it is better to use the ordinary laws of logarithms *before* taking the derivative.

Example 1. Find dy/dx if

$$y = \ln\frac{|x - 1|(x^2 + 2)}{(3x + 4)^2}.$$

Solution. The direct application of the derivative formula would give

$$\frac{dy}{dx} = \frac{1}{\dfrac{(x - 1)(x^2 + 2)}{(3x + 4)^2}} \frac{d}{dx} \frac{(x - 1)(x^2 + 2)}{(3x + 4)^2} = \text{etc.,}$$

where the derivative of this complicated quotient would still have to be taken. By using the formulas for the logarithms of quotients, products, and powers, it follows that

$$y = \ln\left[\,|x - 1|(x^2 + 2)\right] - \ln(3x + 4)^2$$
$$= \ln|x - 1| + \ln(x^2 + 2) - 2\ln|3x + 4|.$$

Now the derivative of each of these is easily obtained:

$$\frac{dy}{dx} = \frac{1}{x - 1} + \frac{2x}{x^2 + 2} - 2\frac{3}{3x + 4}.$$

Even if logarithms are not involved, it may lead to simpler derivatives if the logarithm of both sides is first taken as illustrated in the next example. This method is known as "logarithmic differentiation."

Example 2. Find dy/dx if

$$y = \frac{(x - 1)(x^2 + 2)}{(3x + 4)^2}.$$

Solution. First take the absolute value of both sides and then the natural logarithm of both sides of the resulting equation to obtain

$$\ln|y| = \ln\frac{|x - 1|(x^2 + 2)}{(3x + 4)}$$
$$= \ln|x - 1| + \ln(x^2 + 2) - 2\ln|3x + 4|.$$

Now take the derivative with respect to x of both sides:

$$\frac{1}{y}\frac{dy}{dx} = \frac{1}{x - 1} + \frac{2x}{x^2 + 2} - \frac{6}{3x + 4}.$$

Upon multiplying by y, and then substituting the given expression for y on the right, the result is

$$\frac{dy}{dx} = \frac{(x-1)(x^2+2)}{(3x+4)^2}\left[\frac{1}{x-1} + \frac{2x}{x^2+2} - \frac{6}{3x+4}\right].$$

By using logarithmic differentiation it is possible to derive the formula

(1) $$\frac{dx^p}{dx} = px^{p-1},$$

with p any constant for which x^p is real. This formula was proved (see Sec. 2–8) under the restriction that p be a positive integer, but has been used without this restriction, since it was anticipated that the proof now to be given was forthcoming. Set $y = x^p$ so $|y| = |x|^p$, $\ln|y| = \ln|x|^p = p\ln|x|$. Now take the derivative with respect to x of both sides:

$$\frac{1}{y}\frac{dy}{dx} = \frac{p}{x}, \quad \frac{dy}{dx} = p\frac{y}{x}.$$

Next, set $y = x^p$ throughout:

$$\frac{dx^p}{dx} = p\frac{x^p}{x} = px^{p-1}.$$

From previous work it is known how to take the derivative of a function which is a variable to a constant power. For example,

$$\frac{d}{dx}(x^2 + 4x)^3 = 3(x^2 + 4x)^2(2x + 4) = 6(x + 2)(x^2 + 4x)^2.$$

If, however, the function is a constant to a variable power, the situation is quite different, but may be handled by using logarithmic differentiation.

Example 3. Find $\dfrac{d}{dx}3^{(x^2+4x)}$.

Solution. Set $y = 3^{(x^2+4x)}$. Even if x is negative, the quantity $3^{(x^2+4x)}$ is positive, so absolute values need not be taken. Hence,

$$\ln y = \ln 3^{(x^2+4x)} = (x^2 + 4x)\ln 3.$$

Now the derivative with respect to x of both sides gives

$$\frac{1}{y}\frac{dy}{dx} = (2x + 4)\ln 3, \quad \frac{dy}{dx} = y(2x + 4)\ln 3,$$

and then, upon setting $y = 3^{(x^2+4x)}$,

$$\frac{d}{dx}3^{(x^2+4x)} = 3^{(x^2+4x)}(2x + 4)\ln 3.$$

Problem 1. Find the derivative with respect to x of:

a. $y = \ln\dfrac{(3x+4)^2}{|x-1|(x^2+2)}$.

b. $y = \ln\dfrac{|x\sin x|}{x^2+4}$.

c. $y = \ln\dfrac{1+\sin x}{x^2+5}$.

d. $y = \ln\dfrac{|x + x(x+1)|}{x^2+6}$.

e. $y = \ln\dfrac{|x + x\cos x|}{2+\cos x}$.

f. $y = \ln\left|\dfrac{x^2+x-2}{x-1}\right|$.

Problem 2. Use logarithmic differentiation to find dy/dx if:

a. $y = x(x - 1)(x - 2)$.

b. $y = \dfrac{1}{x(x - 1)(x - 2)}$.

c. $y = \dfrac{x \sin x}{1 + \sin x}$.

d. $y = (1 - x)^2(2 + 7x)$.

e. $y = \sqrt{\dfrac{x^2 \sin x}{x^2 + 4}}$.

f. $y = \dfrac{(x + 2)^4}{(2 - x)^3}$.

Problem 3. Find dy/dx for each of the following functions which is the form of a constant to a variable power:

a. $y = 2^{\sin x}$.

b. $y = 2^{x \sin x}$.

c. $y = 3^{(x - \sin x)}$.

d. $y = 10^{\sqrt{x}}$.

e. $y = \sqrt{10^x}$.

f. $y = 4^{(2 - x + \sin x)}$.

6-6. Variable Exponents

For $a > 0$ but $a \neq 1$, the function $y = a^x$ has a derivetive with respect to x. As in the previous section, the logarithm to base e of both sides gives

$$\ln y = \ln a^x = x \ln a.$$

Now, by taking the derivative with respect to x:

$$\frac{d \ln y}{dx} = \frac{d}{dx}(x \ln a),$$

$$\frac{1}{y}\frac{dy}{dx} = (\ln a)\frac{dx}{dx},$$

so that

$$\frac{dy}{dx} = y \ln a.$$

But since $y = a^x$, the formula

(1) $$\frac{da^x}{dx} = a^x \ln a$$

is obtained. Hence, for the particular constant e,

(2) $$\frac{de^x}{dx} = e^x,$$

since $\ln e = \log_e e = 1$. This is circular reasoning, since (2) is (3) of Sec. 6–4. This formula may also be written as

$$\frac{de^u}{du} = e^u,$$

and now if u is a function of x then, by the Chain Rule,

(3) $$\frac{de^u}{dx} = \frac{de^u}{du}\frac{du}{dx}$$

$$= e^u\frac{du}{dx}.$$

Formula (3) may be used in conjunction with the logarithmic formula*

(4)
$$M^p = e^{p \ln M}$$

to obtain the derivative of a function which has a variable in the exponent (even if the function is a variable raised to a variable power).

Example. With the restriction $x > 0$,

$$\frac{dx^{\cos x}}{dx} = \frac{d}{dx} e^{\cos x \ln x} \qquad \text{from (4)}$$

$$= e^{\cos x \ln x} \frac{d}{dx}(\cos x \ln x) \qquad \text{from (3)}$$

$$= x^{\cos x}\left(\frac{\cos x}{x} - \sin x \ln x\right).$$

If r is a constant, then (3) yields

(5)
$$\frac{de^{rx}}{dx} = re^{rx} \quad \text{and} \quad \frac{d^2 e^{rx}}{dx^2} = r^2 e^{rx}.$$

These equations may be used (as shown below) to find two nontrivial† solutions of the differential equation

(6)
$$\frac{d^2 y}{dx^2} + \frac{dy}{dx} - 12y = 0.$$

Such a differential equation is said to have a function $y(x)$ as a solution if this function $y(x)$ satisfies the differential equation identically, that is, makes the left side equal to zero for all values of x. A method of attack is to see if the function

(7)
$$y = e^{rx}$$

satisfies (6) for some value of r. Direct substitution into the left side of (6) yields

$$r^2 e^{rx} + re^{rx} - 12e^{rx} = e^{rx}(r^2 + r - 12) = e^{rx}(r - 3)(r + 4),$$

which will be zero for all values of x if either $r = 3$ or $r = -4$. It thus follows that the two functions

$$y = e^{3x} \quad \text{and} \quad y = e^{-4x}$$

both satisfy (6) identically.

Mathematical development does not always proceed in an orderly fashion from known results to new facts. Sometimes mathematicians use trial-and-error methods. It is only through experience (as gained from the above illustration) that one might suspect there are values of r such that (7) satisfies (6).

---

*Recall that $\log_e M$ is such that $M = e^{\log_e M}$ [see (1) of Sec. 6–3] and thus, with $b = e$,
$$M = e^{\ln M}.$$
Formula (4) follows by raising both sides to the power p.

†A nontrivial solution is one that is not identically equal to zero.

Problem 1. Find $D_x^2 y$ and $D_x^3 y$ for each of the following:

a. $y = x^{\sin x}$, $x > 0$.

b. $y = (\sin x)^x$, $0 < x < \pi$.

c. $y = |x|^x$, $x \neq 0$.

d. $y = (\ln x)^x$, $x > 1$.

e. $y = (\sqrt{x})^x$, $x > 0$.

f. $y = 5^{\sin x}$.

g. $y = (\sin x)^5$.

h. $y = x^{\ln x}$, $x > 0$.

Note: Problems 2 through 5 furnish background material for later developments (see Sec. 14–6).

Problem 2. Find two nontrivial solutions of each of the differential equations:

a. $\dfrac{d^2 y}{dx^2} + \dfrac{dy}{dx} - 2y = 0$.

b. $\dfrac{d^2 y}{dx^2} - \dfrac{dy}{dx} - 12y = 0$.

c. $2\dfrac{d^2 y}{dx^2} - 7\dfrac{dy}{dx} + 3y = 0$.

d. $3\dfrac{d^2 y}{dx^2} + \dfrac{dy}{dx} - 4y = 0$.

Problem 3. Given the differential equation $4y'' - 4y' + y = 0$:

a. Show that there is only one value of r such that $y = e^{rx}$ is a solution.

b. With r the value obtained in part a, show that $y = xe^{rx}$ is also a solution.

Problem 4. Work Prob. 3 for the differential equation
$$9y'' - 12y' + 4y = 0.$$

Problem 5. Given the differential equation $y'' - 2y' + 5y = 0$:

a. Show that $y = e^{rx}$ will formally satisfy the differential eqation if
$$r^2 - 2r + 5 = 0.$$

b. Show that the quadratic equation $r^2 - 2r + 5 = 0$ has the complex-valued solutions
$$r = 1 \pm 2i, \text{ where } i = \sqrt{-1}.$$

c. Show that $y = e^x \cos 2x$ and $y = e^x \sin 2x$ both satisfy the differential equation.

6-7. Hyperbolic Functions

If mathematicians, or those who apply mathematics, see a particular combination of known functions recurring frequently, they may decide to replace such a combination by a new function. It has been found that the sum and difference of $\frac{1}{2}e^x$ and $\frac{1}{2}e^{-x}$ reappear in certain branches of applied mathematics and it has become standard practice to define new functions sinh x (the **hyperbolic sine** of x) and cosh x (the **hyperbolic cosine** of x) by setting

(1) $\sinh x = \frac{1}{2}(e^x - e^{-x})$ and $\cosh x = \frac{1}{2}(e^x + e^{-x})$.

The reason for the adjective "hyperbolic" is because these functions are related to a rectangular hyperbola in much the same way the ordinary trigonometric sin x and cos x functions are related to a circle, but this relation is unimportant in the uses of these functions and so will not be explained.* Further analogy with trigonometry is made by defining the hyperbolic tangent function and other functions by setting

(2)
$$\tanh x = \frac{\sinh x}{\cosh x}, \qquad \operatorname{sech} x = \frac{1}{\cosh x},$$

$$\coth x = \frac{\cosh x}{\sinh x}, \qquad \operatorname{csch} x = \frac{1}{\sinh x}.$$

By direct use of the definitions (1) it follows that

$$
\begin{aligned}
(3) \qquad \cosh^2 x + \sinh^2 x &= [\tfrac{1}{2}(e^x + e^{-x})]^2 + [\tfrac{1}{2}(e^x - e^{-x})]^2 \\
&= \tfrac{1}{4}(e^{2x} + 2 + e^{-2x}) + \tfrac{1}{4}(e^{2x} - 2 + e^{-2x}) \\
&= \tfrac{1}{2}(e^{2x} + e^{-2x}) = \cosh 2x;
\end{aligned}
$$

whereas, from trigonometry,

$$\cos^2 x + \sin^2 x = 1 \quad \text{and} \quad \cos^2 x - \sin^2 x = \cos 2x.$$

A mental check, with a glance at the above, shows that

$$(4) \qquad\qquad \cosh^2 x - \sinh^2 x = 1.$$

Thus, there are some similarities, but not complete analogies, between identities for hyperbolic functions and trigonometric functions.

The calculus of hyperbolic functions may be worked out from the known calculus formulas for the functions e^x and e^{-x}. Thus,

$$
(5) \qquad \frac{d}{dx} \sinh x = \frac{d}{dx} \frac{1}{2}(e^x - e^{-x}) = \frac{1}{2}\left(\frac{de^x}{dx} - \frac{de^{-x}}{dx}\right)
$$

$$
= \frac{1}{2}(e^x + e^{-x}) = \cosh x,
$$

$$
(6) \qquad \frac{d}{dx} \cosh x = \frac{d}{dx} \frac{1}{2}(e^x + e^{-x}) = \sinh x.
$$

These formulas are just enough like

$$\frac{d}{dx} \sin x = \cos x \quad \text{and} \quad \frac{d}{dx} \cos x = -\sin x$$

to make the presence or absence of the minus sign hard to remember unless the derivation of the formulas is kept in mind.

Notice that the graph of $y = \sinh x$ may be obtained by geometric addition of the graphs $y = \tfrac{1}{2}e^x$ and $y = -\tfrac{1}{2}e^{-x}$ (Fig. 6-7.1) while geometric addition of curves $y = \tfrac{1}{2}e^x$ and $y = \tfrac{1}{2}e^{-x}$ gives the curve $y = \cosh x$ (Fig. 6-7.2). Since e^x and e^{-x} are both positive, then $\cosh x$ is always positive and, from $D_x \sinh x = \cosh x$, the curve $y = \sinh x$ has positive slope throughout. Hence, given a number y there is one and only one number x such that $\sinh x = y$.

*Anyone interested may find the explanation in H. W. Reddick and F. H. Miller, *Advanced Mathematics for Engineers*, 3rd ed., (New York: John Wiley and Sons, Inc., 1955), p. 95.

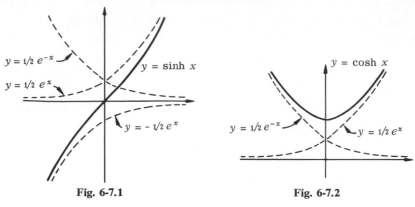

Fig. 6-7.1   Fig. 6-7.2

By interchanging the roles of x and y, the function

(7) $$y = \sinh^{-1} x$$

of x is called the **inverse hyperbolic sine** of x. It so happens, however, that this is not an entirely new function since, as shown below,

(8) $$\sinh^{-1} x = \ln (x + \sqrt{x^2 + 1}).$$

To obtain (8) first note, from (7), that $\sinh y = x$; that is,

$$x = \frac{1}{2}(e^y - e^{-y}) = \frac{e^{2y} - 1}{2e^y}.$$

This equation may be written in the form

$$e^{2y} - 2xe^y - 1 = 0,$$

which is a quadratic equation in e^y whose formal solution for e^y is

$$e^y = \frac{2x \pm \sqrt{(2x)^2 - 4(-1)}}{2} = x \pm \sqrt{x^2 + 1}.$$

Since, however, e^y is never negative, the minus sign gives an extraneous root, which is discarded so that $e^y = x + \sqrt{x^2 + 1}$. Now $\ln e^y = \ln (x + \sqrt{x^2 + 1})$, and since $\ln e^y = y \ln e = y$, then

$$y = \ln (x + \sqrt{x^2 + 1}).$$

But $y = \sinh^{-1} x$ from (7) and hence (8) has been established.

Problem 1. By using formulas (1) and (2) with x replaced by u or v, check that:
a. $\sinh u \cosh v + \cosh u \sinh v = \frac{1}{2}(e^{(u+v)} - e^{-(u+v)}) = \sinh (u + v)$.
b. $\cosh u \cosh v + \sinh u \sinh v = \frac{1}{2}(e^{(u+v)} + e^{-(u+v)}) = \cosh (u + v)$.

Problem 2. Reduce each of the following to a hyperbolic function of $u - v$:
a. $\sinh u \cosh v - \cosh u \sinh v$.
b. $\cosh u \cosh v - \sinh u \sinh v$.

Problem 3. Start with the identities of Probs. 1 and 2 and establish each of the following identities [possibly also using (5) or (6)]:

a. $\sinh 2u = 2 \sinh u \cosh u$.

b. $\cosh 2u = \cosh^2 u + \sinh^2 u = 2 \cosh^2 u - 1 = 1 + 2 \sinh^2 u$.

c. $\sinh x + \sinh y = 2 \sinh \dfrac{x+y}{2} \cosh \dfrac{x-y}{2}$.

d. $\cosh x - \cosh y = 2 \sinh \dfrac{x+y}{2} \sinh \dfrac{x-y}{2}$.

Problem 4. Establish each of the derivative formulas:

a. $D_x \tanh x = \operatorname{sech}^2 x$.

b. $D_x \coth x = -\operatorname{csch}^2 x$.

c. $D_x \operatorname{sech} x = -\operatorname{sech} x \tanh x$.

d. $D_x \ln (\cosh x) = \tanh x$.

e. $D_x \sinh^{-1} x = \dfrac{1}{\sqrt{1 + x^2}}$.

f. $D_x \operatorname{csch} x = -\operatorname{csch} x \coth x$.

Problem 5. Find $D_x y$, given:

a. $y = \sinh (3x^2 - 4x)$.

b. $y = \cosh^3 (2x + 1)$.

c. $y = \tanh^2 \sqrt{x}$.

d. $y = \sinh (\sin x)$.

e. $x + y^2 \sinh x = 4$.

f. $xy + \sinh y = 0$.

g. $y = \sinh^{-1} (x/a)$.

h. $y = \sinh^{-1} (a/x)$.

Chapter 7

Indefinite Integrals

7-1. Tables of Integrals

Given a function $y = f(x)$, it has been seen that some problems lead to the derivative of $f(x)$ with respect to x :

(1) $$D_x y = \frac{dy}{dx} = f'(x) = \lim_{\Delta x \to 0} \frac{\Delta f(x)}{\Delta x} = \lim_{\Delta x \to 0} \frac{f(x + \Delta x) - f(x)}{\Delta x}.$$

For other problems, it is necessary to know the value of the definite integral from a to b of a continuous function $f(x)$:

(2) $$\int_a^b f(x)\, dx = \lim_{n \to \infty} \sum_{k=1}^n f(x_k)\, \Delta x,$$

wherein $\Delta x = (b - a)/n$ and $x_k = a + k\,\Delta x$ for $k = 1, 2, 3, \ldots, n$. So far in this book, the derivative has received the major emphasis, but a few applications of the definite integral were given and more will appear later. It has also been shown that the long process of actually forming the sum in (2), and then taking its limit as $n \to \infty$, may be avoided if a function $F(x)$ can be found such that $F'(x) = f(x)$. In fact, the Fundamental Theorem of Calculus states that

(3) $$\int_a^b f(x)\, dx = F(x)]_a^b, \quad \text{where} \quad F'(x) = f(x).$$

Hence, before becoming involved with problems that lead to definite integrals, it is advisable to have techniques at hand for finding antiderivatives $F(x)$ for a large class of functions $f(x)$.

This chapter is devoted to the development of methods and techniques for finding antiderivatives. Recall also that if a function $f(x)$ is given and $F(x)$ is an antiderivative of $f(x)$, so that $F'(x) = f(x)$, then the notation

$$\int f(x)\, dx = F(x) + c$$

is used and the terminology "indefinite integration" is applied to it. For example, since $D_x \cos x = -\sin x$ [so that $D_x(-\cos x + c) = \sin x$ for any constant c], then

$$\int \sin x \, dx = -\cos x + c.$$

It should therefore be seen that every derivative that has been worked out could be recorded in reverse as a fact about indefinite integration.

A Table of Integrals has been compiled under various methods of cataloging entries according to some classification of the functions involved. Such a table of indefinite integrals is given at the end of this book and should now be turned to for a preliminary examination.

Notice that the first 16 formulas come under the forewarning title "Minimum Memorization List," which should be taken seriously. Actually, most of these 16 formulas are already familiar from their original appearances as derivative formulas or results. In fact, it would be well to take the differential with respect to x of each of the functions on the right of the equality sign and obtain as an answer the function under the integral sign, that is, the integrand. For example, with an eye on formula 15, note that

$$d \ln|\sec x + \tan x| = \frac{d(\sec x + \tan x)}{\sec x + \tan x}$$

$$= \frac{d \sec x + d \tan x}{\sec x + \tan x}$$

$$= \frac{\sec x \tan x \, dx + \sec^2 x \, dx}{\sec x + \tan x}$$

$$= \frac{\sec x(\tan x + \sec x) \, dx}{\sec x + \tan x}$$

$$= \sec x \, dx.$$

The variable x is used throughout the table and all other letters stand for constants. Any other variable may be used in place of x. For example,

$$\int \sin u \, du = -\cos u + c$$

is equivalent to formula 3.

The availability of a Table of Integrals should not lull anyone into a complacent feeling that indefinite integration is as easy as using a logarithmic or trigonometric table. Consider, for example,

(4) $$\int x\sqrt{(4 - x^2)} \, dx.$$

There is a section of the table (formulas 32 through 41) headed "Integrals Involving $\sqrt{a^2 - x^2}$," and it would be natural to look there for the answer to (4), but no such form is found for the simple reason that (4) may be integrated by using the very first formula of the table. To see this, set

(5) $$4 - x^2 = u,$$

so $-2x \, dx = du$, $x \, dx = -\frac{1}{2} \, du$, and hence

$$\int x\sqrt{4 - x^2}\, dx = \int u^{1/2}\left(-\frac{1}{2}\, du\right) = -\frac{1}{2}\int u^{1/2}\, du$$

$$= -\frac{1}{2}\frac{u^{3/2}}{3/2} + c$$

$$= -\frac{1}{3}(4 - x^2)^{3/2} + c.$$

Notice that the above illustration used the fact that "the integral of a constant times a function is the constant times the integral of the function :

$$\int cf(x)\, dx = c\int f(x)\, dx\text{"}$$

which was first shown to hold on p. 95. It should also be recalled that "the integral of the sum of two functions is the sum of their integrals :

$$\int [f(x) \pm g(x)]\, dx = \int f(x)\, dx \pm \int g(x)\, dx.\text{"}$$

By making the proper substitution [similar to (2) above], each of the integrals of the following problems may be reduced to one of the forms 1 through 16 of the Table of Integrals.

Problem 1. Each of the following may be integrated by using only formulas 1 and 2 of the Table of Integrals.

a. $\int (x^3 + 4)^2 x^2\, dx.$

d. $\int \frac{x^2}{x^3 + 4}\, dx.$

g. $\int \frac{dx}{x \ln x}.$

b. $\int \sin^2 x \cos x\, dx.$

e. $\int \frac{\ln(x)}{x}\, dx.$

h. $\int \frac{\sin(\ln |x|)}{x}\, dx.$

c. $\int \frac{2x + 1}{x^2 + x}\, dx.$

f. $\int \frac{1}{x - 1}\, dx.$

i. $\int \frac{\sec x \tan x}{\sqrt{1 + \sec x}}\, dx.$

Problem 2. First divide the numerator by the denominator until a remainder of degree less than the denominator is obtained and thus integrate :

a. $\int \frac{x^2 + x}{2x + 1}\, dx.$

d. $\int \frac{t^8 + t^5 + t^2}{t^3 + 1}\, dt.$

b. $\int \frac{x^3 + 4}{x + 2}\, dx.$

e. $\int \left(\frac{t + 1}{t}\right)^2 dt.$

c. $\int \frac{x^4 + x^2 + x}{x^2 + 1}\, dx.$

f. $\int \left(\frac{x^2 + 3}{x^2}\right)^2 dx.$

Problem 3. Integrate :

a. $\int x \sin x^2\, dx.$

g. $\int \frac{dx}{\sqrt{1 - 4x^2}}.$

b. $\int x \cot x^2\, dx.$

h. $\int \frac{dx}{1 + (4x)^2}.$

c. $\int e^{2x}\, dx.$

i. $\int x \sec (2x)^2 \tan (2x)^2\, dx.$

d. $\int (2x)^e\, dx.$

j. $\int (x + 1) \sec (x^2 + 2x + 1)\, dx.$

e. $\int 2^{4x}\, dx.$

k. $\int \dfrac{\csc \sqrt{x}}{\sqrt{x}}\, dx.$

f. $\int (4x)^2\, dx.$

l. $\int \dfrac{\ln x^2}{x}\, dx.$

7-2. Recommended for Memorization

The previous set of problems should be convincing evidence that the mere ability to rattle off integration formulas from memory is not enough for working integration problems. Even more, a blind search through a table of integrals for an appropriate formula may be fruitless unless an ability has been developed to recognize how the integrand may be changed by algebraic manipulation, trigonometric identities, or substitutions to make this integrand fit a pattern. In other words, a table of integrals so extensive as to include all integration problems ever met would be so ponderous that its bulk and complexity would render it useless.

Thus, a table of integrals must be carefully selected to include a workable set of formulas to fit most situations, assuming the user is familiar with standard facts about derivatives and has developed some skill in recognizing how integrands may be altered to fit into one or another of the formulas. The purpose of this chapter is to develop such skills based upon 100 formulas in the table.

Formulas 17 through 24, those *recommended* for memorization, should now be examined carefully. In one sense, these formulas are largely superfluous since all except formula 22 follow from the first list of 16 formulas, as shown in the following three examples and Prob. 1 below.

Example 1. First check the algebraic identity:

$$\frac{a}{b}\left(\frac{1}{ax} - \frac{1}{ax+b}\right) = \frac{1}{x(ax+b)}.$$

Hence,

$$\int \frac{dx}{x(ax+b)} = \frac{a}{b}\int \frac{dx}{ax} - \frac{a}{b}\int \frac{dx}{ax+b}$$

$$= \frac{1}{b}\int \frac{dx}{x} - \frac{1}{b}\int \frac{d(ax+b)}{ax+b}$$

$$= \frac{1}{b}\left[\ln|x| - \ln|ax+b|\right] \quad \text{from formula 2}$$

$$= \frac{1}{b}\ln\left|\frac{x}{ax-b}\right|, \quad \text{which is formula 17.}$$

Example 2. Solve the trigonometric identity $\cos 2x = 2\cos^2 x - 1$, for $\cos^2 x$:

$$\cos^2 x = \frac{1 + \cos 2x}{2}.$$

Hence,

$$\int \cos^2 x \, dx = \tfrac{1}{2} \int dx + \tfrac{1}{2} \int \cos 2x \, dx$$

$$= \tfrac{1}{2}x + \tfrac{1}{4} \int \cos 2x \, d(2x)$$

$$= \tfrac{1}{2}x + \tfrac{1}{4} \sin 2x \quad \text{from formula 4.}$$

Note that this is essentially formula 24.

Example 3. Toward establishing formula 21, make the substitution $x = a \sin t$ with $-\pi/2 \le t \le \pi/2$ and $a > 0$. Then

$$dx = a \cos t \, dt.$$

Hence,

$$\int \sqrt{a^2 - x^2} \, dx = \int \sqrt{a^2 - a^2 \sin^2 t} \, a \cos t \, dt$$

$$= \int \sqrt{a^2(1 - \sin^2 t)} \, a \cos t \, dt$$

(1)
$$= a^2 \int \sqrt{\cos^2 t} \, \cos t \, dt$$

$$= a^2 \int \cos^2 t \, dt \quad (\text{not } \pm \cos^2 t \text{ since } -\pi/2 \le t \le \pi/2)$$

$$= a^2(\tfrac{1}{2}t + \tfrac{1}{4} \sin 2t) \quad \text{from formula 24.}$$

Since $x = a \sin t$ with $-\pi/2 \le t \le \pi/2$, then $t = \sin^{-1}(x/a)$. Also,

$$\sin 2t = 2 \sin t \cos t = 2 \sin t \sqrt{1 - \sin^2 t}$$

$$= 2\frac{x}{a}\sqrt{1 - \frac{x^2}{a^2}} = \frac{2x}{a^2}\sqrt{a^2 - x^2}.$$

(Recall that $a > 0$; hence, $\sqrt{a^2} = a$.) These expressions substituted into (1) yield

$$\int \sqrt{a^2 - x^2} \, dx = a^2\left(\frac{1}{2} \sin^{-1}\frac{x}{a} + \frac{1}{4}\frac{2x}{a^2}\sqrt{a^2 - x^2}\right),$$

which is equivalent to formula 21.

The type of substitutions and manipulations illustrated in the above three examples (and those of Prob. 1 below) will be studied in more detail later. The student is urged to become thoroughly familiar with all formulas 1 through 24 ; otherwise, further work would be similar to writing a theme and looking up the spellings of such words as "the," "cat," and "man."

Problem 1. a. Check the identity

$$\frac{1}{2a}\left(\frac{1}{x - a} - \frac{1}{x + a}\right) = \frac{1}{x^2 - a^2}$$

and use this to establish formula 18.

b. In the integrand of formula 19, set $x = a \tan t$, use the trigonometric identity $\tan^2 t + 1 = \sec^2 t$, and show that

$$\int \frac{dx}{\sqrt{x^2 + a^2}} = \ln\left(\frac{\sqrt{x^2 + a^2} + x}{a}\right) + c.$$

Explain why this is equivalent to formula 19 with the plus sign. Also explain why $\ln(\ )$ rather than $\ln|\ \ |$ may be used.

    c. Use the substitution $x = a \sec t$ $(0 \le t < \pi/2$ or $\pi/2 < t \le \pi)$ and the trigonometric identity $\sec^2 t = \tan^2 t + 1$ to derive formula 19 with the minus sign.

    d. Use the trigonometric identity $\cos 2t = 1 - 2\sin^2 t$ to derive formula 23.

Problem 2. Check each of the formulas 17 through 24 by finding the differential with respect to x of the right side to obtain the integrand on the left. (At least do this for formula 22.)

    Problem 3. In each of the following parts, find all three integrals:

a. $\int \sqrt{9 - 4x^2}\, dx,$ $\int \frac{1}{\sqrt{9 - 4x^2}}\, dx,$ $\int \frac{x}{\sqrt{9 - 4x^2}}\, dx.$

b. $\int \sqrt{4x^2 - 9}\, dx,$ $\int \frac{1}{\sqrt{4x^2 - 9}}\, dx,$ $\int \frac{x}{\sqrt{4x^2 - 9}}\, dx.$

c. $\int x \sin (4x^2)\, dx,$ $\int \sin^2 4x\, dx,$ $\int \sin^2 4x \cos 4x\, dx.$

d. $\int \frac{dx}{2x(3x + 1)},$ $\int 2x(3x + 1)\, dx,$ $\int \frac{3x + 1}{2x}\, dx.$

e. $\int \sqrt{2x^2 - 3}\, dx,$ $\int \frac{1}{\sqrt{2x^2 - 3}}\, dx,$ $\int x\sqrt{2x^2 - 3}\, dx.$

f. $\int e^x\sqrt{e^{2x} + 1}\, dx,$ $\int \frac{e^x}{\sqrt{e^{2x} + 1}}\, dx,$ $\int \frac{1}{e^x - 1}\, dx.$

7-3. Integration by Parts

    The differential of a sum is the sum of the differentials, and hence the integral of a sum is the sum of the integrals:

$$\int [f(x) + g(x)]\, dx = \int f(x)\, dx + \int g(x)\, dx.$$

The integral of a product is, however, not the product of the integrals. Nevertheless, the formula for the derivative of a product, written as

(1) $$u\, dv + v\, du = d\, uv,$$

has an integral analog which is most useful. From (1),

$$\int u\, dv + \int v\, du = \int d\, uv = uv.$$

Upon transposing the second integral to the right-hand side, the result

(2) $$\int u\, dv = uv - \int v\, du$$

is known as the formula for **integration by parts.**

Example 1. Integrate $\int x \sin x\, dx$.

Solution. Set $u = x$ and $dv = \sin x\, dx$ to make the integrand fit the left member of (2). Hence, $du = dx$ and (by integration, omitting the additive constant) $v = -\cos x$. Then substitute throughout (2) to obtain

$$\int x \sin x\, dx = x(-\cos x) - \int (-\cos x)\, dx$$

$$= -x \cos x + \int \cos x\, dx$$

$$= -x \cos x + \sin x + c.$$

Some of the formulas in the Table of Integrals are merely the results of carrying out integrations by parts.

Example 2. Derive formula 60.

Solution. The integrand in formula 60 is $x^n \ln ax\, dx$. It would seem natural to set u equal to x^n and dv equal to $\ln ax\, dx$, but this is not advisable since then v would have to be found from the integral $\int \ln ax\, dx$, which is formula 60, with $n = 0$. Hence, try

$$u = \ln ax \quad \text{and} \quad dv = x^n\, dx, \quad \text{so that}$$

$$du = \frac{a}{ax}\, dx = \frac{1}{x}\, dx, \quad v = \frac{x^{n+1}}{n+1}.$$

Upon making these substitution into (2), the result is

$$\int (\ln ax)(x^n\, dx) = (\ln ax)\frac{x^{n+1}}{n+1} - \int \frac{x^{n+1}}{n+1}\frac{1}{x}\, dx,$$

$$\int x^n \ln ax\, dx = \frac{x^{n+1}}{n+1} \ln ax - \frac{1}{n+1}\int x^n\, dx$$

$$= \frac{x^{n+1}}{n+1} \ln ax - \frac{1}{n+1}\frac{x^{n+1}}{n+1} + c,$$

which is equivalent to formula 60 of the Table of Integrals.

Example 3. Derive formula 72.

Solution. The integrand is $\cos^{-1}(x/a)\, dx$. Set $u = \cos^{-1}(x/a)$ and dv all the rest of the integrand; that is, $dv = dx$. Hence,

$$du = d\cos^{-1}\frac{x}{a} = -\frac{1}{\sqrt{1-(x/a)^2}}\, d\left(\frac{x}{a}\right) = -\frac{a}{\sqrt{a^2-x^2}}\frac{1}{a}\, dx = -\frac{1}{\sqrt{a^2-x^2}}\, dx,$$

since $\sqrt{a^2} = a$ because the constant a is positive. Since $dv = dx$, then $v = x$. Thus, from the integration by parts formula (2),

$$\int \cos^{-1}\frac{x}{a}\, dx = \left(\cos^{-1}\frac{x}{a}\right)x - \int x\left(-\frac{1}{\sqrt{a^2-x^2}}\, dx\right)$$

$$= x \cos^{-1}\frac{x}{a} + \int \frac{x}{\sqrt{a^2-x^2}}\, dx$$

$$= x \cos^{-1}\frac{x}{a} - \frac{1}{2}\int (a^2-x^2)^{-1/2}\, d(a^2-x^2)$$

$$= x \cos^{-1} \frac{x}{a} - \frac{1}{2} \frac{(a^2 - x^2)^{1/2}}{1/2} + c,$$

which is equivalent to formula 72 of the Table of Integrals.

Sometimes it is necessary to use integration by parts twice.

Example 4. Integrate $\int x^2 e^x \, dx$.

Solution. $u = x^2$, $dv = e^x \, dx$; $du = 2x \, dx$, $v = e^x$, and hence

(3)
$$\int x^2 e^x \, dx = x^2 e^x - \int e^x (2x) \, dx = x^2 e^x - 2 \int x e^x \, dx.$$

Now u and dv may be used again on the resulting integral. This time, set $u = x$, $dv = e^x \, dx$; $du = dx$, $v = e^x$. Hence,

$$\int x e^x \, dx = x e^x - \int e^x \, dx = x e^x - e^x.$$

The substitution of this integration into the right-most term of (3) yields

$$\int x^2 e^x \, dx = x^2 e^x - 2(x e^x - e^x) + c$$
$$= e^x (x^2 - 2x + 2) + c.$$

Example 5. Derive formula 61.

Solution. The integrand is $e^{ax} \sin bx \, dx$, so set

$$u = e^{ax}, \quad dv = \sin bx \, dx,$$

$$du = a e^{ax} \, dx, \quad v = -\frac{1}{b} \cos bx.$$

$$\int e^{ax} \sin bx \, dx = e^{ax} \left(-\frac{1}{b} \cos bx \right) - \int \left(-\frac{1}{b} \cos bx \right) a e^{ax} \, dx$$

$$= -\frac{1}{b} e^{ax} \cos bx + \frac{a}{b} \int e^{ax} \cos bx \, dx.$$

Now in the integral on the right (and only on the integral on the right), set

$$u = e^{ax}, \quad dv = \cos bx,$$

$$du = a e^{ax} \, dx, \quad v = \frac{1}{b} \sin bx,$$

and then the whole result is

$$\int e^{ax} \sin bx \, dx = -\frac{1}{b} e^{ax} \cos bx + \frac{a}{b} \left[e^{ax} \frac{1}{b} \sin bx - \int \frac{1}{b} \sin bx \, a e^{ax} \, dx \right]$$

$$= -\frac{1}{b} e^{ax} \cos bx + \frac{a}{b^2} e^{ax} \sin bx - \frac{a^2}{b^2} \int e^{ax} \sin bx \, dx.$$

The original integral now appears on both sides, so transpose and collect to obtain

$$\left(1 + \frac{a^2}{b^2} \right) \int e^{ax} \sin bx \, dx = -\frac{1}{b} e^{ax} \cos bx + \frac{a}{b^2} e^{ax} \sin bx.$$

This equation should be solved for the desired integral to see that the result is formula 61.

Problem 1. Use integration by parts to obtain each of the following integrals:

a. $\int x \cos x \, dx.$

g. $\int \sec^3 x \, dx.$

b. $\int x \sin (2x) \, dx.$

h. $\int x^3 e^{-x} \, dx.$

c. $\int xe^{2x} \, dx.$

i. $\int x \sec^2 x \, dx.$

d. $\int x\sqrt{1 + x} \, dx.$

j. $\int x 2^x \, dx.$

e. $\int x^2 \sqrt{x + 3} \, dx.$

k. $\int \frac{x \tan^{-1} x}{\sqrt{1 + x^2}} \, dx.$

f. $\int x^2 \cos x \, dx.$

l. $\int x^3 \sqrt{a^2 + x^2} \, dx.$

Problem 2. Use integration by parts to derive each of the following formulas in the Table of Integrals:

a. 27. c. 36. e. 73.
b. 30. d. 63. f. 75.

g. Also, rederive formula 23 by setting $u = \sin x$ and $dv = \sin x \, dx$.

Problem 3. Set $u = f(x)$ and $dv = g(x) \, dx$ in (2) and derive the formula

$$\int f(x) g(x) \, dx = f(x) \int g(x) \, dx - \int \left(\int g(x) \, dx \right) f'(x) \, dx$$

for obtaining the integral of the product of two functions. For example, Prob. 1a. a could now be worked as follows:

$$\int x \cos x \, dx = x \int \cos x \, dx - \int \left(\int \cos x \, dx \right) 1 \cdot dx$$

$$= x \sin x - \int \sin x \, dx$$

$$= x \sin x + \cos x + c.$$

Rework some of the parts of Prob. 1 using this formula.

Problem 4. As practice in recognizing when to use integration by parts and when to use known formulas, evaluate the three integrals in each case.

a. $\int x \sin x^2 \, dx, \quad \int x^2 \sin x \, dx, \quad \int x \sin^2 x \, dx.$

b. $\int \tan 2x \, dx, \quad \int x \tan 2 \, dx, \quad \int 2 \tan x \, dx.$

c. $\int \frac{x}{\sqrt{x^2 + 4}} \, dx, \quad \int x\sqrt{x^2 + 4} \, dx, \quad \int x^2 \sqrt{x + 4} \, dx.$

d. $\int x^2 e^x \, dx, \quad \int xe^{x^2} \, dx, \quad \int x(e^x)^2 \, dx.$

e. $\int \ln |x|^{-1} \, dx, \quad \int x^{-1} \ln |x| \, dx, \quad \int x \ln |x|^{-1} \, dx.$

7-4. Sums and Differences of Squares

In this section it is shown how the trigonometric identities

(1) $\sin^2 A + \cos^2 A = 1, \quad \tan^2 A + 1 = \sec^2 A, \quad$ and $\quad 1 + \cot^2 A = \csc^2 A$

are used in deriving integral formulas.

Example 1. Derive formula 35 of the Table of Integrals.

Solution. The substitution $x = a \sin t$ yields

$$\sqrt{a^2 - x^2} = \sqrt{a^2 - a^2 \sin^2 t} = \sqrt{a^2(1 - \sin^2 t)} = \sqrt{a^2 \cos^2 t} = a|\cos t|,$$

where the absolute value is necessary since it is not known whether $\cos t \geq 0$ or $\cos t < 0$. If, however, t is restricted by

$$(2) \qquad \frac{-\pi}{2} \leq t \leq \frac{\pi}{2},$$

then, in this t-range, $\cos t \geq 0$, so $|\cot t| = \cos t$. Also, from the substitution $x = a \sin t$, it follows that

$$dx = d(a \sin t) = a \cos t \, dt.$$

Hence,

$$\int \frac{\sqrt{a^2 - x^2}}{x^2} \, dx = \int \frac{a \cos t}{(a \sin t)^2} a \cos t \, dt = \int \frac{\cos^2 t}{\sin^2 t} \, dt = \int \cot^2 t \, dt$$

$$= \int (\csc^2 t - 1) \, dt = -\cot t - t + c \quad \text{from formula 8.}$$

It is now necessary to return to the original variable x. To do so, note that, since $x = a \sin t$ and $-\pi/2 \leq t \leq \pi/2$, then* $t = \sin^{-1}(x/a)$ and

$$\cot t = \frac{\cos t}{\sin t} = \frac{\sqrt{1 - \sin^2 t}}{\sin t} = \frac{\sqrt{1 - (x/a)^2}}{x/a} = \frac{\sqrt{a^2 - x^2}}{x}.$$

These resubstitutions into the above result yield

$$\int \frac{\sqrt{a^2 - x^2}}{x^2} \, dx = -\frac{\sqrt{a^2 - x^2}}{x} - \sin^{-1} \frac{x}{a} + c,$$

which is formula 35.

In the Table of Integrals, all of formulas 32 through 54 have integrands involving $\sqrt{a^2 - x^2}$, $\sqrt{x^2 + a^2}$, or $\sqrt{x^2 - a^2}$, each of which may be rationalized by a substitution, depending on the first two trigonometric identities of (1). Since the constant a appears only as a^2, it is customary to assume $a > 0$, so that

$$\sqrt{a^2} = a$$

without the ambiguity "$\pm$." The variable x may, however, be either positive or negative. It is customary to avoid as much ambiguity as possible by imposing restrictions on the new variable t, as given below.

(i) The substitution $x = a \sin t$ with $-\pi/2 \leq t \leq \pi/2$ yields

$$\sqrt{a^2 - x^2} = \sqrt{a^2 - a^2 \sin^2 t} = \sqrt{a^2 \cos^2 t} = a \cos t.$$

(ii) The substitution $x = a \tan t$ with $-\pi/2 < t < \pi/2$ yields

$$\sqrt{x^2 + a^2} = \sqrt{a^2 + a^2 \tan^2 t} = \sqrt{a^2 \sec^2 t} = a \sec t.$$

(iii) The substitution $x = a \sec t$ with $0 \leq t < \pi/2$ or $\pi/2 < t \leq \pi$ yields

*Recall from Sec. 6-2 that $\sin^{-1}$ was restricted to $-\pi/2 \leq \sin^{-1} \leq \pi/2$.

$$\sqrt{x^2 - a^2} = \sqrt{a^2 \sec^2 t - a^2} = \sqrt{a^2 \tan^2 t} = \begin{cases} a \tan t & \text{if } 0 \le t < \pi/2, \\ -a \tan t & \text{if } \pi/2 < t \le \pi. \end{cases}$$

Example 2. Derive formula 42.

Solution. The integrand involves $\sqrt{x^2 - a^2}$, so (iii) is called for, and hence

$$dx = d(a \sec t) = a \sec t \tan t \, dt.$$

If x is positive, then $0 \le t < \pi/2$, but if x is negative, then $\pi/2 < t \le \pi$. Hence, two cases must be considered.

Case 1: $0 \le t < \pi/2$. Then $x = a \sec t > 0$ and

$$\int \frac{\sqrt{x^2 - a^2}}{x} \, dx = \int \frac{a \tan t}{a \sec t} a \sec t \tan t \, dt = a \int \tan^2 t \, dt$$

$$= a \int (\sec^2 t - 1) \, dt = a(\tan t - t) + c$$

$$= a \left[\frac{\sqrt{x^2 - a^2}}{a} - \sec^{-1} \frac{x}{a} \right] + c$$

(3)
$$= \sqrt{x^2 - a^2} - a \cos^{-1} \frac{a}{x} + c, \quad x > 0,$$

where the change from* $\sec^{-1}(x/a)$ to $\cos^{-1}(a/x)$ is made, since most trigonometric tables do not have a secant column.

Case 2: $\pi/2 < t \le \pi$. Then $x = a \sec t < 0$ and

$$\int \frac{\sqrt{x^2 - a^2}}{x} \, dx = \int \frac{(-a \tan t)}{a \sec t} a \sec t \tan t \, dt = -a \int \tan^2 t \, dt$$

$$= -a \int (\sec^2 t - 1) \, dt = -a(\tan t - t) + C$$

$$= -a \left[\frac{\sqrt{x^2 - a^2}}{-a} - \sec^{-1} \frac{a}{x} \right] + C$$

$$= \sqrt{x^2 - a^2} + a \cos^{-1} \frac{a}{x} + C$$

$$= \sqrt{x^2 - a^2} + a \left(\pi - \cos^{-1} \frac{a}{-x} \right) + C$$

$$= \sqrt{x^2 - a^2} - a \cos^{-1} \frac{a}{-x} + C + a\pi$$

(4)
$$= \sqrt{x^2 - a^2} - a \cos^{-1} \frac{a}{|x|} + c \quad \text{for} \quad x < 0,$$

where $-x = |x|$ since $x < 0$. Also, the constant $C + a\pi$ was changed to c, since the additive constant is arbitrary.

Now in (3) the variable x is positive, so $x = |x|$, and hence (3) may be written in exactly the same form as (4) to yield

---

*Recall from Sec. 6-2 that $\sec^{-1}$ was defined by $\sec^{-1} y = \cos^{-1} 1/y$, where $0 \le \cos^{-1} \le \pi$. Hence, either $0 \le \sec^{-1} < \pi/2$ or $\pi/2 < \sec^{-1} \le \pi$, wherein $\pi/2$ is excluded since $\sec \pi/2$ is undefined.

$$\int \frac{\sqrt{x^2 - a^2}}{x}\, dx = \sqrt{x^2 - a^2} - a \cos^{-1} \frac{a}{|x|} + c,$$

which is formula 42.

As mentioned earlier, no table of integrals can contain all integrals ever met. In applications of mathematics, even though tables of integrals are always available, other integrals may have to be obtained by combining known formulas or deriving new ones. Familiarity with standard integrals, and the ability to manipulate integrals, is best gained by rederiving as many of the listed formulas as possible. Thus, the next set of problems consists largely of derivations of formulas of the Table of Integrals.

For one thing, it should not be thought that, just because an integrand contains, say, $\sqrt{x^2 \pm a^2}$, the substitutions (ii) and (iii) should be used.

Example 3. Derive formula 48.

Solution. By adding and subtracting a^2 to the numerator it follows that

$$\int \frac{x^2\, dx}{\sqrt{x^2 \pm a^2}} = \int \frac{x^2 \pm a^2 \mp a^2}{\sqrt{x^2 \pm a^2}}\, dx = \int \frac{x^2 \pm a^2}{\sqrt{x^2 \pm a^2}}\, dx \mp \int \frac{a^2\, dx}{\sqrt{x^2 \pm a^2}}$$

$$= \int \sqrt{x^2 \pm a^2}\, dx \mp a^2 \int \frac{dx}{\sqrt{x^2 \pm a^2}},$$

and now formulas 22 and 19 may be used to see that

$$\int \frac{x^2\, dx}{\sqrt{x^2 \pm a^2}} = \frac{1}{2}(x\sqrt{x^2 \pm a^2} \pm a^2 \ln|x + \sqrt{x^2 \pm a^2}|) \mp a^2 \ln|x + \sqrt{x^2 \pm a^2}| + c$$

$$= \frac{x}{2}\sqrt{x^2 \pm a^2} \mp \frac{a^2}{2} \ln|x + \sqrt{x^2 \pm a^2}|) + c,$$

which is formula 48.

Problem 1. Derive:
a. Formula 34 by using (i).
b. Formula 39 by using formulas 34 and 21.

Problem 2. Derive formula 36 by:
a. Using (i).
b. Using integration by parts $[u = x, \, dv = x(a^2 - x^2)^{-1/2}\, dx]$ and formula 21.
c. By adding and subtracting a^2 in the numerator and then using formulas 11 and 21.

Problem 3. First derive formula 40 and then use this and another formula to derive formula 41.

Problem 4. a. Derive formula 32 by using (i).
b. Multiply both numerator and denominator of the integrand in formula 32 by x, then indicate the integration by parts using $u = x^{-2}, \, dv = x\sqrt{a^2 - x^2}\, dx$, and use the result to find

$$\int \frac{(a^2 - x^2)^{3/2}}{x^3}\, dx.$$

c. In the integrand of formula 32, set $u = \sqrt{a^2 - x^2}$ and $dv = (1/x)\, dx$, indicate the integration by parts, and use the result to find

$$\int \frac{x \ln|x|}{\sqrt{a^2 - x^2}}\, dx.$$

Problem 5. a. Derive formula 46. Note that both (ii) and (iii) must be used.

b. In the integrand of formula 46 set $u = x$, $dv = x\sqrt{x^2 \pm a^2}\, dx$, indicate the integration by parts, and use the result to obtain formula 52.

7-5. Quadratic Terms in Integrands

Section VI of the Table of Integrals has integrands involving the quadratic expression $ax^2 + bx + c$ with a, b, and c constants. Space is conserved by replacing this expression by X. Also the constant $b^2 - 4ac$ occurs frequently and is replaced by q.

The formulas involving X may be derived from previous integration formulas by writing

$$X = ax^2 + bx + c = a\left[x^2 + \frac{b}{a}x + \frac{c}{a}\right]$$

$$= a\left[x^2 + \frac{b}{a}x + \left(\frac{b}{2a}\right)^2 + \frac{c}{a} - \frac{b^2}{4a^2}\right]$$

$$= a\left[\left(x + \frac{b}{2a}\right)^2 - \frac{b^2 - 4ac}{4a^2}\right]$$

(1) $= \begin{cases} a\left[\left(x + \dfrac{b}{2a}\right)^2 - \left(\dfrac{\sqrt{q}}{2a}\right)^2\right] & \text{if } q > 0, \\[2ex] a\left[\left(x + \dfrac{b}{2a}\right)^2 + \left(\dfrac{\sqrt{-q}}{2a}\right)^2\right] & \text{if } q < 0, \\[2ex] a\left(x + \dfrac{b}{2a}\right)^2 & \text{if } q = 0. \end{cases}$

(2)

(3)

Example 1. Derive formula 55.

Solution. Case 1: $q = b^2 - 4ac > 0$. Then, by using (1) above,

$$\int \frac{dx}{X} = \frac{1}{a} \int \frac{dx}{\left(x + \dfrac{b}{2a}\right)^2 - \left(\dfrac{\sqrt{q}}{2a}\right)^2}.$$

The integrand is now in the form of the integrand of formula 18 with, however,

$$x \text{ of formula 18 replaced by } \left(x + \frac{b}{2a}\right) \text{ and}$$

$$a \text{ of formula 18 replaced by } \frac{\sqrt{q}}{2a}.$$

Hence, the integral is (not forgetting to multiply by $1/a$)

$$\frac{1}{a}\frac{1}{2\left(\dfrac{\sqrt{q}}{2a}\right)}\ln\left|\frac{\left(x+\dfrac{b}{2a}\right)-\dfrac{\sqrt{q}}{2a}}{\left(x+\dfrac{b}{2a}\right)+\dfrac{\sqrt{q}}{2a}}\right|+c=\frac{1}{\sqrt{q}}\ln\left|\frac{2ax+b-\sqrt{q}}{2ax+b+\sqrt{q}}\right|+c,$$

which is the upper part of formula 55.

Case 2: $b^2 - 4ac < 0$. The expression (2) above is first used and then formula 12:

$$\int\frac{dx}{X}=\frac{1}{a}\int\frac{dx}{\left(x+\dfrac{b}{2a}\right)^2+\left(\dfrac{\sqrt{-q}}{2a}\right)^2}=\frac{1}{a}\frac{1}{\dfrac{\sqrt{-q}}{2a}}\tan^{-1}\frac{x+\dfrac{b}{2a}}{\dfrac{\sqrt{-q}}{2a}}+c$$

$$=\frac{2}{\sqrt{-q}}\tan^{-1}\frac{2ax+b}{\sqrt{-q}}+c.$$

Notice that formulas 79 through 84 also involved X.

Example 2. Derive formula 81.

Solution. Notice that $dX = d(ax^2 + bx + c) = (2ax + b)\,dx$. Hence, in formula 81 first multiply and divide the integrand by $2a$, then in the numerator add and subtract b:

$$\int\frac{x\,dx}{\sqrt{X}}=\frac{1}{2a}\int\frac{2ax\,dx}{\sqrt{X}}=\frac{1}{2a}\int\frac{2ax+b-b}{\sqrt{X}}\,dx$$

$$=\frac{1}{2a}\int\frac{2ax+b}{\sqrt{X}}\,dx-\frac{b}{2a}\int\frac{dx}{\sqrt{X}}$$

$$=\frac{1}{2a}\int X^{-1/2}\,dX-\frac{b}{2a}\int\frac{dx}{\sqrt{X}}$$

$$=\frac{1}{2a}\frac{X^{1/2}}{1/2}-\frac{b}{2a}\int\frac{dx}{\sqrt{X}}=\frac{\sqrt{X}}{a}-\frac{b}{2a}\int\frac{dx}{\sqrt{X}}.$$

In a specific case in which a, b, and c are given, the integration may now be completed by using formula 56.

Example 3. Find

$$\int\frac{x\,dx}{\sqrt{2+3x-2x^2}}.$$

Solution. From formula 81, with $a = -2$, $b = 3$, and $c = 2$,

$$\int\frac{x\,dx}{\sqrt{2+3x-2x^2}}=\frac{\sqrt{2+3x-2x^2}}{-2}-\frac{3}{2(-2)}\int\frac{dx}{\sqrt{2+3x-2x^2}}.$$

Since $a = -2 < 0$ and $q = 3^2 - 4(-2)(2) = 25 = 5^2 > 0$, the lower portion of formula 56 is used to obtain the answer

$$-\frac{1}{2}\sqrt{2+3x-2x^2}-\frac{3}{4\sqrt{2}}\sin^{-1}\frac{-4x+3}{5}+c.$$

Problem 1. In each of the following obtain all three integrals :

a. $\displaystyle\int \frac{dx}{4x^2 + 12x + 13}, \quad \int \frac{dx}{4x^2 + 12x + 5}, \quad \int \frac{dx}{4x^2 + 12x + 9}.$

b. $\displaystyle\int \frac{dx}{9x^2 - 12x + 4}, \quad \int \frac{dx}{9x^2 - 12x + 3}, \quad \int \frac{dx}{9x^2 - 12x + 5}.$

c. $\displaystyle\int \frac{dx}{x\sqrt{x^2 + 6x + 4}}, \quad \int \frac{dx}{x\sqrt{x^2 + 6x - 7}}, \quad \int \frac{dx}{x^{3/2}\sqrt{x + 6}}.$

d. $\displaystyle\int \frac{dx}{\sqrt{4x^2 + 4x + 3}}, \quad \int \frac{dx}{\sqrt{3 - 4x - 4x^2}}, \quad \int \frac{dx}{\sqrt{4x^2 + 4x + 1}}.$

e. $\displaystyle\int \frac{dx}{\sqrt{x^2 + x + 1}}, \quad \int \frac{x\,dx}{\sqrt{x^2 + x + 1}}, \quad \int \sqrt{x^2 + x + 1}\,dx.$

f. $\displaystyle\int (x^2 - x + 2)\,dx, \quad \int (x^2 - x + 2)^{1/2}\,dx, \quad \int (x^2 - x + 2)^{3/2}\,dx.$

Problem 2. The conditions in formula 56 are either $a > 0$ or else both $a < 0$ and $q > 0$. Show that if both $a < 0$ and $q < 0$ then $X = ax^2 + bx + c < 0$ for all x so that $\sqrt{X}$ could not be real.

Problem 3. In the integrand of formula 57 make the substitution $x = u^{-1}$ and see that the resulting integrand is (if $c \neq 0$) the form of the integrand of formula 56. Thus, derive the first two parts of formula 57. Also use the same substitution to derive the third part of formula 57.

Problem 4. a. Use the form (1) or (2) of X to see that formula 58 may be derived from formula 53.

b. In the integrand of formula 59 make the substitution $x = u^{-1}$ and show that formula 59 follows from formula 58.

Problem 5. Use the scheme of Example 2 to derive formula 79.

Problem 6. In the integrand of formula 80 set $u = \sqrt{X}$, $dv = dx$, and use integration by parts to obtain the first equality below. Also check the following steps :

$$\int \sqrt{X}\,dx = \sqrt{X}x - \int \frac{2ax + b}{2\sqrt{X}}\,x\,dx = x\sqrt{X} - \int \frac{ax^2 + (b/2)x}{\sqrt{X}}\,dx$$

$$= x\sqrt{X} - \int \frac{ax^2 + bx + c}{\sqrt{X}}\,dx + \int \frac{(b/2)x + c}{\sqrt{X}}\,dx$$

$$= x\sqrt{X} - \int \sqrt{X}\,dx + \frac{b}{2}\int \frac{x}{\sqrt{X}}\,dx + c\int \frac{dx}{\sqrt{X}}.$$

Now transpose the second term, use formula 81 on the third term, and then collect terms to prove formula 80.

7-6. Partial Fractions, Linear Factors

In a high school algebra course there was considerable practice in factoring. For example,

$$x^2 - a^2 = (x - a)(x + a),$$

$$x^3 - a^3 = (x - a)(x^2 + ax + a^2), \quad (x^3 + a^3) = (x + a)(x^2 - ax + a^2),$$

$$x^2 - 5x + 6 = (x - 2)(x - 3).$$

Also it was learned, for example, that since $x = 1$ makes $x^3 - 3x + 2$ equal to zero, then $x^3 - 3x + 2$ has $(x - 1)$ as a factor, and this other factor may be found by synthetic division :

$$
\begin{array}{rrrr|r}
1 & 0 & -3 & 2 & \underline{1} \\
 & 1 & 1 & -1 & \\
\hline
1 & 1 & -2 & 0 &
\end{array}
$$

so $x^3 - 3x + 2 = (x - 1)(x^2 + x - 2)$ (see Sec. 5-6). The factor $x^2 + x - 2$ may be further factored and hence

(1)
$$
\begin{aligned}
x^3 - 3x + 2 &= (x - 1)(x - 1)(x + 2) \\
&= (x - 1)^2(x + 2).
\end{aligned}
$$

Another type of high school problem was : Put

$$\frac{1}{2(x - 1)} + \frac{3}{(x - 1)^2} + \frac{2}{x + 2}$$

over the least common denominator. The algebraic problem converse to "putting over a common denominator" is important in obtaining integrals of expressions which are the ratios of two polynomials ; for example,

$$\int \frac{5x^2 - x + 14}{x^3 - 3x + 2}\, dx.$$

The procedure is to first factor the denominator, as given in (1) above, and then to write

(2)
$$\frac{5x^2 - x + 14}{x^3 - 3x + 2} \equiv \frac{A}{x - 1} + \frac{B}{(x - 1)^2} + \frac{C}{x + 2},$$

where $A, B,$ and C are constants to be determined. The symbol "$\equiv$" is read "identically equal to" and means that both sides have the same value for all values of x for which both sides are defined. Since the least common denominator of the right side is $(x - 1)^2(x + 2) \equiv x^3 - 3x + 2$, then, from (2),

(3) $\qquad 5x^2 - x + 14 \equiv A(x - 1)(x + 2) + B(x + 2) + C(x - 1)^2.$

There are two methods for determining the constants $A, B,$ and C.

Method 1: Since (3) is an identity, any three values of x may be substituted to give three equations from which $A, B,$ and C may be determined. Since $x = 1$, and $x = -2$ each makes two terms of (3) equal to zero, these are natural choices. Also, $x = 0$ is easy to substitute :

$$x = 1 \quad : 5 - 1 + 14 = B(1 + 2), \quad B = \tfrac{18}{3} = 6 \,;$$

$$x = -2 : 20 + 2 + 14 = C(-2 - 1)^2, \quad C = \tfrac{36}{9} = 4 \,;$$

$$x = 0 \quad : 14 = -2A + 2B + C = -2A + 12 + 4, \quad A = 1.$$

Method 2: Expand the right side of (3) and collect like powers of x:

$$5x^2 - x + 14 \equiv (A + C)x^2 + (A + B - 2C)x - 2A + 2B + C.$$

This being an identity, the coefficients of like powers of x must be equal:

$$A + C = 5.$$
$$A + B - 2C = -1,$$
$$-2A + 2B + C = 14.$$

The simultaneous solution of these equations is $A = 1$, $B = 6$, $C = 4$.

Hence, either by Method 1 or 2, the identity (2) becomes

$$\frac{5x^2 - x + 14}{x^3 - 3x + 2} \equiv \frac{1}{x - 1} + \frac{6}{(x - 1)^2} + \frac{4}{x + 2}.$$

Now to return to the original problem of integrating the left side :

$$\int \frac{5x^2 - x + 14}{x^3 - 3x + 2}\, dx = \int \frac{dx}{x - 1} + 6 \int (x - 1)^{-2}\, dx + 4 \int \frac{dx}{x + 2}$$

(4)
$$= \ln|x - 1| - 6\frac{1}{x - 1} + 4 \ln|x + 2| + c.$$

The principle involved here is:

   (i) If an integrand is the ratio of two polynomials,

   (ii) If the numerator is of lower degree than the denominator, and

   (iii) If the denominator factors into linear factors some of which may be raised to powers 2, 3, etc.,

then the integrand may be split into partial fractions by setting it identical to the sum of terms each a constant over a linear factor, a constant over a linear factor squared, etc., to the highest power to which a linear factor occurs.

The proof that the constants are uniquely determined is given in a more advanced algebra course.

The condition (ii) should be carefully observed. For example, if

(5)
$$\int \frac{x^5 + 2x^4 - 3x^3 + x^2 + 3x + 14}{x^3 - 3x + 2}\, dx$$

is sought, then, by long division,

$$\frac{x^5 + 2x^4 - 3x^3 + x^2 + 3x + 14}{x^3 - 3x + 2} \equiv x^2 + 2x + \frac{5x^2 - x + 14}{x^3 - 3x + 2},$$

which is carried out until a remainder is obtained with lower degree than the denominator. Hence, the integral (5) is equal to

$$\int x^2\, dx + 2 \int x\, dx + \int \frac{5x^2 - x + 14}{x^3 - 3x + 2}\, dx,$$

and the above principle is then applied to the last integrand.

Problem 1. Integrate each of the following :

a. $\int \dfrac{9x^2 - 5x + 8}{x^3 - 3x + 2}\,dx.$

                      c. $\int \dfrac{x^2 + x - 6}{x^3 - 3x + 2}\,dx.$

b. $\int \dfrac{1}{x^3 - 3x + 2}\,dx.$

                      d. $\int \dfrac{x^3 - 2x + 1}{x^2 + x - 6}\,dx.$

Problem 2. a. Check that $x = 2$ makes the denominator zero and then find

$$\int \frac{x^2 + 10x + 4}{x^3 + 5x^2 - 4x - 20}\,dx.$$

b. Set $x = -2$ in the denominator and use the resulting knowledge to find

$$\int \frac{4x^2 + x - 26}{x^3 + x^2 - 14x - 24}\,dx.$$

Problem 3. Integrate :

a. $\int \dfrac{dx}{(2x - 1)(3x + 2)}.$

                      e. $\int \dfrac{3x^2 + 4x - 1}{x^3 + 2x^2 - x - 2}\,dx.$

b. $\int \dfrac{2x - 1}{3x + 2}\,dx.$

                      f. $\int \dfrac{dx}{(2x - 1)^2 - 4}.$

c. $\int (2x - 1)(3x + 2)\,dx.$

                      g. $\int \dfrac{dx}{(2x - 1)^2 + 4}.$

d. $\int \dfrac{(x - 1)\,dx}{x^3 + 2x^2 - x - 2}.$

                      h. $\int \dfrac{(2x - 1)\,dx}{(2x - 1)^2 - 4}.$

Problem 4. Use the method of this section to derive formulas 17, 18, 25, and 26 of the Table of Integrals.

7-7. Quadratic Partial Fractions

In Sec. 7-6 the integrands had denominators with linear factors or linear factors raised to integer powers. If the denominator has a quadratic factor that cannot be factored further into real linear factors, then there is a partial fraction with this quadratic factor as denominator and a linear expression in the numerator.

Example 1. Find

$$\int \frac{dx}{x(x^2 + 2x + 3)}.$$

Solution. Since $x^2 + 2x + 3 = 0$ has roots that are imaginary,

$$x = \frac{-2 \pm \sqrt{2^2 - 4 \cdot 1 \cdot 3}}{2 \cdot 1} = \frac{-2 \pm \sqrt{-3}}{2} = -1 \pm i\sqrt{2},$$

the factor $x^2 + 2x + 3$ cannot be factored into real linear factors. Hence, set

(1) $\dfrac{1}{x(x^2 + 2x + 3)} \equiv \dfrac{A}{x} + \dfrac{Bx + C}{x^2 + 2x + 3},$ so that

$$1 \equiv A(x^2 + 2x + 3) + x(Bx + C)$$
$$\equiv (A + B)x^2 + (2A + C)x + 3A.$$

Hence, $A + B = 0$, $2A + C = 0$, and $3A = 1$, and therefore

$$A = \tfrac{1}{3}, \quad C = -2A = -\tfrac{2}{3}, \quad \text{and} \quad B = -A = -\tfrac{1}{3}.$$

By substituting these values into (1) and then integrating, it follows that

$$\int \frac{dx}{x(x^2 + 2x + 3)} = \frac{1}{3} \int \frac{dx}{x} - \frac{1}{3} \int \frac{x + 2}{x^2 + 2x + 3}\, dx$$

$$= \frac{1}{3} \ln |x| - \frac{1}{3} \int \frac{x\, dx}{x^2 + 2x + 3} - \frac{2}{3} \int \frac{dx}{x^2 + 2x + 3}.$$

Formula 79 of the table applied to the first integral changes the result to

$$\frac{1}{3} \ln |x| - \frac{1}{3}\left[\frac{1}{2} \ln (x^2 + 2x + 3) - \frac{2}{2} \int \frac{dx}{x^2 + 2x + 3} \right] - \frac{2}{3} \int \frac{dx}{x^2 + 2x + 3}$$

$$= \frac{1}{3} \ln |x| - \frac{1}{6} \ln (x^2 + 2x + 3) - \frac{1}{3} \int \frac{dx}{x^2 + 2x + 3}.$$

Since $q = 2^2 - 4\cdot 1 \cdot 3 = -8 < 0$, the second part of formula 55 now gives (since $\sqrt{-q} = 2\sqrt{2}$) the answer

$$\frac{1}{3} \ln |x| - \frac{1}{6} \ln (x^2 + 2x + 3) - \frac{1}{3} \frac{1}{\sqrt{2}} \tan^{-1} \frac{x + 1}{\sqrt{2}} + c.$$

Similar to repeated linear factors in the denominator, if a quadratic factor is squared, then a linear expression must be put over this quadratic factor plus another term having a linear expression over the quadratic factor squared.

Example 2.

$$\frac{x + 1}{x(x^2 + 3)^2} \equiv \frac{A}{x} + \frac{Bx + C}{x^2 + 3} + \frac{Dx + E}{(x^2 + 3)^2},$$

$$x + 1 \equiv A(x^2 + 3)^2 + x(Bx + C)(x^2 + 3) + x(Dx + E)$$

$$\equiv (A + B)x^4 + Cx^3 + (6A + 3B + D)x^2 + (3C + E)x + 9A,$$

$$A + B = 0, \quad C = 0, \quad 6A + 3B + D = 0, \quad 3C + E = 1, \quad 9A = 1,$$

$$A = \frac{1}{9}, \quad B = -\frac{1}{9}, \quad C = 0, \quad D = -\frac{1}{3}, \quad E = 1.$$

Hence,

$$\int \frac{(x + 1)\, dx}{x(x^2 + 3)^2} = \frac{1}{9} \int \frac{dx}{x} - \frac{1}{9} \int \frac{x\, dx}{x^2 + 3} - \frac{1}{3} \int \frac{x\, dx}{(x^2 + 3)^2} + \int \frac{dx}{(x^2 + 3)^2}$$

(2)

$$= \frac{1}{9} \int \frac{dx}{x} - \frac{1}{18} \int \frac{d(x^2 + 3)}{x^2 + 3} - \frac{1}{6} \int (x^2 + 3)^{-2}\, d(x^2 + 3) + \int \frac{dx}{(x^2 + 3)^2}.$$

The last integral is the only one on the right which is not easily integrated and this one yields to formula 83 of the table, with $a = 1$, $b = 0$, $c = 3$, and hence $q = -12$:

$$\int \frac{dx}{(x^2 + 3)^2} = -\frac{2x}{(-12)} \frac{1}{x^2 + 3} - \frac{2}{(-12)} \int \frac{dx}{x^2 + 3}$$

$$= \frac{1}{6} \frac{x}{x^2 + 3} + \frac{1}{6} \frac{1}{\sqrt{3}} \tan^{-1} \frac{x}{\sqrt{3}} \quad \text{by formula 12.}$$

Upon integrating the other integrals on the right of (2), the answer is

$$\frac{1}{9}\ln|x| - \frac{1}{18}\ln(x^2 + 3) + \frac{1}{6}\frac{1}{x^2 + 3} + \frac{1}{6}\frac{x}{x^2 + 3} + \frac{1}{6\sqrt{3}}\tan^{-1}\frac{x}{\sqrt{3}} + c.$$

Since formula 83 was used above, and will be used in the following problems, its derivation should be seen. The first equality below is obtained from integration by parts using

$$u = \frac{1}{X}, \quad dv = dx; \quad du = -\frac{dX}{X^2} = -\frac{(2ax + b)}{X^2}\,dx, \quad \text{and} \quad v = x.$$

Each succeeding step should be carefully checked to see that the final result is formula 83.

$$\int\frac{dx}{X} = \frac{1}{X}\,x - \int x\left[-\frac{2ax + b}{X^2}\,dx\right] = \frac{x}{X} + \int\frac{2ax^2 + bx}{X^2}\,dx$$

$$= \frac{x}{X} + \int\frac{(2ax^2 + 2bx + 2c) - (bx + 2c)}{X^2}\,dx$$

$$= \frac{x}{X} + 2\int\frac{X}{X^2}\,dx - \int\frac{bx + 2c}{X^2}\,dx$$

$$= \frac{x}{X} + 2\int\frac{dx}{X} - b\int\frac{x}{X^2}\,dx - 2c\int\frac{dx}{X^2},$$

$$-2c\int\frac{dx}{X^2} = \int\frac{dx}{X} - \frac{x}{X} - 2\int\frac{dx}{X} + b\int\frac{x}{X^2}\,dx$$

$$= -\frac{x}{X} - \int\frac{dx}{X} + \frac{b}{2a}\int\frac{2ax + b - b}{X}\,dx$$

$$= -\frac{x}{X} - \int\frac{dx}{X} + \frac{b}{2a}\int\frac{2ax + b}{X^2}\,dx - \frac{b^2}{2a}\int\frac{dx}{X^2},$$

$$\left(\frac{b^2}{2a} - 2c\right)\int\frac{dx}{X^2} = -\frac{x}{X} - \int\frac{dx}{X} + \frac{b}{2a}\int\frac{dX}{X^2},$$

$$\frac{b^2 - 4ac}{2a}\int\frac{dx}{X^2} = -\frac{x}{X} - \int\frac{dx}{X} - \frac{b}{2a}\frac{1}{X},$$

$$\frac{q}{2a}\int\frac{dx}{X^2} = -\left(x + \frac{b}{2a}\right)\frac{1}{X} - \int\frac{dx}{X} = -\frac{(2ax + b)}{2a}\frac{1}{X} - \int\frac{dx}{X},$$

$$\int\frac{dx}{X^2} = -\frac{2ax + b}{q}\frac{1}{X} - \frac{2a}{q}\int\frac{dx}{X}, \quad \text{formula 83.}$$

A theorem of algebra states that every polynomial of nth degree,

$$P(x) = a_n x^n + a_{n-1}x^{n-1} + \cdots + a_1 x + a_0,$$

with real coefficients can be factored into linear and/or quadratic factors. Thus, partial fractions with cubic or higher degree factors need not be considered.

Problem 1. Find each of the following integrals:

a. $\displaystyle\int \frac{2x^2 + x + 2}{(x+1)(x^2+2)}\,dx.$

d. $\displaystyle\int \frac{2x^4 + 6x^3 + 10x^2 + 8x + 4}{(x+1)(x^2+x+1)}\,dx.$

b. $\displaystyle\int \frac{(2x^2 + 4x + 4)\,dx}{(x+1)(x^2+2x+3)}.$

e. $\displaystyle\int \frac{2x^5 + 6x^3 + 5x}{(x^2+1)^2(x^2+2)^2}\,dx.$

c. $\displaystyle\int \frac{2x^2 + x + 1}{(x+1)(x^2+2)}\,dx.$

f. $\displaystyle\int \frac{2x^5 + x^4 + 6x^3 + 2x^2 + 5x + 1}{(x^2+1)^2(x^2+2)^2}\,dx.$

Problem 2. Derive formula 25 of the table.

Problem 3. The method of partial fractions should not be used on some of the following integrals; also, recall that the numerator must be of lower degree than the denominator or the method of partial fractions does not work:

a. $\displaystyle\int \frac{(x-1)(x-2)}{(x-3)(x-4)}\,dx.$

g. $\displaystyle\int \frac{(x^2+1)^2}{x}\,dx.$

b. $\displaystyle\int \frac{(x-3)(x-4)}{(x-1)(x-2)}\,dx.$

h. $\displaystyle\int \frac{x}{(x^2+1)^2}\,dx.$

c. $\displaystyle\int \frac{x^3+1}{x^2}\,dx.$

i. $\displaystyle\int \frac{\cos x}{\sin^2 x - \sin x}\,dx.$

d. $\displaystyle\int \frac{x^2}{x^3+1}\,dx.$

j. $\displaystyle\int \frac{\sin^2 x - \sin x}{\cos x}\,dx.$

e. $\displaystyle\int \frac{dx}{x(x^2-1)^2}.$

k. $\displaystyle\int \frac{ax+b}{cx+d}\,dx.$

f. $\displaystyle\int x(x^2-1)^2\,dx.$

l. $\displaystyle\int \frac{1}{(ax+b)(cx+d)}\,dx.$

7-8. Reduction Formulas

Each of the formulas 77 through 100 of the Table of Integrals has an integral both on the left and on the right, where the integral on the right is either:

1. Given in some other portion of the table or else
2. Has its integrand in the same form as the one on the left, with, however, some power of lower order.

Example 1. Find $I = \int \cos^5 x \sin^4 x\, dx.$

Solution. First use the upper portion of formula 95 with $m = 5$ and $n = 4$:

$$I = \frac{\cos^4 x \sin^5 x}{9} + \frac{4}{9}\int \cos^3 x \sin^4 x\,dx.$$

Now use the same formula with $m = 3$ and $n = 4$:

$$I = \frac{\cos^4 x \sin^5 x}{9} + \frac{4}{9}\left[\frac{\cos^2 x \sin^5 x}{7} + \frac{2}{7}\int \cos x \sin^4 x\,dx\right]$$

$$= \frac{1}{9}\cos^4 x \sin^5 x + \frac{4}{63}\cos^2 x \sin^5 x + \frac{8}{63}\int \sin^4 x\, d\sin x$$

$$= \frac{1}{9}\cos^4 x \sin^5 x + \frac{4}{63}\cos^2 x \sin^5 x + \frac{8}{315}\sin^5 x + c.$$

Example 2. Derive the upper portion of formula 95.

Solution. First write the integrand on the left as

$$\int \cos^m x \sin^n x \, dx = \int \cos^{m-1} x \, (\sin^n x \cos x) \, dx.$$

With the integrand in this form, use integration by parts with

$$u = \cos^{m-1} x, \qquad\qquad dv = \sin^n x \cos x \, dx,$$

$$du = -(m-1)\cos^{m-2} x \sin x \, dx, \quad v = \frac{\sin^{n+1} x}{n+1}$$

to obtain

$$\int \cos^m x \sin^n x \, dx = \cos^{m-1} x \frac{(\sin^{n+1} x)}{n+1} - \int \frac{\sin^{n+1} x}{n+1}[-(m-1)\cos^{m-2} x \sin x \, dx]$$

(1)
$$= \frac{\cos^{m-1} x \sin^{n+1} x}{n+1} + \frac{m-1}{n-1}\int \cos^{m-2} x \sin^{n+2} x \, dx.$$

This formula decreases one exponent by 2 but increases the other by 2. In order to decrease the one without increasing the other, set

$$\sin^{n+2} x = \sin^n x \sin^2 x = \sin^n x \, (1 - \cos^2 x) = \sin^n x - \sin^n x \cos^2 x$$

in the integrand on the right and thus write the integral on the right as

$$\int \cos^{m-2} x \sin^{n+2} x \, dx = \int \cos^{m-2} x \sin^n x \, dx - \int \cos^{m-2} x \sin^n x \cos^2 x \, dx$$

$$= \int \cos^{m-2} x \sin^n x \, dx - \int \cos^m x \sin^n x \, dx,$$

in which the original integral reappears. Upon substituting this difference of integrals for the integral on the right in (1) and then solving for the original integral, the result is the upper portion of formula 95.

Many of the reduction formulas may be derived by methods similar to that used in Example 2.

Problem 1. Each of the following integrals yields to one or more applications of reduction formulas:

a. $\int \sin^5 x \cos^4 x \, dx.$

b. $\int \frac{\sin^5 x}{\cos^4 x} \, dx.$

c. $\int \sec^5 x \, dx.$

d. $\int x^3 e^{2x} \, dx.$

e. $\int x^4 \cos 2x \, dx.$

f. $\int \frac{x \, dx}{\sqrt{x^2 + x + 3}}.$

g. $\int \frac{x^4 \, dx}{(2x^2 + 5)^2}.$

h. $\int \frac{\sqrt{5 - x}}{x} \, dx.$

Problem 2. Reduction formulas should not be used to find any of the following integrals:

a. $\int \sin^5 x \cos x \, dx.$

b. $\int \frac{\sin x}{\cos^4 x} \, dx.$

e. $\int x^4 \cos 2x^5 \, dx.$

f. $\int \frac{2x + 1}{\sqrt{x^2 + x + 3}} \, dx.$

c. $\int \sec^5 x \tan x \, dx.$

g. $\int \dfrac{x^3 \, dx}{(2x^4 + 5)^2}.$

d. $\int x e^{x^2} \, dx.$

h. $\int \dfrac{\sqrt{5} - \sqrt{x}}{x} \, dx.$

7-9. Rationalizing Integrands

The first two examples given below illustrate substitutions that rationalize integrands.

Example 1. Find

$$I = \int \frac{x \, dx}{3 + \sqrt{x + 1}}.$$

Solution. Since $x + 1$ must be positive, it may be replaced by u^2. The substitution $u^2 = x + 1$ must be accompanied by $x = u^2 - 1$ and $2u \, du = dx$ to yield

$$I = \int \frac{(u^2 - 1)2u \, du}{3 + u} = 2 \int \frac{u^3 - u}{3 + u} \, du.$$

The numerator, being of higher degree than the denominator, could be divided by the denominator until a remainder of lower degree than the denominator is obtained, but an alternative method is to set $3 + u = z$, $u = z - 3$, and $du = dz$:

$$I = 2 \int \frac{(z - 3)^3 - (z - 3)}{z} \, dz = 2 \int \frac{z^3 - 9z^2 + 26z - 24}{z} \, dz$$

$$= 2 \int \left(z^2 - 9z + 26 - \frac{24}{z} \right) dz = 2 \left[\frac{1}{3} z^3 - \frac{9}{2} z^2 + 26z - 24 \ln |z| \right] + c.$$

Resubstitution is now necessary to return to the variable x :

$$I = 2[\tfrac{1}{3}(3 + u)^3 - \tfrac{9}{2}(3 + u)^2 + 26(3 + u) - 24 \ln |3 + u|] + c$$

$$= 2[\tfrac{1}{3}(3 + \sqrt{x + 1})^3 - \tfrac{9}{2}(3 + \sqrt{x + 1})^2$$

$$+ 26(3 + \sqrt{x + 1}) - 24 \ln (3 + \sqrt{x + 1})] + c.$$

Example 2. Find

$$I = \int \frac{x^{2/3}}{1 + x^{1/2}} \, dx.$$

Solution. The least common denominator of the exponents $\frac{1}{2}$ and $\frac{2}{3}$ is 6. Hence, upon setting

$$x = u^6, \quad \text{then} \quad x^{1/2} = u^3, \quad \text{and} \quad x^{2/3} = (u^6)^{2/3} = u^4.$$

Also, $dx = 6u^5 \, du$, and the integral becomes

$$I = \int \frac{u^4}{1 + u^3} 6u^5 \, du = 6 \int \frac{u^9}{1 + u^3} \, du$$

$$= 6 \int \left(u^6 - u^3 + 1 - \frac{1}{u^3 + 1} \right) du \quad \text{by division}$$

$$= 6 \left[\frac{1}{7} u^7 - \frac{1}{4} u^4 + u - \int \frac{du}{(u + 1)(u^2 - u + 1)} \right].$$

The method of partial fractions may now be applied to the one remaining integral to yield:

$$I = 6\left[\frac{1}{7} u^7 - \frac{1}{4} u^4 + u - \frac{1}{3}\int \frac{du}{u+1} + \frac{1}{3}\int \frac{u\,du}{u^2-u+1} - \frac{2}{3}\int \frac{du}{u^2-u+1}\right].$$

Formulas 2, 79, and 55 now yield

$$I = 6\left[\frac{1}{7} u^7 - \frac{1}{4} u^4 + u - \frac{1}{3}\ln|u+1| + \frac{1}{6}\ln(u^2-u+1)\right.$$

$$\left. + \left(\frac{1}{6} - \frac{2}{3}\right)\frac{2}{\sqrt{3}}\tan^{-1}\frac{2u-1}{\sqrt{3}}\right] + c.$$

Since $x = u^6$, then $u = x^{1/6}$, and hence the final answer is

$$6\left[\frac{1}{7} x^{7/6} - \frac{1}{4} x^{2/3} + x^{1/6} - \frac{1}{3}\ln(x^{1/6}+1) + \frac{1}{6}\ln|x^{1/3} - x^{1/6} + 1|\right.$$

$$\left. - \frac{1}{\sqrt{3}}\tan^{-1}\frac{2x^{1/6}-1}{\sqrt{3}}\right] + c.$$

The following example is included mainly as an illustration of a method that may work if at some future date an obstinate integral is met involving only sines and cosines.

Example 3. Derive formula 68.

Solution. An ingenious substitution that might not be thought of unless its consequences were pointed out is

(1) $$\tan\frac{x}{2} = u \quad \text{for} \quad 0 \le x < \pi, \quad \text{so that} \quad u \ge 0.$$

It is shown below that (1) leads to

(2) $$\cos x = \frac{1-u^2}{1+u^2}, \quad \sin x = \frac{2u}{1+u^2}, \quad \text{and} \quad dx = \frac{2}{1+u^2}\,du.$$

First set $A = x/2$ in the trigonometric identity $\cos 2A = 2\cos^2 A - 1$:

$$\cos x = 2\cos^2\frac{x}{2} - 1 = \frac{2}{\sec^2 x/2} - 1 = \frac{2}{1+\tan^2 x/2} - 1 = \frac{2}{1+u^2} - 1 \quad \text{from (1)}$$

which simplifies to the first equation in (2). Next,

$$\sin x \doteq \sqrt{1 - \cos^2 x} = \sqrt{1 - \left(\frac{1-u^2}{1+u^2}\right)^2}$$

$$= \frac{\sqrt{1 + 2u^2 + u^4 - (1 - 2u^2 + u^4)}}{1+u^2} = \frac{2u}{1+u^2},$$

which is the second equation of (2). From (1), by taking differentials,

$$du = d\tan\frac{x}{2} = \left(\sec^2\frac{x}{2}\right)\frac{1}{2}dx = \frac{1}{2}\left(1 + \tan^2\frac{x}{2}\right)dx = \frac{1}{2}(1 + u^2)\,dx,$$

from which the third equation of (2) follows.

Now notice that the integral in formula 68 is the one given below and that the above substitutions change the integrand as shown:

$$I = \int \frac{dx}{a + b \cos x} = \int \frac{[2/(1 + u^2)]\, du}{a + b(1 - u^2)/(1 + u^2)} = 2 \int \frac{du}{(a - b)u^2 + (a + b)}.$$

The integrand is now in the form to which formula 55 may be applied with $q = 0^2 - 4(a - b)(a + b) = 4(b^2 - a^2)$. Hence, if $b^2 > a^2$, then $q > 0$ and the upper part of formula 55 yields

$$I = 2 \frac{1}{2\sqrt{b^2 - a^2}} \ln \left| \frac{2(a - b)u + 0 - 2\sqrt{b^2 - a^2}}{2(a - b)u + 0 + 2\sqrt{b^2 - a^2}} \right| + c$$

$$= \frac{1}{\sqrt{b^2 - a^2}} \ln \left| \frac{(a - b)\tan(x/2) - \sqrt{b^2 - a^2}}{(a - b)\tan(x/2) + \sqrt{b^2 - a^2}} \right| + c,$$

which equals the lower part of formula 68. If, however, $b^2 < a^2$, then $q < 0$ and the lower part of formula 55 gives the upper part of formula 68.

Problem 1. Each of the following integrals may be found by using the methods of Examples 1 or 2 above:

a. $\int \dfrac{3 + \sqrt{x + 1}}{x} \, dx.$

b. $\int x\sqrt{2 + x}\, dx.$

c. $\int \dfrac{x\, dx}{1 + \sqrt{3 + 4x}}.$

d. $\int x(2 - x)^{2/3}\, dx.$

e. $\int \dfrac{dx}{1 + (2 + x)^{3/2}}.$

f. $\int \dfrac{x^{1/2}}{1 + x^{1/3}} \, dx.$

g. $\int \dfrac{x^{3/2}}{x^{1/3} - x^{1/4}} \, dx.$

h. $\int \dfrac{x^{1/3} - x^{1/4}}{x^{3/2}} \, dx.$

Problem 2. Establish that:

a. $\displaystyle\int \frac{\sin x}{2 + 3 \sin x}\, dx = \frac{1}{3} x - \frac{2}{3\sqrt{5}} \ln \left| \frac{2 \tan(x/2) + 3 - \sqrt{5}}{2 \tan(x/2) + 3 + \sqrt{5}} \right| + c.$

b. $\displaystyle\int \frac{\cos x}{2 + 3 \sin x}\, dx = \frac{1}{3} \ln |2 + 3 \sin x| + c.$

c. $\displaystyle\int \frac{dx}{2 + 3 \sin x + 4 \cos x} = -\frac{1}{\sqrt{21}} \ln \left| \frac{3 + \sqrt{21} - 2 \tan(x/2)}{3 - \sqrt{21} - 2 \tan(x/2)} \right| + c.$

d. $\displaystyle\int \frac{dx}{4 + 3 \sin x + 2 \cos x} = \frac{2}{\sqrt{3}} \tan^{-1} \frac{3 + 2 \tan(x/2)}{\sqrt{3}} + c.$

7-10. Review Integration Problems

The following set of problems will furnish a review of the methods of integration given in this chapter:

1. $\int \dfrac{x^3}{\sqrt[3]{x}} \, dx.$

2. $\int (3x^2 + 1)^2 x \, dx.$

3. $\int \cos^3 2x \sin 2x \, dx.$

4. $\int \cos^3 x \sin 2x \, dx.$

5. $\int \dfrac{\sec^2 2x}{\tan^4 2x} \, dx.$

6. $\int e^{2 + 4x} \, dx.$

7. $\int \dfrac{2 + e^x}{e^{3x}} \, dx.$

8. $\int 5^{3x} \, dx.$

9. $\int (e^2)^{\sin x} \cos x\, dx.$

10. $\int \dfrac{x\, dx}{4 + 3x^2}.$

11. $\int \dfrac{e^x\, dx}{1 + 2e^x}.$

12. $\int \dfrac{\csc^2 2x}{1 + 2\cot 2x}\, dx.$

13. $\int \csc^2 2x\, dx.$

14. $\int \dfrac{dx}{\cot 5x}.$

15. $\int \dfrac{1}{\csc^2 3x}\, dx.$

16. $\int \dfrac{\sec 2e^{-x}}{e^x}\, dx.$

17. $\int \dfrac{dx}{\sqrt{16 - 9x^2}}.$

18. $\int \dfrac{dx}{16 + 9x^2}.$

19. $\int \dfrac{x^2\, dx}{x^6 - 9}.$

20. $\int x(2x + 3)^{3/2}\, dx.$

21. $\int \dfrac{x\, dx}{\sqrt[3]{2x + 3}}.$

22. $\int \dfrac{\sec^2 x\, dx}{\sqrt{\tan^2 x + 9}}.$

23. $\int \dfrac{dx}{\sqrt{1 + 25x^2}}.$

24. $\int \dfrac{dx}{9x^2 - 24x + 16}.$

25. $\int \dfrac{dx}{9x^2 + 4x - 5}.$

26. $\int \dfrac{dx}{\sqrt{-x^2 - 5x}}.$

27. $\int \dfrac{(2x + 5)\, dx}{\sqrt{6x - x^2 + 7}}.$

28. $\int \dfrac{\sin x \cos x}{\sqrt{9 - \cos^4 x}}\, dx.$

29. $\int \dfrac{x + 1}{x(x^3 - 1)}\, dx.$

30. $\int x^2 \cos 2x\, dx.$

31. $\int x \ln x\, dx.$

32. $\int \cos^2 x \sin^5 x\, dx.$

33. $\int \dfrac{dx}{x\sqrt{1 + 4x}}.$

34. $\int \dfrac{dx}{x - x^{1/3}}.$

35. $\int x(x - 2)^{3/2}\, dx.$

36. $\int x^{3/2} \ln (x + 1)\, dx.$

37. $\int x^3 \sqrt{3x^2 + 1}\, dx.$

38. $\int x^4 \sqrt{3x^2 + 1}\, dx.$

39. $\int \dfrac{x^3}{\sqrt{3x^2 + 1}}\, dx.$

40. $\int \dfrac{\sin^4 x}{\cos^2 x}\, dx.$

Applications of Definite Integrals

Chapter 8

8-1. Area of a Plane Region

In Sec. 3-11 the area between two continuous curves $y = f(x)$ and $y = g(x)$, where $f(x) \geq g(x)$ for $a \leq x \leq b$, was defined as

$$A = \int_a^b [f(x) - g(x)]\, dx.$$

The discussions of Sec. 3-11 should now be reviewed to see that they are general enough to encompass the wider class of functions whose derivatives and indefinite integrals have been derived since that section.

Example 1. Find the area bounded by the x-axis and the first arch in the first quadrant of curve $y = x \cos x$.

Solution. The curve intersects the x-axis when $x = 0$ and $x = \pi/2$. Considering the x-axis as the lower curve having equation $y = g(x) = 0$, the answer is

$$A = \int_0^{\pi/2} x \cos x\, dx = x \sin x \Big]_0^{\pi/2} - \int_0^{\pi/2} \sin x\, dx$$

from integration by parts with $u = x$ and $dy = \cos x\, dx$. Thus,

$$A = \frac{\pi}{2} \sin \frac{\pi}{2} - 0 + \Big[\cos x \Big]_0^{\pi/2} = \frac{\pi}{2} + \Big[\cos \frac{\pi}{2} - \cos 0 \Big] = \frac{\pi}{2} - 1.$$

Example 2. Derive the formula for the area of a circle of radius r.

Solution. The area is four times the area of the first quadrant portion within $x^2 + y^2 = r^2$, so that

$$A = 4 \int_0^r \sqrt{r^2 - x^2}\, dx = \frac{4}{2}\Big[x\sqrt{r^2 - x^2} + r^2 \sin^{-1}\frac{x}{r} \Big]_0^r \quad \text{by formula 21}$$

$$= 2\Big[r \cdot 0 - 0 + r^2 \sin^{-1}\frac{r}{r} - r^2 \cdot 0 \Big] = 2r^2 \sin^{-1} 1 = 2r^2 \frac{\pi}{2} = \pi r^2.$$

The integrand in $\int (x + 4)\sqrt{x}\, dx$ may be written as the sum of two expressions, each of which is easily integrated:

$$\int (x + 4)\sqrt{x}\, dx = \int (x^{3/2} + 4x^{1/2})dx = \tfrac{2}{5}x^{5/2} + \tfrac{8}{3}x^{3/2} + c.$$

The integrand in $\int x\sqrt{x+4}\,dx$ cannot, however, be written directly as a sum since the addition is under the radical. Hence "hide" this addition by substituting a single letter for $x + 4$, say,

$$s = x + 4.$$

Then $x = s - 4$ and $dx = ds$, so that

$$\int x\sqrt{x+4}\,dx = \int (s-4)\sqrt{s}\,ds.$$

Now this second integrand may be written in two parts, each falling under a known formula. Thus,

$$\int x\sqrt{x+4}\,dx = \int (s^{3/2} - 4s^{1/2})\,ds = \tfrac{2}{5}s^{5/2} - \tfrac{8}{3}s^{3/2} + c.$$

But the answer should be in terms of the original variable x; therefore, by resubstitution,

$$\int x\sqrt{x+4}\,dx = \tfrac{2}{5}(x+4)^{5/2} - \tfrac{8}{3}(x+4)^{3/2} + c.$$

If definite integrals are involved, the x limits may be changed to s limits, thus avoiding the resubstitution to x. For example, if the above integral is to be taken from $x = 0$ to $x = 5$, it follows from $x + 4 = s$ that when $x = 0$ then $s = 4$ and when $x = 5$ then $s = 9$, thus giving

$$\int_0^5 x\sqrt{x+4}\,dx = \int_4^9 (s-4)\sqrt{s}\,ds = \tfrac{2}{5}s^{5/2} - \tfrac{8}{3}s^{3/2}\,\Big]_4^9$$

$$= \tfrac{2}{5}(9^{5/2} - 4^{5/2}) - \tfrac{8}{3}(9^{3/2} - 4^{3/2})$$

$$= \tfrac{2}{5}(143 - 32) - \tfrac{8}{3}(27 - 8) = \tfrac{506}{15}.$$

Example 3.

$$\int_1^4 \frac{1}{\sqrt{x}+1}\,dx = \int_1^2 \frac{2s}{s+1}\,ds \quad \text{from } \sqrt{x} = s,\ x = s^2,\ dx = 2s\,ds;$$

$$s = 1 \text{ when } x = 1,\ s = 2 \text{ when } x = 4$$

$$= 2\int_2^3 \frac{t-1}{t}\,dt \quad \text{from } s + 1 = t$$

$$= 2\Big[\,t - \ln t\,\Big]_2^3 = 2\Big[\,1 - \ln 1.5\,\Big].$$

Problem 1. Find the area under the first arch of the curve:

a. $y = x \sin x$.

b. $y = x \sin x^2$.

c. $y = x^2 \cos x/2$.

d. $y = x\sqrt{4 - x}$.

e. $y = 10 \sin 2x \cos 3x$.

f. $y = e^{2x} \sin x/3$.

Problem 2. Find the area under the given curve and above the given interval:

a. $y = \tan x,\quad 0 \le x \le \pi/4$.

e. $y = \sin(\ln x),\quad 1 \le x \le e^{\pi}$.

b. $y = \sec^2 x$, $-\pi/4 \leq x \leq \pi/4$.　　　f. $y = \cos^2 2x$, $-\pi \leq x \leq \pi$.

c. $y = \dfrac{1}{4 + x^2}$, $-2 \leq x \leq 2$.　　　g. $y = \dfrac{\sqrt{3x + 1}}{x}$, $1 \leq x \leq 8$.

d. $y = x^2\sqrt{2x + 3}$, $-1 \leq x \leq 3$.　　　h. $y = x^2\sqrt{x^2 + 4^2}$, $0 \leq x \leq 3$.

Problem 3. Find the area of the region or regions between the given curves. Recall that in some cases it may be easier to set the problem up for integration with respect to y instead of x.

a. $y = x^2 \cos x$, $y = (1/2)x^2$.　　　c. $y = \dfrac{3}{x^2 - 2x - 3}$, $y = \dfrac{2}{x^2 - 2x + 2}$.

b. $x = \sin y$, $x = y^2 - \pi y$.　　　d. $xy = 1$, $y = 2 - x + |x - 2|$.

Problem 4. Find the area in the first quadrant between the pair of curves. Use either Horner's or Newton's Method to find approximations of intersections of the curves.

a. $xy = 1$, $y = -(x - 1)(x - 3)$.　　　b. $2y = x$, $y = \sin x$.

Problem 5. Evaluate each of the following definite integrals by making an appropriate substitution for the variable x and the corresponding substitution for the constant limits of integration:

a. $\displaystyle\int_0^1 \frac{\sqrt{x}}{1 + \sqrt{x}}\, dx$.　　　d. $\displaystyle\int_0^1 \frac{dx}{e^x + 1}$.

b. $\displaystyle\int_1^5 \frac{1}{2 + \sqrt{x - 1}}\, dx$.　　　e. $\displaystyle\int_0^1 x \cos^{-1} x\, dx$.

c. $\displaystyle\int_0^{\pi/2} \frac{\cos x}{\sqrt{\sin x + 1}}\, dx$.　　　f. $\displaystyle\int_1^9 \sqrt[3]{x - 1}\, dx$.

8-2. Moments and Centroids

Consider the xy-plane as being vertical and the x-axis as an inflexible, weightless, horizontal rod. At a point $(x_1, 0)$, apply a vertical force represented by a vector $\vec{f}$ pointing either up or down. By definition, the first moment of this force relative to a point $(c, 0)$ is

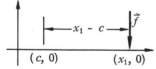

(1) 　　$(x_1 - c)|\vec{f}|$ 　if $\vec{f}$ points downward, but

$-(x_1 - c)|\vec{f}|$ 　if $\vec{f}$ points upward.

Fig. 8-2.1

A system of downward vertical forces $\vec{v}_1, \vec{v}_2, \ldots,$ $\vec{v}_n$ applied at the points $(x_1, 0), (x_2, 0), \ldots, (x_n, 0)$ and a single upward force $\vec{F}$ applied at a point $(\bar{x}, 0)$ are said to be in equilibrium if the vector sum

(2) 　　　　　　$\vec{v}_1 + \vec{v}_2 + \cdots + \vec{v}_n + \vec{F} = \vec{0}$,

and relative to a point $(c, 0)$ the sum of all moments is zero:

(3) 　　$(x_1 - c)|\vec{v}_1| + (x_2 - c)|\vec{v}_2| + \cdots + (x_n - c)|\vec{v}_n| = (\bar{x} - c)|\vec{F}|$.

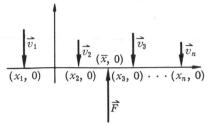

Fig. 8-2.2

Since all the forces $\vec{v}_1, \vec{v}_2, \ldots, \vec{v}_n$ are vertical and directed downward, then, from (2),

$$\vec{F} = -(\vec{v}_1 + \vec{v}_2 + \cdots + \vec{v}_n),$$

so that the upward force $\vec{F}$ has magnitude the sum of the magnitudes of the other forces

(4) $$|\vec{F}| = |\vec{v}_1| + |\vec{v}_2| + \cdots + |\vec{v}_n|.$$

Thus, (3) reduces [since c cancels out because of (4)] to

$$x_1|\vec{v}_2| + x_2|\vec{v}_2| + \cdots + x_n|\vec{v}_n| = \bar{x}(|\vec{v}_1| + |\vec{v}_2| + \cdots + |\vec{v}_n|),$$

which is independent of c and may be solved for $\bar{x}$:

(5) $$\bar{x} = \frac{x_1|\vec{v}_1| + x_2|\vec{v}_2| + \cdots + x_n|\vec{v}_n|}{|\vec{v}_1| + |\vec{v}_2| + \cdots + |\vec{v}_n|}.$$

The point $(\bar{x}, 0)$ is said to be the **centroid** of the system.

Example 1. Bodies of weights 10 lb, 15 lb, 5 lb, and 7 lb are at the points $(-4, 0)$, $(1, 0)$, $(3, 0)$, and $(6, 0)$. Find the centroid of the system.

Solution. Since

$$\bar{x} = \frac{-4 \cdot 10 + 1 \cdot 15 + 3 \cdot 5 + 6 \cdot 7}{10 + 15 + 5 + 7} = \frac{32}{37},$$

the centroid is at the point $(32/37, 0)$.

The above considerations are specializations of equilibrium conditions studied in a branch of mechanics called statics and grew out of such simple problems as two children balancing on a seesaw. If the children weigh 40 lb and 60 lb and the board is 15 ft long, then the fulcrum is placed x ft from the 40-lb child, so that

$$40x = (15 - x)60.$$

Next, consider the xy-plane as an inflexible weightless sheet lying horizontally with downward forces $\vec{v}_1, \vec{v}_2, \ldots, \vec{v}_n$ at the points $(x_1, y_1), (x_2, y_2), \ldots, (x_n, y_n)$. The system will balance on a knife-edge perpendicular to the x-axis at the point $(\bar{x}, 0)$, where

$$\bar{x} = \frac{x_1|\vec{v}_1| + x_2|\vec{v}_2| + \cdots + x_n|\vec{v}_n|}{|\vec{v}_1| + |\vec{v}_2| + \cdots + |\vec{v}_n|},$$

or on a knife-edge perpendicular to the y-axis at the point $(0, \bar{y})$, where

$$\bar{y} = \frac{y_1|\vec{v}_1| + y_2|\vec{v}_2| + \cdots + y_n|\vec{v}_n|}{|\vec{v}_1| + |\vec{v}_2| + \cdots + |\vec{v}_n|}.$$

The point $(\bar{x}, \bar{y})$ is then called the **centroid** of the system.

For example, in Fig. 8-2.3, if $\vec{v}_1, \ldots, \vec{v}_5$ are due to weights of 2 lb, $\frac{3}{2}$ lb, 3 lb, 5 lb, and 4 lb, respectively, Then

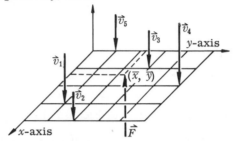

Fig. 8-2.3

$$\bar{x} = \frac{3 \cdot 2 + 4 \cdot \frac{3}{2} + 1 \cdot 3 + 2 \cdot 5 + 0 \cdot 4}{2 + \frac{3}{2} + 3 + 5 + 4} = \frac{50}{31} \quad \text{and} \quad \bar{y} = \frac{86}{31}.$$

A thin circular disk of homogeneous material would, under ideal conditions, balance horizontally on a needle point at its center. But where would the balance point be for a sector consisting of one fourth of a circular disk? This problem is attacked by locating such a sector as the first quadrant portion inside the circle $x^2 + y^2 = r^2$. Consider this sector sliced into many narrow strips, each of width Δx, having sides parallel to the y-axis. If $x_1, x_2, \ldots, x_n$ are such that $(x_k, 0)$ is on the base of the kth strip, then the altitude of the strip is close to $\sqrt{r^2 - x_k^2}$, the area is close to $\sqrt{r^2 - x_k^2}\,\Delta x$, its weight close to $\rho\sqrt{r^2 - x_k^2}\,\Delta x$ (where ρ is the density constant for the sheet; that is, the weight of a piece of unit area), and its moment with respect to the y-axis is close to $x_k\,\rho\sqrt{r^2 - x_k^2}\,\Delta x$. Hence,

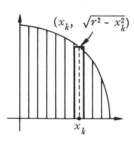

Fig. 8-2.4

(6)

$$\frac{\sum\limits_{k=1}^{n} x_k\,\rho\sqrt{r^2 - x_k^2}\,\Delta x}{\sum\limits_{k=1}^{n} \rho\sqrt{r^2 - x_k^2}\,\Delta x}$$

should be close to the $\bar{x}$ of the centroid $(\bar{x}, \bar{y})$ of the sector. The limits as $\Delta x \to 0$ of the numerator and denominator are the definite integrals in

$$\bar{x} = \frac{\int_0^r x\rho\sqrt{r^2 - x^2}\,dx}{\int_0^r \rho\sqrt{r^2-x^2}\,dx} = \frac{-\frac{1}{3}(r^2 - x^2)^{3/2}\Big]_0^r}{\frac{1}{4}\pi r^2} = \frac{\frac{1}{3}r^3}{\frac{1}{4}\pi r^2} = \frac{4}{3}\frac{r}{\pi}.$$

By symmetry, $\bar{x} = \bar{y}$.

The above discussion for a quadrant of a circle should motivate the following definition:

In a horizontal plane, a homogeneous sheet (density constant ρ), whose projections on the axes are $a \le x \le b$ and $c \le y \le d$, has centroid $(\bar{x}, \bar{y})$ given by

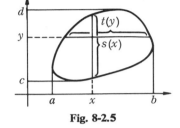

$$(7) \quad \bar{x} = \frac{\int_a^b x\rho s(x)\,dx}{\int_a^b \rho s(x)\,dx} \quad \text{and} \quad \bar{y} = \frac{\int_c^d y\rho t(y)\,dy}{\int_c^d \rho t(y)\,dy},$$

Fig. 8-2.5

where $s(x)$ is the height and $t(y)$ the width of the sheet through a point (x, y) of the sheet.

The quantites $x\rho s(x)\,dx$ and $y\rho t(y)\,dy$ are called the **differential moments** with respect to the y-axis and x-axis, respectively.

Example 2. A sheet of homogeneous material is cut to fit the first quadrant region under $y = \sin x$ for $0 \le x \le \pi/2$. Find the centroid of the sheet.

Solution. At $(x, 0)$ the height of the sheet is merely $\sin x$, so the differential moment with respect to the y-axis is $x\rho \sin x\,dx$ and

$$\bar{x} = \frac{\int_0^{\pi/2} x\rho \sin x\,dx}{\int_0^{\pi/2} \rho \sin x\,dx} = \frac{\rho\int_0^{\pi/2} x \sin x\,dx}{\rho\int_0^{\pi/2} \sin x\,dx}$$

$$= \frac{-x\cos x + \sin x\Big]_0^{\pi/2}}{-\cos x\Big]_0^{\pi/2}} \quad \text{by integration by parts in the numerator.}$$

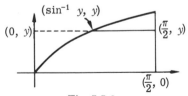

Fig. 8-2.6

Hence, $\bar{x} = 1$. Now take a point $(0, y)$ with $0 \le y \le 1$ and draw the line perpendicular to the y-axis at $(0, y)$. The segment of this line crossing the region has left end at $(\sin^{-1} y, y)$ and right end at $(\pi/2, y)$. This segment has length $\pi/2 - \sin^{-1} y$, and the differential moment relative to the x-axis is $\rho y(\pi/2 - \sin^{-1} y)\,dy$ and

$$\bar{y} = \frac{\int_0^1 \rho y \left(\frac{\pi}{2} - \sin^{-1} y \right) dy}{\int_0^1 \rho \left(\frac{\pi}{2} - \sin^{-1} y \right) dy} = \frac{\frac{\pi}{2} \int_0^1 y \, dy - \int_0^1 y \sin^{-1} y \, dy}{\frac{\pi}{2} \int_0^1 dy - \int_0^1 \sin^{-1} y \, dy}.$$

The second integral in the numerator (from integration by parts using $u = \sin^{-1} y$ and $dv = y \, dy$) is evaluated as

$$\int_0^1 y \sin^{-1} y \, dy = (\sin^{-1} y) \frac{y^2}{2} \Big]_0^1 - \int_0^1 \frac{1}{\sqrt{1 - y^2}} \frac{y^2}{2} \, dy$$

$$= \frac{\pi}{4} - \frac{1}{2} \left[-\frac{y}{2} \sqrt{1 - y^2} + \frac{1}{2} \sin^{-1} y \right]_0^1 \quad \text{by formula 36}$$

$$= \frac{\pi}{4} - \frac{\pi}{8} = \frac{\pi}{8}.$$

The first integral in the numerator of $\bar{y}$ has value $\pi/4$, and thus the numerator of $\bar{y}$ is $\pi/4 - \pi/8 = \pi/8$. The integrals in the denominator of $\bar{y}$ need not be evaluated, since this denominator has the same value (namely, 1) as the denominator of $\bar{x}$. Thus, $\bar{y} = \pi/8$, and the centroid is $(1, \pi/8)$.

In computing the centroid of a homogeneous sheet, it should be noticed that the density constant ρ cancels out. Hence, it is customary to speak of the centroid of an area rather than of the centroid of a homogeneous sheet cut to fit the area.

Problem 1. Prove that if (2) and (3) hold, then the sum of the moments relative to any other point $(d, 0)$ is also zero.

Problem 2. In Fig. 8-2.3, find the centroid if $\vec{v}_1, \ldots, \vec{v}_5$ are due to weights of:
a. 4 lb, 3 lb, 2 lb, 1 lb, and 1 lb, respectively.
b. 1 lb, 1 lb, 2 lb, 3 lb, and 4 lb, respectively.

Problem 3. Find the centroid of each of the regions whose bounding curves are given:
a. Under $y = x^2$ and above $0 \le x \le 2$.
b. $x = \sqrt{y}$, $x = 0$, $y = 4$.
c. $y = x^2$, $y = x + 2$.
d. Under $y = \cos x$ and above $-\pi/2 \le x \le \pi/2$.
e. $y = \cos x$, $y = 1$, $x = \pi/2$.
f. $3y^2 + 4(x - 3) = 0$, y-axis.
g. First quadrant portion inside the ellipse $b^2x^2 + a^2y^2 = a^2b^2$.
h. $y = 6x - x^2$, $y = x$.
i. $y^2 + 4y = x$, $y = x$.

Problem 4. A triangular area has vertices $(0, 0)$, (a, b), and $(c, 0)$, with a, b, and c positive. Show that the centroid is the intersection of the medians. Be sure to consider two cases according to whether $c > a$ or $c \le a$.

Problem 5. Let R_1 and R_2 be two regions with no more than boundary points in common. Show that if the areas are A_1 and A_2, the centroids $(\bar{x}_1, \bar{y}_1)$ and $(\bar{x}_2, \bar{y}_2)$, respectively, then

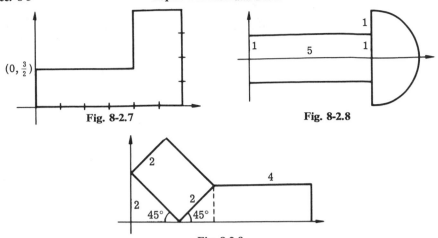

Fig. 8-2.7   Fig. 8-2.8

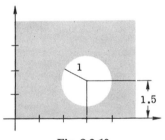

Fig. 8-2.9

$$\bar{x} = \frac{\bar{x}_1 A_1 + \bar{x}_2 A_2}{A_1 + A_2} \quad \text{and} \quad \bar{y} = \frac{\bar{y}_1 A_1 + \bar{y}_2 A_2}{A_1 + A_2}$$

give the centroid of the combined regions. Use this fact, together with known centroids, to find the centroids of the regions of Figs. 8-2.7, 8-2.8, and 8-2.9.

Problem 6. If a region has a hole in it, then the formulas of Prob. 5 may be used with $\bar{x}$ and $\bar{y}$ known and either $(\bar{x}_1, \bar{y}_1)$ or $(\bar{x}_2, \bar{y}_2)_2$ known, with the other to be solved for. Find the centroid of the regions shown in Figs. 8-2.10, 8-2.11, and 8-2.12.

Fig. 8-2.10

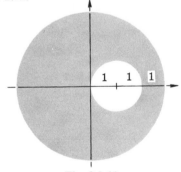

Fig. 8-2.11

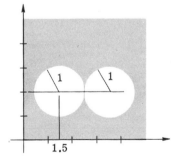

Fig. 8-2.12

8-3. Liquid Pressure and Force

At a point within a liquid at rest, the pressure (or force per unit area) is the same in all directions. Also, a liquid, such as water, is essentially incompressible, which means that a cubic unit of liquid weighs the same whether near the bottom or top of a tank of the liquid. Thus, on the plane verti-

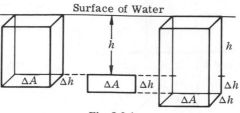

Surface of Water

Fig. 8-3.1

cal side of a tank, an area of ΔA square units sustains a force between the weight of the liquid which would be directly above ΔA if ΔA were turned horizontal about its highest or lowest points. For example, on a plane vertical side of a water tank, a rectangle of length l ft, width Δh ft, and upper

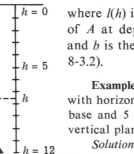

Fig. 8-3.2

edge h ft below the surface of water (weight 62.5 lb/ft³) sustains a force between

$$62.5 \, hl \, \Delta h \text{ lb} \quad \text{and} \quad 62.5(h+\Delta h)l \, \Delta h \text{ lb}.$$

Hence, the force on an area A on a plane vertical side of a water tank is close to the sum of such elements of force for many narrow strips and is defined to be

$$(1) \qquad \text{force} = \int_a^b 62.5 \, hl(h) \, dh,$$

where $l(h)$ is the function of h giving the width of A at depth h, a is the depth of the top of A, and b is the depth of the bottom of A (see Fig. 8-3.2).

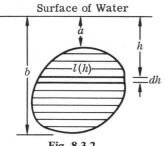

Fig. 8-3.3

Example 1. Find the force on a triangular area with horizontal base 6 ft, altitude 7 ft, vertex above base and 5 ft below the surface of water on the vertical plane face of a dam.

Solution 1. See Fig. 8-3.3. Here $a = 5$, $b = 5 + 7 = 12$, and for $5 \leq h \leq 12$, the width l of the triangle at depth h is such that

$$\frac{l}{h-5} = \frac{6}{7}, \quad \text{so that} \quad l = \frac{6}{7}(h-7).$$

Thus,

$$\text{force} = 62.5 \int_5^{12} h \frac{6}{7}(h-5) \, dh = 62.5 \frac{6}{7} \int_5^{12} (h^2 - 5h) \, dh$$

$$= 62.5 \frac{6}{7} \left[\frac{h^3}{3} - \frac{5}{2}h^2 \right]_5^{12} = (62.5)(203) \text{ lb}.$$

Solution 2. See Fig. 8-3.4. Sometimes it is better to use a scale especially selected for the problem at hand. In this case, select a y-scale along the altitude of the triangle, with $y = 0$ at the vertex and $y = 7$ at the base. Now for $0 \leq y \leq 7$, the width l of the triangle at level y is such that

$$\frac{l}{y} = \frac{6}{7}, \quad \text{so that} \quad l = \frac{6}{7} y.$$

But this level is $5 + y$ ft from the surface, so that

$$\text{force} = 62.5 \int_0^7 (5 + y) \frac{6}{7} y \, dy$$

$$= 62.5 \frac{6}{7} \int_0^7 (5y + y^2) \, dy = 62.5 \frac{6}{7} \left[\frac{5}{2} y^2 + \frac{y^3}{3} \right]_0^7$$

$$= (62.5)(203) \text{ lb}.$$

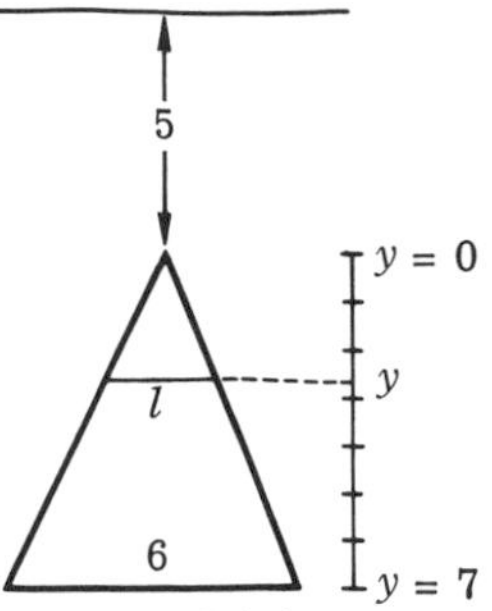

Fig. 8-3.4

An orientation on a page of the axes of a coordinate system is quite arbitrary, and it is merely long association that makes it seem natural to have the positive x-axis to the right and the positive y-axis directed upward. For some problems, in particular those concerned with gravity, it is convenient to have the positive y-axis directed downward, especially since most people think in terms of positive numbers more freely than in negative numbers.

Example 2. With the positive y-axis directed downward, find the force on one side of a plane section bounded by $x^2 = y - 1$ and $y = 3$, which is submerged vertically in water if the x-axis is in the surface of the water (see Fig. 8-3.5).

Solution. The vertex of the parabola is $(0, 1)$ and hence is 1 ft below the origin, which is in the surface of the water. Thus, for $1 \leq y \leq 3$, the differential of force is $62.5y \, 2\sqrt{y - 1} \, dy$ and

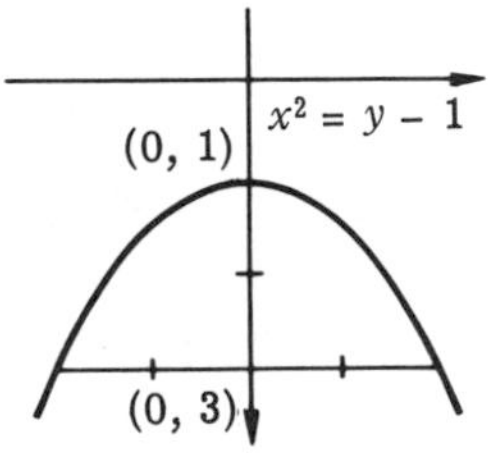

Fig. 8-3.5

$$\text{force} = 2(62.5) \int_1^3 y \sqrt{y - 1} \, dy = 2(62.5) \frac{44\sqrt{2}}{15} \text{ lb}.$$

Again, let the positive y-axis be downward. A region of the (x, y)-plane, such that $l(y)$ is the function of y giving the horizontal distance across the strip for $a \leq y \leq b$, has centroid $(\bar{x}, \bar{y})$, where

$$\bar{y} = \frac{\int_a^b y l(y) \, dy}{\int_a^b l(y) \, dy} = \frac{\int_a^b y l(y) \, dy}{\text{area}}.$$

If $a > 0$ and the region is on the vertical plane face of a dam, with the x-axis at the surface of the water, then

$$\text{force} = 62.5 \int_a^b yl(y)\, dx = 62.5\bar{y} \text{ (area)}.$$

This formula, derived by using calculus, makes it unnecessary to use calculus in finding the force on a region of the vertical face of a dam if the area and centroid of the region are known by symmetry considerations or previous use of calculus. As an illustration, in Example 1 the centroid is

$$5 + \tfrac{2}{3}\cdot 7 = \frac{29}{3} \text{ ft}$$

from the surface of water. Since area = 21, then

$$\text{force} = 62.5 \left(\frac{29}{3}\right) 21 = 62.5\,(29\cdot 7) = 62.5\,(203).$$

Consider now a circular cylindrical tank lying horizontally with its circular ends vertical and with the tank full of water. What is the force on one end? A horizontal strip across one end of the tank has more water directly above its center point than above an off-center point. It might be thought the center point sustains a greater force than other points, but this is not so. In fact, the downward containing force of the upper portion of the tank is

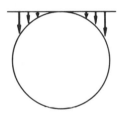

exactly the same (because liquid pressure is the same in all directions) as if the upper semicircle were replaced by a rectangle. Thus, the force on an end is the same as if the circle were on the vertical face of a dam and tangent to the surface of the water (see Fig. 8-3.6). Hence, if the tank has a 5-ft radius, the centroid is 5 ft below the surface and

$$\text{force} = 62.5(5)\pi 5^2 \text{ lb}.$$

Fig. 8-3.6

Furthermore, if a 10-ft long, 1-in. diameter, vertical feed pipe to the top of the tank is also full of water, then the force on one end of the tank is (disregarding capillary attraction)

$$62.5(15)\pi 5^2 \text{ lb}.$$

This is an increase of $62.5(10)\pi 5^2 = 4.91 \times 10^4$ lb of force on an end due to only $62.5(10)\pi(1/24)^2 = 3.41$ lb of water in the feed pipe.

Problem 1. A dam is 50 ft across the top at water line and 30 ft high from its lowest point. Find the force in tons on the dam if the shape is:

    a. Parabolic.

    b. Semi-elliptical.

    c. One arch of a cosine curve.

Problem 2. In a dam there is a rectangular gate 2 ft wide and 3 ft high, with upper edge 1 ft below the surface. Find the force on:

    a. The whole gate.

    b. The upper and lower triangular parts of the gate formed by a diagonal of the gate.

Problem 3. The gate of Prob. 2 is to have a horizontal swivel placed at such a depth that if the gate is closed it will (theoretically) stay closed by the force of water alone; that is, such that the sum of moments above and below this level is zero. Find the depth at which to put the swivel.

Problem 4. Replace the gate of Prob. 3 by a circular gate of radius 2 ft, with center 3 ft below the surface.

Problem 5. Replace the gate of Prob. 3 by a triangular gate with horizontal base 4 ft, altitude 3 ft, and vertex 1 ft below the surface.

Problem 6. Turn the triangular gate of Prob. 5 over so the base is 1 ft below the surface and the vertex is 3 ft below the base.

Problem 7. Two cylindrical tanks are 10 ft long, one has vertical circular cross sections of radius 3 ft, the other has vertical elliptical cross sections with horizontal major axis 8 ft and vertical minor axis 4.5 ft. Show that the tanks have the same volume and find the force on an end of each tank if the tanks are full of water.

8-4. Work by Variable Force

If a body is moved along the x-axis (with unit 1 ft) from $x = a$ to $x = b$ by a variable force (acting in the line of motion) whose value at x is $f(x)$ lb, then the work done (see Sec. 3-6) is

(1) $$W = \int_a^b f(x)\, dx \text{ ft-lb.}$$

Example 1. A particle at x is attracted toward the origin by a force whose magnitude is kx^2, where k is a positive constant (depending on the units used). Find the work done by an oppositely directed force in moving the particle from:

    a. $x = -1$ to $x = 2$.   b. $x = 2$ to $x = -1$.

Solution. Since the given force (the attraction) is always toward the origin, the force function $f(x)$, either helped or hindered by the attraction, is

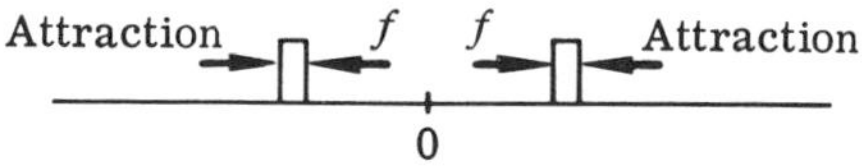

Fig. 8-4.1

$$f(x) = \begin{cases} -kx^2 & \text{if } x < 0, \\ kx^2 & \text{if } x \geq 0. \end{cases}$$

Thus,

    a. $$W = \int_{-1}^2 f(x)\, dx = \int_{-1}^0 -kx^2\, dx + \int_0^2 kx^2\, dx = \tfrac{7}{3}k.$$

    b. $$W = \int_2^{-1} f(x)\, dx = -\int_{-1}^2 f(x)\, dx = -\tfrac{7}{3}k.$$

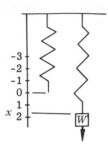

Fig. 8-4.2

A spring hung by one end has a natural length if no weight is attached. It will extend in direct proportion to the mass of a weight attached to its lower end. Thus, for a given spring there is a constant k (depending on the units used) such that the extension due to a force F is

$$F = kx.$$

If, for example, a spring extends 2 in. beyond its natural length when a 6-lb weight is attached, then $6 = k \cdot 2$ so $k = 3$ and for this spring

(2) $$F = 3x \text{ lb}, \quad \text{with } x \text{ in inches.}$$

Hence, if an 8-lb weight is attached, the extension is

$$\tfrac{8}{3} = 2\tfrac{2}{3} \text{ in.}$$

If one now grasps the free end of this unweighted spring and pulls it from its natural length to an extension of 4 in., how much work is done? Recall that, by definition, work W is force times distance *if the force is constant.* But for the spring the force varies, so that the formula (1) must be used with the force given by (2). Hence, the required answer to the above question is

$$W = \int_0^4 3x\,dx = 24 \text{ in.-lb.}$$

In formula (1) it is assumed that the body is rigid and all points move the same distance so the body may be considered as a mass point; that is, as a particle. The integrand $f(x)\,dx$ is then considered as an "element of work."

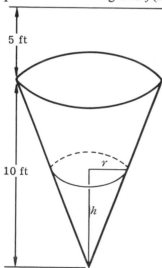

Fig. 8-4.3

In some problems, the body does not retain its shape; for example, a dangling cable may be coiled up at the level of its original upper end or all water in a tank may be pumped to the same level above the tank, with some particles of water moved farther than others. In such cases, the element of work has a different form than in (1) and may have a variable distance as well as a variable force.

The following example is the same as Example 2 of Sec. 3-6 but is worked more from an engineering point of view.

Example 2. A conical tank having radius of base 4 ft, altitude 10 ft, and vertex down is full of water (weight 62.5 lb/ft³). Find the work done in pumping the water to a level 5 ft above the top of the tank.

Solution. When pumping has lowered the surface to h ft from the vertex (see Fig. 8-4.3) then, by similar triangles, the surface radii r and h are related by

$$\frac{r}{h} = \frac{4}{10}, \quad \text{so that} \quad r = 0.4h,$$

and the surface area is $\pi r^2 = 0.16\pi h^2$. Thus, at this level, the element of volume (that is, a thin sheet of thickness dh) is $\pi 0.16\pi h^2\, dh$ ft^3. The element of force is the weight of this element of volume:

$$\text{element of force} = 62.5\pi(0.16)h^2\, dh \text{ lb.}$$

The element of volume is to be raised the $10 - h$ ft to the top of the tank and then 5 ft more. Thus, the element of force acts through a distance of $15 - h$ ft, so that

$$\text{element of work} = (15 - h)\pi 62.5(0.16)h^2\, dh \text{ ft-lb.}$$

Since this holds for all h from $h = 0$ at the vertex to $h = 10$ at the top of the tank (not to $h = 15$), then

$$\text{work} = \int_0^{10} (15 - h)\pi 62.5(0.16)h^2\, dh$$

$$= \pi(62.5)(0.16)\int_0^{10} (15h^2 - h^3)\, dh$$

$$= \text{etc.} = 25{,}000\pi = 7.85 \times 10^4 \text{ ft-lb.}$$

Example 3. A rope weighing $\frac{1}{2}$ lb/ft is used to raise a leaky bucket of water from a 20-ft well. The bucket of water, starting at 40 lb and ending at 25 lb, is raised at a constant velocity. Find the work done.

Solution. Use a coordinate system with $x = 0$ at ground level and $x = 70$ at water level. The bucket loses water at the rate of

$$(40 - 25) \text{ lb/20 ft} = \tfrac{15}{20} \text{ lb/ft} = \tfrac{3}{4} \text{ lb/ft.}$$

Thus, when the bucket is x ft below ground level, it is $20 - x$ ft above water level, weighs

$$f(x) = 40 - \tfrac{3}{4}(20 - x) = 25 + \tfrac{3}{4}x \text{ lb,}$$

and if it were raised by a weightless rope would require, by (1),

$$\int_0^{20} (25 + \tfrac{3}{4}x)\, dx = 650 \text{ ft-lb of work.}$$

A dx-ft section of rope weighs $\frac{1}{2}\, dx$ lb; such a section x ft below ground level requires $x\frac{1}{2}\, dx$ ft-lb to raise to ground level, and

$$\int_0^{20} \tfrac{1}{2}x\, dx = 100 \text{ ft-lb}$$

of work raises the whole rope to ground level. Thus, rope and bucket require

$$650 + 100 = 750 \text{ ft-lb of work.}$$

Problem 1. The natural length of a spring is 12 in. and a force of 25 lb stretches the spring 3 in. Find the work done in stretching the length from:

a. 12 in. to 15 in.   d. a in. to $a + h$ in.

b. 14 in. to 17 in.   e. a in. to $a + 2h$ in.
c. a in. to $a + 3$ in.   f. $a + h$ in. to $a + 2h$ in.

Problem 2. Work Prob. 1 if the natural length is 1 ft and a force of 40 lb stretches the spring 1 in.

Problem 3. Find the work in pumping all water from a tank to H ft above the top of the tank if the tank has the form of:

  a. A right circular cone, vertex down, altitude 6 ft, radius of base 3 ft, and $H = 5$.
  b. The cone of part a with altitude a, radius of base b, and $H \geq 0$.
  c. The cone of part a with vertex up.
  d. A hemispherical bowl of radius 3 ft and $H = 10$ ft.
  e. A vertical right-circular cylinder of altitude 8 ft, radius 3 ft, and $H = 2$.
  f. The bowl of part d as bottom and the cylinder of part e attached at the rim of the bowl, with $H = 2$.
  g. A trough of length 8 ft whose vertical cross sections are all isosceles triangles with bases 3 ft and altitudes 2 ft, and $H = 5$.
  h. A trough as in part g but with cross sections all semicrcles of diameter 3 ft and $H = 0$.
  i. The trough of part h but with $H = 5$.

Problem 4. An empty tank stands on a tower 50 ft high. The tank is to be filled by pumping water from a well in which the water level is always 25 ft below ground. Find the work in filling the tank if the tank has the form of the one in the various parts of Prob. 3.

Problem 5. A 60-ft rope weighs 40 lb. The upper end of the rope is attached to a windlass H ft above ground. Find the work in winding all the rope onto the windlass if the height H above ground of the windlass is:

a. 60 ft.   c. 50 ft, so 10 ft of rope lies on the ground.
b. 75 ft.   d. 20 ft, so 40 ft of rope lies on the ground.

Problem 6. A cable weighing 5 lb/ft is wound on a windlass 75 ft above ground. To the end of the cable is attached a 300-lb weight. A brake allows the weight to be lowered at a steady rate to the ground. Find the work the brake must do in lowering the weight:

  a. All the way to the ground.
  b. Over the first half of the distance to the ground.
  c. Over the second half of the distance to the ground.

8-5. Solids of Revolution

If the circular disk with center $(3, 0)$ and radius 2 is revolved about the y-axis, then a doughnut-shaped solid (called a torus) is formed whose volume may be calculated by means of definite integrals. The disk is bounded by

(1) $(x - 3)^2 + y^2 = 2^2$,   so that $1 \leq x \leq 5$ and $-2 \leq y \leq 2$.

There are two methods of attack.

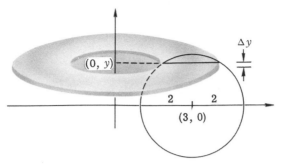

Fig. 8-5.1

Method 1 (Stacked Washers): Think of slicing the solid, as in Fig. 8-5.1, by a plane perpendicular to the y-axis at $(0, y)$, where $-2 \leq y \leq 2$. The cut surface is a ring whose area $A(y)$ is a function of y. A washer with this ring as base and altitude Δy has volume $A(y) \Delta y$ that approximates the volume of a thin slice of the torus between the levels y and $y + \Delta y$. By summing the volumes of such slices and then taking the limit as the thickness of each slice approaches zero, the volume is defined to be

$$(2) \qquad \text{volume} = \int_{-2}^{2} A(y)\, dy.$$

The analytic expression for $A(y)$ must now be found. The equation (1) has two solutions for x in terms of y:

$$x = 3 \pm \sqrt{4 - y^2}.$$

The inner radius of $A(y)$ is $3 - \sqrt{4 - y^2}$, the outer radius is $3 + \sqrt{3 - y^2}$, and

$$A(y) = \pi(3 + \sqrt{4 - y^2})^2 - \pi(3 - \sqrt{4 - y^2})^2$$
$$= \pi[9 + 6\sqrt{4 - y^2} + 4 - y^2 - (9 - 6\sqrt{4 - y^2} + 4 - y^2)]$$
$$= 12\pi\sqrt{4 - y^2}.$$

Thus, from (2),

$$(3) \qquad \text{volume} = \int_{-2}^{2} 12\pi\sqrt{4 - y^2}\, dx = 12\pi\, \frac{1}{2}\left[y\sqrt{4 - y^2} + 4 \sin^{-1}\frac{y}{2} \right]_{-2}^{2}$$

$$= 6\pi[4 \sin^{-1} 1 - 4 \sin^{-1}(-1)] = 24\pi\left[\frac{\pi}{2} - \left(\frac{-\pi}{2} \right) \right] = 24\pi^2.$$

Method 2 (Cylindrical Shells): For $1 \leq x \leq 5$ the vertical chord, as in Fig. 8-5.2, of the disk through $(x, 0)$ has lower end (x, y_1), upper end (x, y_2), and length $y_2 - y_1$. As this chord revolves about the y-axis, it generates the surface of a cylinder of radius x, altitude $y_2 - y_1$, and area $2\pi x(y_2 - y_1)$. If this cylindrical surface is used as the inner surface of a cylindrical shell of thickness Δx, the cylindrical shell has volume close to

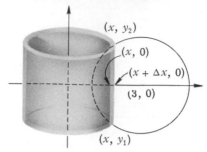

Fig. 8-5.2

$$2\pi x(y_2 - y_1)\,\Delta x,$$

which approximates the volume of a portion of the whole solid. By the usual method, this leads to the definition

(4) $\text{volume} = \int_1^5 2\pi x(y_2 - y_1)\,dx.$

Since y_2 and y_1 are the solutions of (1) for y, in terms of x, they are functions of x:

$$y_1 = -\sqrt{4 - (x - 3)^2}, \quad y_2 = \sqrt{4 - (x - 3)^2}, \quad y_2 - y_1 = 2\sqrt{4 - (x - 3)^2},$$

and

$$\text{volume} = 4\pi \int_1^5 x\sqrt{4 - (x - 3)^2}\,dx.$$

Make the substitution $u = x - 3$ to see that

$$\text{volume} = 4\pi \int_{-2}^2 (u + 3)\sqrt{4 - u^2}\,du$$

$$= 4\pi \left\{ \int_{-2}^2 u\sqrt{4 - u^2}\,du + 3\int_{-2}^2 \sqrt{4 - u^2}\,du \right\}$$

$$= 4\pi \left\{ -\frac{1}{3}(4 - u^2)^{3/2} + 3\left(\frac{1}{2}\right)\left[u\sqrt{4 - u^2} + 4\sin^{-1}\frac{u}{2} \right] \right\}_{-2}^2$$

$$= 4\pi \frac{3}{2}\cdot 4\pi = 24\pi^2.$$

A plane region may be revolved about a line other than an axis, as illustrated in the following examples.

Example. A region is bounded by $y = x^2$, $y = 0$, and $x = 2$. Find the volume of the solid obtained by revolving this region about the line $y = -1$.

Solution 1 (Stacked Washers). The solid cut by the plane perpendicular to the x-axis at $(x, 0)$, with $0 \le x \le 2$, leads to

$$\text{volume} = \int_0^2 [\pi(1 + x^2)^2 - \pi(1)^2]\,dx = \pi\int_0^2 (2x^2 + x^4)\,dx$$

$$= \pi\left[\frac{2}{3}x^3 + \frac{x^5}{5} \right]_0^2 = \frac{176}{15}\pi.$$

Solution 2 (Cylindrical Shells). For the region $0 \leq y \leq 2^2$ and at the level y, the horizontal segment across the region has endpoints $(\sqrt{y}, y)$ and $(2, y)$ and thus length $2 - \sqrt{y}$. Hence, the cylindrical shell has radius $1 + y$, altitude $2 - \sqrt{y}$, and differential volume $2\pi(1 + y)(2 - \sqrt{y}) \, dy$. Thus,

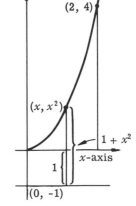

Fig. 8-5.3

$$\text{volume} = 2\pi \int_0^4 (2 - \sqrt{y} + 2y - y^{3/2}) \, dy$$

$$= 2\pi \left[2y - \tfrac{2}{3}y^{3/2} + y^2 - \tfrac{2}{5}y^{5/2} \right]_0^4$$

$$= 2\pi[8 - \tfrac{16}{3} + 16 - \tfrac{64}{5}]$$

$$= 16\pi(3 - \tfrac{2}{3} - \tfrac{8}{5}) = \tfrac{176}{15}\pi.$$

Problem 1. Find the volume obtained by revolving the region of Example 1 about:

a. The x-axis.

b. The y-axis.

c. The line $x = -1$.

d. The line $y = 4$.

Problem 2. Find the volume obtained by revolving the region described about the x-axis.

    a. The semi-ellipse $b^2x^2 + a^2y^2 = a^2b^2, y \geq 0$.

    b. One arch of $y = \sin x$, $y = 0$.

    c. Bounded by $y = e^x$, $x = 0$, $x = 1$, and $y = 0$.

    d. Bounded by $y = \ln x$, $y = 0$, and $x = e$.

    e. Bounded by $y = \tfrac{1}{2}(e^x + e^{-x})$, $y = 0$, $x = \pm 1$.

    f. Bounded, by $xy = 4$, $y = 0$, $x = 1$, and $x = 4$.

    g. The two finite regions bounded by $y = x(x - 1)(x - 3)$ and the x-axis.

Problem 3. A region is bounded by $y = x(6 - x)$ and the x-axis. Find the volume obtained by revolving the region about:

a. The y-axis.

b. The line $x = -2$.

c. The line $y = -1$.

Problem 4. Replace the region of Prob. 3 by the one bounded by $y = 8/(4 + x^2)$, $x = 2$, $x = 4$, and $y = 0$.

Problem 5. Use volumes of revolution to find the volume of:

    a. A sphere of radius r.

    b. A right circular cone of altitude h and radius r.

    c. The frustum of a cone with radii r and R and altitude h.

Problem 6. In a circle of radius 3 or more, draw a chord of length 6 and note the smaller area bounded by this chord and the circle. Revolve this area about the diameter parallel to the chord and show that the resulting solid is independent of the size circle used (so long as its radius is greater than or equal to 3).

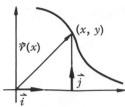

Fig. 8-6.1

8-6.   Length of a Curve

The graph of the scalar function $y = f(x)$ may also be thought of as the path traced by the terminal end of the position vector function of x,

(1) $$\vec{r}(x) = \vec{i}x + \vec{j}y,$$

with each vector $\vec{r}(x)$ having its initial end at the origin. By taking differentials of both sides of (1), the result is

$$d\vec{r}(x) = \vec{i}\,dx + \vec{j}\,dy.$$

The length of $d\vec{r}(x)$ is $|d\vec{r}(x)| = \sqrt{(dx)^2 + (dy)^2}$. Since, by definition, the differential of $y = f(x)$ is $dy = f'(x)\,dx$, it follows, assuming $dx > 0$, that

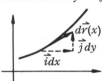

Fig. 8-6.2

$$|d\vec{r}(x)| = \sqrt{(dx)^2 + [f'(x)]^2(dx)^2}$$
$$= \sqrt{1 + f'^2(x)}\,dx.$$

The geometric interpretation is that $d\vec{r}(x)$ is a small vector tangent to the curve $y = f(x)$, and thus $|d\vec{r}(x)|$ seems close to the length of a small portion of the curve. In more advanced work it is shown that the length of the curve $y = f(x)$ between $x = a$ and $x = b$ is

(2) $$\text{length} = \int_a^b |dr(x)| = \int_a^b \sqrt{1 + f'^2(x)}\,dx = \int_a^b \sqrt{1 + y'^2}\,dx.$$

Example 1. Find the length of the curve $y = x^{3/2}$ between $x = 0$ and $x = 4$.

Solution. Since $y' = \frac{3}{2}x^{1/2}$, it follows that

$$\text{length} = \int_0^4 \sqrt{1 + (\tfrac{3}{2}x^{1/2})^2}\,dx = \int_0^4 \sqrt{1 + \tfrac{9}{4}x}\,dx = \tfrac{4}{9} \cdot \tfrac{2}{3}(1 + \tfrac{9}{4}x)^{3/2}\Big]_0^4$$
$$= \tfrac{8}{27}[(1 + 9)^{3/2} - 1] = \tfrac{8}{27}(10^{3/2} - 1).$$

An intuitive feeling for the formula (2) may be gained by considering increments, instead of differentials,

(3) $$\Delta\vec{r} = \vec{i}\,\Delta x + \vec{i}\,\Delta y,$$

and noticing that if these are taken at closely selected points along the curve then the vectors $\Delta_1\vec{r}, \Delta_2\vec{r}, \ldots, \Delta_n\vec{r}$ are chords hardly distinguishable from the curve itself. Thus, the sum of the lengths of these increments of $\vec{r}$ should approximate the length of the curve. Also, as $\Delta x \to 0$ (which it does as finer selections of points are made along the curve), then

(4) $$\left|\frac{\Delta\vec{r}}{\Delta x}\right| = \left|\vec{i}\frac{\Delta y}{\Delta x} + \vec{j}\frac{\Delta y}{\Delta x}\right| = \sqrt{1 + \left(\frac{\Delta y}{\Delta x}\right)^2}$$

approaches the expression

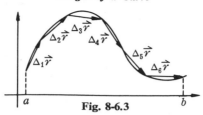

Fig. 8-6.3

$$\sqrt{1 + \left(\frac{dy}{dx}\right)^2} = \sqrt{1 + y'^2}$$

in the integrand of (2).

If the curve is thought of as the path of a moving point, then x and y are both functions of a third independent variable t. Equation (3) still holds, but an increment Δt of t caused the increments Δx and Δy. Thus, it is natural to divide by Δt to obtain, instead of (4),

(5)
$$\left|\frac{\Delta \vec{r}}{\Delta t}\right| = \left|\vec{i}\frac{\Delta x}{\Delta t} + \vec{j}\frac{\Delta y}{\Delta t}\right| = \sqrt{\left(\frac{\Delta x}{\Delta t}\right)^2 + \left(\frac{\Delta y}{\Delta t}\right)^2},$$

which approaches, as $\Delta t \to 0$,

$$\left|\frac{d\vec{r}}{dt}\right| = \sqrt{\left(\frac{dx}{dt}\right)^2 + \left(\frac{dy}{dt}\right)^2}.$$

Hence, when t is the independent varible (instead of x), then the length of the path from time $t = t_0$ to time $t = t_1$ is, instead of (2),

(6)
$$\int_{t_0}^{t_1} \sqrt{\left(\frac{dx}{dt}\right)^2 + \left(\frac{dy}{dt}\right)^2}\, dt = \int_{t_0}^{t_1} \sqrt{x'^2 + y'^2}\, dt,$$

where the dt indicates integration with respect to t.

Example 2. Find the distance traveled during the time from $t = 0$ to $t = 4$ by a moving point whose position vector is

$$\vec{r}(t) = \vec{i}5\cos 2t + \vec{j}5\sin 2t.$$

Show that the path is on a circle and the distance traveled is more than all the way around the circle.

Solution. In this case, x and y are functions of t:

$$x(t) = 5\cos 2t \quad \text{and} \quad y(t) = 5\sin 2t.$$

Hence, the derivatives (with respect to t) to be substituted into (6) are

$$x' = -10\sin 2t \quad \text{and} \quad y' = 10\cos 2t,$$

and the length of the path is

$$\int_0^4 \sqrt{(-10\sin 2t)^2 + (10\cos 2t)^2}\, dt = \int_0^4 \sqrt{100(\sin^2 2t + \cos^2 2t)}\, dt$$

$$= 10\int_0^4 dt = 10t \Big]_0^4 = 40.$$

Since $|\vec{r}(t)| = \sqrt{(5 \cos 2t)^2 + (5 \sin 2t)^2} = 5$ for all t, the point is always 5 units from the origin and thus the path is on a circle. The moving point starts (when $t = 0$) at the end of $\vec{r}(0) = \vec{i}5 \cos 0 + \vec{j}5 \sin 0 = 5\vec{i}$; that is, at the point $(5, 0)$. The point then moves counterclockwise around the circle and returns to $(5, 0)$ when $t = \pi$, since

$$\vec{r}(\pi) = \vec{i}5 \cos 2\pi + \vec{j}5 \sin 2\pi = 5\vec{i}.$$

Since $\pi = 3.14159\ldots$, the point will have retraced part of its path by the time $t = 4$.

Problem 1. Find the length of the indicated arc for the curve:

a. $y = \frac{1}{2}(e^x + e^{-x})$, $x = -1$ to $x = 1$.

b. $x^{2/3} + y^{2/3} = 1$, whole curve. [Hint: Four times length in first quadrant.]

c. $y = \frac{x^3}{6} + \frac{1}{2x}$, $x = 1$ to $x = 3$. $\left[\text{Hint: } \frac{x^4}{4} + \frac{1}{2} + \frac{1}{4x^4} = \left(\frac{x^2}{2} + \frac{1}{2x^2} \right)^2. \right]$

d. $9y^2 = 4x^3$, $x = 0$ to $x = 3$. [Hint: Twice first quadrant length.]

e. $y = e^x$, $x = 0$ to $x = 1$.

f. $y = \ln x$, $x = 1$ to $x = e$.

g. $y = \ln(x + \sqrt{x^2 - 1})$, $x = 2$ to $x = 5$.

h. $y = \frac{x^3}{3} + \frac{1}{4x}$, $x = 1$ to $x = 2$.

Problem 2. Show that the curve $3y^2 = x(x - 1)^2$ has a loop. Find the length of this loop.

Problem 3. The position vector $\vec{r}$ of a moving point during a time interval is given. Find the length of the path.

a. $\vec{r}(t) = \vec{i}3t^2 + \vec{j}2t^3$, $0 \leq t \leq 3$.

b. $\vec{r}(t) = \vec{i}4(1 - \sin t) + \vec{j}4 \cos t$, $0 \leq t \leq 2\pi$.

c. $\vec{r}(t) = \vec{i}a \cos^3 t + \vec{j}a \sin^3 t$, $0 \leq t \leq \pi$.

d. $\vec{r}(t) = e^t(\vec{i} \sin t + \vec{j} \cos t)$, $0 \leq t \leq \pi$.

e. $\vec{r}(t) = 2\vec{i} + 3\vec{j} + (\vec{i} \sin t + \vec{j} \cos t)$, $0 \leq t \leq 2\pi$.

f. $\vec{r}(t) = \vec{i}(2 + 3t) + \vec{j}(5 - 4t)$, $0 \leq t \leq 10$.

8-7. Area of Surface of Revolution

A curve $y = f(x)$ from $x = a$ to $x = b$ when revolved about the x-axis generates a surface of revolution. A point (x, y) of the curve generates a circle of circumference $2\pi|y|$; that is, the point traverses a path of length $2\pi|y|$. Length times length is area. At (x, y), visualize a small portion of the curve with element of length ds. Thus, the length $2\pi|y|$ times the element of length ds is considered as an element dA of area of the surface of revolution:

(1) $$dA = 2\pi|y| \, ds.$$

This element of area dA is visualized as a thin strip around the surface. The integral from $x = a$ to $x = b$ of such elements of area is defined to be the area of the surface of revolution:

(2)
$$A = \int_{x=a}^{x=b} 2\pi |y| \, ds.$$

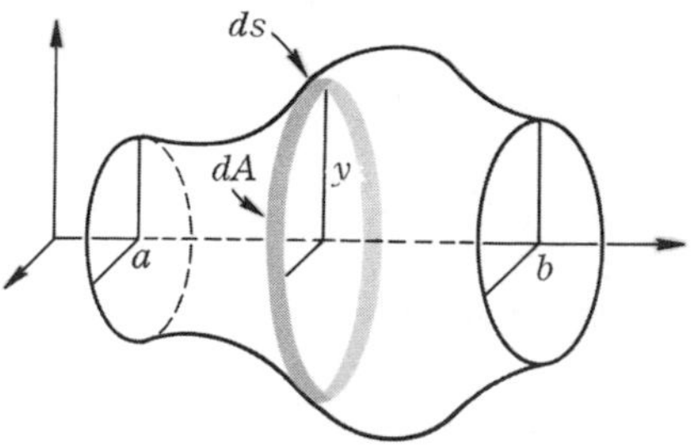

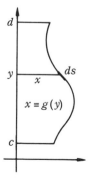

Fig. 8-7.1

Before the integral is evaluated, it is necessary to express the variables x, y, and ds all in terms of a single variable (usually x or y).

Example 1. Find the area of the surface generated by revolving about the x-axis the portion of the curve $4y = x^2$ from $x = 0$ to $x = 16$.

Solution. It is natural to express y and ds in terms of x. Since $y = \frac{1}{4}x^2$, then $ds = \sqrt{1 + y'^2} \, dx$ becomes

$$ds = \sqrt{1 + \left(\frac{2x}{4}\right)^2} \, dx = \sqrt{1 + \left(\frac{x}{2}\right)^2} \, dx = \frac{1}{2}\sqrt{4 + x^2} \, dx.$$

Hence, upon substituting into (2),

$$A = \int_0^{16} 2\pi \left(\frac{1}{4}x^2\right) \frac{1}{2} \sqrt{4 + x^2} \, dx = \frac{\pi}{4} \int_0^{16} x^2 \sqrt{4 + x^2} \, dx$$

By using formula 46 of the Table of Integrals,

$$A = \frac{\pi}{4} \left[\frac{x}{8} (2x^2 + 4)\sqrt{x^2 + 4} - \frac{4^2}{8} \ln |x + \sqrt{x^2 + 4}| \right]_0^{16}$$

$$= \frac{\pi}{2} [1032\sqrt{65} - \ln (8 + \sqrt{65})].$$

If a portion of a curve $x = g(y)$ between $y = c$ and $y = d$ is revolved about the y-axis, then a point (x, y) generates a circle of radius $|x|$, an element of area is $2\pi |x| \, ds$, and

(3)
$$A = \int_{y=c}^{y=d} 2\pi |x| \, ds.$$

Example 2. Find the area generated by revolving the curve of Example 1 about the y-axis (instead of the x-axis).

Solution. Since $4y = x^2$, the curve between $x = 0$ and $x = 16$ has y-limits $y = 0$ and $y = 64$. Thus, ds expressed in terms of y is, since $x = 2y^{1/2}$,

Fig. 8-7.2

$$ds = \sqrt{1 + x'^2}\, dy = \sqrt{1 + (y^{-1/2})^2}\, dy = \frac{\sqrt{y+1}}{\sqrt{y}}\, dy.$$

Hence,

$$A = \int_0^{64} 2\pi(2\sqrt{y})\frac{\sqrt{y+1}}{\sqrt{y}}\, dy = 4\pi \int_0^{64} \sqrt{y+1}\, dy$$

$$= 4\pi \frac{2}{3}(y+1)^{3/2}\Big]_0^{64} = \frac{8}{3}\pi\,(65\sqrt{65} - 1).$$

Problem 1. Find the area of the surface generated by revolving each of the given arcs about the x-axis:

a. $y^2 = 4x$ in the first quadrant from $x = 0$ to $x = 8$.
b. $y^2 = 4 - x$ in the first quadrant.
c. $y = x^3$ from $x = 0$ to $x = 1$.
d. $y = \frac{1}{2}(e^x + e^{-x})$ from $x = -1$ to $x = 1$.
e. $y^2 = 4x + 20$ from $x = -5$ to $x = -2$.
f. $x^2 - y^2 = 16$ from $x = 4$ to $x = 8$.
g. $y = \sin x$, first arch.

Problem 2. Find the area of the surface generated by revolving each of the given arcs about the y-axis.

a. $x^2 = 8 - 4y$ from $y = 3/4$ to $y = 2$.
b. $y = x^2$ from $y = 0$ to $y = 2$.
c. $x = y^3$ from $y = 0$ to $y = 3$.
d. The line segment from $(0, h)$ to $(b, 0)$.
e. $x^{2/3} + y^{2/3} = a^{2/3}$. [Hint: Even though revolution is about the y-axis, use integration with respect to x.]

Problem 3. Circumscribe a right-circular cylinder about a sphere of radius a. Show that:

a. The lateral area of the cylinder and the area of the sphere are equal.
b. Two parallel planes perpendicular to the axis of the cylinder and h units apart, where $h \le 2a$, have between them equal areas on the sphere and the cylinder.

Problem 4. With $b > a$, place a circle of radius a with center $(b, 0)$. Revolve this circle about the y-axis and find the area of the resulting figure.

Chapter 9

Alternative Representations

9-1. Parametric Equations

Given a vector function $\vec{F}(t)$ of the independent variable t, then

(1) $$\vec{F}(t) = \vec{i}x(t) + \vec{j}y(t)$$

determines two functions of t:

(2) $$x = x(t) \quad \text{and} \quad y = y(t).$$

By representing $\vec{F}(t)$ with initial end at the origin then, as t varies, the terminal end of $\vec{F}(t)$ traces a curve. This curve is also said to have the equations (2) as **parametric equations,** and in this context t is called a **parameter.**

Parametric equations have, in fact, already been used. For example, in Sec. 3-4 the position at time t of a projectile traveling in vacuum was given by

$$x = tv_0 \cos \alpha, \quad y = tv_0 \sin \alpha - \tfrac{1}{2}gt^2.$$

Also, the fact that the variable vector

$$\vec{F}(\theta) = r(\vec{i} \cos \theta + \vec{j} \sin \theta)$$

has length $|\vec{F}(\theta)| = \sqrt{(r \cos \theta)^2 + (r \sin \theta)^2} = r$ independent of θ leads to the parametric equations

$$x = r \cos \theta, \quad y = r \sin \theta$$

of the circle with center at the origin and radius r.

With a and b positive constants, then

(3) $$x = a \cos \theta, \quad y = b \sin \theta$$

are parametric equations whose graph lies on the ellipse

(4) $$\frac{x^2}{a^2} + \frac{y^2}{b^2} = 1,$$

since, for any value of θ, the x and y given by (3) are such that

$$\left(\frac{x}{a}\right)^2 + \left(\frac{y}{b}\right)^2 = \cos^2 \theta + \sin^2 \theta = 1.$$

Conversely, if (x, y) is a point on the ellipse (4), then there are many values of θ for which both equations of (3) hold simultaneously. To see this, let x and y be numbers satisfying (4). Plot the point $(x/a, y/b)$ and join this point to the origin (see Fig. 9-1.1 in which $a = 3$ and $b = 2$).

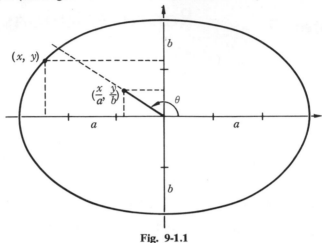

Fig. 9-1.1

Any angle in standard position with this line segment as terminal side is a θ for which (3) holds.

    Now consider the parametric equations

(5) $$x = a \operatorname{sech} t, \quad y = b \tanh t.$$

From the fact that $\operatorname{sech}^2 t + \tanh^2 t = 1$ (see Sec. 6-7), it follows that the graph of (5) also lies on the ellipse (4), but in this case the whole ellipse is not covered. In fact, $\operatorname{sech} t > 0$ for all values of t, so the graph of (5) does

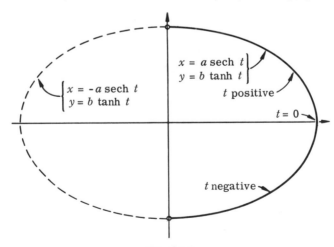

Fig. 9-1.2

not include any point on the left half of the ellipse nor the points $(0, \pm b)$.

Figure 9-1.2 illustrates the graph of (5) as the solid curve and the graph of

$$x = -a \text{ sech } t, \quad y = b \tanh t$$

as the dashed curve with the points $(0, \pm b)$ on neither curve.

The above example illustrates that if parametric equations

(6) $$x = x(t), \quad y = y(t)$$

are given and the "elimination of the parameter" yields an ordinary cartesion equation

(7) $$f(x, y) = 0,$$

then the graph of (6) may be only part of the graph of (7).

The following example illustrates a parameterization of a locus.

Example 1. A wheel has radius of a units, and on one spoke there is a spot b units from the center of the hub. As the wheel rolls, without slipping, along a straight line the spot describes a locus. Find parametric equations of this locus in terms of the parameter θ through which the spoke rotates.

Solution. On a coordinate system, place the wheel tangent to the x-axis at the origin, with the spot S directly below the hub on the y-axis (dotted circle of Fig. 9-1.3). Now roll the wheel (without slipping) along the x-axis and picture its

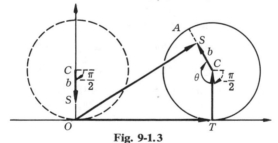

Fig. 9-1.3

position when the spotted spoke has turned through an angle θ. Note θ has been generated clockwise, which is opposite to the usually considered counterclockwise generation of positive angles.

In order to find the parametric equations of the locus described by S, it is only necessary to express the vector $\overrightarrow{OS}$ in terms of the unit vectors $\vec{i}$ and $\vec{j}$. This is done by first using vector addition to see that (from Fig. 9-1. 3)

(8) $$\overrightarrow{OS} = \overrightarrow{OT} + \overrightarrow{TC} + \overrightarrow{CS}$$

and then to express each of $\overrightarrow{OT}$, $\overrightarrow{TC}$, and $\overrightarrow{CS}$ in terms of $\vec{i}$ and $\vec{j}$.

First, the distance $|\overrightarrow{OT}|$ is the same as the length of circular arc TA since the wheel rolled without slipping. Since θ is positive, arc $TA = a\theta$, which means incidentally that θ is measured in radians. Thus,

$$\overrightarrow{OT} = \vec{i} \, a\theta.$$

Next, $\vec{TC}$ is perpendicular to the x-axis and has length a, so that

$$\vec{TC} = \vec{j}a.$$

Now $\vec{CS}$ has length b. But what is an amplitude of $\vec{CS}$? By definition, an amplitude must be measured from the positive x-axis (or a half-line parallel to it) around to the vector, with counterclockwise rotation considered positive. Hence, an amplitude of $\vec{CS}$ is something more negative than $-\pi/2$ and is thus $-\pi/2 - \theta$ (whereas one might be careless and think that $-\pi/2 + \theta$ would be an amplitude of $\vec{CS}$). Consequently,

$$\vec{CS} = b\left[\vec{i}\cos\left(-\frac{\pi}{2} - \theta\right) + \vec{j}\sin\left(-\frac{\pi}{2} - \theta\right)\right]$$

$$= b\left[\vec{i}\cos\left(\frac{\pi}{2} + \theta\right) - \vec{j}\sin\left(\frac{\pi}{2} + \theta\right)\right]$$

$$= b[-\vec{i}\sin\theta - \vec{j}\cos\theta].$$

By substitution into (8) it therefore follows that

$$\vec{OS} = \vec{i}a\theta + \vec{j}a + b[-\vec{i}\sin\theta - \vec{j}\cos\theta]$$

$$= \vec{i}(a\theta - b\sin\theta) + \vec{j}(a - b\cos\theta).$$

Hence, parametric equations of the path described by S are

$$x = a\theta - b\sin\theta, \quad y = a - b\cos\theta.$$

Note: If S is on the rim of the circle, then $b = a$, the curve is called a **cycloid**, and its parametric equations are

(9) $x = a(\theta - \sin\theta), \quad y = a(1 - \cos\theta).$

Example 2. Find the length of the first arc of a cycloid.

Solution. The spot S is on the x-axis if the y of (9) is equal to zero and hence if $1 - \cos\theta = 0$, which has solutions $\theta = 0$, $\theta = 2\pi$, $\theta = 4\pi$, etc. Hence, the first arch has $0 \leq \theta \leq 2\pi$ (which should also be visualized geometrically). The length of the first arch is therefore (see Sec. 8-6)

$$\int_0^{2\pi} \sqrt{\left(\frac{dx}{d\theta}\right)^2 + \left(\frac{dy}{d\theta}\right)^2}\, d\theta = \int_0^{2\pi} \sqrt{\left[\frac{d}{d\theta}a(\theta - \sin\theta)\right]^2 + \left[\frac{d}{d\theta}a(1 - \cos\theta)\right]^2}\, d\theta$$

$$= a\int_0^{2\pi} \sqrt{(1 - \cos\theta)^2 + (\sin\theta)^2}\, d\theta = a\int_0^{2\pi} \sqrt{2 - 2\cos\theta}\, d\theta$$

$$= a\sqrt{2}\int_0^{2\pi} \sqrt{1 - \cos\theta}\, d\theta$$

$$= a\sqrt{2}\int_0^{2\pi} \sqrt{2\sin^2\frac{\theta}{2}}\, d\theta$$

$$= a\sqrt{2}\sqrt{2}\int_0^{2\pi} \sin\frac{\theta}{2}\, d\theta,$$

since $\sqrt{\sin^2\theta/2} = \sin\theta/2 \geq 0$ for $0 \leq \theta \leq 2\pi$. This integral should now be evaluated to see that the length of the first arch is $8a$.

Example 3. Given that distances are measured in feet and that the wheel makes one revolution per half second, find the speed of the point S for a cycloid when $\theta = \pi/4$.

Solution. "One revolution per half second" is translated into

$$\frac{d\theta}{dt} = 2\pi \text{ radians}/\tfrac{1}{2} \text{ sec} = 4\pi \text{ radians/sec}$$

and thus (with $\theta \doteq 0$ when $t = 0$) into

$$\theta = 4\pi t,$$

with t measured in seconds. This condition together with (9) yields the vector function

$$\vec{F}(t) = a\,[\vec{i}(4\pi t - \sin 4\pi t) + \vec{j}(1 - \cos 4\pi t)],$$

and since $t = 1/16$ when $\theta = \pi/4$, the answer is

$$\left| \vec{F'}\left(\frac{1}{16}\right) \right| = \left| a\left[\vec{i}\left(4\pi - 4\pi \cos \frac{\pi}{4}\right) + \vec{j}4\pi \sin \frac{\pi}{4}\right]\right|$$

$$= 4\pi a\,\sqrt{2 - \sqrt{2}}.$$

Problem 1. Figure 9-1.4 has circles of radii a and b with centers at the origin. An arbitrary angle θ is drawn in standard position, with terminal side intersecting the circles at C and D, respectively. AC is perpendicular to the x-axis, BD to the y-axis, and these lines intersect at $P(x, y)$. Show that

$$x = a \cos \theta \quad \text{and} \quad y = b \sin \theta.$$

Problem 2. a. Prove that the graph of the parametric equations

(10) $$x = a \sec \theta, \; y = b \tan \theta$$

is the hyperbola

(11) $$\frac{x^2}{a^2} - \frac{y^2}{b^2} = 1.$$

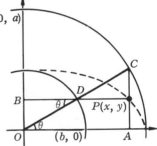

Fig. 9-1.4

b. Show that the graph of the parametric equations

$$x = a \cosh t, \; y = b \sinh t$$

is one branch of the hyperbola of part a.

c. Figure 9-1.5 has circles of radii a and b with centers at the origin. An angle in standard position has terminal side intersecting the a-radius circle at T, where the tangent to the circle is drawn intersecting the x-axis at A. The b-radius circle intersects the x-axis at S, where the tangent to the circle is drawn intersecting the terminal side of θ at B. From A and B, perpendiculars are drawn to the x-axis and y-axis, respectively, and the point in which these intersect is labeled $P(x, y)$. Show that

$$x = a \sec \theta \quad \text{and} \quad y = b \tan \theta.$$

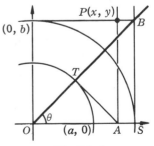

Fig. 9-1. 5

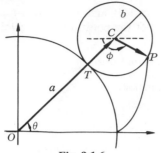

Fig. 9-1.6

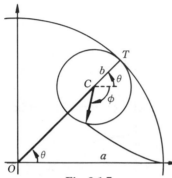

Fig. 9-1.7

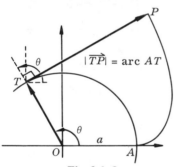

Fig. 9-1. 8

Problem 3. Show that each pair of parametric equations has its graph on the parabola $y = 2x^2$. In each case, describe the part included.

    a. $x = \cos\theta$, $y = 1 + \cos 2\theta$.
    b. $x = \sin\theta$, $y = 1 - \cos 2\theta$.
    c. $x = 1/t$, $y = 2/t^2$.
    d. $x = t$, $y = 2t^2$.
    e. $x = \cosh t$, $y = 1 + \cosh 2t$.
    f. $x = \operatorname{sech} t$, $y = 4/(1 + \cosh 2t)$.

Problem 4. Show that the graph of the pair of parametric equations is a portion of a straight line:

    a. $x = t^2$, $y = 3t^2 + 1$.
    b. $x = |t|$, $y = 3|t| + 1$.
    c. $x = 3\sin\theta - 1$, $y = \sin\theta + 2$.
    d. $x = 3e^t - 1$, $y = e^{t+2}$.
    e. $x = \cosh t$, $y = 1 - \cosh t$.

Problem 5. A circle of radius b rolls without slipping around a circle radius a with center at the origin. Let P be the point of the b-radius circle that was at the point $(a, 0)$ when the circles were tangent at $(a, 0)$. Find parametric equations of the path of P if:

    a. The b-radius circle is tangent externally to the a-radius circle as shown in Fig. 9-1.6. [Note: The path of P is called an **epicycloid**.]

    b. The b-radius circle is tangent internally to the a-radius circle as shown in Fig. 9-1.7. [Note: The path of P is called an **hypocycloid**.] [Hint: As shown θ is measured positively counterclockwise, but ϕ is measured positively clockwise. Hence, in this case an amplitude of $\overrightarrow{CP}$ is $-\phi$.]

Problem 6. a. A circle with center at the origin and radius a has had a string wrapped around it with the free end P initially at the point $(a, 0)$. The string is now unwound and kept taut so that the unwound portion is a straight line segment tangent to the circle (such as $\overrightarrow{TP}$ in Fig. 9-1. 8). Find parametric equation of the path of P. [Note: The curve obtained is called the **evolute** of the circle.]

    b. Find how far P travels as θ increases from 0 to π.

Problem 7. Sketch the graph of the pair of parametric equations for the given range of the parameter. Also determine an xy-equation of the curve on which the graph lies.

    a. $x = 1 + 1/t$, $y = 1 - t$, $1 \le t$.

    b. $x = t + 1$, $y = t^2 - 2$, $0 \leq t$.
    c. $x = \cos 2\theta$, $y = \sin \theta$; $0 \leq \theta \leq 2\pi$.
    d. $x = 2 + \sin \theta$, $y = - (3 + \cos \theta)$; $0 \leq \theta \leq 2\pi$.

9-2.   Parametric Derivatives

    Given a pair of parametric equations

(1) $$x = x(t), \quad y = y(t),$$

then $$\frac{dx(t)}{dt} = x'(t) \quad \text{and} \quad \frac{dy(t)}{dt} = y'(t)$$

(assumed to exist) give the rates of change of x and y with respect to t. It is, however, sometimes desirable to know how a change in x determines a change in y. More specifically, it may be desirable to know the derivative of y with respect to (not t, but) x:

(2) $$\frac{dy}{dx} = \lim_{\Delta x \to 0} \frac{\Delta y}{\Delta x}.$$

The variable y is not given directly in terms of x in (1). It might not even be possible to eliminate t between the equations (1) to express y as a usable function of x.* It is expedient to cause the increments Δy and Δx by means of the increment Δt. Hence, upon the supposition that $\Delta x \neq 0$ for $\Delta t \neq 0$ but $\Delta x \to 0$ if and only if $\Delta t \to 0$, then upon dividing both numerator and denominator of the right side of (2) by Δt it follows that

(3) $$\frac{dy}{dx} = \lim_{\Delta x \to 0} \frac{\Delta y / \Delta t}{\Delta x / \Delta t} = \frac{dy/dt}{dx/dt} = \frac{y'(t)}{x'(t)}.$$

In the D-notation, this formula is

(3') $$D_x y = \frac{D_t y}{D_t x}.$$

    Example 1. Given $x = t - \sin t$, $y = t + \cos t$, find the rate of change of y with respect to x.

    Solution. From (3),

$$D_x y = \frac{D_t (t + \cos t)}{D_t (t - \sin t)} = \frac{1 - \sin t}{1 - \cos t}, \qquad \text{provided} \quad t \neq 2m\pi, \quad m = 0, \pm 1, \pm 2, \ldots.$$

    Notice in this example that $D_x y$ turned out to be a function of t. This is the typical situation.

    Once $D_x y$ is found, it might also be desirable to find $D_x^2 y$, the second derivative of y with respect again to x. Hence, in the above example,

$$D_x^2 y = D_x (D_x y) = D_x \left(\frac{1 - \sin t}{1 - \cos t} \right) = ?$$

    *For example, try to express y as an explicit function of x if $x = t - \sin t$, $y = t + \cos t$.

Note that the expression in the parentheses is a function of t, but the derivative is to be taken with respect to x. It is therefore necessary to again use (3) with y replaced by the new function of t, that is,

$$D_x \left(\frac{1 - \sin t}{1 - \cos t} \right) = \frac{D_t \left(\frac{1 - \sin t}{1 - \cos t} \right)}{D_t x}$$

$$= \frac{\dfrac{(1 - \cos t)\, D_t\, (1 - \sin t) - (1 - \sin t)\, D_t\, (1 - \cos t)}{(1 - \cos t)^2}}{D_t x}.$$

Now, as given in the example, $x = t - \sin t$, and thus

$$D_x^2 y = \frac{\dfrac{(1 - \cos t)(- \cos t) - (1 - \sin t)(\sin t)}{(1 - \cos t)^2}}{D_t\, (t - \sin t)}$$

$$= \frac{\dfrac{- \cos t + \cos^2 t - \sin t + \sin^2 t}{(1 - \cos t)^2}}{1 - \cos t} = \frac{1 - \cos t - \sin t}{(1 - \cos t)^3}.$$

It is well to write formula (3′) in the form

(3″)
$$D_x [\ ] = \frac{D_t [\ ]}{D_t\, x},$$

with the understanding that any function of t may be placed in the brackets, provided the same function of t is placed in both brackets. Thus, if y is a function of t, then $D_x y$ is again a function of t, so that $D_x y$ may be placed in both brackets to yield

$$D_x [D_x y] = \frac{D_t [D_x y]}{D_t\, x}.$$

By definition, $D_x^2 y = D_x [D_x y]$, so that

$$D_x^2 y = \frac{D_t [D_x y]}{D_t\, x}.$$

If a formula for $D_x^2 y$ is desired involving only derivatives with respect to t, then, by using (3″),

$$D_x^2 y = \frac{D_t \left[\dfrac{D_t\, y}{D_t\, x} \right]}{D_t\, x} = \frac{\dfrac{D_t x\, D_t\, (D_t y) - D_t y\, D_t\, (D_t x)}{(D_t x)^2}}{D_t\, x}.$$

Since $D_t\, (D_t y) = D_t^2 y$ and $D_t\, (D_t x) = D_t^2 x$, it follows that

(4)
$$D_x^2 y = \frac{D_t x\, D_t^2 y - D_t y\, D_t^2 x}{(D_t x)^3}.$$

By using the prime notation for indicating the derivative with respect to t, formula (4) appears as

(4')
$$D_x^2 y = \frac{x'y'' - y'x''}{(x')^3}.$$

Notice that the left side of (4') may not be replaced by y'', since the second derivative on the left is with respect to x whereas the primes on the right indicate derivatives with respect to t. In the d-notation, the formula

(4'')
$$\frac{d^2 y}{dx^2} = \frac{\dfrac{dx}{dt}\dfrac{d^2 y}{dt^2} - \dfrac{dy}{dt}\dfrac{d^2 x}{dt^2}}{\left(\dfrac{dx}{dt}\right)^3}$$

appears more complicated than either (4) or (4').

Actually, a rote memorization of (4), (4'), or (4'') is not recommended; instead, time should be spent in becoming thoroughly familiar with the use of (3'') first to compute $D_x y$ and then $D_x^2 y$.

Example 2. Find $D_x^2 y$ if

$$x = \cos^2 t, \quad y = 3 \sin t.$$

Solution. First, from (3'') with the brackets filled with $y = 3 \sin t$,

$$D_x[y] = \frac{D_t [3 \sin t]}{D_t \cos^2 t}$$

$$= \frac{3 \cos t}{2 \cos t (- \sin t)} = -\frac{3}{2} \csc t.$$

Now again use (3') with the brackets filled with $D_x y = -\dfrac{3}{2} \csc t$:

$$D_x[D_x y] = \frac{D_t [-\frac{3}{2} \csc t]}{D_t \cos^2 t},$$

$$D_x^2 y = \frac{-\frac{3}{2} D_t \csc t}{-2 \cos t \sin t} = \frac{3}{4} \frac{-\csc t \cot t}{\cos t \sin t} = -\frac{3}{4} \csc^3 t.$$

Problem 1. In each of the following, find $D_x y$ by using formula (3') and then again by first expressing y as an explicit function of x before taking the derivative:

a. $x = 2t, \quad y = t^3$.
b. $x = 2t, \quad y = \sin t$.
c. $x = e^t, \quad y = t^2$.
d. $x = t + 3, \quad y = 4 + t^3$.
e. $x = \sin t, \quad y = \cos t$ for $-\pi/2 < t < \pi/2$.
f. $x = \ln t, \quad y = \cos t$ for $t > 0$.

Problem 2. Find $D_x y$ and $D_x^2 y$ if:

a. $x = 3 \sin t, \quad y = \cos t$.
b. $x = t + \ln t, \quad y = \cos t$.
c. $x = \sin t, \quad y = \sin t + \cos t$.
d. $x = \sinh t, \quad y = \sinh t + \cosh t$.

Problem 3. By interchanging the roles of $x = x(t)$ and $y = y(t)$, formulas for $D_y x$ and $D_y^2 x$ may be obtained. Prove that

$$D_y x = \frac{1}{D_x y}.$$

Use $x = \sin t, y = \cos t$ to show that $D_y^2 x$ need not be the same as $1/D_x^2 y$.

Problem 4. In dy/dx, consider dy and dx as differentials of y and x, respectively. Upon dividing both numerator and denominator by the differential dt, the result is

$$\frac{dy}{dt} = \frac{dy/dt}{dx/dt},$$

which, according to (3), is correct. Now d^2y/dx^2 is an accepted notation for the second derivative of y with respect to x. Divide both numerator and denominator by dt^2 to obtain

$$\frac{d^2y/dt^2}{dx^2/dt^2}.$$

It is natural here to interpret d^2y/dt^2 as the second derivative of y with respect to t and to interpret dx^2/dt^2 as $(dx/dt)^2$.

  a. Show that the quotient of d^2y/dt^2 by $(dx/dt)^2$ is not equal to d^2y/dx^2. [Hint: The "not equal" may be shown by one example.]

  b. Show that $(dx/dt)^2 \neq d^2x/dt^2$.

  c. Show that the second derivative of y with respect to t divided by the second derivative of x with respect to t is not equal (in all cases) to the second derivative of y with respect to x.

Problem 5. Find an equation of the tangent to the graph of the parametric equations at the point of the graph determined by the given value of the parameter. Also, determine whether the curve is concave upward or concave downward at this point.

  a. $x = \cos t$, $y = \cot t$; $t = \pi/4$.
  b. $x = 2t^2$, $y = 8t^3$; $t = -\frac{1}{2}$.
  c. $x = 1 - \sqrt{t}$, $y = 12 - t^2$, $t = 4$.

9-3. Circle of Curvature

The following facts, which were established earlier, are recalled for use presently.

  (i) Nonzero vectors $\vec{u}$ and $\vec{v}$ are perpendicular if and only if $\vec{u} \cdot \vec{v} = 0$, since $\vec{u} \cdot \vec{v} = |\vec{u}||\vec{v}| \cos \theta$ will be zero if and only if $\cos \theta = 0$.

  (ii) If $\vec{u} = \vec{i}a + \vec{j}b$ and $\vec{v} = \vec{i}c + \vec{j}d$, then

$$\vec{u} \cdot \vec{v} = ac + bd.$$

  (iii) $\vec{u} = \vec{i}a + \vec{j}b$ and $\vec{v} = \vec{i}(-b) + \vec{j}a$ are perpendicular since

$$\vec{u} \cdot \vec{v} = a(-b) + ba = 0.$$

Consider a vector function $\vec{F}(t) = \vec{i}x(t) + \vec{j}y(t)$; the curve traced by its terminal end as the initial end is always kept at the origin. With a fixed value of t and an increment Δt, the vectors

$$\vec{F} \quad \text{and} \quad \vec{F} + \Delta\vec{F}$$

have terminal ends at neighboring points of the curve. At these points, normals to the curve are drawn, and the point where these normals intersect is denoted by D in Fig. 9-3.1. As $\Delta t \to 0$, these normals become more nearly parallel, but (in most cases) the point D approaches a point C. With C as center, draw the circle whose radius r is the distance from C to the terminal end of $\vec{F}$. This circle is called the **circle of curvature,** C is called the **center of curvature,** and r is called the **radius of curvature** of the curve at the terminal end of $\vec{F}$.

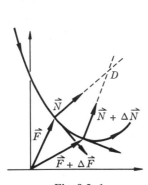

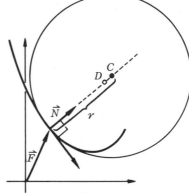

Fig. 9-3. 1   Fig. 9-3. 2

The purpose is now to derive formulas for obtaining the center and radius of curvature.

The increment Δt caused increments $\Delta \vec{F}$, Δx, Δy, and also increments $\Delta x'$ and $\Delta y'$ in the derivatives x' and y' with respect to t. All of these increments approach zero as $\Delta t \to 0$, but

(1) $$\lim_{\Delta t \to 0} \frac{\Delta x}{\Delta t} = x' \quad \text{and} \quad \lim_{\Delta t \to 0} \frac{\Delta y}{\Delta t} = y',$$

and furthermore it should be carefully noted that

(2) $$\lim_{\Delta t \to 0} \frac{\Delta x'}{\Delta t} = x'' \quad \text{and} \quad \lim_{\Delta t \to 0} \frac{\Delta y'}{\Delta t} = y'',$$

since x' is already a derivative and $\Delta x'$ is the increment of this derivative.

Now $\vec{F'} = \vec{i}x' + \vec{j}y'$ drawn from the terminal end of $\vec{F}$ is tangent to the curve and thus [see (iii) above],

$$\vec{N} = -\vec{i}y' + \vec{j}x'$$

is normal to the curve at the terminal end of $\vec{F}$. In the same way, $\vec{N} + \Delta\vec{N}$ $= -\vec{i}(y' + \Delta y') + \vec{j}(x' + \Delta x')$ is normal to the curve at the terminal end of $\vec{F} + \Delta\vec{F}$. As defined above, with D the intersection of these normals, then there is a number a such that

$$\vec{OD} = \vec{F} + a\vec{N}$$

and a number b such that

(3) $$\vec{OD} = \vec{F} + \Delta\vec{F} + b(\vec{N} + \Delta\vec{N}).$$

Consequently, $\vec{F} + a\vec{N} = \vec{F} + \Delta\vec{F} + b(\vec{N} + \Delta\vec{N})$, and hence

$$(a - b)\vec{N} - b\,\Delta\vec{N} = \Delta\vec{F}.$$

This equation, in terms of the unit vectors $\vec{i}$ and $\vec{j}$, is

$$(a - b)(-\vec{i}y' + \vec{j}x') - b(-\vec{i}\,\Delta y' + \vec{j}\,\Delta x') = \vec{i}\,\Delta x + \vec{j}\,\Delta y.$$

By equating the coefficients of $\vec{i}$ and $\vec{j}$ on each side, the simultaneous equations

$$-(a - b)y' + b\,\Delta y' = \Delta x,$$
$$(a - b)x' - b\,\Delta x' = \Delta y$$

are obtained for determining a and b. Upon multiplying the first by x' and the second by y', addition gives

$$b(x'\,\Delta y' - y'\,\Delta x') = x'\,\Delta x + y'\,\Delta y,$$

and hence

$$b = \frac{x'\,\Delta x + y'\,\Delta y}{x'\,\Delta y' - y'\,\Delta x'}.$$

It is not necessary to find a since this expression for b substituted into (3) yields

$$\vec{OD} = \vec{F} + \Delta\vec{F} + \frac{x'\,\Delta x + y'\,\Delta y}{x'\,\Delta y' - y'\,\Delta x'}(\vec{N} + \Delta\vec{N}).$$

Now all the Δ's approach zero as $\Delta t \to 0$, and the expression on the right reduces to

$$\vec{F} + \frac{0}{0}\vec{N},$$

which is not meaningful. Before letting $\Delta t \to 0$, however, both numerator and denominator of the quotient term are divided by Δt to yield

$$\vec{OD} = \vec{F} + \Delta\vec{F} + \frac{x'(\Delta x/\Delta t) + y'(\Delta y/\Delta t)}{x'(\Delta y'/\Delta t) - y'(\Delta x'/\Delta t)}(\vec{N} + \Delta\vec{N}).$$

Now as $\Delta t \to 0$, the equations (1) and (2) are used to see that D approaches C, where

(4) $$\vec{OC} = \vec{F} + \frac{x'^2 + y'^2}{x'y'' - y'x''}\vec{N}.$$

The variable t was held constant (and omitted during this derivation), so in terms of t the formula is

(5) $$\vec{OC} = \vec{i}x(t) + \vec{j}y(t) + \frac{x'^2(t) + y'^2(t)}{x'(t)y''(t) - y'(t)x''(t)}[-\vec{i}y'(t) + \vec{j}x'(t)].$$

This is an important formula to remember since it involves all necessary information for determining the radius and center of curvature for any value of t.

Example Given the curve determined by

$$\vec{F}(t) = \vec{i}2t^2 + \vec{j}t^3,$$

find the equation of the circle of curvature when $t = -1$.

Solution. Since $x(t) = 2t^2$ and $y(t) = t^3$, then

$$x'(t) = 4t, \quad x''(t) = 4, \quad y'(t) = 3t^2, \quad y''(t) = 6t,$$

so that when $t = -1$ then

$$\vec{OC} = \vec{i}\,2 + \vec{j}(-1)^3 + \frac{(-4)^2 + 3^2}{(-4)(-6) - 3(4)}[-\vec{i}3 + \vec{j}(-4)]$$

(6)
$$= 2\vec{i} - \vec{j} + \tfrac{25}{12}(-3\vec{i} - 4\vec{j}).$$

From the definition of the radius of curvature r, it follows that r is the absolute value of the second term:

$$r = |\tfrac{25}{12}(-3\vec{i} - 4\vec{j})| = \tfrac{25}{12}\sqrt{9 + 16} = \tfrac{125}{12}.$$

The abscissa of the center of curvature C is the coefficient of $\vec{i}$ on the right of (6) and is hence

$$2 + \tfrac{25}{12}(-3) = -\tfrac{17}{4}.$$

The ordinate of C is the coefficient of $\vec{j}$:

$$-1 + \tfrac{25}{12}(-4) = -\tfrac{28}{3}.$$

Hence, the circle of curvature has equation

$$(x + \tfrac{17}{4})^2 + (y + \tfrac{28}{3})^2 = (\tfrac{125}{12})^2.$$

The intuitive notion inspiring the definition of the circle of curvature of a curve at a point is the feeling that this circle of curvature "fits the curve close to the point" better than any other circle would.

It is usual to set

(7)
$$\vec{R}(t) = \frac{x'^2(t) + y'^2(t)}{x'(t)y''(t) - y'(t)x''(t)}[-\vec{i}y'(t) + \vec{j}x'(t)]$$

and to call this the **vector radius of curvature** since it is the vector from the terminal end of $\vec{F}(t)$ to C. Note that near the terminal end of $\vec{F}(t)$ the curve is concave toward C (since the normals at neighboring points must converge on a point D close to C). This means that $\vec{R}(t)$ *is the internal normal at this point.*

It now follows that the vector

$$\vec{F}''(t) = \vec{i}x''(t) + \vec{j}y''(t)$$

is also on the concave side of the curve. To see this, let θ be the number of

degrees in the angle between $\vec{F}''(t)$ and $\vec{R}(t)$, so that by definition of the dot
product

$$\vec{R}(t) \cdot \vec{F}''(t) = |\vec{R}(t)||\vec{F}''(t)| \cos \theta.$$

But $[-\vec{i}y'(t) + \vec{j}x'(t)] \cdot [\vec{i}x''(t) + \vec{j}y''(t)] = -y'(t)x''(t) + x'(t)y''(t)$, by (ii) at
the beginning of this section, so that

$$\vec{R}(t) \cdot \vec{F}(t) = \frac{x'^2(t) + y'^2(t)}{x'(t)y''(t) - y'(t)x''(t)} [-y'(t)x''(t) + x'(t)y''(t)]$$

$$= x'^2(t) + y'^2(t) > 0.$$

From these two expressions for $\vec{R}(t) \cdot \vec{F}(t)$, it follows that $\cos \theta > 0$ and hence
$0 < \theta < 90°$. Since $\vec{R}(t)$ is the internal normal (as established above) and
$\vec{F}''(t)$ is directed less than 90° away from $\vec{R}(t)$, then $\vec{F}''(t)$ is also on the concave side of the curve.

Considering t as time and a particle traveling the path determined by
$\vec{F}(t)$, the above result has the physical interpretation:

*The acceleration vector is always on the concave side of the path of a mov-
ing particle.*

For reference later on (Sec. 9-5), note that the radius of curvature $r(t)$
is given by

$$(8) \qquad r(t) = |\vec{R}(t)| = \frac{[x'^2(t) + y'^2(t)]^{3/2}}{|x'(t)y''(t) - y'(t)x''(t)|}.$$

9-4. Nonparametric Circle of Curvature

If a curve is the graph of a function

$$y = f(x)$$

of the independent variable x, then at each point this graph also has a circle
of curvature. Rather than present a completely new discussion in ordinary
cartesian terminology, it is better to use the results of the previous section
by considering the curve "parameterized," with x as parameter. This is done
by defining the same curve as the graph of the vector function

$$\vec{F}(x) = \vec{i}x + \vec{j}f(x).$$

In (5) of Sec. 9-3, the "prime" indicated the "derivative with respect to the
parameter." Hence, now

$$x' = D_x x = 1, \qquad x'' = D_x^2 x = 0,$$

$$y' = D_x f(x) = f'(x), \quad y'' = D_x^2 f(x) = f''(x).$$

Thus, (5) of Sec. 9-3 transcribes into

$$(1) \qquad \vec{OC} = \vec{i}x + \vec{j}f(x) + \frac{1 + f'^2(x)}{f''(x)} [-\vec{i}f'(x) + \vec{j}],$$

in which "prime" means "derivative with respect to x."

Example. Find the equation of the circle of curvature for the graph of $x^3 + 3y = 0$ at the point having $x = 1$.

Solution. Here $f(x) = -\frac{1}{3}x^3$, $f'(x) = -x^2$, $f''(x) = -2x$ so that $f(1) = -\frac{1}{3}$, $f'(1) = -1$, $f''(1) = -2$. Hence,

$$\overrightarrow{OC} = \vec{i} + \vec{j}(-\tfrac{1}{3}) + \frac{1 + (-1)^2}{-2}[-\vec{i}(-1) + \vec{j}]$$

$$= \vec{i} - \tfrac{1}{3}\vec{j} - (\vec{i} + \vec{j}) = 0\vec{i} - \tfrac{4}{3}\vec{j}.$$

The center is at $(0, -\frac{4}{3})$, and $r = \sqrt{1 + 1} = \sqrt{2}$, so the equation of the circle is

$$x^2 + (y + \tfrac{4}{3})^2 = 2.$$

For reference in the next section, note that the radius of curvature $r(x)$ is given by

(2)
$$r(x) = \frac{[1 + f'^2(x)]^{3/2}}{|f''(x)|}$$

Problem 1. Show that, at each point of a circle, the circle of curvature is the circle itself.

Problem 2. Find the center and radius of the circle of curvature of the graph of the pair of parametric equations at the point determined by the given value of the parameter:
   a. $x = t^2$, $y = (2t - 1)$; $t = 2$.
   b. $x = t$, $y = e^t$; $t = 0$.
   c. $x = \sin t$, $y = \cos 2t$; $t = \pi/6$.
   d. $x = t - 1$, $y = 1/t$; $t = 2$.

Problem 3. At the indicated point, find the center and radius of the circle of curvature of the curve:
a. $y = x^2$, $(0, 0)$. e. $y = \cos x$; $(\pi/4, 1/\sqrt{2})$.
b. $y = x^2$; $(1, 1)$. f. $y = \cosh x$; $(0, 1)$.
c. $y = x^3$; $(1, 1)$. g. $y = x^3 + x^2 + x + 1$; $(0, 1)$.
d. $y = \ln x$; $(1, 0)$. h. $y = 3 \sin x + 4 \cos x$; $(0, 4)$.

Problem 4. a. With $p > 0$ constant, show that the graph of $y = x^p$ has a circle of curvature at $(0, 0)$ if and only if $p = 2$.
   b. Show that if a curve has a point of inflection, then at this inflection the curve has no circle of curvature.

9-5. Curvature

On the graph in Fig. 9-5.1 the two sections A and B have the same arc length Δs. As illustrated, the graph "curves" less throughout section A than throughout section B. Think of a point moving along the graph and of a

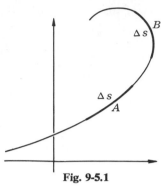

Fig. 9-5.1

tangent to the graph at each position of the point. As the point traverses section A, the amplitude of the tangent varies less than the amplitude varies over section B, although both sections have the same arc length Δs. The intuitive notion of a graph "curving" more or less over one section than over another led to the following definition assigning a quantitative measure of "average curvature over a section" and then "curvature at a point."

Consider a graph and a point P_0 on it from which arc length s along the graph is measured. A fixed value of s determines a point $P(x, y)$ and then $Q(x + \Delta x, y + \Delta y)$ corresponds to $s + \Delta s$. At P and Q let amplitudes of the tangents on the graph be ϕ and $\phi + \Delta\phi$. Then, by definition,

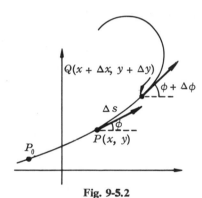

Fig. 9-5.2

$$(1) \qquad \text{(average curvature from } P \text{ to } Q) = \frac{\Delta\phi}{\Delta s},$$

and curvature at P is denoted by κ, where

$$(2) \qquad \kappa = \lim_{\Delta s \to 0} \frac{\Delta\phi}{\Delta s}.$$

Even if Δs is positive, it may be that $\Delta\phi$ is negative (as in Fig. 9-5.3), and then the average curvature will be negative. It is also possible for a single curve to have positive average curvature on some section but negative average curvature on another section, and the same is true of curvatures at different points.*

---

*This situation is analogous to having positive and negative velocities in straight-line motion, or to having positive or negative work.

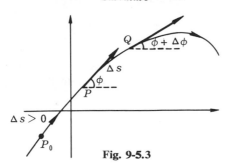

Fig. 9-5.3

The purpose is now to derive formulas expressing curvature at a point in terms of the functions defining the graph.

Consider the graph as defined by the parametric equations

(3) $$x = x(t), \quad y = y(t)$$

or, equivalently, by the vector function

$$\vec{F}(t) = \vec{i}x(t) + \vec{j}y(t).$$

Arc length s is now a function of t and, although it is not at all necessary, it is convenient to think of s as increasing as t increases, so that $ds/dt > 0$. Under this convention, the positive square root is used in

(4) $$\frac{ds}{dt} = \sqrt{\left(\frac{dx}{dt}\right)^2 + \left(\frac{dy}{dt}\right)^2}$$

rather than the indefinite plus or minus square root as in some books. Inversely, t is then a function of s for which

(5) $$\frac{dt}{ds} = \frac{1}{\sqrt{(dx/dt)^2 + (dy/dt)^2}}.$$

Derivatives with respect to the intermediate variable s, as well as derivatives with respect to the independent variable t, are involved in the following derivations. In order to save space, x' and y' will be used to indicate derivatives with respect to t.

Since $\vec{F}' = \vec{i}x' + \vec{j}y'$ is the tangent to the graph, it follows that the amplitude ϕ of this tangent is a function of t such that

(6) $$\tan \phi = \frac{y'}{x'}$$

at all points where $x' \neq 0$.* From this equation $d\phi/ds = \kappa$ is extracted by taking the derivative of both sides with respect to s:

$$\sec^2 \phi \, \frac{d\phi}{ds} = \frac{d}{ds}\left(\frac{y'}{x'}\right),$$

*If $x' = 0$ and $y' \neq 0$ at some point, then $\cot \phi = x'/y'$ may be used, as the following Prob. 6 shows.

$$\kappa = \frac{d\phi}{ds} = \frac{1}{\sec^2 \phi} \frac{d}{ds}\left(\frac{y'}{x'}\right) = \frac{1}{1 + (y'/x')^2} \frac{d}{ds}\left(\frac{y'}{x'}\right)$$

since $\sec^2 \phi = 1 + \tan^2 \phi$. The curvature κ is to be expressed entirely in terms of the independent variable t, so the Chain Rule is used on the right:

$$\kappa = \frac{x'^2}{x'^2 + y'^2} \frac{d}{dt}\left(\frac{y'}{x'}\right)\frac{dt}{ds}$$

$$= \frac{x'^2}{x'^2 + y'^2} \frac{x'y'' - y'x''}{x'^2} \frac{1}{\sqrt{x'^2 + y'^2}},$$

where the last factor comes from (5). Hence, the desired formula is

(7) $$\kappa = \frac{x'y'' - y'x''}{(x'^2 + y'^2)^{3/2}}.$$

Example 1. Find the curvature of

$$x = \sec t, \quad y = \tan t$$

at the points where $t = 0$, $t = \pi/4$. (For the graph, see Prob. 2, Sec. 9-1.)

Solution. $x' = \sec t \tan t, \quad x'' = \sec^3 t + \sec t \tan^2 t,$
            $y' = \sec^2 t, \quad y'' = 2 \sec^2 t \tan t.$

Thus, $x'(0) = 0$, $x''(0) = 1$, $y'(0) = 1$, $y''(0) = 0$, so that

$$\kappa(0) = \frac{0 \cdot 1 - 1 \cdot 1}{(0^2 + 1^2)} = -1.$$

Also, $x'(\pi/4) = \sqrt{2}$, $x''(\pi/4) = 3\sqrt{2}$, $y'(\pi/4) = 2$, $y''(\pi/4) = 4$, so that

$$\kappa\left(\frac{\pi}{4}\right) = \frac{\sqrt{2} \cdot 4 - 2 \cdot 3\sqrt{2}}{(2 + 4)^{3/2}} = \frac{-2\sqrt{2}}{6\sqrt{6}} = -\frac{1}{3\sqrt{3}}.$$

Example 2. Show that the circle of radius a has $|\kappa| = 1/a$ at each point, with $\kappa = +1/a$ if the parameterization sends the points counterclockwise around the circle, but $\kappa = -1/a$ if clockwise.

Solution. Counterclockwise rotation is given by

$$x = a \cos t, \quad y = a \sin t.$$

Since $x' = -a \sin t$, $x'' = -a \cos t$, $y' = a \cos t$, $y'' = -a \sin t$, then

$$\kappa = \frac{(-a \sin t)(-a \sin t) - (a \cos t)(-a \cos t)}{[(-a \sin t)^2 + (a \cos t)^2]^{3/2}} = \frac{a^2}{a^3} = \frac{1}{a}.$$

Clockwise rotation is given by

$$x = a \cos t, \quad y = -a \sin t.$$

Thus, y' and y'' change sign, which changes the sign of the numerator but not that of the denominator, and thus changes the sign of κ.

Recall that the parametric form of the radius of curvature was given in (8) of Sec. 9-3 by

$$r = \frac{[x'^2 + y'^2]^{3/2}}{|x'y'' - y'x''|},$$

where it was tacitly assumed that $x'y'' - y'x'' \neq 0$. Thus, by comparing this with (7) above, it follows that

$$|\kappa| = \frac{1}{r} \quad \text{and} \quad r = \frac{1}{|\kappa|}$$

wherever $\kappa \neq 0$. It is natural to extend the definition of r by setting $r = \infty$ wherever $\kappa = 0$.

The nonparametric form of the curvature means an expression of curvature at points of the graph of

(8) $$y = f(x).$$

The previous parametric form may be used to derive the nonparametric form by temporarily parameterizing the graph by

$$\vec{F}(x) = \vec{i}x + \vec{j}f(x)$$

and, of course, considering s as an increasing function of the temporary parameter x. Now $x' = 1$, $x'' = 0$, while $y' = f'(x)$ and $y'' = f''(x)$ are derivatives with respect to x. Thus, (7) becomes

(9) $$\kappa(x) = \frac{f''(x)}{[1 + f'^2(x)]^{3/2}}$$

as the nonparametric form (or the ordinary rectangular form) of the expression of the curvature for the graph of (8).

Recall that if:

1. $f''(x) > 0$, the graph is concave upward, so at such points the curvature is positive.
2. $f''(x) < 0$, the graph is concave downward, so at such points the curvature is negative.
3. $f''(x) = 0$, the graph may have an inflection point, so at such points the graph has zero curvature.

Example 3. Find the curvature of $y = x^4$ when $x = 1$ and when $x = 0$.

Solution. Here $f(x) = x^4$, $f'(x) = 4x^3$ and $f''(x) = 12x^2$. Thus,

$$\kappa(1) = \frac{12}{[1 + 4^2]^{3/2}} = \frac{12}{17\sqrt{17}},$$

$$\kappa(0) = \frac{0}{[1 + 0^2]^{3/2}} = 0.$$

Note: The fact that $\kappa(0) = 0$ in the above example shows that the curvature can be zero at a point that is not an inflection point of the curve.

Problem 1. Find the curvature of the graph at the point indicated:

a. $x = t^2$, $y = (2t - 1)$; $t = 2$.
b. $x = \sin t$, $y = \cos 2t$; $t = \pi/6$.

c. $y = x^2$; $(2, 4)$.
d. $y = \ln x$; $(1, 0)$.
e. $y = \cosh x$; $(0, 1)$.
f. $y = \cos x$; $(0, 1)$.

Problem 2. a. Show that the graphs $y = x^2 + x + 1$ and $y = x^3 + x^2 + x + 1$ both pass through the same point when $x = 0$ and at this point have the same tangent and curvature.

b. Show that $y = \cos x$ and $y = 1 - x^2$ pass through the same point with the same tangent when $x = 0$ but have different curvatures there.

Problem 3. Let $y = f_1(x)$ and $y = f_2(x)$ be such that their graphs intersect at a point (x_0, y_0). By taking the average of these two, let

$$y = \tfrac{1}{2}[f_1(x) + f_2(x)].$$

a. Show that this third graph also passes through (x_0, y_0) with slope the average of the slopes of the other two.

b. Is the curvature of the third graph the average of the curvatures of the first two?

Problem 4. Let a graph be defined by $x = g(y)$.

a. Show that in this case

$$\kappa(y) = \frac{-g''(y)}{[g'^2(y) + 1]^{3/2}},$$

where g' stands for the derivative with respect to y.

b. Is the minus sign consistent with the previously mentioned notion of positive and negative curvature?

Problem 5. a. For the hyperbola $x^2 - y^2 = 1$ considered as the graphs of $y = \sqrt{x^2 - 1}$ and $y = -\sqrt{x^2 - 1}$, show that curvature is negative on the first and second quadrant portions but positive on the other two portions.

b. Let the same hyperbola be parametrized by

$$x = \sec t, \quad y = \tan t.$$

Show that this parameterization gives negative curvature on the whole right branch and positive curvature on the whole left branch.

c. Explain.

Problem 6. Rederive the formula for curvature by starting with the equation $\cot \phi = x'/y'$, as mentioned in the footnote on p. 295.

Problem 7. a. Find the curvature of $y = 2x^2$ at the point $(1, 2)$.

b. Show that the graph of

$$x = \sin t, \quad y = 1 - \cos 2t$$

lies on the parabola and contains the point $(1, 2)$ when $t = \pi/2$, but the curvature of this graph does not exist when $t = \pi/2$.

c. For $\kappa(t)$ and the radius of curvature $r(t)$ obtained from part b, show that

$$\lim_{t \to \pi/2} \kappa(t) \quad \text{does not exist but} \quad \lim_{t \to \pi/2} r(t) = \frac{17\sqrt{17}}{4}.$$

9-6. Components of Acceleration

Let $\vec{u} \neq 0$ be a vector and let $\vec{v}$ be a vector considered as having the same initial end as $\vec{u}$. The directed segment from the common initial end to the projection of the terminal end of $\vec{v}$ on the line containing $\vec{u}$ is called the **vector projection** of $\vec{v}$ on $\vec{u}$ and is denoted by $\vec{v}_u$.

As previously defined, the dot product of $\vec{u}$ and $\vec{v}$ is

(1) $$\vec{u} \cdot \vec{v} = |\vec{u}||\vec{v}| \cos \theta,$$

where θ is the angle formed by the vectors $\vec{u}$ and $\vec{v}$; that is, θ is not considered to be a directed angle.

The absolute value of the part $|\vec{v}| \cos \theta$ is the length of $\vec{v}_u$. The vector

$$\frac{1}{|\vec{u}|} \vec{u}$$

has unit length and is directed the same as $\vec{u}$. Thus

$$|\vec{u}| \cos \theta \frac{1}{|\vec{u}|} \vec{u}$$

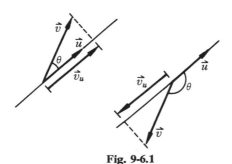

Fig. 9-6.1

has the same length as $\vec{v}_u$ and is directed the same as $\vec{v}_u$, so is in fact equal to $\vec{v}_u$:

$$\vec{v}_u = \frac{|\vec{v}|}{|\vec{u}|} (\cos \theta) \vec{u}.$$

Upon multiplying both numerator and denominator by $|\vec{u}|$, then

$$\vec{v}_u = \frac{|\vec{u}||\vec{v}| \cos \theta}{|\vec{u}|^2} \vec{u} \quad \text{and}$$

(2) $$\vec{v}_u = \frac{\vec{u} \cdot \vec{v}}{\vec{u} \cdot \vec{u}} \vec{u}.$$

from (1) and the fact that $\vec{u} \cdot \vec{u} = |\vec{u}| |\vec{u}| \cos 0° = |\vec{u}|^2$. Formula (2) is an easy way of finding the vector projection of one vector on another. Thus, if $\vec{u} = \vec{i}a + \vec{j}b$ and $\vec{v} = \vec{i}c + \vec{j}d$, then

(3)
$$\vec{v}_u = \frac{ac + bd}{a^2 + b^2}(\vec{i}a + \vec{j}b).$$

Given a law of motion

$$\vec{F}(t) = \vec{i}x(t) + \vec{j}y(t),$$

then

$$\vec{v}(t) = \vec{F}'(t) = \vec{i}x'(t) + \vec{j}y'(t)$$

is geometrically a tangent vector to the path and physically the velocity vector of the motion. Also, the acceleration vector $\vec{a}(t)$ is

$$\vec{a}(t) = \vec{F}''(t) = \vec{i}x''(t) + \vec{j}y''(t).$$

As noted earlier,

$$\vec{N}(t) = -\vec{i}y'(t) + \vec{j}x'(t)$$

is along the normal to the curve.

It is sometimes desirable to resolve the acceleration vector into its tangential component $\vec{a}_T(t)$ and its normal component $\vec{a}_N(t)$. By using formula (3), these components are (with t omitted for convenience)

(4)
$$\vec{a}_T = \frac{\vec{F}' \cdot \vec{a}}{\vec{F}' \cdot \vec{F}'} \vec{F}' = \frac{x'x'' + y'y''}{x'^2 + y'^2}(\vec{i}x' + \vec{j}y')$$

(5)
$$\vec{a}_N = \frac{\vec{N} \cdot \vec{a}}{\vec{N} \cdot \vec{N}} \vec{N} = \frac{-y'x'' + x'y''}{(-y')^2 + x'^2}(-\vec{i}y' + \vec{j}x')$$

$$= \frac{x'y'' - y'x''}{x'^2 + y'^2}(-\vec{i}y' + \vec{j}x').$$

For some purposes it is desirable to have these components expressed by formulas looking quite different from (4) and (5). These new formulas, and the derivations of them, do not involve an ordinary rectangular coordinate system but use instead a linear coordinate system bent to fit the curve with origin at an arbitrary point P_0 of the curve. A particle is to be visualized as moving on the curve with position at time t denoted by $s(t)$. If the particle travels back and forth along the curve, then at some time the function s will be increasing and at other times decreasing; but in any case the scalar

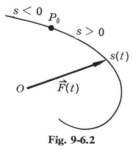

Fig. 9-6.2

$$\frac{ds}{dt} \quad \text{curvilinear units/time unit}$$

is the *velocity of the particle along the path*.

Relative to some point 0 as common initial point, let the position of the particle be denoted by $\vec{F}(t)$. Hence,

$$\frac{d\vec{F}}{dt} = \frac{d\vec{F}}{ds}\frac{ds}{dt}.$$

The vector $d\vec{F}/ds$ times a scalar is thus equal to $d\vec{F}/dt$, which is known to be tangent to the path. Hence, upon setting

(6) $$\vec{\tau} = \frac{d\vec{F}}{ds}$$

then $\vec{\tau}$ is a tangent vector, which moreover has $|\vec{\tau}| = 1$, since

$$\left|\frac{\Delta\vec{F}}{\Delta s}\right|$$

is the ratio of a chord length to the corresponding arc length and this ratio approaches 1 as these increments approach zero.

The fact that $\vec{\tau}$ has length 1 may be denoted by

$$\vec{\tau}\cdot\vec{\tau} = 1.$$

Even though $\vec{\tau}$ has constant length, $\vec{\tau}$ is variable in direction and

$$\frac{d}{dt}(\vec{\tau}\cdot\vec{\tau}) = \frac{d(1)}{dt}, \quad \text{so} \quad 2\vec{\tau}\frac{d\vec{\tau}}{dt} = 0.*$$

This dot product of $\vec{\tau}$ and $d\vec{\tau}/dt$ being zero says that

(7) $$\frac{d\vec{\tau}}{dt} \quad \text{is normal to the curve,}$$

since it is perpendicular to the tangent vector $\vec{\tau}$.

From any fixed direction, let ϕ be the directed angle to $\vec{\tau}$. Thus, ϕ is a function of t and

$$\frac{d\vec{\tau}}{dt} = \frac{d\vec{\tau}}{d\phi}\frac{d\phi}{dt}.$$

Hence, upon setting

(8) $$\vec{\eta} = \frac{d\vec{\tau}}{d\phi},$$

then $\vec{\eta}$ is normal to the curve but in addition, as shown below, $\vec{\eta}$ is a unit vector.

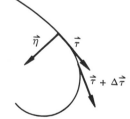

Fig. 9-6.3

*Recall that the usual formula for the derivative of a product also holds for vector functions and dot products:

$$\frac{d}{dt}(\vec{u}\cdot\vec{v}) = \vec{u}\cdot\frac{d\vec{v}}{dt} + \vec{v}\cdot\frac{d\vec{u}}{dt}.$$

The fact that $|\vec{\tau}| = 1$ for all t means also that $|\vec{\tau} + \Delta\vec{\tau}| = 1$. Move $\vec{\tau} +$ $\Delta\vec{\tau}$ to have the same initial point as $\vec{\tau}$ (as in Fig. 9-6.4). Then $|\Delta\phi|$ radians is the central angle of a circular sector of radius 1 and hence circular arc $|\Delta\phi|$ units. The chord length is $|\Delta\vec{\tau}|$ units. Thus,

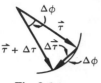

Fig. 9-6.4

$$\frac{|\Delta\vec{\tau}|}{|\Delta\phi|}$$

approaches unity as these increments approach zero; that is, $|\vec{\eta}| = 1$.

Consequently,

$$\vec{\tau} = \frac{d\vec{F}}{ds} \quad \text{and} \quad \vec{\eta} = \frac{d\vec{\tau}}{d\phi}$$

are unit tangent and unit normal vectors.

The material is now at hand for obtaining the tangential and normal components of acceleration in forms useful in some theoretical discussions. The velocity vector is

$$\vec{v} = \frac{d\vec{F}}{dt} = \frac{d\vec{F}}{ds}\frac{ds}{dt} = \vec{\tau}\frac{ds}{dt}.$$

Hence, the acceleration vector is

$$\vec{a} = \frac{d\vec{v}}{dt} = \frac{d}{dt}\left(\vec{\tau}\frac{ds}{dt}\right)$$

$$= \vec{\tau}\left(\frac{d^2s}{dt^2}\right) + \frac{ds}{dt}\left(\frac{d\vec{\tau}}{dt}\right)$$

$$= \vec{\tau}\frac{d^2s}{dt^2} + \frac{ds}{dt}\left(\frac{d\vec{\tau}}{d\phi}\frac{d\phi}{ds}\frac{ds}{dt}\right)$$

$$= \vec{\tau}\frac{d^2s}{dt^2} + \vec{\eta}\frac{d\phi}{ds}\left(\frac{ds}{dt}\right)^2.$$

Now recall that the very definition of curvature κ is

$$\kappa = \frac{d\phi}{ds}$$

[see (2) Sec. 9-5]. Consequently,

(9) $$\vec{a} = \vec{\tau}\frac{d^2s}{dt^2} + \vec{\eta}\kappa\left(\frac{ds}{dt}\right)^2.$$

Thus, the tangential and normal components $\vec{a}_T$ and $\vec{a}_N$ are

(10) $$\vec{a}_T = \vec{\tau}\frac{d^2s}{dt^2}$$

(11)
$$\vec{a}_N = \vec{\eta}\kappa \left(\frac{ds}{dt}\right)^2.$$

Since $|\vec{\tau}| = 1$, the formula (10) gives the intuitive result, "the component of acceleration in the direction of the tangent is the acceleration in the path." It can hardly be considered intuitive, however, that "the component of acceleration normal to the path is the curvature of the path times the square of the velocity in the path," which is what (11) states, since $|\vec{\eta}| = 1$.

Example Show how formula (4) for $\vec{a}_T$ is equivalent to (10).

Solution. Since $s'^2 = x'^2 + y'^2$, then

$$\frac{ds'^2}{dt} = \frac{d}{dt}(x'^2 + y'^2)$$

$$2s'\frac{ds'}{dt} = 2x'\frac{dx'}{dt} + 2y'\frac{dy'}{dt}$$

$$s'\frac{d^2 s}{dt^2} = x'x'' + y'y''.$$

Hence, upon substitution into (4),

$$\vec{a}_T = \frac{s'\dfrac{d^2 s}{dt^2}}{s'^2}(\vec{i}x' + \vec{j}y')$$

$$= \frac{d^2 s}{dt^2}\left(\vec{i}\frac{x'}{s'} + \vec{j}\frac{y'}{s'}\right) = \vec{\tau}\frac{d^2 s}{dt^2},$$

by setting $\vec{i}(x'/s') + \vec{j}(y'/s') = \vec{\tau}$ and noting that $\vec{\tau}$ is a tangent vector with

$$|\vec{\tau}| = \sqrt{\left(\frac{x'}{s'}\right)^2 + \left(\frac{y'}{s'}\right)^2} = \sqrt{\frac{x'^2 + y'^2}{s'^2}} = \sqrt{\frac{s'^2}{s'^2}} = 1.$$

Problem 1. Transform the form of $\vec{a}_N$ as given by (5) into the form as given by (11).

Problem 2. In the derivation of (5), the normal vector $\vec{N} = -\vec{i}y' + \vec{j}x'$ was used. Note that $\vec{M} = \vec{i}y' - \vec{j}x'$ is also a normal vector. Will the same formula (5) follow if $\vec{a}$ is projected onto $\vec{M}$ instead of onto $\vec{N}$?

Problem 3. If the normal component of acceleration is zero, is there necessarily motion on a straight line?

Problem 4. Given that a particle of mass m moves in its path with constant speed. Show that the force (mass times acceleration) is always directed along the normal to the path.

9-7. One-Parameter Families

It is standard practice to use the term "parameter" in two different ways: one as in the previous few sections, the other to be considered now. For example, the graph of

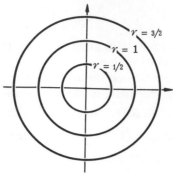

Fig. 9-7.1

(1) $$x^2 + y^2 - r^2 = 0$$

is a circle with center at the origin and radius $|r|$, and any circle with center at the origin has an equation in the form (1). The collection of all circles centered at the origin will now be described as "The family of circles centered at the origin," and r will be called "the parameter of this family."

Given a relation between x, y, and c expressed by

(2) $$f(x, y, c) = 0,$$

then x and y are considered in their usual roles as variables, while (2) is called a **family of equations** with **parameter** c. This means that the equation and its graph are to be considered for c mentally fixed at one value, then another graph for c fixed at another value, etc., for all possible values. The collection of all possible graphs so obtainable from (2) is a **family** of curves with parameter c.

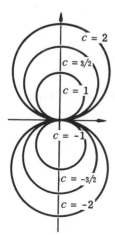

Fig. 9-7.2

In the past, individual curves have been studied. The emphasis will now be on distinctive properties of the whole family. By this is meant a property or properties which each member of the family possesses but that any curve not in the family fails to have. For example,

(3) $$x^2 + y^2 - cy = 0$$

is a family of circles. But (1) is also a family of circles. However, (3) written as

$$x^2 + \left(y - \frac{c}{2}\right)^2 = \left(\frac{c}{2}\right)^2$$

shows that each actual circle* of (3) is tangent to the x-axis at the origin, since any such circle corresponds to a fixed $c \neq 0$ and has center at $(0, c/2)$ with radius $|c|/2$. However, any circle not in the family (3) is not tangent to the x-axis at $(0, 0)$.

*The origin $(0, 0)$ is a "curve" of the family (3) corresponding to $c = 0$ and also of the family (1) for $r = 0$.

Example 1. Find the equation of the family of lines tangent to the parabola $y = x^2$.

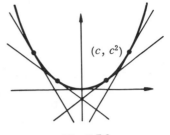

Fig. 9-7.3

Solution. A line is a member of this family if and only if it is tangent to $y = x^2$. To find the equation of the family, take any one member of the family and note that its point of contact with $y = x^2$ is (c, c^2) for one and only one number c. The tangency condition means that this line has slope

$$\frac{dx^2}{dx}\bigg]_{x=c} = 2x]_{x=c} = 2c$$

and thus has equation $y - c^2 = 2c\,(x-c)$, which simplifies to

(4) $$y = 2cx - c^2.$$

Conversely, no matter what number is substituted for c in (4) the resulting equation will have a straight-line graph tangent to $y = x^2$. Therefore, (4) is the equation of the family.

The family-parameter terminology is used in connection with differential equations. Thus, the differential equation

(5) $$\frac{dy}{dx} = x^2$$

is said to have the one-parameter* family of solutions

(6) $$y = \tfrac{1}{3}x^3 + c.$$

Conversely, given the family (6), then (5) is said to be the differential equation of this family according to the following procedure.

Given a one-parameter family of equations, then:
1. Consider any arbitrary, but fixed, value of the parameter.
2. Take a derivative of the resulting function (which may be explicit or implicit).
3. Eliminate the parameter between the given equation (of the family) and the equation of step 2.

The resulting equation will involve a derivative (but not the parameter) and is called the **differential equation of the family.**

Example 2. Find the differential equation of the family

(7) $$x^2 + y^2 - cy = 0.$$

Solution. Take a derivative with respect to x:

(8) $$2x + 2y\frac{dy}{dx} - c\frac{dy}{dx} = 0.$$

Solve (7) for c and substitute into (8):

$$2x + 2y\frac{dy}{dx} - \frac{x^2 + y^2}{y}\frac{dy}{dx} = 0.$$

*This forecasts the eventual use of two or more parameter families.

This is the differential equation of the family but it would ordinarily be simplified and written as

(9)
$$(y^2 - x^2)\frac{dy}{dx} + 2xy = 0.$$

Also, (9) is called the differential equation of the family of circles tangent to the x-axis at the origin; this, of course, because (7) is the same as (3).

Methods will be developed later on for starting with (9) and obtaining the family (7) of its solution.

Problem 1. Find the one-parameter equation of the family described:

a. All lines tangent to $y = x^3$.
b. All lines tangent to $xy = 1$.
c. All lines, each of which intersects $y = x^3$ at right angles.
d. All lines, each of which intersects $xy = 1$ at right angles.
e. All circles of radius 2 such that each member and $x^2 + y^2 = 1$ are tangent externally.
f. All circles of radius 2 such that $x^2 + y^2 = 1$ is tangent internally to each member.
g. All parabolas symmetric to the x-axis and confocal at $(2, 0)$.
h. All parabols symmetric to the line $x = 2$ and confocal at $(2, 1)$.
i. All central conics confocal at $(2, 0)$ and $(-2, 0)$.

Problem 2. Find the differential equation of the family of equations:

a. $x^2 + y^2 + cx = 0$.
b. $x^2 + 2y^2 + cy = 0$.
c. $y^2 = x + cy$.
d. $y = x^2 + cy$.
e. $x^3 - 2cx + y^4 = 5$.
f. $cx + c^2y = 1$.

Problem 3. Find the differential equation of the family of curves described:

a. All lines tangent to the parabola $y = x^2$.
b. All lines tangent to the parabola $y = 2x^2$.
c. All circles with centers on the line $y = x$ and passing through $(0, 0)$.
d. All hyperbolas having the axes as asymptotes.

9-8. Polar Coordinates

If each of the vectors

$$-4(\vec{i} \cos 30° + \vec{j} \sin 30°)$$

$$4(\vec{i} \cos 210° + \vec{j} \sin 210°)$$

$$4(\vec{i} \cos -150° + \vec{j} \sin -150°)$$

$$-4(\vec{i} \cos -330° + \vec{j} \sin -330°)$$

is drawn with its initial end at the origin, then, in fact, there is only one vector and its terminal end has rectangular coordinates

$$(-2\sqrt{3}, -2).$$

According to the following definition, this same point will be assigned innumerable pairs of polar coordinates, and among them are

$$(-4, 30°), (4, 210°), (4, -150°),$$
$$(-4, -330°), (-4, 390°) (4, 570°).$$

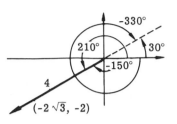

Fig. 9-8.1

In the plane, a half-line is drawn (usually horizontally) and is called the **initial ray**. Angles are to be measured from this initial ray with counter-clockwise rotation as positive. The end of the initial ray is called the **pole**. The unit vector $\vec{i}$ is on the initial ray with initial end at the pole, and $\vec{j}$ is $\vec{i}$ rotated 90°. With ρ a number (which may be positive, negative, or zero) and θ an angle, the vector

$$\rho(\vec{i} \cos \theta + \vec{j} \sin \theta)$$

with initial end at the pole has terminal end at a point that is assigned, by definition, the **polar coordinates**

(1) $(\rho, \theta).$

The pole is therefore $(0, \theta)$ for any angle θ. Also, the point (1) has polar coordinates $(-\rho, \theta \pm 180°)$, $(\rho, \theta \pm 360°)$ and, in fact,

$$((-1)^n \rho, \theta \pm n\, 180°) \quad \text{for any integer } n.$$

The graph of an equation in ρ and θ as variables is obtained by finding pairs (ρ, θ) that satisfy the equation, plotting the corresponding points on a polar coordinate system, and then joining these points by a curve.

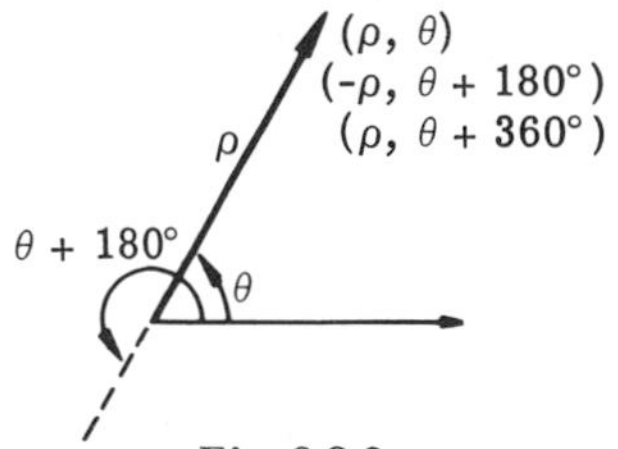

Example 1. Sketch the graph of

$$\rho = 4 \cos \theta.$$

(ρ, θ)
$(-\rho, \theta + 180°)$
$(\rho, \theta + 360°)$

$\theta + 180°$

Fig. 9-8.2

Solution. The table shows corresponding values of ρ and θ; these are plotted and joined in sequence on Fig. 9-8.3. If θ is assigned the additional special values 210°,

θ	0°	30°	45°	60°	90°	120°	135°	150°	180°
ρ	4	$2\sqrt{3}$	$2\sqrt{2}$	2	0	-2	$-2\sqrt{2}$	$-2\sqrt{3}$	-4

225°, etc. to 360°, the points travel around the curve again.

A geometric point P is on the polar graph of a (ρ, θ)-equation if and only if *at least one* of the pairs of polar coordinates of P satisfy the equation and the graph is (by definition) the totality of all such points.

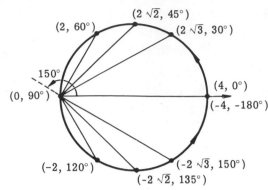

Fig. 9-8.3

For example, there is one and only one point P having polar coordinates
$$(-\tfrac{3}{2}, 60°).$$
Is this point P on the graph of

(2) $$\rho = 2 + \cos\theta?$$

Substitution of $\theta = 60°$ yields $\rho = 2 + \tfrac{1}{2} = \tfrac{5}{2}$, so at first glance it seems that P is not on the graph. However, the same point P also has among its polar coordinates the pair

$$(\tfrac{3}{2}, 240°),$$

which satisfies the equation (2). Hence, the answer is "yes."

The rectangular equation $x = 2$ is the straight line perpendicular to the x-axis since a point $(2, y)$ has coordinates satisfying the equation regardless of the value of y. In the same way, the polar graph of

$$\rho = 2$$

is the circle of radius 2 and center at the pole. The point $(-2, 30°)$ is on this graph, even though the coordinates fail to satisfy the equation, because the same point may be designated as $(2, 210°)$.

Also, the graph of

$$\theta = 60°$$

is not just a half-line, but is a whole line through the pole. For example, $(2, 60°)$ and $(-2, 60°)$ both satisfy the equation.

Example 2. Sketch the graphs of each of the equations

$$\rho = \sin 2\theta, \quad \rho = 2, \quad \text{and} \quad \rho = 2 + \sin 2\theta.$$

Solution. The graph of $\rho = \sin 2\theta$ passes through the origin for each angle θ such that $\sin 2\theta = 0$, and thus if

$$2\theta = m\,180°, \quad \text{so} \quad \theta = m\,90°$$

for $m = 0, 1, 2, 3, \ldots$. For $0 < \theta < 90°$, then $\sin 2\theta > 0$, and reaches its maximum value when $\theta = 45°$, since $\sin(2 \cdot 45°) = 1$. For $90° < \theta < 180°$, then $\sin 2\theta < 0$ and $\sin(2 \cdot 135°) = -1$ is the minimum value. By noting the behavior of $\sin 2\theta$ as θ varies in $180° < \theta < 270°$ and in $270° < \theta < 360°$, the graph of $\rho = \sin 2\theta$ is the four-leaf clover of Fig. 9-8.4. The arrow heads show how passage through the pole

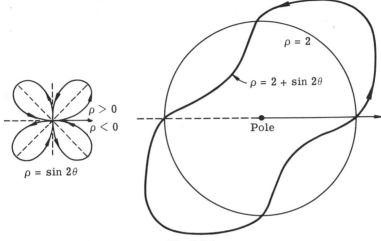

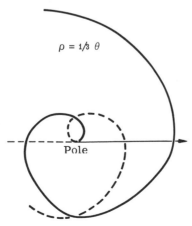

Fig. 9-8.4

is made as θ increases.

In the other part of Fig. 9-8.4, the circle is the graph of $\rho = 2$. The graph of $\rho = 2 + \sin 2\theta$ is then obtained by the geometric addition of the four-leaf clover and the circle. Note how (and why) the graph is outside the circle for those values of θ for which $\sin 2\theta > 0$ but inside if $\sin 2\theta < 0$.

The variable θ may be measured in any units, such as degrees, hours, radians. However, ρ is measured in linear units determined by the scale put on the initial half-line.

Fig. 9-8.5

Example 3. Sketch the graph (called a Spiral of Archimedes) of

$$\rho = \tfrac{1}{3}\theta.$$

Solution. The interpretation is that the number of linear units in any ρ is one third the number of radians in the corresponding θ. The following table gives approximations of values of ρ obtained from 3.1416 as an approximation of π and then rounding to two decimal places.

θ	0	$\frac{1}{4}\pi$	$\frac{1}{2}\pi$	$\frac{3}{4}\pi$	π	$\frac{5}{4}\pi$	$\frac{3}{2}\pi$	$\frac{7}{4}\pi$	2π	$\frac{9}{4}\pi$	$\frac{5}{2}\pi$
ρ	0	0.26	0.52	0.79	1.05	1.31	1.57	1.83	2.09	2.36	2.62

Problem 1. Sketch the polar coordinate graph of:

a. $\rho = \sin 2\theta$.

b. $\rho = 2 \sin \theta$.

c. $\rho = -3 \sin \theta$.

d. $\rho = \sin 3\theta$.

e. $\rho = \cos 4\theta$.

f. $\rho = 1 - 2 \sin^2 \theta$.

g. $\rho = -1 + 2 \cos^2 \theta$.

h. $\rho = \theta$.

Problem 2. a. Sketch the graph of $\rho = \sin \theta/2$ for $0 \le \theta \le 4\pi$.

b. Show that the same graph is obtained for $\rho = \cos \theta/2$ with, however, a different starting point when $\theta = 0$.

c. Solve the equation $\sin \theta/2 = \cos \theta/2$ for values of θ in $0 \le \theta \le 4\pi$. Explain why there are only two solutions even though the graphs of $\rho = \sin \theta/2$ and $\rho = \cos \theta/2$ coincide.

Problem 3. Sketch the graph of $\rho = a + \cos \theta$ for:

a. $a = 2$.

b. $a = 1$.

c. $a = \tfrac{1}{2}$.

d. $a = \tfrac{1}{4}$.

e. $a = 0$.

f. $a = -1$.

Problem 4. Show that the point having the given coordinates lies on the graph of the given equation even though these polar coordinates of the point do not satisfy the equation.

a. $(-2, 90°)$, $\rho = 2 + \cos \theta$.

b. $(2, 90°)$, $\rho = -2 + \cos \theta$.

c. $\left(\dfrac{\sqrt{3}}{2}, 60°\right)$, $\rho = \sin \dfrac{\theta}{2}$.

d. $\left(-\dfrac{\sqrt{3}}{2}, 60°\right)$, $\rho = \sin \dfrac{\theta}{2}$.

e. $(1, 3\pi)$, $\pi\rho = \theta$.

f. $(0, 60°)$, $\rho = \sin \theta$.

g. $(0, 0°)$, $\rho = \cos \theta$.

h. $(-\tfrac{3}{2}, 30°)$, $\rho = 1 - \sin \theta$.

9-9. Different Equations of a Curve

Interplay between a rectangular and a polar coordinate system is effected by using the positive x-axis as the initial ray. Any specific point in the plane has unique rectangular coordinates

$$(x, y)$$

but innumerable pairs (ρ, θ) of polar coordinates. For example,

$$(1, \sqrt{3})$$

has (2, 60°) as its simplest polar coordinates but also has polar coordinates

$$(-2, -120°), \quad (-2, 240°), \quad (2, -300°), \quad \text{etc.}$$

But $1 = 2 \cos 60° = -2 \cos(-120°) = -2 \cos 240° = 2 \cos(-300°) = $ etc. In the same way, $\sqrt{3}$ is $\rho = 2$ or -2 times the sine of the corresponding θ.

If the definition of polar coordinates is reread, it will be seen that the

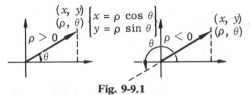

Fig. 9-9.1

rectangular coordinates (x, y) of a point and any pair (ρ, θ) of polar coordinates of the same point are related by

(1) $$x = \rho \cos \theta, \quad y = \rho \sin \theta.$$

Example 1. Find an equation whose polar graph is the same curve as the rectangular graph of $xy = 4$.

Solution. The rectangular graph of $xy = 4$ is a hyperbola with the axes as asymptotes. This same hyperbola has a polar coordinate equation obtained by substituting (1) into $xy = 4$:

$$(\rho \cos \theta)(\rho \sin \theta) = 4$$

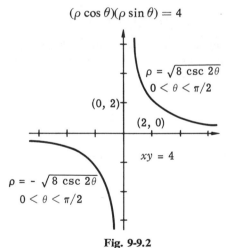

Fig. 9-9.2

or, equivalently, $\rho^2 \sin \theta \cos \theta = 4$, $\rho^2 \sin 2\theta = 8$, or

$$\rho = \pm\sqrt{8 \csc 2\theta}, \quad \csc 2\theta > 0.$$

There is no doubt that $xy = 4$ is easier to graph in rectangular coordinates than $\rho^2 = 8 \csc 2\theta$ is in polar coordinates. The situation is, however, sometimes reversed.

Example 2. Sketch the graph of

(2) $$(x^2 + y^2)^{3/2} = 2xy.$$

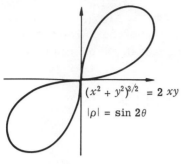

$(x^2 + y^2)^{3/2} = 2\,xy$

$|\rho| = \sin 2\theta$

Fig. 9-9.3

Solution. Substitution of (1) into (2) yields

$$(\rho^2 \cos^2 \theta + \rho^2 \sin^2 \theta)^{3/2} = 2(\rho \cos \theta)(\rho \sin \theta),$$
$$(\rho^2)^{3/2} = \rho^2(2 \sin \theta \cos \theta),$$
$$|\rho|^3 = \rho^2 \sin 2\theta.$$

This equation is satisfied if $\rho = 0$, whose total graph is the pole, or if

(2′) $$|\rho| = \sin 2\theta,$$

whose graph includes the pole. Hence, (2′) represents the entire graph and is easier than (2) to work with.

Sometimes information about a graph is obtained by considering an equation involving both rectangular and polar coordinates.

Example 3. Sketch the graph of

(3) $$\rho = \frac{4}{\theta} \quad \text{for} \quad \theta > 0.$$

Solution. When $\theta = \pi$, $\rho = 4/\pi$; when $\theta = \pi/2$, $\rho = 8/\pi$; and when $\theta = \pi/10$, $\rho = 40/\pi$; but the value 0 may not be assumed by θ, although

$$\lim_{\theta \to 0+} \rho = \lim_{\theta \to 0+} \frac{4}{\theta} = \infty.$$

This merely says that ρ increases without bound as θ is assigned smaller and smaller positive values, but gives only the information that the curve goes off into the remote portion of the first quadrant.

From the first equation of (1),

$$\rho = \frac{x}{\cos \theta},$$

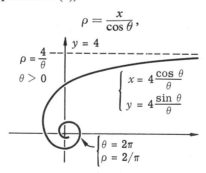

$\rho = \dfrac{4}{\theta}$

$\theta > 0$

$y = 4$

$\begin{cases} x = 4 \dfrac{\cos \theta}{\theta} \\ y = 4 \dfrac{\sin \theta}{\theta} \end{cases}$

$\begin{cases} \theta = 2\pi \\ \rho = 2/\pi \end{cases}$

Fig. 9-9.4

and this result substituted into (3) may be written

(4) $$x = 4\frac{\cos \theta}{\theta}.$$

From the second equation of (1), and (3),

(5)
$$y = 4\frac{\sin\theta}{\theta}.$$

Consequently,

$$\lim_{\theta\to 0+} x = 4\lim_{\theta\to 0+}\frac{\cos\theta}{\theta} = \infty$$

and*

$$\lim_{\theta\to 0+} y = 4\lim_{\theta\to 0+}\frac{\sin\theta}{\theta} = 4.$$

These two limit expressions reveal that the line $y = 4$ is an asymptote of the curve, a definite gain in information about the graph of (3).

The mixed rectangular-polar equations (4) and (5) reveal more about the behavior of the curve for θ close to 0 than would be easily extracted from the polar equation (3) alone. On the other hand, the given polar equation (3) shows the spiraling nature of the curve as θ increases.

Another contact with previously studied methods is to consider (4) and (5) taken together as a pair of parametric equations (parameter θ) of the curves.

A graph is a mathematical model of a law relating variables. Examples 1 and 2 show how a single model (graph) may express different relations between the variables according to whether the model is interpreted in rectangular or polar coordinates. On the other hand, a single law may have different looking models. For example, consider the following law: "Two variables are inversely proportional." This law (with proportionality constant 4) may be symbolized as

$$y = \frac{4}{x} \quad \text{or as} \quad \rho = \frac{4}{\theta},$$

according to whether rectangular or polar representation of the law is anticipated. Hence, Figs. 9-9.2 and 9-9.4 are both models of the "Inverse Proportionality Law."

It is to be expected that a curve will have different looking rectangular and polar equations. It may come as a surprise, however, to learn that a single curve may have two (or even more) different looking polar equations. In fact:

The graph of the equation

(6)
$$\rho = f(\theta)$$

also has the equation

(7)
$$\rho = -f(\theta + \pi).$$

PROOF. Let (ρ_1, θ_1) satisfy (6) so that

$$\rho_1 = f(\theta_1).$$

*Recall that (5) of Sec. 2-11 is $\lim_{h\to 0}(\sin h)/h = 1$.

Think of plotting the point $P(\rho_1, \theta_1)$. This same geometric point may also be written $P(-\rho_1, \theta_1 - \pi)$. Now in the right side of (7) substitute $\theta = \theta_1 - \pi$ and obtain

$$-f(\theta_1 - \pi + \pi) = -f(\theta_1) = -\rho_1,$$

which shows that $(-\rho_1, \theta_1 - \pi)$ satisfies (7). Thus, any point on the graph of (6) is also on the graph of (7). In the same way, any point on the graph of (7) is on the graph of (6).

Example 4. Show that the two equations

$$\rho = -1 + \sin\theta \quad \text{and} \quad \rho = 1 + \sin\theta$$

have exactly the same graph.

Solution. The graph of $\rho = -1 + \sin\theta$ also [according to the statement about (6) and (7)] has the equation

$$\rho = -[-1 + \sin(\theta + \pi)]$$
$$= -(-1 - \sin\theta) = 1 + \sin\theta.$$

Now start with $\rho = 1 + \sin\theta$ and see that its graph also has equation

$$\rho = -[1 + \sin(\theta + \pi)] = -[1 - \sin\theta] = -1 + \sin\theta.$$

The points of intersection of two rectangular graphs are obtained by solving the equations of the graphs simultaneously, but not so for polar graphs. The procedure for finding the intersection of two polar graphs is to:
(i) Find all equations of both graphs.
(ii) Solve each equation of the first graph with each equation of the second graph.
(iii) Check whether the pole is on both graphs.

Example 5. Find all intersections of the graphs of

(8') $$\rho = -1 + \sin\theta \quad \text{and}$$
(9') $$\rho = 2\sin^2\theta$$

Solution. As in Example 4, the only additional equation of the graph of (8') is

(8'') $$\rho = 1 + \sin\theta.$$

The graph of (9') has another equation:

$$\rho = -2\sin^2(\theta + \pi) = -2(-\sin\theta)^2; \quad \text{that is,}$$

(9'') $$\rho = -2\sin^2\theta,$$

and a check will show that $\rho = -[2\sin^2(\theta + \pi)]$ agrees with (9').
Attempted simultaneous solution of (8') and (9') leads to

$$2\sin^2\theta - \sin\theta + 1 = 0,$$

$$\sin\theta = \frac{1 \pm \sqrt{1 - 8}}{2},$$

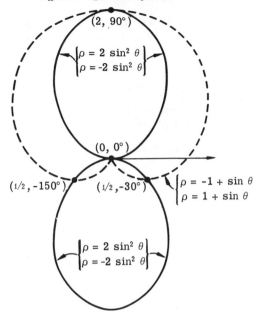

Fig. 9-9.5

showing that (8′) and (9′) have no real solution. But (8′) and (9″) give

$$2 \sin^2\theta + \sin \theta - 1 = 0,$$

$$(2 \sin \theta - 1)(\sin \theta + 1) = 0,$$

$$\sin \theta = \tfrac{1}{2}, \qquad \theta = \begin{cases} 30° + m\,360°, \\ 150° + m\,360°, \end{cases}$$

$$\sin \theta = -1, \quad \theta = -90° + m\,360°,$$

and hence the points of intersection

(10) $(-\tfrac{1}{2}, 30° + m\,360°),\quad (-\tfrac{1}{2}, 150° + m\,360°),\quad (-2, -90° + m\,360°).$

Now (8″) and (9′) give

$$2 \sin^2\theta = 1 + \sin \theta, \quad 2 \sin^2\theta - \sin \theta - 1 = 0,$$

$$(2 \sin \theta + 1)(\sin \theta - 1) = 0,$$

and hence the points of intersection

(11) $(\tfrac{1}{2}, -30° + m\,360°),\quad (\tfrac{1}{2}, -150° + m\,360°),\quad (2, 90° + m\,360°).$

It is still necessary to check (8″) and (9″) simultaneously, but these lead to $2 \sin^2\theta + \sin \theta + 1 = 0$, which has no real solution.

All the points of (11) are the points of (10) with alternate polar coordinates, so actually there are only the three points

(12) $(\tfrac{1}{2}, -30°),\quad (\tfrac{1}{2}, -150°),\quad (2, 90°).$

But do not forget (iii) of the above procedure. Set $\rho = 0$ in (8') and obtain $\sin \theta = 1$, $\theta = 90°$. Also, the pole is on the second graph since $2 \sin^2 \theta = 0$ for $\theta = 0°$.

Hence, if the four geometric points are plotted by using

$$(\tfrac{1}{2}, -30°), \quad (\tfrac{1}{2}, -150°), \quad (2, 90°), \quad \text{and the pole,}$$

then these four points are the only points on both curves.

The curves are most easily plotted by using (8'') and (9').

Problem 1. Find a polar equation of the graph having rectangular equation:

a. $4x + 3y = 6$.

b. $x - y = 1$.

c. $x^2 + y^2 - 4x = 0$.

d. $x^2 + y^2 + 6y = 0$.

e. $(x^2 + y^2)^{3/2} = 2(x + y)$.

f. $(x^2 + y^2)^2 = x^2 - y^2$.

g. $y^2 = 4a(x + a)$.

h. $16(x - 3)^2 + 25y^2 = 400$.

Problem 2. Find the rectangular equation of the graph having polar equation:

a. $\rho(2 + \cos \theta) = 6$.

b. $\rho = 4 \cos \theta$.

c. $\rho = 4 \sin \theta$.

d. $\rho = 2(\cos \theta - \sin \theta)$.

e. $\rho = 4 \cos 2\theta$.

f. $\rho = 4 \sin 2\theta$.

Problem 3. a. Show that the four equations have the same graph:

$$\rho = \sin \frac{\theta}{2}, \quad \rho = -\cos \frac{\theta}{2}, \quad \rho = -\sin \frac{\theta}{2}, \quad \rho = \cos \frac{\theta}{2}.$$

b. Show that the graph of $\rho = \sqrt{3} \cos (\theta/3) - \sin (\theta/3)$ also has equation

$$\rho = \sin (\theta/3).$$

c. Show that both answers of Prob. 1. g have the same graph.

Problem 4. Find all points of intersection of the graphs of the pair of equations:

a. $\rho = 2 \cos^2 \theta$, $\quad \rho = -1 + \cos \theta$.

b. $\rho = 2 \cos^2 \theta$, $\quad \rho = -1 + \sin \theta$,

c. $\rho = \cos 2\theta$, $\quad \rho = \cos \theta$.

d. $\rho = \sin 2\theta$, $\quad \rho = \sin \theta$.

e. $\rho = \sin 2\theta$, $\quad \rho = 2 \sin^2 \theta$.

f. $\rho = \dfrac{1}{1 + \cos \theta}$, $\quad \rho = \dfrac{-2}{2 + \cos \theta}$.

Problem 5. Prove that the graph of $\rho = f(\theta)$ also has equation of the form $\rho = (-1)^n f(\theta + n\pi)$ for each integer n.

9-10. Polar Equations of Conics

A conic with axis on the initial ray and a focus at the pole has two equations

(1) $$\rho = \frac{eq}{1 - e \cos \theta} \quad \text{and} \quad \rho = \frac{-eq}{1 + e \cos \theta},$$

where e is the eccentricity and a directrix is perpendicular to the initial ray at the point $(q, 180°)$.

PROOF. The vector $\vec{u}$ from the focus (pole) to the point $P(\rho, \theta)$ is

$$\vec{u} = \rho(\vec{i}\cos\theta + \vec{j}\sin\theta).$$

As illustrated in Fig. 9-10.1, q is positive, but in Fig. 9-10.2, q is negative.

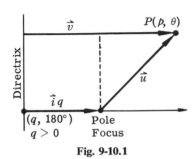

Fig. 9-10.1

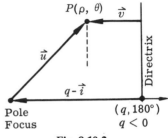

Fig. 9-10.2

In either case, $\vec{i}q$ with initial end at $(q, 180°)$ has terminal end at the focus. The horizontal vector $\vec{v}$ from the directrix to $P(\rho, \theta)$ is $\vec{i}q$ plus the $\vec{i}$ component of $\vec{u}$:

$$\vec{v} = \vec{i}q + \vec{i}\rho\cos\theta = \vec{i}(q + \rho\cos\theta).$$

By the eccentricity-directrix definition of a conic (see Example 2, Sec. 4-7), $P(\rho, \theta)$ is on the conic if and only if

$$\frac{|\vec{u}|}{|\vec{v}|} = e.$$

Hence, $|\vec{u}| = e|\vec{v}|$, so that $|\rho| = e|q + \rho\cos\theta|$, which leads to

$$\rho = e(q + \rho\cos\theta) \quad\text{or}\quad \rho = -e(q + \rho\cos\theta).$$

These equations solved for ρ are the two equations (1), respectively.

The emergence of two polar equations is to be expected, since the graph of the first equation of (1) also has equation [see (6) and (7) of Sec. 9–9]

$$\rho = -\left[\frac{eq}{1 - e\cos(\theta + 180°)}\right] = -\frac{eq}{1 + e\cos\theta},$$

which is the second equation of (1). Thus, either equation of (1) may be used for the complete graph and neither equation has precedence over the other.

Recall that a conic is a:

Parabola   if $e = 1$.
Ellipse   if $0 < e < 1$.
Hyperbola if $e > 1$.

Example 1. Show that the graph of

(2)
$$\rho(3 - \cos \theta) = -16$$

is a hyperbola.

Solution. Upon solving for ρ, the result is

$$\rho = \frac{-16}{3 - 5 \cos \theta},$$

which resembles the equations (1). The 1 in both denominators of (1) is the only absolute constant appearing there, since e and q are in the nature of parameters.* Hence, in the last equation, divide both denominator and numerator by 3:

(3)
$$\rho = \frac{-\dfrac{16}{3}}{1 - \dfrac{5}{3} \cos \theta}.$$

Because of the two minus signs this may not appear to be in either of the forms (1). Remember, however, that e is positive but q may be either positive or negative. Hence, (3) matches the first equation of (1) with

(4)
$$e = \tfrac{5}{3} \quad \text{and} \quad eq = -\tfrac{16}{3}.$$

Since $e > 1$, the graph is a hyperbola.

Recall the following designations:

	Ellipse	*Hyberbola*
Center-Focus Distance	c	c
Center-Vertex Distance	$a > c$	$a < c$
b, Semimajor or Semiconjugate	$b = \sqrt{a^2 - c^2}$	$b = \sqrt{c^2 - a^2}$
e Eccentricity	$e = \dfrac{c}{a} < 1$	$e = \dfrac{c}{a} > 1$
c, a, e Relation	$c = ae$	$c = ae$
Center-Directrix Distance	$\dfrac{a}{e} > a$	$\dfrac{a}{e} < a$
Focus-Directrix Distance	$\dfrac{a}{e} - ae > 0$	$ae - \dfrac{a}{e} > 0$

With q as introduced in this section, $|q|$ is the focus-directrix distance, so that q is related to the above by

$$|q| = \begin{cases} \dfrac{a}{e} - ae & \text{for ellipse,} \\[2mm] ae - \dfrac{a}{e} & \text{for hyperbola,} \end{cases}$$

$$q = 2p \quad \text{for parabola.}$$

Example 2. For the hyperbola of Example 1, find the center, other focus, directrices, b; draw the asymptotes; and sketch the hyperbola.

*The second type of parameter discussed in Sec. 9-7.

Solution. Since e and eq are already known from (4), it follows that

$$q = -\frac{16}{3e} = -\frac{16}{5}.$$

Hence, from the above $|q|$, a, e relation,

$$|q| = \frac{16}{5} = ae - \frac{a}{e} = a\left[\frac{5}{3} - \frac{3}{5}\right] = \frac{16}{15}a,$$

so that $a = 3$. Now from the c, a, e relation, $c = ae = 3 \cdot \frac{5}{3} = 5$. The number b is therefore

$$b = \sqrt{c^2 - a^2} = \sqrt{25 - 9} = 4.$$

At this stage, it is highly recommended that a figure be drawn. In this case, $q = -16/5$ is negative, so the point $(q, 180°)$, where a directrix is drawn, is the point $(-16/5, 180°)$, which, of course, is also $(16/5, 0°)$ to the right of the focus (pole).

For a hyperbola, the directrices are between the foci, so the second focus (in this case) must be to the right of the known focus at the pole and $2c$ units away. Hence, the second focus is at $(10, 0°)$:

$$F_1(0, 0°), \quad F_2(10, 0°).$$

Halfway between these foci is the center

$$(5, 0°).$$

The vertices are three units on both sides of the center:

$$V_1(2, 0°), \quad V_2(8, 0°).$$

Since $b = 4$, the rectangle can be drawn whose diagonals are the asymptotes. The hyperbola is now easily sketched.

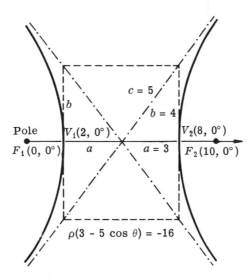

Fig. 9-10.3

Example 3. Sketch the graph of $2\rho(1 + \cos\theta) = -5$.

Solution. This equation solved for ρ is

$$\rho = \frac{-\frac{5}{2}}{1 + \cos\theta},$$

which is in the form of the second equation of (1), with

$$e = 1, \quad -eq = -\tfrac{5}{2}, \quad \text{and hence} \quad q = \tfrac{5}{2}.$$

Thus, the graph is a parabola with vertex at the pole, directrix to the left at $(\tfrac{5}{2}, 180°)$. Hence, the vertex is at $(\tfrac{5}{4}, 180°)$, the parabola opens to the right, with $p = 2q = 5$ the length of the latus rectum (see Fig. 9-10.4).

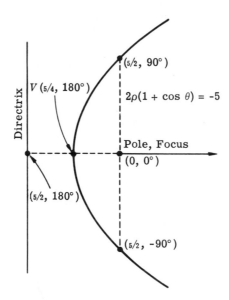

Fig. 9-10.4

Example 4. Find the two polar equations of the ellipse with axis on the initial ray, right-hand focus at the pole, major axis 10, and minor axis 6.

Solution. $2a = 10, \quad 2b = 6; \quad a = 5, \quad b = 3,$

$$c = \sqrt{a^2 - b^2} = 4, \quad e = \frac{c}{a} = \frac{4}{5},$$

and therefore $|q| = (a/e) - ae = (25/4) - 4 = \tfrac{9}{4}$. Since the right-hand focus is at the pole, the point $(q, 180°)$, where the corresponding directrix is drawn, must be to the right of the focus, so

$$q = -\tfrac{9}{4}.$$

Hence, $eq = -\tfrac{9}{5}$, and the equations are, from (1), respectively,

$$\rho = \frac{-\frac{9}{5}}{1 - \frac{4}{5}\cos\theta} \quad \text{and} \quad \rho = \frac{\frac{9}{5}}{1 + \frac{4}{5}\cos\theta}.$$

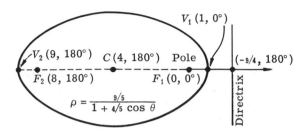

Fig. 9-10.5

Ellipses and hyperbolas are generally centered at the origin in rectangular coordinates, but conics are focused at the pole in polar coordinates, mainly because in each case the choice leads to simpler equations than the other choice would. Also, the study of orbital notions (such as planets, comets, and satellites, either natural or man-made) yields more readily to polar than to rectangular analysis because the attracting body is focal, rather than central, to the orbit.

Problem 1. Transform the rectangular equation to polar form as nearly like (1) as possible:

a. $\dfrac{x^2}{a^2} + \dfrac{y^2}{a^2 - c^2} = 1.$ c. $\dfrac{(x + c)^2}{a^2} + \dfrac{y^2}{a^2 - c^2} = 1.$

b. $\dfrac{(x - c)^2}{a^2} + \dfrac{y^2}{a^2 - c^2} = 1.$ d. $y^2 = 4p(x + p).$

Problem 2. Find the usual information about the conic and sketch the curve:

a. $\rho(5 + 3\cos\theta) = -16.$ c. $\rho(2 + \cos\theta) = 3.$

b. $\rho(13\cos\theta - 12) = 25.$ d. $\rho(2 + 2\cos\theta) = 3.$

Problem 3. In the answers to Prob. 1. b and 1. c, hold a constant but let $e \to 0$ and see that the limits are $\rho = \pm a$. [Note: For this reason a circle may be considered as an ellipse with eccentricity zero.]

Problem 4. Find the polar equations of a conic with focus at the pole and corresponding directrix the horizontal line through $(q, -90°)$.

Problem 5. Sketch the pair of graphs and find all their points of intersection:

a. $\rho(1 + \cos\theta) = 1, \quad \rho(2 + \cos\theta) = -2.$

b. $\rho = \dfrac{1}{1 + \cos\theta}, \quad \rho = \dfrac{-1}{3 + 3\cos\theta}.$

9-11. Polar Interpretation of Derivatives

The previous few sections were concerned with analytic geometry based on polar coordinates; now calculus will be considered in terms of polar coordinates. A function

$$\rho = f(\theta)$$

of the independent variable θ has a derivative whose definition

$$\frac{d\rho}{d\theta} = \lim_{\Delta\theta \to 0} \frac{f(\theta + \Delta\theta) - f(\theta)}{\Delta\theta} = \lim_{\Delta\theta \to 0} \frac{\Delta\rho}{\Delta\theta}$$

is purely analytical, but the letters used forecast the intention of giving this derivative an interpretation in terms of the polar coordinates.

At the outset, it should be understood that "the derivative is the slope of the curve" requires that many supplementary conditions be understood, not the least of which stipulates interpretation in terms of rectangular coordinates. Hence, prepare for a fresh approach to a polar interpretation of derivatives.

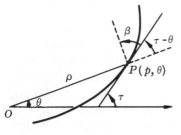

On the polar graph of $\rho = f(\theta)$, select a point P, draw the tangent to the curve at P, and let τ be the amplitude of the tangent as in Fig. 9-11.1 It turns out that

Fig. 9-11.1   (1) $\dfrac{d\rho}{d\theta} = \rho \cot (\tau - \theta).$

To obtain an intuitive concept of this formula, hold θ fixed while $\Delta\theta$ approaches zero. This θ and its ρ determine a point $P(\rho, \theta)$ on the curve. Corresponding to an increment $\Delta\theta$ there is an increment $\Delta\rho$ such that

$$Q(\rho + \Delta\rho, \theta + \Delta\theta)$$

is also on the curve, as in Fig. 9-11.2. With center at the pole and with

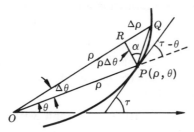

Fig. 9-11.2

radius $\rho = OP$, strike the arc $\overset{\frown}{PR}$ of central angle $\Delta\theta$. Thus, circular arc $\overset{\frown}{PR}$ has length $\rho\,\Delta\theta$:

$$\overset{\frown}{PR} = \rho\,\Delta\theta \quad \text{and} \quad RQ = \Delta\rho.$$

Consequently,

$$\frac{\Delta\rho}{\Delta\theta} = \frac{RQ}{\overset{\frown}{PR}/\rho} = \rho\,\frac{RQ}{\overset{\frown}{PR}}.$$

Hence,

$$\frac{d\rho}{d\theta} = \lim_{\Delta\theta\to 0}\frac{\Delta\rho}{\Delta\theta} = \rho\lim_{\Delta\theta\to 0}\frac{RQ}{\overset{\frown}{PR}}.$$

The angle β, in Fig. 9-11.1, from the tangent to the perpendicular to OP, is independent of $\Delta\theta$, but the angle α opposite RQ and adjacent to $\overset{\frown}{PR}$ approaches β as $\Delta\theta \to 0$, so that also

$$\lim_{\Delta\theta\to 0}\tan\alpha = \tan\beta.$$

Since the two quantities

$$\tan\alpha \quad \text{and} \quad \frac{RQ}{\overset{\frown}{PR}}$$

are so nearly equal, intuition is relied upon to conjure up the fact that they both approach $\tan\beta$ and hence that

$$\frac{d\rho}{d\theta} = \rho\lim_{\Delta\theta\to 0}\frac{RQ}{\overset{\frown}{PR}} = \rho\lim_{\Delta\theta\to 0}\tan\alpha = \tan\beta.$$

But $\beta + (\tau - \theta) = 90°$, so $\tan\beta = \cot(\tau - \theta)$, and hence (1) follows.

The figures and discussion above were for θ, $\Delta\theta$, ρ, and $\Delta\rho$, all positive. Hence, there are 15 other cases to consider, all more involved than the one intuitively discussed. It thus seems advisable to take a different attack on establishing (1) for all cases.

With ρ a function of θ as before, let $\vec{F}(\theta)$ be the vector from the pole to a typical point (ρ, θ) of the curve:

$$\vec{F}(\theta) = \rho(\vec{i}\cos\theta + \vec{j}\sin\theta).$$

Hence, by taking a derivative with respect to θ, and using the prime notation,

$$\vec{F}' = \rho(-\vec{i}\sin\theta + \vec{j}\cos\theta) + \rho'(\vec{i}\cos\theta + \vec{j}\sin\theta)$$

(2) $$= \vec{i}(\rho'\cos\theta - \rho\sin\theta) + \vec{j}(\rho'\sin\theta + \rho\cos\theta)$$

is the tangent vector to the graph at (ρ, θ). The square of the length of this tangent vector is

$$|\vec{F}'|^2 = (\rho'\cos\theta - \rho\sin\theta)^2 + (\rho'\sin\theta + \rho\cos\theta)^2$$

$$= \rho'^2(\cos^2\theta + \sin^2\theta) + \rho^2(\sin^2\theta + \cos^2\theta)$$

$$+ 2\rho\rho'(-\cos\theta\sin\theta + \sin\theta\cos\theta)$$

$$= \rho'^2 + \rho^2.$$

The tangent vector $\vec{F}'$ then has amplitude τ such that $\vec{F}'$ itself is

$$\vec{F}' = |\vec{F}'|(\vec{i}\cos\tau + \vec{j}\sin\tau)$$

$$= \sqrt{\rho'^2 + \rho^2}\,(\vec{i}\cos\tau + \vec{j}\sin\tau).$$

Since this expression for $\vec{F}'$ and the expression (2) must agree, the coefficients of $\vec{i}$ must be equal and the coefficients of $\vec{j}$ must be equal. Hence, τ must be such that

$$(3) \qquad \rho' \cos\theta - \rho \sin\theta = \sqrt{\rho'^2 + \rho^2} \cos\tau \quad \text{and}$$

$$(4) \qquad \rho' \sin\theta + \rho \cos\theta = \sqrt{\rho'^2 + \rho^2} \sin\tau.$$

The objective is to find an expression for ρ'. But in both of these equations, ρ' appears under a radical, and squaring might introduce extraneous values. However, upon multiplying (3) by $\cos\theta$ and (4) by $\sin\theta$ and adding, the result is

$$\rho'(\cos^2\theta + \sin^2\theta) = \sqrt{\rho'^2 + \rho^2}\,(\cos\tau\cos\theta + \sin\tau\sin\theta),$$

$$\rho' = \sqrt{\rho'^2 + \rho^2}\cos(\tau - \theta),$$

again with the radical. Next, multiply (3) by $-\sin\theta$, (4) by $\cos\theta$, add, and then simplify to obtain

$$\rho = \sqrt{\rho'^2 + \rho^2}\sin(\tau - \theta),$$

Finally, by division,

$$\frac{\rho'}{\rho} = \frac{\sqrt{\rho'^2 + \rho^2}\cos(\tau - \theta)}{\sqrt{\rho'^2 + \rho^2}\sin(\tau - \theta)},$$

the radicals cancel, and the result may be written

$$\rho' = \rho\cot(\tau - \theta),$$

which is the same as (1) but obtained without the necessity of considering special cases.

    Example. The graphs of

$$\rho = 1 + \sin\theta \quad \text{and} \quad \rho = 2\sin^2\theta$$

intersect at the point $(\frac{1}{2}, -30°)$. Find the acute angle of intersection at this point (see Fig. 9-9.5).

    Solution. First check that these actual coordinates satisfy both equations. Write the equation, for distinguishing purposes, as

$$\dot{\rho}_1(\theta) = 1 + \sin\theta \quad \text{and} \quad \rho_2(\theta) = 2\sin^2\theta.$$

Then $\rho_1'(\theta) = \cos\theta$, $\rho_2'(\theta) = 4\sin\theta\cos\theta$, so that

$$\rho_1'(-30°) = \frac{\sqrt{3}}{2} \quad \text{and} \quad \rho_2'(-30°) = 4\left(-\frac{1}{2}\right)\frac{\sqrt{3}}{2} = -\sqrt{3}.$$

Let τ_1 and τ_2 be the positive amplitudes less than $180°$ of the tangents, respectively. Since $\rho_1(-30°) = \rho_2(-30°) = \frac{1}{2}$, then, by formula (1),

$$\frac{\sqrt{3}}{2} = \frac{1}{2}\cot[\tau_1 - (-30°)] \quad \text{and} \quad -\sqrt{3} = \frac{1}{2}\cot(\tau_2 + 30°).$$

Hence,

(5) $\cot(\tau_1 + 30°) = \sqrt{3}$ and $\cot(\tau_2 + 30°) = -2\sqrt{3}$.

By using a table to find the second of these angles,

$$\tau_1 + 30° = 30°, \quad \tau_2 + 30° = 163°54',$$

$$\tau_1 = 0°, \quad \text{and} \quad \tau_2 = 133°54'.$$

Consequently, $\tau_2 - \tau_1 = 133°54'$, so the acute answer requested is

$$180° - 133°54' = 46°6'.$$

Another method of extracting this answer from (5) is to use the trigonometric formula

$$\cot(A - B) = \frac{\cot A \cot B + 1}{\cot B - \cot A}.$$

Hence,

$$\cot(\tau_2 - \tau_1) = \cot[(\tau_2 + 30°) - (\tau_1 + 30°)] = \frac{(-2\sqrt{3})\sqrt{3} + 1}{-2\sqrt{3} - \sqrt{3}}$$

$$= \frac{-5}{-3\sqrt{3}} = \frac{5}{3\sqrt{3}},$$

from which, by table, the answer $46°6'$ is again obtained.

Problem 1. Let the graphs of two equations

$$\rho = \rho_1(\theta) \quad \text{and} \quad \rho = \rho_2(\theta)$$

intersect at a point (ρ_0, θ_0) such that $\rho_1(\theta_0) = \rho_2(\theta_0) = \rho_0$.

     a. Show that

$$\cot(\tau_2 - \tau_1) = \frac{\rho_1'(\theta_0)\,\rho_2'(\theta_0) + \rho_0^2}{\rho_0[\rho_1'(\theta_0) - \rho_2'(\theta_0)]}, \quad \text{if} \quad \rho_1'(\theta_0) \neq \rho_2'(\theta_0) \quad \text{and} \quad \rho_0 \neq 0.$$

     b. Show that if $\rho_1'(\theta_0) = \rho_2'(\theta_0)$, then the curves intersect at $0°$; that is, have a common tangent at (ρ_0, θ_0).

     c. If two curves intersect at the pole, how can their angle of intersection be determined?

Problem 2. Find the acute angle of intersection of $\rho = 1 + \sin\theta$ and $\rho = 2\sin^2\theta$ at the points:

a. $(\frac{1}{2}, -150°)$.   b. $(2, 90°)$.   c. The pole.

Problem 3. Find the acute angle of intersection of the graphs of the given equations at the given points:

     a. $\rho = 4\sin\theta$, $\rho\sin\theta = 1$; $(2, 30°)$.

     b. $\rho = \sin 2\theta$, $\rho = \sin\theta$; $\left(\frac{\sqrt{3}}{2}, 60°\right)$,   pole.

     c. $\rho(1 + \cos\theta) = 1$, $\rho(2 - \cos\theta) = 2$, $(1, 90°)$.

     d. $\rho = 2a\cos(\theta - 30°)$, $\rho\cos(\theta - 30°) = a$; $(\sqrt{2}\,a, 75°)$.

Problem 4. a. Find all acute angles of intersection of the polar graphs of

$$\rho = 2\cos^2\theta \quad \text{and} \quad \rho = -1 + \cos\theta.$$

b. Show that the rectangular graphs of

$$y = 2 \cos^2 x \quad \text{and} \quad y = -1 + \cos x$$

do not intersect.

c. Find all acute angles of intersection of the rectangular graphs of

$$y = -2 \cos^2 x \quad \text{and} \quad y = -1 + \cos x.$$

9-12. Length and Area

Let $\rho = \rho(\theta)$ be a function of the independent variable θ, let α and β be constant angles with $\alpha < \beta$, and watch the vector

$$\vec{r}(\theta) = \rho(\theta)(\vec{i} \cos \theta + \vec{j} \sin \theta)$$

as θ increases from $\theta = \alpha$ to $\theta = \beta$. The terminal end of $\vec{r}$ follows the polar graph and traverses an arc of

(1) $$\text{length} = \int_\alpha^\beta \sqrt{\rho'^2 + \rho^2} \, d\theta,$$

while the vector itself sweeps out a region of

(2) $$\text{area} = \int_\alpha^\beta \frac{1}{2} \rho^2 \, d\theta.$$

These facts are not proved in this book, and so must be taken as definitions of arc length between points of a polar graph, and area bounded by two rays and a portion of a polar graph. The original formulation could have been based upon the following line of thought, which now provides a guide for recalling (1) and (2) if some detail (such as, does $\frac{1}{2}$ appear in the length or area formula?) is needed when no reference is available.

The following suggestive presentation rests upon the concept of a definite integral as the limit of sums in which each term *resembles* the integrand.

Figure 9-12.1 shows an inscribed polygon, the sum of whose lengths

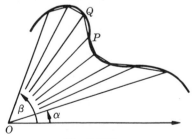

Fig. 9-12.1

presumably approximates the length of the curve between the endpoints. Take $P(\rho, \theta)$ as a typical vertex and $Q(\rho + \Delta\rho, \theta + \Delta\theta)$ as the next vertex of the polygon. Then PQ would, as shown on the right, be the hypotenuse of a right triangle if $\overparen{PR}$ were only straight. There is an error in setting

$$PQ = \sqrt{(RQ)^2 + (\overparen{PR})^2} = \sqrt{(\Delta\rho)^2 + (\rho\Delta\theta)^2} = \sqrt{\left(\frac{\Delta\rho}{\Delta\theta}\right)^2 + \rho^2}\,\Delta\theta,$$

but the close resemblence of this and the integrand of (1) should make (1) seem reasonable and easy to recover if forgotten.

Returning to Fig. 9-12.1, consider the region as approximated by the "sector-like" pieces. The figure OPQ contains the circular sector OPR of area

$$\tfrac{1}{2}\rho^2\,\Delta\theta,$$

which resembles the integrand of (2). Even though $\tfrac{1}{2}\rho^2\,\Delta\theta$ is smaller than area OPQ, these two are approximately* equal since their ratio approaches 1 as $\Delta\theta \to 0$. This follows since OPQ is contained in a circular sector (not shown) of area $\tfrac{1}{2}(\rho + \Delta\rho)^2\,\Delta\theta$, so that

$$1 \leq \lim_{\Delta\theta \to 0}\frac{\text{area } OPQ}{\tfrac{1}{2}\rho^2\,\Delta\theta} \leq \lim_{\Delta\theta \to 0}\frac{\tfrac{1}{2}(\rho+\Delta\rho)^2\Delta\theta}{\tfrac{1}{2}\rho^2\,\Delta\theta} = \lim_{\Delta\theta \to 0}\left(\frac{\rho + \Delta\rho}{\rho}\right)^2 = 1.$$

Example 1. a. Show that the graph of

(3) $$\rho = 2a \cos\theta$$

is a circle of radius $|a|$ and center $(a, 0°)$.

b. By using (1) and (2), find the distance traveled by the terminal end of the vector

$$\vec{F}(\theta) = 2a\cos\theta\,(\vec{i}\cos\theta + \vec{j}\sin\theta)$$

and the area swept over by the vector as θ increases from $\theta = 0$ to $\theta = 2\pi$.

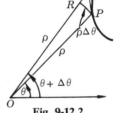

Fig. 9-12.2

Solution. a. Multiply both sides of (3) by ρ:

$$\rho^2 = 2a\rho\cos\theta.$$

Change to rectangular coordinates:

$$x^2 + y^2 = 2ax.$$

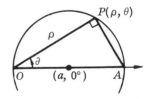

Fig. 9-12.3

Hence, obtain the equation $(x - a)^2 + y^2 = a^2$ of the circle of radius $|a|$ and center with rectangular coordinates $(a, 0)$ or polar coordinates $(a, 0°)$.

Another method (in case $a > 0$) is to draw the circle with center $(a, 0°)$ and radius a as in Fig. 9-12.3. Then a typical point $P(\rho, \theta)$ on the circle is (at least for $0 < \rho$ and $0 < \theta < \pi/2$) at the right angle of the triangle OPA inscribed in the semicircle, so that

---

*Two small quantities are approximations of one another if their ratio is close to 1. For example, 0.001 and 0.0001 are not approximately equal (even though their difference is only 0.0009) since the first is 10 times the second.

$$\frac{OP}{OA} = \cos\theta; \quad \text{that is,} \quad \frac{\rho}{2a} = \cos\theta,$$

which is (3).

Solution. b. Direct substitution of $\rho = 2a\cos\theta$ into (1) gives

$$\int_0^{2\pi} \sqrt{\left(\frac{d\,2a\cos\theta}{d\theta}\right)^2 + (2a\cos\theta)^2}\,d\theta = \int_0^{2\pi} \sqrt{(-2a\sin\theta)^2 + (2a\cos\theta)^2}\,d\theta$$

$$= \int_0^{2\pi}\sqrt{4a^2}\,d\theta = 2|a|\int_0^{2\pi}d\theta = 4|a|\pi.$$

This is twice the circumference of the circle, as it should be since the point (ρ, θ) travels twice around the circle as θ increases from 0 to 2π.

Substitution of $\rho = 2a\cos\theta$ into (2) gives

$$\int_0^{2\pi} \tfrac{1}{2}(2a\cos\theta)^2\,d\theta = 2a^2\int_0^{2\pi}\cos^2\theta\,d\theta = \text{etc.} = 2\pi a^2,$$

which is twice the area of the circle.

Example 2. Find the length of the polar graph of

$$\rho = e^\theta \quad \text{for} \quad -\pi \le \theta \le \pi$$

and the length of the rectangular graph of

$$y = e^x \quad \text{for} \quad -\pi \le x \le \pi.$$

Solution.

$$\text{Polar length} = \int_{-\pi}^{\pi}\sqrt{\left(\frac{de^\theta}{d\theta}\right)^2 + (e^\theta)^2}\,d\theta = \int_{-\pi}^{\pi}\sqrt{2(e^\theta)^2}\,d\theta$$

$$= \sqrt{2}\int_{-\pi}^{\pi}e^\theta\,d\theta = \sqrt{2}\,(e^\pi - e^{-\pi}).$$

$$\text{Rec. length} = \int_{-\pi}^{\pi}\sqrt{1 + \left(\frac{de^x}{dx}\right)^2}\,dx = \int_{-\pi}^{\pi}\sqrt{1 + e^{2x}}\,dx$$

$$= \int_{e^{-\pi}}^{e^\pi}\frac{\sqrt{1+u^2}}{u}\,du \quad \text{by substituting } e^x = u$$

$$= \sqrt{1+u^2} - \ln\frac{1+\sqrt{1+u^2}}{u}\Bigg]_{e^{-\pi}}^{e^\pi} \quad \text{by formula 43}$$

$$= \sqrt{1+e^{2\pi}} - \sqrt{1+e^{-2\pi}} - \ln\frac{1+\sqrt{1+e^{2\pi}}}{1+\sqrt{1+e^{-2\pi}}} + 2\pi$$

9-13. The Inverse Square Law

Tycho Brahe (1546–1601) kept voluminous data on careful observations of the planets. Exhaustive analysis of this data by Johannes Kepler (1571–1630) led to the following conclusions, known as Kepler's Laws:

1. The planets travel in ellipses, each with the sun as a focus.
2. The vector from the sun to a planet sweeps out equal areas in equal times (indicated in Fig. 9-13.1).

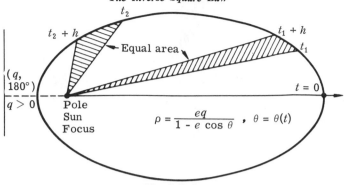

Fig. 9-13.1

3. The squares of the periods of two planets are proportional to the cubes of their mean distances from the sun.

Kepler's first law means that, with appropriate choice of polar coordinates having pole at the sun, a planet's orbit has equation [see (1) of Sec. 9-10]

(1) $$\rho = \frac{eq}{1 - e \cos \theta}, \quad 0 < \theta < 1, \quad q > 0.$$

Hence, ρ is always positive and the focus is at the pole. The independent variable is no longer θ, but $\theta = \theta(t)$ is a function of time t, and hence

$$d\theta = \theta'(t)\, dt.$$

Also, it is convenient to start measuring time so that

$$\theta(0) = 0.$$

Kepler's second law means [from (2) of Sec. 9-12] that, for any number h,

$$\int_{t=t_1}^{t_1+h} \tfrac{1}{2}\rho^2\, d\theta = \int_{t=t_2}^{t_2+h} \tfrac{1}{2}\rho^2\, d\theta$$

for any times t_1 and t_2. Hence,

$$\lim_{h \to 0} \frac{1}{h} \int_{t_1}^{t_1+h} \rho^2(t)\, \theta'(t)\, dt = \lim_{h \to 0} \frac{1}{h} \int_{t_2}^{t_2+h} \rho^2(t)\, \theta'(t)\, dt;$$

that is (this is really the Fundamental Theorem of Calculus),

$$\rho^2(t_1)\theta'(t_1) = \rho^2(t_2)\theta'(t_2).$$

Since this equality holds for all t_1 and t_2, the functions ρ and θ vary with t in such a way that at all times t

(2) $$\rho^2(t)\theta'(t) = \rho^2 \frac{d\theta}{dt} = c_1,$$

where c_1 is a constant.

Kepler's first and second laws, translated into (1) and (2), lead to the famous "inverse square law" of acceleration, as shown below.

Before starting the actual development, note from (1) that

$$\frac{d\rho}{dt} = -\frac{eq}{(1 - e\cos\theta)^2}(e\sin\theta)\frac{d\theta}{dt}$$

$$= -\frac{\sin\theta}{q}\left(\frac{eq}{1 - e\cos\theta}\right)^2\frac{d\theta}{dt} = -\frac{\sin\theta}{q}\rho^2\frac{d\theta}{dt}$$

$$= -\frac{\sin\theta}{q}c_1 \quad \text{from (2).}$$

The vector from the pole to a typical point of the orbit (1) is

$$\vec{r}(t) = \rho(\vec{i}\cos\theta + \vec{j}\sin\theta).$$

Hence, the velocity vector is

$$\vec{v}(t) = \frac{d\vec{r}}{dt} = \rho(-\vec{i}\sin\theta + \vec{j}\cos\theta)\frac{d\theta}{dt} + (\vec{i}\cos\theta + \vec{j}\sin\theta)\frac{d\rho}{dt}$$

$$= \frac{1}{\rho}(-\vec{i}\sin\theta + \vec{j}\cos\theta)\rho^2\frac{d\theta}{dt} + (\vec{i}\cos\theta + \vec{j}\sin\theta)\left(-\frac{\sin\theta}{q}c_1\right)$$

$$= \left\{\frac{1 - e\cos\theta}{eq}(-\vec{i}\sin\theta + \vec{j}\cos\theta) - \frac{\sin\theta}{q}(\vec{i}\cos\theta + \vec{j}\sin\theta)\right\}c_1,$$

wherein both (1) and (2) were used again. Thus,

$$\vec{v}(t) = \left\{\vec{i}\left[-\frac{\sin\theta}{eq} + \frac{\sin\theta\cos\theta}{q} - \frac{\sin\theta\cos\theta}{q}\right]\right.$$

$$\left. + \vec{j}\left[\frac{\cos\theta}{eq} - \frac{\cos^2\theta}{q} - \frac{\sin^2\theta}{q}\right]\right\}c_1$$

$$= \frac{c_1}{eq}(-\vec{i}\sin\theta + \vec{j}\cos\theta) - \frac{c_1}{q}\vec{j}.$$

Hence, the acceleration is [since $(c_1/q)\vec{j}$ is constant]

$$\vec{a}(t) = \frac{d\vec{v}}{dt} = \frac{c_1}{eq}(-\vec{i}\cos\theta - \vec{j}\sin\theta)\frac{d\theta}{dt}$$

$$= -\frac{c_1}{eq}\frac{1}{\rho^2}(\vec{i}\cos\theta + \vec{j}\sin\theta)\rho^2\frac{d\theta}{dt}$$

$$= -\frac{c_1^2}{eq}\frac{1}{\rho^2}(\vec{i}\cos\theta + \vec{j}\sin\theta).$$

The numbers c_1^2, e, and q are all positive, while $-(\vec{i}\cos\theta + \vec{j}\sin\theta)$ is directed exactly opposite to $\vec{r}$. Hence, the acceleration is directed toward the focus, with magnitude inversely porportional to ρ^2.

The point of the orbit which is farthest from the focus, where the attracting body is located, is called the **apogee** (a word with the same root as apex) and the closest point of the orbit is the **perigee**.* Hence,

*Before the advent of man-made satellites of the earth, "apogee" and "perigee" were used in connection with the orbit of the moon. Corresponding terms for satellites of the sun are "aphelion" and "perihelion." The suffix *gee* has the same root as "geography," while *Heliopolis* is the Latin word for "sun."

$$\rho = \frac{eq}{1 - e\cos\theta}, \quad q > 0, \quad \text{and} \quad \theta(0) = 0$$

means that ρ is always positive and time is reckoned from an instant when the planet was at its apogee, as shown in Fig. 9-13.1. In case the alternate equation

$$\rho = \frac{-eq}{1 + e\cos\theta}$$

is used, it is customary to have $q < 0$ and $\theta(0) = 0$, so at all times ρ will be positive and time is reckoned from a perigee passage (see Fig. 9-13.2.).

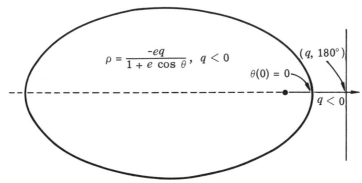

$$\rho = \frac{-eq}{1 + e\cos\theta}, \quad q < 0$$

$\theta(0) = 0$

$(q, 180°)$

$q < 0$

Fig. 9-13.2

Let T be the period of a planet, that is, the time required for one complete revolution of this planet. Kepler's third law states that there is a constant κ (the same for all planets) such that

$$T^2 = \kappa[\tfrac{1}{2}(\text{apogee distance} + \text{perigee distance})]^3$$
$$= \kappa[\text{semimajor axis}]^3.$$

A derivation of this law will be given later.

    Problem 1. Find the area bounded by the polar graph of

$$\rho = e^\theta, \quad -\pi \le \theta \le \pi$$

and the rays to its endpoints. Also, find the area under the rectangular graph of

$$y = e^x$$

and above the interval $-\pi \le x \le \pi$.

    Problem 2. Find the length traveled by the terminal end, and the area swept out, by the vector:

    a. $\vec{r}(\theta) = \theta(\vec{i}\cos\theta + \vec{j}\sin\theta), \quad -\pi \le \theta \le \pi$.

    b. $\vec{r}(\theta) = (1 + \cos\theta)(\vec{i}\cos\theta + \vec{j}\sin\theta), \quad 0 \le \theta \le 2\pi$.

    c. $\vec{r}(\theta) = (3\cos\theta + 4\sin\theta)(\vec{i}\cos\theta + \vec{j}\sin\theta), \quad 0 \le \theta \le \pi$. Why are the answers the same as for a circle of radius $\tfrac{5}{2}$?

    d. $\vec{r}(\theta) = (a\cos\theta + b\sin\theta)(\vec{i}\cos\theta + \vec{j}\sin\theta), \quad 0 \le \theta \le \pi$.

Problem 3. a. Find the length of the graph of

$$\rho = a \sec \theta \quad \text{for} \quad -\frac{\pi}{4} \le \theta \le \frac{\pi}{4}.$$

b. Show that part a is a complicated way of finding the length of a straight-line segment.

c. Find the length of the graph of

$$\rho = a \sec \left(\theta - \frac{\pi}{3}\right) \quad \text{for} \quad 0 \le \theta \le \frac{\pi}{2}.$$

d. Find the area bounded by the graph of part c and the rays to its endpoints, first by using (2) and again by seeing that the graph is a straight line.

Problem 4. Find the area enclosed by one loop of:

a. $\rho = a \sin 2\theta$.   b. $\rho = a \sin 3\theta$.   c. $\rho = a \sin n\theta$.

Problem 5. Given $\rho = \rho(\theta)$ as a function of θ, the polar graph is the rectangular graph of the pair of parametric equations

$$x = \rho(\theta) \cos \theta, \quad y = \rho(\theta) \sin \theta.$$

a. Substitute these into formula (6) of Sec. 8-6 for $\alpha \le \theta \le \beta$ and see that the result is (1) of the present section.

b. For the same parametric equations check that

$$\frac{1}{2}\left(x \frac{dy}{d\theta} - y \frac{dx}{d\theta}\right) d\theta = \frac{1}{2}\rho^2 \, d\theta,$$

which is the integrand in (2).

Problem 6. Start with an orbit having the alternate equation

$$\rho = \frac{-eq}{1 + e \cos \theta}, \quad q < 0, \quad 0 < e < 1$$

of an ellipse, and show that the acceleration vector is

$$\vec{a} = \frac{c^2}{eq} \frac{1}{\rho^2} (\vec{i} \cos \theta + \vec{j} \sin \theta).$$

Does the absence of a minus sign mean that this $\vec{a}$ is directed away (instead of toward) the focus?

Problem 7. Let a planetary orbit have eccentricity $e < 1$ and semimajor axis a. With c_1 the constant of (2) for this planet and T the period for this planet, show that

$$T^2 = 4\pi^2 \frac{1 - e^2}{c_1^2} a^4.$$

[Note: This is not Kepler's third law since there is a different constant, and a is raised to the fourth (instead of the third) power.]

9-14. Complex Numbers and Functions

Mathematical, scientific, and engineering literature is replete with complex numbers and functions, thus attesting to their practical value. The adjective "imaginary" associated with these numbers was a most unfortunate choice since a practical mind is inclined to reject anything labeled to suggest tenuousness. The purpose of the present and the following section is to at least start breaking down whatever prejudice against complex numbers may exist by showing how complex numbers have a close relation to vectors but in addition have distinct manipulative advantages in many situations.

A vector

$$\vec{v} = \vec{i}x + \vec{j}y$$

with initial end at the origin is determined by the ordered pair (x, y), which

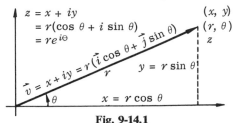

Fig. 9-14.1

plotted as a point is the terminal end of $\vec{v}$. The complex number

(1) $$z = x + iy$$

is represented graphically by the same point (x, y). The i appearing here is the so-called imaginary unit and has, by definition, the property

(2) $$i^2 = -1.$$

The imaginary unit i is representationally the unit vector $\vec{j}$, but not so manipulatively, since $\vec{j}\vec{j}$ (without a dot or cross between them) is usually undefined.*

In the following review of the algebra of complex numbers, all letters except i represent real numbers.

Equality of complex numbers is defined by

1.　　　$a + ib = c + id$ if and only if $a = c$ and $b = d$.

Addition, subtraction, multiplication, and division of complex numbers are defined by carrying over the ordinary rules supplemented by i having the property (2).

2.　　　$(a + ib) \pm (c + id) = (a \pm c) + i(b \pm d).$

Both 1 and 2 are duplications of vector laws. Multiplication and division do not, however, have vector analogs. From

$$(a + ib)(c + id) = ac + iad + ibc + i^2bd,$$

*Engineers use $z = x + jy$, which is even closer to vector notation than $z = x + iy$.

3. $$(a + ib)(c + id) = (ac - bd) + i(ad + bc).$$

4. $$\frac{a + ib}{c + id} = \frac{a + ib}{c + id}\frac{c - id}{c - id} = \frac{ac + bd + i(bc - ad)}{c^2 + d^2}$$

$$= \frac{ac + bd}{c^2 + d^2} + i\frac{bc - ad}{c^2 + d^2} \quad \text{if } c^2 + d^2 \neq 0.$$

Let $x(t)$ and $y(t)$ be two ordinary (that is, real-valued) functions of the real variable t, and consider the complex-valued function of the real variable* t defined by

$$z(t) = x(t) + iy(t).$$

The derivative is then defined as if i were any constant by

$$\frac{dz}{dt} = \frac{dx}{dt} + i\frac{dy}{dt}.$$

For example,

$$\frac{d}{d\theta}(\cos\theta + i\sin\theta) = \frac{d\cos\theta}{d\theta} + i\frac{d\sin\theta}{d\theta}$$

$$= -\sin\theta + i\cos\theta$$

$$= i^2\sin\theta + i\cos\theta \quad \text{since} \quad i^2 = -1$$

$$= i(i\sin\theta + \cos\theta)$$

(3) $$= i(\cos\theta + i\sin\theta);$$

that is,

$$\frac{d}{d\theta}(\cos\theta + i\sin\theta) = i(\cos\theta + i\sin\theta).$$

This equality and its close relation to the previously derived formula

$$\frac{de^{cx}}{dx} = ce^{cx} \quad \text{for } c \text{ a constant}$$

lead to the definition (and it must be emphasized that it is only a definition)

(4) $$e^{i\theta} = \cos\theta + i\sin\theta,$$

so that upon substituting (4) into (3)

(5) $$\frac{de^{i\theta}}{d\theta} = ie^{i\theta}.$$

The expression $\cos\theta + i\sin\theta$ takes only a little longer to write than $e^{i\theta}$, so it might seem that (4) is hardly worth the trouble. As further courses in science and mathematics are taken it will be found, however, that (4), known

---

*The situation is more involved, but eminently more useful, if the independent variable is also complex. The study of complex-valued functions of a complex variable comes in a higher level course than this one.

as Euler's* Formula, holds an honorable position far transcending mere economy in writing.

Example 1. Establish the law of exponents,

(6)
$$e^{i\theta}e^{i\phi} = e^{i(\theta+\phi)}.$$

Solution.

$$
\begin{aligned}
e^{i\theta}e^{i\phi} &= (\cos\theta + i\sin\theta)(\cos\phi + i\sin\phi)\\
&= \cos\theta\cos\phi - \sin\theta\sin\phi + i(\sin\theta\cos\phi + \cos\theta\sin\phi)\\
&= \cos(\theta+\phi) + i\sin(\theta+\phi)\\
&= e^{i(\theta+\phi)}.
\end{aligned}
$$

For $\phi = \theta$, the equality (6) shows that

$$(e^{i\theta})^2 = e^{i2\theta},$$

and this generalizes for any positive integer n:

(7)
$$(e^{i\theta})^n = e^{in\theta}.$$

Those having had previous experience with complex numbers will recognize (7) as de Moivre's Theorem:

$$(\cos\theta + i\sin\theta)^n = \cos n\theta + i\sin n\theta.$$

For m any integer,

(8)
$$e^{i2m\pi} = \cos 2m\pi + i\sin 2m\pi = 1 + i\cdot 0 = 1,$$

and hence the function $e^{i\theta}$ is a periodic function of θ with period 2π:

$$e^{i(\theta+2m\pi)} = e^{i\theta}e^{i2m\pi} = e^{i\theta}(1) = e^{i\theta}.$$

Example 2. Find all complex cube roots of unity; that is, find all complex numbers such that each of them has its cube equal to 1.

Solution. For m an integer, use an exponent one third of the exponent in (8) and then cube the result:

$$(e^{i(2m\pi/3)})^3 = e^{i2m\pi} = 1.$$

Thus, any of the numbers

$$e^{i(2m\pi/3)}, \quad m = 0, \pm 1, \pm 2, \cdots$$

is a cube root of 1. The three substitutions $m = -1, 0, 1$ give, respectively,

$$e^{i(-2/3)\pi} = \cos\left(-\frac{2}{3}\pi\right) + i\sin\left(-\frac{2}{3}\pi\right) = -\frac{1}{2} - i\frac{\sqrt{3}}{2},$$

$$e^{i\cdot 0} = \cos 0 + i\sin 0 = 1 + i\cdot 0 = 1,$$

$$e^{i(2/3)\pi} = \cos\frac{2}{3}\pi + i\sin\frac{2}{3}\pi = -\frac{1}{2} + i\frac{\sqrt{3}}{2},$$

*Euler, 1707–1783.

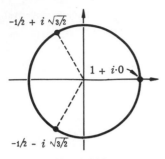

Fig. 9-14.2

and any other integer m will duplicate one or another of these. Figure 9-14.2 shows the graphical representation of three cube roots of unity as points on the unit circle.

Euler's Formula (4) gives e to a pure imaginary power

$$e^{ib} = \cos b + i \sin b,$$

and it is natural to extend the additive law of exponents by defining

$$(9) \qquad e^a e^{ib} = e^{a+ib},$$

so e to any complex exponent may be used.

Given a complex number

$$z = x + iy, \quad z \neq 0,$$

there is one and only one positive number r, but many angles θ, such that

$$(10) \qquad z = r(\cos \theta + i \sin \theta)$$
$$= re^{i\theta}, \quad r > 0.$$

This follows directly from the fact that the point (x, y) has many polar coordinates (ρ, θ), some with $\rho = \sqrt{x^2 + y^2} > 0$, so that

$$\vec{i}x + \vec{i}y = \sqrt{x^2 + y^2}\,(\vec{i} \cos \theta + \vec{j} \sin \theta).$$

Either version of (10) is called the **polar form** of z. The positive number r is called the **absolute value** of z,

$$|z| = r = \sqrt{x^2 + y^2},$$

and θ is called an **amplitude** of z. The θ such that

$$-\pi < \theta \leq \pi$$

is called the **principal amplitude** of z.

Note carefully that r must be positive in the polar form of $z \neq 0$. For example,

$$z = -\sqrt{3} - i = -2 \cos \frac{\pi}{6} - i 2 \sin \frac{\pi}{6}$$

$$= -2\left(\cos \frac{\pi}{6} + i \sin \frac{\pi}{6}\right) = -2e^{i\pi/6}$$

is a perfectly good complex number, but -2 is **not** its absolute value nor is $\pi/6$ an amplitude. However, the same z written as

$$z = 2[\cos\left(-\tfrac{5}{6}\pi\right) + i \sin\left(-\tfrac{5}{6}\pi\right)] = 2e^{-i5\pi/6}$$

shows the absolute value $|z| = 2$ and the principal amplitude $-\tfrac{5}{6}\pi$.

The equality of complex numbers written in polar form

$$r_1 e^{i\theta_1} = r_2 e^{i\theta_2}$$

demands that $r_1 = r_2$ but permits θ_1 and θ_2 to be different provided their difference is 2π multiplied by an integer:

$$\theta_1 - \theta_2 = 2m\pi.$$

Problem 1. Find:
a. The three cube roots of -1.
b. The three cube roots of i.
c. The four fourth roots of 16.
d. The four fourth roots of $8(-1 + i\sqrt{3})$.

Problem 2. With a and b real and $z = a + ib$, the conjugate $\bar{z}$ of z is defined by $\bar{z} = a - ib$. Prove:
a. $\overline{z_1 + z_2} = \bar{z_1} + \bar{z_2}$.
b. $\overline{z_1 z_2} = \bar{z_1} \bar{z_2}$.
c. $z + \bar{z}$ is real.
d. $z\bar{z} = |z|^2$.
e. If $z = re^{i\theta}$, then $\bar{z} = re^{-i\theta}$.

Problem 3. A polynomial in t and of degree n

$$P(t) = a_0 + a_1 t + a_2 t^2 + \cdots + a_n t^n$$

is given. Show that:
a. For $x + iy = re^{i\theta}$, then $x - iy = re^{-i\theta}$ and
$$P(x \pm iy) = a_0 + a_1 r \cos \theta + a_2 r^2 \cos 2\theta + \cdots + a_n r^n \cos n\theta$$
$$\pm i(a_1 r \sin \theta + a_2 r^2 \sin 2\theta + \cdots + a_n r^n \sin n\theta).$$

b. If $a_0, a_2 \ldots, a_n, x$, and y are all real, then
$$P(x - iy) = 0 \text{ if and only if } P(x + iy) = 0.$$

Problem 4. a. Show that:
$$\sin \theta = \frac{e^{i\theta} - e^{-i\theta}}{2i} \quad \text{and} \quad \cos \theta = \frac{e^{i\theta} + e^{-i\theta}}{2}.$$

[Note the similarity of these expressions and the definitions of $\sinh \theta$ and $\cosh \theta$.]
b. For z a complex number, define
$$\sin z = \frac{e^{iz} - e^{-iz}}{2i} \quad \text{and} \quad \cos z = \frac{e^{iz} + e^{-iz}}{2}.$$

For x and y real, show that
$$\sin (x + iy) = \sin x \, \frac{e^y + e^{-y}}{2} + i \cos x \, \frac{e^y - e^{-y}}{2}$$
$$= \sin x \cosh y + i \cos x \sinh y.$$

c. Find at least one solution of $\sin z = 2$.
d. Find at least one solution of $\cos z = -2$.

9-15.   Universal Gravitation

Based largely on the inverse square law of acceleration for planets of the sun (as deduced from Kepler's Laws), Isaac Newton (1642–1727) announced his Universal Law of Gravitation in 1686 and was knighted in 1705 in recognition of his scientific achievements. According to this law, there is a universal gravitational constant, G, whose value depends only on the units used, such that two spherical bodies of masses M and m are attracted toward each other along their line of centers by a force of magnitude

$$(1) \qquad\qquad G\frac{Mm}{r^2},$$

where r is the distance between their centers. Also,

$$(2) \qquad\qquad \text{Force} = \text{mass} \times \text{acceleration}.$$

A coordinate system is selected with origin (or pole) at the center of the body of larger mass M. The position of the second body is then given as

$$(3) \qquad\qquad z = re^{i\theta}.$$

Motion of the second body means that r and θ are functions of time and, because of the vector interpretation of complex numbers, the velocity is

$$v = \frac{dz}{dt} = r\frac{de^{i\theta}}{dt} + e^{i\theta}\frac{dr}{dt} = rie^{i\theta}\frac{d\theta}{dt} + e^{i\theta}\frac{dr}{dt},$$

$$(4) \qquad\qquad v = \frac{dz}{dt} = \left[\frac{dr}{dt} + ir\frac{d\theta}{dt}\right]e^{i\theta},$$

and the acceleration is

$$a = \frac{dv}{dt} = \frac{d^2z}{dt^2} = \left[\frac{dr}{dt} + ir\frac{d\theta}{dt}\right]\frac{de^{i\theta}}{dt} + e^{i\theta}\frac{d}{dt}\left[\frac{dr}{dt} + ir\frac{d\theta}{dt}\right]$$

$$= \left[\frac{dr}{dt} + ir\frac{d\theta}{dt}\right]ie^{i\theta}\frac{d\theta}{dt} + e^{i\theta}\left[\frac{d^2r}{dt^2} + ir\frac{d^2\theta}{dt^2} + i\frac{d\theta}{dt}\frac{dr}{dt}\right]$$

$$(5) \qquad\qquad = \left\{\left[\frac{d^2r}{dt^2} - r\left(\frac{d\theta}{dt}\right)^2\right] + i\left[r\frac{d^2\theta}{dt^2} + 2\frac{dr}{dt}\frac{d\theta}{dt}\right]\right\}e^{i\theta},$$

Since the mass M is held stationary at the origin, the only motion is of the second body, so the "acceleration" in (2) is d^2z/dt^2 and hence the force of attraction is

$$m\frac{d^2z}{dt^2}.$$

But also (1) gives the magnitude of the force of attraction. Furthermore, the vector force of attraction is from the smaller toward the larger mass and thus has amplitude exactly $180°$ from θ, so the polar form of the force of attraction is

$$G\frac{Mm}{r^2}e^{i(\theta+\pi)}.$$

These two expressions for the force of attraction yield the equation

$$m\frac{d^2z}{dt^2} = G\frac{Mm}{r^2}e^{i\theta}e^{i\pi} = -m\frac{GM}{r^2}e^{i\theta}.$$

By canceling m and making the substitution

(6) $$k = GM,$$

the result is

(7) $$\frac{d^2z}{dt^2} = -\frac{k}{r^2}e^{i\theta}.$$

The purpose is to use these various differential equations to extract an equation, without derivatives, of the path of the body of mass m.

On the left of (7) substitute (5), cancel $e^{i\theta}$, and obtain

$$\frac{d^2r}{dt^2} - r\left(\frac{d\theta}{dt}\right)^2 + i\left[r\frac{d^2\theta}{dt^2} + 2\frac{dr}{dt}\frac{d\theta}{dt}\right] = -\frac{k}{r^2}.$$

From the equality of complex numbers, the following two equations are obtained:

$$\frac{d^2r}{dt^2} - r\left(\frac{d\theta}{dt}\right)^2 = -\frac{k}{r^2}$$

and

(8) $$r\frac{d^2\theta}{dt^2} + 2\frac{dr}{dt}\frac{d\theta}{dt} = 0.$$

It is now a matter of insight to notice that the left side of (8) will appear as a factor in

$$\frac{d}{dt}\left(r^2\frac{d\theta}{dt}\right) = r^2\frac{d^2\theta}{dt^2} + \frac{d\theta}{dt}2r\frac{dr}{dt}$$

$$= r\left[r\frac{d^2\theta}{dt^2} + 2\frac{dr}{dt}\frac{d\theta}{dt}\right].$$

It therefore follows from (8), since $r \neq 0$, that

$$\frac{d}{dt}\left(r^2\frac{d\theta}{dt}\right) = 0.$$

Consequently, there is a constant c_1 such that

(9) $$r^2\frac{d\theta}{dt} = c_1.$$

The choice $c_1 > 0$ is made, which merely means that the coordinate system is viewed so that θ increases as t increases.

Hence, again the "constant areal velocity" property is arrived at [see (2) of Sec. 9-13] this time, however, for all paths due to a mass M rather than for only elliptical planetary orbits of the solar system, as before.

From (9) written as

$$\frac{1}{r^2} = \frac{1}{c_1}\frac{d\theta}{dt},$$

substitution into (7) yields

$$\frac{d^2 z}{dt^2} = -\frac{k}{c_1} e^{i\theta} \frac{d\theta}{dt},$$

which is in a form easily integrated once with respect to t. Thus, by adding a complex constant of integration,

(10) $$\frac{dz}{dt} = -\frac{k}{c_1} \frac{1}{i} e^{i\theta} + c_2 e^{i\gamma}, \quad c_2 > 0$$

$$= \frac{k}{c_1} i e^{i\theta} + c_2 e^{i\gamma} \quad \text{since} \quad -1 = i^2.$$

This expression and (4) both represent the velocity, so that

$$\left[\frac{dr}{dt} + ir\frac{d\theta}{dt}\right] e^{i\theta} = \frac{k}{c_1} i e^{i\theta} + c_2 e^{i\gamma},$$

$$\frac{dr}{dt} + ir\frac{d\theta}{dt} = \frac{k}{c_1} i + c_2 e^{i(\gamma - \theta)}$$

$$= i\frac{k}{c_1} + c_2[\cos(\gamma - \theta) + i\sin(\gamma - \theta)].$$

Again, equality of complex numbers yields

(11) $$\frac{dr}{dt} = c_2 \cos(\theta - \gamma),$$

(12) $$r\frac{d\theta}{dt} = \frac{k}{c_1} - c_2 \sin(\theta - \gamma).$$

Multiplying by r and again using (9), this last equation yields

$$c_1 = r\left[\frac{k}{c_1} - c_2 \sin(\theta - \gamma)\right],$$

and this solved for r,

(13) $$r = \frac{c_1}{(k/c_1) - c_2 \sin(\theta - \gamma)},$$

is the polar equation of the path of the body of mass m about the stationary (at the pole) body of mass M.

The choice $\gamma = -\pi/2$ yields

(14) $$r = \frac{c_1^2/k}{1 - (c_1 c_2/k)\cos\theta},$$

which is one of the typical polar equations of a conic [see (1) of Sec. 9-10] having eccentricity e and focus-directrix distance q, where

(15) $$e = \frac{c_1 c_2}{k}, \quad eq = \frac{c_1^2}{k}, \quad \text{and} \quad q = \frac{c_1}{c_2}.$$

Thus, $\gamma = -\pi/2$ merely orients the conic to have its axis of symmetry along the initial ray.

Note that if $c_2 = 0$ then the path is a circle, as seen from (14), (13), or (11).

Example. Establish Kepler's Third Law not only for planetary orbits of the sun but for any elliptical orbit about an attracting body.

Solution. For an elliptical orbit, $0 \leq e < 1$, so the body retraces its path periodically. Let T be the period of one revolution. With a the semimajor axis (not the acceleration) and $b = a\sqrt{1 - e^2}$ the semiminor axis, the area of the ellipse is πab. Hence, by using the polar formula for area, and the fact that (9) holds,

$$\pi ab = \int_0^T \frac{1}{2} r^2 \frac{d\theta}{dt} dt = \frac{1}{2} \int_0^T c_1 \, dt = \frac{1}{2} c_1 T,$$

so that

$$T^2 = 4\pi^2 \frac{a^2 b^2}{c_1^2} = 4\pi^2 \frac{a^4(1 - e^2)}{c_1^2}.$$

Since $q > 0$, it follows that (see page 318)

$$q = \frac{a}{e} - ae = a\frac{1 - e^2}{e},$$

so that, by using the second equation in (15),

$$1 - e^2 = \frac{eq}{a} = \frac{c_1^2}{ak}.$$

Thus,

(16) $$T^2 = \frac{4\pi^2}{k} a^3.$$

Since G is the universal constant, then $k = GM$ is the same for all elliptical orbits about the attracting body of mass M, so that (16) says "the squares of the periods of two such orbits are to each other as the cubes of their mean distances from the body."

Problem 1. Given that $c_1 c_2 < k$, so the graph of (14) is an ellipse, find the semimajor axis a and semiminor axis b in terms of c_1, c_2, and k.

Problem 2. a. Show that $\gamma = \pi/2$ also reduces (13) to a typical form of a conic with

$$e = \frac{c_1 c_2}{k} \quad \text{and} \quad q = -\frac{c_1^2}{ke}.$$

b. In this case and with $c_1 c_2 < k$, for what values of θ is r greatest and least?

9-16. Space Travel

Because of interest in space travel originating on the earth, the Universal Law of Gravitation will be applied with the earth as the attracting body. Gravity will therefore mean "the attraction of our earth on objects near its surface." The weight of the space vehicle is taken as mg, where g is the acceleration of gravity, which in foot-second units is approximately (and used as)

$$g = 32.2 \text{ ft/sec}^2.$$

With R the radius of the earth (approximately 3930×5280 ft), it follows from (1) of Sec. 9-15 that

$$mg = G\frac{Mm}{R^2},$$

and hence the k in formulas of Sec. 9-15 takes the value

(1) $k = MG = gR^2 = 32.2(3930 \times 5280)^2 = 1.386 \times 10^{16}.$

The vehicle is launched from the earth, but its path in space is determined by conditions holding at the instant it is released by the last rocket stage. This instant is taken as time $t = 0$. The choice (in the plane of the path) of the initial ray of the polar coodinate system is arbitrary and is taken as passing through the point of release, so that

(2) $\theta = 0$ when $t = 0.$

The other pertinent initial conditions are given as

(3) $r = r_0,$ $\dfrac{dr}{dt} = \mu_0,$ and $\dfrac{d\theta}{dt} = \omega_0 > 0$ when $t = 0.$

Although the whole system leaves the launching pad in a vertical straight line, the last stage curves so that at separation θ is varying, that is, $\omega_0 > 0$. It may be, however, that at this instant the path is perpendicular to the initial ray, so that $\mu_0 = 0$, and, in fact, this is desirable.

It will be shown that these constants are parameters of the path. By this is meant that if exact values of these constants were known, then the position of the vehicle could be predicted at any future time until a force other than gravity alters its course. The engineering problem is to design and construct launching equipment that will produce sufficiently close approximations of previously specified constants (3) known in advance to produce the desired course.

High-speed electronic computers stand by with programs all ready to go as soon as approximations for (3) are received from the vehicle's instruments at the instant of release. The computer then calculates positions ahead of the vehicle and the times at which it should reach these positions. As tracking stations over the world report positions and times (again approximations), the computer notes variations from predictions, adjusts the parameters, calculates still further advanced positions, etc., until an accurate determination of the path is achieved.

The constants (3) will now be fitted into appropriate formulas to see that they determine the course of the vehicle.

Since (9) of Sec. 9-15 holds at all times t, it holds in particular when $t = 0$, so that

(4) $$c_1 = r_0^2 \omega_0 > 0 \quad \text{since} \quad \omega_0 > 0.$$

Since $\theta = 0$ for $t = 0$, (11) and (12) of Sec. 9-15 yield

(5) $$\mu_0 = c_2 \cos(-\gamma) = c_2 \cos\gamma \quad \text{and}$$

(6) $$r_0 \omega_0 = \frac{k}{c_1} - c_2 \sin(-\gamma) = \frac{gR^2}{r_0^2 \omega_0} + c_2 \sin\gamma.$$

Thus,

$$\mu_0^2 = c_2^2 \cos^2\gamma = c_2^2 - c_2^2 \sin^2\gamma = c_2^2 - \left(r_0 \omega_0 - \frac{gR^2}{r_0^2 \omega_0}\right)^2 \quad \text{and}$$

(7) $$c_2 = \left[\mu_0^2 + \left(\frac{r_0^3 \omega_0^2 - gR^2}{r_0^2 \omega_0}\right)^2\right]^{1/2} \quad \text{since} \quad c_2 \geq 0.$$

If the calculated value is $c_2 = 0$, then the path is a circle (see the note of Sec. 9-15) and further calculations are easy, but if $c_2 \neq 0$ then

(8) $$\sin\gamma = \frac{r_0^3 \omega_0^2 - gR^2}{c_2 r_0^2 \omega_0}, \quad \cos\gamma = \frac{\mu_0}{c_2},$$

and γ is obtained by computing the first quadrant angle

$$\gamma_0 = \tan^{-1}\left|\frac{r_0^3 \omega_0^2 - gR^2}{\mu_0 r_0^2 \omega_0}\right|.$$

Then $\gamma = \gamma_0$ or $\gamma = -\gamma_0$ or $\gamma = \pi \pm \gamma_0$, according to the signs of the numerators

$$r_0^3 \omega_0^2 - gR^2 \quad \text{and} \quad \mu_0$$

of $\sin\gamma$ and $\cos\gamma$, since both denominators are positive.

Now all of the parameters c_1, c_2 and γ in

(9) $$r = \frac{c_1}{(k/c_1) - c_2 \sin(\theta - \gamma)}$$

[which is (13) of Sec. 9-15] have been expressed in terms of the initial conditions (3), and calculations proceed to obtain many (r, θ) points of the path. Then the time t_1 when a specified point (r_1, θ_1) should be reached is obtained from the constant areal velocity property (9) of Sec. 9-15 written as

$$dt = \frac{1}{c_1} r^2 \, d\theta = \frac{1}{r_0^2 \omega_0} r^2 \, d\theta,$$

so that

$$t_1 = \int_0^t dt = \frac{1}{r_0^2 \omega_0} \int_0^{\theta_1} r^2 \, d\theta,$$

and then the right member is numerically integrated* by using the many (r, θ) values previously computed.

*See Sec. 13-16 for methods of numerical integration.

In order to obtain a feeling for how relative sizes of the constants (3) determine the type of curve followed by the vehicle, further discussion will be under the desirable situation that $\mu_0 = 0$, so that actual space fight begins perpendicular to the initial ray of the polar coordinate system, which has already been chosen so $\omega_0 > 0$.

The first observation is that $\mu_0 = 0$ simplifies (7) to

$$c_2 = \frac{|r_0^3\omega_0^2 - gR^2|}{r_0^2\omega_0}$$

If, in addition to $\mu_0 = 0$, also $r_0^3\omega_0^2 - gR^2 = 0$, then $c_2 = 0$ and the orbit is a circle. Hence, further discussion is based upon the two requirements

$$\mu_0 = 0 \quad \text{and} \quad r_0^3\omega_0^2 - gR^2 \neq 0.$$

Under these conditions, it follows from (8) that

$$\sin\gamma = \frac{r_0^3\omega_0^2 - gR^2}{|r_0^3\omega_0^2 - gR^2|} \quad \text{and} \quad \cos\gamma = 0.$$

Consequently,

(10)
$$\gamma = \begin{cases} -\pi/2 \ \text{ if } \ r_0^3\omega_0^2 < gR^2, \\ +\pi/2 \ \text{ if } \ r_0^3\omega_0^2 > gR^2. \end{cases}$$

These two cases will be considered separately.

CASE 1: $\mu_0 = 0$, $r_0^3\omega_0^2 < gR^2$.

Hence, $\gamma = -\pi/2$, while c_2 may be written without absolute values as

$$c_2 = \frac{gR^2 - r_0^3\omega_0^2}{r_0^2\omega_0}.$$

Recall that $c_1 = r_0^2\omega_0$ and $k = gR^2$. Hence (9) becomes

$$r = \frac{r_0^2\omega_0}{\dfrac{gR^3}{r_0^2\omega_0} - \dfrac{gR^2 - r_0^3\omega_0^2}{r_0^2\omega_0}\sin\left(\theta + \dfrac{\pi}{2}\right)}$$

(11)
$$= \frac{r_0^4\omega_0^2/(gR)^2}{1 - \left(1 - \dfrac{r_0^3\omega_0^2}{gR^2}\right)\cos\theta}.$$

This is in the typical form of a conic [see (1) of Sec. 9-10] with eccentricity e, where

(12)
$$0 < e = 1 - \frac{r_0^3\omega_0^2}{gR^2}.$$

Thus, the conic is an ellipse. Moreover, the maximum r is obtained when the positive denominator in (11) is smallest and thus occurs (because of the minus sign) when $\cos\theta$ is largest at $\theta = 0$. By substituting $\theta = 0$ in (11), the result is

$$r = r_0 \quad \text{when} \quad \theta = 0,$$

showing that the vehicle starts its orbit at apogee (the largest distance from the focus). In the same way, (11) is smallest when $\theta = \pi$:

(13) $$r = r_\pi = \frac{r_0^4 \omega_0^2}{2gR^2 - r_0^3 \omega_0^2}, \quad \text{when} \quad \theta = \pi,$$

is the perigee distance from the focus (center of the earth).

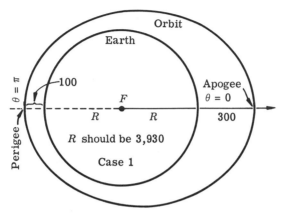

Fig. 9-16.1

Example 1. Given that castoff is 300 mi above the earth and that the closest approach to the earth is 100 mi, find:

    a. The eccentricity of the elliptical orbit.
    b. The initial speed (at apogee).
    c. The speed at perigee.
    d. The time of one revolution.

Solution a. The closest-approach condition means that $r_\pi = r_0 - 200$, and thus, from (13),

$$\frac{r_0^4 \omega_0^2}{2gR^2 - r_0^3 \omega_0^2} = r_0 - 200,$$

$$r_0^4 \omega_0^2 = 2gR^2(r_0 - 200) - r_0^3 \omega_0^2(r_0 - 200),$$

$$r_0^3 \omega_0^2(r_0 + r_0 - 200) = 2gR^2(r_0 - 200),$$

(14) $$\frac{r_0^3 \omega_0^2}{gR^2} = \frac{r_0 - 200}{r_0 - 100} = \frac{R + 100}{R + 200}.$$

Now, from (12), since $R = 3930$,

$$e = 1 - \frac{R + 100}{R + 200} = \frac{100}{R + 200} = \frac{100}{4130} - 0.0242.$$

Solution b. Since $\omega_0 = d\theta/dt]_{\theta=0}$ and the vehicle is at the end of an r_0-mi radius, the initial velocity is $v_0 = r_0 \omega_0$. From (14),

(15) $$v_0 = r_0 \omega_0 = \sqrt{\frac{gR^2(R + 100)}{r_0(R + 200)}} = \sqrt{\frac{gR^2(R + 100)}{(R + 300)(R + 200)}}$$

$$= \sqrt{\frac{(32.2)(3930)^2(4030)5280}{(4230)(4130)}} \text{ ft/sec}$$

$$= \sqrt{\frac{(32.2)(3930)^2(4030)}{(4230)(4130)(5280)}} = 4.691 \text{ mi/sec.}$$

Solution c. Let $\omega_\pi = d\theta/dt]_{\theta=\pi}$ and v_π be the velocity at perigee, so that $v_\pi = (R + 100)\omega_\pi$. From the constant areal velocity property (9) of Sec. 9-15, it follows that

$$(R + 100)^2 \omega_\pi = r_0^2 \omega_0.$$

Consequently,

$$v_\pi = (R + 100)\omega_\pi = \frac{1}{R + 100} r_0^2 \omega_0$$

and hence, from (15),

(16) $$v_\pi = \frac{1}{R + 100} \sqrt{\frac{r_0^2 gR^2(R + 100)}{r_0(R + 200)}} = \sqrt{\frac{gR^2 (R + 300)}{(R + 100)(R + 200)}}$$

$$= \sqrt{\frac{(32.2)(3930)^2(4230)}{(4030)(4130)(5280)}} = 4.867 \text{ mi/sec.}$$

Solution d. The ellipse has semimajor axis of length

$$a = 3930 + \tfrac{1}{2}(300 + 100) = 4130 \text{ mi,}$$

which is the mean distance to be substituted (using the proper units) into (16) of Sec. 9-15 to obtain

$$T^2 = \frac{4\pi^2}{32.2(3930 \times 5280)^2}(4130 \times 5280)^3; \quad T = 5434 \text{ sec} = 90.57 \text{ min.*}$$

This finishes the discussion of Case 1.

CASE 2: $\mu_0 = 0$, $r_0^3 \omega_0^2 > gR^2$.

Referring back to (10), it is seen that $\gamma = \pi/2$, while c_2 may be written without absolute values as

$$c_2 = \frac{r_0^3 \omega_0^2 - gR^2}{r_0^2 \omega_0},$$

and (since $c_1 = r_0^2 \omega_0$ and $k = gR^2$, as before) equation (9) becomes

$$r = \frac{r_0^2 \omega_0}{\dfrac{gR^2}{r_0^2 \omega_0} - \dfrac{r_0^3 \omega_0^2 - gR^2}{r_0^2 \omega_0} \sin\left(\theta - \dfrac{\pi}{2}\right)}$$

(17) $$= \frac{r_0^4 \omega_0^2/gR^2}{1 + \left(\dfrac{r_0^3 \omega_0^2}{gR^2} - 1\right) \cos\theta},$$

---

*The time between two successive crossings of a meridian may be as much as 5.5 min greater than this. During the hour and a half circuit the earth will have turned on its axis $\tfrac{3}{2}(1/24) = 1/16$ of a revolution, so that $(1/16)(90.57)$, or about 5.5, additional minutes would be necessary (at the equator) for the vehicle to reach the same meridian.

which is a typical form of a conic [see (1) of Sec. 9-10] with eccentricity e:

$$(18) \qquad 0 < e = \frac{r_0^3 \omega_0^2}{gR^2} - 1.$$

If $e = 1$, the path is a parabola, and if $e > 1$, it is a hyperbola, and in either case the vehicle becomes a spaceship not destined to return to the earth.

If $e < 1$, the path is again an ellipse, but this time $\theta = 0$ gives r_0 as the smallest distance from the earth, while $\theta = \pi$ gives

$$(19) \qquad r_\pi = \frac{r_0^4 \omega_0^2}{2gR^2 - r_0^3 \omega_0^2},$$

the largest distance from the earth.

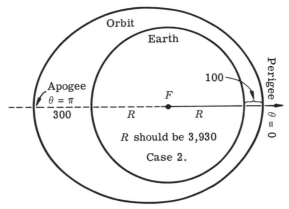

Fig. 9-16.2

Example 2. Given that $e = 1$ and the rockets release the vehicle 100 mi from the earth, find the initial speed.

Solution. The initial speed is $r_0 \omega_0$, where $r_0 = 4030$. From (18) with $e = 1$, it follows that

$$r_0 \omega_0 = \sqrt{\frac{2gR^2}{r_0}} = \sqrt{\frac{2(32.2)(3930)^2 \, 5280}{4030}} \quad \text{ft/sec}$$

$$= \sqrt{\frac{2(32.2)(3930)^2}{4030(5280)}} = 6.829 \text{ mi/sec}.$$

This is the "escape speed" in this case.

Problem 1. Given (in Case 2) that castoff is 100 mi from the earth and apogee is 300 mi from earth, check that the same orbit is obtained as the one in Example 1 of Case 1.

This problem shows that in Case 2 the rockets need not boost the vehicle so high but must give it a greater velocity than in Case 1 to produce the same orbit.

Problem 2. Find (in Case 2) the initial velocity to send the vehicle on an elliptic orbit to the vicinity of the moon (that is, some 237,000 mi away).

Problem 3. Find the escape velocity (see Example 3) if:

a. $e = 1$, $r_0 = R + 300$ mi.

b. $e = 1$, $r_0 = R$ (of course, no atmosphere).

c. $e = 1.1$, $r_0 = R + 100$.

d. $e = 1.5$, $r_0 = R + 100$.

e. $e = 1.5$, $r_0 = R$.

Solid
Geometry

Chapter 10

10-1. Rectangular Coordinates

The unit vectors $\vec{i}$ on the x-axis and $\vec{j}$ on the y-axis are kept with their initial ends at the origin. A third vector $\vec{k}$ is taken having initial end at the origin and perpendicular to the (x, y)-plane. Also, $\vec{k}$ is directed so that an ordinary screw (with right-handed threading) pointed to agree with $\vec{k}$ would advance along $\vec{k}$ if twisted by rotation from $\vec{i}$ toward $\vec{j}$. If $\vec{i}$ and $\vec{j}$ are drawn in the page as before, then Fig. 10-1.1 represents $\vec{k}$ sticking out of the page.

Fig. 10-1.1   Fig. 10-1.2

It is customary, however, to reorient the system as in Fig. 10-1.2, representing $\vec{j}$ and $\vec{k}$ in the page and $\vec{i}$ pointing out of the page. The line containing $\vec{k}$ is the z-axis of the rectangular (x, y, z)-coordinate system established below.

With P a point in space, let $\vec{u}$ be the vector from the origin to P. The line of $\vec{u}$ and the x-axis determine a plane in which the vector projection of $\vec{u}$ on the x-axis is a multiple of $\vec{i}$; that is, there is a number x such that this vector projection is $x\vec{i}$. In the same way, there are numbers y and z such that $y\vec{j}$ and $z\vec{k}$ are the vector projections of $\vec{u}$ on

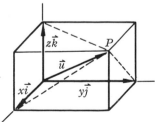

Fig. 10-1.3

the y-axis and z-axis, respectively. The point P is assigned the ordered triple (x, y, z) as its coordinates.

349

Conversely, if x, y, and z are given numbers, then the vector

$$\vec{u} = x\vec{i} + y\vec{j} + z\vec{k},$$

with initial end at the origin, has terminal end at the point (x, y, z). This one-to-one correspondence between points is spaced, and ordered triples (x, y, z) establishs a rectangular coordinate system—rectangular since $\vec{i}, \vec{j}$, and $\vec{k}$ are mutually perpendicular.

Recall that the dot product of two vectors is zero if and only the vectors are perpendicular. Hence,

$$(1) \qquad \vec{i}\cdot\vec{j} = \vec{i}\cdot\vec{k} = \vec{j}\cdot\vec{k} = 0,$$

and since the order of the factors of a dot product is immaterial, then also $\vec{j}\cdot\vec{i} = \vec{k}\cdot\vec{i} = \vec{k}\cdot\vec{j} = 0$. Also, the dot product of a vector by itself is the square of the length of the vector, so that

$$(2) \qquad \vec{i}\cdot\vec{i} = \vec{j}\cdot\vec{j} = \vec{k}\cdot\vec{k} = 1.$$

Example 1. Consider the line determined by the origin and the point $(3, -4, 7)$ and the line determined by the origin and the point $(2, 5, 2)$. Show that these lines intersect at right angles.

Solution. Draw the vectors from the origin to each of these points:

$$\vec{u} = 3\vec{i} - 4\vec{j} + 7\vec{k} \quad \text{and} \quad \vec{v} = 2\vec{i} + 5\vec{j} + 2\vec{k}$$

These two vectors lie in a plane, and the properties of the dot product hold as before, so that

$$\vec{u}\cdot\vec{v} = (3\vec{i} - 4\vec{j} + 7\vec{k})\cdot(2\vec{i} + 5\vec{j} + 2\vec{k})$$
$$= 6(\vec{i}\cdot\vec{i}) + 15(\vec{i}\cdot\vec{j}) + 6(\vec{i}\cdot\vec{k}) - 8(\vec{j}\cdot\vec{i}) - 20(\vec{j}\cdot\vec{j}) - 8(\vec{j}\cdot\vec{k}) + 14(\vec{k}\cdot\vec{i})$$
$$+ 35(\vec{k}\cdot\vec{j}) + 14(\vec{k}\cdot\vec{k}).$$

But (1) and (2) simplify this to

$$\vec{u}\cdot\vec{v} = 6 - 20 + 14 = 0.$$

Hence, the vectors intersect at right angles and the same is true of the lines on which they lie.

The expansion of a dot product, as used in the above example, shows that

$$(3) \qquad (a_1\vec{i} + b_1\vec{j} + c_1\vec{k})\cdot(a_2\vec{i} + b_2\vec{j} + c_2\vec{k}) = a_1a_2 + b_1b_2 + c_1c_2.$$

As in the plane, a vector may be moved parallel to itself. Figure 10-1.4 illustrates how a vector $\vec{u}$ from a point (x_1, y_1, z_1) to a point (x_2, y_2, z_2) may be moved to have its initial point at the origin and terminal point at $(x_2 - x_1, y_2 - y_1, z_2 - z_1)$, and hence that

$$(4) \qquad \vec{u} = (x_2 - x_1)\vec{i} + (y_2 - y_1)\vec{j} + (z_2 - z_1)\vec{k}.$$

Thus, to express a vector in terms of the coordinates of its initial and terminal points, subtract each initial coordinate from its corresponding terminal coordinate and use the respective differences as coefficients of $\vec{i}, \vec{j},$ and $\vec{k}$.

The square of the length of the vector (4) is $\vec{u} \cdot \vec{u}$:

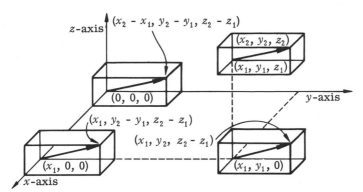

Fig. 10-1.4

$$|\vec{u}|^2 = \vec{u} \cdot \vec{u} = (x_2 - x_1)^2 + (y_2 - y_1)^2 + (z_2 - z_1)^2,$$

where (3) was used in expanding this dot product. Hence, the formula for the distance between two points (x_1, y_1, z_1) and (x_2, y_2, z_2) is

(5) $\text{distance} = \sqrt{(x_2 - x_1)^2 + (y_2 - y_1)^2 + (z_2 - z_1)^2}.$

It therefore follows that the equation of a sphere with center (c_1, c_2, c_3) and radius r is

(6) $(x - c_1)^2 + (y - c_2)^2 + (z - c_3)^2 = r^2.$

This follows since a variable point (x, y, z) is always exactly r units from (c_1, c_2, c_3) if and only if

$$r = \sqrt{(x - c_1)^2 + (y - c_2)^2 + (z - c_3)^2}.$$

Example 2. Show that the graph of

$$2x^2 + 2y^2 + 2z^2 - 4x + 6y + 5z = 4$$

is a sphere, and find its center and radius.

Solution. First divide by 2 and write the equation, preparatory to completing the square, as

$$(x^2 - 2x \quad) + (y^2 + 3y \quad) + (z^2 + \tfrac{5}{2}z \quad) = 2.$$

Hence,

$$(x^2 - 2x + 1) + (y^2 + 3y + \tfrac{9}{4}) + (z^2 + \tfrac{5}{2}y + \tfrac{25}{16}) = 2 + 1 + \tfrac{9}{4} + \tfrac{25}{16},$$

$$(x - 1)^2 + (y + \tfrac{3}{2})^2 + (z + \tfrac{5}{4})^2 = \tfrac{109}{16}.$$

This is in the form (6), so the graph is a sphere with

center $(1, -\frac{3}{2}, \frac{5}{4})$ and radius $\frac{\sqrt{109}}{4}$.

Example 3. A triangle has vertices $A(6, -1, 1)$, $B(3, -1, 7)$, and $C(2, -3, 3)$. Find the interior angles of the triangles.

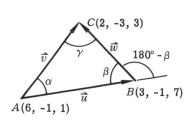

C(2, -3, 3)

$\vec{v}$ γ $\vec{w}$ $180° - \beta$

α β

$\vec{u}$ B(3, -1, 7)

A(6, -1, 1)

Fig. 10-1.5

Solution. It is not necessary to make a three-dimensional representation, but it is helpful to draw a plane figure (Fig. 10-1.5) to aid in visualizing relations. The figure need not even have the proper proportions. Let

$$\vec{AB} = \vec{u} = (3 - 6)\vec{i} + (-1 + 1)\vec{j} + (7 - 1)\vec{k}$$
$$= -3\vec{i} + 0 \cdot \vec{j} + 6\vec{k},$$
$$\vec{AC} = \vec{v} = -4\vec{i} - 2\vec{j} + 2\vec{k},$$
$$\vec{BC} = \vec{w} = -\vec{i} - 2\vec{j} - 4\vec{k},$$

where subtraction in the proper order has been carefully followed. Let α, β, γ be the interior angles at A, B, C, respectively. Since $\vec{u}$ and $\vec{v}$ both emanate from A, then

$$\cos \alpha = \frac{\vec{u} \cdot \vec{v}}{|\vec{u}| \, |\vec{v}|} = \frac{(-3)(-4) + 0(-2) + (6)(2)}{\sqrt{3^2 + 0^2 + 6^2} \sqrt{4^2 + 2^2 + 2^2}} = \frac{24}{\sqrt{45} \sqrt{24}} = \sqrt{\frac{8}{15}}.$$

Think of translating $\vec{u}$ along itself until its initial end is at B. Then the angle between $\vec{u}$ and $\vec{w}$ is $180° - \beta$ instead of β, so that

$$\cos(180° - \beta) = \frac{\vec{u} \cdot \vec{w}}{|\vec{u}| \, |\vec{w}|} = \frac{(-3)(-1) + (-2)0 + (-4)6}{\sqrt{45} \sqrt{1 + 2^2 + 4^2}} = \frac{3 - 24}{\sqrt{45}\sqrt{21}} = \frac{-21}{\sqrt{45}\sqrt{21}}.$$

Hence, $180° - \beta > 90°$, so $\beta < 90°$ and

$$\cos \beta = \frac{12}{\sqrt{45}\sqrt{21}} = \sqrt{\frac{7}{15}}.$$

Since $\vec{v}$ and $\vec{w}$ both terminate at the same point C, then

$$\cos \gamma = \frac{4 + 4 - 8}{\sqrt{24}\sqrt{21}} = 0,$$

and thus $\gamma = 90°$. By the use of tables, $\alpha = 43°05'$ and in this case it is unnecessary to use tables to find $\beta = 46°55'$ except as a check.

10-2. Parametric Equations of a Line

Two distinct points $P_1(x_1, y_1, z_1)$ and $P_2(x_2, y_2, z_2)$ determine a line, and the constant vector

$$\vec{u} = (x_2 - x_1)\vec{i} + (y_2 - y_1)\vec{j} + (z_2 - z_1)\vec{k},$$

with initial end at P_1, lies on this line. Given a typical point $P(x, y, z)$ on the vector

$$\vec{v} = (x - x_1)\vec{i} + (y - y_1)\vec{j} + (z - z_1)\vec{k},$$

with initial end at P_1, must also be on the line and is therefore a scalar multiple of $\vec{u}$:

$$\vec{v} = t\,\vec{u}.$$

Hence,

$$(x - x_1)\vec{i} + (y - y_1)\vec{j} + (z - z_1)\vec{k}$$
$$= t(x_2 - x_1)\vec{i} + t(y_2 - y_1)\vec{j} + t(z_2 - z_1)\vec{k}.$$

But this equation holds only if the coefficients of $\vec{i}, \vec{j}$, and $\vec{k}$ on one side are equal to the respective coefficients on the other side:

$$x - x_1 = t(x_2 - x_1), \quad y - y_1 = t(y_2 - y_1), \quad z - z_1 = t(z_2 - z_1).$$

These equations written as

(1) $\qquad x = x_1 + t(x_2 - x_1), \quad y = y_1 + t(y_2 - y_1), \quad z = z_1 + t(z_2 - z_1)$

are called **parametric equations**, with parameter t, of the line.

Example 1. Show that the line determined by the points $(2, 1, 3)$ and $(-1, 7, 2)$ intersects the line determined by the points $(-1, -3, -3)$ and $(2, -7, -1)$.

Solution. Parametric equations of the first line are

$$x = 2 + t(-1 - 2), \quad y = 1 + t(7 - 1), \quad z = 3 + t(2 - 3),$$

(2) $\qquad\qquad = 2 - 3t \qquad\qquad\quad = 1 + 6t \qquad\qquad = 3 - t.$

For the second line, it is better to use some letter other than t for the parameter:

(3) $\qquad\qquad x = -1 + 3s, \quad y = -3 - 4s, \quad z = -3 + 2s.$

The problem is now to determine whether there is a value of t and a value of s such that this value of t in (2) and this value of s in (3) will yield the same x, y, z values. It is therefore necessary to decide whether the three equations

$$2 - 3t = -1 + 3s,$$

(4) $\qquad\qquad\qquad 1 + 6t = -3 - 4s,$

$$3 - t = -3 + 2s,$$

in two unknowns t and s, have a simultaneous solution. The first two equations, written as

$$t + s = 1,$$
$$3t + 2s = -2,$$

have the simultaneous solution $t = -4$, $s = 5$, and a check shows that these values also satisfy the third equation. By substituting $t = -4$ in (2), the point

$$(14, -23, 7)$$

is obtained and it should be checked that $s = 5$ in (3) yields the same point.

Notice that if t has been used for the parameter of both lines, then, instead of (4), the three equations

$$2 - 3t = -1 + 3t,$$

(5) $$1 + 6t = -3 - 4t,$$

$$3 - t = -3 + 2t$$

in one unknown would be obtained, and no value of t satisfies all three. A physical interpretation is that a particle moving on the first line has position at time t given by (2) and at the same time t a particle moving on the second line has location

$$x = -1 + 3t, \quad y = -3 - 4t, \quad z = -3 + 2t.$$

Both particles pass through the point $(14, -23, 7)$, but the nonsimultaneous solution of (5) means that they do so at different times (the first when $t = -4$ and the second when $t = 5$).

Example 2. Show that the lines having parametric equations

$$x = -1 - 6t, \quad y = 7 + 12t, \quad z = 2 - 2t, \quad \text{and}$$
$$x = 2 - 3t, \quad y = 1 + 6t, \quad z = 3 - t$$

are actually the same line.

Solution. Change the parameter of the second line to s:

(6) $$x = 2 - 3s, \quad y = 1 + 6s, \quad z = 3 - s,$$

set corresponding $x, y,$ and z expressions equal:

$$-1 - 6t = 2 - 3s$$
$$7 + 12t = 1 + 6s,$$
$$2 - 2t = 3 - s,$$

and note that all of these equations reduce to

$$s = 2t + 1.$$

This means that any point on either line is also on the other. In fact, $s = 2t + 1$ substituted into (6) yields the first set of equations.

Problem 1. The plane determined by the x- and y-axes is called the (x, y)-plane and in the same way the (x, z)-plane and (y, z)-plane are determined. For each of the given points, find the point symmetric to the given plane, axis, or point:

a. $(2, 1, 4)$, (x, y)-plane.
b. $(-2, 5, 3)$, (y, z)-plane.
c. $(3, -1, 7)$, (x, y)-plane.
d. $(2, -3, 5)$, z-axis.

e. $(5, 7, -4)$, x-axis.
f. $(4, -2, 3)$, origin.
g. $(4, -2, 3)$, point $(1, 0, 0)$.
h. $(3, 5, -6)$, point $(1, 2, 3)$.

Problem 2. Show that the given points are vertices of a right triangle. Find the other angles and the area of the triangle.

a. $A(-3, 0, 1)$, $B(-2, 2, 4)$, $C(4, -2, 0)$.
b. $A(3, -1, 0)$, $B(1, 2, 5)$, $C(5, -3, 2)$.

Problem 3. Prove that the line segment joining (x_1, y_1, z_1) and (x_2, y_2, z_2) has midpoint $\left(\dfrac{x_1 + x_2}{2}, \dfrac{y_1 + y_2}{2}, \dfrac{z_1 + z_2}{2}\right)$.

Problem 4. Show that the given points are vertices of an isosceles triangle. Find the angle between the equal sides and find the area.

a. $A(0, 2, 5)$, $B(2, 2, 3)$, $C(-1, 0, 2)$ b. $A(1, 1, 0)$, $B(3, 0, 3)$, $C(-1, 4, 1)$.

Problem 5. Find the points on the given sphere that are closest to and farthest from the origin:

a. $x^2 + y^2 + z^2 - 10x + 8y - 12z + 73 = 0$.
b. $x^2 + y^2 + z^2 - 4x + 8y - 12z + 42 = 0$.

Problem 6. Find the points on the two spheres that are a minimum distance apart:

a. $(x + 1)^2 + (y - 1)^2 + (z + 5)^2 = 6$,
$$(x - 3)^2 + (y - 9)^2 + (z + 1)^2 = 24.$$
b. $x^2 + y^2 + z^2 + 2x - 2y + 4z + 3 = 0$, $x^2 + (y - 2)^2 + (z + 1)^2 = 12$.

Problem 7. Determine whether or not the pair of lines intersect:

a. $x = 1 + t$, $y = 2 - t$, $z = 4 + 3t$; joining $(1, -4, 7)$, $(6, 8, -2)$.
b. Joining $(1, -1, 3)$, $(2, 1, -1)$; joining $(1, 3, -9)$, $(-1, 1, -7)$.

10-3. Direction Cosines and Numbers

The angle between two vectors (whether as given they intersect or not) is defined as the angle between the parallel translations of these vectors, so that each has its initial end at the origin (see Fig. 10-3.1).

Also, an angle between two lines, whether or not they intersect, is defined as the angle between any vectors on the lines.

Example 1. One line contains the points $(1, 0, -3)$ and $(2, 1, 4)$, while another line contains the points $(-1, 2, 3)$ and $(0, -2, 1)$. Find the acute angle between these lines.

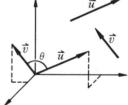

Fig. 10-3.1

Solution. By subtracting coordinates in a consistent order, vectors considered on the respective lines are

$$\vec{u} = \vec{i} + \vec{j} + 7\vec{k} \quad \text{and} \quad \vec{v} = \vec{i} - 4\vec{j} - 2\vec{k}.$$

An angle between these vectors is such that its cosine equals

$$\frac{\vec{u} \cdot \vec{v}}{|\vec{u}|\,|\vec{v}|} = \frac{1 - 4 - 14}{\sqrt{51}\,\sqrt{21}} = \frac{-17}{\sqrt{(51)(21)}}.$$

Since an acute angle θ is asked for, then

$$\cos \theta = \frac{17}{\sqrt{(51)(21)}} \quad \text{and} \quad \theta = 58°41'.$$

In the previous section, it was shown how to find parametric equations of a line passing through two points. Notice now that if $a, b,$ and c are not all zero, then the graph of the parametric equations

(1) $$x = x_1 + at \quad y = y_1 + bt, \quad z = z_1 + ct$$

is a straight line. In particular, $t = 0$ and $t = 1$ shows that the graph passes through the points

$$(x_1, y_1, z_1) \quad \text{and} \quad (x_1 + a, \ y_1 + b, \ z_1 + c).$$

Now if the rule for finding parametric equations of the line through these two points is applied, the result is (1), thus showing that the graph of (1) is a straight line.

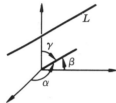

Fig. 10-3.2

The angles α, β, γ that a line makes with the positive $x, y,$ and z-axes are called **direction angles** of the line, and $\cos \alpha$, $\cos \beta$, $\cos \gamma$ are called **direction cosines** of the line.

A vector considered on the line (1) is

$$\vec{u} = a\vec{i} + b\vec{j} + c\vec{k}.$$

Hence the direction cosines of the line (1) are

$$\cos \alpha = \frac{\vec{u} \cdot \vec{i}}{|\vec{u}||\vec{i}|}, \quad \cos \beta = \frac{\vec{u} \cdot \vec{j}}{|\vec{u}||\vec{j}|}, \quad \text{and} \quad \cos \gamma = \frac{\vec{u} \cdot \vec{k}}{|\vec{u}||\vec{k}|}.$$

But $\vec{u} \cdot \vec{i} = (a\vec{i} + b\vec{j} + c\vec{k}) \cdot \vec{i} = a\vec{i} \cdot \vec{i} + b\vec{j} \cdot \vec{i} + c\vec{k} \cdot \vec{i} = a.$

Therefore,

(2) $$\cos \alpha = \frac{a}{\sqrt{a^2 + b^2 + c^2}}, \quad \cos \beta = \frac{b}{\sqrt{a^2 + b^2 + c^2}},$$

$$\cos \gamma = \frac{c}{\sqrt{a^2 + b^2 + c^2}}.$$

Thus, in (1) the numbers a, b, c are proportional to the direction cosines [the proportionality factor being $(a^2 + b^2 + c^2)^{-1/2}$].

It is customary to say that numbers $a, b,$ and c are **direction numbers** of a line if $a, b,$ and c are proportional to the direction cosines of the line.

Let two lines have direction numbers a_1, b_1, c_1 and $a_2, b_2, c_2,$ and let

$$\vec{v}_1 = a_1\vec{i} + b_1\vec{j} + c_1\vec{k} \quad \text{and} \quad \vec{v}_2 = a_2\vec{i} + b_2\vec{j} + c_2\vec{k}$$

be vectors on these lines, respectively. Then an angle θ between the lines is such that

(3) $$\cos \theta = \frac{\vec{v}_1 \cdot \vec{v}_2}{|\vec{v}_1||\vec{v}_2|} = \frac{a_1 a_2 + b_1 b_2 + c_1 c_2}{\sqrt{a_1^2 + b_1^2 + c_1^2} \sqrt{a_2^2 + b_2^2 + c_2^2}}.$$

The lines are then perpendicular if and only $\cos \theta = 0$, that is, if and only if

(4) $$a_1 a_2 + b_1 b_2 + c_1 c_2 = 0.$$

On the other hand, the lines are parallel if and only if (after translating $\vec{v}_1$ and $\vec{v}_2$ to the origin) $\vec{v}_2$ is a constant multiple of $\vec{v}_1$:

$$\vec{v}_2 = \lambda \vec{v}_1$$

$$a_2 \vec{i} + b_2 \vec{j} + c_2 \vec{k} = \lambda a_1 \vec{i} + \lambda b_2 \vec{j} + \lambda c_3 \vec{k}$$

By equating coefficients of $\vec{i}, \vec{j}$, and $\vec{k}$, it follows that the lines are parallel if and only if there is a constant λ such that

(5) $$a_2 = \lambda a_1, \quad b_2 = \lambda b_1, \quad c_2 = \lambda c_1.$$

Example 2. Given the point $P_0(-2, 1, -6)$ and the line L having parametric equations

$$L: x = -1 + 2t, \quad y = -6 + 4t, \quad z = 10 - 7t,$$

find parametric equations of the line through P_0 and:
   a. Parallel to L.
   b. Intersecting L at right angles.

Solution a. In this case, the new line has direction numbers proportional to the direction numbers $2, 4, -7$ of L. Any proportionality factor may be used, and a convenient one is $\lambda = 1$. Answer:

$$x = -2 + 2t, \quad y = 1 + 4t, \quad z = -6 - 7t.$$

Solution b. The requested line passes through P_0, must intersect L, and in addition must be perpendicular to L. First take a general point on L:

(6) $$(-1 + 2t, \quad -6 + 4t, \quad 10 - 7t).$$

The line containing this point and P_0 then intersects L and has direction numbers

$$-1 + 2t - (-2), \quad -6 + 4t - 1, \quad 10 - 7t - (-6); \quad \text{that is,}$$

$$2t + 1, \quad 4t - 7, \quad -7t + 16.$$

But L has direction numbers $2, 4, -7$, and hence t must be found so that [using (4)]

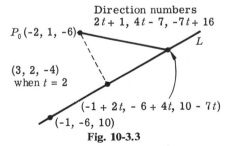

Direction numbers
$2t + 1, \ 4t - 7, \ -7t + 16$

$P_0(-2, 1, -6)$

L

$(3, 2, -4)$
when $t = 2$

$(-1 + 2t, -6 + 4t, 10 - 7t)$

$(-1, -6, 10)$

Fig. 10-3.3

$$(2t + 1)2 + (4t - 7)4 + (-7t + 16)(-7) = 0,$$

$$(4 + 16 + 49)t = -2 + 28 + 112,$$

$$69t = 138, \quad t = 2.$$

Substitute $t = 2$ into (6), or the equations of L, to obtain the point

$$(3, 2, -4)$$

on L. This point and $P_0(-2, 1, -6)$ determine a line not only intersecting L but also perpendicular to L. Answer:

$$x = -2 + 5t, \quad y = 1 + t, \quad z = -6 + 2t.$$

Two lines are said to be **skew** to one another if they are neither parallel nor intersecting. A theorem of solid geometry says that if two lines are skew, then there is one and only one line intersecting both and perpendicular to both.

Example 3. Show that the two lines

$$L_1: x = 4 - t, \quad y = -2 + 2t, \quad z = 7 - 3t,$$
$$L_2: x = 3 + 2s, \quad y = -7 - 3s, \quad z = 6 + 4s$$

are skew. Also, find the points on the lines such that the segment joining these points is perpendicular to both lines.

Solution. The x's and y's are equal if $t = -13$ and $s = 7$. These values give $z = 46$ on L_1, but $z = 34$ on L_2, so the lines do not intersect. The lines are not parallel since their direction numbers are not proportional.

General points on the lines are, respectively,

$$(4 - t, -2 + 2t, 7 - 3t) \quad \text{and} \quad (3 + 2s, -7 - 3s, 6 + 4s).$$

Direction numbers of the line joining these points are

$$3 + 2s - (4 - t), \quad -7 - 3s - (-2 + 2t), \quad 6 + 4s - (7 - 3t); \text{ that is,}$$
$$t + 2s - 1, \quad -2t - 3s - 5, \quad 3t + 4s - 1.$$

This line will be perpendicular to L_1 (whose direction numbers are $-1, 2, -3$) if

$$(-1)(t + 2s - 1) + 2(-2t - 3s - 5) - 3(3t + 4s - 1) = 0,$$

which reduces to

$$-14t - 20s = 6.$$

In the same way, the line is perpendicular to L_2 if

$$20t + 29s = -9.$$

The simultaneous solution of these equations is $t = 1, s = -1$. Finally, $t = 1$ in L_1 and $s = -1$ in L_2 yield the desired points

$$(3, 0, 4) \quad \text{and} \quad (1, -4, 2).$$

Problem 1. Find direction cosines of the line joining the points:

a. $(2, 1, -3)$, $(6, 1, 0)$.   b. $(-1, 5, 3)$, $(2, 1, 4)$.

Problem 2. a. Prove that if $\cos \alpha$, $\cos \beta$, $\cos \gamma$ are direction cosines of a line, then

$$\cos^2 \alpha + \cos^2 \beta + \cos^2 \gamma = 1.$$

b. Show there is no line having $\alpha = 30°, \beta = 45°$.

c. Show that if α and β are positive acute direction angles of a line, then
$\alpha + \beta \geq 90°$.

d. What condition must hold if $0 < \alpha < 90°$ and $90° < \beta < 180°$?

e. Given $\cos \alpha$ and $\cos \beta$ of a line, show that

$$\cos^2 \gamma = (\sin \alpha + \cos \beta)(\sin \alpha - \cos \beta).$$

Problem 3. Show there are two lines having the two given direction angles α and β. In each case, find the acute angle between these lines:

a. $\alpha = 60°, \quad \beta = 45°$.

b. $\alpha = 120°, \quad \beta = 60°$.

c. $\alpha = 55°, \quad \beta = 42°$.

d. $\alpha = 37°, \quad \beta = 116°$.

Problem 4. Use calculus to find the perpendicular distance from the point P_0 to the line L:

a. $P_0(-2, 1, -6)$, $L: x = -1 + 2t, \quad y = -6 + 4t, \quad z = 10 - 7t$.

b. $P_0(1, 9, 6)$, $L: x = 1 + 2t, \quad y = 2 - t, \quad z = -1 - 3t$.

Problem 5. Show that the pairs of lines are skew, and find the points on the lines that are ends of a segment perpendicular to both lines:

a. $L_1: x = 5 + t, \quad y = 8 - 3t, \quad z = -t$.
$L_2: x = -5 + s, \quad y = -5 + 2s. \quad z = -9 + 4s$.

b. $L_1: x = 4 + t, \quad y = 1 + t, \quad z = 3 + 3t$.
$L_2: x = -1, \quad y = -2 + s, \quad z = 2 + s$.

Problem 6. Find parametric equations of the line L through A perpendicular to the plane of $A, B,$ and C. [Note: A line is perpendicular to a plane if it is perpendicular to two lines in the plane.]

a. $A(1, -2, 3), \quad B(4, 3, -2), \quad C(-2, 1, 4)$.

b. $A(0, 0, 0), \quad B(1, 0, 0), \quad C(0, 1, 1)$.

10-4. Equation of a Plane

Let $A, B,$ and C be three numbers not all zero, let $P_0(x_0, y_0, z_0)$ be a point, and let L_0 be the line through P_0 with direction numbers A, B, C. Think of a vector $\vec{v}$ with initial point P_0 and $\vec{v}$ perpendicular to L_0. Let the vector $\vec{v}$ vary with all possible lengths and directions but always remain perpendicular to L_0 and have initial end at P_0. All terminal ends (x, y, z) of such vectors form a plane. But

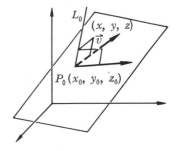

$$\vec{v} = (x - x_0)\vec{i} + (y - y_0)\vec{j} + (z - z_0)\vec{k},$$

so that $x - x^0, y - y_0, z - z_0$ are direction numbers of the line containing $\vec{v}$. All such lines and L_0 are perpendicular so x, y, z must satisfy

(1) $\quad A(x - x_0) + B(y - y_0) + C(z - z_0) = 0.$

Fig. 10-4.1

Conversely, $x = x_0, y = y_0, z = z_0$ satisfy (1), and for any other x, y, z satisfying (1) the points (x, y, z) and (x_0, y_0, z_0) determine a line perpendicular to L_0. Hence, (1) is the equation of the plane through $P_0(x_0, y_0, z_0)$ perpendicular to L_0 and thus perpendicular to any line with direction numbers A, B, C.

It will now be shown that:

If A, B, and C are constants not all zero and D is a constant, then the graph of

(2) $$Ax + By + Cz = D$$

is a plane and any line normal (that is, perpendicular) to this plane has direction numbers A, B, C.

PROOF. Assuming $A \neq 0$, choose any constants y_0 and z_0 and set

$$x_0 = \frac{1}{A}(D - By_0 - Cz_0) \quad \text{so that} \quad D = Ax_0 + By_0 + Cz_0.$$

Hence, (x_0, y_0, z_0) is a point on the graph of (2). Also, any variable point (x, y, z) on the graph of (2) is such that

$$Ax + By + Cz = Ax_0 + By_0 + Cz_0; \quad \text{that is,}$$
$$A(x - x_0) + B(y - y_0) + C(z - z_0) = 0,$$

which is in the form (1) already known to be the equation of a plane.

Example 1. Find the point where the line

$$L : x = 1 + t, \quad y = -2 + 3t, \quad z = 8 - 2t$$

pierces the plane $5x - 3y + 2z = 3$.

Solution. The point $(1 + t, -2 + 3t, 8 - 2t)$ will be on the plane if t satisfies the equation

$$5(1 + t) - 3(-2 + 3t) + 2(8 - 2t) = 3.$$

This equation is $-8t + 27 = 3$, and hence $t = 3$. This value substituted into L yields the point

$$(4, 7, 2),$$

which is both on the line and on the plane.

Example 2. Show that the line

$$L : x = 1 + 2t, \quad y = -2 - 4t, \quad z = 3 - 2t$$

lies on the plane $2x + 3y - 4z + 16 = 0$.

Solution. By proceeding as if the point where the line pierces the plane were sought, the result is

$$2(1 + 2t) + 3(-2 - 4t) - 4(3 - 2t) + 16 = 0,$$
$$t(4 - 12 + 8) + 2 - 6 - 12 + 16 = 0,$$
$$t \cdot 0 + 0 = 0.$$

Hence, an equation is obtained that holds for all t, and thus the entire line L lies on the given plane.

In a plane two lines are parallel if they do not intersect, but in space two lines may be neither parallel nor intersecting (skew lines as mentioned above). In space, two planes are parallel if they do not intersect, and also a line and a plane are parallel if they do not intersect.

Example 3. Show that the line

$$L: x = 1 - 2t, \quad y = 2t, \quad z = 3 + 4t$$

and the plane $2x - 4y + 3z = 7$ are parallel.

Solution. As before, substitute from L into the equation of the plane

$$2(1 - 2t) - 4(2t) + 3(3 + 4t) = 0,$$

$$t(-4 - 8 + 12) + 2 + 9 = 0, \quad t \cdot 0 + 11 = 0,$$

and this equation is never satisfied. Thus, the line and plane have no point in common and are therefore parallel.

Two planes

$$A_1 x + B_1 y + C_1 z = D_1, \quad A_2 x + B_2 y + C_2 z = D_2$$

are parallel (or coincide) if and only if their normals are parallel, and the condition for this is the proportionality

$$A_1 : A_2 = B_1 : B_2 = C_1 : C_2.$$

If the planes are not parallel, they intersect in a line and the figure so formed is called a **dihedral angle**. A dihedral angle is measured by the plane angle θ between lines in the planes perpendicular to the intersection at a point. But θ is also the angle between the normals to the planes. Thus, from the direction numbers A_1, B_1, C_1 and A_2, B_2, C_2 of the normals,

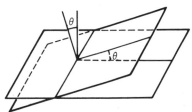

Fig. 10-4.2

(3)
$$\cos \theta = \frac{A_1 A_2 + B_1 B_2 + C_1 C_2}{\sqrt{A_1^2 + B_1^2 + C_1^2} \sqrt{A_2^2 + B_2^2 + C_2^2}}.$$

In particular, the planes intersect at right angles whenever

$$A_1 A_2 + B_1 B_2 + C_1 C_2 = 0.$$

Some analogies will now be pointed out.

The equation $x = 2$ represents:

1. A point in one dimension.
2. A line in two dimensions ($x + 0 \cdot y = 2$).
3. A plane in three dimensions ($x + 0 \cdot y + 0 \cdot z = 2$).

The equation $2x + 3y = 4$ represents:

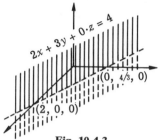

1. A line in two dimensions.
2. A plane in three dimensions ($2x + 3y + 0 \cdot z = 4$). (See Fig. 10-4.3.)

The intersection of:

1. Two lines in the plane is a point.
2. Two planes in space is a line.

The fact that the simultaneous solution of

Fig. 10-4.3

$$x + y = 3 \quad \text{and} \quad x + 2y = 5$$

is $x = 1$, $y = 2$ illustrates the interpretation:

In the plane, the intersection of any two lines may be expressed as the intersection of two lines each parallel to an axis.

The following analogous situation will be illustrated in Example 4:

In space, the intersection of any two planes may be expressed as the intersection of three planes each parallel to an axis.

Note first that the plane

$$Ax + By + Cz = D, \quad \text{with} \quad A, B, \text{ or } C \text{ zero,}$$

is parallel to a coordinate axis. For example, $0 \cdot x + By + Cz = D$ is perpendicular to the (y, z)-plane and thus parallel to the x-axis.

Example 4. Express the line of intersection of the planes

(4) $$6x - y - 2z = -3 \quad \text{and} \quad 3x - 2y + 2z = 9$$

as the intersection of planes parallel to the axes.

Solution. For k any constant, the graph of

(5) $$(6x - y - 2z + 3) + k(3x - 2y + 2z - 9) = 0$$

is a plane that contains the line of intersection of the planes (4); any point (x, y, z) on this line makes both parenthetic expressions zero. Write (5) in the form

$$(6 + 3k)x + (-1 - 2k)y + (-2 + 2k)z = -3 + 9k.$$

By inspection there are three choices of k to make a coefficient zero:

$$k = -2: \quad 0 \cdot x + 3y - 6z = -21,$$

$$k = -\tfrac{1}{2}: \quad \tfrac{9}{2}x + 0 \cdot y - 3z = -\tfrac{15}{2},$$

$$k = 1: \quad 9x - 3y + 0 \cdot z = 6.$$

Thus, any two of the equations

$$y - 2z = -7,$$

(6) $$3x - 2z = -5,$$

$$3x - y = 2$$

may be used to represent the line of intersection of the planes (4). Each of planes (6) is parallel to an axis.

Example 5. Find a parametric representation of the line in Example 4. Determine direction numbers of the line.

Solution. First obtain any two of the equations (6) and solve these two for the common variable. As illustration, the first and second are chosen:

$$z = \frac{y + 7}{2} = \frac{3x + 5}{2}.$$

These are all equal, so set each equal to a parameter t and solve for $x, y,$ and z in terms of t:

$$\frac{3x + 5}{2} = t, \quad x = \frac{2t - 5}{3},$$

$$\frac{y + 7}{2} = t, \quad y = 2t - 7,$$

$$z = t, \quad z = t.$$

Thus, the parametric equations

(7) $$x = -\tfrac{5}{3} + \tfrac{2}{3}t, \quad y = -7 + 2t, \quad z = 0 + 1 \cdot t$$

of the line are obtained.

It follows that the coefficients of t

$$\tfrac{2}{3}, \quad 2, \quad 1$$

are direction numbers of the line (and these multiplied by any nonzero constant are direction numbers; for example, 2, 6, 3).

If there is any doubt that the line (7) lies on both planes (4), substitute x, y, z from (7) into both equations (4) and see that the result is $0 \cdot t = 0$, which is satisfied by any number t.

It will now be shown that the perpendicular distance from (x_0, y_0, z_0) to the plane

$$Ax + By + Cz = D$$

is

(8) $$\text{distance} = \frac{|Ax_0 + By_0 + Cz_0 - D|}{\sqrt{A^2 + B^2 + C^2}}.$$

First, the vector $\vec{u} = \vec{i}A + \vec{j}B + \vec{k}C$ is perpendicular to the plane. At least one of the axes cuts the plane. In particular, if $C \neq 0$ the z-axis cuts the plane at $(0, 0, z)$, where $A \cdot 0 + B \cdot 0 + Cz = D$, and hence at the point

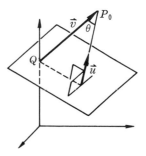

Fig. 10-4.4

$$Q\left(0, 0, \frac{D}{C}\right).$$

Then the vector $\vec{v} = \overrightarrow{QP_0} = \vec{i}(x_0 - 0) + \vec{j}(y_0-0)+\vec{k}(z_0 - D/C)$ has the length of its projection on the line of $\vec{u}$ equal to

$$|\vec{v}||\cos\theta| = \frac{|\vec{u}\cdot\vec{v}|}{|\vec{u}|} = \frac{\left|Ax_0 + By_0 + C\left(z_0 - \frac{D}{C}\right)\right|}{\sqrt{A^2 + B^2 + C^2}},$$

which is also the perpendicular distance from P_0 to the plane. This expression simplifies to (8).

Problem 1. Find an equation of the plane passing through the three points:
a. $(3, 2, 1)$, $(5, 1, 2)$, $(2, 3, 3)$.   b. $(1, 3, 0)$, $(-1, 4, -1)$, $(4, 1, -1)$.

Problem 2. Find an equation of the plane determined by the given point and the given line:
a. $(4, 1, -1)$; $L: x = 3 + 2t$, $y = 2 - t$, $z = 1 + t$.
b. $(5, 1, 2)$; $L: x = 3-t$, $y = 2 + t$, $z = 1 + 2t$.

Problem 3. Show that the two lines intersect and find an equation of the plane they determine:
a. $L_1: x = 1 + 2t$, $y = 3 - t$, $z = t$.
   $L_2: x = 3 - t$, $y = 2 + t$, $z = 1 + 2t$.
b. $L_1: x = 3 + t$, $y = 2 - \frac{1}{2}t$, $z = 1 + \frac{1}{2}t$.
   $L_2: x = -7 - t$, $y = 12 + t$, $z = 21 + 2t$.

Problem 4. Find an equation of the plane through the given point parallel to the given plane:
a. $(-1, 4, 3)$; $3x + 5y - z = 18$.   b. $(4, -8, 3)$; $x - y + z = 10$.

Problem 5. Find an equation of the plane through the given point and perpendicular to the given line.
a. $(2, -3, -5)$; $L: x = 25 - 2t$, $y = -52 + 3t$. $z = 47 - t$.
b. $(-2, 0, 1)$; $L: x = 16 - \frac{5}{2}t$, $y = -20 + \frac{2}{3}t$, $z = 15 + t$.
c. $(2, 15, 45)$; $L: x = 5t$, $y = 4$, $z = 5$.

Problem 6. Find direction numbers of the line of intersection of the two planes:
a. $4x + 2y - 2z = -6$, $7x + 2y - 4z = -7$.
b. $6x + 10y - 15z = -60$, $4x + 5y - 5z = -20$.
c. $x + 3y = 14$, $2y + z = 10$.
d. $2x - 3z = -2$, $x + y - z = 4$.

Problem 7. Derive the distance formula (8) by expressing the distance between P_0 and the point where

$$L: x = x_0 + At, \quad y = y_0 + Bt, \quad z = z_0 + Ct$$

pierces the plane.

10-5. Determinants

The purpose of this section is to present those few properties of determinants that will be used in succeeding sections. The square arrays of numbers

$$\begin{pmatrix} a_1 & b_1 \\ a_2 & b_2 \end{pmatrix} \quad \text{and} \quad \begin{pmatrix} a_1 & b_1 & c_1 \\ a_2 & b_2 & c_2 \\ a_3 & b_3 & c_3 \end{pmatrix}$$

are called **matrices** of **second** and **third** order, respectively. When vertical lines instead of parentheses are used, the result is called the **determinant** of the matrix and is assigned a value by the following definition:

$$(1) \qquad\qquad \begin{vmatrix} a_1 & b_1 \\ a_2 & b_2 \end{vmatrix} = a_1 b_2 - b_1 a_2,$$

$$(2) \qquad \begin{vmatrix} a_1 & b_1 & c_1 \\ a_2 & b_2 & c_2 \\ a_3 & b_3 & c_3 \end{vmatrix} = a_1 \begin{vmatrix} b_2 & c_2 \\ b_3 & c_3 \end{vmatrix} - b_1 \begin{vmatrix} a_2 & c_2 \\ a_3 & b_3 \end{vmatrix} + c_1 \begin{vmatrix} a_2 & b_2 \\ a_3 & b_3 \end{vmatrix}.$$

Notice carefully the position of the minus sign in each case. As examples:

$$\begin{vmatrix} 2 & 3 \\ 4 & -5 \end{vmatrix} = 2(-5) - (3)(4) = -10 - 12 = -22,$$

$$\begin{vmatrix} 4 & -5 \\ 2 & 3 \end{vmatrix} = 4(3) - (-5)2 = 12 + 10 = 22,$$

$$\begin{vmatrix} 6 & 2 & -1 \\ 0 & 2 & 3 \\ 7 & 4 & -5 \end{vmatrix} = 6 \begin{vmatrix} 2 & 3 \\ 4 & -5 \end{vmatrix} - 2 \begin{vmatrix} 0 & 3 \\ 7 & -5 \end{vmatrix} + (-1) \begin{vmatrix} 0 & 2 \\ 7 & 4 \end{vmatrix}$$

$$= 6(-22) - 2(0 - 21) - (0 - 14)$$

$$= -132 + 42 + 14 = -76.$$

If the two rows of a second-order determinant are interchanged, the sign of the determinant is changed. This is seen by merely interchanging the rows in (1) and then following the rule for evaluating the resulting determinant:

$$\begin{vmatrix} a_2 & b_2 \\ a_1 & b_1 \end{vmatrix} = a_2 b_1 - b_2 a_1 = -(a_1 b_2 - b_1 a_2) = - \begin{vmatrix} a_1 & b_1 \\ a_2 & b_2 \end{vmatrix}.$$

If any two rows of a third-order determinant are interchanged, the sign of the determinant is changed. As an illustration, the second and third rows of (2) are interchanged:

$$\begin{vmatrix} a_1 & b_1 & c_1 \\ a_3 & b_3 & c_3 \\ a_2 & b_2 & c_2 \end{vmatrix} = a_1 \begin{vmatrix} b_3 & c_3 \\ b_2 & c_2 \end{vmatrix} - b_1 \begin{vmatrix} a_3 & c_3 \\ a_2 & c_2 \end{vmatrix} + c_1 \begin{vmatrix} a_3 & b_3 \\ a_2 & b_2 \end{vmatrix}.$$

and each second-order determinant on the right is the negative of the corresponding second-order determinant on the right of (2).

Vector determinants are also defined if one row consists of vectors and the other rows contain only numbers. For example,

$$\begin{vmatrix} \vec{i} & \vec{j} & \vec{k} \\ 0 & 2 & -3 \\ 7 & 4 & 5 \end{vmatrix} = \vec{i}(10 + 12) - \vec{j}(0 + 21) + \vec{k}(0 - 14)$$

$$= 22\vec{i} - 21\vec{j} - 14\vec{k}.$$

It is this type of vector determinant that will appear most frequently in the following sections.

Example Given the vectors $\vec{u} = 2\vec{i} - 3\vec{j} + \vec{k}$ and $\vec{v} = 4\vec{i} + \vec{j} - 2\vec{k}$, show that each of these is perpendicular to

(3)
$$\vec{w} = \begin{vmatrix} \vec{i} & \vec{j} & \vec{k} \\ 2 & -3 & 1 \\ 4 & 1 & -2 \end{vmatrix}.$$

[Note how the coefficients in $\vec{u}$ and $\vec{v}$ are used in the determinant.]

Solution. First expand the determinant representing $\vec{w}$:

$$\vec{w} = \vec{i}\begin{vmatrix} -3 & 1 \\ 1 & -2 \end{vmatrix} - \vec{j}\begin{vmatrix} 2 & 1 \\ 4 & -2 \end{vmatrix} + \vec{k}\begin{vmatrix} 2 & -3 \\ 4 & 1 \end{vmatrix}$$

$$= \vec{i}(6 - 1) - \vec{j}(-4 - 4) + \vec{k}(2 + 12)$$

$$= 5\vec{i} + 8\vec{j} + 14\vec{k}.$$

Now

$$\vec{u}\cdot\vec{w} = (2\vec{i} - 3\vec{j} + \vec{k})\cdot(5\vec{i} + 8\vec{j} + 14\vec{k}) = 2(5) + (-3)(8) + 1(14)$$

$$= 10 - 24 + 14 = 0;$$

hence, $\vec{u}$ and $\vec{w}$ are perpendicular. In the same way,

$$\vec{v}\cdot\vec{w} = 4(5) + 1(8) + (-2)(14) = 20 + 8 - 28 = 0.$$

Note the same property, "interchange of rows changes the sign," holds for vector determinants. For example, interchange the second and third rows in (3):

$$\begin{vmatrix} \vec{i} & \vec{j} & \vec{k} \\ 4 & 1 & -2 \\ 2 & -3 & 1 \end{vmatrix} = \vec{i}(1 - 6) - \vec{j}(4 + 4) + \vec{k}(-12 - 2)$$

$$= -5\vec{i} - 8\vec{j} - 14\vec{k} = -\vec{w}.$$

Matrices and determinants are useful in many connections, and there is a big temptation to include more about them in this book. It seems wise, however, not to break the trend of development more than to obtain facility in expanding determinants, as provided by the following problems.

Problem 1. Evaluate each of the determinants:

a. $\begin{vmatrix} -5 & 6 \\ 2 & 3 \end{vmatrix}$.

c. $\begin{vmatrix} \sin\theta & -\cos\theta \\ \cos\theta & \sin\theta \end{vmatrix}$.

e. $\begin{vmatrix} 3 & 2 & 4 \\ 1 & 0 & -2 \\ 3 & 4 & -3 \end{vmatrix}$.

g. $\begin{vmatrix} \frac{1}{2} & 2 & \frac{3}{2} \\ 4 & 2 & \frac{1}{3} \\ 0 & 0 & 2 \end{vmatrix}$.

b. $\begin{vmatrix} \frac{1}{2} & 5 \\ 3 & 4 \end{vmatrix}$.

d. $\begin{vmatrix} \tan\theta & \sec\theta \\ \sec\theta & \tan\theta \end{vmatrix}$.

f. $\begin{vmatrix} 2 & -5 & 7 \\ 0 & 1 & 2 \\ 1 & -1 & 3 \end{vmatrix}$.

Problem 2. Establish each of the following. In each case, look for a property that may be generalized.

a. $\begin{vmatrix} 2 & 5 & -7 \\ 3 & -4 & 3 \\ 0 & 0 & 0 \end{vmatrix} = 0.$

b. $\begin{vmatrix} 2 & 5 & -7 \\ 3 & -4 & 3 \\ 3 & -4 & 3 \end{vmatrix} = 0.$

c. $\begin{vmatrix} -2 & 1 & 3 \\ 4 & 1 & 8 \\ 3 & 2 & 6 \end{vmatrix} = -\begin{vmatrix} 1 & -2 & 3 \\ 1 & 4 & 8 \\ 2 & 3 & 6 \end{vmatrix} = 35.$

d. $\begin{vmatrix} \vec{i} & \vec{j} & \vec{k} \\ 2+3 & 5-3 & 1+2 \\ 5 & & -1 & 4 \end{vmatrix} = \begin{vmatrix} \vec{i} & \vec{j} & \vec{k} \\ 2 & 5 & 1 \\ 5 & -1 & 4 \end{vmatrix} + \begin{vmatrix} \vec{i} & \vec{j} & \vec{k} \\ 3 & -3 & 2 \\ 5 & -1 & 4 \end{vmatrix}.$

e. $(2\vec{i} - 3\vec{j} + \vec{k})\cdot\begin{vmatrix} \vec{i} & \vec{j} & \vec{k} \\ -1 & 4 & 2 \\ 3 & -2 & 3 \end{vmatrix} = \begin{vmatrix} 2 & -3 & 1 \\ -1 & 4 & 2 \\ 3 & -2 & 3 \end{vmatrix} = -5.$

f. $\begin{vmatrix} x & y & 1 \\ -2 & 3 & 1 \\ 4 & 5 & 1 \end{vmatrix} = 0$ is the equation (in the plane) of the line through $(-2, 3)$ and $(4, 5)$.

g. $\begin{vmatrix} \vec{i} & \vec{j} & \vec{k} \\ 4 & 0 & -1 \\ 6 & 2 & 4 \end{vmatrix} = 2\begin{vmatrix} \vec{i} & \vec{j} & \vec{k} \\ 4 & 0 & -1 \\ 3 & 1 & 2 \end{vmatrix} = 2(\vec{i} - 11\vec{j} + 4\vec{k}).$

10-6. The Cross Product

The definition of the dot product of two vectors $\vec{u}$ and $\vec{v}$ is

$$\vec{u}\cdot\vec{v} = |\vec{u}||\vec{v}|\cos\theta,$$

where θ is the angle, less than or equal to a straight angle, between $\vec{u}$ and $\vec{v}$. From Fig. 10-6.1, it is seen that, if $0 \le \theta \le 90°$, then

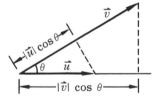

Fig. 10-6.1

(1) $\vec{u}\cdot\vec{v} = |\vec{u}|$ (length of the projection of $\vec{v}$ on $\vec{u}$)

$= |\vec{v}|$ (length of the projection of $\vec{u}$ on $\vec{v}$).

If $90° \le \theta \le 180°$, then the negative of the actual length of the projection must be used.

Toward defining the cross product of $\vec{u}$ and $\vec{v}$ (moved to a common initial point), let $\vec{e}$ be the unit vector with the same initial point and uniquely determined by the two conditions:

1. $\vec{e}$ is perpendicular to the plane of $\vec{u}$ and $\vec{v}$.
2. A rotation from $\vec{u}$ toward $\vec{v}$ advances a right-hand screw along $\vec{e}$.

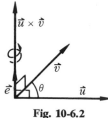

Fig. 10-6.2

By definition, the cross product $\vec{u} \times \vec{v}$ ($\vec{u}$ first, $\vec{v}$ second) is

$$(2) \qquad \vec{u} \times \vec{v} = \vec{e}|\vec{u}||\vec{v}| \sin \theta,$$

where θ is, as before, the angle less than a straight angle between $\vec{u}$ and $\vec{v}$.

Of course, no vector $\vec{e}$ exists if $\vec{u} = \vec{0}$, or if $\vec{v} = \vec{0}$, or if $\theta = 0°$, or if $\theta = 180°$. In any of these situations, then, by definition,

$$(3) \qquad \vec{u} \times \vec{v} = \vec{0}.$$

Thus, $\vec{u} \cdot \vec{v}$ is a scalar, but $\vec{u} \times \vec{v}$ is a vector. For this reason, the dot product is sometimes called the "scalar" product and the cross product is called the "vector" product.*

The cross product $\vec{v} \times \vec{u}$, with factors in the opposite order, differs only by the rotation from $\vec{v}$ toward $\vec{u}$, sending the unit vector $\vec{e}$ in the opposite direction; everything else remains the same. Consequently,

$$(4) \qquad \vec{v} \times \vec{u} = -\vec{u} \times \vec{v}.$$

The fact that $\vec{u} \cdot \vec{v} = \vec{v} \cdot \vec{u}$ is stated as "the dot product is commutative," and $\vec{u} \times \vec{v} = -\vec{v} \times \vec{u}$ as "the cross product is anticommutative."

With $\vec{e}$ the proper unit vector for $\vec{u} \times \vec{v}$ and θ the angle between $\vec{u}$ and $\vec{v}$, then the angle between $-\vec{u}$ and $\vec{v}$ is $180° - \theta$; rotation from $-\vec{u}$ toward $\vec{v}$ is opposite that from $\vec{u}$ toward $\vec{v}$, and hence

$$(5) \qquad (-\vec{u}) \times \vec{v} = -\vec{e}|-\vec{u}||\vec{v}| \sin (180° - \theta)$$
$$= -\vec{e}|\vec{u}||\vec{v}| \sin \theta$$
$$= -(\vec{u} \times \vec{v}).$$

In the same way, $\vec{u} \times (-\vec{v}) = -(\vec{u} \times \vec{v})$.

The factor $|\vec{u}||\vec{v}| \sin \theta$ has a geometric interpretation that will be used presently. Consider the $(\vec{u}, \vec{v})$ parallelogram, that is, the parallelogram with

---

*Other names (less descriptive) are the "inner" product and the "outer" product, respectively.

$\vec{u}$ and $\vec{v}$ as adjacent sides. If $\vec{u}$ is considered the base, then $h = |\vec{v}| \sin \theta$ is the altitude of the parallelogram (even if $90° < \theta < 180°$, Fig. 10-6.3A), so that

Fig. 10-6.3

(6)
$$|\vec{u} \times \vec{v}| = |\vec{e}||\vec{u}||\vec{v}| \sin \theta$$
$$= \text{area of } (\vec{u}, \vec{v}) \text{ parallelogram.}$$

Consider three vectors $\vec{u}, \vec{v}, \vec{w}$ all moved to the same initial point. These vectors need not be perpendicular, but in the order $\vec{u}, \vec{v}, \vec{w}$ they are said to form a **right-handed system** if they are in the same relative positions as the. thumb, forefinger, and middle finger of the right hand. If any one (and only

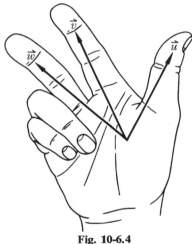

Fig. 10-6.4

one) of the vectors is reversed, the system becomes a **left-handed system**.

For $\vec{u}, \vec{v}$, and $\vec{w}$ given, $\vec{u} \times \vec{v}$ is a vector but $(\vec{u} \times \vec{v}) \cdot \vec{w}$ is a scalar, and the geometric interpretation,

$$(\vec{u} \times \vec{v}) \cdot \vec{w} = \text{volume of the } (\vec{u}, \vec{v}, \vec{w})$$
$$\text{parallelepiped}$$

for $\vec{u}, \vec{v}, \vec{w}$ a right-handed system, will now be established. Notice first that since $\vec{u}, \vec{v}, \vec{w}$ is a right-handed system, the angle (say, ϕ) between $\vec{u} \times \vec{v}$ and $\vec{w}$ is no more than $90°$, so that (as in Fig. 10-6.5)

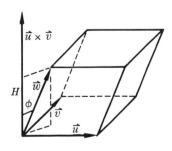

Fig. 10-6.5

$$H = |\vec{w}| \cos \phi = \text{length of projection of } \vec{w} \text{ on } \vec{u} \times \vec{v}$$

$$= \text{altitude of } (\vec{u}, \vec{v}, \vec{w}) \text{ parallelepiped,}$$

with the $(\vec{u}, \vec{v})$ parallelogram considered as base. Thus, by using the definition of the dot product of $\vec{u} \times \vec{v}$ and $\vec{w}$,

$$(\vec{u} \times \vec{v}) \cdot \vec{w} = |\vec{u} \times \vec{v}||\vec{w}| \cos \phi$$

$$= [\text{area } (\vec{u}, \vec{v}) \text{ parallelogram}][\text{altitude } (\vec{u}, \vec{v}, \vec{w}) \text{ parallelepiped}]$$

$$= \text{volume } (\vec{u}, \vec{v}, \vec{w}) \text{ parallelepiped.}$$

In exactly the same way (considering the parallelepiped as having the $(\vec{v}, \vec{w})$ parallelogram as base), it follows that

$$(\vec{v} \times \vec{w}) \cdot \vec{u} = \text{volume } (\vec{u}, \vec{v}, \vec{w}) \text{ parallelepiped.}$$

Consequently, the expressions for the volume are equal:

$$(\vec{u} \times \vec{v}) \cdot \vec{w} = (\vec{v} \times \vec{w}) \cdot \vec{u} = \vec{u} \cdot (\vec{v} \times \vec{w}),$$

the last equality following since the dot product is commutative.

The cross and dot product, therefore, have the joint property

(7) $$(\vec{u} \times \vec{v}) \cdot \vec{w} = \vec{u} \cdot (\vec{v} \times \vec{w}),$$

which turns out to be most useful. This is stated as the "cross-dot-switch" law, but it must be understood that the grouping must be such that the result has meaning. For example, $\vec{u} \cdot \vec{v}$ is a scalar, so that

$$(\vec{u} \cdot \vec{v}) \times \vec{w} \text{ is meaningless,}$$

since a cross or a dot may occur only between vectors.

It is almost universal practice to put even more responsibility on the reader and to use $(\vec{u}\vec{v}\vec{w})$ to stand for either $\vec{u} \cdot (\vec{v} \times \vec{w})$ or $(\vec{u} \times \vec{v}) \cdot \vec{w}$:

(8) $$(\vec{u}\vec{v}\vec{w}) = \vec{u} \cdot (\vec{v} \times \vec{w}) = (\vec{u} \times \vec{v}) \cdot \vec{w}.$$

Thus, $(\vec{u}\,\vec{v}\,\vec{w})$ means, "Insert one dot and one cross and then group the terms so the result has meaning."

Notice also that the order in $(\vec{u}\vec{v}\vec{w})$ is important. For example,

$$(\vec{v}\vec{u}\vec{w}) = (\vec{v} \times \vec{u}) \cdot \vec{w}$$

$$= -(\vec{u} \times \vec{v}) \cdot \vec{w} = -(\vec{u}\vec{v}\vec{w}).$$

Actually, (7) has been established only for $\vec{u}, \vec{v}, \vec{w}$ a right-handed system. Note, however, that if $\vec{u}, \vec{v}, \vec{w}$ is left-handed, then $(-\vec{u}), \vec{v}, \vec{w}$ is right-handed and, from (7),

$$[(-\vec{u}) \times \vec{v}] \cdot \vec{w} = (-\vec{u}) \cdot (\vec{v} \times \vec{w}),$$

$$[-(\vec{u}) \times \vec{v}] \cdot \vec{w} = -(\vec{u}) \cdot (\vec{v} \times \vec{w}),$$
$$-[(\vec{u} \times \vec{v}) \cdot \vec{w}] = -[\vec{u} \cdot (\vec{v} \times \vec{w})],$$

and multiplication by -1 yields (7) itself.

It is already known that "the dot product is distributive over addition, meaning that the usual rule for removing parentheses holds:

(9) $$\vec{u} \cdot (\vec{v} + \vec{w}) = \vec{u} \cdot \vec{v} + \vec{u} \cdot \vec{w}.$$

It will now be shown that "the cross product is distributive over addition":

(10) $$\vec{u} \times (\vec{v} + \vec{w}) = \vec{u} \times \vec{v} + \vec{u} \times \vec{w}$$

or, what is equivalent,

(11) $$\vec{u} \times (\vec{v} + \vec{w}) - \vec{u} \times \vec{v} - \vec{u} \times \vec{w} = \vec{0}.$$

PROOF. Let $\vec{p}$ be the vector defined by setting.

$$\vec{p} = \vec{u} \times (\vec{v} + \vec{w}) - \vec{u} \times \vec{v} - \vec{u} \times \vec{w},$$

and note that if it turns out that $|\vec{p}|$ is zero this will show that (11), and thus (10), holds. Since $|\vec{p}|^2 = \vec{p} \cdot \vec{p}$, merely compute this dot product in the following way:

$$\begin{aligned}|\vec{p}|^2 = \vec{p} \cdot \vec{p} &= \vec{p} \cdot [\vec{u} \times (\vec{v} + \vec{w}) - \vec{u} \times \vec{v} - \vec{u} \times \vec{w}] \\ &= \vec{p} \cdot [\vec{u} \times (\vec{v} + \vec{w})] - \vec{p} \cdot (\vec{u} \times \vec{v}) - \vec{p} \cdot (\vec{u} \times \vec{w}) \qquad \text{by (9)} \\ &= (\vec{p} \times \vec{u}) \cdot (\vec{v} + \vec{w}) - (\vec{p} \times \vec{u}) \cdot \vec{v} - (\vec{p} \times \vec{u}) \cdot \vec{w},\end{aligned}$$

by the cross-dot-switch law. But again, since the dot product is distributive over addition,

$$|\vec{p}|^2 = (\vec{p} \times \vec{u}) \cdot \vec{v} + (\vec{p} \times \vec{u}) \cdot \vec{w} - (\vec{p} \times \vec{u}) \cdot \vec{v} - (\vec{p} \times \vec{u}) \cdot \vec{w} = 0.$$

Thus, $|\vec{p}| = 0$, which, as noted above, means that (10) holds.

Since $\vec{i}, \vec{j}, \vec{k}$ is a right-handed system, with these unit vectors also orthogonal, it follows from the definitions [(3) and (2)] that

(12) $$\vec{i} \times \vec{i} = \vec{0}, \quad \vec{j} \times \vec{j} = \vec{0}, \quad \vec{k} \times \vec{k} = \vec{0},$$

(13) $$\vec{i} \times \vec{j} = \vec{k}, \quad \vec{j} \times \vec{k} = \vec{i}, \quad \vec{k} \times \vec{i} = \vec{j},$$

which may be remembered by writing the cyclic order

$$\vec{i}, \vec{j}, \vec{k}, \vec{i}, \vec{j}$$

and noting that a cross between any two is equal to the following member. By reversing the factors, the sign is changed:

(14) $$\vec{j} \times \vec{i} = -\vec{k}, \quad \vec{k} \times \vec{j} = -\vec{i}, \quad \vec{i} \times \vec{k} = -\vec{j}.$$

By using the distributivity (10) of the cross product and these formulas, the cross product of two vectors

$$\vec{u}_1 = a_1\vec{i} + b_1\vec{j} + c_1\vec{k} \quad \text{and} \quad \vec{u}_2 = a_2\vec{i} + b_2\vec{j} + c_2\vec{k}$$

may now be expanded (and then contracted):

$$\vec{u}_1 \times \vec{u}_2 = (a_1\vec{i} + b_1\vec{j} + c_1\vec{k}) \times \vec{u}_2$$
$$= a_1\vec{i} \times \vec{u}_2 + b_1\vec{j} \times \vec{u}_2 + c_1\vec{k} \times \vec{u}_2$$
$$= a_1\vec{i} \times a_2\vec{i} + a_1\vec{i} \times b_2\vec{j} + a_1\vec{i} \times c_2\vec{k}$$
$$\quad + b_1\vec{j} \times a_2\vec{i} + b_1\vec{j} \times b_2\vec{j} + b_1\vec{j} \times c_2\vec{k}$$
$$\quad + c_1\vec{k} \times a_2\vec{i} + c_1\vec{k} \times b_2\vec{j} + c_1\vec{k} \times c_2\vec{k}$$
$$= a_1a_2\vec{0} + a_1b_2\vec{k} - a_1c_2\vec{j}$$
$$\quad - b_1a_2\vec{k} + b_1b_2\vec{0} + b_1c_2\vec{i}$$
$$\quad + c_1a_2\vec{j} - c_1b_2\vec{i} + c_1c_2\vec{0}$$
$$= \vec{i}(b_1c_2 - c_1b_2) - \vec{j}(a_1c_2 - c_1a_2) + \vec{k}(a_1b_2 - b_1a_2)$$
$$= \vec{i}\begin{vmatrix} b_1 & c_1 \\ b_2 & c_2 \end{vmatrix} - \vec{j}\begin{vmatrix} a_1 & c_1 \\ a_2 & c_2 \end{vmatrix} + \vec{k}\begin{vmatrix} a_1 & b_1 \\ a_2 & b_2 \end{vmatrix}.$$

In terms of the $\vec{i}, \vec{j}, \vec{k}$ components, the cross product of two vectors has, therefore, the most convenient determinant expression:

$$(15) \qquad (a_1\vec{i} + b_1\vec{j} + c_1\vec{k}) \times (a_2\vec{i} + b_2\vec{j} + c_2\vec{k}) = \begin{vmatrix} \vec{i} & \vec{j} & \vec{k} \\ a_1 & b_1 & c_1 \\ a_2 & b_2 & c_2 \end{vmatrix}.$$

Example 1. Find the area of the triangle having vertices

$$A(8, -5, 2), \quad B(10, -8, 3), \quad C(12, -4, 5).$$

Solution. Let

$$\vec{u} = \vec{AB} = (10 - 8)\vec{i} + (-8 + 5)\vec{j} + (3 - 2)\vec{k} = 2\vec{i} - 3\vec{j} + \vec{k},$$
$$\vec{v} = \vec{AC} = 4\vec{i} + \vec{j} + 3\vec{k}.$$

The triangle is half the $(\vec{u}, \vec{v})$ parallelogram whose area is $|\vec{u} \times \vec{v}|$. But

$$\vec{u} \times \vec{v} = \begin{vmatrix} \vec{i} & \vec{j} & \vec{k} \\ 2 & -3 & 1 \\ 4 & 1 & 3 \end{vmatrix} = \vec{i}(-9 - 1) - \vec{j}(6 - 4) + \vec{k}(2 + 12)$$
$$= -10\vec{i} - 2\vec{j} + 14\vec{k}.$$

Answer:

$$\tfrac{1}{2}|\vec{u} \times \vec{v}| = \tfrac{1}{2}\sqrt{(-10)^2 + (-2)^2 + (14^2)} = \tfrac{1}{2}\sqrt{300}.$$

Example 2. Find parametric equations of the line of intersection of the planes

(16) $\qquad\qquad 6x - y - 2z = -3 \quad$ and $\quad 3x - 2y + 2z = 9.$

Also, express this line as the intersection of planes parallel to the axes.

Solution. A vector perpendicular to the first plane has direction numbers $6, -1,$ $-2,$ and hence

$$\vec{u} = 6\vec{i} - \vec{j} - 2\vec{k}$$

is such a vector. Also,

$$\vec{v} = 3\vec{i} - 2\vec{j} + 2\vec{k}$$

is perpendicular to the second plane. The line of intersection of the planes is perpendicular to both of these vectors, and since

$$\vec{u} \times \vec{v} = \begin{vmatrix} \vec{i} & \vec{j} & \vec{k} \\ 6 & -1 & -2 \\ 3 & -2 & 2 \end{vmatrix} = \begin{aligned} &\vec{i}(-2 - 4) - \vec{j}(12 + 6) + \vec{k}(-12 + 3) \\ &= -6\vec{i} - 18\vec{j} - 9\vec{k} \\ &= -3(2\vec{i} + 6\vec{j} + 3\vec{k}) \end{aligned}$$

is also perpendicular to $\vec{u}$ and $\vec{v}$, the line has direction numbers

$$2, \quad 6, \quad 3.$$

Hence, to write parametric equations of the line, one point on the line is necessary. A convenient point is one where the line pierces a coordinate plane. In this case, set $x = 0$ in (16) and solve the resulting equations

$$-y - 2z = -3,$$
$$-2y + 2z = 9$$

to find the point $(0, -2, \frac{5}{2})$. Thus,

$$L: x = 0 + 2t, \quad y = -2 + 6t, \quad z = \tfrac{5}{2} + 3t$$

are parametric equations of the line.

For the rest of the requested information, solve each of the equations of L for the parameter t:

$$t = \frac{x}{2} = \frac{y + 2}{6} = \frac{2z - 5}{6}.$$

By using the x, y, z equations in pairs, the results

$$3x - y = 2, \quad 3x - 2z = -5, \quad y - 2z = -7$$

are equations of planes, each parallel to an axis such that any pair intersects in the same line as the intersection of the planes (16).

Notice that this example is the same as Examples 4 and 5 of Sec. 10–4, but that the solution is considerably simplified by the use of a cross product.

Problems 1-6. Work Probs. 1 through 6 of Sec. 10-4, but use cross products to simplify the work wherever possible. The answers are, of course, the same as those in Sec. 10-4, but in the answers for the present section hints are given in case they are needed.

Problem 7. Let T be the area of the triangle with vertices A, B, C and let $T_1,$

T_2, T_3 be the areas of the projections of the triangle on the three coordinate planes. Find these four areas and then check that

$$T = \sqrt{T_1^2 + T_2^2 + T_3^2}:$$

a. $A(1, 2, 3)$, $B(0, 5, 4)$, $C(2, 3, 1)$.
b. $A(-8, -2, 5)$, $B(2, 4, 7)$, $C(-2, -1, 8)$.

Problem 8. Find the volume of the tetrahedron with the given vertices:
a. $A(-1, 4, 6)$, $B(1, 7, 8)$, $C(-2, 6, 3)$, $D(3, 5, 13)$.
b. $A(0, 0, 0)$, $B(1, 0, 0)$, $C(0, 2, 0)$, $D(0, 0, 3)$.

Problem 9. Find the equation of a plane containing L_1 and parallel to L_2:
a. $L_1: x = 2 + 3t$, $y = -1 + t$, $z = 4 - 2t$,
   $L_2: x = 5 - 6t$, $y = 3 + t$, $z = 4 + 3t$.
b. $L_1: x = 1 + 6t$, $y = -2 + 4t$, $z = 4$,
   $L_2: x = 10 + 7t$, $y = -15 + 5t$, $z = 35 + t$.

Problem 10. Find the equation of the plane containing the two points and parallel to the intersection of the two planes:
a. $P_1(5, -1, 6)$, $P_2(4, 1, 7)$; $4x + 2y - z = 5$, $3x + z = 17$.
b. $P_1(0, 3, 3)$, $P_2(2, -1, 1)$; $19x + 8y - 3z = 6$, $15x + 6y - 2z = 45$.

Problem 11. Without using the distributive law proved in the text, give a direct proof of

$$(\vec{u} + \vec{v}) \times \vec{w} = \vec{u} \times \vec{w} + \vec{v} \times \vec{w};$$

that is, prove that the vector

$$\vec{q} = (\vec{u} + \vec{v}) \times \vec{w} - \vec{u} \times \vec{w} - \vec{v} \times \vec{w}$$

is the null vector.

10-7. Multiple Products

As shown in Sec. 10-6, the triple products

(1) $\qquad (\vec{u} \times \vec{v}) \cdot \vec{w}$ and $\vec{u} \cdot (\vec{v} \times \vec{w})$, written as $(\vec{u}\,\vec{v}\,\vec{w})$,

have the same scalar value, which is the volume or its negative, of the $(\vec{u}, \vec{v}, \vec{w})$-parallelepiped, depending on whether $\vec{u}, \vec{v}, \vec{w}$ is a right- or left-handed system.

With two crosses, the triple products

(2) $\qquad (\vec{u} \times \vec{v}) \times \vec{w}$ and $\vec{u} \times (\vec{v} \times \vec{w})$

are vector valued and, as seen below, are usually not equal.

As an aid to visualizing $(\vec{u} \times \vec{v}) \times \vec{w}$, arrange five pencils in the following manner with their eraser ends together. For $\vec{u}$ and $\vec{v}$, lay two pencils on the table, hold the third pencil normal to the table for $\vec{u} \times \vec{v}$, and the fourth not normal to the table for $\vec{w}$. The third and fourth pencils determine a plane, and the fifth pencil may be laid on the table normal to this plane to represent $(\vec{u} \times \vec{v}) \times \vec{w}$. Thus, the vector $(\vec{u} \times \vec{v}) \times \vec{w}$ is in the $(\vec{u}, \vec{v})$-plane, and there are scalars l and m such that

(3) $$(\vec{u} \times \vec{v}) \times \vec{w} = l\vec{u} + m\vec{v}.$$

The purpose is now to express the scalars l and m in terms of $\vec{u}, \vec{v}$, and $\vec{w}$. Think of a temporary right-handed system of unit vectors $\vec{I}, \vec{J}$, and $\vec{K}$, with $\vec{I}$ along $\vec{u}, \vec{J}$ in the $(\vec{u}, \vec{v})$-plane, and $\vec{K} = \vec{I} \times \vec{J}$. In terms of components along these unit vectors,

$$\vec{u} = a_1\vec{I},$$

(4) $$\vec{v} = a_2\vec{I} + b_2\vec{J},$$

$$\vec{w} = a_3\vec{I} + b_3\vec{J} + c_3\vec{K}.$$

Hence $(\vec{u} \times \vec{v}) \times \vec{w}$ is equal to

$$\begin{vmatrix} \vec{I} & \vec{J} & \vec{K} \\ a_1 & 0 & 0 \\ a_2 & b_2 & 0 \end{vmatrix} \times \vec{w} = a_1 b_2 \vec{K} \times (a_3\vec{I} + b_3\vec{J} + c_3\vec{K}) = \begin{vmatrix} \vec{I} & \vec{J} & \vec{K} \\ 0 & 0 & a_1 b_2 \\ a_3 & b_3 & c_3 \end{vmatrix}$$

$$= \vec{I}(-a_1 b_2 b_3) - \vec{J}(-a_1 a_3 b_2) + \vec{K}(0) = b_2\vec{J}(a_1 a_3) - a_1\vec{I}(b_2 b_3)$$

$$= (\vec{v} - a_2\vec{I})(a_1 a_3) - \vec{u}(b_2 b_3),$$

since $b_2\vec{J} = \vec{v} - a_2\vec{I}$ and $a_1\vec{I} = \vec{u}$ from (4). Thus,

$$(\vec{u} \times \vec{v}) \times \vec{w} = a_1 a_3\vec{v} - a_1\vec{I}(a_2 a_3) - \vec{u}(b_2 b_3)$$

$$= a_1 a_3\vec{v} - (a_2 a_3 + b_2 b_3)\vec{u},$$

where $a_1\vec{I} = \vec{u}$ was used again. Now check from (4) that

$$\vec{u} \cdot \vec{w} = a_1 a_3 \quad \text{and} \quad \vec{v} \cdot \vec{w} = a_2 a_3 + b_2 b_3.$$

It therefore follows that

(5) $$(\vec{u} \times \vec{v}) \times \vec{w} = (\vec{u} \cdot \vec{w})\vec{v} - (\vec{v} \cdot \vec{w})\vec{u}.$$

Formula (5) is sometimes called the "mean-minus-first" law, since the result is the mean vector minus the first vector, with coefficients the dot products of the other two vectors in each case.

Notice that $\vec{u} \times (\vec{v} \times \vec{w}) = -(\vec{v} \times \vec{w}) \times \vec{u}$ and thus, by applying the mean-minus-first law to the right side,

(6) $$\vec{u} \times (\vec{v} \times \vec{w}) = -[(\vec{v} \cdot \vec{u})\vec{w} - (\vec{w} \cdot \vec{u})\vec{v}]$$

$$= (\vec{w} \cdot \vec{u})\vec{v} - (\vec{v} \cdot \vec{u})\vec{w},$$

and this is the "mean-minus-last" law. On the left of the equality, the **first** two factors are grouped in the mean-minus-first law, but the **last** two factors are grouped in the mean-minus-last law.

The cross-dot-switch law together with the mean-minus-first and mean-minus-last laws are used to manipulate a variety of multiple products that arise in physical and engineering problems. And, of course, the fact that parentheses may be removed by the distributive laws for both cross and dot products is used.

Since it hardly seems right to use $\vec{x}$ and $\vec{y}$ for vectors, it is better to go to the first of the alphabet and use $\vec{A}, \vec{B}, \vec{C}, \vec{D}$ for vectors. Anyway, it is better to think of the laws rather than specific letters used in formalistic expressions of the laws.

Example 1. Show that

$$(\vec{A} \times \vec{B}) \times (\vec{C} \times \vec{D}) = (\vec{A}\vec{C}\vec{D})\vec{B} - (\vec{B}\vec{C}\vec{D})\vec{A}.$$

Solution. To hide some of the complexity, set $\vec{V} = \vec{C} \times \vec{D}$, so that

$$(\vec{A} \times \vec{B}) \times (\vec{C} \times \vec{D}) = (\vec{A} \times \vec{B}) \times \vec{V}$$
$$= (\vec{A} \cdot \vec{V})\vec{B} - (\vec{B} \cdot \vec{V})\vec{A}$$

by the mean-minus-first law. But

$$\vec{A} \cdot \vec{V} = \vec{A} \cdot (\vec{C} \times \vec{D}) = (\vec{A}\vec{C}\vec{D}) \quad \text{and} \quad \vec{B} \cdot \vec{V} = (\vec{B}\vec{C}\vec{D}),$$

and thus the desired result follows.

Example 2. Express $(\vec{A} \times \vec{B}) \cdot (\vec{C} \times \vec{D})$ as a determinant whose elements are dot products in pairs. [Note: The result is known as the Lagrange identity.]

Solution. Set $\vec{u} = \vec{A} \times \vec{B}$, so that

$$(\vec{A} \times \vec{B}) \cdot (\vec{C} \times \vec{D}) = \vec{u} \cdot (\vec{C} \times \vec{D})$$
$$= (\vec{u} \times \vec{C}) \cdot \vec{D} \quad \text{by cross-dot-switch}$$
$$= [(\vec{A} \times \vec{B}) \times \vec{C}] \cdot \vec{D}$$
$$= [(\vec{A} \cdot \vec{C})\vec{B} - (\vec{B} \cdot \vec{C})\vec{A}] \cdot \vec{D} \quad \text{by mean-minus-first}$$
$$= (\vec{A} \cdot \vec{C})(\vec{B} \cdot \vec{D}) - (\vec{B} \cdot \vec{C})(\vec{A} \cdot \vec{D}) = \begin{vmatrix} \vec{A} \cdot \vec{C} & \vec{A} \cdot \vec{D} \\ \vec{B} \cdot \vec{C} & \vec{B} \cdot \vec{D} \end{vmatrix}.$$

It should be clear that possible geometric interpretations of multiple products are too involved to be helpful. Suffice it to say, however, that the equalities in the above two examples, and in the following problems, have a great deal of helpful interpretive value when vectors are used to represent electric fields and in many physical situations.

When using $\vec{A}, \vec{B}$, etc., for vectors, it is better to use

$$\vec{A} = a_1\vec{i} + a_2\vec{j} + a_3\vec{k}, \quad \vec{B} = b_1\vec{i} + b_2\vec{j} + b_3\vec{k}, \quad \text{etc.,}$$

rather than

$$a_1\vec{i} + b_1\vec{j} + c_1\vec{k}, \quad a_2\vec{i} + b_2\vec{j} + c_2\vec{k},$$

if the $\vec{i}, \vec{j}, \vec{k}$ components are desired.

Problem 1. Compute each of the following in two ways, once by using determinants and again by using the mean-minus-last or mean-minus-first law, whichever is appropriate:

a. $(2\vec{i} - 3\vec{j} + \vec{k}) \times [(\vec{i} + 4\vec{j} - 2\vec{k}) \times (3\vec{i} - \vec{j} + \vec{k})]$.

b. $[(2\vec{i} - 3\vec{j} + \vec{k}) \times (\vec{i} + 4\vec{j} - 2\vec{k})] \times (3\vec{i} - \vec{j} + \vec{k})$.

c. $(2\vec{i} + \vec{j}) \times [(\vec{j} + 5\vec{k}) \times (2\vec{i} + \vec{k})]$.

d. $[(2\vec{i} + \vec{j}) \times (\vec{j} + 5\vec{k})] \times (2\vec{i} + \vec{k})$.

Problem 2. In Example 1, what result follows if the substitution $\vec{u} = \vec{A} \times \vec{B}$ is made?

Problem 3. a. Show that $(\vec{B}\vec{B}\vec{C}) = 0$ for any two vectors $\vec{B}$ and $\vec{C}$.

b. With $x, y,$ and z scalars and

$$\vec{A}x + \vec{B}y + \vec{C}z = \vec{D},$$

show that

$$(\vec{A}\vec{B}\vec{C})x = (\vec{D}\vec{B}\vec{C}), \quad (\vec{A}\vec{B}\vec{C})y = (\vec{A}\vec{D}\vec{C}), \quad (\vec{A}\vec{B}\vec{C})z = (\vec{A}\vec{B}\vec{D}).$$

c. Use the result of part b to solve the equations:

$$x + 2y - 4z = -12,$$
$$2x - y + z = 7,$$
$$3x + z = -3.$$

Problem 4. Establish each of the equalities:

a. $(\vec{A} + \vec{B})\cdot(\vec{C} \times \vec{D}) = (\vec{A}\vec{C}\vec{B}) + (\vec{B}\vec{C}\vec{D})$.

b. $[\vec{D} \times (\vec{A} \times \vec{B})]\cdot(\vec{A} \times \vec{C}) = (\vec{A}\vec{B}\vec{C})(\vec{A}\cdot\vec{D})$; that is,

$$(\vec{D} \quad \vec{A} \times \vec{B} \quad \vec{A} \times \vec{C}) = (\vec{A}\vec{B}\vec{C})(\vec{A}\cdot\vec{D}).$$

c. $\vec{A} \times (\vec{B} \times \vec{C}) + \vec{B} \times (\vec{C} \times \vec{A}) + \vec{C} \times (\vec{A} \times \vec{B}) = 0$. (Called the Jacobi identity.)

d. $(\vec{A} \times \vec{B})\cdot[(\vec{B} \times \vec{C}) \times (\vec{C} \times \vec{A})] = (\vec{A}\vec{B}\vec{C})^2$; that is,

$$(\vec{A} \times \vec{B} \quad \vec{B} \times \vec{C} \quad \vec{C} \times \vec{A}) = (\vec{A}\vec{B}\vec{C})^2.$$

Problem 5. Show that:

a. $(\vec{A}\vec{A}\vec{B}) = 0$.

b. $(\vec{A}\vec{B}\vec{A}) = 0$.

c. $[(\vec{A} \times \vec{A}) \times \vec{B}] = \vec{0}$.

d. $[\vec{A} \times (\vec{B} \times \vec{A})]$ is not ordinarily equal to $\vec{0}$.

e. $(\vec{i}\,\vec{j}\,\vec{k}) = 1$.

10-8.   Differentiation Rules

A vector function $\vec{u}(t)$ of a single variable t is differentiable at those (fixed) values of t [and has derivative $\vec{u}'(t)$ or $d\vec{u}(t)/dt$], provided the limit in

(1) $$\lim_{\Delta t \to 0} \frac{\vec{u}(t + \Delta t) - \vec{u}(t)}{\Delta t} = \lim_{\Delta t \to 0} \frac{\Delta \vec{u}}{\Delta t} = \frac{d\vec{u}(t)}{dt}$$

exists. This is the definition whether $\vec{u}$ is on a line, in the plane, or in space; and if $\vec{u}(t) = \vec{i}f_1(t) + \vec{j}f_2(t) + \vec{k}f_3(t)$, then

(2) $$\frac{d\vec{u}(t)}{dt} = \vec{i}\frac{df_1(t)}{dt} + \vec{j}\frac{df_2(t)}{dt} + \vec{k}\frac{df_3(t)}{dt}.$$

Moreover, if $\vec{u}$ is a function of θ, and θ is a function of t, then

(3) $$\frac{d\vec{u}}{dt} = \frac{d\vec{u}}{d\theta}\frac{d\theta}{dt}.$$

Also, if $\vec{u}$ is the ordinary product of a scalar function $r(t)$ and of a vector function $\vec{R}(t)$, so that $\vec{u}(t) = r(t)\vec{R}(t)$, then

$$\frac{d\vec{u}}{dt} = \lim_{\Delta t \to 0} \frac{\Delta \vec{u}}{\Delta t} = \lim_{\Delta t \to 0} \frac{r(t + \Delta t)\vec{R}(t + \Delta t) - r(t)\vec{R}(t)}{\Delta t}$$

$$= \lim_{\Delta t \to 0} \frac{[r(t) + \Delta r][\vec{R}(t) + \Delta \vec{R}] - r(t)\vec{R}(t)}{\Delta t}$$

$$= \lim_{\Delta t \to 0} \left[r(t)\frac{\Delta \vec{R}}{\Delta t} + \frac{\Delta r}{\Delta t}\vec{R}(t) + \Delta r \frac{\Delta \vec{R}}{\Delta t} \right]$$

$$= r(t)\frac{d\vec{R}(t)}{dt} + \frac{dr(t)}{dt}\vec{R}(t) + 0\frac{d\vec{R}(t)}{dt}.$$

Thus, the usual formula for the derivative of a product holds:

(4) $$\frac{d(r\vec{R})}{dt} = r\frac{d\vec{R}}{dt} + \vec{R}\frac{dr}{dt}.$$

Example 1. Let the position of a particle in the plane at time t be the end of the vector (initial point at the origin)

$$\vec{u} = r(\vec{i}\cos\theta + \vec{j}\sin\theta),$$

with r and θ both scalar functions of t. Derive formulas for the velocity and acceleration.

Solution. First let $\vec{R} = \vec{i}\cos\theta + \vec{j}\sin\theta$ and note that

(5) $$\frac{d\vec{R}}{d\theta} = -\vec{i}\sin\theta + \vec{j}\cos\theta, \quad \frac{d^2\vec{R}}{d\theta^2} = -\vec{i}\cos\theta - \vec{j}\sin\theta = -\vec{R}.$$

Hence, $\vec{u} = r\vec{R}$, so the velocity vector is

$$\vec{v} = \frac{d\vec{u}}{dt} = r\frac{d\vec{R}}{d\theta}\frac{d\theta}{dt} + \vec{R}\frac{dr}{dt}.$$

The acceleration vector is

$$\vec{a} = \frac{d\vec{v}}{dt} = r\frac{d\vec{R}}{d\theta}\frac{d^2\theta}{dt^2} + r\left(\frac{d^2\vec{R}}{d\theta^2}\frac{d\theta}{dt}\right)\frac{d\theta}{dt} + \frac{d\vec{R}}{d\theta}\frac{d\theta}{dt}\frac{dr}{dt} + \vec{R}\frac{d^2r}{dt^2} + \frac{dr}{dt}\frac{d\vec{R}}{d\theta}\frac{d\theta}{dt}.$$

Since $d^2\vec{R}/d\theta^2 = -\vec{R}$, the acceleration may be expressed as

$$\vec{a} = \left[\frac{d^2r}{dt^2} - r\left(\frac{d\theta}{dt}\right)^2\right]\vec{R} + \left[r\frac{d^2\theta}{dt^2} + 2\frac{dr}{dt}\frac{d\theta}{dt}\right]\frac{d\vec{R}}{d\theta}$$

$$= \left[\frac{d^2r}{dt^2} - r\left(\frac{d\theta}{dt}\right)^2\right]\vec{R} + \frac{1}{r}\frac{d}{dt}\left(r^2\frac{d\theta}{dt}\right)\frac{d\vec{R}}{d\theta}.$$

It should be recognized that these formulas for $\vec{v}$ and $\vec{a}$ are equivalent to those used in discussing universal gravitation [(4) and (5) of Sec. 9-15].

Note, from the definition of $\vec{R}$ and (5), that

(6) $$\vec{R}\cdot\vec{R} = 1, \quad \frac{d\vec{R}}{d\theta}\cdot\frac{d\vec{R}}{d\theta} = 1 \quad \text{and} \quad \vec{R}\cdot\frac{d\vec{R}}{d\theta} = 0,$$

so that $\vec{R}$ and $d\vec{R}/d\theta$ are unit orthogonal vectors.

The meaning of the limit of a vector function should be made more precise.

For $\vec{u}(t)$ a vector function and $\vec{U}$ a constant vector,

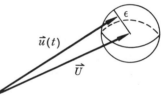

(7) $$\lim_{t\to c}\vec{u}(t) = \vec{U}$$

means that, if a sphere of arbitrary given radius ϵ is drawn with the tip of $\vec{U}$ as center, then there is a $\delta > 0$ such that, whenever

Fig. 10-8.1

$0 < |t - c| < \delta$, the length and direction of $\vec{u}(t)$ differ so little from those of $\vec{U}$ that the tip of $\vec{u}(t)$ is within the sphere; that is,

(8) $$\text{if} \quad 0 < |t - c| < \delta, \quad \text{then} \quad |\vec{u}(t) - \vec{U}| < \epsilon.$$

Since $|\vec{u}(t) - \vec{U}|$ is a scalar function, criteria for limits of vector functions reduce to limits of scalar functions. For example, let

$$\lim_{t\to c}\vec{v}(t) = \vec{V}$$

hold in addition to (7). Then

$$|\vec{u}(t) \times \vec{v}(t) - \vec{U} \times \vec{V}| = |\vec{u}(t) \times \vec{v}(t) - \vec{u}(t) \times \vec{V} + \vec{u}(t) \times \vec{V} - \vec{U} \times \vec{V}|$$

$$= |\vec{u}(t) \times [\vec{v}(t) - \vec{V}] + [\vec{u}(t) - \vec{U}] \times \vec{V}|$$

$$\leq |\vec{u}(t) \times [\vec{v}(t) - \vec{V}]| + |[\vec{u}(t) - \vec{U}] \times \vec{V}|,$$

$$|\vec{u}(t) \times \vec{v}(t) - \vec{U} \times \vec{V}| \leq |\vec{u}(t)||\vec{v}(t) - \vec{V}| + |\vec{u}(t) - \vec{U}||\vec{V}|.$$

As $t \to c$, the scalar on the right approaches zero, and thus the one on the left does also, so that

(9)
$$\lim_{t \to c} \vec{u}(t) \times \vec{v}(t) = \vec{U} \times \vec{V}.$$

Hence, the limit of a cross product is the cross product (in the same order) of the limits.

With (9) established, the same formal procedure as used for scalar functions establishes the derivative formula

(10)
$$\frac{d(\vec{u} \times \vec{v})}{dt} = \vec{u} \times \frac{d\vec{v}}{dt} + \frac{d\vec{u}}{dt} \times \vec{v},$$

with only the difference that the order of factors in each cross product must be carefully preserved; for

$$\frac{d(\vec{u} \times \vec{v})}{dt} = \lim_{\Delta t \to 0} \frac{(\vec{u} + \Delta\vec{u}) \times (\vec{v} + \Delta\vec{v}) - \vec{u} \times \vec{v}}{\Delta t}$$

$$= \lim_{\Delta t \to 0} \frac{\vec{u} \times \vec{v} + \vec{u} \times \Delta\vec{v} + \Delta\vec{u} \times \vec{v} + \Delta\vec{u} \times \Delta\vec{v} - \vec{u} \times \vec{v}}{\Delta t}$$

$$= \lim_{\Delta t \to 0} \left[\vec{u} \times \frac{\Delta\vec{v}}{\Delta t} + \frac{\Delta\vec{u}}{\Delta t} \times \vec{v} + \frac{\Delta\vec{u}}{\Delta t} \times \Delta\vec{v} \right]$$

$$= \vec{u} \times \frac{d\vec{v}}{dt} + \frac{d\vec{u}}{dt} \times \vec{v} + \frac{d\vec{u}}{dt} \times \vec{0}.$$

In a similar way, the limit of a dot product is the dot product (in either order) of the limits:

$$\lim_{t \to c} (\vec{u} \cdot \vec{v}) = (\lim_{t \to c} \vec{u}) \cdot (\lim_{t \to c} \vec{v})$$

$$= (\lim_{t \to c} \vec{v}) \cdot (\lim_{t \to c} \vec{u}).$$

Also,

(11)
$$\frac{d\vec{u} \cdot \vec{v}}{dt} = \vec{u} \cdot \frac{d\vec{v}}{dt} + \frac{d\vec{u}}{dt} \cdot \vec{v}$$

$$= \vec{u} \cdot \frac{d\vec{v}}{dt} + \vec{v} \cdot \frac{d\vec{u}}{dt}.$$

Example 2. Let a particle move in such a way that its position vector $\vec{u}(t)$ has constant length, with $\vec{u}$ a differentiable function of t. Show that the velocity and position vectors are perpendicular.

Solution. The constant length condition may be expressed by

$$\vec{u} \cdot \vec{u} = c.$$

Hence, from (11), with both factors equal to $\vec{u}$:

$$2\vec{u}\cdot\frac{d\vec{u}}{dt} = \frac{dc}{dt} = 0, \quad \text{so that} \quad \vec{u}\cdot\frac{d\vec{u}}{dt} = 0.$$

This dot product says that $\vec{u}$ (assumed not the zero vector) and the velocity vector $d\vec{u}/dt$ are perpendicular whenever this velocity vector is not the zero vector. If $d\vec{u}/dt = \vec{0}$ in an interval of time, then during this time interval there is no motion. If $d\vec{u}/dt$ is $\vec{0}$ only at $t = t_0$, then the particle experiences an instantaneous halt at this time.

The formulas (10) and (11) may be combined to yield

$$(12) \qquad \frac{d}{dt}(\vec{u}\vec{v}\vec{w}) = \left(\frac{d\vec{u}}{dt}\,\vec{u}\,\vec{w}\right) + \left(\vec{u}\frac{d\vec{v}}{dt}\vec{w}\right) + \left(\vec{u}\,\vec{v}\,\frac{d\vec{w}}{dt}\right).$$

Notice that if $(\vec{u}\vec{v}\vec{w})$ is interpreted as $\vec{u}\cdot(\vec{v}\times\vec{w})$, then it is not at all necessary to use dot first and cross second on the right. The most natural form for (12) is, however,

$$\frac{d}{dt}[\vec{u}\cdot(\vec{v}\times\vec{w})] = \frac{d\vec{u}}{dt}\cdot(\vec{v}\times\vec{w}) + \vec{u}\cdot\left(\frac{d\vec{v}}{dt}\times\vec{w}\right) + \vec{u}\cdot\left(\vec{v}\times\frac{d\vec{w}}{dt}\right).$$

If the component forms of the vectors are

$$\vec{u} = \vec{i}f_1 + \vec{j}f_2 + \vec{k}f_3, \quad \vec{v} = \vec{i}g_1 + \vec{j}g_2 + \vec{k}g_3, \quad \vec{w} = \vec{i}h_1 + \vec{j}h_2 + \vec{k}h_3,$$

and if the determinant equivalents of $\vec{u}\cdot(\vec{v}\times\vec{w})$, $(d\vec{u}/dt)\cdot(\vec{v}\times\vec{w})$, etc., are used, then the result is a theorem about derivatives of determinants of functions:

$$\frac{d}{dt}\begin{vmatrix} f_1 & f_2 & f_3 \\ g_1 & g_2 & g_3 \\ h_1 & h_2 & h_3 \end{vmatrix} = \begin{vmatrix} f_1' & f_2' & f_3' \\ g_1 & g_2 & g_3 \\ h_1 & h_2 & h_3 \end{vmatrix} + \begin{vmatrix} f_1 & f_2 & f_3 \\ g_1' & g_2' & g_3' \\ h_1 & h_2 & h_3 \end{vmatrix} + \begin{vmatrix} f_1 & f_2 & f_3 \\ g_1 & g_2 & g_3 \\ h_1' & h_2' & h_3' \end{vmatrix}.$$

Problem 1. Show that:

a. $\dfrac{d}{dt}\left(\vec{u}\times\dfrac{d\vec{u}}{dt}\right) = \vec{u}\times\dfrac{d^2\vec{u}}{dt^2}.$ \qquad c. $\dfrac{d}{dt}\,|\vec{u}|^2 = 2\vec{u}\cdot\dfrac{d\vec{u}}{dt}.$

b. $\dfrac{d}{dt}\left(\vec{u}\cdot\dfrac{d\vec{u}}{dt}\right) = \vec{u}\cdot\dfrac{d^2\vec{u}}{dt^2} + \left|\dfrac{d\vec{u}}{dt}\right|^2.$

Problem 2. a. Obtain the formula

$$\frac{d}{dt}\left[\vec{u}\times(\vec{v}\times\vec{w})\right] = \frac{d\vec{u}}{dt}\times(\vec{v}\times\vec{w}) + \vec{u}\times\frac{d\vec{v}}{dt}\times\vec{w} + \vec{u}\times\left(\vec{v}\times\frac{d\vec{w}}{dt}\right).$$

b. Is $\dfrac{d}{dt}[(\vec{u}\times\vec{v})\times\vec{w}]$ equal to $\dfrac{d}{dt}[\vec{u}\times(\vec{v}\times\vec{w})]$?

c. First use the mean-minus-last law and then derivative formulas to find

$$\frac{d}{dt}[\vec{u}\times(\vec{v}\times\vec{w})].$$

d. By using the answers themselves, check that the answers in parts a and c are equal.

Problem 3. With primes also denoting derivatives with respect to t, show that:

a. $\dfrac{d}{dt}\,(\vec{u}\vec{u}'\vec{u}'') = (\vec{u}\vec{u}'\vec{u}''')$.   b. $\dfrac{d}{dt}\,(\vec{u}\vec{u}''\vec{u}') = (\vec{u}\vec{u}'''\vec{u}')$.

Problem 4. With ω a scalar constant, $\vec{a}$ and $\vec{b}$ vector constants, and

$$\vec{u} = \vec{a}\cos\omega t + \vec{b}\sin\omega t,$$

show that:

    a. $\vec{u} \times \vec{u}' = \omega\vec{a} \times \vec{b}$.

    b. $\vec{u}'' = -\omega^2\vec{u}$.

    c. $(\vec{u}\vec{u}'\vec{u}'') = 0$.

    d. Define $\vec{u}$ by $\vec{u} = \vec{a}e^{\omega t} + \vec{b}e^{-\omega t}$ and find expressions similar to those in parts a, b, and c for

$$\vec{u} \times \vec{u}',\quad \vec{u}'',\quad \text{and}\quad (\vec{u}\vec{u}'\vec{u}'').$$

10-9. Curves in Space

With C a given curve in space, select a point P_0 on C and measure arc length s along C from P_0. Then there are functions $x(s)$, $y(s)$, $z(s)$ such that the vector from the origin to a point on C is

(1) $$\vec{u}(s) = \vec{i}x(s) + \vec{j}y(s) + \vec{k}z(s),$$

and

$$\vec{u}(s + \Delta s) = \vec{i}x(s + \Delta s) + \vec{j}y(s + \Delta s) + \vec{k}z(s + \Delta s)$$

is from the origin to a neighboring point of C. Thus, the vector

$$\Delta\vec{u} = \vec{i}\Delta x + \vec{j}\Delta y + \vec{k}\Delta z$$

is from the first to the second point, and the vector $\vec{t}$,

(2) $$\vec{t} = \frac{d\vec{u}}{ds} = \lim_{\Delta s \to 0}\frac{\Delta\vec{u}}{\Delta s} = \lim_{\Delta s \to 0}\left[\vec{i}\frac{\Delta x}{\Delta s} + \vec{j}\frac{\Delta y}{\Delta s} + \vec{k}\frac{\Delta z}{\Delta s}\right]$$

$$= \vec{i}\frac{dx}{ds} + \vec{j}\frac{dy}{ds} + \vec{k}\frac{dz}{ds},$$

is tangent to C and has length

$$|\vec{t}| = \sqrt{\vec{t}\cdot\vec{t}} = \left|\frac{d\vec{u}}{ds}\right| = \sqrt{\frac{d\vec{u}}{ds}\cdot\frac{d\vec{u}}{ds}} = \sqrt{\left(\frac{dx}{ds}\right)^2 + \left(\frac{dy}{ds}\right)^2 + \left(\frac{dz}{ds}\right)^2}.$$

But the ratio of chord length to corresponding increment Δs of arc length approaches 1 as $\Delta s \to 0$:

$$1 = \lim_{\Delta s \to 0} \frac{\sqrt{(\Delta x)^2 + (\Delta y)^2 + (\Delta z)^2}}{\Delta s} = \sqrt{\left(\frac{dx}{ds}\right)^2 + \left(\frac{dy}{ds}\right)^2 + \left(\frac{dz}{ds}\right)^2}$$

Hence, $\vec{t}$ has length 1 and

(3)
$$\vec{t} = \frac{d\vec{u}}{ds}$$

is the unit tangent vector at the point.

The lines passing through the point and normal to C (that is, perpendicular to $\vec{t}$) form the **normal plane** to C at the point. In this plane, two specific normal vectors will be singled out for special attention; they are called the **principal unit normal** and the **unit binormal**.

One way of expressing "$\vec{t}$ has length 1" is $\vec{t} \cdot \vec{t} = 1$, and from this equation, by differentiation,

(4)
$$0 = \vec{t} \cdot \frac{d\vec{t}}{ds} + \frac{d\vec{t}}{ds} \cdot \vec{t} = 2\vec{t} \cdot \frac{d\vec{t}}{ds}.$$

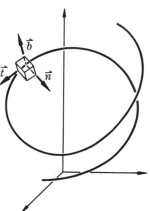

If $\vec{t}$ is constant in direction (as well as length), then C is a straight line, $d\vec{t}/ds = 0$, and $|d\vec{t}/ds| = 0$. If $|d\vec{t}/ds| \neq 0$, then C actually curves and $d\vec{t}/ds$ is perpendicular to $\vec{t}$, since the dot product in (4) is zero. Hence, the vector $\vec{n}$ defined by

(5)
$$\vec{n} = \frac{1}{|d\vec{t}/ds|} \frac{d\vec{t}}{ds}$$

is a unit vector and is called the **principal unit normal** vector.

Fig. 10-9.1

A second unit normal vector $\vec{b}$, called the **unit binormal**, is now defined by

(6)
$$\vec{b} = \vec{t} \times \vec{n}.$$

Thus, $\vec{t}, \vec{n}, \vec{b}$ is a right-handed system of mutually orthogonal unit vectors which may be thought of as riding along the curve, varying in orientation from point to point. As already noted, $|d\vec{t}/ds| \neq 0$ indicates that C is curving, and the more it curves the greater will be $|d\vec{t}/ds|$. Hence, the scalar κ is introduced by setting

(7)
$$\kappa = \left|\frac{d\vec{t}}{ds}\right|$$

and is called the **curvature** of C at whatever point it is evaluated. Thus, (5) becomes

(8)
$$\frac{d\vec{t}}{ds} = \kappa\vec{n}, \quad \text{so that} \quad \kappa\vec{n} = \frac{d^2\vec{u}}{ds^2}.$$

If C is a plane curve, then $\vec{b}$ is normal to this plane, and thus from point to point $\vec{b}$ stays constant in direction as well as length, so that $d\vec{b}/ds = 0$. Thus, $d\vec{b}/ds \neq 0$ means that C is not plane but is twisted in space, and a scalar τ will be introduced for judging the amount of twisting. First, however, note that $d\vec{b}/dt$ not only is back in the $(\vec{t}, \vec{n})$-plane but is in the line of $\vec{n}$; for $\vec{b} \cdot \vec{b} = 1$, and hence

$$\vec{b} \cdot \frac{d\vec{b}}{ds} = 0,$$

showing that $d\vec{b}/ds$ is perpendicular to $\vec{b}$ and thus is in the $(\vec{t}, \vec{n})$-plane. But the perpendicularity of $\vec{b}$ with both $\vec{t}$ and $\vec{n}$ means

(9)
$$\vec{b} \cdot \vec{t} = 0 \quad \text{and} \quad \vec{b} \cdot \vec{n} = 0.$$

The first of these, by differentiation, gives

$$0 = \frac{d\vec{b}}{ds} \cdot \vec{t} + \vec{b} \cdot \frac{d\vec{t}}{ds}$$

$$= \frac{d\vec{b}}{ds} \cdot \vec{t} + \kappa(\vec{b} \cdot \vec{n}) \quad \text{by (8)}$$

$$= \frac{d\vec{b}}{ds} \cdot \vec{t} + 0 \quad \text{by the second equation of (9),}$$

so that $d\vec{b}/ds$ is also perpendicular to $\vec{t}$ and thus is in the same line as n. Hence, there is a scalar τ such that

(10)
$$\frac{d\vec{b}}{ds} \doteq \tau\vec{n},$$

and this scalar τ is called the **torsion** of the curve at whatever point it is evaluated.

The fact that $\vec{t}, \vec{n}, \vec{b}$ is a right-handed system of vectors gives [including (6) again]

(11)
$$\vec{t} \times \vec{n} = \vec{b}, \quad \vec{n} \times \vec{b} = \vec{t}, \quad \vec{b} \times \vec{t} = \vec{n}.$$

From the last of these, by differentiation,

(12)
$$\frac{d\vec{n}}{ds} = \vec{b} \times \frac{d\vec{t}}{ds} + \frac{d\vec{b}}{ds} \times \vec{t}$$

$$= \kappa\vec{b} \times \vec{n} + \tau\vec{n} \times \vec{t} \quad \text{by (8) and (10)}$$

$$= -\kappa\vec{n} \times \vec{b} - \tau\vec{t} \times \vec{n}$$

$$= -\kappa\vec{t} - \tau\vec{b} \quad \text{by the first and second of (11).}$$

Hence, the derivatives with respect to s of the three unit vectors $\vec{t}, \vec{n}$, and $\vec{b}$ are expressed in terms of the vectors themselves:

$$\frac{d\vec{t}}{ds} = \kappa\vec{n},$$

$$\frac{d\vec{n}}{ds} = -\kappa\vec{t} - \tau\vec{b},$$

$$\frac{d\vec{b}}{ds} = \tau\vec{n}.$$

These are known as the Frenet-Serret formulas and are used extensively in a branch of mathematics called differential geometry, which was basic to the development of relativity theory.

Space curves usually are not delivered already parameterized in terms of their own arc lengths s but come as paths of particles in terms of a time parameter t:

$$\vec{u}(t) = \vec{i}x(t) + \vec{j}y(t) + \vec{k}z(t).$$

(The scalar time t should not be confused with the unit normal vector $\vec{t}$.) A tangent vector to the path (or the velocity of the particle) is

$$(13) \qquad \frac{d\vec{u}}{dt} = \vec{i}\frac{dx}{dt} + \vec{j}\frac{dy}{dt} + \vec{k}\frac{dz}{dt},$$

and the unit tangent vector is

$$(14) \qquad \vec{t} = \frac{d\vec{u}}{dt}\frac{1}{\left|\frac{d\vec{u}}{dt}\right|} = \left[\vec{i}\frac{dx}{dt} + \vec{j}\frac{dy}{dt} + \vec{k}\frac{dz}{dt}\right] \frac{1}{\sqrt{\left(\frac{dx}{dt}\right)^2 + \left(\frac{dy}{dt}\right)^2 + \left(\frac{dz}{dt}\right)^2}}.$$

The point $P_0(x(0), y(0), z(0))$ is a convenient one from which to measure arc lengths s along the path, with s increasing at t increases. Then, $s(t)$ is an increasing function of t with $ds/dt > 0$. It follows inversely that t is an increasing function of s and

$$\frac{dt}{ds} = \frac{1}{ds/dt}.$$

From the original definition (2) of the unit tangent vector $\vec{t}$, and by using the formula for the derivative of a function,

$$\vec{t} = \frac{d\vec{u}}{ds} = \frac{d\vec{u}}{dt}\frac{dt}{ds}$$

$$= \vec{t}\left|\frac{d\vec{u}}{dt}\right|\frac{dt}{ds} \quad \text{from (14),}$$

and this shows that

(15)
$$\frac{dt}{ds} = \frac{1}{|d\vec{u}/dt|},$$

(16)
$$\frac{ds}{dt} = \left|\frac{d\vec{u}}{dt}\right| = \sqrt{\left(\frac{dx}{dt}\right)^2 + \left(\frac{dy}{dt}\right)^2 + \left(\frac{dz}{dt}\right)^2}.$$

Example 1. A particle moves according to the law

$$\vec{u}(t) = e^t(\vec{i}\cos t + \vec{j}\sin t + \vec{k}).$$

For the path of the particle, find the vectors $\vec{t}, \vec{n}, \vec{b}$ and the scalars κ, τ.

Solution. The arc length s need not be expressed explicitly as a function of t, but these variables are linked together through their derivatives as expressed by (16), or the equivalent (15). Hence, first compute

(17)
$$\frac{ds}{dt} = \sqrt{[e^t(\cos t - \sin t)]^2 + [e^t(\sin t + \cos t)]^2 + [e^t]^2} = \sqrt{3}\, e^t.$$

Having computed the derivatives of the components of $\vec{u}$, the unit tangent vector may be written down (being sure not to confuse $\vec{t}$ and t):

(18)
$$\vec{t} = \frac{d\vec{u}}{ds} = \frac{d\vec{u}}{dt}\frac{dt}{ds}$$

$$= e^t[\vec{i}(\cos t - \sin t) + \vec{j}(\sin t + \cos t) + \vec{k}]\frac{1}{\sqrt{3}\,e^t}$$

$$= \frac{1}{\sqrt{3}}[\vec{i}(\cos t - \sin t) + \vec{j}(\sin t + \cos t) + \vec{k}].$$

The curvature κ and principal normal $\vec{n}$ are such that

(19)
$$\kappa\vec{n} = \frac{d\vec{t}}{ds} = \frac{d\vec{t}}{dt}\frac{dt}{ds}$$

$$= \frac{1}{\sqrt{3}}[\vec{i}(-\sin t - \cos t) + \vec{j}(\cos t - \sin t)]\frac{1}{\sqrt{3}\,e^t}$$

$$= \frac{\sqrt{2}}{3e^t}\frac{1}{\sqrt{2}}[\vec{i}(-\sin t - \cos t) + \vec{j}(\cos t - \sin t)]$$

(where $\sqrt{2}$ was introduced to obtain a unit vector), so that

(20)
$$\kappa = \frac{\sqrt{2}}{3e^t} \quad \text{and} \quad \vec{n} = \frac{1}{\sqrt{2}}[\vec{i}(-\sin t - \cos t) + \vec{j}(\cos t - \sin t)].$$

The unit binormal is obtained from a cross product:

(21)
$$\vec{b} = \vec{t} \times \vec{n} = \frac{1}{\sqrt{3}}\frac{1}{\sqrt{2}}\begin{vmatrix} \vec{i} & \vec{j} & \vec{k} \\ \cos t - \sin t & \sin t + \cos t & 1 \\ -\sin t - \cos t & \cos t - \sin t & 0 \end{vmatrix}$$

$$= \frac{1}{\sqrt{6}}[\vec{i}(-\cos t + \sin t) + \vec{j}(-\sin t - \cos t) + \vec{k}2].$$

The torsion τ is such that

$$\tau \vec{n} = \frac{d\vec{b}}{ds} = \frac{d\vec{b}}{dt}\frac{dt}{ds}$$

$$= \frac{1}{\sqrt{6}}[\vec{i}(\sin t + \cos t) + \vec{j}(-\cos t + \sin t)]\frac{1}{\sqrt{3}\,e^t}$$

$$= \frac{-1}{3e^t}\cdot\frac{1}{\sqrt{2}}[\vec{i}(-\sin t - \cos t) + \vec{j}(\cos t - \sin t)]$$

$$= \frac{-1}{3e^t}\vec{n} \quad \text{and hence}$$

$$\tau = -\frac{1}{3e^t}\,.$$

The velocity and acceleration of the particle are kinematic properties and these are connected with geometric properties of the curve. First, the velocity $\vec{v}$,

$$\vec{v} = \frac{d\vec{u}}{dt} = \frac{d\vec{u}}{ds}\frac{ds}{dt} = \vec{t}\frac{ds}{dt},$$

is in the direction of the tangent $\vec{t}$, with scalar coefficient the instantaneous speed along the curve. The acceleration $\vec{a}$ resolves naturally into tangential and normal components:

(22)
$$\vec{a} = \frac{d\vec{v}}{dt} = \frac{d}{dt}\left(\vec{t}\frac{ds}{dt}\right) = \vec{t}\frac{d^2 s}{dt^2} + \frac{ds}{dt}\frac{d\vec{t}}{dt}$$

$$= \vec{t}\frac{d^2 s}{dt^2} + \frac{ds}{dt}\left(\frac{d\vec{t}}{ds}\frac{ds}{dt}\right) = \vec{t}\frac{d^2 s}{dt^2} + \frac{d\vec{t}}{ds}\left(\frac{ds}{dt}\right)^2$$

$$= \vec{t}\frac{d^2 s}{dt^2} + \vec{n}\kappa\left(\frac{ds}{dt}\right)^2.$$

The actual (scalar) acceleration $d^2 s/dt^2$ along the curve seems natural for the coefficient of $\vec{t}$, but the curvature times the square of the scalar speed may not be as intuitive for the normal component.

The resolution (22) shows that the portion of the path near a point is so nearly in the $(\vec{t}, \vec{n})$-plane for the point that the acceleration vector lies in this plane.* Moreover, the positiveness of the coefficient of $\vec{n}$ shows that the acceleration vector is directed no more than 90° from the direction of the normal; and if this descriptive argument is not convincing, then formally

$$\vec{a}\cdot\vec{n} = \vec{t}\cdot\vec{n}\frac{d^2 s}{dt^2} + \vec{n}\cdot\vec{n}\kappa\left(\frac{ds}{dt}\right)^2$$

$$= 0 + \kappa\left(\frac{ds}{dt}\right)^2 \geq 0$$

---

*The intimacy of this plane and the curve is described by calling the $(\vec{t}, \vec{n})$-plane the **osculating** plane of the curve at the point.

shows that the angle θ between $\vec{a}$ and $\vec{n}$ has $\cos \theta \geq 0$, so $\theta \leq 90°$.

Example 2. The motions of two particles are governed by the laws

$$\vec{u}_1(t) = 3t^2\vec{i} - t^2\vec{j} + \tfrac{1}{3}t^3\vec{k}, \quad t > 0 \quad \text{and}$$

$$\vec{u}_2(t) = 3e^{2t}\vec{i} - e^{2t}\vec{j} + \tfrac{1}{3}e^{3t}\vec{k}.$$

Let P_1 be a point on either path, and show that P_1 is also on the other path; that is, the paths are identical. Show that both particles pass through $Q(3, -1, \tfrac{1}{3})$ with the same velocity but different accelerations. Find relations between the tangential and normal components of acceleration of the particles at Q.

Solution. Let P_1 be on the first graph and $t = t_1 > 0$ be the time the first particle passes through P_1, so that

$$P_1 = (3t_1^2, -t_1^2, \tfrac{1}{3}t_1^3).$$

The second particle passes through P_1 when t is such that

$$e^t = t_1 \quad \text{so that} \quad t = \ln t_1.$$

In a similar way, a point on the second path is also on the first path.

Denoting derivatives with respect to t by primes, the respective velocities are

$$\vec{u}_1'(t) = \vec{v}_1(t) = 6t\vec{i} - 2t\vec{j} + t^2\vec{k} \quad \text{and} \quad \vec{u}_2'(t) = \vec{v}_2(t) = 6e^{2t}\vec{i} - 2e^{2t}\vec{j} + e^{3t}\vec{k}.$$

Hence, at Q, time $t = 1$ for the first but $t = 0$ for the second particle, and

$$\vec{v}_1(1) = 6\vec{i} - 2\vec{j} + \vec{k} \quad \text{and} \quad \vec{v}_2(0) = 6\vec{i} - 2\vec{j} + \vec{k} = \vec{v}_1(1).$$

The accelerations at time t are

$$\vec{v}_1'(t) = \vec{a}_1(t) = 6\vec{i} - 2\vec{j} + 2t\vec{k} \quad \text{and} \quad \vec{v}_2'(t) = \vec{a}_2(t) = 12e^{2t}\vec{i} - 4e^{2t}\vec{j} + 3e^{3t}\vec{k}.$$

Hence, at Q,

$$\vec{a}_1(1) = 6\vec{i} - 2\vec{j} + 2\vec{k}, \quad \text{but} \quad \vec{a}_2(0) = 12\vec{i} - 4\vec{j} + 3\vec{k}.$$

Thus, for any scalar constant c,

$$\vec{a}_1(t) \neq c\vec{a}_2(0).$$

The tangential and normal components of acceleration depend on $\vec{t}, \vec{n}$, and κ at Q, but since these are the same for both parameterizations their exact values are not necessary. It is, however, necessary to have the first and second time derivatives of both arc lengths:

$$s_1'(t) = \sqrt{(6t)^2 + (-2t)^2 + (t^2)^2} = t\sqrt{40 + t^2}, \quad s_1'(1) = \sqrt{41};$$

$$s_1''(t) = \frac{t^2}{\sqrt{40 + t^2}} + \sqrt{40 + t^2} = \frac{40 + 2t^2}{\sqrt{40 + t^2}}, \quad s_1''(1) = \frac{42}{\sqrt{41}};$$

$$s_2'(t) = \sqrt{(6e^{2t})^2 + (-2e^{2t})^2 + (e^{3t})^2} = e^{2t}\sqrt{40 + e^{2t}}, \quad s_2'(0) = \sqrt{41};$$

$$s_2''(t) = \frac{e^{4t}}{\sqrt{40 + e^{2t}}} + 2e^{2t}\sqrt{40 + e^{2t}} = \frac{80e^{2t} + 3e^{4t}}{\sqrt{40 + e^{2t}}}, \quad s_2''(0) = \frac{83}{\sqrt{41}}.$$

Thus, at Q, from the resolution formula (22),

$$\vec{a}_1(1) = \vec{t}\,\frac{42}{\sqrt{41}} + \vec{n}\kappa(\sqrt{41})^2,$$

$$\vec{a}_2(0) = \vec{t}\,\frac{83}{\sqrt{41}} + \vec{n}\kappa(\sqrt{41})^2.$$

Hence, in this particular case and at the particular point Q, the accelerations have the same normal component but different tangential components.

Problem 1. Check formula (12) for the path of Example 1.

Problem 2. With a and c positive constants a particle moves according to the law

$$\vec{u}(t) - \vec{i}a \cos t + \vec{j}a \sin t + \vec{k}ct.$$

a. Show that the particle is always a units from the z-axis. [Note: The path is called a **circular helix.**]
b. Find how far the particle travels for $0 \le t \le 2\pi$.
c. Find $\vec{t}, \vec{n}, \vec{b}, \kappa,$ and τ for the path. [Note: κ and τ are constants in this case.]
d. Describe the path in case $c = 0$.

Problem 3. Find $\vec{t}, \kappa,$ and $\vec{n}$ if:
a. $\vec{u}(t) = \vec{i}\cosh 2t + \vec{j}\sinh 2t + \vec{k}2t.$
b. $\vec{u}(t) = \vec{i}4 \cos 3t + \vec{j}4 \sin 3t + \vec{k}5t.$
c. $\vec{u}(t) = \vec{i}(3t - t^3) + \vec{j}3t^2 + \vec{k}(3t + t^3).$

Problem 4. Work out $\vec{t}, \vec{n},$ and κ for both parameterizations of the path in Example 2 and show that they are the same at any one point.

Problem 5. Show that

$$\frac{d^3\vec{u}}{ds^3} = -\kappa^2\vec{t} + \frac{d\kappa}{ds}\,\vec{n} - \kappa\tau\vec{b}.$$

10-10. Surfaces and Solids

Through the point $(0, 0, 1)$ there is a plane parallel to the (x, y)-plane. In this plane, there is an elliptical disk with center $(0, 0, 1)$, major axis $2a$ units long and parallel to the x-axis, and minor axis $2b$ units long. Thus, a point $(x, y, 1)$ is on this surface if and only if

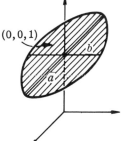

$$\frac{x^2}{a^2} + \frac{y^2}{b^2} \le 1.$$

A compact way of indicating that each point of this elliptical disk has three coordinates, instead of two, is to write

(1) $$\left\{(x, y, 1)\,\Big|\,\frac{x^2}{a^2} + \frac{y^2}{b^2} \le 1\right\}$$

Fig. 10-10.1

and to read "the set of all points $(x, y, 1)$ such that $x^2/a^2 + y^2/b^2 \leq 1$." This symbolic way of expressing a set of points is a fairly recent introduction into mathematical literature, but its utility has already won its assured acceptance.

Consider now the three sets

$$\left\{(x, y) \Big| \frac{x^2}{a^2} + \frac{y^2}{b^2} \leq 1\right\}, \quad \left\{(x, y, 0) \Big| \frac{x^2}{a^2} + \frac{y^2}{b^2} \leq 1\right\}, \quad \left\{(x, y, z) \Big| \frac{x^2}{a^2} + \frac{y^2}{b^2} \leq 1\right\}.$$

The first is an elliptical disk in the (x, y)-plane with no third dimension even contemplated. The second is also an elliptical disk visualized as embeded in three-dimensional space but confined to the (x, y)-plane of that space. The third is an elliptical solid cylinder of infinite extent, since the third coordinate z is present, but not restricted in any way. The set

$$\left\{(x, y, z) \Big| \frac{x^2}{a^2} + \frac{y^2}{b^2} = 1\right\}$$

is the surface of this elliptical solid cylinder, while

$$\left\{(x, y, z) \Big| 0 \leq z \leq 2, \frac{x^2}{a^2} + \frac{y^2}{b^2} \leq 1\right\}$$

is a solid elliptical cylinder of altitude 2 standing on the (x, y)-plane.

Many solids or surfaces are best perceived by visualizing plane sections perpendicular to coordinate axes. For example,

(2)
$$\left\{(x, y, z) \Big| \frac{x^2}{a^2} + \frac{y^2}{b^2} - \frac{z^2}{c^2} = 1\right\}$$

is a surface, but there is too much to keep in mind if all three variables are allowed to vary at once. Thus, write this set as

$$\left\{(x, y, z) \Big| \frac{x^2}{a^2} + \frac{y^2}{b^2} = 1 + \frac{z^2}{c^2}\right\}$$

$$= \left\{(x, y, z) \Big| \frac{x^2}{a^2[1 + (z^2/c^2)]} + \frac{y^2}{b^2[1 + (z^2/c^2)]} = 1\right\},$$

and consider the surface as made up of a family of ellipses, with z the parameter of the family. Hold z at a fixed arbitrary value and note that

$$\frac{x^2}{a^2[1 + (z^2/c^2)]} + \frac{y^2}{b^2[1 + (z^2/c^2)]} = 1$$

represents an ellipse with semimajor and semiminor axes of lengths

$$a\sqrt{1 + \frac{z^2}{c^2}}, \quad b\sqrt{1 + \frac{z^2}{c^2}},$$

but this ellipse is to be located in the plane perpendicular to the z-axis at $(0, 0, z)$. Thus, planes perpendicular to the z-axis intersect the surface (2) in ellipses, with both semiaxes increasing as the sections are taken farther and farther from the (x, y)-plane. Also, a conception of how these semi-axes vary

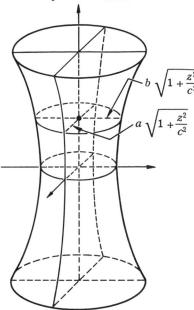

Fig. 10-10.2

may be obtained from the intersection of (2) with the (y, z)-plane and the (x, z)-plane; that is,

(3) $$\left\{(0, y, z)\Big|\frac{y^2}{b^2} - \frac{z^2}{c^2} = 1\right\} \quad \text{and} \quad \left\{(x, 0, z)\Big|\frac{x^2}{a^2} - \frac{z^2}{c^2} = 1\right\},$$

respectively. The first is a hyperbola in the (y, z)-plane with vertices at $(0, \pm b, 0)$ and having as asymptotes the lines

(4) $$\left\{(0, y, z)\Big|\frac{y^2}{b^2} - \frac{z^2}{c^2} = 0\right\} = \left\{(0, y, z)\Big|\frac{y}{b} = \frac{z}{c} \quad \text{or} \quad \frac{y}{b} = \frac{-z}{c}\right\}.$$

In the same way, the second set in (3) is a hyperbola in the (x, z)-plane.

Notice the difference between the lines (4), which are not on the surface, and the lines

$$\left\{(a, y, z)\Big|\frac{y^2}{b^2} - \frac{z^2}{c^2} = 0\right\},$$

which constitute the intersection of the surface (2) and the plane $x = a$. As curved as the surface (2) appears, it may be surprising that it contains all of these two straight lines, but the following example shows even more.

Example 1. a. Show that through each point of the surface

(5) $$\{(x, y, z)|x^2 + y^2 - z^2 = 1\}$$

there are two lines that lie completely on the surface.*

*Such a surface is said to be **doubly ruled**.

b. Use the result of part a to show that the surface (2) is also doubly ruled.

Solution a. Let (x_0, y_0, z_0) be an arbitrary point on the surface (5), so that

(6) $x_0^2 + y_0^2 - z_0^2 = 1$ or $x_0^2 + y_0^2 = 1 + z_0^2$

and, for later use, note that x_0 and y_0 cannot both be zero. Pass a line through (x_0, y_0, z_0) with direction numbers A, B, C, and write the line in parametric form,

$$x = x_0 + At, \quad y = y_0 + Bt, \quad z = z_0 + Ct,$$

so A, B, C are not all zero. This line will be on the surface (5) if

$$(x_0 + At)^2 + (y_0 + Bt)^2 - (z_0 + Ct)^2 \equiv 1 \,;$$

that is, if the equation holds for all t. Write this equation in the form

$$x_0^2 + y_0^2 - z_0^2 + 2(Ax_0 + By_0 - Cz_0)t + (A^2 + B^2 - C^2)t^2 = 1.$$

Next, use (6) to simplify this to

$$2(Ax_0 + By_0 - Cz_0)t + (A^2 + B^2 - C^2)t^2 = 0,$$

which will hold for all t if and only if the coefficients of t and t^2 are both zero; that is, if A, B, C simultaneously satisfy

$$Ax_0 + By_0 - Cz_0 = 0 \quad \text{and} \quad A^2 + B^2 - C^2 = 0.$$

From the second of these,

$$A^2 + B^2 = C^2$$

shows that $C \neq 0$ (for otherwise all three of the direction numbers A, B, C would be zero). Thus, C may be assigned any nonzero number, and hence set $C = 1$ to obtain the simpler simultaneous equations

$$Ax_0 + By_0 = z_0,$$
$$A^2 + B^2 = 1.$$

Since x_0 and y_0 cannot both be zero, assume $x_0 \neq 0$ and solve the first equation for A :

(7) $$A = \frac{z_0 - By_0}{x_0}.$$

Then substitute into the second equation :

$$\left(\frac{z_0 - By_0}{x_0}\right)^2 + B^2 = 1, \quad B^2(x_0^2 + y_0^2) - 2y_0z_0B + z_0^2 - x_0^2 = 0.$$

This quadratic equation in B yields

(8) $$B = \frac{2y_0z_0 \pm \sqrt{4y_0^2z_0^2 - 4(x_0^2 + y_0^2)(z_0^2 - x_0^2)}}{2(x_0^2 + y_0^2)}.$$

It is now an algebraic exercise to reduce this expression [by using (6) at least once] to

(9) $$B = \frac{y_0z_0 \pm x_0}{x_0^2 + y_0^2}.$$

The substitution into (7) yields the corresponding values

$$A = \frac{x_0 z_0 \mp y_0}{x_0^2 + y_0^2}.$$

Hence, the lines through (x_0, y_0, z_0) (with either of the direction numbers A, B, 1 given by the above expressions) will lie completely on the surface (5).

Solution b. This time, the equation in (2) is to be used, but the simplifying substitutions

$$X = \frac{x}{a}, \quad Y = \frac{y}{b}, \quad Z = \frac{z}{c}$$

reduce this equation to

$$Z^2 + Y^2 - Z^2 = 1,$$

which is identical in form to the equation in (5). Hence, the work of part a need not be duplicated to obtain $C=1$,

$$A = \frac{X_0 Z_0 \mp Y^0}{X_0^2 + Y_0^2} = \frac{(x_0/a)(z_0/c) \mp (y_0/b)}{(x_0/a)^2 + (y_0/b)^2} = \frac{b x_0 z_0 \mp a c y_0}{b^2 x_0^2 + a^2 y_0^2} \frac{ab}{c}$$

and

$$B = \frac{a y_0 z_0 \pm b c x_0}{b^2 x_0^2 + a^2 y_0^2} \frac{ab}{c}.$$

Another feature of some surfaces may be seen by turning the surface (2) so the y-axis is the axis of symmetry,

$$\left\{ (x, y, z) \middle| \frac{x^2}{a^2} - \frac{y^2}{b^2} + \frac{z^2}{c^2} = 1 \right\},$$

and then considering only the half (Fig. 10-10.3) above the (x, y)-plane:

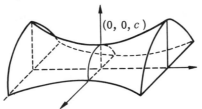

Fig. 10-10.3

$$\left\{ (x, y, z) \middle| z = c\sqrt{1 + \frac{y^2}{b^2} - \frac{x^2}{a^2}} \right\}.$$

The intersection of the (y, z)-plane with this surface is a branch of a hyperbola

$$\left\{ (0, y, z) \middle| z = c\sqrt{1 + \frac{y^2}{b^2}} \right\},$$

which has its minimum point at the vertex $(0, 0, c)$. The intersection of the same surface with the (x, z)-plane is the semiellipse

$$\left\{(x, 0, z) \middle| z = c\sqrt{1 - \frac{x^2}{a^2}}\right\},$$

which has the same point $(0, 0, c)$ as its maximum. Such a point is called a **minimax** point of the surface or, in another terminology, the surface is said to have a **saddlepoint** there.

The following equation differs from the equation in (2) only by having -1 instead of 1:

$$\frac{x^2}{a^2} + \frac{y^2}{b^2} - \frac{z^2}{c^2} = -1.$$

The graph of this equation does not intersect the (x, y)-plane, but sections parallel to the (x, y)-plane

$$\left\{(x, y, z) \middle| \frac{x^2}{a^2\left(\frac{z^2}{c^2} - 1\right)} + \frac{y^2}{b^2\left(\frac{z^2}{c^2} - 1\right)} = 1\right\}, \quad z \text{ constant},$$

are ellipses for $|z| > c$. However, as with (2), sections parallel to the (x, z)-plane

$$\left\{(x, y, z) \middle| \frac{z^2}{c^2\left(1 + \frac{y^2}{b^2}\right)} - \frac{x^2}{a^2\left(1 + \frac{y^2}{b^2}\right)} = 1\right\}, \quad y \text{ constant},$$

are hyperbolas and the same is true of sections parallel to the (y, z)-plane.

The graph of the similar looking equation

(10) $$\frac{x^2}{a^2} + \frac{y^2}{b^2} - \frac{z^2}{c^2} = 0$$

contains the origin and intersects planes parallel to the (x, y)-plane in

$$\left\{(x, y, z) \middle| \frac{x^2}{a^2 \frac{z^2}{c^2}} + \frac{y^2}{b^2 \frac{z^2}{c^2}} = 1\right\}, \quad z \neq 0 \text{ constant},$$

which are ellipses. The (x, z)-plane itself intersects this surface in

$$\left\{(x, 0, z) \middle| \frac{x^2}{a^2} - \frac{z^2}{c^2} = 0\right\} = \left\{(x, 0, z) \middle| \frac{x}{a} = \frac{z}{c} \text{ or } \frac{x}{a} = -\frac{z}{c}\right\},$$

which are lines. In the same way, the (y, z)-plane intersects the surface (10) in two lines and the graph of (10) is an **elliptic cone**.

Of the surfaces having equations,

$$\frac{x^2}{a^2} + \frac{y^2}{b^2} - \frac{z^2}{c^2} = 1, \quad \frac{x^2}{a^2} + \frac{y^2}{b^2} - \frac{z^2}{c^2} = -1, \quad \frac{x^2}{a^2} + \frac{y^2}{b^2} - \frac{z^2}{c^2} = 0,$$

the first two are labeled an **elliptic hyperboloid of one sheet** and an **elliptic hyperboloid of two sheets,** respectively, and the third is an **elliptic cone** to which the first two are both asymptotic. In fact, the family of surfaces

(11)
$$\frac{x^2}{a^2} + \frac{y^2}{b^2} - \frac{z^2}{c^2} = \lambda$$

of parameter λ are one-sheeted or two-sheeted elliptic hyperboloids for $\lambda > 0$ or $\lambda < 0$, respectively, and the member with $\lambda = 0$ is the asymptotic cone for all other members.

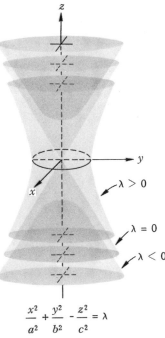

$$\frac{x^2}{a^2} + \frac{y^2}{b^2} - \frac{z^2}{c^2} = \lambda$$

$\lambda > 0$: Hyperboloid of one sheet
$\lambda = 0$: Elliptia cone
$\lambda < 0$: Hyperboloid of two sheets

Fig. 10-10.4

Other surfaces having equations of second degree (called **quadric surfaces**), their equations, and their labels are given in Figure 10-10.5. In each case, a few sections by planes parallel to the coordinate planes should be visualized.

Even though an equation involves only two variables, such as

(12) $y^2 = 4px,$

but it is certain that three dimensions are being considered, then this shorter notation for the graph is used instead of

$$\{(x, y, z)|y^2 = 4px\}.$$

If a surface can be completely ruled by parallel lines, then the graph is said to be a cylindrical surface. Thus, the graph of (12) is a parabolic cylinder.

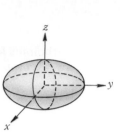

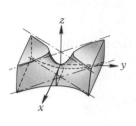

Ellipsoid:

$$\frac{x^2}{a^2} + \frac{y^2}{b^2} + \frac{z^2}{c^2} = 1$$

Elliptic paraboloid:

$$\frac{x^2}{a^2} + \frac{y^2}{b^2} = z$$

Hyperbolic paraboloid:

$$\frac{y^2}{b^2} - \frac{x^2}{a^2} = z$$

Cylindrical Surfaces

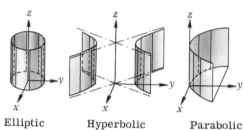

Elliptic

$$\frac{x^2}{a^2} + \frac{y^2}{b^2} = 1$$

Hyperbolic

$$\frac{y^2}{a^2} - \frac{x^2}{b^2} = 1$$

Parabolic

$$x^2 = 4py$$

Fig. 10-10.5

Problem 1. Describe each of the sets:

a. $\{(x, y)|y^2 = 4x\}, \quad \{(x, y, 0)|y^2 = 4x\}, \quad \{(x, y, z)|y^2 = 4x\}$.

b. $\{(y, z)|(y - 1)^2 + z^2 = 4\}, \quad \{(2, y, z)|(y-1)^2+z^2 = 4\},$

$$\{(x, y, z)|(y - 1)^2 + z^2 = 4\}.$$

c. $\{(x, z)|xz = 2\}, \quad \{(x, 2, z)|xz = 2\}, \quad \{(x, y, z)|xz = 2\}$.

Problem 2. By making a translation of axes, name the surface having equation:

a. $x^2 + y^2 - z^2 - 2x = 0$.

b. $x^2 - y^2 + 4x + 6y = z$.

c. $x^2 + y^2 - z^2 - 2x + 4y - 6z = 4$.

d. $x^2 - 2y^2 - z^2 - 2x + 8y - 6z = 16$.

Problem 3. a. Show that the special hyperbolic paraboloid

$$y^2 - x^2 = z$$

is a doubly ruled surface.

b. Use the result of part a to show that the general hyperbolic paraboloid

$$\frac{y^2}{b^2} - \frac{x^2}{a^2} = z$$

is also doubly ruled.

Problem 4. Without relying on geometry (that is, by purely algebraic means), show that the circular cone $x^2 + y^2 - z^2 = 0$ is singly ruled through any point except the origin.

Problem 5. Given the equation $xy = z$ of a surface:
a. Show that the surface contains the x- and y-axes.
b. Show that the surface is doubly ruled.
c. Prove that the surface is a hyperbolic paraboloid.

Problem 6. Show that the graph of each of the equations is an elliptic cone:
a. $3x^2 - 2xy + 3y^2 - 2z^2 = 0$.   b. $x^2 + yz = 0$.
c. $x^2 + yz - 2x - 3y + 2z = 5$.

Problem 7. First translate to remove first-degree terms, then rotate to remove product terms, and name the graph from the resulting equation;
a. $x^2 - y^2 + z^2 + 2xz + 2y - 1 = 0$.
b. $3(x^2 + y^2) + 2z^2 + 2xy - 6x - 2y + 5 = 0$,
c. $xy + xz = 4$. [Hint; Rotate $45°$ in (y, z)-plane.]
d. $z^2 - 4xy - 8x + 4y - 4z + 12 = 0$.

10-11. Cylindrical and Spherical Coordinates

A coordinate system is a frame of reference whereby any point may be specified. In the plane, both rectangular and polar coordinates were used. In addition to rectangular coordinates in space, the two systems in the title of this section are used.

Cylindrical coordinates have a polar coordinate system (ρ, θ) in the (x, y)-plane and z as the third coordinate. Thus, the cylindrical coordinates (ρ, θ, z) and the rectangular coordinates (x, y, z) of a point P are related (Fig. 10-11.1) by

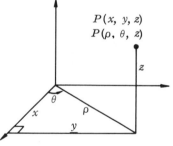

Fig. 10-11.1

(1) $x = \rho \cos \theta, \quad y = \rho \sin \theta, \quad z = z.$

Spherical coordinates are (r, θ, ϕ), with r a number but θ and ϕ angles. The z-axis and a point P not on this axis determine a plane. In this plane, P has polar coordinates (r, ϕ), with ϕ measured from the z-axis. In the (x, y)-plane, the projection of P has polar coordinates $(r \sin \phi, \theta)$. Hence, the spherical coordinates (r, θ, ϕ) and cylindrical coordinates (ρ, θ, z) of P are related by

(2) $\rho = r \sin \phi, \quad \theta = \theta, \quad z = r \cos \phi,$

as shown in Fig. 10-11.2 with $r > 0$.

By combining (1) and (2), the rectangular and spherical coordinates of P are related by

(3) $x = r \sin \phi \cos \theta, \quad y = r \sin \phi \sin \theta, \quad z = r \cos \phi.$

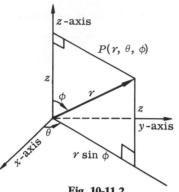

z-axis

$P(r, \theta, \phi)$

y-axis

$r \sin \phi$

Fig. 10-11.2

The point set notation introduced in the previous sections is particularly useful when more than one coordinate system is involved. For example,

$$I = \{(x, y, z)|x = 2, \quad y = 1.5, \quad 0 \le z \le 3\}$$

and

$$J = \{\rho, \theta, z)|\rho = 2, \quad \theta = 1.5, \quad 0 \le z \le 3\}$$

are both line segments of length 3 but have different locations, as shown in Fig. 10-11.3. Of course, $\theta = 1.5$ means that θ is an angle of 1.5 radians or about $1.5(57°10') = 85°45'$.

With sets T and S defined by

$$T = \{(x, y, z)|x = 3, \quad 0 \le y \le 2, \quad z = 1\},$$
$$S = \{(\rho, \theta, z)|\rho = 3, \quad 0 \le \theta \le 2, \quad z = 1\},$$

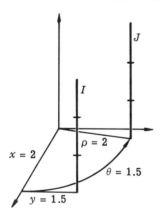

Fig. 10-11.3

T is a line segment while S is an arc of a circle of radius 3. The arc S subtends a central angle of 2 radians and thus has length 6, as shown in Fig. 10-11.4. This same arc S written in spherical coordinates is

$$S = \{(r, \theta, \phi)|r = \sqrt{10},$$
$$0 \le \theta \le 2, \quad \phi = \tan^{-1}3\}.$$

Whenever there is no question about the coordinate system to be used, the set notation is neither necessary nor desirable. The graphs of

$$z = 1, \quad \rho = 1, \quad \text{and} \quad r = 1$$

are a plane, cylinder, and a sphere, respectively. It is, moreover, clear which coordinate system is to be used when a sphere is represented by

$$x^2 + y^2 + z^2 = 4, \quad \rho^2 + z^2 = 4,$$
$$\text{or} \qquad\qquad r = 2.$$

It is immaterial whether rectangular or cylindrical coordinates are used for the plane

$$z = 1$$

and whether cylindrical or spherical coordinates are used for the plane

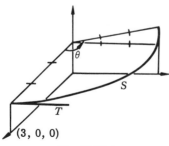

Fig. 10-11.4

$$\theta = \pi/4.$$

On the other hand, a function of two variables such as

$$f(s, t) = s \sin t$$

has a considerably different-looking graph if plotted as

$$z = f(x, y) = x \sin y \quad \text{or as} \quad z = f(\rho, \theta) = \rho \sin \theta.$$

The first is a surface of waves, with each plane perpendicular to the x-axis intersecting the surface in a sine curve of amplitude $|x|$, but the surface is

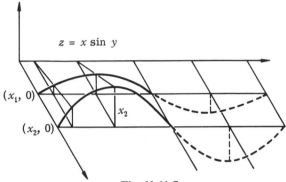

Fig. 10-11.5

ruled by lines in planes perpendicular to the y-axis. The second surface is best visualized (but hard to draw) by noting that its intersection with each cylinder $\rho = $ const. is one period of the sine curve wrapped around the cylinder, but again the surface is ruled by lines in planes $\theta = $ const.

Problem 1. Find cylindrical and spherical coordinates of the point whose rectangular coordinates are given. Also, find the direction angles of the vector from the origin to the point:

a. $(1, 1, 1)$.   c. $(2, 1, -2)$.   e. $(-1, \sqrt{3}, 2)$.
b. $(1, -1, 1)$.   d. $(-1, 2, 3)$.   f. $(1, -\sqrt{3}, -2)$.

Problem 2. For each of the following points, give the spherical coordinates in which $r > 0$ and the angles have as small positive values as possible:

a. $(-2, 30°, 30°)$.   b. $(-2, -30°, 30°)$.   c. $(-2, -30°, -30°)$.

Problem 3. Find spherical coordinates with $r > 0$ of the reflections of the given points in the axes and in the coordinate planes:

a. $(-2, -30°, 60°)$.   b. $(-2, 30°, 60°)$.

Problem 4. Show that each of the sets is an arc of a circle and find the length of the arc. In each case, $0 < h < 2\pi$:

a. $\{(r, \theta, \phi)|r = 5, \theta_0 \le \theta \le \theta_0 + h, \phi = 60°\}$,
b. $\{(r, \theta, \phi)|r = -5, \theta_0 \le \theta \le \theta_0 + h, \phi = -60°\}$,
c. $\{(r, \theta, \phi)|r = 5, \theta = 60°, \phi_0 \le \phi \le \phi_0 + h\}$,
d. $\{(\rho, \theta, z)|\rho = 5, \theta_0 \le \theta \le \theta_0 + h, z = 2\}$.

Chapter 11

Partial Derivatives

11-1. Heat in a Rod

A thin metal rod 10 cm long is cooled to $0°$ C. At time $t = 0$, a flame is placed near one end of the rod. Considering expansion under heat to be so small that it may be neglected, then:

(1) At any given time, the temperatures at points along the rod depend on the distances of the points from the heated end.

(2) At any given point on the rod, the temperature at that point increases with time.

By considering a 10-cm scale along the rod, with 0 at the heated end, the temperature T is a function $T(x, t)$ of two variables, x the distance along the rod and t the time after the experiment started. Upon placing a thermometer at a point x, then the time variation of temperature at that point may be observed. Thus, by keeping x fixed, $T(x, t)$ becomes a function of t alone. The derivative of this function with respect to t is denoted by either

$$(1) \qquad \frac{\partial T(x, t)}{\partial t} \quad \text{or} \quad T_t(x, t).$$

For example, $T_t(5, 3)$ is the time rate at which the temperature is increasing at the point $x = 5$ when $t = 3$. This same information is indicated in the first (curly delta) notation of (1) by

$$\frac{\partial T(x, t)}{\partial t}\bigg|_{(5,3)}.$$

It is not possible to make "time stand still," but at any specified time the temperature $T(x, t)$ is a function of x alone. The derivative with respect to x of this function is denoted by

$$(2) \qquad \frac{\partial T(x, t)}{\partial x} \quad \text{or} \quad T_x(x, t).$$

The symbols in (1) are read, "the partial derivative of $T(x, t)$ with respect to t"; those in (2), "the partial* of $T(x, t)$ with respect to x." By definition,

*Often "partial" is said without following it by "derivative."

400

$$\frac{\partial T(x, t)}{\partial t} = T_t(x; t) = \lim_{\Delta t \to 0} \frac{T(x, t + \Delta t) - T(x, t)}{\Delta t},$$

$$\frac{\partial T(x, t)}{\partial x} = T_x(x, t) = \lim_{\Delta x \to 0} \frac{T(x + \Delta x, t) - T(x, t)}{\Delta x}.$$

From physical considerations, it is reasonable to expect that, at any one point x, the temperature increases with time; that is, $T_t(x, t) > 0$. On the other hand, at any time $t > 0$, the temperature at a point near the flame should be higher than at a point farther along the rod in such a way that $T_x(x, t) < 0$.

No simple algebraic expression for $T(x, t)$ can be given, but an overall general feeling for the variation of $T(x, t)$ can be obtained from a three-dimensional model. The graph of

$$T = T(x, t)$$

is visualized as a surface above the first quadrant of an (x, t)-plane. In Fig. 11-1.1 the straight line AB in the (t, T)-plane shows the constant temperature

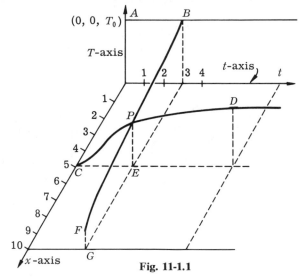

Fig. 11-1.1

T_0 at the flame-end of the rod. The profile CPD represents how the temperature varies with time when $x = 5$. Thus,

$$T(5, 0) = 0, \quad T(5, 3) = EP, \quad \text{and} \quad T_t(5, t) > 0$$

is represented by the curve rising to the right. Similarly, the curve BPF is the intersection of the surface $T = T(x, t)$ and the plane $t = 3$. Here

$$T(0, 3) = T_0, \quad T(5, 3) = EP, \quad T(10, 3) = GF, \quad T_x(x, t) < 0.$$

It also might be suspected that, for $0 < x \le 10$ fixed, $T(x, t) < T_0$, but

$$\lim_{t\to\infty} T(x, t) = T_0.$$

This merely means that, at any fixed point along the rod, the temperature at that point is never as much as T_0 but will be greater than any preassigned temperature less than T_0 after a sufficiently long time.

The purpose here is not to study the physics of heat. The rod example was introduced to indicate how partials arise in practical situations and how a surface may serve as an aid in visualizing relationships. In the remainder of this chapter, partials and their mathematical properties are given for their own sake and also so that they will be available for various interpretations in other fields.

11-2. Partial Derivatives

Let $z = f(x, y)$ be a function of two independent variables x and y. The graph of $z = f(x, y)$ is visualized as a surface in three-dimensional space. Let y have a fixed value such that the plane perpendicular to the y-axis at $(0, y, 0)$ cuts the surface in a curve. Then, with y so fixed, $z = f(x, y)$ becomes a function of the single independent variable x. Think of holding x fixed only temporarily while an increment Δx is made to approach zero in

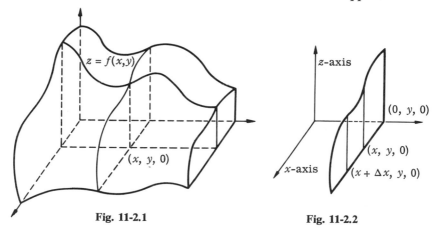

Fig. 11-2.1   Fig. 11-2.2

(1)
$$\lim_{\Delta x\to 0} \frac{f(x + \Delta x, y) - f(x, y)}{\Delta x}.$$

Whenever this limit exists, it is called the *partial derivative* of $z = f(x, y)$ *with respect to* x, and is denoted by either

$$\frac{\partial z}{\partial x} = \frac{\partial f(x, y)}{\partial x} \quad \text{or} \quad z_x = f_x(x, y).$$

These notations for the same thing are used* interchangeably; each has an advantage over the other in some situations.

*Other notations sometimes met are $D_x f(x, y)$, $f'_x x, y)$, and $f_1(x, y)$.

No new formulas are required for finding partial derivatives of explicitly expressed functions of two or more variables. Since

$$\frac{d \sin (a^2 x)}{dx} = a^2 \cos a^2 x$$

for any constant a, it follows for the function $\sin (xy^2)$ of two variables that

$$\frac{\partial \sin (xy^2)}{\partial x} = y^2 \cos (xy^2),$$

since y is held constant while taking the partial derivative with respect to x.

Recall that, for functions of one variable, if $f(x) = \sin 4x$, then by convention

$$\frac{df(\pi/3)}{dx} = \frac{d}{dx} \sin \left(\frac{4\pi}{3}\right) = \frac{d}{dx}\left(-\frac{\sqrt{3}}{2}\right) = 0, \quad \text{but}$$

$$f'\left(\frac{\pi}{3}\right) = 4 \cos \left(\frac{4\pi}{3}\right) = 4\left(-\frac{1}{2}\right) = -2.$$

An analogous convention prevails for the two notations for partial derivatives. Thus, if

$$f(x, y) = \sin (xy^2),$$

then

$$\frac{\partial f(x, y)}{\partial x} = y^2 \sin (xy^2) \quad \text{and} \quad f_x(x, y) = y^2 \sin (xy^2)$$

are the same whenever the variables x and y are not assigned specific values. The convention is to have

$$\frac{\partial f(\pi/3, y)}{\partial x} = \frac{\partial}{\partial x} \sin \left(\frac{\pi}{3} y^2\right) = 0;$$

that is, for the curly delta notation, $x = \pi/3$ is substituted *first* and then the constant (as far as x is concerned) is differentiated with respect to x. For the subscript notation, however,

$$f_x\left(\frac{\pi}{3}, y\right) = y^2 \sin \left(\frac{\pi}{3} y^2\right),$$

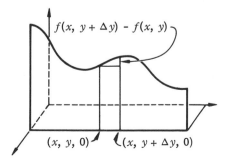

Fig.11-2.3

in which the partial is taken *first* and, after completing this, then x is re-placed by $\pi/3$.

A function $z = f(x, y)$ of two variables also has a partial derivative with respect to y:

$$\frac{\partial z}{\partial y} = \frac{\partial f(x, y)}{\partial y} \quad \text{or} \quad z_y = f_y(x, y),$$

which is defined, whenever the limit exists, by

(2) $$\lim_{\Delta y \to 0} \frac{f(x, y + \Delta y) - f(x, y)}{\Delta y}.$$

For example, with $z = \sin(xy^2)$,

$$\frac{\partial z}{\partial y} = \frac{\partial \sin(xy^2)}{\partial y} = \cos(xy^2)\frac{\partial(xy^2)}{\partial y} = 2xy \cos(xy^2),$$

and also

$$z_y = 2xy \cos(xy^2).$$

Again, by convention, if $f(x, y) = \sin(xy^2)$, then

$$\frac{\partial f(x, 2)}{\partial y} = \frac{\partial \sin(4x)}{\partial y} = 0, \quad \text{but}$$

$$f_y(x, 2) = 2x\ 2 \cos(x2^2) = 4x \cos 4x.$$

The following problems are for the purpose of developing facility in finding partial derivatives.

Problem 1. Find each of the indicated partials:

a. $\dfrac{\partial(x^2y^3 + xy^2)}{\partial x}$ and $\dfrac{\partial(x^2y^3 + xy^2)}{\partial y}$.

b. $\dfrac{\partial \sin(x^2y^3)}{\partial x}$ and $\dfrac{\partial \sin(x^2y^3)}{\partial y}$.

c. $\dfrac{\partial x^y}{\partial x}$ and $\dfrac{\partial x^y}{\partial y}$.

d. $\dfrac{\partial e^{x/y}}{\partial x}$ and $\dfrac{\partial e^{x/y}}{\partial y}$.

Problem 2. Find $f_x(x, y)$ and $f_y(x, y)$:

a. $f(x, y) = \tan^{-1}\dfrac{y}{x}$.   c. $f(x, y) = \sin^{-1}\dfrac{y}{x}$.

b. $f(x, y) = x \ln\left|\dfrac{x}{y}\right|$.   d. $f(x, y) = \cos(2x^2 - 3y^2)$.

Problem 3. Find z_x and z_y:

a. $z = (x^2 + 1)^y$.   c. $z = \dfrac{x + y}{x - y}$.

b. $z = x^2 e^y$.   d. $z = \ln|x \sin y|$.

Problem 4. Given $f(x, y) = x \cos(xy)$, find:

a. $\dfrac{\partial f(x, y)}{\partial x}$, $f_x(x, y)$, $\dfrac{\partial f(x, y)}{\partial y}$, $f_y(x, y)$.

b. $\dfrac{\partial f(2, y)}{\partial x}$, $f_x(2, y)$, $\dfrac{\partial f(2, y)}{\partial y}$, $f_y(2, y)$.

c. $f_x(x, 3)$, $f_y(x, 3)$, $\dfrac{\partial f(x, 3)}{\partial x}$, $\dfrac{\partial f(x, 3)}{\partial y}$.

d. $f_x\left(1, \dfrac{\pi}{4}\right)$, $f_y\left(1, \dfrac{\pi}{4}\right)$, $\dfrac{\partial f(1, \pi/4)}{\partial x}$, $\dfrac{\partial f(1, \pi/4)}{\partial y}$.

Problem 5. Work Prob. 4 with $f(x, y) = y^2 \tan(x^2 y)$.

Problem 6. Without using formulas for derivatives, obtain each of the following partial derivatives; in other words, use the definitions (1) and (2):

a. $\dfrac{\partial(x^2 y)}{\partial x}$ and $\dfrac{\partial(x^2 y)}{\partial y}$.

b. z_x and z_y, given $z = \sqrt{xy + y^2}$.

c. $f_x(x, y)$ and $f_y(x, y)$, given $f(x, y) = x \sin(xy)$.

d. $\dfrac{\partial f(2, y)}{\partial x}$ and $\dfrac{\partial f(2, y)}{\partial y}$, given $f(x, y) = (x^2 - 1)\sqrt{y + 1}$.

11-3. Increments and Mean Values

For a function $z = f(x, y)$, there are two independent variables x and y that may take on independent increments Δx and Δy. The corresponding *increment* of the function is then defined by

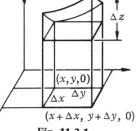
Fig. 11-3.1

(1) $\Delta z = f(x + \Delta x, y + \Delta y) - f(x, y)$.

Figure 11-3.1 illustrates these increments as all being positive, although any of them may be negative or zero.

As the ordinary derivative of a function of one variable may be interpreted as the slope of the tangent to a plane curve, so the partial derivatives $f_x(x, y)$ and $f_y(x, y)$ have geometric representations as slopes of tangent lines to plane curves imbedded in three-dimensional space. Thus, for $x = x_1$ fixed, the graph of

$$z = f(x_1, y)$$

is a curve illustrated in Fig. 11-3.2. The assumption that the arc of this graph between the point P and Q has a tangent at each point means that $f_y(x_1, y)$ exists for y between y_1 and $y_1 + \Delta y$.

The interpretation of the Law of the Mean as the existence of a tangent line parallel to the chord of an arc of a plane curve then has the analytic expression

(2) $$\frac{f(x_1, y_1 + \Delta y) - f(x_1, y_1)}{\Delta y} = f_y(x_1, \eta)$$

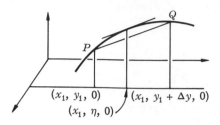

Fig. 11-3.2

for some η between y_1 and $y_1 + \Delta y$. Also, (2) may be written

(3) $$f(x_1, y_1 + \Delta y) - f(x_1, y_1) = f_y(x_1, \eta)\,\Delta y.$$

In the same way, if $f_x(x, y)$ exists for x between x_1 and $x_1 + \Delta x$, then there is a number ξ between x_1 and $x_1 + \Delta x$ such that

(4) $$f(x_1 + \Delta x, y_1) - f(x_1, y_1) = f_x(\xi, y_1)\,\Delta x.$$

Formulas (3) and (4) will be used repeatedly; it would therefore be well to reflect upon their meaning and to reexamine the conditions under which they hold. The Law of the Mean may now be extended as follows:

TWO-DIMENSIONAL LAW OF THE MEAN. *Let $d > 0$ be a number such that $f_x(x, y)$ and $f_y(x, y)$ both exist at each (x, y) satisfying*

$$|x - x_0| < d \quad \text{and} \quad |y - y_0| < d.$$

Then, corresponding to each pair of increments Δx and Δy for which

$$|\Delta x| < d \quad \text{and} \quad |\Delta y| < d,$$

there are numbers ξ and η such that ξ is between x_0 and $x_0 + \Delta x$, η is between y_0 and $y_0 + \Delta y$, and

(5) $$\Delta z = f_x(\xi, y_0 + \Delta y)\,\Delta x + f_y(x_0, \eta)\,\Delta y.$$

PROOF. First rewrite (1) at the point (x_0, y_0), then subtract and add $f(x_0, y_0 + \Delta y)$ to the right side:

$$\Delta z = f(x_0 + \Delta x, y_0 + \Delta y) - f(x_0, y_0)$$
$$= [f(x_0 + \Delta x, y_0 + \Delta y) - f(x_0, y_0 + \Delta y)] + [f(x_0, y_0 + \Delta y) - f(x_0, y_0)].$$

Now match the first bracket with (4) to see the existence of a number ξ such that

$$f(x_0 + \Delta x, y_0 + \Delta y) - f(x_0, y_0 + \Delta y) = f_x(\xi, y_0 + \Delta y)\,\Delta x.$$

In a similar way, the second bracket is [from (3)] equal to $f_y(x_0, \eta)\,\Delta y$ for some η between y_0 and $y_0 + \Delta y$. Thus, (5) is seen to hold.

By looking only at the (x, y)-plane, Fig. 11-3.3 illustrates how $\xi, \eta, x_0, y_0, \Delta x,$ and Δy are related.

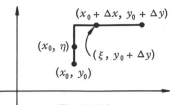

Fig. 11-3.3

The full significance of the following definition and the reason for using the word "differentiable" may not be apparent at this time; however, the notion is an important one.

DEFINITION. *A function $z = f(x, y)$ is said to be* **differentiable** *at a point (x_0, y_0) if there exist two functions ϵ_1 and ϵ_2 of Δx and Δy such that*

(6) $$\Delta z = f_x(x_0, y_0)\,\Delta x + f_y(x_0, y_0)\,\Delta y + \epsilon_1\,\Delta x + \epsilon_2\,\Delta y,$$

where both $\epsilon_1 \to 0$ and $\epsilon_2 \to 0$ as $(\Delta x, \ \Delta y) \to (0, 0)$.

Before proving the first theorem about differentiability, recall that the continuity of the partial $f_x(x, y)$ at (x_0, y_0) is equivalent to the existence of the limit and the equality in

$$\lim_{(\Delta x, \Delta y) \to (0,0)} [f_x(x_0 + \Delta x, y_0 + \Delta y) - f_x(x_0, y_0)] = 0.$$

THEOREM 11-3.1. *If both partials $f_x(x, y)$ and $f_y(x, y)$ are continuous at (x_0, y_0), then $f(x, y)$ is differentiable at (x_0, y_0).*

PROOF. Write

$$\Delta z = f(x_0 + \Delta x, y_0 + \Delta y) - f(x_0, y_0)$$
$$= f_x(\xi, y_0 + \Delta y)\,\Delta x + f_y(x_0, \eta)\,\Delta y \quad \text{by the Law of the Mean.}$$

Then add and subtract $f_x(x_0, y_0)\,\Delta x + f_y(x_0, y_0)\,\Delta y$ to obtain

$$\Delta z = f_x(x_0, y_0)\,\Delta x + f_y(x_0, y_0)\,\Delta y + [f_x(\xi, y_0 + \Delta y) - f_x(x_0, y_0)]\,\Delta x$$
$$+ [f_y(x_0, \eta) - f_y(x_0, y_0)]\,\Delta y.$$

Compare this equation with (6); the two will look the same upon setting

$$\epsilon_1 = f_x(\xi, y_0 + \Delta y) - f_x(x_0, y_0) \quad \text{and} \quad \epsilon_2 = f_y(x_0, \eta) - f_y(x_0, y_0).$$

It is then only necessary to show that this ϵ_1 and this ϵ_2 both approach zero as $(\Delta x, \Delta y) \to (0, 0)$. But it follows immediately from the continuity of $f_x(x, y)$ at (x_0, y_0) that

$$\lim_{(\Delta x, \Delta y) \to (0,0)} [f_x(\xi, y_0 + \Delta y) - f_x(x_0, y_0)] = 0,$$

since $(\xi, y_0 + \Delta y)$ is even closer to (x_0, y_0) than $(x_0 + \Delta x, y_0 + \Delta y)$ is. Hence, this $\epsilon_1 \to 0$ as $(\Delta x, \Delta y) \to (0, 0)$. In the same way, $\epsilon_2 \to 0$. Thus, by the definition, $z = f(x, y)$ is differentiable at (x_0, y_0).

For a function of one variable, the existence of the derivative ensures the continuity of the function. It is, however, possible in functions of two variables to have $f_x(x, y)$ and $f_y(x, y)$ both exist and still for the function $z = f(x, y)$ to be discontinuous at a point. An example of this phenomenon is

$$f(x, y) = \begin{cases} \dfrac{xy}{x^2 + y^2} & \text{for } x^2 + y^2 \neq 0, \\ 0 & \text{for } x^2 + y^2 = 0. \end{cases}$$

This function has, for $x^2 + y^2 \neq 0$,

$$f_x(x, y) = \frac{(x^2 + y^2)y - xy(2x)}{(x^2 + y^2)^2} = \frac{y^3 - x^2 y}{(x^2 + y^2)^2} \quad \text{and}$$

$$f_y(x, y) = \frac{x^3 - xy^2}{(x^2 + y^2)^2}.$$

The partials at $(0, 0)$ must be computed directly:

$$f_x(0, 0) = \lim_{\Delta x \to 0} \frac{f(0 + \Delta x, 0) - f(0, 0)}{\Delta x}$$

$$= \lim_{\Delta x \to 0} \frac{1}{\Delta x} \left[\frac{(\Delta x)0}{(0 + \Delta x)^2 + 0^2} - 0 \right] = \lim_{\Delta x \to 0} \frac{1}{\Delta x} \cdot 0 = 0,$$

and, in the same way, $f_y(0, 0) = 0$. Thus, $f_x(x, y)$ and $f_y(x, y)$ exist for all (x, y), but $z = f(x, y)$ is not continuous at $(0, 0)$, as shown in the answer to Prob. 7a of Sec. 11-4.

The following theorem shows, however, that differentiability not only implies continuity but a good deal more.

THEOREM 11-3.2. *If a function $z = f(x, y)$ is differentiable at (x_0, y_0), then it is also continuous at (x_0, y_0); that is,*

(7) $$\lim_{(\Delta x, \Delta y) \to (0,0)} \Delta z = 0 \quad \text{or} \quad \lim_{(\Delta x, \Delta y) \to (0,0)} f(x_0 + \Delta x, y_0 + \Delta y) = f(x_0, y_0),$$

but, in addition,

(8) $$\lim_{(\Delta x, \Delta y) \to (0,0)} \frac{\Delta z - [f_x(x_0, y_0)\, \Delta x + f_y(x_0, y_0)\, \Delta y]}{\sqrt{(\Delta x)^2 + (\Delta y)^2 + (\Delta z)^2}} = 0.$$

PROOF. The limit (7) follows from (6), since each term on the right of (6) approaches zero as $(\Delta x, \Delta y) \to (0, 0)$.

In (8), as $(\Delta x, \Delta y) \to (0, 0)$, there is one restriction on how $\Delta x \to 0$ and $\Delta y \to 0$, and this restriction is that at no place in the approach may Δx and Δy both be zero. This restriction is to ensure that in the approach the point $(x_0 + \Delta x, y_0 + \Delta y)$ is never actually at (x_0, y_0). Also, the denominator then never assumes the value zero, but note that

$$|\Delta x| \leq \sqrt{(\Delta x)^2 + (\Delta y)^2 + (\Delta z)^2} \quad \text{and}$$

(9) $$0 \leq \frac{|\Delta x|}{\sqrt{(\Delta x)^2 + (\Delta y)^2 + (\Delta z)^2}} \leq 1.$$

In (8), both numerator and denominator approach zero, but from this alone it cannot be told what the ratio approaches. It will be shown that the absolute value of this ratio can be made arbitrarily small by choosing $|\Delta x|$ and $|\Delta y|$ sufficiently small. For, by (6), the absolute value of the ratio in (8) is equal to

$$\left| \frac{\epsilon_1 \Delta x + \epsilon_2 \Delta y}{\sqrt{(\Delta x)^2 + (\Delta y)^2 + (\Delta z)^2}} \right| \leq |\epsilon_1| \frac{|\Delta x|}{\sqrt{(\Delta x)^2 + (\Delta y)^2 + (\Delta z)^2}}$$

$$+ |\epsilon_2| \frac{|\Delta y|}{\sqrt{(\Delta x)^2 + (\Delta y)^2 + (\Delta z)^2}}$$

$$\leq |\epsilon_1| + |\epsilon_2|.$$

The last inequality follows from (9), and (9) with $|\Delta x|$ in the numerator replaced by $|\Delta y|$. Since $\epsilon_1 \to 0$ and $\epsilon_2 \to 0$ as $(\Delta x, \Delta y) \to (0, 0)$, then (8) follows.

Comment: The inequalities (9) remain valid if Δz is erased from them. Hence, upon altering (8) by removing Δz from the denominator, the limit is still zero. For later reference, this fact is written out:

(10) $$\lim_{(\Delta x, \Delta y) \to (0,0)} \frac{\Delta z - [f_x(x_0, y_0) \Delta x + f_y(x_0, y_0) \Delta y]}{\sqrt{(\Delta x)^2 + (\Delta y)^2}} = 0.$$

11-4. Tangent Planes and Normal Lines

Let (x_0, y_0) be such that $f_x(x_0, y_0)$ and $f_y(x_0, y_0)$ both exist. The intersection of the surface $z = f(x, y)$ with the plane $x = x_0$ is a curve having a tangent line at (x_0, y_0, z_0), where $z_0 = f(x_0, y_0)$. With (x_0, y_0, z_0) as initial end, the vector

(1) $$\vec{v} = \vec{j} + \vec{k} f_y(x_0, y_0)$$

lies along this tangent line, as illustrated in Fig. 11-4.1.

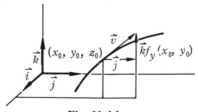

Fig. 11-4.1

In the same way,

(2) $$\vec{u} = \vec{i} + \vec{k} f_x(x_0, y_0); \text{ that is,}$$

$$\vec{u} = \vec{i} + 0\vec{j} + \vec{k}f_x(x_0, y_0)$$

drawn at (x_0, y_0, z_0) is on the tangent line to the curve $z = f(x, y)$, $y = y_0$.

The vector $\vec{N}$ defined by $\vec{N} = \vec{u} \times \vec{v}$ is perpendicular to both $\vec{u}$ and $\vec{v}$. The determinant form of the cross product gives

$$\vec{N} = \vec{u} \times \vec{v} = \begin{vmatrix} \vec{i} & \vec{j} & \vec{k} \\ 1 & 0 & f_x(x_0, y_0) \\ 0 & 1 & f_y(x_0, y_0) \end{vmatrix}.$$

By expanding this determinant,

(3) $$\vec{N} = -\vec{i}f_x(x_0, y_0) - \vec{j}f_y(x_0, y_0) + \vec{k}.$$

A representation for a smooth surface is shown in Fig. 11-4.2.

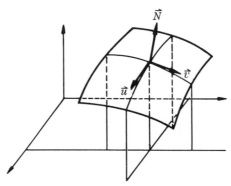

Fig. 11-4.2

The vectors $\vec{u}$ and $\vec{v}$ issue from the point (x_0, y_0, z_0), they determine a plane, and $\vec{N}$ is normal to this plane. Under the proviso that $z = f(x, y)$ is differentiable at (x_0, y_0), then this plane is tangent to the surface (as shown below in Theorem 11-4.1). This statement anticipates the definition of a tangent plane to a surface.

DEFINITION. *A plane is said to be the **tangent plane** to a surface $z = f(x, y)$ at a point (x_0, y_0, z_0), provided the line determined by the points*

$$(x_0, y_0, z_0) \quad \text{and} \quad (x, y, f(x, y))$$

approaches the plane as $(x, y) \rightarrow (x_0, y_0)$.

THEOREM 11-4.1. *If $z = f(x, y)$ is differentiable at (x_0, y_0), then the surface has a tangent plane at (x_0, y_0, z_0), where $z_0 = f(x_0, y_0)$.*

PROOF. For Δx and Δy not both zero, the vector

$$\vec{w} = \vec{i}\,\Delta x + \vec{j}\,\Delta y + \vec{k}\,\Delta z$$

is drawn from (x_0, y_0, z_0) to a second point $(x_0 + \Delta x, y_0 + \Delta y, z_0 + \Delta z)$ of the surface. The line determined by these points will approach the plane determined by $\vec{u}$ and $\vec{v}$ if and only if $\vec{w}$ approaches perpendicularity to $\vec{N}$ as $(\Delta x, \Delta y) \to (0, 0)$. To see that it does, let θ be the angle between $\vec{N}$ and $\vec{w}$. Then

$$
\begin{aligned}
\cos \theta &= \frac{\vec{N} \cdot \vec{w}}{|\vec{N}| \, |\vec{w}|} \\
&= \frac{-f_x(x_0, y_0)\,\Delta x - f_y(x_0, y_0)\,\Delta y + \Delta z}{\sqrt{f_x^2(x_0, y_0) + f_y^2(x_0, y_0) + 1} \, \sqrt{(\Delta x)^2 + (\Delta y)^2 + (\Delta z)^2}} .
\end{aligned}
$$

This ratio approaches zero as $(\Delta x, \Delta y) \to (0, 0)$, by Theorem 11-3.2, since $\sqrt{f_x^2(x_0, y_0) + f_y^2(x_0, y_0) + 1}$ is a constant as far as Δx and Δy are concerned. Thus, $\cos \theta \to 0$, so that $\theta \to 90°$ as $(\Delta x, \Delta y) \to (0, 0)$. The plane determined by $\vec{u}$ and $\vec{v}$ is, therefore, tangent to the surface and the theorem is proved.

The equation of this plane is easily obtained. For a point (x, y, z) is on this plane if and only if the vector

$$
\vec{i}(x - x_0) + \vec{j}(y - y_0) + \vec{k}(z - z_0)
$$

is perpendicular to the vector $\vec{N}$, which [from (3)] is

$$
\vec{N} = -\vec{i} f_x(x_0, y_0) - \vec{j} f_y(x_0, y_0) + \vec{k}.
$$

Hence, the equation of the plane is obtained by setting the dot product of these two vectors equal to zero:

(4) $\qquad -f_x(x_0, y_0)(x - x_0) - f_y(x_0, y_0)(y - y_0) + 1(z - z_0) = 0.$

Upon using $z_0 = f(x_0, y_0)$, the more commonly met form of the equation of the tangent plane is

(5) $\qquad z = f(x_0, y_0) + f_x(x_0, y_0)(x - x_0) + f_y(x_0, y_0)(y - y_0).$

Since $z = f(x, y)$, then $z_0 = f(x_0, y_0)$, and the above equation may be written in terms of z as

(6) $\qquad z = z_0 + z_x(x_0, y_0)(x - x_0) + z_y(x_0, y_0)(y - y_0).$

The line containing $\vec{N}$ is said to be **normal** to the surface at (x_0, y_0, z_0). Hence, this normal has direction numbers

$$
-f_x(x_0, y_0), \quad -f_y(x_0, y_0), \quad 1 \quad \text{or} \quad f_x(x_0, y_0), \quad f_y(x_0, y_0), \quad -1
$$

whichever set happens to be preferred. It is usual to use the second set and write parametric equations of the normal as

(7) $\qquad x = x_0 + t f_x(x_0, y_0), \quad y = y_0 + t f_y(x_0, y_0), \quad z = f(x_0, y_0) - t.$

Example 1. Find the equation of the tangent plane and parametric equations of the normal line to the surface

$$
z = x^2 y + xy^3
$$

at the point on the surface having $x_0 = -1$ and $y_0 = 2$.

Solution. For easier substitution, set $f(x, y) = x^2 y + xy^3$. Thus,

$$z_0 = f(-1, 2) = 2 - 8 = -6.$$

Also, $f_x(x, y) = 2xy + y^3$ and $f_y(x, y) = x^2 + 3xy^2$, so that

$$f_x(-1, 2) = 4 \quad \text{and} \quad f_y(-1, 2) = -11.$$

Thus, the desired equation of the tangent plane is

$$z = -6 + 4(x + 1) - 11(y - 2)$$

or $z = 4x - 11y + 20$. Parametric equations of the normal line are

$$x = -1 + 4t, \quad y = 2 - 11t, \quad z = -6 - t.$$

Example 2. Show that there is a value of b such that the plane

$$z = 4x - y + b$$

is tangent to the surface $z = x^2 + xy + y^2$.

Solution. With $f(x, y) = x^2 + xy + y^2$, then

$$f_x(x, y) = 2x + y \quad \text{and} \quad f_y(x, y) = x + 2y.$$

A point (x_0, y_0, z_0) on the surface must have

$$f_x(x_0, y_0) = 2x_0 + y_0 = 4 \quad \text{and} \quad f_y(x_0, y_0) = x_0 + 2y_0 = -1.$$

The simultaneous solution of these equations is $x_0 = 3$, $y_0 = -2$. Hence,

$$z_0 = f(x_0, y_0) = 3^2 + 3(-2) + (-2)^2 = 7.$$

The tangent plane to the surface at $(3, -2, 7)$ is

$$z = 7 + 4(x - 3) - 1(y + 2)$$
$$= 4x - y - 7.$$

Thus, $b = -7$.

An example of a function of three variables is

$$F(x, y, z) = x^2 y + xz + y^2 z^3.$$

For this function, $F_x = 2xy + z$, $F_y = x^2 + 2yz^3$, and $F_z = x + 3y^2 z^2$. If, however,

(8) $$x^2 y + xz + y^2 z^3 = 9,$$

then the variables x, y, and z must be interrelated. Upon considering (8) as defining z as an implicit function of x and y, then z_x and z_y may be expressed. Take the partial of both sides of (8) with respect to x (thus holding y constant) and obtain

$$2xy + (xz_x + z) + 3y^2 z^2 z_x = \frac{\partial 9}{\partial x} = 0.$$

Hence, upon solving for z_x, it follows that

$$z_x = -\frac{2xy + z}{x + 3y^2 z^2} = -\frac{F_x}{F_z}.$$

This specific example generalizes as follows: If $w = F(x, y, z)$ is a function of three variables, then

(9) $$F(x, y, z) = c$$

may be considered as defining $z = z(x, y)$ as a function of x and y. Then by taking the partial of both sides of (9) with respect to x,

$$F_x \frac{\partial x}{\partial x} + F_y \frac{\partial y}{\partial x} + F_z \frac{\partial z}{\partial x} = \frac{\partial c}{\partial x} = 0.$$

But $\partial x/\partial x = 1$ and $\partial y/\partial x = 0$, since y is held constant while taking the partial with respect to x, so that $F_x + F_z z_x = 0$ and

$$z_x = -\frac{F_x}{F_z}.$$

In the same way,

$$z_y = -\frac{F_y}{F_z}.$$

Let (x_0, y_0, z_0) be a point on the surface defined by (9). The equation of the tangent plane to this surface at this point may be put in the symmetric form

(10) $$F_x(x_0, y_0, z_0)(x - x_0) + F_y(x_0, y_0, z_0)(y - y_0)$$
$$+ F_z(x_0, y_0, z_0)(z - z_0) = 0.$$

To see this, note that $z_0 = z(x_0, y_0)$,

$$z_x(x_0, y_0) = -\frac{F_x(x_0, y_0, z_0)}{F_z(x_0, y_0, z_0)}, \quad \text{and} \quad z_y(x_0, y_0) = -\frac{F_y(x_0, y_0, z_0)}{F_z(x_0, y_0, z_0)}.$$

These expressions substituted into (6) yield

$$z = z_0 - \frac{F_x(x_0, y_0, z_0)}{F_z(x_0, y_0, z_0)}(x - x_0) - \frac{F_y(x_0, y_0, z_0)}{F_z(x_0, y_0, z_0)}(y - y_0),$$

and this equation may be put in the form (10).

Example 3. Find the equation of the tangent plane to the surface
$$x^2 y + xz + y^2 z^3 = 9 \text{ at } (1, -1, 2).$$

Solution. First check that the point is on the surface. With $F(x, y, z) = x^2 y + xz + y^2 z^3$, it follows [from the partials of this function taken above (8)] that

$$F_x(1, -1, 2) = 0, \quad F_y(1, -1, 2) = -15, \quad F_z(1, -1, 2) = 13.$$

Thus, the equation of the tangent plane is
$$0(x - 1) - 15(y + 1) + 13(z - 2) = 0; \quad \text{that is,} \quad -15y + 13z = 41.$$

Problem 1. Use the scalar triple product of $\vec{u}, \vec{v},$ and $\vec{i}(x - x_0) + \vec{j}(y - y_0) + \vec{k}(z - z_0)$ to express the equation of the tangent plane as

$$\begin{vmatrix} x - x_0 & y - y_0 & z - z_0 \\ 1 & 0 & f_x(x_0, y_0) \\ 0 & 1 & f_y(x_0, y_0) \end{vmatrix} = 0.$$

Problem 2. In each case, check that the given point is on the surface $z = f(x, y)$, then find the equation of the tangent plane and the parametric equations of the normal line to the surface at the point.

a. $z = x^2 + y^2$, $(-3, 4, 25)$.

b. $z = x^2 - xy$, $(2, -1, 6)$.

c. $z = \tan^{-1}(x^2 y)$, $\left(-1, 1, \dfrac{\pi}{4}\right)$.

d. $z = \sqrt{3x^2 - xy + y^2}$, $(1, -2, 3)$.

e. $z = \ln(x^2 + y^2)$, $(1, 0, 0)$.

f. $z = \sin(xy^2)$, $\left(\dfrac{\pi}{2}, -1, 1\right)$.

Problem 3. A surface has equation $z^2 = 3x^2 + 4y^2$ and a line has parametric equations $x = 2t$, $y = t$, $z = 4t$.

a. Show that the line lies on the surface.

b. Show that at each point on the line (except the origin) the tangent plane to the surface has equation

$$2z = 3x + 2y.$$

Problem 4. Find $\partial z / \partial x$, $\partial z / \partial y$, and $\partial y / \partial x$ and check that

$$\frac{\partial z}{\partial x} = -\frac{\partial z}{\partial y} \frac{\partial y}{\partial x}$$

even though formally

$$\frac{\Delta z}{\Delta x} = +\frac{\Delta z}{\Delta y} \frac{\Delta y}{\Delta x}.$$

a. $xy + yz + zx = 1$.

b. $x \ln y - x^2 e^z + y \sin z = 4$.

Problem 5. Find the equation of the tangent plane to the given surface at the given point:

a. $\dfrac{x}{y} + yz - z^3 = \dfrac{3}{2}$, $(1, 2, 1)$.

b. $e^{xy} + xz - \tan y = 3$, $(1, 0, 2)$.

Problem 6. Let $\vec{N}(x, y)$ be the normal vector to $z = f(x, y)$ at the point (x, y, z). Given that the partials f_x and f_y are both continuous at (x_0, y_0), prove that

$$\lim_{(\Delta x, \Delta y) \to (0, 0)} \vec{N}(x_0 + \Delta x, y_0 + \Delta y) = \vec{N}(x_0, y_0).$$

[Note: It is necessary to cite reasons why the initial point of $\vec{N}(x_0 + \Delta x, y_0 + \Delta y)$ approaches the initial point of $\vec{N}(x_0, y_0)$ as well as why the first approaches both the length and direction of the second.]

Problem 7. Consider the surface

$$z = f(x, y) = \begin{cases} \dfrac{xy}{x^2 + y^2} & \text{for } x^2 + y^2 \neq 0 \\ 0 & \text{for } x^2 + y^2 = 0, \end{cases}$$

discussed in Sec. 11-3. Use the notation $\vec{N}(x, y)$ introduced in Prob. 6. Note that $\vec{N}(0, 0) = \vec{k}$.

a. For $h \neq 0$, show that $\vec{N}(h, h)$ is also a unit vector in the direction $\vec{k}$ but that $\lim\limits_{h \to 0} \vec{N}(h, h) \neq \vec{N}(0, 0)$.

b. For $h \neq 0$, find $\vec{N}(h, 2h)$. Show that as $h \to 0$ the vector $\vec{N}(h, 2h)$ approaches perpendicularity (instead of parallelism) to $\vec{N}(0, 0)$.

c. Does this surface have a tangent plane at $(1, 2, \frac{2}{5})$?

Problem 8. Show that the formula in the two-dimensional Law of the Mean could have been given in the slightly different form

$$\Delta z = f_x(\xi, y_0) \, \Delta x + f_y(x_0 + \Delta x, \eta) \, \Delta y.$$

Problem 9. Prove that if $z = f(x, y)$ has a tangent plane at a point (x_0, y_0, z_0), then there is only one tangent plane at this point.

11-5. Differentials

Recall that, if $y = f(x)$ is a function of a single independent variable x, then an increment Δx and a differential dx were themselves independent variables which, if desired, could be chosen equal. In this case, y is the dependent variable and its increment Δy and differential dy were defined by

$$\Delta y = f(x + \Delta x) - f(x) \quad \text{but} \quad dy = f'(x) \, dx.$$

Even for $dx = \Delta x$, it may very well be that

$$\Delta y = f(x + dx) - f(x) \quad \text{is not equal to} \quad dy = f'(x) \, dx,$$

but their difference is so small compared to dx that

$$(1) \qquad \lim_{dx \to 0} \frac{\Delta y - dy}{dx} = \lim_{dx \to 0} \left[\frac{f(x + dx) - f(x)}{dx} - \frac{f'(x) \, dx}{dx} \right]$$

$$= f'(x) - f'(x) = 0.$$

Now let $z = f(x, y)$ be a function of two independent variables x and y. First hold y fixed. Then, corresponding to a differential dx of x,

$$(2) \qquad d_x z = f_x(x, y) \, dx$$

is called the **partial differential** of z with respect to x. But y is also an independent variable and, corresponding to a differential dy of it, the dependent variable z has a partial differential with respect to y :

$$(3) \qquad d_y z = f_y(x, y) \, dy.$$

The **total differential** dz is defind by

$$(4) \qquad dz = d_x z + d_y z$$

$$= f_x(x, y) \, dx + f_y(x, y) \, dy.$$

Often the adjective "total" is omitted.

As used earlier, the increment Δz is

$$\Delta z = f(x + \Delta x, y + \Delta y) - f(x, y).$$

Upon choosing $dx = \Delta x$ and $dy = \Delta y$, the increment Δz may be expressed as

$$\Delta z = f(x + dx, y + dy) - f(x, y).$$

As illustrated in Fig. 11-5.1, the point $(x + \Delta x, y + \Delta y, z + \Delta z)$ is on the surface $z = f(x, y)$, but $(x + dx, y + dy, z + dz)$ is on the tangent plane

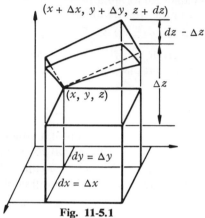

Fig. 11-5.1

drawn at (x, y, z). To see the second part of this statement, fix the point under consideration as (x_0, y_0, z_0) to free x, y, and z in expressing the tangent plane as

$$z = z_0 + f_x(x_0, y_0)(x - x_0) + f_y(x_0, y_0)(y - y_0).$$

Now let $x = x_0 + dx$ and $y = y_0 + dy$ in this equation, so that

$$z = z_0 + f_x(x_0, y_0)\, dx + f_y(x_0, y_0)\, dy = z_0 + dz.$$

Hence, $(x_0 + dx, y_0 + dy, z_0 + dz)$ is on the tangent plane to the surface $z = f(x, y)$ at (x_0, y_0, z_0).

Even if $dx = \Delta x$ and $dy = \Delta y$, it should be expected that Δz and dz are more likely to have different values than equal ones. In a sense, they are, however, not much different, as the following theorem shows:

THEOREM 11-5.1. *If $z = f(x, y)$ is differentiable at a point, then, with $dx = \Delta x$ and $dy = \Delta y$,*

(5) $$\lim_{(dx, dy) \to (0,0)} \frac{\Delta z - dz}{\sqrt{(dx)^2 + (dy)^2}} = 0.$$

This theorem has already been proved. To see that this is so, look at the comment on p. 409 and reconcile the notation used there and here.

The relation (5) between increments and differentials for functions of two variables is as near the relation (1) for functions of one variable as could be expected.

Because of (5), dz is an approximation of Δz whenever $dx = \Delta x$ and $dy = \Delta y$.

Example. Given $z = f(x, y) = \ln(2x^2 + 3y)$, find $\Delta f(2, 4)$ and $df(2, 4)$ for $dx = \Delta x = 0.1$ and $dy = \Delta y = -0.2$.

Solution. Here $x + \Delta x = 2 + 0.1 = 2.1$ and $y + \Delta y = 3.8$. Hence,

$$\Delta f(2, 4) = \ln(8.82 + 11.4) - \ln(8 + 12)$$
$$= (0.4343)[\log_{10} 20.22 - \log_{10} 20]$$
$$= (0.4343)[1.3058 - 1.3010] = 0.0021,$$

$$f_x(x, y) = \frac{4x}{2x^2 + 3y}, \quad f_y(x, y) = \frac{3}{2x^2 + 3y},$$

$$df(2, 4) = \frac{8}{20}(0.1) + \frac{3}{20}(-0.2) = 0.01.$$

In this case,

$$\frac{df - \Delta f}{\sqrt{(dx)^2 + (dy)^2}} = \frac{0.0079}{\sqrt{0.05}} = \frac{0.0079}{(0.1)(2.24)} = 0.035.$$

11-6. Functions of Functions

Let $z = f(x, y)$ be differentiable as a function of x and y. Now let $x = x(s)$ and $y = y(s)$ be differentiable functions of a single variable s. Then z is a function of the single variable s, and its derivative with respect to s is

(1)
$$\frac{dz}{ds} = f_x(x, y)\frac{dx}{ds} + f_y(x, y)\frac{dy}{ds}.$$

This is seen by returning to the definition of a derivative. Let s take an increment Δs. Then x takes the increment

$$\Delta x = x(s + \Delta s) - x(s)$$

and similarly y takes an increment $\Delta y = y(s + \Delta s) - y(s)$. Hence, z is forced to take an increment

$$\Delta z = f(x + \Delta x, y + \Delta y) - f(x, y)$$
$$= f_x(\xi, y + \Delta y)\,\Delta x + f_y(x, \eta)\,\Delta y,$$

with ξ between x and $x + \Delta x$, η between y and $y + \Delta y$. Divide throughout by Δs:

(2)
$$\frac{\Delta z}{\Delta s} = f_x(\xi, y + \Delta y)\frac{\Delta x}{\Delta s} + f_y(x, \eta)\frac{\Delta y}{\Delta s}.$$

As $\Delta s \to 0$, both $\Delta x \to 0$ and $\Delta y \to 0$, so that

$$f_x(\xi, y + \Delta y) \to f_x(x, y) \quad \text{and} \quad f_y(x, \eta) \to f_y(x, y)$$

by the continuity of these partials. Since the ratio of increments approaches the corresponding derivatives, the limit as $\Delta s \to 0$ in (2) yields (1).

Formula (1) may be written

(1′)
$$\frac{dz}{ds} = \frac{\partial f}{\partial x}\frac{dx}{ds} + \frac{\partial f}{\partial y}\frac{dy}{ds}.$$

This formula is easily remembered since it looks exactly like the differential

$$dz = \frac{\partial f}{\partial x}\,dx + \frac{\partial f}{\partial y}\,dy$$

divided by ds, but do not be fooled into thinking that this is what was really done.

If $x = x(s, t)$ and $y = y(s, t)$ are functions of two variables, then by holding first t fixed and then s fixed it follows from (1′) that

(3)
$$\frac{\partial z}{\partial s} = \frac{\partial f}{\partial x}\frac{\partial x}{\partial s} + \frac{\partial f}{\partial y}\frac{\partial y}{\partial s} \quad \text{and}$$

$$\frac{\partial z}{\partial t} = \frac{\partial f}{\partial x}\frac{\partial x}{\partial t} + \frac{\partial f}{\partial y}\frac{\partial y}{\partial t}.$$

The relative positions of the variables in (3) should be remembered rather than the specific letters used for the variables. The next example uses (3), but the ultimate independent variables are ρ and θ rather than s and t.

Example 1. The function $z = x^2 + xy$ is given. Translate to polar coordinates and find how z varies with respect to ρ and θ.

Solution. Since $x = \rho \cos \theta$ and $y = \rho \sin \theta$, then

$$\frac{\partial z}{\partial \rho} = \frac{\partial}{\partial x}(x^2 + xy)\frac{\partial}{\partial \rho}(\rho \cos \theta) + \frac{\partial}{\partial y}(x^2 + xy)\frac{\partial}{\partial \rho}(\rho \sin \theta)$$

$$= (2x + y)\cos \theta + x \sin \theta,$$

$$\frac{\partial z}{\partial \theta} = \frac{\partial}{\partial x}(x^2 + xy)\frac{\partial}{\partial \theta}(\rho \cos \theta) + \frac{\partial}{\partial y}(x^2 + xy)\frac{\partial}{\partial \theta}(\rho \sin \theta)$$

$$= (2x + y)(-\rho \sin \theta) + x\rho \cos \theta.$$

If these partials are desired entirely in terms of ρ and θ, then

$$\frac{\partial z}{\partial \rho} = (2\rho \cos \theta + \rho \sin \theta)(\cos \theta) + \rho \cos \theta \sin \theta$$

$$= 2\rho(\cos^2 \theta + \sin \theta \cos \theta) \quad \text{and}$$

$$\frac{\partial z}{\partial \theta} = (2\rho \cos \theta + \rho \sin \theta)(-\rho \sin \theta) + (\rho \cos \theta)(\rho \cos \theta)$$

$$= \rho^2(\cos^2 \theta - \sin^2 \theta - 2 \sin \theta \cos \theta).$$

Of course, the transformation to polar coordinates could have been made first,

$$z = (\rho \cos \theta)^2 + \rho \cos \theta\, \rho \sin \theta$$

$$= \rho^2(\cos^2 \theta + \sin \theta \cos \theta),$$

and then the partials taken. Should there be any lack of confidence in formulas (3), the partials of z so expressed should be taken and matched with the above.

As shown above, a function $z = f(x, y)$ of two independent variables may be used to form a function of a single independent variable by setting $x = x(s)$ and $y = y(s)$. The opposite process of starting with a function of a single independent variable and using it to form a function of two independent variables is shown below.

The function $\sin u$ is a function of the single independent variable u whose derivative with respect to u is $\cos u$. Upon setting $u = x + 2t$, then

$$z = \sin(x + 2t)$$

is an example of using a function of a single independent variable to form a function of two independent variables. Then z has a partial with respect to x and a partial with respect to t:

$$\frac{\partial z}{\partial x} = \cos(x + 2t)\frac{\partial(x + 2t)}{\partial x}, \qquad \frac{\partial z}{\partial t} = \cos(x + 2t)\frac{\partial(x + 2t)}{\partial t}$$

$$= \cos(x + 2t); \qquad\qquad = 2\cos(x + 2t).$$

An additional abstraction frequently occurs. A function $f(u)$ of a single independent variable u is used to form a function of two independent variables. For example,

$$z = f(x + 2t).$$

No specific formula for $f(u)$ is given. How should the partials of z be written in terms of the f function? In the above case, when $f(u) = \sin u$ there was no question about using the derivative $f'(u) = \cos u$ and then replacing u by $x + 2t$. When no formula for $f(u)$ is given, then as much as can be said is

$$\frac{\partial z}{\partial x} = f'(x + 2t)\frac{\partial(x + 2t)}{\partial x}, \qquad \frac{\partial z}{\partial t} = f'(x + 2t)\frac{\partial(x + 2t)}{\partial t}$$

$$= f'(x + 2t) \qquad\qquad = 2f'(x + 2t).$$

The general notation is

(4) $$\frac{\partial z}{\partial x} = \frac{df(u)}{du}\frac{\partial u}{\partial x}, \qquad \frac{\partial z}{\partial y} = \frac{df(u)}{du}\frac{\partial u}{\partial t}.$$

Example 2. Given $z = \dfrac{1}{y} f\!\left(\dfrac{x}{y}\right)$, show that $x\dfrac{\partial z}{\partial x} + y\dfrac{\partial z}{\partial y} = -z$.

Solution. The notation $f(x/y)$ means that actually the f function is a function $f(u)$ of a single variable whose derivative with respect to this variable is $f'(u)$. This function $f(u)$ is then used to form the function z of two independent variables. Thus,

$$\frac{\partial z}{\partial x} = \frac{1}{y} f'\!\left(\frac{x}{y}\right)\frac{\partial(x/y)}{\partial x} = \frac{1}{y^2} f'\!\left(\frac{x}{y}\right).$$

A scratch-paper computation should now be made to obtain

$$\frac{\partial z}{\partial y} = -\frac{x}{y^3} f'\!\left(\frac{x}{y}\right) - \frac{1}{y^2} f\!\left(\frac{x}{y}\right).$$

The problem is not to derive the answer but merely to check it. Hence, write

$$x\frac{\partial z}{\partial x} + y\frac{\partial z}{\partial y} = x\left[\frac{1}{y^2}f'\left(\frac{x}{y}\right)\right] + y\left[\frac{-x}{y^3}f'\left(\frac{x}{y}\right) - \frac{1}{y^2}f\left(\frac{x}{y}\right)\right]$$

$$= \frac{x}{y^2}f'\left(\frac{x}{y}\right) - \frac{x}{y^2}f'\left(\frac{x}{y}\right) - \frac{1}{y}f\left(\frac{x}{y}\right) = -\frac{1}{y}f\left(\frac{x}{y}\right) = -z.$$

Example 3. Show that the transformation from rectangular to polar coordinates yields the formula

(5) $$\left(\frac{\partial z}{\partial\rho}\right)^2 + \frac{1}{\rho^2}\left(\frac{\partial z}{\partial\theta}\right)^2 = \left(\frac{\partial z}{\partial x}\right)^2 + \left(\frac{\partial z}{\partial y}\right)^2.$$

Solution. This form of statement requires the reader to think "z must have been given originally as a function of x and y, but then a new function of two new variables ρ and θ was formed by setting $x = \rho\cos\theta$, $y = \rho\sin\theta$." This new function (again called z)* as a function of ρ and θ has its partials with respect to ρ and θ related to the partials with respect to x and y of the original function z by

$$\frac{\partial z}{\partial\rho} = \frac{\partial z}{\partial x}\frac{\partial x}{\partial\rho} + \frac{\partial z}{\partial y}\frac{\partial y}{\partial\rho} = \frac{\partial z}{\partial x}\cos\theta + \frac{\partial z}{\partial y}\sin\theta,$$

$$\frac{\partial z}{\partial\theta} = \frac{\partial z}{\partial x}(-\rho\sin\theta) + \frac{\partial z}{\partial y}(\rho\cos\theta) = \rho\left[\frac{\partial z}{\partial x}(-\sin\theta) + \frac{\partial z}{\partial y}\cos\theta\right].$$

As in Example 1, the formula is to be checked, so write

$$\left(\frac{\partial z}{\partial\rho}\right)^2 + \frac{1}{\rho^2}\left(\frac{\partial z}{\partial\theta}\right)^2 = \left[\frac{\partial z}{\partial x}\cos\theta + \frac{\partial z}{\partial y}\sin\theta\right]^2$$

$$+ \frac{\rho^2}{\rho^2}\left[\frac{\partial z}{\partial x}(-\sin\theta) + \frac{\partial z}{\partial y}\cos\theta\right]^2.$$

After squaring out the right side, the terms may be collected as the right side of (5).

Example 4. Show that if z is a function of x and y, but x and y are functions of s and t, then

(6) $$dz = \frac{\partial z}{\partial s}ds + \frac{\partial z}{\partial t}dt.$$

Solution. From z being a function of x and y, it follows from the definition of a differential that

(7) $$dz = \frac{\partial z}{\partial x}dx + \frac{\partial z}{\partial y}dy.$$

From this same definition of a differential applied, however, to x and y as functions of s and t,

$$dx = \frac{\partial x}{\partial s}ds + \frac{\partial x}{\partial t}dt \quad \text{and} \quad dy = \frac{\partial y}{\partial s}ds + \frac{\partial y}{\partial t}dt.$$

The substitution of these expressions for dx and dy into (7) yields

---

*It would be much better to use a letter other than z for the new function of ρ and θ, but other books do not do so and other books may have to be deciphered later on.

$$dz = \frac{\partial z}{\partial x}\left(\frac{\partial x}{\partial s}\,ds + \frac{\partial x}{\partial t}\,dt\right) + \frac{\partial z}{\partial y}\left(\frac{\partial y}{\partial s}\,ds + \frac{\partial y}{\partial t}\,dt\right).$$

This may be collected as

$$dz = \left[\frac{\partial z}{\partial x}\frac{\partial x}{\partial s} + \frac{\partial z}{\partial y}\frac{\partial y}{\partial s}\right]ds + \left[\frac{\partial z}{\partial x}\frac{\partial x}{\partial t} + \frac{\partial z}{\partial y}\frac{\partial y}{\partial t}\right]dt.$$

The expression in the first bracket contracts to $\partial z/\partial s$ and in the second bracket to $\partial z/\partial t$, as a glance at (3) shows. This contraction yields (6).

Problem 1. Express dz/ds in terms of s by two methods: (i) differentiating first by using (1) and then substituting, and (ii) by substituting first and then differentiating:

a. $z = x^2 + y^2$; $\quad x = e^s \cos s$, $\quad y = e^s \sin s$.
b. $z = x^2 y$; $\quad x = s \cos s$, $\quad y = s \sin s$.
c. $z = (1 + x)(1 - y)$; $\quad x = s^2$, $\quad y = s^3$.
d. $z = \ln|x^2 - y^2|$; $\quad x = a \cos s$, $\quad y = a \sin s$.

Problem 2. Find $\partial z/\partial s$ and $\partial z/\partial t$ by two methods:

a. $z = x^2 + y^2$; $\quad x = e^t \cos s$, $\quad y = e^t \sin s$.
b. $z = x^2 y$; $\quad x = t \cos s$, $\quad y = t \sin s$.
c. $z = (1 + x)(1 - y)$; $\quad x = st$, $\quad y = st^2$.
d. $z = \ln|x^2 - y^2|$; $\quad x = t \cos s$, $\quad y = t \sin s$.

Problem 3. Establish each of the following:

a. If $z = f(x^2 y)$, then $x\frac{\partial z}{\partial x} - 2y\frac{\partial z}{\partial y} = 0.$

b. If $z = f(x - at)$, then $a\frac{\partial z}{\partial x} + \frac{\partial z}{\partial t} = 0.$

c. If $z = f(x^2 + y^2)$, then $y\frac{\partial z}{\partial x} - x\frac{\partial z}{\partial y} = 0.$

d. If $z = xf\left(\frac{y}{x}\right)$, then $x\frac{\partial z}{\partial x} + y\frac{\partial z}{\partial y} = z.$

e. If $z = x + f(xy)$, then $x\frac{\partial z}{\partial x} - y\frac{\partial z}{\partial y} = x.$

f. If $z = x^4 y^2 f\left(\frac{y}{x}\right)$, then $x\frac{\partial z}{\partial x} + y\frac{\partial z}{\partial y} = 6z.$

g. If $z = x^m y^n f\left(\frac{y}{x}\right)$, then $x\frac{\partial z}{\partial x} + y\frac{\partial z}{\partial y} = (m + n)z.$

Problem 4. Given that $f(u)$ is a function of a single variable u, then by the Law of the Mean,

$$f(u + \Delta u) - f(u) = f'(\xi)\,\Delta u$$

for some number ξ between u and $u + \Delta u$. Now let $u = u(x, y)$ be a function of x and y and set $z = f[u(x, y)]$. Hold y fixed, but let x take an increment Δx. With this as a start, derive the formulas in (4).

Problem 5. A function z of two variables x and y is given, but then the translation to polar coordinates $x = \rho \cos \theta$, $y = \rho \sin \theta$ is made. Show that:

a. If $z = x^2 + y^2$, then $dz = 2\rho\, d\rho$. (Do this in two ways.)
b. If $z = f(x^2 + y^2)$, then $dz = 2f'(\rho^2)\rho\, d\rho$.
c. If $z = f(x^2) + f(y^2)$, then
$$dz = 2\rho[f'(x^2)\cos^2\theta + f'(y^2)\sin^2\theta]d\rho$$
$$+ 2\rho^2[-f'(x^2) + f'(y^2)]\sin\theta\cos\theta\, d\theta.$$
d. If $z = x^2 - y^2$, then $dz = 2\rho\cos 2\theta\, d\rho - 2\rho^2\sin 2\theta\, d\theta$.

11-7. Directional Derivative, Gradient

A function $z = f(x, y)$ of variables x and y may be expressed as a function of variables t and θ by means of the substitutions

$$x = a + t\cos\theta, \quad y = b + t\sin\theta.$$

Then with θ held fixed,

$$\frac{\partial z}{\partial t} = \frac{\partial f}{\partial x}\frac{\partial x}{\partial t} + \frac{\partial f}{\partial y}\frac{\partial y}{\partial t}$$

(1)
$$= f_x\cos\theta + f_y\sin\theta.$$

This is called the **directional derivative** (not partial) of $z = f(x, y)$ in the direction θ. The notion has many uses, and there are several different notations used in connection with it. Some books set

(2)
$$\frac{dz}{ds} = f_x\cos\theta + f_y\sin\theta,$$

although no s appears anywhere else. The s is a vestige of seeing how $z = f(x, y)$ varies over a curve of the (x, y)-plane, where arc length is denoted by s. With (x, y) on the curve, with Δx and Δy restricted so that $(x + \Delta x, y + \Delta y)$ is also on the curve, and with Δs the increment of arc length of the curve between these points, then

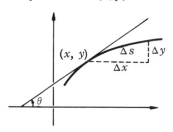

$$\frac{\Delta z}{\Delta s} = \frac{f(x + \Delta x, y + \Delta y) - f(x, y)}{\Delta s}$$

$$= f_x(\xi, y + \Delta y)\frac{\Delta x}{\Delta s} + f_y(x, \eta)\frac{\Delta y}{\Delta s}.$$

Fig. 11-7.1   The limit is then taken as the increments approach zero. With $m = \tan\theta$, the slope in the (x, y)-plane of the tangent to the curve, $\Delta x/\Delta s \to \cos\theta$, $\Delta y/\Delta s \to \sin\theta$ and (2) is obtained.

Another notation for the directional derivative in the direction θ is

$$D_\theta z = f_x\cos\theta + f_y\sin\theta,$$

which, from all other standard notation, should indicate that θ is the variable of differentiation, whereas θ is the one thing that is held constant while forming the directional derivative.

These remarks about notation were made in the hope they will be recalled to aid in deciphering the symbolism, should directional derivatives be met in other books on mathematics or its applications.

The less frequently seen notation

(3) $$D(z, \vec{\theta}) = z_x \cos \theta + z_y \sin \theta$$

will be used for the directional derivative of $z = f(x, y)$ in the direction θ determined by the unit vector

(4) $$\vec{\theta} = \vec{i} \cos \theta + \vec{j} \sin \theta.$$

At least this notation (3) fits in with the notion of the gradient of $z = f(x, y)$. The **gradient** of z has two common notations: they are $\overrightarrow{\text{grad}}\ z$ and $\vec{\nabla} z$, where $\vec{\nabla}$ is read "del." By definition,

(5) $$\overrightarrow{\text{grad}}\ z = \vec{\nabla} z = \vec{i} z_x + \vec{j} z_y.$$

Notice, therefore, that the dot product of the vectors $\vec{\nabla} z$ and $\vec{\theta}$ is the scalar $D(z, \vec{\theta})$:

(6) $$(\vec{\nabla} z) \cdot \vec{\theta} = (\vec{i} z_x + \vec{j} z_y) \cdot (\vec{i} \cos \theta + \vec{j} \sin \theta)$$
$$= z_x \cos \theta + z_y \sin \theta = D(z, \vec{\theta}).$$

For a geometric interpretation of the gradient of $z = f(x, y)$, the usual three-dimensional representation is replaced by the "topographical map" method. Figure 11-7.2, taken from the back of a U.S. Coast and Geodetic Survey map, shows this method of representing elevation by "level curves." Closely packed level curves indicate rapid change in elevation.

Think of drawing an (x, y)-coordinate system on the lower frame of Fig. 11-7.2. Select any point and from it draw a unit vector $\vec{\theta} = \vec{i} \cos \theta + \vec{j} \sin \theta$ for any angle θ. Then $D(z, \vec{\theta})$ is the instantaneous rate of change of z, equal to the elevation at that point, in the direction $\vec{\theta}$. Now keep the point fixed, but let $\vec{\theta}$ rotate. Then $D(z, \vec{\theta})$ is a function of θ whose first and second derivatives with respect to θ are

(7) $$\frac{d}{d\theta} D(z, \vec{\theta}) = z_x(-\sin \theta) + z_y(\cos \theta) \quad \text{and}$$
$$\frac{d^2}{d\theta^2} D(z, \vec{\theta}) = -z_x \cos \theta - z_y \sin \theta.$$

The first derivative is zero when θ is such that

(8) $$\frac{\sin \theta}{\cos \theta} = \frac{z_y}{z_x}.$$

For this to hold,

(9) $$\sin \theta = \frac{\pm z_y}{\sqrt{z_x^2 + z_y^2}} \quad \text{and} \quad \cos \theta = \frac{\pm z_x}{\sqrt{z_x^2 + z_y^2}},$$

where either both plus signs or both minus signs are used. The values (9) with plus substituted into the second derivative (7) give

$$-\frac{z_x^2 + z_y^2}{\sqrt{z_x^2 + z_y^2}} < 0.$$

This being negative shows that the values (9) with plus signs furnish the maximum value of the directional derivative $D(z, \vec{\theta})$. Also, these values (9) with plus substituted into (4) give

$$\vec{\theta} = \frac{1}{\sqrt{z_x^2 + z_y^2}}(\vec{i}z_x + \vec{j}z_y) = \frac{1}{\sqrt{z_x^2 + z_y^2}}\vec{\nabla}z.$$

Thus, since $\sqrt{z_x^2 + z_y^2}$ is positive, the vector

$\vec{\nabla}z$ is in the direction of maximum increase in z and $|\vec{\nabla}z| = \sqrt{z_x^2 + z_y^2}$ is the maximum rate of increase of z.

At any point, the direction $\vec{\theta}$ of the level curve through that point is obtained by setting $D(z, \vec{\theta})$ equal to zero:

$$D(z, \vec{\theta}) = z_x \cos\theta + z_y \sin\theta = 0.$$

Thus, $\tan\theta = -z_x/z_y$, showing that this θ is exactly 90° from the one [given by (8)] of maximum increase in z. Hence:

At any point, the direction of maximum increase of z is perpendicular to the level curve at that point.

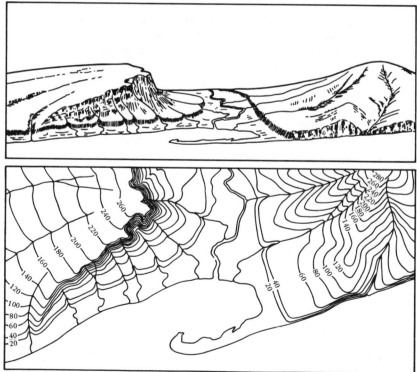

Fig. 11-7.2

Consequently, through each point of the (x, y)-plane there is a curve in the (x, y)-plane that is the projection of a curve on the actual terrain along which a person walking would always be headed in the direction of maximum increase in elevation z. These curves [of the (x, y)-plane] are called **curves of quickest ascent.**

Thus, each curve of quickest ascent cuts each level curve at right angles. The family of level curves and the family of curves of quickest ascent are an example of a pair of **orthogonal families.**

Pairs of orthogonal families of curves arise in many practical situations. For example, a thin metal sheet of nonconstant heat distribution will have curves along which temperature is constant. These **isothermal curves** are analogous to level curves. The flow of heat is then most rapid in the direction opposite to the direction of maximum increase in temperature. Hence, the **curves of flow** are analogous to curves of quickest descent (which are the curves of quickest ascent but thought of as traversed in the opposite direction). Hence, curves of flow and isothermal curves form a pair of orthogonal families.

Orthogonal families are described in more detail in books on differential equations and on functions of a complex variable.

Given a pair of orthogonal families, then either family is said to be the **orthogonal trajectory** of the other.

Example 1. a. Represent $z = x^2 - y^2$ by the topographical map method. b. Find the directional derivative and the gradient at $(2, 1)$. c. Without using the above theory, show that at $(2, 1)$ the direction of maximum $D(z, \vec{\theta})$ is perpendicular to the level curve through $(2, 1)$.

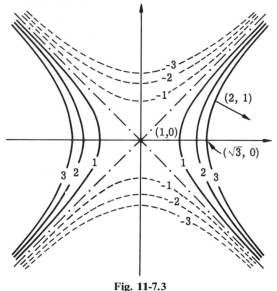

Fig. 11-7.3

Solution a. In Fig. 11-7.3, all actual curves are hyperbolas: solid for positive z, dotted for negative z. The dash-dot lines are both zero-elevation "level curves" $x^2 - y^2 = 0$, as well as the asymptotes of all the hyperbolas.

Solution b. Since $z_x = 2x$ and $z_y = -2y$, then $z_x(2, 1) = 4$, $z_y(2, 1) = -2$, $D[z(2, 1), \vec{\theta}] = 4 \cos \theta - 2 \sin \theta$, and $\vec{\nabla} z(2, 1) = 4\vec{i} - 2\vec{j}$.

Solution c. $\dfrac{d}{d\theta} (4 \cos \theta - 2 \sin \theta) = -4 \sin \theta - 2 \cos \theta = 0$ for $\tan \theta = -2/4$ $= -1/2$.

The level curve through $(2, 1)$ has equation $x^2 - y^2 = 2^2 - 1^2 = 3$. With (x, y) restricted to this curve,

$$\frac{d}{dx}(x^2 - y^2) = \frac{d3}{dx}, \quad 2x - 2y\frac{dy}{dx} = 0, \quad \frac{dy}{dx} = \frac{x}{y}.$$

Hence, at $(2, 1)$ the level curve has slope $m = 2/1$, which is the negative reciprocal of $\tan \theta = -1/2$ found above.

On Fig. 11-7.3, the unit vector at $(2, 1)$ is

$$\vec{\theta} = \frac{1}{\sqrt{z_x^2(2, 1) + z_y^2(2, 1)}} [\vec{i} z_x(2, 1) + \vec{j} z_y(2, 1)]$$

$$= \frac{1}{\sqrt{4^2 + (-2)^2}} [4\vec{i} - 2\vec{j}]$$

and hence is in the direction of the curve of quickest ascent through $(2, 1)$.

Further general theory will be illustrated by using the specific family $z = x^2 - y^2$ of the above example.

With (x, y) restricted to the level curve over which the elevation is a constant k, then $x^2 - y^2 = k$, so that $2x \, dy - 2y \, dy = 0$, and hence

(10) $$\frac{dy}{dx} = \frac{x}{y}.$$

Any curve of quickest ascent intersects any level curve at right angles, and hence the slopes of the curves are negative reciprocals of each other. Thus, with (x, y) restricted to a curve of quickest ascent (instead of to a level curve), then

(11) $$\frac{dy}{dx} = -\frac{y}{x}.$$

This differential equation may be written

$$\frac{dy}{y} = -\frac{dx}{x}.$$

By integration, $\ln |y| = -\ln |x| + \ln |c|$. The arbitrary additive constant was written as $\ln |c|$ so that $\ln |y| = \ln |c/x|$. Hence, the equation without logarithms is $|y| = |c/x|$ or, since c is arbitrary,

(12) $$y = \frac{c}{x}.$$

This is the parametric equation of the family of curves of quickest ascent. Figure. 11-7.4 shows a few members of this family. The fact that each curve

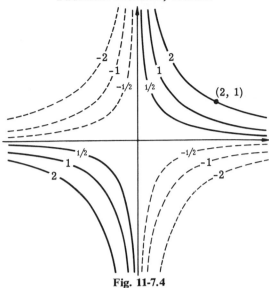

Fig. 11-7.4

of quickest ascent intersects each level curve at right angles could be visualized by superimposing Figs. 11-7.3 and 11-7.4.

The family $x^2 - y^2 = k$ of level curves is said to have (10) as its differential equation and (11) is the differential equation of the orthogonal family (which turned out to have parametric equation $y = c/x$).

Example 2. Find the family of curves orthogonal to the family of parabolas

(13) $$y^2 = 4px.$$

Solution. In (13), p is a parameter that is held constant while taking differentials

(14) $$2y\, dy = 4p\, dx.$$

The elimination of p between (13) and (14) yields the differential equation

(15) $$\frac{2y\, dy}{y^2} = \frac{dx}{x} \quad \text{or} \quad \frac{dy}{dx} = \frac{1}{2}\frac{y}{x}$$

of the given family of parabolas. The negative reciprocity property of slopes of perpendicular curves is used next. With (x, y) referring now to the orthogonal family, then

$$\frac{dy}{dx} = -\frac{2x}{y} \quad \text{or} \quad y\, dy + 2x\, dx = 0$$

is the differential equation of the orthogonal family. By integration,

$$\frac{y^2}{2} + x^2 = c^2,$$

where c^2 is used since the left side can never be negative. Thus, the family of ellipses

$$\frac{x^2}{c^2} + \frac{y^2}{(\sqrt{2c})^2} = 1$$

is orthogonal to the given family of parabolas $y^2 = 4px$.

The general way of giving the parametric equation of a family of curves is

$$f(x, y, k) = 0.$$

Next take differentials (holding the parameter k fixed) to obtain a second equation,

$$f_x(x, y, k)\, dx + f_y(x, y, k)\, dy = 0.$$

The differential equation of the family is now obtained by eliminating k between these two equations. To see that this is what was done in Example 2, write (13) as

$$f(x, y, p) = 4px - y^2 = 0.$$

Then

$$f_x(x, y, p)\, dx + f_y(x, y, p)\, dy = -4p\, dx - 2y\, dy = 0$$

is the same as (14). The elimination of p between these equations may now be carried out to give the differential equation (15) of the family.

The parametric equation $f(x, y, k) = 0$ of a family of curves has the parameter k present. It is important to note that the differential equation of the family *does not have the parameter k present*. Thus, starting with $y^2 = 4px$, then $2y\, dy = 4p\, dx$ is a differential equation but is not the differential equation of the family. The parameter p must be eliminated, as in Example 2.

Problem 1. Find the directional derivative of each of the following functions at the given point and in the direction indicated:

  a. $z = x^2 - xy + y^2$ at $(1, 2)$; from $(1, 2)$ toward $(4, 6)$.
  b. $z = x - x^2y + y^3$ at $(1, 2)$; from $(1, 2)$ toward $(4, -2)$.
  c. $z = e^x \sin y$ at $(0, \pi/3)$; making the angle $\pi/6$ with the x-axis.
  d. $z = x^2 + xy + y^2$ at $(3, 1)$; outward normal to $y^2 = x - 2$ at $(3, 1)$.

Problem 2. Given $z = \ln(x^2 + y^2)$ for $x^2 + y^2 \neq 0$, find the directional derivative at (x, y) in the direction:

  a. Toward the origin.
  b. Opposite to the direction of part a.
  c. Perpendicular to the direction of part a.

Problem 3. With c a constant, find the point on the line $x = c$, where the maximum directional derivative of:

  a. $z = x^2 + xy + y^2$ is minimum.
  b. $z = e^{-(x^2 + y^2)}$ is maximum.

Problem 4. Find the orthogonal trajectory of each of the families:

a. $y = kx^3$.

b. $3y^2 = 2x^3 + k$.

c. $2x^2 - y^2 = k^2$.

d. $y = 2x + b$.

e. $y = k \sin x$.

f. $\dfrac{x^2}{4} + \dfrac{y^2}{4 - k} = 1$.

Problem 5. Show that the family of parabolas $y^2 = 4p(x + p)$ is self-orthogonal; that is, whenever two members intersect they do so at right angles.

Problem 6. Show that

$$D(z, \vec{\theta}) = \sqrt{z_x^2 + z_y^2} \cos (\theta - \alpha),$$

where $\quad \cos \alpha = \dfrac{z_x}{\sqrt{z_x^2 + z_y^2}} \quad$ and $\quad \sin \alpha = \dfrac{z_y}{\sqrt{z_x^2 + z_y^2}}.$

[Note: This angle α is such that, for any angle θ,

$$D(z, \vec{\alpha}) \geq D(z, \vec{\theta});$$

that is, α furnishes the maximum directional derivative.]

Problem 7. Let $z = f(x, y)$ and $w = g(x, y)$ be two differentiable functions. Establish the following formulas for the gradient:

a. $\vec{\nabla}(z + w) = \vec{\nabla}z + \vec{\nabla}w$.

b. $\vec{\nabla}(zw) = z \vec{\nabla}w + w \vec{\nabla}z$.

c. $\vec{\nabla}\left(\dfrac{w}{z}\right) = \dfrac{z \vec{\nabla}w - w \vec{\nabla}z}{z^2}$.

d. $\vec{\nabla} \cos z = (-\sin z)\vec{\nabla}z$.

Problem 8. Let $\vec{r} = \vec{i}x + \vec{j}y$ be the vector from the origin to the point (x, y). It is then natural to set $d\vec{r} = \vec{i}\,dx + \vec{j}\,dy$:

a. Show that, for any function $z = f(x, y)$,

$$dz = (\vec{\nabla}z) \cdot d\vec{r}.$$

b. With $r = |\vec{r}|$, show that

$$\vec{\nabla}r^n = nr^{n-2}\vec{r}.$$

Problem 9. Given that $f_x(x, y)$ and $f_y(x, y)$ are continuous on the rectangle R defined by $a \leq x \leq b, c \leq y \leq d$, show that

$$f(b, d) - f(a, c) = \vec{\nabla}f(x_1, y_1) \cdot [\vec{i}(b - a) + \vec{j}(d - c)]$$

for some point (x_1, y_1) in R. [Hint: Apply the Law of the Mean to the function $h(t)$ of one variable defined by

$$h(t) = f[a + t(b - a), c + t(d - c)] \quad \text{for} \quad 0 \leq t \leq 1.]$$

11-8.   Second Partial Derivatives

Given the function $f(x, y) = \sin (x^2y)$ then

$$\frac{\partial f(x, y)}{\partial x} = 2xy \cos (x^2y).$$

But now $2xy \cos{(x^2y)}$ is a function whose partial with respect to either x or y may be taken:

$$\frac{\partial}{\partial x}\left[\frac{\partial f(x,y)}{\partial x}\right] = \frac{\partial}{\partial x}[2xy \cos{(x^2y)}]$$

$$= -4x^2y^2 \sin{(x^2y)} + 2y \cos{(x^2y)},$$

$$\frac{\partial}{\partial y}\left[\frac{\partial f(x,y)}{\partial x}\right] = \frac{\partial}{\partial y}[2xy \cos{(x^2y)}]$$

$$= -2x^3y \sin{(x^2y)} + 2x \cos{(x^2y)}.$$

This last result is written

(1) $$\frac{\partial^2 f(x,y)}{\partial y\,\partial x} = -2x^3y \sin{(x^2y)} + 2x \cos{(x^2y)},$$

and is read, "the second partial of $f(x, y)$ taken first with respect to x and then with respect to y."

In the subscript notation for partials,

(2) $$f_x(x,y) = 2xy \cos{(x^2y)} \quad \text{and}$$

$$f_{xy}(x,y) = -2x^3y \sin{(x^2y)} + 2x \cos{(x^2y)}.$$

Notice that the second partial with respect to x and then with respect to y is indicated in (1) by having in the denominator ∂x to the right of ∂y, but in (2) the subscript x is to the left of subscript y.

The second partial of $f(x, y)$ taken both times with respect to x is written

$$\frac{\partial^2 f(x,y)}{\partial x^2} \quad \text{rather than as} \quad \frac{\partial^2 f(x,y)}{\partial x\,\partial x},$$

but $f_{xx}(x, y)$ is not condensed* to $f_{x^2}(x, y)$.

For the same function $f(x, y) = \sin{(x^2y)}$, the second partial with respect to y first and then x is obtained by

(3) $$\frac{\partial f(x,y)}{\partial y} = x^2 \cos{(x^2y)} = f_y(x,y),$$

$$\frac{\partial^2 f(x,y)}{\partial x\,\partial y} = -2x^3y \sin{(x^2y)} + 2x \cos{(x^2y)} = f_{yx}(x,y).$$

The final expression in (1) and (2) being the same as in (3) shows that, at least for $f(x, y) = \sin{(x^2y)}$,

(4) $$\frac{\partial^2 f(x,y)}{\partial y\,\partial x} = \frac{\partial^2 f(x,y)}{\partial x\,\partial y} \quad \text{or} \quad f_{xy}(x,y) = f_{yx}(x,y).$$

These equalities (4) also hold for other functions, as shown in Theorem 11-8.1 below. The following lemma is used in the proof of the theorem.

---

*Recall (from footnote p. 402) that in some books f_1 means f_x. In these books, f_{xy} is written as f_{12}, f_{xx} as f_{11}, and f_{yx} as f_{21}.

LEMMA. If $f_{xy}(x, y)$ and $f_{yx}(x, y)$ both exist within and on a rectangle having corners (a, b), $(a + h, b + k)$, $(a + h, b)$, $(a, b + k)$, where $h > 0$ and $k > 0$, then there are points (x_1, y_1) and (x_2, y_2) within this rectangle such that

(5) $$f_{xy}(x_2, y_2) = f_{yx}(x_1, y_1).$$

PROOF. Such a rectangle is illustrated in Fig. 11-8.1, with $-$ and $+$ signs at corners agreeing with the signs assigned to $f(x, y)$ at these corners in the expression

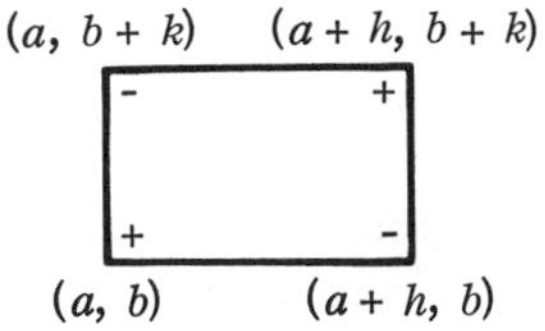

$(a, b + k)$ $(a + h, b + k)$

(a, b) $(a + h, b)$

Fig. 11-8.1

$$F(h, k) = f(a + h, b + k) + f(a, b) - f(a + h, b) - f(a, b+k).$$

The only reason for this expression and the following two,

$$G(x) = f(x, b + k) - f(x, b).$$

$$H(y) = f(a + h, y) - f(a, y),$$

is that someone saw how to use them in proving the result.

The substitutions $y = b + k$ and $y = b$ into $H(y)$ yield

$$H(b + k) = f(a + h, b + k) - f(a, b + k) \quad \text{and}$$

$$H(b) = f(a + h, b) - f(a, b).$$

By the subtraction $H(b + k) - H(b)$, the resulting expression is

$$F(h, k) = H(b + k) - H(b).$$

The Law of the Mean applied to the right side yields

$$F(h, k) = H'(y_1)k$$

for some y_1 between b and $b + k$. The "prime" means the derivative with respect to y, so that

$$H'(y) = f_y(a + h, y) - f_y(a, y).$$

Hence,

$$F(h, k) = [f_y(a + h, y_1) - f_y(a, y_1)]k.$$

The Law of the Mean may be applied again, this time to the expression in the bracket (where $y = y_1$ is fixed, but x takes the two separate values $a + h$ and a). Thus,

$$F(h, k) = [f_{yx}(x_1, y_1)h]k$$

for some x_1 between a and $a + h$.

A check on understanding of the proof so far is to go back and do almost the same thing to $G(x)$ that was done to $H(y)$. If no mistake is made, it will be found that

$$F(h, k) = [f_{xy}(x_2, y_2)k]h,$$

with $a < x_2 < a + h$ and $b < y_2 < b + k$.

Upon setting these last two expressions for $F(h, k)$ equal, and then canceling out hk, the equation (5) is obtained, and the lemma is proved.

THEOREM 11-8.1. *If $f_{xy}(x, y)$ and $f_{yx}(x, y)$ are both continuous at a point (a, b), then*

(6) $$f_{xy}(a, b) = f_{yx}(a, b).$$

PROOF. Since both these partials are continuous at (a, b), they must both exist in some rectangle having corners

$$(a \pm h, b \pm k),$$

with $h > 0$ and $k > 0$. Hence, by the above lemma, there are points (x_1, y_1) and (x_2, y_2) within the upper right-hand portion of this rectangle, where $f_{xy}(x_2, y_2) = f_{yx}(x_1, y_1)$. Now let $(h, k) \to (0, 0)$ so that both $(x_1, y_1) \to (a, b)$ and $(x_2, y_2) \to (a, b)$ and see, from the continuity of the partials, that also (6) must hold. Thus, the theorem is proved.

The interchange of order in taking partials, as expressed by (6), will be used repeatedly, especially in the next section.

Recall that if $z = f(x, y)$ is a function of two variables x and y, but $x = x(t)$ and $y = y(t)$ are functions of a single variable t, then z is a function of t whose derivative with respect to t is given by the formula

(7)
$$\frac{dz}{dt} = \frac{\partial f}{\partial x}\frac{dx}{dt} + \frac{\partial f}{\partial y}\frac{dy}{dt}$$
$$= z_x x' + z_y y'.$$

All derivatives and partials written down, both here and in what follows, are assumed to exist and be continuous.

Upon applying the same formula to z_x, then

(8)
$$\frac{dz_x}{dt} = \frac{\partial z_x}{\partial x}\frac{dx}{dt} + \frac{\partial z_x}{\partial y}\frac{dy}{dt}$$
$$= z_{xx} x' + z_{xy} y'.$$

Extreme care should be taken to check and understand each step in the following computation of the second derivative of z with respect to t. Start with (7) and see that

$$\frac{d^2 z}{dt^2} = \frac{d}{dt}(z_x x' + z_y y') = \frac{d}{dt}(z_x x') + \frac{d}{dt}(z_y y')$$
$$= \left[z_x \frac{dx'}{dt} + x' \frac{dz_x}{dt} \right] + \left[z_y \frac{dy'}{dt} + y' \frac{dz_y}{dt} \right]$$
$$= z_x x'' + x' \frac{dz_x}{dt} + z_y y'' + y' \frac{dz_y}{dt}.$$

Now use (8) as it stands and also with x and y interchanged:

$$\frac{d^2z}{dt^2} = z_x x'' + x'(z_{xx}x' + z_{xy}y') + z_y y'' + y'(z_{yy}y' + z_{yx}x').$$

But $z_{yx} = z_{xy}$ by (6), and the above result may be collected as

(9) $$\frac{d^2z}{dt^2} = z_{xx}(x')^2 + 2z_{xy}x'y' + z_{yy}(y'^2) + z_x x'' + z_y y''.$$

If $z = f(x, y)$ but $x = x(u, v)$ and $y = y(u, v)$, then

(10) $$\frac{\partial^2 z}{\partial u^2} = z_{xx}(x_u)^2 + 2z_{xy}x_u y_u + z_{yy}(y_u)^2 + z_x x_{uu} + z_y y_{uu}$$

is obtained from (9) by replacing x' with x_u, x'' with x_{uu}, y' with y_u, and y'' with y_{uu}. Similarly, $\partial^2 z/\partial v^2$ may be obtained. For practice, the following formula should be derived:

(11) $$\frac{\partial^2 z}{\partial v\,\partial u} = z_{xx}x_u x_v + z_{xy}(x_u y_v + x_v y_u) + z_{yy}y_u y_v + z_x x_{uv} + z_y y_{uv}.$$

Problem 1. Compute all four second partials for each of the following functions:

a. $z = \sin(xy^2)$.

b. $z = \ln|2x - 3y|$.

c. $z = 2xy^2 + x^2 y + x^3 y^4$.

d. $z = e^{(3x+4y)}$.

Problem 2. For each of the functions, check (but do not expect this always to happen) that

$$z_{xx} = z_{yy}.$$

a. $z = \sin(x + y)$.

b. $z = \sin(x + y) + \cos(x - y)$.

c. $z = e^{(2x+2y)} + \tan(2x - 2y)$.

d. $z = (x + y)^2 - (x - y)^2$.

Problem 3. With $f(u)$ and $g(v)$ twice differentiable functions of one variable, let $z = f(x + ct) + g(x - ct)$. Check that

$$z_{tt} = c^2 z_{xx} = c^2[f''(u) + g''(v)].$$

Problem 4. In many applications, the **Laplace equation**

$$z_{xx} + z_{yy} = 0$$

plays an important role. A function is said to be **harmonic** if it satisfies the Laplace equation. Check that z is harmonic if:

a. $z = x^2 - y^2$.

b. $z = \ln(x^2 + y^2)$.

c. $z = e^{-2x}\sin 2y$.

d. $z = 3x^2 y - y^3$.

e. $z = e^{(x^2-y^2)}\cos 2xy$.

f. $z = \ln\sqrt{x^2 + y^2} + \tan^{-1}(y/x)$.

Problem 5. Check that if:

a. $z = \sqrt{x^2 + y^2}$, then $\left(\dfrac{\partial z}{\partial x}\right)^2 + \left(\dfrac{\partial z}{\partial y}\right)^2 = 1$ and $\left(\dfrac{\partial^2 z}{\partial x^2}\right) + \left(\dfrac{\partial^2 z}{\partial y^2}\right) = \dfrac{1}{z}$.

b. $z = x^2 - y^2$, then $z_x^2 - z_y^2 = 4z$ and $z_{xx} - z_{yy} = 4$.

c. $z = (x - y)^{-1}$, then $z_x^2 = z_y^2$ and $z_{xx} + z_{xy} = 0$.

d. $z = \dfrac{xy}{x + y}$, then $x^2\dfrac{\partial^2 z}{\partial x^2} + 2xy\dfrac{\partial^2 z}{\partial x\,\partial y} + y^2\dfrac{\partial^2 z}{\partial y^2} = 0$.

Problem 6. Given $z = f(x, y)$, make the:

a. Transformation $x = \rho \cos \theta$, $y = \rho \sin \theta$ to polar coordinates, and show that $\left(\dfrac{\partial z}{\partial \rho}\right)^2 + \dfrac{1}{\rho^2}\left(\dfrac{\partial z}{\partial \theta}\right)^2 = \left(\dfrac{\partial z}{\partial x}\right)^2 + \left(\dfrac{\partial z}{\partial y}\right)^2$ and

$$\frac{\partial^2 z}{\partial \rho^2} + \frac{1}{\rho^2}\frac{\partial^2 z}{\partial \theta^2} = \frac{\partial^2 z}{\partial x^2} + \frac{\partial^2 z}{\partial y^2} - \frac{\cos \theta}{\rho}\frac{\partial z}{\partial x} - \frac{\sin \theta}{\rho}\frac{\partial z}{\partial y}.$$

b. Rotation of axes $x = X \cos \theta - Y \sin \theta$, $y = X \sin \theta + Y \cos \theta$ and show that

$$\frac{\partial^2 z}{\partial X^2} + \frac{\partial^2 z}{\partial Y^2} = \frac{\partial^2 z}{\partial x^2} + \frac{\partial^2 z}{\partial y^2}.$$

c. Translation of axes $x = X + h$, $y = Y + k$, and obtain the same formula as in part b.

d. The linear transformation $x = aX + bY$, $y = cX + dY$, with $ad - bc \neq 0$, and show that

$$\frac{\partial^2 z}{\partial x^2} + \frac{\partial^2 z}{\partial y^2} = \frac{1}{(ad - bc)^2}[(b^2 + d^2)z_{XX} - 2(ab + dc)z_{XY} + (a^2 + c^2)z_{YY}]$$

[Hint: First express X and Y in terms of x and y.]

Problem 7. Two functions $u(x, y)$ and $v(x, y)$ have their second-order partials all continuous. These functions are related by having both of the equations.

$$\frac{\partial u}{\partial x} = \frac{\partial v}{\partial y} \quad \text{and} \quad \frac{\partial u}{\partial y} = -\frac{\partial v}{\partial x}$$

hold. These are called the **Cauchy-Riemann Equations.**

a. Show that

$$\frac{\partial^2 u}{\partial x^2} + \frac{\partial^2 u}{\partial y^2} = 0 \quad \text{and} \quad \frac{\partial^2 v}{\partial x^2} + \frac{\partial^2 v}{\partial y^2} = 0.$$

b. Transform to polar coordinates and check that

$$\frac{\partial u}{\partial \rho} = \frac{1}{\rho}\frac{\partial v}{\partial \theta} \quad \text{and} \quad \frac{1}{\rho}\frac{\partial u}{\partial \theta} = -\frac{\partial v}{\partial \rho}.$$

11-9. Exact Differentials

As functions of two variables have partial derivatives, they also have partial integrals. Thus,

$$\int (x^2 + 3xy + 2y^2)\, dx = \tfrac{1}{3}x^3 + \tfrac{3}{2}x^2 y + 2xy^2 + g(y),$$

since y is held fixed during the process of taking the integral with respect to x. The additive constant, as far as x is concerned, is an arbitrary function $g(y)$ of y alone. Thus, for $f(x, y)$ a continuous function, it follows that

$$\int f(x, y)\, dx = F(x, y) + g(y) \quad \text{if and only if} \quad \frac{\partial F(x, y)}{\partial x} = f(x, y)$$

since $\partial g(y)/\partial x = 0$ no matter what function of y alone $g(y)$ stands for. Hence,

(1)
$$\frac{\partial}{\partial x}\int f(x, y)\, dx = f(x, y).$$

Notice, however, that $f(x, y)$ is merely one of the functions represented by

$$\int \frac{\partial}{\partial x} f(x, y)\, dx.$$

For example,

$$\int \frac{\partial}{\partial x}(x^2 + 3xy + 2y^2)\, dx = \int (2x + 3y + 0)\, dx = x^2 + 3xy + g(y),$$

and the result is $x^2 + 3xy + 2y^2$ if and only if the choice $g(y) = 2y^2$ is made, but there is no *a priori* reason for this choice.

Also, a partial with respect to one variable and an integral with respect to the other may appear together:

$$\frac{\partial}{\partial y}\int (x^2 + 3xy + 2y^2)\, dx = \frac{\partial}{\partial y}\left[\frac{x^3}{3} + \frac{3}{2}x^2 y + 2xy^2 + g(y)\right]$$

$$= 0 + \tfrac{3}{2}x^2 + 4xy + ?$$

The question mark may be replaced formally by $dg(y)/dy$, since the partial with respect to y of a function of y alone is merely the derivative with respect to y. There is still a question, however, since $g(y)$ is arbitrary and may very well not have a derivative.

To avoid such difficulties, it is customary to call

$$\int^x f(x, y)\, dx \quad \text{the principal part of} \quad \int f(x, y)\, dx$$

and to mean by this that no addition is made to the simplest function whose partial with respect to x is $f(x, y)$. Thus,

$$\int^x (x^2 + 3xy + 2y^2)\, dx = \tfrac{1}{3}x^3 + \tfrac{3}{2}x^2 y + 2xy^2,$$

with no arbitrary function of y added. Hence, (1) also holds for the principal parts:

(1')
$$\frac{\partial}{\partial x}\int^x f(x, y)\, dx = f(x, y) \quad \text{and} \quad \frac{\partial}{\partial y}\int^y f(x, y)\, dy = f(x, y).$$

The following lemma is used in the proof of the next theorem.

LEMMA. *If $P(x, y)$ and $Q(x, y)$ are functions whose partial derivatives are continuous and if*

(2)
$$\frac{\partial P(x, y)}{\partial y} = \frac{\partial Q(x, y)}{\partial x},$$

then the function

(3)
$$Q(x, y) - \frac{\partial}{\partial y}\int^x P(x, y)\, dx$$

is a constant as far as x is concerned: that is, (3) depends at most upon y even though x is present.

PROOF. The partial of (3) with respect to x is

$$\frac{\partial Q}{\partial x} - \frac{\partial}{\partial x}\frac{\partial}{\partial y}\int^x P\,dx = \frac{\partial Q}{\partial x} - \frac{\partial}{\partial y}\frac{\partial}{\partial x}\int^x P\,dx \qquad \text{by Theorem 11-8.1}$$

$$= \frac{\partial Q}{\partial x} - \frac{\partial}{\partial y}P \qquad \text{by (1)}$$

$$= 0 \qquad \text{from (2).}$$

Since the function (3) has its partial with respect to x equal to zero, this function (3) is a constant as far as x is concerned.

THEOREM 11-9.1. *If $P(x, y)$ and $Q(x, y)$ satisfy the conditions of the lemma, then there is a function $f(x, y)$ such that*

(4) $$df(x, y) = P(x, y)\,dx + Q(x, y)\,dy.$$

PROOF. The proof is accomplished by checking that the function $f(x, y)$ defined by

(5) $$f(x, y) = \int^x P\,dx + \int^y\left[Q - \frac{\partial}{\partial y}\int^x P\,dx\right]dy$$

satisfies (4). First note from the lemma that everything following the plus sign is constant as far as x is concerned, and hence its partial with respect to x is equal to zero:

$$\frac{\partial f(x, y)}{\partial x} = \frac{\partial}{\partial x}\int^x P\,dx + 0 = P.$$

But also

$$\frac{\partial f(x, y)}{\partial y} = \frac{\partial}{\partial y}\int^x P\,dx + \frac{\partial}{\partial y}\int^y\left[Q - \frac{\partial}{\partial y}\int^x P\,dx\right]dy$$

$$= \frac{\partial}{\partial y}\int^x P\,dx + \left[Q - \frac{\partial}{\partial y}\int^x P\,dx\right] = Q.$$

Thus, $df = f_x\,dx + f_y\,dy = P\,dx + Q\,dy$. After seeing how neatly the result follows, it is possible to reconstruct how someone could have thought of defining $f(x, y)$ as in (5).

The converse of the statement in Theorem 11-9.1 is also a theorem.

THEOREM 11-9.2. *If $f(x, y)$, $P(x, y)$, and $Q(x, y)$ have continuous partials and if*

(6) $$df(x, y) = P(x, y)\,dx + Q(x, y)\,dy,$$

then (2) holds, that is, $P_y = Q_x$.

PROOF. By definition, $df = f_x\,dx + f_y\,dy$, so that, from (6),

$$P = f_x \quad \text{and} \quad Q = f_y.$$

Thus, $P_y = f_{xy} = f_{yx} = Q_x$, which shows that (2) holds.

The following definition helps to simplify statements.

DEFINITION. *The expression*

(7) $$P(x, y)\, dx + Q(x, y)\, dy$$

is said to be an **exact differential** *if and only if there is a function $f(x, y)$ having (7) as its differential; that is, having $df = P\, dx + Q\, dy$.*

The following theorem then embodies both Theorems 11-9.1 and 11-9.2.

THEOREM 11-9.3. *Given that $P(x, y)$ and $Q(x, y)$ have continuous partials, then*

(8) $$P(x, y)\, dx + Q(x, y)\, dy$$

is an exact differential if and only if

(9) $$P_y(x, y) = Q_x(x, y).$$

Example 1. Show that one of the expressions

(10) $(x^2y^3 + e^x + \sin y)\, dx + (x^3y^2 + \cos y + \ln |y|)\, dy,$

(11) $(x^2y^3 + e^x + \sin y)\, dx + (x^3y^2 + x \cos y + \ln |y|)\, dy$

is an exact differential but the other is not. Find a function whose differential is the exact differential.

Solution. In (10),

$$P = x^2y^3 + e^x + \sin y, \qquad Q = x^3y^2 + \cos y + \ln |y|,$$
$$P_y = x^2(3y^2) + 0 + \cos y, \qquad Q_x = 3x^2y^2 + 0 + 0.$$

Since $P_y \neq Q_x$, then (10) is not an exact differential.

For (11), P is the same as above, but

$$Q = x^3y^2 + x \cos y + \ln |y| \quad \text{and} \quad Q_x = 3x^2y^2 + \cos y + 0.$$

In this case, $P_y = Q_x$. Hence, (11) is an exact differential.

To find a function having (11) as its differential, the formula (5) may be used. First,

$$\int^x P\, dx = \int^x (x^2y^3 + e^x + \sin y)\, dx = \tfrac{1}{3}x^3y^3 + e^x + x \sin y,$$

$$\frac{\partial}{\partial y} \int^x P\, dx = x^3y^2 + 0 + x \cos y,$$

$$Q - \frac{\partial}{\partial y} \int^x P\, dx = x^3y^2 + x \cos y + \ln |y| - [x^3y^2 + x \cos y] = \ln |y|,$$

$$\int^y \left[Q - \frac{\partial}{\partial y} \int^x P\, dx \right] dy = \int^y \ln |y|\, dy = y \ln |y| - y.$$

All of the parts of formula (5) are now at hand to see that

(12) $$f(x, y) = \tfrac{1}{3}x^3y^3 + e^x + x \sin y + y \ln |y| - y.$$

For practice it should be confirmed by actual computation that $df(x, y)$ turns out to be (11).

From long experience, it is known that few people remember for more than two weeks the sequence of steps in actually constructing $f(x, y)$ from formula (5). The following scheme, however, is easily remembered.

Scheme: After checking (11) for $P_y = Q_x$, it is known that a function $f(x, y)$ exists, with (11) as its differential. Hence, f must be such that both

$$f_x = P = x^2 y^3 + e^x + \sin y \quad \text{and} \quad f_y = Q = x^3 y^2 + x \cos y + \ln |y|.$$

Thus, f must satisfy, respectively,

$$f = \int P \, dx = \frac{x^3}{3} y^3 + e^x + x \sin y + g(y) \quad \text{and}$$

$$f = \int Q \, dy = x^3 \frac{y^3}{3} + x \sin y + y \ln |y| - y + h(x)$$

for some functions $g(y)$ of y alone and $h(x)$ of x alone. By inspection, both expressions for f are the same upon choosing

$$g(y) = y \ln |y| - y \quad \text{and} \quad h(x) = e^x.$$

Hence, (12) is again obtained, but by a more easily remembered method.

One reason for the above discussion of exact differentials is that differential equations of the form

(13) $$P(x, y) \, dx + Q(x, y) \, dx = 0$$

are encountered in practice. If there is a function $f(x, y)$, such that $df = P \, dx + Q \, dy$, then (13) is said to be an **exact differential equation** and its solution is $f(x, y) = c$. If, however, no such function $f(x, y)$ exists, then the solution of (13) is harder to find. Several methods of attacking nonexact differential equations are given in differential equations books, but there is no known method that will work in all cases.

Example 2. Solve the differential equation and supplementary condition
$$(1 + y^2 + xy^2) \, dx + (x^2 y + 2xy + y) \, dy = 0; \quad y = 2 \quad \text{when} \quad x = 1.$$

Solution. First check

$$\frac{\partial}{\partial y} (1 + y^2 + xy^2) = 2y + 2xy = \frac{\partial}{\partial x} (x^2 y + 2xy + y)$$

to see that the equation is exact. Hence, $g(y)$ and $h(x)$ exist, such that

$$f(x, y) = \int (1 + y^2 + xy^2) \, dx = x + xy^2 + \tfrac{1}{2} x^2 y^2 + g(y)$$

$$= \int (x^2 y + 2xy + y) \, dy = \tfrac{1}{2} x^2 y^2 + xy^2 + \tfrac{1}{2} y^2) + h(x).$$

The terms involving both x and y agree, so the two expressions for $f(x, y)$ are the same upon choosing $g(y) = \tfrac{1}{2} y^2$ and $h(x) = x$. Thus, the general solution of the differential equation is

$$\tfrac{1}{2}x^2y^2 + xy^2 + x + \tfrac{1}{2}y^2 = c.$$

The constant c is determined by setting $y = 2$ and $x = 1$. Hence, the solution is $\tfrac{1}{2}x^2y^2 + xy^2 + x + \tfrac{1}{2}y^2 = 9$ or, in more compact form,

$$y^2(x + 1)^2 + 2x = 18.$$

Problem 1. Without looking back in the text, prove that if $P_y = Q_x$, then

$$P(x, y) - \frac{\partial}{\partial x}\int^y Q(x, y)\,dy$$

is a constant as far as y is concerned. Then check that the function

$$f(x, y) = \int^y Q\,dy + \int^x \left[P - \frac{\partial}{\partial x}\int^y Q\,dy \right] dx$$

is such that $df = P\,dx + Q\,dy$.

Problem 2. Test each of the expressions for exactness, and for each that is exact find a function of which it is the differential:

a. $(x^2 + y^2)\,dx + (y^2 + 2xy)\,dy$.   d. $e^{-x}\cos y\,dx - e^{-x}\sin y\,dy$.
b. $(y^2 + 2xy)\,dx + (x^2 + y^2)\,dy$.   e. $(e^x + 3x^2y)\,dx + (x^3 - \tan y)\,dy$.
c. $e^{-x}\sin y\,dx - e^{-x}\cos y\,dy$.   f. $(x^3 - \tan y)\,dx + (e^x + 3x^2y)\,dy$.

Problem 3. Find which of the following are exact differential equations and solve those that are:

a. $(2x - y)\,dx + (2y - x)\,dy = 0$.   d. $\dfrac{y\,dx - x\,dy}{x^2} = 0$.

b. $(x^2 - y^2)\,dx - (y^2 + 2xy)\,dy = 0$.   e. $(3x^2y + 2x)\,dx + (x^3 - 1)\,dy = 0$.
c. $x\,dx + y\,dy = 0$.   f. $(2xy - y^3)\,dx = (3xy^2 - x^2)\,dy$.

Problem 4. Solve the differential equation with side condition:

a. $(y^2 + \cos x)\,dx + (2xy + e^y)\,dy = 0$; $y = 0$ when $x = \dfrac{\pi}{2}$.

b. $(y^2 + 2x)\,dx + \left(2xy + \dfrac{1}{y}\right)dy = 0$; $y = -e$ when $x = 2$.

Problem 5. Carry out the operations in the indicated order to show that:

a. $\dfrac{\partial}{\partial y}\displaystyle\int^x e^{xy}\,dx = \dfrac{xye^{xy} - e^{xy}}{y^2}$ and $\displaystyle\int^x \dfrac{\partial e^{xy}}{\partial y}\,dx = x\dfrac{e^{xy}}{y} - \dfrac{e^{xy}}{y^2}$.

b. To avoid any question, take $x > 0$ and $y > 0$ in this part:

$$\frac{\partial}{\partial y}\int^x x\ln(x + y)\,dx = \frac{\partial}{\partial y}\left[\frac{x^2}{2}\ln(x + y) - \frac{1}{2}\int^x \frac{x^2}{x + y}\,dx\right]$$

from using integration by parts

$$= \text{etc.} = x - y\ln(x + y) - \tfrac{1}{2}y, \quad \text{and}$$

$$\int^x \frac{\partial[x\ln(x + y)]}{\partial y}\,dx = x - y\ln(x + y)$$

c. For $y > 0$,

$$\frac{d}{dy}\int_1^2 x\ln(x + y)\,dx = 1 + y\ln\frac{1 + y}{2 + y},$$

$$\int_1^2 \frac{\partial[x \ln(x+y)]}{\partial y} dx = 1 + y \ln \frac{1+y}{2+y}.$$

[Note: The point brought out in this problem is that, even with all partials existing and everything being continuous, it is possible for

$$\frac{\partial}{\partial y} \int^x f(x,y)\,dx \quad \text{and} \quad \int^x \frac{\partial f(x,y)}{\partial y} dx$$

to be the same for some functions but different for others. In more advanced work it is shown, however, that for definite integrals

$$\frac{d}{dy} \int_a^b f(x,y)\,dx = \int_a^b \frac{\partial f(x,y)}{\partial y} dx,$$

provided f and f_y are continuous.]

   Problem 6. The differential

$$\frac{x}{(x^2+y^2)^{3/2}} dx + \frac{y}{(x^2+y^2)^{3/2}} dy$$

arises in the next section in connection with the inverse square law of attraction. Show that it is an exact differential and find a function of which it is the differential.

11-10.   Curvilinear Integrals

   A particle is moved from the initial to the terminal end of a vector $\vec{v}$ by a force $\vec{F}$ of constant magnitude and constant angle θ to $\vec{v}$ (Fig. 11-10.1).

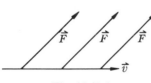

Fig. 11-10.1

The distance $|\vec{v}|$ moved times the force $|\vec{F}| \cos \theta$ in the line of motion gives

(1) $\text{work} = |\vec{v}||\vec{F}| \cos \theta = \vec{F} \cdot \vec{v},$

by the definitions of the work and the dot product. Do not forget that (1) was arrived at only for $\vec{F}$ constant.

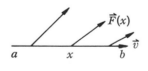

Fig. 11-10.2

   Straight-line motion over a vector $\vec{v}$ may be under a varying force. Thus, if $\vec{v} = (b-a)\vec{i}$ is on the x-axis and the force $\vec{F}(x)$ varies with x as in Fig. 11-10.2, then a new definition of work is necessary. Over a vector $\vec{i}\,\Delta x$ from x to $x + \Delta x$, the work is approximately $\vec{F}(x) \cdot \vec{i}\,\Delta x$, assuming $\vec{F}(x)$ continuous. By considering $\vec{v} = \vec{i}\,\Delta_1 x + \vec{i}\,\Delta_2 x + \cdots + \vec{i}\,\Delta_n x$, then

$$\sum_{k=1}^n \vec{F}(x_k) \cdot \vec{i}\,\Delta_k x$$

is considered an approximation of the whole work. Assuming that the limit exists as $n \to \infty$ in such a way that each $\Delta_k x \to 0$, then the work is defined to be this limit, and the symbolism

$$\text{work} = \int_a^b \vec{F}(x) \cdot \vec{i} \, dx$$

is introduced.

This definition is preliminary to defining work over a smooth-directed curve by a varying force. Let $\vec{F}(x, y)$ be a vector force function of two variables defined at least for each point (x, y) on a curve C. Now restrict y to be the function of x such that

$$\vec{r} = \vec{i}x + \vec{j}y$$

traces the curve C from (a, c) to (b, d). The symbolic definition of work over the directed curve C by the force $\vec{F}(x, y)$ is now given as

(2) $$\text{work} = \int_a^b \vec{F}(x, y) \cdot d\vec{r} = \int_a^b \vec{F}(x, y) \cdot [\vec{i} \, dx + \vec{j} \, dy].$$

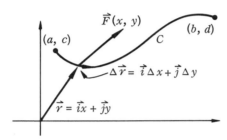

Fig. 11-10.3

The symbolism should suggest summing terms of the form

$$\vec{F}(x_k, y_k) \cdot [\vec{i} \, \Delta_k x + \vec{j} \, \Delta_k y]$$

for polygonal approximations of the curve, and then taking the limit (assumed to exist) of such sums as all inscribed vector chords approach zero in length.

The evaluation of such a limit of sums is, however, not attempted directly. $\vec{F}(x, y)$ has $\vec{i}$ and $\vec{j}$ components, say,

$$\vec{F}(x, y) = \vec{i}P(x, y) + \vec{j}Q(x, y).$$

If C has equation $y = f(x)$, then $\vec{r} = \vec{i}x + \vec{j}f(x)$, and

$$d\vec{r} = \vec{i} \, dx + \vec{j}f'(x) \, dx = [\vec{i} + \vec{j}f'(x)] \, dx.$$

Moreover, $\vec{F}(x, f(x))$ is the value of the force function at a point on the curve C. Hence, formally,

$$\int_a^b \vec{F} \cdot d\vec{r} = \int_a^b [\vec{i}P(x, f(x)) + \vec{j}Q(x, f(x))] \cdot [\vec{i} + \vec{j}f'(x)] \, dx$$

$$= \int_a^b [P(x, f(x)) + Q(x, f(x)) f'(x)] \, dx.$$

Continuity of the functions P, Q, and f' are sufficient for the existence of this last integral. These conditions are satisfied in most applications, and hence this method of evaluation is used whenever C has its equation in the form $y = f(x)$.

Example 1. Given $\vec{F}(x, y) = \vec{i}(2y - x^2) - \vec{j}y^2$, find the work done in moving along the parabola $C: y = x^2$ from $(-1, 1)$ to $(1, 1)$.

Solution. Upon replacing y by x^2 throughout, it follows that

$$\text{work} = \int_{-1}^{1} [\vec{i}(2x^2 - x^2) - \vec{j}(x^2)^2] \cdot \left[\vec{i} + \vec{j}\frac{dx^2}{dx}\right] dx$$

$$= \int_{-1}^{1} (\vec{i}x^2 - \vec{j}x^4) \cdot (\vec{i} + \vec{j}2x) \, dx$$

$$= \int_{-1}^{1} (x^2 - 2x^5) \, dx = \frac{2}{3}.$$

With the curve C, its endpoints, and the direction along it all given, the integral in (2) may be simplified to

$$(3) \qquad\qquad \int_C \vec{F} \cdot d\vec{r}.$$

This is called a **curvilinear integral.*** Any simplified notation is open to liberal interpretation. Hence, if C has parametric representation $x = x(t)$, $y = y(t)$ for $a \leq t \leq b$, then

$$\vec{r}(t) = \vec{i}x(t) + \vec{j}y(t), \quad d\vec{r}(t) = [\vec{i}x'(t) + \vec{j}y'(t)] \, dt,$$

and (3) stands for

$$(4) \qquad\qquad \int_a^b \vec{F}(x(t), y(t)) \cdot [\vec{i}x'(t) + \vec{j}y'(t)] \, dt.$$

With C and the direction along it as above, let C' denote the same set of points but traversed in the opposite direction. A fact that will be used repeatedly is

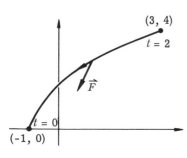

(3, 4)

$t = 2$

$\vec{F}$

$t = 0$

(-1, 0)

Fig. 11-10.4

$$(5) \qquad \int_{C'} \vec{F} \cdot d\vec{r} = -\int_C \vec{F} \cdot d\vec{r}.$$

This follows from (4) by interchanging a and b.

The force function of Example 1 is a mathematical fiction, but the inverse square law of the next example has stature.

Example 2. A fixed mass at the origin attracts a particle elsewhere by the inverse square law. Find the work done in moving the particle

along the parabola $x = t^2 - 1$, $y = 2t$ from $(3, 4)$ to $(-1, 0)$. (Fig. 11-10.4.)

*Some books call it a "line integral."

Solution. With the particle at (x, y), then $\vec{F}(x, y)$ has magnitude

$$\frac{c}{(\sqrt{x^2 + y^2})^2} = \frac{c}{x^2 + y^2}$$

and $\vec{F}(x, y)$ has direction $-\vec{i}x - \vec{j}y$ directly opposite to $\vec{r} = \vec{i}x + \vec{j}y$. The constant $c > 0$ of proportionality depends on the units used. The scalar magnitude of $\vec{F}(x, y)$ times the *unit* vector in the proper direction is $\vec{F}(x, y)$ itself, so that

$$\vec{F}(x, y) = \frac{c}{x^2 + y^2} \frac{-\vec{i}x - \vec{j}y}{\sqrt{x^2 + y^2}} = \frac{-c}{(x^2 + y^2)^{3/2}}(\vec{i}x + \vec{j}y).$$

From the parametric equations of the curve,

$$\vec{r} = \vec{i}(t^2 - 1) + \vec{j}(2t), \quad \text{so that} \quad d\vec{r} = (\vec{i}t + \vec{j})2dt.$$

The particle is at $(3, 4)$ when $t = 2$, moves along the curve, and arrives at $(-1, 0)$ when $t = 0$. Thus,

$$\text{work} = \int_2^0 \frac{-c}{[(t^2 - 1)^2 + (2t)^2]^{3/2}} [\vec{i}(t^2 - 1) + \vec{j}(2t)] \cdot (\vec{i}t + \vec{j})2dt$$

$$= -2c \int_2^0 \frac{1}{(t^4 + 2t^2 + 1)^{3/2}} [(t^3 - t) + 2t] \, dt$$

$$= -2c \int_2^0 \frac{t^3 + t}{(t^2 + 1)^3} \, dt = -2c \int_2^0 \frac{t}{(t^2 + 1)^2} \, dt$$

$$= c\frac{1}{t^2 + 1} \Big]_2^0 = \frac{4}{5}c.$$

Statements involving "infinite," as the one in the next example, are not at all uncommon, even in practical settings.

Example 3. With the curve and force as in Example 2, find the work done to bring the particle in from infinity along the curve to $(-1, 0)$.

Solution. This means to find the limit of the works needed to bring the particle in from increasingly remote (without bounds) points of the curve. More precisely, find

(6) $$\lim_{a \to \infty} \int_a^0 \vec{F} \cdot d\vec{r}.$$

From the calcuations of Example 2, the answer is

$$\lim_{a \to \infty} \frac{c}{t^2 + 1} \Big]_a^0 = c - \lim_{a \to \infty} \frac{1}{a^2 + 1} = c.$$

If it is understood that (6) is meant, then

$$\int_\infty^0 \vec{F} \cdot d\vec{r}$$

may be written. Such "improper" integrals are discussed in Sec. 13-6.

The curvilinear integral $\vec{F} \cdot d\vec{r}$ over C was defined for C not only continuous but smooth, meaning it has a one-sided tangent at each endpoint and a tangent at its other points. Keeping the continuity of C, the definition

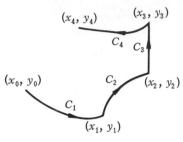

(x_4, y_4) (x_3, y_3)

C_4 C_3

(x_0, y_0)

C_2 (x_2, y_2)

C_1

(x_1, y_1)

Fig. 11-10.5

is extended by allowing C to be "piecewise smooth," meaning it is made up of subarcs $C_1, C_2, \ldots, C_n$, each of which is smooth. Then, by definition,

$$(7) \qquad \int_C \vec{F} \cdot \vec{dr} = \sum_{k=1}^{n} \int_{C_k} \vec{F} \cdot \vec{dr}.$$

A fictitious force function is again used in the next example for illustrative purposes without unduly complicated computations.

Example 4. For $\vec{F}(x, y) = (3x + 1)\vec{i} + (xy - 2)\vec{j}$, evaluate $\int_C \vec{F} \cdot \vec{dr}$ from $(0, 1)$ to $(2, 3)$, where C is made up of intervals C_1 and C_2 with:

     a. C_1 from $(0, 1)$ to $(2, 1)$; C_2 from $(2, 1)$ to $(2, 3)$.
     b. C_1 from $(0, 1)$ to $(0, 3)$; C_2 from $(0, 3)$ to $(2, 3)$.
     c. C_1 from $(0, 1)$ to $(0, 0)$; C_2 from $(0, 0)$ to $(2, 3)$.

Solution. First draw a picture to aid in visualizing the following substitutions:
     a. The equation of C_1 is $y = 1$. Thus, $(x, 1)$ is on C_1 for $0 \leq x \leq 2$,

$$\vec{F} = (3x + 1)\vec{i} + (x - 2)\vec{j}, \quad \vec{r} = x\vec{i} + 1\vec{j}, \quad \text{and}$$

$$\int_{C_1} \vec{F} \cdot \vec{dr} = \int_{C_1} [(3x + 1)\vec{i} + (x - 2)\vec{j}] \cdot [dx\,\vec{i} + 0\vec{j}]$$

$$= \int_0^2 [(3x + 1)\,dx + 0(x - 2)] = \frac{3x^2}{2} + x \Big]_0^2 = 8.$$

C_2 is $x = 2$, $1 \leq y \leq 3$, so that

$$\int_{C_2} \vec{F} \cdot \vec{dr} = \int_{C_2} [7\vec{i} + (2y - 2)\vec{j}] \cdot d(2\vec{i} + y\vec{j})$$

$$= \int_{C_2} [7\vec{i} + (2y - 2)\vec{j}] \cdot (0\vec{i} + \vec{j}\,dy) = \int_1^3 (2y - 2)\,dy = 4.$$

Thus, the answer for part a is $8 + 4 = 12$.
     b. Mentally check that, for the C_1 and C_2 of this part,

$$\int_{C_1} [\vec{i} - 2\vec{j}] \cdot \vec{j}\,dy + \int_{C_2} [(3x + 1)\vec{i} + (3x - 2)\vec{j}] \cdot d(x\vec{i} + 3\vec{j})$$

$$= \int_1^3 (-2)\,dy + \int_0^2 (3x + 1)\,dx = -4 + 8 = 4.$$

     c. The point must travel down along the y-axis to the origin and then along $y = \frac{3}{2}x$ to $(2, 3)$. Note how the limits of integration take care of the direction of motion in

$$\int_{C_1} (\vec{i} - 2\vec{j}) \cdot d(0\vec{i} + \vec{j}y) + \int_{C_2} [(3x + 1)\vec{i} + (\tfrac{3}{2}x^2 - 2)\vec{j}] \cdot d(x\vec{i} + \tfrac{3}{2}x\vec{j})$$

$$= \int_1^0 (-2)\,dy + \int_0^2 [(3x + 1) + (\tfrac{3}{2}x^2 - 2)\tfrac{3}{2}]\,dx$$

$$= -2y \Big]_1^0 + \int_0^2 (\tfrac{9}{4}x^2 + 3x - 2)\,dx = 2 + \Big[\tfrac{3}{4}x^3 + \tfrac{3}{2}x^2 - 2x \Big]_0^2 = 10.$$

The answers to parts a, b, and c are 12, 4, and 10, respectively, although all three paths are from (0, 1) to (2, 3). The force function

$$\vec{F}(x, y) = (3x + 1)\vec{i} + (xy - 2)\vec{j}$$

is an example where the value of the curvilinear integral between two poins depends on the path taken between the points.

Problem 1. For $\vec{F}$ the inverse square attraction exerted by a mass at the origin (as in Example 2), show that the same answer as in Example 2 is obtained for $\int_C \vec{F} \cdot d\vec{r}$ from (3, 4) to (−1, 0) if:

     a. C is the line segment from (3, 4) to (−1, 0).
     b. C consists of the line segments from (3, 4) to (−1, 4) to (−1, 0).
     c. C consists of the line segments from (3, 4) to (3, −1), to (−1, −1), and finally to (−1, 0).

[Note: For this problem, of the inverse square law with the attracting mass at the origin, no path is allowed to pass through the origin. The reason is that $\vec{F}$ "becomes infinite" at the origin. Many mistakes have been made by practical men who learned how to "manipulate" calculus while ignoring the theory. The theory of such singularities is given in Sec. 13-6.]

Problem 2. $\vec{F} = \vec{i}(x^2 + 2xy) + \vec{j}(3xy + 1)$ is to be integrated from (0, 0) to (3, 2) over three different paths. Show that the value is 29 for the path of part a and of b, but is 35 for the path of part c:

     a. Line segments from (0, 0) to (0, 2), then to (3, 2).
     b. Line segments from (0, 0) to (3, 0) then to (3, 2).
     c. Line segment from (0, 0) to (3, 2).

Problem 3. $\vec{F} = \vec{i}x + \vec{j}xy$ is to be integrated from (1, 0) around a path C and back to (1, 0). Show that the value is zero for the path of part a, but is $\frac{1}{2}$ for the path of b; also work parts c and d:

     a. C is the circle $x = \cos\theta$, $y = \sin\theta$, $0 \le \theta \le 2\pi$.
     b. C consists of the line segments from (1, 0) to (1, 1), to (0, 1), to (0, 0), to (1, 0).
     c. C is traced by $\vec{r} = \vec{i}(1 + \sin\theta) + \vec{j}(1 - \cos\theta)$, $0 \le \theta \le 2\pi$. Evaluate the integral and describe the path.
     d. C is traced by $\vec{r} = \frac{1}{2}[\vec{i}(1 + \sin 2\theta) + \vec{j}\cos 2\theta]$, $0 \le \theta \le \pi$.

Problem. 4. A wire is along the z-axis, with current flowing in the direction $\vec{k}$. A magnetic force field $\vec{F}$ is thus created in the (x, y)-plane. According to the theory of electricity, the magnitude of $\vec{F}$ at the end of $\vec{r} = \vec{i}x + \vec{j}y$ is inversely proportional to the distance $|\vec{r}|$ (not the square of the distance). Also, $\vec{F}$ is directed perpendicular to $\vec{r}$ and in the direction determined by rotating $\vec{i}$ toward $\vec{j}$ (considered the counterclockwise direction since $\vec{i}, \vec{j}, \vec{k}$ form a right-handed system) (see Fig. 11-10.6). Call the constant of

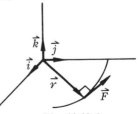

Fig. 11-10.6

proportionality $2c$ (for a technical reason) and find the work done by $\vec{F}$ in moving a particle:

a. Along the line segment from $(3, 4)$ to $(-1, 0)$.
b. Along the parabola $x = t^2 - 1$, $y = 2t$ from $(3, 4)$ to $(-1, 0)$.
c. From infinity along this parabola to $(-1, 0)$.
d. Once counterclockwise around the circle

$$x = a \cos \theta, \quad y = a \sin \theta.$$

e. Once counterclockwise around the square with vertices $(\pm 1, \pm 1)$.
f. Once counterclockwise around the rectangle with vertices $(1, 1), (1, 2), (-1, 2), (-1, 1)$.

11-11. Gradients, Exact Differentials, Curvilinear Integrals

The items of the heading are all related; the purpose of this section is to show how.

Recall that a function $z = f(x, y)$ of two variables was represented in the plane, using the topographical map method, by drawing level curves for each constant value of z. This $f(x, y)$ is now called a **scalar field** (there being no vectors) or, in some contexts, a **potential field** (it being a duty of physicists to explain the connotation of "potential"). The gradient of $f(x, y)$ was defined as

(1) $$\vec{\nabla}f(x, y) = \vec{i}f_x(x, y) + \vec{j}f_y(x, y).$$

Given $P(x, y)$ and $Q(x, y)$, then

(2) $$\vec{F}(x, y) = \vec{i}P(x, y) + \vec{j}Q(x, y)$$

is now called a **vector field** (or **force field**). Hence, the gradient of a scalar field is an example of a vector field, but some other vector field may not be the gradient of any scalar field.

In fact, with P and Q given, the holding of the equality

(3) $$P_y(x, y) = Q_x(x, y)$$

(and some continuity) is a necessary and sufficient condition for the existence of a function $f(x, y)$ for which $df = f_x \, dx + f_y \, dy = P \, dx + Q \, dy$, as Theorem 11-9.3 states. Translated into "field" terminology, (3) is necessary and sufficient for the existence of a scalar field $f(x, y)$ whose gradient $\vec{\nabla}f$ is $\vec{F} = \vec{i}P + \vec{j}Q$; that is,

$$\vec{\nabla}f(x, y) = \vec{i}f_x(x, y) + \vec{j}f_y(x, y)$$
$$= \vec{i}P(x, y) + \vec{j}Q(x, y).$$

As used in connection with curvilinear integrals, $\vec{r} = \vec{i}x + \vec{j}y$ is the position vector of any point (x, y) on the curve C, and

$$\vec{dr} = \vec{i}\,dx + \vec{j}\,dy.$$

Thus, the dot product of the vector field $\vec{F} = \vec{i}P + \vec{j}Q$ and $\vec{dr}$ is

$$\vec{F}\cdot\vec{dr} = (\vec{i}P + \vec{j}Q)\cdot(\vec{i}\,dx + \vec{j}\,dy) = P\,dx + Q\,dy,$$

whose exactness as a differential is equivalent to the holding of (3). Also, the line integral now takes the form

$$\int_C \vec{F}\cdot\vec{dr} = \int_C (P\,dx + Q\,dy).$$

With $\vec{F} = \vec{i}P + \vec{j}Q$ given, let (3) hold and let f be such that $f_x = P$ and $f_y = Q$, so that $\vec{F} = \vec{\nabla}f$. Thus,

$$\int_C \vec{F}\cdot\vec{dr} = \int_C \vec{\nabla}f\cdot\vec{dr} = \int_C (\vec{i}f_x + \vec{j}f_y)\cdot(\vec{i}\,dx + \vec{j}\,dy)$$

$$= \int_C (f_x\,dx + f_y\,dy) = \int_C df,$$

which looks like an ordinary integral of an ordinary differential and might be expected to have value f plus a constant. In a sense it does, as the next theorem shows.

Before stating the theorem, the notion of a "region" is clarified. First, a set of points in the plane is said to be **open** if each of its points is the center of a circular disk (possibly very small), all of whose points belong to the set. For example, the interior of a rectangle is an open set. Also, for any simple closed curve that is drawn on paper, the set of points actually inside the curve is an open set. Next, an open set is said to be **connected** if any two of its points may be joined by a piecewise smooth curve lying completely in the set.* Finally, a **region** is an open connected set.

THEOREM 11-11.1. *Let R be a region and f(x, y) a scalar field having continuous partials in R. In R take (a, c) and (b, d) arbitrarily. Then the vector field $\vec{\nabla}f(x, y)$ in R is such that*

(4) $$\int_C \vec{\nabla}f\cdot\vec{dr} = f(b, d) - f(a, c)$$

for any piecewise smooth curve C in R with initial end (a, c) and terminal end (b, d).

PROOF. First, the theorem will be proved under the additional restriction that

(5)   *(a, c) and (b, d) are joinable by a smooth curve.*

With C such a smooth curve, let $\vec{r}(t) = \vec{i}x(t) + \vec{j}y(t)$ trace C from (a, c) when $t = t_0$ to (b, d) when $t = t_1$. Define $g(t)$ by

---

*Some books would say "arcwise connected" since there are other types of connectedness that mathematicians study.

$$g(t) = f[x(t), y(t)].$$

Note that $g(t_0) = f(a, c)$, $g(t_1) = f(b, d)$, and that

$$g'(t) = f_x[x(t), y(t)]x'(t) + f_y[x(t), y(t)]y'(t) \quad \text{for} \quad t_0 \le t \le t_1.$$

Then

$$\int_C \vec{\nabla} f \cdot d\vec{r} = \int_{t_0}^{t_1} \{\vec{i} f_x[x(t), y(t)] + \vec{j} f_y[x(t), y(t)]\} \cdot \{\vec{i} x'(t) + \vec{j} y'(t)\} \, dt$$

$$= \int_{t_0}^{t_1} \{f_x[x(t), y(t)]x'(t) + f_y[x(t), y(t)]y'(t)\} \, dt$$

$$= \int_{t_0}^{t_1} g'(t) \, dt = g(t) \Big]_{t_0}^{t_1} = g(t_1) - g(t_0)$$

$$= f(b, d) - f(a, c).$$

This proves the theorem under the additional restriction (5).

In case (a, c) and (b, d) are not joinable by a smooth curve, then let C be a piecewise smooth curve in R joining them. Then C is made up of smooth pieces $C_1, C_2, \ldots, C_n$, joining in succession points

$$(x_0, y_0), (x_1, y_1), \ldots, (x_n, y_n),$$

with $x_0 = a$, $y_0 = c$, $x_n = b$, $y_n = d$. Upon applying the restrictedly proved theorem to each piece C_k, then

$$\int_C \vec{\nabla} f \cdot d\vec{r} = \sum_{k=1}^{n} \int_{C_k} \vec{\nabla} f \cdot d\vec{r} = \sum_{k=1}^{n} [f(x_k, y_k) - f(x_{k-1}, y_{k-1})].$$

All terms of the last sum cancel out except

$$f(x_n, y_n) - f(x_0, y_0) = f(b, d) - f(a, c).$$

Two apparently small but important points are:

Point 1: The final number $f(b, d) - f(a, c)$ does not depend on the specific curve used in arriving at this value. Stated loosely:

Curvilinear integrals of vector fields in a region R, which are gradients of scalar fields, are independent of the path in R.

Point 2: The point (b, d) need not be different from (a, c). Hence, take $b = a$ and $d = c$ and see what can be said. Then the curve C [assumed to have more than (a, c) on it] becomes a **closed curve**, and the result is

$$\int_C \vec{\nabla} f \cdot d\vec{r} = f(a, c) - f(a, c) = 0.$$

The essentials (proper restrictions assumed, of course) are:

Any vector field that is the gradient of a scalar field in R has the value zero for its curvilinear integral around any closed path in R.

An important fact is that the converse of this statement is also a theorem.

THEOREM 11-11.2. *Let* $\vec{F}(x, y) = \vec{i} P(x, y) + \vec{j} Q(x, y)$ *be a continuous vector field on a region R. If* $\vec{F} \cdot d\vec{r}$ *has its curvilinear integral equal to zero around*

every piecewise smooth closed curve lying in R, then there is a scalar field
f(x,y) whose gradient is $\vec{F}(x, y)$; that is, such that

$$\vec{\nabla}f(x, y) = \vec{F}(x, y) \quad for \quad (x, y) \ in \ R.$$

PROOF. First observe that:

(6)   *The curvilinear integral of $\vec{F}\cdot d\vec{r}$ from any point of R to any other*
        point of R is independent of the path that stays in R.

For assume there are two points $P_1(x_1, y_1)$ and $P_2(x_2, y_2)$ in R and piecewise
smooth curves C_1 and C_2 in R from P_1 to P_2 for which

$$\int_{C_1} \vec{F}\cdot d\vec{r} \neq \int_{C_2} \vec{F}\cdot d\vec{r}.$$

Let C_2' be the same as C_2 but traversed from P_2 to P_1. Then the curve C,
consisting of C_1 followed by C_2', is a closed curve such that

$$\int_C \vec{F}\cdot d\vec{r} = \int_{C_1} \vec{F}\cdot d\vec{r} + \int_{C_2'} \vec{F}\cdot d\vec{r} = \int_{C_1} \vec{F}\cdot d\vec{r} - \int_{C_2} \vec{F}\cdot d\vec{r} \neq 0$$

[see (5) of Sec. 11-10]. This contradiction shows the assumption is wrong
and hence that the statement (6) is true.

Now select a fixed point (a, c) in R. For (x, y) variable, but restricted
to R, let $f(x, y)$ be befined by

(7) $$f(x, y) = \int_{(a, c)}^{(x, y)} \vec{F}\cdot d\vec{r}.$$

Only the endpoints are indicated on the integral, since the value depends
only on these endpoints and not on whatever piecewise smooth curve is
chosen in R to get from (a, c) to (x, y). This is what statement (6) says.

Next, it will be shown that:

This function f(x, y) has its gradient equal to $\vec{F}(x, y)$; that is,

(8) $$f_x(x, y) = P(x, y) \quad and \quad f_y(x, y) = Q(x, y).$$

For let (x_1, y_1) in R be arbitrary but fixed for the moment. There is a circular disk in R with center at (x_1, y_1), since R is an open set. Choose $\Delta x \neq 0$

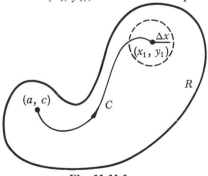

Fig. 11-11.1

with $|\Delta x|$ less than the radius of this disk. The whole horizontal line segment L joining (x_1, y_1) and $(x_1 + \Delta x, y_1)$ is now in R. Then

$$f(x_1 + \Delta x, y_1) = \int_{(a,\,c)}^{(x_1 + \Delta x,\, y_1)} \vec{F} \cdot \vec{dr}$$

is evaluated by following any piecewise smooth curve in R from (a, c) to $(x_1 + \Delta x, y_1)$. The choice of a path C from (a, c) to (x_1, y_1) followed by the segment L to $(x_1 + \Delta x, y_1)$ makes it easy to see that

$$f(x_1 + \Delta x, y_1) - f(x_1, y_1) = \left[\int_C \vec{F} \cdot \vec{dr} + \int_L \vec{F} \cdot \vec{dr} \right] - \int_C \vec{F} \cdot \vec{dr}$$

$$= \int_L \vec{F} \cdot \vec{dr} = \int_L [\vec{i} P(x, y_1) + \vec{j} Q(x, y_1)] \cdot [\vec{i}\, dx + \vec{j}\, dy_1]$$

$$= \int_{x_1}^{x_1 + \Delta x} P(x, y_1)\, dx \quad \text{(since } dy_1 = 0 \text{ along } L)$$

$$= \Delta x\, P(\xi, y_1) \quad \text{(for some } \xi \text{ between } x_1 \text{ and } x_1 + \Delta x).$$

The last equality follows by the ordinary Mean Value Theorem for integrals, since y_1 is being held constant. Consequently,

$$\lim_{\Delta x \to 0} \frac{f(x_1 + \Delta x, y_1) - f(x_1, y_1)}{\Delta x} = \lim_{\Delta x \to 0} P(\xi, y_1) = P(x_1, y_1).$$

Since (x_1, y_1) was any arbitrary point of R, it follows that

$$f_x(x, y) = P(x, y) \quad \text{for} \quad (x, y) \text{ in } R.$$

A similar proof establishes the second equality of (8).

Hence, the particular function $f(x, y)$ defined by (7) is such that

$$\vec{\nabla} f(x, y) = \vec{i} f_x(x, y) + \vec{j} f_y(x, y) = \vec{i} P(x, y) + \vec{j} Q(x, y)$$

$$= \vec{F}(x, y),$$

and the theorem is proved.

Now a word about curvilinear integrals being zero around closed curves in a region R. A force field for which this is true of every piecewise smooth closed curve in the region R is said to be **conservative;** whatever energy (kinetic energy plus potential energy*) that is lost is regained in "working" a particle from any point around any such path in R and back to the same point. It is physically significant that the only conservative force fields are those obtainable as gradients of scalar fields as shown in Theorem 11-11.1 (and Point 2, made about it) and Theorem 11-11.2.

Thus, within a region R the following statements are equivalent (they are either all true or all false for any given $\vec{F} = \vec{i} P + \vec{j} Q$):

a. $\vec{F}$ is conservative in R.

*These technical terms are made clear in a physics book.

b. $\vec{F}$ is the gradient of some scalar field in R.

c. With C_1 and C_2 arbitrary (except with the same initial and terminal ends) piecewise smooth curves in R,

$$\int_{C_1} \vec{F} \cdot d\vec{r} = \int_{C_2} \vec{F} \cdot d\vec{r}.$$

d. For each piecewise closed curve C in R,

$$\int_C \vec{F} \cdot d\vec{r} = 0.$$

Problem 1. Show that each of the following integrals is in fact independent of the path. Compute each value by finding an appropriate function $f(x, y)$ for which (4) may be used. Also, it is instructive to compute each value by following the line segment between the points.

a. $\displaystyle\int_{(1, 2)}^{(3, 4)} (2xy\, dx + x^2\, dy) = 34.$

b. $\displaystyle\int_{(1, 2)}^{(3, 4)} [(2xy - x^2)\, dx + (x^2 - y^3)\, dy] = -\dfrac{104}{3}.$

c. $\displaystyle\int_{(0, 0)}^{(\pi, 1)} (\cos x\, dx - e^y\, dy) = 1 - e.$

d. $\displaystyle\int_{(0, 0)}^{(\pi, 1)} [(3 + y + \cos x)\, dx + (x - e^y)\, dy] = 4\pi + 1 - e.$

e. $\displaystyle\int_{(-1, 0)}^{(1, 0)} [(2xy - 1)\, dx + (x^2 + 1)\, dy] = -2.$

Problem 2. Check how each of the following is related to an elementary derivative formula:

a. $\displaystyle\int_{(0, 5)}^{(3, 1)} (x\, dx + y\, dy) = -\dfrac{15}{2}.$

b. $\displaystyle\int_{(0, 5)}^{(3, 1)} (y\, dx + x\, dy) = 3.$

c. $\displaystyle\int_{(0, 5)}^{(3, 1)} \dfrac{y\, dx - x\, dy}{y^2} = 3.$ (Curve must not intersect the x-axis.)

d. $\displaystyle\int_{(0, 1)}^{(\pi/2, 3)} \cos (xy)(x\, dy + y\, dx) = -1.$

e. $\displaystyle\int_{(a, b)}^{(c, d)} (\sin y\, dx + x \cos y\, dy) = c \sin d - a \sin b.$

Problem 3. Figure 11-11.2 shows a "triangulation" of a region enclosed by a polygon. Given that $\vec{F}$ is continuous in a region containing the figure, show that the integral of $\vec{F} \cdot d\vec{r}$ counterclockwise around the polygon may be expressed as the sum of the integrals counterclockwise around the triangles.

Problem 4. Show that the integral of $(\vec{i}y + \vec{j}2x) \cdot d\vec{r}$ counterclockwise around the polygon of Fig. 11-11.2 is the area of region enclosed by the polygon. [Hint:

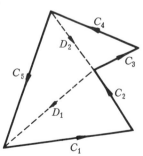

Fig. 11-11.2

First evaluate the integral counterclockwise around any rectangle with sides parallel to the axes, then any triangle with two sides parallel to the axes, and use them to get the integral around any triangle. Then use Prob. 3.]

Problem 5. This problem should be attempted only by the very best students, and even then only if at least an hour is available for it. The problem concerns the differential

$$P\,dx + Q\,dy = \frac{-y}{x^2 + y^2}\,dx + \frac{x}{x^2 + y^2}\,dy,$$

which arose in connection with electrical theory (see Prob. 4 of Sec. 11-10) and thus has practical significance. It is all right to have $x = 0$ or $y = 0$, but they must not both be zero. Hence, all discussion is for

$$x^2 + y^2 \neq 0.$$

a. First check that $P_y = Q_x$. Hence, there is a function $f(x, y)$ such that $df = P\,dx + Q\,dy$, or equivalently, that $\vec{\nabla}f = \vec{i}P + \vec{j}Q$.

b. Note from $f_x = P$ and $f_y = Q$ that, respectively,

(9)
$$f(x, y) = \int \frac{-y}{x^2 + y^2}\,dx = -\tan^{-1}\frac{x}{y} + g(y) \quad \text{and}$$

$$f(x, y) = \int \frac{x}{x^2 + y^2}\,dy = \tan^{-1}\frac{y}{x} + h(x).$$

The trouble arises in finding $g(y)$ not depending on x and $h(x)$ not depending on y, which will make these two expressions for $f(x, y)$ have the same value. Both $g(y)$ and $h(x)$ will be constants, but these constants depend on which quadrant (x, y) lies in.

c. Recall that for A any number, then $\tan^{-1}A$ was defined in such a way that

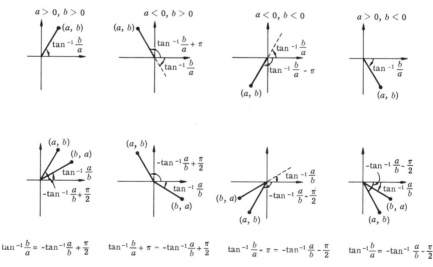

$$\tan^{-1}\frac{b}{a} = -\tan^{-1}\frac{a}{b} + \frac{\pi}{2} \qquad \tan^{-1}\frac{b}{a} + \pi = -\tan^{-1}\frac{a}{b} + \frac{\pi}{2} \qquad \tan^{-1}\frac{b}{a} - \pi = -\tan^{-1}\frac{a}{b} - \frac{\pi}{2} \qquad \tan^{-1}\frac{b}{a} = -\tan^{-1}\frac{a}{b} - \frac{\pi}{2}$$

Fig. 11-11.3

$$-\frac{\pi}{2} < \tan^{-1}A < \frac{\pi}{2}.$$

Very carefully examine the facts illustrated in Fig. 11-11.3. Do not proceed to the next part until it is thoroughly understood why different formulas hold according to the quadrant in which (a, b) lies.

d. By identifying x with a and y with b, check how $f(x, y)$ may be given according to quadrants as follows:

$$\text{I: } f(x, y) = \tan^{-1}\frac{y}{x} = -\tan^{-1}\frac{x}{y} + \frac{\pi}{2}$$
$$\text{II: } f(x, y) = \tan^{-1}\frac{y}{x} + \pi = -\tan^{-1}\frac{x}{y} + \frac{\pi}{2}$$
$$\left.\right\} f(0, y) = \frac{\pi}{2} \text{ for } y > 0.$$

$$\text{III: } f(x, y) = \tan^{-1}\frac{y}{x} - \pi = -\tan^{-1}\frac{x}{y} - \frac{\pi}{2}$$
$$\text{IV: } f(x, y) = \tan^{-1}\frac{y}{x} = -\tan^{-1}\frac{x}{y} - \frac{\pi}{2}$$
$$\left.\right\} f(0, y) = -\frac{\pi}{2} \text{ for } y < 0.$$

e. Note that the formal substitution of $y = 0$ in the formulas for quadrants II and III yield, respectively,

$$f(x, 0) = +\pi, \quad \text{but} \quad f(x, 0) = -\pi, \quad x < 0.$$

Thus, there is no way of matching the formulas on the negative x-axis. The expressions after the brackets show, however, that the formulas match on the y-axis (origin excluded).

What this means is that

$$\int_{(a, c)}^{(b, d)} \vec{\nabla}f \cdot \vec{dr}$$

is independent of the path from (a, c) to (b, d) *provided the path does not cross the negative x-axis*.

f. Check for the specific expression for $P\,dx + Q\,dy$ of this problem, that

$$\int_{(-1, 2)}^{(3, 4)} P\,dx + Q\,dy = f(3, 4) - f(-1, 2)$$

$$= \tan^{-1}\frac{4}{3} - \left[\tan^{-1}\frac{2}{-1} + \pi\right] = \tan^{-1}\frac{4}{3} + \tan^{-1}2 - \pi$$

from the first formulas for $f(x, y)$, but is $-\tan^{-1}\frac{3}{4} - \tan^{-1}\frac{1}{2}$ from the second.

g. Compute the integral of part f by going along the straight line from $(-1, 2)$ to $(3, 4)$ and see that the value is

$$-2\int_{-1}^{3} \frac{dx}{(x+1)^2 + 4} = -\tan^{-1}\frac{x+1}{2}\Big]_{-1}^{3} = -\tan^{-1}2.$$

h. Show that the answers in part f and the answer in part g all have the same value. If you want a harder one to check, integrate over the line segments from $(-1, 2)$ to $(3, 2)$ then to $(3, 4)$.

i. Integrate $P\,dx + Q\,dy$ around the circle of radius a and center at the origin (see Prob. 4. d of Sec. 11-10). Explain why the answer should not be expected to be zero even though $P_y = Q_x$.

11-12. Functions of Three Variables

Much of the analytic development of functions $z = f(x, y)$ of two variables extends naturally to functions

(1) $$w = f(x, y, z)$$

of three independent variables x, y, z. For example, if

(2) $$w = f(x, y, z) = x^2 y + xyz + yz^2,$$

then by holding any two of x, y, z constant and taking the partial with respect to the third,

$$w_x = \frac{\partial w}{\partial x} = 2xy + yz, \quad w_y = \frac{\partial w}{\partial y} = x^2 + xz + z^2, \quad \text{and}$$

$$w_z = \frac{\partial w}{\partial z} = xy + 2yz.$$

Also, for the specific function (2),

$$w_{yz} = \frac{\partial}{\partial z}\left(\frac{\partial w}{\partial y}\right) = \frac{\partial^2 w}{\partial z\, \partial y} = \frac{\partial}{\partial z}(x^2 + xz + z^2) = x + 2z,$$

$$w_{zy} = \frac{\partial}{\partial y}\left(\frac{\partial w}{\partial z}\right) = \frac{\partial^2 w}{\partial y\, \partial z} = \frac{\partial}{\partial y}(xy + 2yz) = x + 2z.$$

In the general situation there are nine second-order partials:

$$w_{xx}, \ w_{xy}, \ w_{xz}, \ w_{yx}, \ w_{yy}, \ w_{yz}, \ w_{zx}, \ w_{zy}, \ w_{zz}.$$

If the mixed partials of a pair are continuous, then they are equal:

(3) $$w_{xy} = w_{yx}, \quad w_{xz} = w_{zx}, \quad w_{yz} = w_{zy},$$

and the proof is the same as before by merely holding the unused variable constant.

Also, if $x = x(u, v)$, $y = y(u, v)$, and $z = z(u, v)$ are themselves functions, then the same form as before, but with an additional term, is obtained:

(4) $$w_u = w_x x_u + w_y y_u + w_z z_u,$$

$$w_v = w_x x_v + w_y y_v + w_z z_v.$$

The previous technique is used for second partials under change of variables:

$$\frac{\partial^2 w}{\partial v\, \partial u} = \frac{\partial w_u}{\partial v} = \frac{\partial}{\partial v}(w_x x_u + w_y y_u + w_z z_u)$$

$$= \left[w_x \frac{\partial x_u}{\partial v} + x_u \frac{\partial w_x}{\partial v} \right] + \left[w_y \frac{\partial y_u}{\partial v} + y_u \frac{\partial w_y}{\partial v} \right] + \left[w_z \frac{\partial z_u}{\partial v} + z_u \frac{\partial w_z}{\partial v} \right]$$

$$= w_x x_{uv} + x_u(w_{xx} x_v + w_{xy} y_v + w_{xz} z_v) + \quad \text{terms for the other two brackets.}$$

However, by noting the pattern being established, and using the equality of mixed partials, the following systematic collection should be checked:

(5) $\qquad w_{uv} = w_{xx}x_u x_v + w_{yy}y_u y_v + w_{zz}z_u z_v$

$$+ w_{xy}(x_u y_v + x_v y_u) + w_{xz}(x_u z_v + x_v z_u) + w_{yz}(y_u z_v + y_v z_u)$$

$$+ w_x x_{uv} + w_y y_{uv} + w_z z_{uv}.$$

If all this had been carried through using u both times, then

(6) $\qquad w_{uu} = w_{xx}(x_u)^2 + w_{yy}(y_u)^2 + w_{zz}(z_u)^2$

$$+ 2(w_{xy}x_u y_u + w_{xz}x_u z_u + w_{yz}y_u z_u)$$

$$+ w_x x_{uu} + w_y y_{uu} + w_z z_{uu}.$$

Example. Transform the function (2) from rectangular to spherical coordinates and find $w_{\rho\rho}$.

Solution. From the above partials already taken, it follows that the additional partials of w necessary in (6) are

$$w_{xx} = 2y, \quad w_{yy} = 0, \quad w_{zz} = 2y,$$

$$w_{xy} = w_{yx} = 2x + z, \quad w_{xz} = w_{zx} = y.$$

The transformation $x = \rho \cos \theta \sin \varphi$, $y = \rho \sin \theta \sin \varphi$, $z = \rho \cos \varphi$ is to be made. It follows that

$$x_\rho = \cos \theta \sin \varphi, \quad x_{\rho\rho} = 0;$$

$$y_\rho = \sin \theta \cos \varphi, \quad y_{\rho\rho} = 0;$$

$$z_\rho = \cos \varphi, \qquad z_{\rho\rho} = 0,$$

Hence,

$$w_{\rho\rho} = 2y (\cos \theta \sin \varphi)^2 + 0 + 2y (\cos \varphi)^2$$

$$+ 2[(2x + z) \cos \theta \sin \theta \sin \varphi \cos \varphi + y \cos \theta \sin \varphi \cos \varphi$$

$$+ (x + 2z) \cos \theta \sin \varphi \cos\varphi] + 0.$$

Continuing the analogy, by definition, the differential dw of w is

(7) $$dw = \frac{\partial w}{\partial x} dx + \frac{\partial w}{\partial y} dy + \frac{\partial w}{\partial z} dz,$$

assuming the partials exist. Again, however, just because w has a differential does not guarantee that w is differentiable. For, by definition, w is differentiable if there are three functions $\epsilon_1, \epsilon_2, \epsilon_3$ all of which approach zero as $(\Delta x, \Delta y, \Delta z) \to (0, 0, 0)$, such that

(8) $$\Delta w = \frac{\partial w}{\partial x} \Delta x + \frac{\partial w}{\partial y} \Delta y + \frac{\partial w}{\partial z} \Delta z + \epsilon_1 \Delta x + \epsilon_2 \Delta y + \epsilon_3 \Delta z.$$

Of course, $\Delta w = f(x + \Delta x, y + \Delta y, z + \Delta z) - f(x, y, z)$.

The notion of a directional derivative extends from two to three variables, but the notation has to be changed slightly. In the plane, a single angle θ, made with the positive x-axis, determines a unique unit vector in that direction, and it was unambiguous to use

$$\vec{\theta} = \vec{i}\cos\theta + \vec{j}\sin\theta$$

in $D[f(x, y), \vec{\theta}]$ for the directional derivative. In three dimensions, the unit vector

$$\vec{v} = \vec{i}\cos\alpha + \vec{j}\cos\beta + \vec{k}\cos\gamma,$$

with direction angles α, β, γ, is used in the notation

(9) $$D[f(x_0, y_0, z_0), \vec{v}]$$

for the directional derivative of $w = f(x, y, z)$ at (x_0, y_0, z_0) in the direction of $\vec{v}$. In order to give the definition, first introduce the function

(10) $$F(s) = f(x_0 + s\cos\alpha, \quad y_0 + s\cos\beta, \quad z_0 + s\cos\gamma)$$

of the single variable s. Thus, $F(s)$ is the f-function evaluated at the end of the vector $s\vec{v}$, with initial end at (x_0, y_0, z_0), and $F(0) = f(x_0, y_0, z_0)$. Hence, $F(s) - F(0)$ is the change of f in going from (x_0, y_0, z_0) a distance s in the direction $\vec{v}$. The quotient

(11) $$\frac{F(s) - F(0)}{s}$$

is the average of this change, and the limit as $s \to 0$ is the instantaneous rate of change of f at (x_0, y_0, z_0) in the direction $\vec{v}$. Thus, by definition,

$$F'(0) = D[f(x_0, y_0, z_0), \vec{v}].$$

From (10),

$$F'(s) = f_x \cos\alpha + f_y \cos\beta + f_z \cos\gamma,$$

with each partial evaluated at $(x_0 + s\cos\alpha, y_0 + s\cos\beta, z_0 + s\cos\gamma)$. Upon setting $s = 0$ and using (x, y, z), since (x_0, y_0, z_0) was an arbitrarily chosen point,

(12) $$D[f(x, y, z), \vec{v}] = f_x(x, y, z)\cos\alpha + f_y(x, y, z)\cos\beta$$
$$+ f_z(x, y, z)\cos\gamma.$$

The gradient of $w = f(x, y, z)$ is now

(13) $$\overrightarrow{\text{grad}}\ w = \vec{\nabla}w = \vec{i}w_x + \vec{j}w_y + \vec{k}w_z.$$

Hence, with $\vec{v} = \vec{i}\cos\alpha + \vec{j}\cos\beta + \vec{k}\cos\gamma$, then

(14) $$D[w, \vec{v}] = \vec{\nabla}w \cdot \vec{v}.$$

Also, with $\vec{r} = \vec{i}x + \vec{j}y + \vec{k}z$ and $\vec{dr} = \vec{i}\,dx + \vec{j}\,dy + \vec{k}\,dz$, then

(15) $$dw = \vec{\nabla}w \cdot \vec{dr}.$$

Problem 1. From the transformation

$$x = \rho\cos\theta\sin\varphi, \quad y = \rho\sin\theta\sin\varphi, \quad z = \rho\cos\varphi$$

between rectangular and spherical coordinates, show that:

a. $x_\rho^2 + \dfrac{1}{\rho^2 \sin^2 \varphi} x_\theta^2 + \dfrac{1}{\rho^2} x_\varphi^2 = 1.$

    b. The same result for y and for z.

c. $x_\rho y_\rho + \dfrac{1}{\rho^2 \sin^2 \varphi} x_\theta y_\theta + \dfrac{1}{\rho^2} x_\varphi y_\varphi = 0.$

    d. The same result for the other two pairs of x, y, z.

e. $\dfrac{2}{\rho} x_\rho + \dfrac{1}{\rho^2 \sin^2 \varphi} x_{\theta\theta} + \dfrac{1}{\rho^2} x_{\varphi\varphi} + \dfrac{\cos \varphi}{\rho^2 \sin \varphi} x_\varphi = 0.$

    f. The same result for y and for z.

    g. Use the above results to show that

$$w_{\rho\rho} + \frac{2}{\rho} w_\rho + \frac{1}{\rho^2 \sin^2 \varphi} w_{\theta\theta} + \frac{1}{\rho^2} w_{\varphi\varphi} + \frac{\cos \varphi}{\rho^2 \sin \varphi} w_\varphi = w_{xx} + w_{yy} + w_{zz}.$$

    h. Show that the left side in part g may be written

(16) $$\frac{1}{\rho^2} \frac{\partial}{\partial \rho} \left(\rho^2 \frac{\partial w}{\partial \rho} \right) + \frac{1}{\rho^2 \sin^2 \varphi} \frac{\partial^2 w}{\partial \theta^2} + \frac{1}{\rho^2 \sin \varphi} \frac{\partial}{\partial \varphi} \left(\sin \varphi \frac{\partial w}{\partial \varphi} \right).$$

[Note: $w_{xx} + w_{yy} + w_{zz}$ is called the **Laplacian** in three rectangular coordinates and (16) the Laplacian in spherical coordinates.]

Problem 2. Show that the Laplacian in cylindrical coordinates is

$$\frac{1}{\rho} \frac{\partial}{\partial \rho} \left(\rho \frac{\partial w}{\partial \rho} \right) + \frac{1}{\rho^2} \frac{\partial^2 w}{\partial \theta^2} + \frac{\partial^2 w}{\partial z^2}.$$

Problem 3. Assuming all partials exist, establish the following mean value theorem:

    a. $\Delta f = f_x(\xi, y + \Delta y, z + \Delta z) \Delta x + f_y(x, \eta, z + \Delta z) \Delta y + f_z(x, y, \zeta) \Delta z$

        for some ξ between x and $x + \Delta x$,

                      η between y and $y + \Delta y$,

                      ζ between z and $z + \Delta z$.

    b. There is a number c such that $0 < c < 1$ for which

$$\Delta f = f_x(x + c \Delta x, y + c \Delta y, z + c \Delta z) \Delta x$$
$$+ f_y(x + c \Delta x, y + c \Delta y, z + c \Delta z) \Delta y$$
$$+ f_z(x + c \Delta x, y + c \Delta y, z + c \Delta z) \Delta z.$$

[Hint: Introduce the function

$$F(s) = f(x + s \Delta x, y + s \Delta y, z + s \Delta z), \quad 0 \le s \le 1$$

and apply the ordinary Mean Value Theorem to obtain

$$F(1) - F(0) = F'(c).]$$

Chapter 12   Multiple Integrals

12-1. Double Integrals

The rectangle R of Fig. 12-1.1 is divided into smaller rectangles by lines perpendicular to the axes. With m and n positive integers, let length increments of x and y be

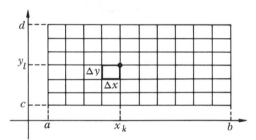

Fig. 12-1.1

$$(1) \qquad \Delta x = \frac{b-a}{m} \quad \text{and} \quad \Delta y = \frac{d-c}{n}.$$

The corresponding **area increment** $\Delta(x, y)$ is denoted by

$$(2) \qquad \Delta(x, y) = \Delta x \, \Delta y.$$

The lines are drawn through the points $(x_k, 0)$ and $(0, y_l)$, where

$$(3) \qquad x_k = a + k \, \Delta x \quad \text{for} \quad k = 1, 2, \ldots, m,$$
$$y_l = c + l \, \Delta y \quad \text{for} \quad l = 1, 2, \ldots, n.$$

Now think of a z-axis perpendicular to the plane of the paper and of a continuous surface having equation

$$z = f(x, y).$$

Take the value of this function at (x_k, y_l) and multiply by $\Delta(x, y)$:

$$(4) \qquad f(x_k, y_l) \, \Delta(x, y).$$

If $f(x, y)$ is positive, then (4) is the volume of a prism of altitude $f(x_k, y_l)$ and base of area $\Delta(x, y)$; it is called an **element of volume**. The sum

(5)
$$\sum_{l=1}^{n} \sum_{k=1}^{m} f(x_k, y_l)\, \Delta(x, y),$$

of these elements of volume seems to approximate the volume of the solid

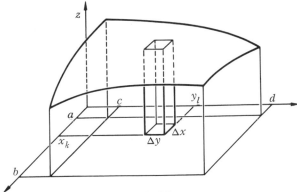

Fig. 12-1.2

under the surface $z = f(x, y)$ and above the rectangle. In fact, the volume V of this solid is defined to be

(6)
$$V = \lim_{(m,n) \to (\infty, \infty)} \sum_{l=1}^{n} \sum_{k=1}^{m} f(x_k, y_l)\, \Delta(x, y)$$

whenever the limit exists. Note that m and n may increase without bound in any manner whatever, but as they do, more and more elements of volume are summed.

In a more advanced text it will be shown that the limit in (6) exists if $z = f(x, y)$ is continuous (whether it is positive or not). The value of this limit is defined to be the **double integral**

(7)
$$\iint_{R} f(x, y)\, d(x, y)$$

of $z = f(x, y)$ over the rectangle R.

Even if $z = f(x, y)$ is a fairly simple function, it may be tedious to evaluate the double integral (7) from the definition; that is, by evaluating the limit in (6). The next section shows, however, that the double integral may be evaluated by performing in succession two ordinary integrals.

12-2. Iterated Integrals

Let y be any number such that $c \le y \le d$. With y held fixed for the moment, form the sum

(1)
$$\sum_{k=1}^{m} f(x_k, y)\, \Delta x,$$

where $\Delta x = (b - a)/m$ and $x_k = a + k\, \Delta x$ for $k = 1, 2, \ldots, m$. Since y is fixed, the limit as $m \to \infty$ of this sum is the ordinary integral from a to b of the continuous function $f(x, y)$ of the single variable x:

$$(2) \qquad \lim_{m \to \infty} \sum_{k=1}^{m} f(x_k, y) \, \Delta x = \int_a^b f(x, y) \, dx.$$

The fact that this integral depends upon y is emphasized by setting

$$(3) \qquad F(y) = \int_a^b f(x, y) \, dx.$$

Since $F(y)$ is defined for each y such that $c \leq y \leq d$, then $F(y)$ is a function of y and has an integral from c to d:

$$(4) \qquad \int_c^b F(y) \, dy = \lim_{n \to \infty} \sum_{l=1}^{n} F(y_l) \, \Delta y,$$

where $\Delta y = (d - c)/n$ and $y_l = c + l \, \Delta y$ for $l = 1, 2, \ldots, n$.

In case $f(x, y) \geq 0$, visualize the solid under the surface $z = f(x, y)$ and above the rectangle R as cut by a plane perpendicular to the y-axis at the point $(0, y_l, 0)$. The area of the section is then $F(y_l)$. Hence, $F(y_l) \, \Delta y$ is an area times a length and is thus a volume visualized as approximating a thin slice of the solid as shown in Fig. 12-2.1. The sum of such slices, and then

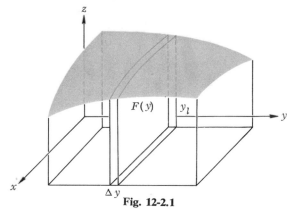

Fig. 12-2.1

the limit of such sums as the slices are taken thinner and thinner, indicates that the whole volume V may likely be

$$V = \int_c^d F(y) \, dy.$$

In Sec. 12-1, the process of forming the double integral

$$\iint_R f(x, y) \, d(x, y)$$

of a continuous function $z = f(x, y)$ was given. In the present section, a single integral defined $F(y)$ by (3) and then the integral from c to d of this function was taken:

$$\int_c^d \left\{ \int_a^b f(x, y)\, dx \right\} dy.$$

Actually, then, the iteration of two single integrals was performed. Different as the double and iterated processes are, it is shown in a more advanced text that, if $f(x, y)$ is continuous, then

(5)
$$\iint_R f(x, y)\, d(x, y) = \int_c^d \left\{ \int_a^b f(x, y)\, dx \right\} dy.$$

This fact will be accepted together with the companion result,

$$\iint_R f(x, y)\, d(x, y) = \int_a^b \left\{ \int_c^d f(x, y)\, dy \right\} dx,$$

that the iteration may be carried out in reverse order: first with respect to y and then with respect to x. Hence, it follows that

(6)
$$\int_a^b \int_c^d f(x, y)\, dy\, dx = \int_c^d \int_a^b f(x, y)\, dx\, dy.$$

Example 1. Find the volume of the solid under $z = x^2 y$ and above the rectangle $0 \le x \le 2, 0 \le y \le 1$.

Solution.

$$V = \int_0^1 \int_0^2 x^2 y\, dx\, dy$$

$$= \int_0^1 \left[\frac{1}{3} x^3 y \right]_{x=0}^{x=2} dy = \frac{1}{3} \int_0^1 8y\, dy$$

$$= \frac{8}{3} \left[\frac{y^2}{2} \right]_0^1 = \frac{4}{3}.$$

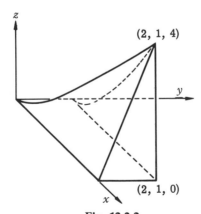

Fig. 12-2.2

It should be checked that the reverse iteration, namely,

$$\int_0^2 \int_0^1 x^2 y \, dy \, dx,$$

gives the same result.

Integration may be over regions other than rectangles. For example, a region G of the (x, y)-plane may be bounded below by $y = g_1(x)$, above by

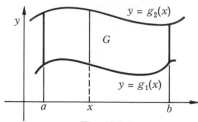

Fig. 12-2.3

$y = g_2(x)$, and on the sides by $x = a$ and $x = b$. In this case, define $A(x)$ for $a \le x \le b$ by

$$A(x) = \int_{g_1(x)}^{g_2(x)} f(x, y) \, dy.$$

Then

(7) $$\int_a^b A(x) \, dx = \int_a^b \int_{g_1(x)}^{g_2(x)} f(x, y) \, dy \, dx$$

is an iterated integral in which the "inside" integral has the variable x in the limits of integration as well as in the integrand $f(x, y)$.

This is an iterated integral over G, but there is also a double integral over G defined as follows: Divide the region G into, say, p subregions and index these subregions in any way. The ith subregion, $i = 1, 2, \ldots, p$, has an area which is designated by

$$\Delta_i(x, y).$$

Let $(\underline{x}_i, \underline{y}_i)$ and $(\bar{x}_i, \bar{y}_i)$ be points of the ith subregion where the minimum

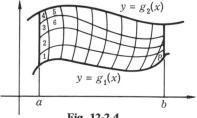

Fig. 12-2.4

and maximum of $f(x, y)$ occur on that subregion. Form the sums

$$\sum_{i=1}^p f(\underline{x}_i, \underline{y}_i) \, \Delta_i(x, y), \quad \sum_{i=1}^p f(\bar{x}_i, \bar{y}_i) \, \Delta_i(x, y).$$

The limits of these sums are taken as $p \to \infty$ in such a way that each sub-region shrinks toward a point. All of this is made much more definite in an advanced text where it is proved that both sums have the same limit, which is called the double integral

$$\iint_G f(x, y) \, d(x, y),$$

and it is proved that the iterated integral in (7) has this same value; that is,

(8) $$\iint_G f(x, y) \, d(x, y) = \int_a^b \int_{g_1(x)}^{g_2(x)} f(x, y) \, dy \, dx.$$

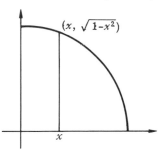

$(x, \sqrt{1-x^2})$

Fig. 12-2.5

Example 2. Find the volume under $z = x^2y$ and above the first quadrant portion of the (x, y)-plane enclosed by the circle $x^2 + y^2 = 1$.

Solution. In this case, consider $g_1(x) = 0$ but $g_2(x) = \sqrt{1 - x^2}$. Then

$$V = \int_0^1 \int_0^{\sqrt{1-x^2}} x^2y \, dy \, dx = \int_0^1 x^2 \left[\frac{y^2}{2} \right]_0^{\sqrt{1-x^2}} dx$$

$$= \frac{1}{2} \int_0^1 x^2(1 - x^2) \, dx = \frac{1}{2} \left[\frac{x^3}{3} - \frac{x^5}{5} \right]_0^1 = \frac{1}{15}.$$

In case G lies between $y = c$ and $y = d$, with left boundary $x = h_1(y)$ and right boundary $x = h_2(y)$, then

(9) $$\iint_G f(x, y) \, d(x, y) = \int_c^d \int_{h_1(y)}^{h_2(y)} f(x, y) \, dx \, dy.$$

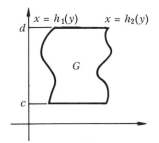

$x = h_1(y)$ $x = h_2(y)$

G

Fig. 12-2.6

Note that in both (8) and (9) the outside limits of integration are constants. The inside limits, if variable, must be in terms of the last variable of integration.

Example 3. Solve the problem of Example 2 by integrating first with respect to x.

Solution. The equation $x^2 + y^2 = 1$ must now be solved for x in terms of y: $x = \sqrt{1 - y^2}$. Then

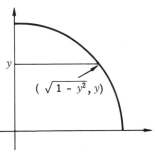

$(\sqrt{1 - y^2}, y)$

Fig. 12-2.7

$$V = \int_0^1 \int_0^{\sqrt{1-y^2}} x^2y \, dx \, dy$$

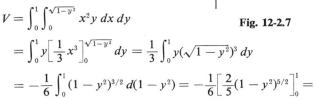

$$= \int_0^1 y \left[\frac{1}{3} x^3 \right]_0^{\sqrt{1-y^2}} dy = \frac{1}{3} \int_0^1 y(\sqrt{1 - y^2})^3 \, dy$$

$$= -\frac{1}{6} \int_0^1 (1 - y^2)^{3/2} \, d(1 - y^2) = -\frac{1}{6} \left[\frac{2}{5}(1 - y^2)^{5/2} \right]_0^1 =$$

$$= -\frac{1}{6} \cdot \frac{2}{5} \left\{ 0^{5/2} - 1^{5/2} \right\} = \frac{1}{15}.$$

Problem 1. Evaluate each of the iterated integrals:

a. $\displaystyle\int_0^1 \int_x^{x^2} (x+y)\, dy\, dx.$

b. $\displaystyle\int_{-1}^1 \int_{-y}^y (x^2+y)\, dx\, dy.$

c. $\displaystyle\int_0^1 \int_0^y \sin y^2\, dx\, dy.$

d. $\displaystyle\int_{-2}^2 \int_0^y x e^{y^2}\, dx\, dy.$

e. $\displaystyle\int_{-1}^1 \int_{2x^2-2}^{x^2+x} x\, dy\, dx.$

f. $\displaystyle\int_0^\pi \int_0^{\cos x} y \sin x\, dy\, dx.$

Problem 2. Evaluate the double integral of $z = x^2 + xy$ over each of the regions G of the (x, y)-plane:

    a. The square $0 \le x \le 1, 0 \le y \le 1$.
    b. The triangle with vertices $(0, 0), (1, 0), (1, 1)$.
    c. The triangle with vertices $(0, 0), (0, 1), (1, 1)$.
    d. The rectangle $1 \le x \le 3, 0 \le y \le 2$.
    e. The triangle with vertices $(1, 0), (3, 0), (3, 2)$.
    f. The first quadrant portion of the (x, y)-plane inside the circle $x^2 + y^2 = 1$.

Problem 3. Find the volume of the solid:

    a. Above the (x, y)-plane, inside the cylinder $x^2 + y^2 = 1$, and below the plane $z = x + y + 3$.
    b. In part a replace the plane $z = x + y + 3$ by the surface $z = x^2 + y^2 + 3$. [Hint: Use the symmetry of the solid.]
    c. Replace the cylinder of part a by the vertical prism whose base in the (x, y)-plane is the triangle having vertices $(0, 0, 0), (1, 0, 0)$, and $(0, 1, 0)$.
    d. Bounded below by the (x, y)-plane and above by the surface $z = 4 - x^2 - y^2$.
    e. Bounded by the planes $x = 0, x = 1, y = 0, y = 2, z = 0$, and the surface $z = 4 - x^2$.
    f. Bounded by the planes $y = 0, y = 2, z = 0$, and the surface $3z = 9 - x^2$.
    g. The solid inside both the cylidrical surfaces $x^2 + z^2 = a^2$ and $y^2 + z^2 = a^2$.

12-3.   First Moments and Centroids

Double integrals are used for purposes other than finding volumes of solids. If, for example, G is a region of the (x, y)-plane bounded by $x = a$, $x = b$, $y = g_1(x)$, and $y = g_2(x)$, as in Fig. 12-2.3, then

$$\text{area } G = \int_a^b \int_{g_1(x)}^{g_2(x)} dy\, dx = \int_a^b [g_2(x) - g_1(x)]\, dx$$

and the single integral used earlier (Sec. 3-11) is obtained.

A convenient way of thinking of this is to consider $\Delta(x, y) = \Delta x\, \Delta y$ as an "element of area," then summing (and taking the limit of the sum) first with respect to one variable and then with respect to the other according to how the boundary of G is given.

Now consider a lamina cut to the pattern of G, the lamina consisting of material of uniform density δ. This merely means that any element of the lamina has mass δ times the area $\Delta(x, y)$ over which the thin element lies. Then, by the method of integration (summing and taking the limit of sums),

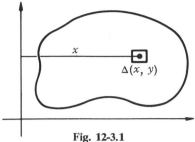

Fig. 12-3.1

the total mass of the lamina is

$$\text{mass} = \iint_G \delta\, d(x, y).$$

Also, with (x, y) a point of the element of the lamina, each of

(1) $x\, \delta\, \Delta(x, y)$ and

(2) $y\, \delta\, \Delta(x, y)$

is "an arm times a mass." These are called "elements of first moments," (1) relative to the y-axis from which the arm x is measured and (2) relative to the x-axis. By definition,

$$M_y = \iint_G x\, \delta\, d(x, y) \quad \text{and} \quad M_x = \iint_G y\, \delta\, d(x, y)$$

are the **first moments** of the lamina relative to the y-axis and the x-axis, respectively

Next, let l_λ be the line having equation $x = \lambda$. Then the first moment of the lamina relative to l_λ is defined by

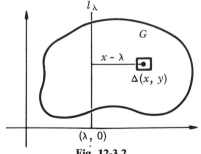

Fig. 12-3.2

(3) $$\iint_G (x - \lambda)\, \delta\, d(x, y) = \iint_G x\, \delta\, d(x, y) - \lambda \iint_G \delta\, d(x, y).$$

This arises naturally by considering the element of mass $\delta \Delta(x, y)$ times the arm $(x - \lambda)$ from a point (x, y) of the element perpendicular to the line. There is a value $\lambda = \bar{x}$ which makes (3) equal to zero. This value $\bar{x}$ is

$$\bar{x} = \frac{\iint_G x \, \delta \, d(x, y)}{\iint_G \delta \, d(x, y)} = \frac{M_y}{\text{mass}\,(G)} \, .$$

The line $l_{\bar{x}}$ is called a **centroidal line**. Intuitively, if the lamina is horizontal, then it would balance on a knife-edge along $l_{\bar{x}}$.

In the same way,

$$\iint_G (y - \mu) \, \delta \, d(x, y)$$

is the first moment relative to the line $y = \mu$. Also, with

$$\bar{y} = \frac{\iint_G y \, \delta \, d(x, y)}{\iint_G \delta \, d(x, y)} = \frac{M_x}{\text{mass}\,(G)} \, ,$$

the line $y = \bar{y}$ is a centroidal line.

By definition, the point $(\bar{x}, \bar{y})$ is the **centroid** (or center of gravity) of the lamina.

Example 1. Find the centroid of a homogeneous lamina cut to fit a quarter of a circle of radius r.

Solution. Locate G as the portion of the first quadrant enclosed by the circle $x^2 + y^2 = r^2$. Then

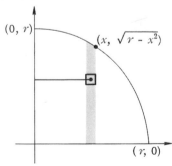
Fig. 12-3.3

$$M_y = \int_0^r \int_0^{\sqrt{r^2 - x^2}} x \, \delta \, dy \, dx$$

$$= \delta \int_0^r x\sqrt{r^2 - x^2} \, dx = -\frac{\delta}{3}(r^2 - x^2)^{3/2} \Big]_0^r$$

$$= \frac{1}{3}\delta r^3.$$

Clearly, mass $= \delta \cdot \text{area} = \delta \tfrac{1}{4}\pi r^2$. Thus,

$$\bar{x} = \frac{\frac{1}{3}\delta r^3}{\frac{1}{4}\pi \delta r^2} = \frac{4}{3\pi}r = 0.42r \text{ approximately.}$$

By symmetry, $\bar{y} = \bar{x}$.

In the above discussion, the lamina was homogeneous, so that δ was constant and could have been factored outside the integral signs (as it was in Example 1). In many practical applications, however, δ is a function.

Example 2. G is the same as in the solution of Example 1, but the density at a point is a constant times the distance of the point from the y-axis. Find the centroid.

Solution. Now $\delta(x, y) = kx$. Thus,

$$M_y = \int_0^r \int_0^{\sqrt{r^2 - x^2}} x(kx)\, dy\, dx$$

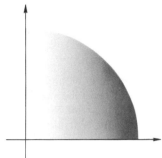

$$= k \int_0^r x^2 \sqrt{r^2 - x^2}\, dx$$

$$= k\,\frac{r^4}{16}\pi \quad \text{by Table formula (34).}$$

In this case, mass is not δ times area but

$$\text{mass} = \int_0^r \int_0^{\sqrt{r^2 - x^2}} kx\, dy\, dx = \frac{k}{3}r^3.$$

Fig. 12-3.4

Thus,

$$\bar{x} = \frac{3\pi}{16}r = 0.589r \quad \text{approximately.}$$

Also, in this case, it is not possible to give a symmetry argument to obtain $\bar{y}$ from $\bar{x}$. However,

$$M_x = \int_0^r \int_0^{\sqrt{r^2 - x^2}} y(kx)\, dy\, dx = k \int_0^r \frac{r^2 - x^2}{2} x\, dx = \frac{k}{8}r^4$$

(and the mass need not be recomputed), so that

$$\bar{y} = \tfrac{3}{8}r = 0.375r \quad \text{approximately.}$$

Note that M_y could just as well have been computed by using iteration in the reverse order:

$$M_y = \int_0^r \int_0^{\sqrt{r^2 - y^2}} x(kx)\, dx\, dy = k \int_0^r \frac{x^3}{3}\Big]_0^{\sqrt{r^2 - y^2}} dy$$

$$= \frac{k}{3} \int_0^r (r^2 - y^2)^{3/2}\, dy = k\frac{r^4}{16}\pi \quad \text{by Table formula (39).}$$

In case the density function δ is in fact a constant, it is customary to speak of the centroid of the region G, rather than of a lamina lying on G.

Problem 1. A lamina is on the rectangle $0 \leq x \leq a,\ 0 \leq y \leq b$. Find the centroid if:

a. The lamina is homogeneous.
b. The density varies as the distance from the x-axis.
c. The density varies as the square of the distance from the origin.

Problem 2. Replace the rectangle of Prob. 1 by the triangle having vertices $(0, 0), (a, h), (b, h)$, where $h > 0$ and $a < b$. In part a, show that the centroid is the intersection of the medians of the triangle.

Problem 3. Replace the rectangle of Prob. 1 by the portion of the parabola $y = 4 - x^2$ for which $x \geq 0$ and $y \geq 0$.

Problem 4. Find the centroid of the region bounded by:

a. $y = x^2$ and $y = x + 2$.
b. $y^2 = 4 - x$, $y^2 = 4 - 4x$, $y \geq 0$.
c. $y = \sin x$, $y = 0$, $0 \leq x \leq \pi$.
d. $y = 1/x$, $y = 0$, $1 \leq x \leq b$.
e. $y = \sec^2 x$, $y = 0$, $0 \leq x \leq \pi/4$.
f. $y = \ln x$, $y = 0$, $1 \leq x \leq b$.

Problem 5. Let G_1 and G_2 be regions with no more than boundary points in common, and let G be the union of G_1 and G_2; that is, G consists of those points which belong to either G_1 or G_2. If $(\bar{x}_1, \bar{y}_1)$ and $(\bar{x}_2, \bar{y}_2)$ are the centroids of G_1 and G_2, show that the centroid $(\bar{x}, \bar{y})$ of G is given by

$$\bar{x} = \frac{\bar{x}_1 \, \text{mass } G_1 + \bar{x}_2 \, \text{mass } G_2}{\text{mass } G_1 + \text{mass } G_2}, \qquad \bar{y} = \frac{\bar{y}_1 \, \text{mass } G_1 + \bar{y}_2 \, \text{mass } G_2}{\text{mass } G_1 + \text{mass } G_2}.$$

Use this fact to find the centroids of the homogeneous laminas shown in Fig. 12-3.5.

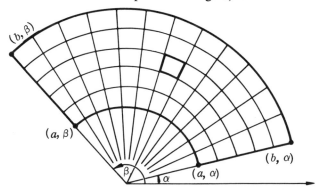

Fig. 12-3.5

12-4. Polar Coordinates

In terms of polar coordinates (ρ, θ), let R be a region (Fig. 12-4.1) bounded by the circles $\rho = a$ and $\rho = b$, and the lines $\theta = \alpha$ and $\theta = \beta$ measured in radians. With m and n positive integers, let

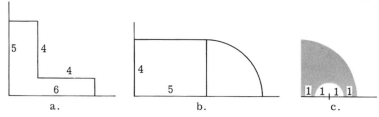

Fig. 12-4.1

$$\Delta \rho = \frac{b - a}{m}, \qquad \Delta \theta = \frac{\beta - \alpha}{n},$$

and set

$$\rho_k = a + k\,\Delta\rho \quad \text{for} \quad k = 1, 2, \ldots, m \quad \text{and}$$
$$\theta_l = \alpha + l\,\Delta\theta \quad \text{for} \quad l = 1, 2, \ldots, n.$$

Also, let $\Delta(\rho_k, \theta_l)$ be the area bounded by the circles $\rho = \rho_k$ and $\rho = \rho_k + \Delta\rho$ and the lines $\theta = \theta_l$ and $\theta = \theta_l + \Delta\theta$. With $f(\rho, \theta)$ a function of ρ and θ, the double integral of $f(\rho, \theta)$ over R is defined by

$$\iint_R f(\rho, \theta)\,d(\rho, \theta) = \lim_{(m,n)\to(\infty,\infty)} \sum_{l=1}^{n} \sum_{k=1}^{m} f(\rho_k, \theta_l)\,\Delta(\rho_k, \theta_l),$$

whenever the limit exists.

This is all very much the same as for rectangular coordinates. There is, however, a difference whenever this double integral is evaluated by means of iterated integrals. In rectangular coordinates,

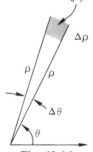

$$d(x, y) = dx\,dy \quad \text{or} \quad d(x, y) = dy\,dx,$$

but for polar coordinates, some justification for

(1) $\qquad d(\rho, \theta) = \rho\,d\rho\,d\theta \quad \text{or} \quad d(\rho, \theta) = \rho\,d\theta\,d\rho$

will now be given.

To indicate why the "extra" ρ is absolutely necessary, a typical area element $\Delta(\rho, \theta)$ is shown in Fig. 12-4.2. The area $\Delta(\rho, \theta)$ is then the difference of the areas of two circular sectors, each of central angle $\Delta\theta$ radians. Thus,

Fig. 12-4.2

$$\Delta(\rho, \theta) = \frac{1}{2}(\rho + \Delta\rho)^2\,\Delta\theta - \frac{1}{2}\rho^2\,\Delta\theta$$

$$= \left(\rho + \frac{\Delta\rho}{2}\right)\Delta\rho\,\Delta\theta,$$

so that approximately $\Delta(\rho, \theta) = \rho\,\Delta\rho\,\Delta\theta$, in the sense that

$$\lim_{(\Delta\rho, \Delta\theta)\to(0,0)} \frac{\Delta(\rho, \theta)}{\Delta\rho\,\Delta\theta} = \rho.$$

This discussion falls short of a full justification of the equations

(2) $\qquad \displaystyle\iint_R f(\rho, \theta)\,d(\rho, \theta) = \int_{\alpha}^{\beta}\int_{a}^{b} f(\rho, \theta)\rho\,d\rho\,d\theta$

$$= \int_{a}^{b}\int_{\alpha}^{\beta} f(\rho, \theta)\rho\,d\theta\,d\rho$$

(which will be used without proof), but should be sufficient to emphasize that the "extra" ρ must always be inserted.

Also, if G is a region between two polar coordinate curves $\rho = g_1(\theta)$ and $\rho = g_2(\theta)$ and lines $\theta = \alpha$ and $\theta = \beta$, as in Fig. 12-4.3, then

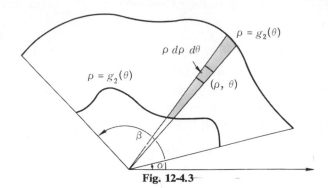

Fig. 12-4.3

$$(3) \qquad \iint_G f(\rho, \theta)\, d(\rho, \theta) = \int_\alpha^\beta \int_{g_1(\theta)}^{g_2(\theta)} f(\rho, \theta)\rho\, d\rho\, d\theta.$$

Example 1. Find the volume under the graph of $z = 4 - \rho^2$ (cylindrical coordinates) and the loop $\rho = \sin 2\theta$, $0 \le \theta \le \pi/2$, of the (ρ, θ)-plane.

Solution. Think of a typical element $d(\rho, \theta)$ in the region G of the loop. This element is expanded into a sector from the origin out to $\rho = \sin 2\theta$, θ constant, by the first integration. Then the sector sweeps out the whole loop for $\theta = 0$ to $\theta = \pi/2$ by the second integration. Thus,

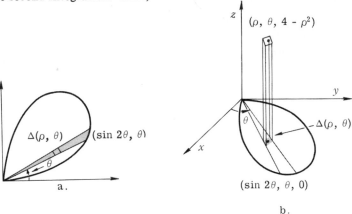

Fig. 12-4.4

$$\iint_G (4 - \rho^2)\, d(\rho, \theta) = \int_0^{\pi/2} \int_0^{\sin 2\theta} (4 - \rho^2)\rho\, d\rho\, d\theta$$

$$= \int_0^{\pi/2} \left[2\rho^2 - \frac{1}{4}\rho^4 \right]_0^{\sin 2\theta} d\theta$$

$$= \int_0^{\pi/2} \left(2\sin^2 2\theta - \frac{1}{4}\sin^4 2\theta \right) d\theta = \frac{29}{64}\pi.$$

It is left as an exercise to make this evaluation.

Sometimes an interplay between an (x, y)- and a (ρ, θ)-system is used to advantage.

Example 2. Find the centroid of the region enclosed by $\rho = \sin 2\theta$, $0 \le \theta \le \pi/2$.

Solution. By symmetry, the centroid is on the 45° line, so that $\bar{\theta} = \pi/4$, but it is necessary to find $\bar{\rho}$. In terms of rectangular coordinates, $\bar{x} = \bar{y}$, so that $\bar{\rho} = \bar{x}\sqrt{2}$. Previous theory yields

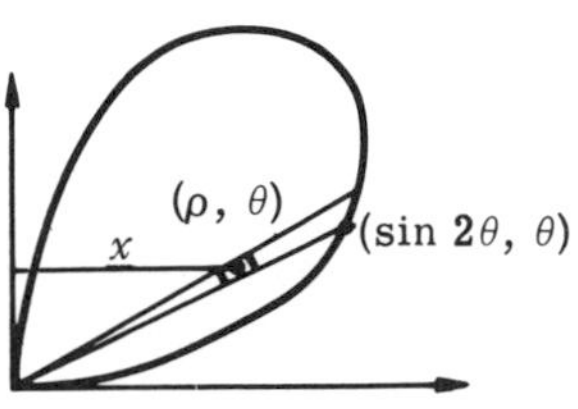

$$M_y = \iint_G x \, d(\rho, \theta) \quad \text{and} \quad \text{area} = \iint_G d(\rho, \theta).$$

Fig. 12-4.5

But only one coordinate system may be used in the actual integration. Since $x = \rho \cos \theta$, it follows that

$$M_y = \int_0^{\pi/2} \int_0^{\sin 2\theta} (\rho \cos \theta) \rho \, d\rho \, d\theta = \frac{1}{3} \int_0^{\pi/2} \rho^3 \Big]_0^{\sin 2\theta} \cos \theta \, d\theta$$

$$= \frac{1}{3} \int_0^{\pi/2} \sin^3 2\theta \cos \theta \, d\theta = \frac{8}{3} \int_0^{\pi/2} \sin^3 \theta \cos^4 \theta \, d\theta$$

$$= \frac{8}{3} \int_0^{\pi/2} (1 - \cos^2 \theta) \cos^4 \theta \sin \theta \, d\theta = \text{etc.} = \frac{16}{105}.$$

The area $= \pi/8$, as should be checked. Thus,

$$\bar{x} = \bar{y} = \frac{16}{105} \cdot \frac{8}{\pi} = \frac{128}{105\pi} = 0.388,$$

$$\bar{\theta} = \frac{\pi}{4}, \quad \bar{\rho} = \bar{x}\sqrt{2} = 0.549.$$

If a region G is bounded by the circles $\rho = a$ and $\rho = b$ and the polar curves $\theta = h_1(\rho)$ and $\theta = h_2(\rho)$, as in Fig. 12-4.6, then

$$(4) \quad \iint_G f(\rho, \theta) \, d(\rho, \theta) = \int_a^b \int_{h_1(\rho)}^{h_2(\rho)} f(\rho, \theta) \rho \, d\theta \, d\rho.$$

12-5. Jacobians

This section is inserted as a warning to consult a book on advanced calculus should a situation arise in which it is desirable to substitute new variables for the independent variables in double integrals.

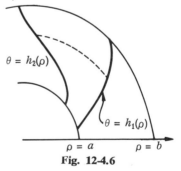

Fig. 12-4.6

To point up an analogy, first recall that the single integral

$$\int_0^1 \sqrt{1 - x^2} \, dx$$

may be evaluated by substituting $x = \sin u$. When $x = 0$, then $u = 0$, but when $x = 1$, then $u = \pi/2$. A formal way of keeping things straight is to multiply and divide by du:

$$\int_0^1 \sqrt{1 - x^2}\, dx = \int_0^{\pi/2} \sqrt{1 - \sin^2 u}\, \frac{d \sin u}{du}\, du$$

$$= \int_0^{\pi/2} \cos u \cdot \cos u\, du = \text{etc.}$$

In general, if the substitution $x = x(u)$ is made and it is found that $u = c$ when $x = a$ and $u = d$ when $x = b$, then

$$\int_a^b f(x)\, dx = \int_c^d f(x(u))\frac{dx(u)}{du}\, du, \quad \text{where} \quad \frac{dx(u)}{du} = x'(u).$$

With G a region of the (x, y)-plane, it may be desirable to make substitutions of the form

(1) $$x = x(u, v), \quad y = y(u, v).$$

The region G will be transformed to a region H of the (u, v)-plane much as (but more complicated than) the above transformation of an interval $a \le x \le b$ into an interval $c \le u \le d$. Then a mechanical procedure is to write

$$\iint_G f(x, y)\, d(x, y) = \iint_H f(x(u, v), y(u, v))\frac{d(x(u, v), y(u, v))}{d(u, v)}\, d(u, v).$$

Here is where an advanced calculus text should be consulted to see why the interpretation

$$\frac{d(x(u, v), y(u, v))}{d(u, v)} = \begin{vmatrix} x_u & x_v \\ y_u & y_v \end{vmatrix}$$

has to be made. The determinant on the right* is called the **Jacobian** of the transformaton (1). Jacobians play much the same role in transformations involving two or more independent variables that derivatives play in transformations of a single variable.

As an illustration, the transformation

$$x = \rho \cos \theta, \quad y = \rho \sin \theta,$$

from rectangular to polar coordinates, has Jacobian

$$\frac{d(x, y)}{d(\rho, \theta)} = \begin{vmatrix} \dfrac{\partial \rho \cos \theta}{\partial \rho} & \dfrac{\partial \rho \cos \theta}{\partial \theta} \\ \dfrac{\partial \rho \sin \theta}{\partial \rho} & \dfrac{\partial \rho \sin \theta}{\partial \theta} \end{vmatrix} = \begin{vmatrix} \cos \theta & -\rho \sin \theta \\ \sin \theta & \rho \cos \theta \end{vmatrix}$$

$$= \rho \cos^2 \theta + \rho \sin^2 \theta = \rho.$$

This ρ is the factor of $\rho\, d\rho\, d\theta$ seen in Sec. 12-4 to be necessary when dealing with iterated integrals in polar coordinates.

*A more common notation for the left side is $\dfrac{\partial(x, y)}{\partial(u, v)}$.

To reiterate, this section is mainly to caution the reader that much more is to be learned before transformations involving two or more independent variables may be handled with confidence.

Problem 1. a. Find the area inside the circle $x^2 + y^2 = \frac{9}{4}$ and to the right of the line $x = \frac{3}{4}$.
 b. Work the same problem in polar coordinates.
 c. Find M_y first in rectangular and then in polar coordinates.

Problem 2. Find the centroid of the region:
 a. Inside one loop of $\rho = a \cos 2\theta$.
 b. Inside the cardioid $\rho = a(1 + \cos \theta)$.
 c. Inside the circle $\rho = 2a \cos \theta$ and outside the circle $\rho = a$.
 d. Inside $\rho = (1 + \cos \theta)$ and outside $\rho = 1$.

Problem 3. Find the centroid of the quarter circle $\rho = r$, $0 \leq \theta \leq \pi/2$, given that the density δ is:

 a. A constant.
 b. Varies as the distance from the y-axis.
 c. Varies as the distance from the x-axis.
 d. Varies as the distance from the pole.

Problem 4. Find the volume under the given surface and above the region of the (ρ, θ)-plane whose bounding curve is given:
 a. $z^2 = 4 - \rho^2$; $\rho = 2 \sin 2\theta$, $0 \leq \theta \leq \pi/2$.
 b. $z^2 = 4 - \rho^2$; $\rho = 2 \cos \theta$, $-\pi/2 \leq \theta \leq \pi/2$.
 c. $z = 3 - \rho$; $\rho = 2 \cos \theta$, $-\pi/2 \leq \theta \leq \pi/2$.
 d. $z = \rho$; $\rho = r$, $0 \leq \theta \leq 2\pi$.
 e. $z = h - (h/r)\rho$; $\rho = r$, $0 \leq \theta \leq 2\pi$.

12-6. Moment of Inertia

A particle of mass m at a distance r from a line l is said to have **moment of inertia**, or **second moment**,

(1) $$I = r^2 m$$

with respect to l. A system of particles of masses $m_1, m_2, \ldots, m_n$ at respective distances $r_1, r_2, \ldots, r_n$ from a line l is said to have moment of inertia

$$I = \sum_{k=1}^{n} r_k^2 m_k.$$

The usual sum-limit process of integration then defines the moment of inertia of a lamina of density δ over a plane region G with respect to a line. In the (x, y)-plane with l_λ having equation $x = \lambda$, then

(2) $$I_{x=\lambda} = \iint_G (x - \lambda)^2 \, \delta \, d(x, y).$$

Here the typical element of mass is $\delta \, d(x, y)$, the arm to l_λ is $|x - \lambda|$, and thus the element of second moment is $(x - \lambda)^2 \, \delta \, d(x, y)$.

Note that $I_{x=0} = I_y$.

Example 1. Find the moment of inertia of a lamina of constant density δ over a quadrant of a circle of radius a with respect to a bounding radius.

Solution. Consider G as $0 \le \rho \le a, 0 \le \theta \le \pi/2$, and take moments with respect to the line $\theta = \pi/2$. Then

$$I = \int_0^{\pi/2} \int_0^a (\rho \cos \theta)^2 \, \delta \rho \, d\rho \, d\theta$$

$$= \delta \int_0^{\pi/2} \frac{a^4}{4} \cos^2 \theta \, d\theta = \delta \frac{\pi}{16} a^4.$$

For lamina over a region G of the (x, y)-plane, it is usual to use I_x, I_y, and I_0 for the moments of inertia with respect to the x-, y-, and z-axes respectively. Thus,

(3) $$I_x = \iint_G y^2 \, \delta \, d(x, y), \quad I_y = \iint_G x^2 \, \delta \, d(x, y), \quad \text{and}$$

$$I_0 = \iint_G (x^2 + y^2) \, \delta \, d(x, y) = I_y + I_x.$$

The physical significance of the second moment is somewhat more elusive than that of the first moment. Moments of inertia are, however, used extensively in designing airplanes, ships, and moving parts of machines. Other terms related to the moment of inertia are the radius of gyration and kinetic energy given below.

First note that the mass of the lamina of Example 1 is $\delta \frac{1}{4} \pi a^2$. Thus, the answer of Example 1 could be written as

$$I = \frac{a^2}{4} \left(\delta \frac{1}{4} \pi a^2 \right) = \left(\frac{a}{2} \right)^2 \text{mass},$$

which looks like (1), with $r = a/2$. Thus, if the mass of the lamina were concentrated into a single particle at distance $a/2$ from the line $\theta = \pi/2$, this particle would have the same moment of inertia as the lamina with respect to the line. In general, the moment of inertia of a lamina may be written as

(4) $$I = R^2(\text{mass}).$$

For example, (2) could be written

$$I_{x=\lambda} = \frac{\displaystyle\iint_G (x - \lambda)^2 \, \delta \, d(x, y)}{\displaystyle\iint_G \delta \, d(x, y)} \cdot \iint_G \delta \, d(x, y).$$

Since the numerator of the first term has the square of a linear dimension more than the denominator, this fraction has dimension (linear)^2. Thus, the positive number R defined by (4) is linear. This number R is called the **radius of gyration**.

In the study of dynamics, a particle of mass m moving with velocity v is said to have

$$\text{momentum} = mv.$$

The kinetic energy to increase the velocity from a value a to a value b is

$$\int_a^b mv \, dv = \tfrac{1}{2}mv^2 \Big]_a^b.$$

Thus, the **instantaneous kinetic energy** is defined as

$$(5) \qquad\qquad E = \tfrac{1}{2}mv^2.$$

Now consider the (x, y)-plane rotating about the x-axis with constant angular velocity ω. A point (x, y) will move along the arc of a circle of radius $|y|$. In Δt sec, the angle generated is $\omega \, \Delta t$ radians, and the point will move $\omega(\Delta t)|y|$ linear units. Thus, the velocity will be

$$\lim_{\Delta t \to 0} \frac{\omega \, \Delta t \, |y|}{\Delta t} = \omega|y|.$$

An element of mass $\delta \, d(x, y)$ will have, from (5),

$$\tfrac{1}{2} \delta \, d(x, y)(\omega|y|)^2$$

as its element of kinetic energy. Hence, a lamina over a region G will have **kinetic energy**

$$(6) \qquad\qquad E = \iint_G \tfrac{1}{2}\omega^2 y^2 \, \delta \, d(x, y) = \tfrac{1}{2}\omega^2 I_x.$$

This shows how moments of inertia and kinetic energies are related.

Desiderata in machines are to have moving parts with as small kinetic energies as possible and hence, from (6), minimal moments of inertia. This leads to the question, in (2) what value of λ will make $I_{x=\lambda}$ a minimum? Note that (2) may be written

$$I_{x=\lambda} = \iint_G (x^2 - 2\lambda x + \lambda^2) \, \delta \, d(x, y)$$

$$= \iint_G x^2 \, \delta \, d(x, y) - 2\lambda \iint_G x \, \delta \, d(x, y) + \lambda^2 \iint_G \delta \, d(x, y)$$

$$(7) \qquad\qquad = I_y - 2\lambda M_y + \lambda^2(\text{mass}),$$

where M_y is the first moment of the lamina with respect to the y-axis as defined in Sec. 12-3. Since I_y, M_y, and the mass are independent of λ, the problem is to find the minimum of the function

$$f(\lambda) = I_y - 2\lambda M_y + \lambda^2(\text{mass})$$

of λ. Derivations with respect to λ yield

$$f'(\lambda) = -2M_y + 2\lambda(\text{mass}) \quad \text{and} \quad f''(\lambda) = 2\text{mass} > 0.$$

Since $f'(\lambda) = 0$ if

$$\lambda = \frac{M_y}{\text{mass}} = \bar{x} = \text{abscissa of the centroid}$$

and $f''(\lambda)$ is always positive, it follows that:

Relative to a set of parallel lines, the one through the centroid furnishes the minimum moment of inertia of a lamina.

The minimum value of $I_{x=\lambda}$ is

$$I_{\lambda=\bar{x}} = I_y - 2\bar{x}M_y + \bar{x}^2(\text{mass})$$

$$= I_y - 2\frac{M_y}{\text{mass}}M_y + \left(\frac{M_y}{\text{mass}}\right)^2 \text{mass}$$

$$= I_y - \frac{M_y^2}{\text{mass}}.$$

As with first moments, if a lamina is uniform (density δ a constant) it is customary to speak of the second moment of the region. Also, a curve, thought of as a wire of uniform density, has a moment of inertia about an axis.

Example 2. Find the moment of inertia of the curve $y = x^2$, $0 \le x \le 1$, with respect to the y-axis.

Solution. It should be seen that it is only necessary to replace the element of area by the element of arc length in the above discussion. Thus,

$$I_y = \int_0^1 x^2\sqrt{1 + \left(\frac{dy}{dx}\right)^2}\,dx = \int_0^1 x^2\sqrt{1 + (2x)^2}\,dx$$

$$= \frac{1}{64}\{18\sqrt{5} - \ln(2 + \sqrt{5})\} \quad \text{by Table formula (46)}.$$

Problem 1. Find I_x, I_y, and the corresponding radii of gyration of the region:

a. Within the triangle with vertices $(0, 0)$, (a, h), (b, h), where $a < b$ and $h > 0$.
b. Right triangle with vertices $(0, 0)$, $(b, 0)$, and (b, h).
c. Right triangle with vertices $(0, 0)$, $(b, 0)$, and $(0, h)$.
d. The circle $x^2 + y^2 = a^2$.
e. The circle $(x - a)^2 + y^2 = a^2$.
f. Bounded by $y = 6x - x^2$ and $y = x$.
g. Bounded by $y = x^2 - 2x$ and $y = 6x - 3x^2$.

Problem 2. Find the moment of inertia of the region $0 \le y \le \cos x$, $0 \le x \le \pi/2$, with respect to the line:

a. $x = \pi/2$.　　　　b. $y = 1$.　　　　c. $y = x$.

Problem 3. A semicircular lamina has density varying as the distance from its diameter. Find the radius of gyration about:

a. The diameter.

b. Its line of symmetry.

c. The tangent line parallel to the diameter.

Problem 4. A lamina over a region G of the (x, y)-plane is said to have **product moment of inertia**

$$I_{xy} = \iint_G xy \, \delta \, d(x, y).$$

Show that the moment of inertia with respect to the line through the origin having inclination θ is

$$I_y \sin^2 \theta + I_x \cos^2 \theta - I_{xy} 2 \sin \theta \cos \theta.$$

[Hint: See the hint in the answer to Prob. 2c.]

Problem 5. Find the moment of inertia of the rectangle $0 \le x \le b$, $0 \le y \le h$, about a diagonal.

12-7. Surface Area

The portion of a surface $z = f(x, y)$ which projects vetically onto a region G of the (x, y)-plane has

(1) $$\text{area} = \iint_G \sqrt{1 + f_x^2(x, y) + f_y^2(x, y)} \, d(x, y)$$

if the partials are continuous. Supporting reasons are given below.

Example 1. Find the area of the portion of the plane

$$z = 4 - 2x + 3y$$

over the rectangle $0 \le x \le 1$, $0 \le y \le 2$, of the (x, y)-plane.

Solution. Since $z_x = -2$ and $z_y = 3$, then

$$\text{area} = \int_0^1 \int_0^2 \sqrt{1 + (-2)^2 + 3^2} \, dy \, dx = 2\sqrt{14}.$$

Note that the surface in Example 1 is a parallelogram having vertices

$$(0, 0, 4), \quad (1, 0, 2), \quad (0, 2, 10), \quad \text{and} \quad (1, 2, 8).$$

Designate as $\vec{u}$ and $\vec{v}$ the vectors from the first to the second and third of these points, respectively; then

$$\vec{u} = \vec{i} + 0 \cdot \vec{j} - 2\vec{k}, \quad \vec{v} = 0 \cdot \vec{i} + 2\vec{j} + 6\vec{k}.$$

Hence,

$$\vec{u} \times \vec{v} = \begin{vmatrix} \vec{i} & \vec{j} & \vec{k} \\ 1 & 0 & -2 \\ 0 & 2 & 6 \end{vmatrix} = 4\vec{i} - 6\vec{j} + 2\vec{k}.$$

Recall (Sec. 10-6) that $\vec{u} \times \vec{v}$ is normal to the parallelogram with sides $\vec{u}$ and $\vec{v}$, and that $|\vec{u} \times \vec{v}|$ is the area of the parallelogram. Therefore, a check on the answer in Example 1 is to compute

$$|\vec{u} \times \vec{v}| = \sqrt{4^2 + (-6)^2 + 2^2} = 2\sqrt{4 + 9 + 1} = 2\sqrt{14}.$$

This property of the vector cross product was recalled since it is the basis on which the definition (1) is justified.

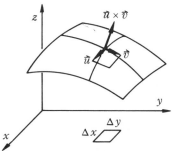

Fig. 12-7.1

In the region G, consider a typical elementary rectangle $\Delta(x, y) = \Delta x \, \Delta y$. At the point (x, y, z) on the surface, draw the vectors

$$\vec{u} = \vec{i} \, \Delta x + \vec{j} 0 + \vec{k} f_x(x, y) \, \Delta x,$$

$$\vec{v} = \vec{i} \, 0 + \vec{j} \, \Delta y + \vec{k} f_y(x, y) \, \Delta y.$$

These vectors are adjacent edges of a parallelogram that is in the tangent plane to the surface at (x, y, z), as shówn in Sec. 11-4. Also, this parallelogram projects onto $\Delta(x, y)$. Since

$$\vec{u} \times \vec{v} = \begin{vmatrix} \vec{i} & \vec{j} & \vec{k} \\ \Delta x & 0 & \Delta x f_x \\ 0 & \Delta y & \Delta y f_y \end{vmatrix} = (-\vec{i} f_x - \vec{j} f_y + \vec{k}) \, \Delta x \, \Delta y,$$

then

$$|\vec{u} \times \vec{v}| = \sqrt{f_x^2 + f_y^2 + 1} \, \Delta x \, \Delta y$$

approximates the area of the portion of the surface that projects onto $\Delta(x, y)$. Hence, the pattern is set for the sum-limit process of integration that leads to (1).

After setting up the double integral in rectangular coordinates, it may be advantageous to shift to polar coordinates for the iterated integral evaluation, as shown in the next example. This example also illustrates the care that must be taken always to set $\sqrt{a^2} = |a|$.

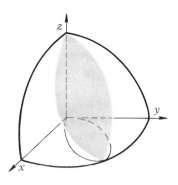

Fig. 12-7.2

Example 2. Find the area of the portion of the sphere $x^2 + y^2 + z^2 = 9$ which lies above the region G of the (x, y)-plane enclosed by
$$\rho = 3 \sin 2\theta \quad \text{for} \quad 0 \le \theta \le \pi/2.$$

Solution. From the equation of the sphere, $2x + 2zz_x = 0$ and $2y + 2zz_y = 0$, so that

$$z_x = -\frac{x}{z}, \quad z_y = -\frac{y}{z}.$$

Thus,

$$\sqrt{1 + z_x^2 + z_y^2} = \sqrt{1 + \frac{x^2}{z^2} + \frac{y^2}{z^2}} = \sqrt{\frac{z^2 + x^2 + y^2}{z^2}} = \sqrt{\frac{9}{z^2}} = \frac{3}{|z|}.$$

But for the upper portion of the sphere, $0 \le z = \sqrt{9 - x^2 - y^2}$, so that

$$\text{area} = \iint_G \frac{3}{\sqrt{9 - x^2 - y^2}} \, d(x, y).$$

Since the iterated integral in rectangular coordinates is somewhat involved, the shift to polar coordinates is made. Since $x^2 + y^2 = \rho^2$ and the element of area is $\rho \, d\rho \, d\theta$ (and not just $d\rho \, d\theta$), then

$$\text{area} = \int_0^{\pi/2} \int_0^{3 \sin 2\theta} \frac{3}{\sqrt{9 - \rho^2}} \rho \, d\rho \, d\theta$$

$$= -3 \int_0^{\pi/2} (9 - \rho^2)^{1/2} \Big]_0^{3 \sin 2\theta} \, d\theta$$

$$= -3 \int_0^{\pi/2} \{\sqrt{9 - 9 \sin^2 2\theta} - \sqrt{9}\} \, d\theta$$

$$= -9 \int_0^{\pi/2} \{\sqrt{1 - \sin^2 2\theta} - 1\} \, d\theta$$

$$= 9 \int_0^{\pi/2} d\theta - 9 \int_0^{\pi/2} \sqrt{\cos^2 2\theta} \, d\theta$$

$$= \frac{9}{2}\pi - 9 \int_0^{\pi/2} |\cos 2\theta| \, d\theta.$$

Since $\cos A$ is positive in the first quadrant but negative in the second quadrant, then

$$\text{area} = \frac{9}{2}\pi - 9 \left\{ \int_0^{\pi/4} \cos 2\theta \, d\theta + \int_{\pi/4}^{\pi/2} - \cos 2\theta \, d\theta \right\}$$

$$= \frac{9}{2}\pi - 9,$$

as should be checked. Also check that the careless replacement of $\sqrt{\cos^2 2\theta}$ by $\cos 2\theta$ would have given the answer $\frac{9}{2}\pi$, which is the area of all of the spherical surface over the first quadrant of the (x, y)-plane,

Problem 1. A sphere $x^2 + y^2 + z^2 = (2a)^2$ and a cylinder $x^2 + z^2 = 2ax$ are given.

a. Show that the intersection of these surfaces projects onto the (x, y)-plane as the portion of the parabola $y^2 + 2ax = 4a^2$ having $x \ge 0$ and the segment joining $(0, -2a, 0)$ and $(0, 2a, 0)$.

b. Find the area of the portion of the cylindrical surface inside the sphere.

Problem 2. Find the area of the portion of the sphere $x^2 + y^2 + z^2 = a^2$ inside the cylinder:

a. $x^2 + y^2 = ay$.
b. $\rho = a \cos 2\theta$, $\quad -\pi/4 \le \theta \le \pi/4$.
c. $\rho = (a/2)(1 - \cos \theta)$, $\quad -\pi \le \theta \le \pi$. [Hint: $1 - \cos \theta = 2 \sin^2 (\theta/2)$.]
d. $x^2 + 2y^2 = a^2$.

Problem 3. Change Prob. 2a to find the area of the portion of the cylinder inside the sphere. [Hint: Project the first octant portion on the (y, z)-plane and adjust formula (1) appropriately.]

Problem 4. Find the total surface area of the solid inside the sphere $x^2 + y^2 + z^2 = 2a^2$ and the cone $z = \sqrt{x^2 + y^2}$.

Problem 5. Show that the portion of the cone $z = a\sqrt{x^2 + y^2}$, $a > 0$, which projects onto a region G of the (x, y)-plane has area $= \sqrt{1 + a^2}$ (area G).

Problem 6. Find the area above the triangle with vertices $(0, 0, 0)$, $(b, 0, 0)$, and $(b, h, 0)$ and on the surface:

a. $z = x^2 + y$.   b. $z = x + y^2$.

Problem 7. Find the area of the ellipse on the plane $Ax + By + Cz + D = 0$ and inside the cylinders:

a. $x^2 + y^2 = a^2$.   b. $x^2 + z^2 = a^2$.

Problem 8. Show that the areas on the sphere $x^2 + y^2 + z^2 = a^2$ and the cylinder $x^2 + z^2 = a^2$ between the parallel planes $y = c$ and $y = c + h$ for $-a \leq c \leq c + h \leq a$, are the same.

Problem 9. Find the total surface area of the solid common to $x^2 + y^2 \leq a^2$ and $x^2 + z^2 \leq a^2$.

12-8. Reversing Order of Integration

An iterated integral in which all limits of integration are constants may by evaluated by performing integration in either order. This is so because both iterated integrals are equal to the double integral over a rectangle. Thus,

$$\int_a^b \int_c^d f(x, y) \, dy \, dx = \int_c^d \int_a^b f(x, y) \, dx \, dy = \iint_R f(x, y) \, d(x,y),$$

where R is the rectangle $a \leq x \leq b$, $c \leq y \leq d$.

If, however, the inside integral has variable limits of integration, then some additional analysis is necessary. For example,

$$(1) \qquad \int_0^1 \int_0^x (x - y)y \, dy \, dx = \int_0^1 \left[\frac{xy^2}{2} - \frac{y^3}{3} \right]_{y=0}^{y=x} dx$$

$$= \int_0^1 \left[\frac{x^3}{2} - \frac{x^3}{3} \right] dx = \frac{1}{24}, \quad \text{but}$$

$$\int_0^x \int_0^1 (x - y)y \, dx \, dy = \int_0^x \left[\frac{x^2}{2}y - y^2 x \right]_{x=0}^{x=1} dy$$

$$= \int_0^x \left(\frac{y}{2} - y^2 \right) dy = \frac{x^2}{4} - \frac{x^3}{3},$$

and the results are not the same.

Whenever the inside integral has variable limits of integration, the order of integration may, however, be reversed, but the limits of integration must be adjusted (as shown below). The technique will be illustrated by using (1).

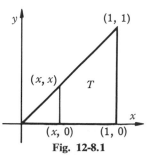

Fig. 12-8.1

First select a fixed x, with $0 \leq x \leq 1$. Then the inside integral of (1) is over the line segment $(x, 0)$ to (x, x), as shown in Fig. 12-8.1. The set of points on all such segments (as x varies from $x = 0$ to $x = 1$) make up the triangle T of Fig. 12-8.1. Hence, the iterated integral of (1) is equal to the double integral over T; that is,

$$(2) \qquad \int_0^1 \int_0^x (x - y)y \, dy \, dx = \iint_T (x - y)y \, d(x, y).$$

Now this double integral is equal to an integral iterated in the other order,

$$\iint (x - y)y \, dx \, dy,$$

but the limits of integration must be supplied properly. Since the final integration is with respect to y, then y must have constant limits. Any point (x, y) of T has $0 \leq y \leq 1$. With y fixed, $0 \leq y \leq 1$, then a point (x, y) of the triangle must have x such that $y \leq x \leq 1$, as shown in Fig. 12-8.2. Thus, also

$$\int_0^1 \int_y^1 (x - y)y \, dx \, dy = \iint_T (x - y)y \, d(x, y).$$

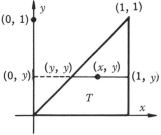

Fig. 12-8.2

Hence, from (2),

$$\int_0^1 \int_0^x (x - y)y \, dy \, dx = \int_0^1 \int_y^1 (x - y)y \, dx \, dy.$$

As confirmation, show that this second iterated integral has the same value, $1/24$, that the first has.

The result of the following example will be used in Sec. 13-16.

Example 1. Given that $f(y)$ is continuous on $0 \leq y \leq 1$, let

$$E = \int_0^1 \int_0^x (x - y)f(y) \, dy \, dx - \tfrac{1}{2} \int_0^1 (1 - y)f(y) \, dy.$$

Show there is a number η such that $0 \leq \eta \leq 1$ and

$$E = -\tfrac{1}{12}f(\eta).$$

Solution. First reverse the order of integration in the iterated integral:

$$\int_0^1 \int_0^x (x - y)f(y) \, dy \, dx = \int_0^1 \int_y^1 (x - y)f(y) \, dx \, dy =$$

$$= \int_0^1 f(y) \left[\int_y^1 (x - y)\, dx \right] dy$$

$$= \int_0^1 f(y) \left[\frac{(x - y)^2}{2} \right]_{x=y}^{x=1} dy$$

$$= \frac{1}{2} \int_0^1 (1 - y)^2 f(y)\, dy.$$

Thus,

$$E = \frac{1}{2} \left\{ \int_0^1 (1 - y)^2 f(y)\, dy - \int_0^1 (1 - y) f(y)\, dy \right\}$$

$$= \frac{1}{2} \int_0^1 [(1 - y)^2 - (1 - y)] f(y)\, dy = -\frac{1}{2} \int_0^1 y(1 - y) f(y)\, dy.$$

Since $y(1 - y)$ does not change sign on $0 \le y \le 1$, then by the Second Law of the Mean for Integrals (Prob. 13, Sec. 3-12) there is a number η such that $0 \le \eta \le 1$ and

$$\int_0^1 y(1 - y) f(y)\, dy = f(\eta) \int_0^1 y(1 - y)\, dy$$

$$= \tfrac{1}{6} f(\eta).$$

Not forgetting the $-\frac{1}{2}$, the desired expression for E is obtained.

Example 2. Evaluate $\int_0^1 \int_{2y}^2 \sin x^2\, dx\, dy.$

Solution. The Table of Integrals contains no formula for

$$\int \sin x^2\, dx.$$

A discussion of this omission is given in Sec. 13-15. Hence, try reversing the order of integration. This time, y has constant limits $y = 0$ and $y = 1$. Take a point $(0, y)$ of the unit interval on the y-axis and note that x must then be limited by $2y \le x \le 2$, as shown in Fig. 12-8.3. Thus, the appropriate triangle T has its hypotenuse on the line $2y = x$; that is, $y = \frac{1}{2}x$. It should then be carefully checked that the reversal of order of integration yields

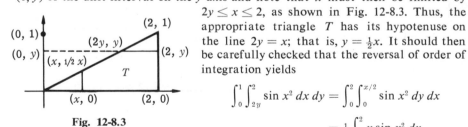

Fig. 12-8.3

$$\int_0^1 \int_{2y}^2 \sin x^2\, dx\, dy = \int_0^2 \int_0^{x/2} \sin x^2\, dy\, dx$$

$$= \tfrac{1}{2} \int_0^2 x \sin x^2\, dx.$$

This integral is easily evaluated, and gives the answer $\frac{1}{4}(1 - \cos 4)$.

Problem 1. Establish each of the following:

a. $\int_0^1 \int_0^{2x} f(x, y)\, dy\, dx = \int_0^2 \int_{y/2}^1 f(x, y)\, dx\, dy.$

b. $\int_0^1 \int_{2x}^2 f(x, y)\, dy\, dx = \int_0^2 \int_0^{y/2} f(x, y)\, dx\, dy.$ [Hint: See Fig. 2-1.3.]

c. $\displaystyle\int_1^2 \int_1^x f(x, y)\, dy\, dx = \int_1^2 \int_y^2 f(x, y)\, dx\, dy.$

d. $\displaystyle\int_1^2 \int_1^{x^2} f(x, y)\, dy\, dx = \int_1^4 \int_{\sqrt{y}}^2 f(x, y)\, dx\, dy.$

e. $\displaystyle\int_0^{\pi/2} \int_0^{\sin x} f(x, y)\, dy\, dx = \int_0^1 \int_{\sin^{-1} y}^{\pi/2} f(x, y)\, dx\, dy.$

f. $\displaystyle\int_0^{\pi} \int_0^{\sin x} f(x, y)\, dy\, dx = \int_0^1 \int_{\sin^{-1} y}^{\pi - \sin^{-1} y} f(x, y)\, dx\, dy.$

Problem 2. Work each of the following as it is and then again after interchanging the order of integration:

a. $\displaystyle\int_0^1 \int_0^{\tan^{-1} x} x\, dy\, dx = \frac{1}{2}\left(\frac{\pi}{2} - 1\right).$ c. $\displaystyle\int_0^1 \int_0^{\cos^{-1} x} y\, dy\, dx = \frac{\pi}{2} - 1.$

b. $\displaystyle\int_0^1 \int_x^1 \frac{dy\, dx}{1 + y^2} = \ln \sqrt{2}.$ d. $\displaystyle\int_0^2 \int_0^{\sqrt{2x - x^2}} y\, dy\, dx = \frac{2}{3}.$

e. $\displaystyle\int_0^1 \int_{x^2/4}^{x^2} x\, dy\, dx + \int_1^2 \int_{x^2/4}^1 x\, dy\, dx = \frac{3}{4}.$

Problem 3. Save the solution of this problem for later use in the note to Prob. 1, Sec. 13-16.

Let $f(t)$ be such that its fourth derivative $f^4(t)$ is continuous on $0 \le t \le 1$. Show that:

a. $\displaystyle\int_0^1 \int_0^x (x - t)^3 f^4(t)\, dt\, dx = \frac{1}{4} \int_0^1 (1 - t)^4 f^4(t)\, dt.$

b. $\displaystyle\int_{-1}^0 \int_0^x (x - t)^3 f^4(t)\, dt\, dx = -\int_{-1}^0 \int_x^0 (x - t)^3 f^4(t)\, dt\, dx$

$\displaystyle\qquad\qquad\qquad\qquad = -\int_{-1}^0 \int_{-1}^t (x - t)^3 f^4(t)\, dx\, dt.$

[Note: The first integral was written in the second form so both variables would increase from their smallest to their largest limit.]

c. With

$$E = \frac{1}{3!} \left\{ \int_{-1}^1 \int_0^x (x - t)^3 f^4(t)\, dt \right.$$
$$\left. - \frac{1}{3}\left[\int_0^{-1} (-1 - t)^3 f^4(t)\, dt + \int_0^1 (1 - t)^3 f^4(t)\, dt \right] \right\},$$

show that

$$E = -\frac{1}{3 \cdot 4!} \int_{-1}^1 g(t) f^4(t)\, dt, \quad \text{where}$$

$$g(t) = \begin{cases} (1 + t)^3(1 - 3t) & \text{if } -1 \le t \le 0, \\ (1 - t)^3(1 + 3t) & \text{if } 0 \le t \le 1. \end{cases}$$

d. Show there is a number ξ such that $-1 < \xi < 1$ and

$$E = -\frac{1}{90} f^4(\xi).$$

12-9. Triple Integrals

In three-dimensional space, consider a solid V and let f be a continuous function defined at each point of V. Divide V up into a number of small solids $\Delta_1 V, \Delta_2 V, \ldots, \Delta_n V$. Multiply the value of f at some point in each $\Delta_k V$ by the number of cubic units in $\Delta_k V$. Sum such products from $k = 1$ to $k = n$. Take the limit of these sums as the dimensions of each small volume approach zero. This limit, assumed to exist, is denoted by

$$\iiint_V f\, dV$$

and is called the **triple integral** of f over V.

As an example let V be a solid ball with surface

$$x^2 + y^2 + z^2 = a^2$$

and made of homogeneous material of density δ. Let a particle of mass m be located at the point $(0, 0, h)$, with $h > a$. The $\vec{i}$-, $\vec{j}$-, and $\vec{k}$-components of the attraction of the ball on the particle may be expressed as triple integrals. Think of a point (x, y, z) in the ball. The distance between this point and the particle at $(0, 0, h)$ is

$$\sqrt{x^2 + y^2 + (h - z)^2}.$$

A small piece of volume $\Delta x\, \Delta y\, \Delta z$ containing (x, y, z) then has the mass $\delta\, \Delta x\, \Delta y\, \Delta z$. This piece attracts the particle by a force of magnitude approximately

(1) $$K \frac{m\, \delta\, \Delta x\, \Delta y\, \Delta z}{[\sqrt{x^2 + y^2 + (h - z)^2}\,]^2} = K \frac{\text{product of masses}}{(\text{distance})^2}$$

for some constant K, depending upon the units used. A force is a vector quantity, so the separate attractions add vectorially, but the components in any fixed direction add algebraically. The element of the force vector from $(0, 0, h)$ toward (x, y, z) has $\vec{k}$-component equal to the magnitude (1) times the cosine of the angle this force makes with $-\vec{k}$; namely,

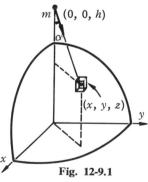

$$\cos \alpha = \frac{h - z}{\sqrt{x^2 + y^2 + (h - z)^2}},$$

as shown in Fig. 12-9.1. Hence, the element of the $\vec{k}$-component of attraction is

$$K(-\vec{k})m\, \delta\, \frac{h - z}{[x^2 + y^2 + (h - z)^2]^{3/2}} \Delta x\, \Delta y\, \Delta z.$$

By summing such elements and then letting each dimension of the elements of volume approach zero, the $\vec{k}$-component of attraction is

Fig. 12-9.1

(2) $$-K\vec{k}m\, \delta \iiint_V \frac{h - z}{[x^2 + y^2 + (h - z)^2]^{3/2}}\, d(x, y, z).$$

Such a triple integral is evaluated by using iterated integrals, just as for double integrals, but the limits of integration must be determined carefully. First think of a fixed value of x such that $-a \le x \le a$. Then a point $(x, y, 0)$ will be in the equatorial section of the ball if

$$-\sqrt{a^2 - x^2} \le y \le \sqrt{a^2 - x^2}.$$

With x and y so fixed, a point (x, y, z) will be in the ball if

$$-\sqrt{a^2 - x^2 - y^2} \le z \le \sqrt{a^2 - x^2 - y^2}.$$

Thus, the ball is

$$\{(x, y, z) \mid -a \le x \le a, \ -\sqrt{a^2 - x^2} \le y \le \sqrt{a^2 - x^2},$$
$$-\sqrt{a^2 - x^2 - y^2} \le z \le \sqrt{a^2 - x^2 - y^2}\}.$$

Thus, the triple integral in (2) may be expressed as the 3-fold iterated integral

(3) $$\int_{-a}^{a} \int_{-\sqrt{a^2-x^2}}^{\sqrt{a^2-x^2}} \int_{-\sqrt{a^2-x^2-y^2}}^{\sqrt{a^2-x^2-y^2}} \frac{h - z}{[x^2 + y^2 + (h-z)^2]^{3/2}} \, dz \, dy \, dx.$$

The above discussion was entirely in rectangular coordinates. Since the ball is a sphere, it is natural to expect that spherical coordintes (r, θ, ϕ) (see Sec. 10-11) would lead to a simpler integral. Now the ball may be considered as

$$\{(r, \theta, \phi) \mid 0 \le r \le a, \ 0 \le \theta \le 2\pi, \ 0 \le \phi \le \pi\},$$

and the integral (3) transforms into

(4) $$\int_{0}^{a} \int_{0}^{2\pi} \int_{0}^{\pi} [\text{integrand}] \, d(r, \theta, \phi).$$

But the integrand must be in (r, θ, ϕ) terms and the proper expression for $d(r, \theta, \phi)$ used. As given in Sec. 10-11,

(5) $$x = r \sin \phi \cos \theta, \ y = r \sin \phi \sin \theta, \ z = r \cos \phi,$$

so that

$$\text{integrand} = \frac{h - r \cos \phi}{[(r \sin \phi \cos \theta)^2 + (r \sin \phi \sin \theta)^2 + (h - r \cos \phi)^2]^{3/2}}$$

$$= \frac{h - r \cos \phi}{[r^2 + h^2 - 2hr \cos \phi]^{3/2}}.$$

As for $d(r, \theta, \phi)$, first consider a point (r, θ, ϕ), hold r and ϕ constant, and let θ increase by $\Delta\theta$ radians. As it does so, an arc of a circle is traced, but note that the center is on the z-axis and the radius is $r \sin \theta$, as shown in Fig. 12-9.2. Thus, the length of the arc is

$$r(\sin \phi) \, \Delta\theta.$$

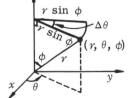

Fig. 12-9.2

Next, hold r and θ fixed and increase ϕ to $\phi + \Delta\phi$. Again an arc of a circle is obtained, but the center is at the origin and the radius is r. This arc has length

$$r\,\Delta\phi.$$

Finally, hold θ and ϕ fixed and let r increase by an increment Δr. Hence, $\Delta(r, \theta, \phi)$ is taken to be

$$\Delta(r, \theta, \phi) = (r \sin \phi\,\Delta\theta)(r\,\Delta\phi)\,\Delta r = r^2 \sin \phi\,\Delta\theta\,\Delta\phi\,\Delta r.$$

The integral (4) is thus

$$\int_0^a \int_0^{2\pi} \int_0^{\pi} \frac{h - r \cos \phi}{[r^2 + h^2 - 2hr \cos \phi]^{3/2}} r^2 \sin \phi \, d\phi \, d\theta \, dr.$$

Even though the limits of integration are constants and the integrand is simpler than in (3), it is better to use the third standard space coordinate system (as called for in Prob. 1 below).

Triple integrals are used for many purposes other than attraction. Also, higher order integrals often appear in applications, but further details will not be given here.

Problem 1. Go through an analysis to see that the integral for obtaining the $\vec{k}$-component of attraction in the above discussion may be expressed in cylindrical coordinates as

$$\int_0^{2\pi} \int_0^a \int_{-\sqrt{a^2-\rho^2}}^{\sqrt{a^2-\rho^2}} \frac{h - z}{[\rho^2 + (h - z)^2]^{3/2}} \rho \, dz \, d\rho \, d\theta, \text{ or}$$

$$\int_0^{2\pi} \int_{-a}^a \int_0^{\sqrt{a^2-z^2}} \frac{h - z}{[\rho^2 + (h - z)^2]^{3/2}} \rho \, d\rho \, dz \, d\theta.$$

Evaluate either of these integrals. [Answer: $\frac{4}{3}a^3/h^2$, which shows that the attraction is the same as if the ball were concentrated at its center.]

Problem 2. From symmetry considerations, the $\vec{i}$- and $\vec{j}$-components of attraction of the ball on the particle are zero. Show this analytically.

Problem 3. The Jacobian of the transformation (5) is, by definition, the determinant

$$\begin{vmatrix} x_r & x_\phi & x_\theta \\ y_r & y_\phi & y_\theta \\ z_r & z_\phi & z_\theta \end{vmatrix},$$

in which the subscripts mean partial derivatives. Show that this determinant has value $r^2 \sin \phi$, the term used in $d(r, \theta, \phi) = r^2 \sin \phi \, dr \, d\theta \, d\phi$.

Problem 4. The length of a line segment is used to find the area of a circle $x^2 + y^2 = a^2$ from

$$\int_{-a}^a \sqrt{a^2 - y^2} \, dy.$$

The area of a circle is used to find the volume of a sphere $x^2 + y^2 + z^2 = a^2$ from

$$\int_{-a}^{a} \pi(\sqrt{a^2 - z^2})^2 \, dz.$$

Find the "volume" of a 4-dimensional sphere $x^2 + y^2 + z^2 + w^2 = a^2$.

Problem 5. A spherical shell of homogeneous material has inner radius a and outer radius b. The problem is to show that the attraction of the shell on a particle of mass m is:

    (i) Zero if the particle is within the cavity.

    (ii) The same as though the mass of the shell were concentrated at its center if the particle is outside the shell.

Locate the shell so its center is at the origin and the positive z-axis passes through the particle. Figure 12-9.3 represents a cross section in any plane containing the z-

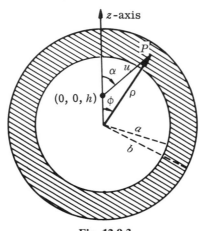

Fig. 12-9.3

axis. The particle is at the point $(0, 0, h)$. If the particle is within the shell, then $0 \le h \le a$ (as shown in the figure), but if the particle is outside the shell, then $h > b$. By symmetry and homogeneity, the $\vec{i}$- and $\vec{j}$-components of attraction are zero.

    a. Show that the $\vec{k}$-component of attraction is expressed in spherical coordinates as

$$F_k = \vec{k} K \, \delta m \int_a^b \int_0^{2\pi} \int_0^{\pi} \frac{\cos \alpha}{u^2} \rho^2 \sin \phi \, d\phi \, d\theta \, d\rho,$$

with the variables u and α as illustrated in the figure. K is the constant of attraction and δ is the density constant.

    b. Show that

$$u^2 = h^2 + \rho^2 - 2h\rho \cos \phi \quad \text{and} \quad \rho^2 = h^2 + u^2 + 2hu \cos \alpha$$

and that:

        If $\phi = 0$, then $u = \sqrt{(h - \rho)^2} = |h - \rho|$, and

        If $\phi = \pi$, then $u = \sqrt{(h + \rho)^2} = h + \rho$.

c. With ρ fixed, show that

$$u \, du = h\rho \sin \phi \, d\phi.$$

d. Check the following evaluation of the innermost integral of part a:

$$\int_0^\pi \frac{\cos \alpha}{u^2} \sin \phi \, d\phi = \int_{|h-\rho|}^{h+\rho} \frac{1}{u^2} \frac{\rho^2 - h^2 - u^2}{2hu} \frac{u}{h\rho} \, du$$

$$= \text{etc.} = \begin{cases} 0 & \text{if } 0 \le h \le a \\ -2/h^2 & \text{if } h > b. \end{cases}$$

[Hint: Since $a \le \rho \le b$, then $|h - \rho| = \rho - h$ if $0 \le h < a$, but on the other hand, $|h - \rho| = h - \rho$ if $h > b$.]

e. Finish the problem.

Sequences and Series

Chapter 13

13-1. Precautions

Everyone knows that

$$1 - \frac{1}{2} + \frac{1}{3} = 1 + \frac{1}{3} - \frac{1}{2} = \frac{4}{3} - \frac{1}{2} = \frac{5}{6},$$

$$1 - \frac{1}{2} + \frac{1}{3} - \frac{1}{4} = 1 + \frac{1}{3} - \left(\frac{1}{2} + \frac{1}{4}\right) = \frac{4}{3} - \frac{3}{4} = \frac{7}{12},$$

and it would only take patience to compute

$$1 - \frac{1}{2} + \frac{1}{3} - \cdots + \frac{1}{99} - \frac{1}{100} = \left(1 + \frac{1}{3} + \cdots + \frac{1}{99}\right)$$

$$- \left(\frac{1}{2} + \frac{1}{4} + \cdots + \frac{1}{100}\right).$$

What is meant, however, by

(1) $$1 - \frac{1}{2} + \frac{1}{3} - \frac{1}{4} + \frac{1}{5} - \frac{1}{6} + \cdots,$$

proceeding endlessly with the nth term $(-1)^{n+1}/n$? Is, for example, this infinite sum equal, in some sense, to

(2) $$\left(1 + \frac{1}{3} + \frac{1}{5} + \cdots\right) - \left(\frac{1}{2} + \frac{1}{4} + \frac{1}{6} + \cdots\right)?$$

The purpose of this chapter is to develop methods for handling infinite sums. The purpose of this section to indicate why careful definitions are necessary in extending finite sums to infinite sums.

In Fig. 13-1.1, the curve has equation $y = 1/x$. Imagine the figure extended to include n rectangles. The sum of the areas of these n rectangles is then greater than the area under the curve from $x = 1$ to $x = n + 1$, so that

$$1 + \frac{1}{2} + \frac{1}{3} + \cdots + \frac{1}{n} > \int_1^{n+1} \frac{1}{x} \, dx = \ln x \Big]_1^{n+1} = \ln (n+1).$$

Hence, if some large number G is given, then by taking N such that $\ln (N + 1) > G$ it follows that:

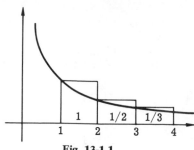

Fig. 13-1.1

For any integer $n \geq N$,

$$1 + \frac{1}{2} + \frac{1}{3} + \cdots + \frac{1}{n} > \ln(n+1) \geq \ln(N+1) > G.$$

Thus, any preassigned number G may be exceeded by adding a finite number of reciprocals of integers. This will be symbolized later as

$$1 + \frac{1}{2} + \frac{1}{3} + \cdots = \infty \quad \text{and as} \quad \sum_{k=1}^{\infty} \frac{1}{k} = \infty.$$

Again, let G be a large number, but then look at $2G$ and take N so that $\ln(N+1) > 2G$. Then

$$1 + \frac{1}{2} + \frac{1}{3} + \cdots + \frac{1}{n} > 2G \text{ if } n \geq N; \text{ that is,}$$

$$\frac{1}{2} + \frac{1}{4} + \frac{1}{6} + \cdots + \frac{1}{2n} > G \text{ if } n \geq N,$$

and also

$$1 + \frac{1}{3} + \frac{1}{5} + \cdots + \frac{1}{2n-1} > G \text{ if } n \geq N,$$

since $1 > \frac{1}{2}, \frac{1}{3} > \frac{1}{4}, \ldots, 1/(2n-1) > 1/2n$. Hence, symbolically,

$$\sum_{k=1}^{\infty} \frac{1}{2k} = \infty \quad \text{and} \quad \sum_{k=1}^{\infty} \frac{1}{2k-1} = \infty.$$

The positive and negative terms of (1) may therefore not be collected as in (2), for this would lead to $\infty - \infty$.

This still leaves the question of whether a reasonable meaning may be given the unending process (1).

First consider adding an even number of terms of (1) and set

$$s_{2n} = 1 - \frac{1}{2} + \frac{1}{3} - \frac{1}{4} + \cdots + \frac{1}{2n-1} - \frac{1}{2n}.$$

This is a finite sum, so that any of the ordinary arithmetic operations may be applied to it. For example,

$$s_{2n} = \left(1 - \frac{1}{2}\right) + \left(\frac{1}{3} - \frac{1}{4}\right) + \cdots + \left(\frac{1}{2n-1} - \frac{1}{2n}\right)$$

$$= \frac{1}{2} + \frac{1}{3 \cdot 4} + \cdots + \frac{1}{(2n-1)\,2n} > \frac{1}{2},$$

or, by a different grouping,

$$s_{2n} = 1 - \left(\frac{1}{2} - \frac{1}{3}\right) - \left(\frac{1}{4} - \frac{1}{5}\right) - \cdots - \left(\frac{1}{2n-2} - \frac{1}{2n-1}\right) - \frac{1}{2n}$$

$$= 1 - \frac{1}{2 \cdot 3} - \frac{1}{4 \cdot 5} - \cdots - \frac{1}{(2n-2)(2n-1)} - \frac{1}{2n} < 1.$$

Now add to s_{2n} the next two terms to obtain

$$s_{2n+2} = s_{2n} + \frac{1}{2n+1} - \frac{1}{2n+2} = s_{2n} + \frac{1}{(2n+1)(2n+2)} > s_{2n}.$$

Hence,

$$\tfrac{1}{2} \leq s_2 < s_4 < s_6 \cdots < s_{2n} < s_{2n+2} < 1.$$

Therefore (as shown in the next section), this sequence has a limit; that is, there is a number s, with $\frac{1}{2} < s \leq 1$, such that

$$\lim_{n \to \infty} s_{2n} = s.$$

Since $s_{2n+1} = s_{2n} + 1/(2n+1)$, then also

$$\lim_{n \to \infty} s_{2n+1} = \lim_{n \to \infty} \left(s_{2n} + \frac{1}{2n+1}\right)$$

$$= \lim_{n \to \infty} s_{2n} + \lim_{n \to \infty} \frac{1}{2n+1} = \lim_{n \to \infty} s_{2n} = s.$$

As defined later, the value s will be assigned to (1) and this will be written*

(3) $$s = 1 - \frac{1}{2} + \frac{1}{3} - \frac{1}{4} + \cdots + \frac{1}{2n-1} - \frac{1}{2n} + \cdots.$$

Thus, (1) will be assigned a meaning, but (as shown above) it will not be permissible to add all the positive terms, then all the negative terms, and subtract to get the sum s. Moreover, it will not be permissible to rearrange the terms indiscriminately into a single series, even though each term is used once and only once. This is shown by the following manipulation, carried out as if (which is not so) the ordinary arithmetic of finite sums applied as well to infinite sums:

$$s = 1 - \frac{1}{2} - \frac{1}{4} + \frac{1}{3} - \frac{1}{6} - \frac{1}{8} + \frac{1}{5} - \frac{1}{10}$$

$$- \frac{1}{12} + \frac{1}{7} - \frac{1}{14} - \frac{1}{16} + \frac{1}{9} - \cdots.$$

*In Sec. 13-10 it is shown that $s = \ln 2$.

Note that each term in (3) is used once and only once, but two negative terms are together, followed by the first unused positive term, then the next two negative terms, etc. By continuing as though the equality held,

$$s = \left(1 - \frac{1}{2}\right) - \frac{1}{4} + \left(\frac{1}{3} - \frac{1}{6}\right) - \frac{1}{8} + \left(\frac{1}{5} - \frac{1}{10}\right)$$

$$- \frac{1}{12} + \left(\frac{1}{7} - \frac{1}{14}\right) - \frac{1}{16} + \cdots$$

$$= \frac{1}{2} - \frac{1}{4} + \frac{1}{6} - \frac{1}{8} + \frac{1}{10} - \frac{1}{12} + \frac{1}{14} - \frac{1}{16} + \cdots$$

$$= \frac{1}{2}\left(1 - \frac{1}{2} + \frac{1}{3} - \frac{1}{4} + \frac{1}{5} - \frac{1}{6} + \frac{1}{7} - \frac{1}{8} + \cdots\right)$$

$$= \frac{1}{2} s.$$

This was done to show that (finite) arithmetic is not always permissible for infinite terms.

13-2. Sequences

In common usage sequence, series, and succession are synonymous, according to The American College Dictionary. A distinction is, however, made in mathematics. A **sequence** is a function whose domain consists of all integers greater than or equal to some integer (usually 0 or 1). For example,

(1) $$1, \frac{1}{2}, \frac{1}{2^2}, \frac{1}{2^3}, \dots, \frac{1}{2^n}, \dots.$$

is understood as indicating the sequence (function) f defined by

$$f(n) = \frac{1}{2^n}, \quad n = 0, 1, 2, \dots.$$

It is customary to use subscript notation:

$$a_n = \frac{1}{2^n}, \quad n = 0, 1, 2, \dots,$$

rather than functional notation. Since the law of formation is of primary importance, this sequence may be indicated by

$$\left\{\frac{1}{2^n}\right\}.$$

Whereas a sequence $\{a_n\}$ may be displayed as

$$a_1, a_2, a_3, \dots, a_n, \dots,$$

the word "series" in mathematical context is used for the formalism

$$a_1 + a_2 + a_3 + \cdots + a_n + \cdots,$$

or, more concisely,

$$\sum_{n=1}^{\infty} a_n.$$

The question of whether or not a series is assigned a "sum" is described in the next section and depends specifically on the properties of sequences discussed in the remainder of the present section.

A geometric model of a sequence $\{a_n\}$ is the set of line segments from the points (n, a_n), $n = 1, 2, 3, \ldots$ perpendicular to the x-axis. Figure 13-2.1 is the beginning of such a graph for the sequence $\{a_n\}$, where

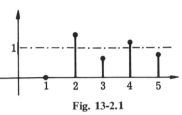

Fig. 13-2.1

$$a_n = \frac{n + (-1)^n}{n}, \quad n = 1, 2, 3, \ldots; \quad \text{that is,}$$

(2) $$0, \frac{3}{2}, \frac{2}{3}, \frac{5}{4}, \frac{4}{5}, \frac{7}{6}. \ldots$$

For any number $\epsilon > 0$, the spikes having tops above the line $y = 1 + \epsilon$ or below the line $y = 1 - \epsilon$ are finite in number. Hence, there is an integer N such that,

whenever $n \geq N$, then $1 - \epsilon < \dfrac{n + (-1)^n}{n} < 1 + \epsilon.$

In fact, this holds for the sequence (2), if $N > 1/\epsilon$.

DEFINITION 13-2.1. *A sequence $\{a_n\}$ is said to have a number a as limit, and*

$$\lim_{n \to \infty} a_n = a$$

is written, provided:
For each number $\epsilon > 0$ (no matter how small) there is an integer N such that,

whenever $n \geq N$, then $|a_n - a| < \epsilon.$

A sequence that has a limit is said to be **convergent** *and to converge to its limit. A sequence that is not convergent is said to be* **divergent**.

Another geometric representation of a sequence $\{a_n\}$ is to use a single coordinate line and to label with n the point having coordinate a_n. The sequence (2) is so represented in Fig. 13-2.2. In this model, a convergent sequence is visualized as having at most a finite number of the representing points outside any interval with center at $x = a$, as in Fig. 13-2.3. The sequence

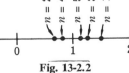

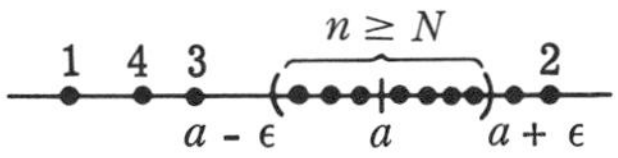

Fig. 13-2.2

Fig. 13-2.3

(3)
$$1, \frac{3}{2}, \frac{1}{3}, \frac{5}{4}, \frac{1}{5}, \frac{8}{7}, \ldots, \frac{1}{n} + \frac{1 + (-1)^n}{2}, \ldots$$

has one infinite cluster around $x = 0$ and another around $x = 1$. Hence, this sequence does not converge to 0 or to 1 or to any other number; that is, it is a divergent sequence.

THEOREM 13-2.1. *Given a sequence $\{a_n\}$ having the properties*

(4)
$$a_1 \le a_2 \le a_3 \le \cdots \le a_n \le \cdots,$$

and for some number B

(5)
$$a_n \le B, \quad n = 1, 2, 3, \ldots,$$

then this sequence converges to a number $a \le B$.

PROOF. This follows easily from the Axiom of Continuity (p. 37). For let S be the set defined by

$$S = \{a_n | n = 1, 2, 3, \ldots\}.$$

This is a nonempty set bounded above by B, so it has a least upper bound $a \le B$. Since a is an upper bound, then

$$a_n \le a, \quad n = 1, 2, 3, \cdots.$$

Since a is the least upper bound, then for each number $\epsilon > 0$ the number $a - \epsilon$ is not an upper bound, which means there is an integer N such that $a - \epsilon < a_N$. Hence, by using (4),

whenever $n \ge N$, then $a - \epsilon < a_N \le a_n \le a < a + \epsilon$.

Thus, by definition, the sequence $\{a_n\}$ converges to a.

This theorem will be used repeatedly, especially in connection with series.

From previous work (Sec. 3-8), it is understood how sequences $\{a_n\}$, $\{b_n\}$, and a number c may be used to form sequences

$$\{a_n + b_n\}, \quad \{a_n - b_n\}, \quad \{a_n b_n\}, \quad \{c a_n\}, \quad \{a_n + c\}$$

and, provided all terms of $\{b_n\}$ are nonzero, also

(6)
$$\left\{\frac{a_n}{b_n}\right\}.$$

If, however, $\{b_n\}$ has zero terms *but they are finite in number*, then it is convenient to consider (6) as the sequence of respective quotients beginning after the last zero term of $\{b_n\}$.

DEFINITIONS 13-2.2. *A sequence $\{a_n\}$ is said to be:*
1. *Bounded if there are numbers b and B such that*

$$b \le a_n \le B, \quad n = 1, 2, 3, \ldots.$$

2. *Increasing if $a_1 < a_2 < a_3 < \cdots$; **nondecreasing** if*

$$a_1 \leq a_2 \leq \cdots.$$

3. *Decreasing if* $a_1 > a_2 > a_3 > \cdots$; *nonincreasing if*

$$a_1 \geq a_2 \geq \cdots.$$

4. *A* **null** *sequence if it converges to zero; that is,*

$$\lim_{n \to \infty} a_n = 0.$$

Thus, Theorem 13-2.1 may be restated as:
A bounded nondecreasing sequence converges and its limit is less than or equal to each of its upper bounds.

THEOREM 13-2.2 *A sequence* $\{a_n\}$ *converges to* a *if and only if* $\{a_n - a\}$ *is a null sequence.*

PROOF. The statements
   1. $\{a_n\}$ converges to a, and
   2. $\{a_n - a\}$ is a null sequence
both mean:
   Corresponding to an arbitrary number $\epsilon > 0$, there is an N such that,

$$\text{whenever} \quad n \geq N, \quad \text{then} \quad |a_n - a| < \epsilon.$$

Thus, if either statement 1 or 2 is known to be true, the other is also true.

In Sec. 3-8, a theorem about limits of products and quotients was stated (and used) without proof. These missing proofs will be given after the following two lemmas on null sequences and a third lemma on non-null sequences.

LEMMA 1. *Any null sequence* $\{b_n\}$ *is bound. In particular, there is a number* B *such that*

$$|b_n| < B, \quad n = 1, 2, 3, \ldots.$$

PROOF. Corresponding to $\epsilon = 1$, let N be such that whenever $n \geq N$, then $|b_n| < 1$. Let B be the largest of the (finite) number of values

$$|b_1| + 1, \quad |b_2| + 1, \ldots, \quad |b_N| + 1.$$

Then each of $|b_1|, |b_2|, \ldots, |b_N|$ is $< B$, and $|b_n| < 1 \leq B$ for $n \geq N$. Thus, $|b_n| < B$ for $n = 1, 2, 3, \ldots, N, \ldots.$

LEMMA 2. *Given null sequences* $\{a_n\}$ *and* $\{b_n\}$, *then*
   (i) $\{a_n + b_n\}$, $\{a_n - b_n\}$,
   (ii) $\{a_n b_n\}$, *and*
   (iii) $\{c a_n\}$, *with* c *a constant*,
are also null sequences.

PROOF OF (i). Let $\epsilon > 0$ be arbitrary. Corresponding to $\epsilon/2$, let N_1 and N_2 be such that,

$$\text{whenever} \quad n \geq N_1, \quad \text{then} \quad |a_n| < \epsilon/2 \quad \text{and}$$

$$\text{whenever} \quad n \geq N_2, \quad \text{then} \quad |b_n| < \epsilon/2.$$

Let N be the larger of N_1 and N_2. Hence, whenever $n \geq N$, then both $|a_n| < \epsilon/2$ and $|b_n| < \epsilon/2$, so that

$$-\epsilon < -(|a_n| + |b_n|) \leq |a_n \pm b_n| \leq |a_n| + |b_n| < \epsilon.$$

Thus, $\{a_n + b_n\}$ and $\{a_n - b_n\}$ are both null sequences.

PROOF OF (ii). By Lemma 1, take B such that $|b_n| < B$, $n = 1, 2, 3, \ldots$. Let $\epsilon < 0$ be arbitrary. Corresponding to ϵ/B, let N be such that,

$$\text{whenever} \quad n \geq N, \quad \text{then} \quad |a_n| < \epsilon/B.$$

Thus, whenever $n \geq N$, then

$$|a_n b_n| = |a_n|\,|b_n| < \frac{\epsilon}{B}B = \epsilon.$$

Hence, $\{a_n b_n\}$ is a null sequence.

PROOF OF (iii). The proof of (ii) used $\{b_n\}$ only as a bounded sequence. Thus, (iii) follows by considering the (bounded) sequence all of whose terms are equal to c.

LEMMA 3. *Let $\{b_n\}$ be a convergent sequence converging to $b \neq 0$. Then $\{1/b_n\}$ is a convergent sequence converging to $1/b$; that is,*

$$(7) \qquad \lim_{n \to \infty} \frac{1}{b_n} = \frac{1}{\lim_{n \to \infty} b_n} = \frac{1}{b}, \quad b \neq 0.$$

PROOF. Since $b \neq 0$, then $|b| > 0$ and $\frac{1}{2}|b| > 0$. Corresponding to $\frac{1}{2}|b|$, let N_1 be such that,

$$\text{whenever} \quad n \geq N_1, \quad \text{then} \quad |b_n - b| < \frac{1}{2}|b|.$$

Hence, whenever $n \geq N_1$, then

$$|b| = |b - b_n + b_n| \leq |b - b_n| + |b_n| < \frac{1}{2}|b| + |b_n|; \text{ that is,}$$

$$|b_n| > \frac{1}{2}|b|.$$

Thus, $\{b_n\}$ has at most a finite number of zero terms. In particular, for all $n \geq N_1$, then $b_n \neq 0$ and $1/b_n$ is defined, and

$$\frac{1}{|b_n|} < \frac{2}{|b|}.$$

Let $\epsilon > 0$ be arbitrary. Corresponding to $(\epsilon/2)|b|^2$, let $N > N_1$ be such that,

$$\text{whenever} \quad n \geq N, \quad \text{then} \quad |b_n - b| < \frac{\epsilon}{2}|b|^2.$$

Hence, whenever $n \geq N$, then

$$\left| \frac{1}{b_n} - \frac{1}{b} \right| = \frac{|b - b_n|}{|b_n| \, |b|} \leq |b_n - b| \frac{2}{|b|^2} < \frac{\epsilon}{2} |b|^2 \frac{2}{|b|^2} = \epsilon.$$

This says that $\{1/b_n\}$ converges to $1/b$; that is, that (7) holds.

THEOREM 13-2.3. *Let $\{a_n\}$ and $\{b_n\}$ be convergent sequences converging to a and b, respectively:*

$$\lim_{n \to \infty} a_n = a \quad \text{and} \quad \lim_{n \to \infty} b_n = b.$$

Then $\{a_n \pm b_n\}$ and $\{a_n b_n\}$ are convergent sequences, with

(i) $\displaystyle \lim_{n \to \infty} (a_n \pm b_n) = \lim_{n \to \infty} a_n \pm \lim_{n \to \infty} b_n = a \pm b$ *and*

(ii) $\displaystyle \lim_{n \to \infty} (a_n b_n) = \left(\lim_{n \to \infty} a_n \right) \left(\lim_{n \to \infty} b_n \right) = ab.$

Moreover, if $b \neq 0$, then $\{a_n/b_n\}$ is a convergent sequence, with

(iii) $\displaystyle \lim_{n \to \infty} \frac{a_n}{b_n} = \frac{\lim_{n \to \infty} a_n}{\lim_{n \to \infty} b_n} = \frac{a}{b}.$

PROOF. Since $\{a_n - a\}$ and $\{b_n - b\}$ are null sequences, then by (i) of Lemma 2,

$$\{(a_n - a) + (b_n - b)\} = \{(a_n + b_n) - (a + b)\}$$

is a null sequence. This (by Theorem 13-2.2) means that $\{a_n + b_n\}$ converges to $a + b$; that is, (1) with plus holds. In the same way, (i) with minus holds.

Also, $\{(a_n - a)(b_n - b)\}$ is a null sequence, as are both $\{b(a_n - a)\}$ and $\{a(b_n - b)\}$ by (ii) and (iii) of Lemma 2. Hence, by Lemma 2(i) extended to three sequences,

$$\{(a_n - a)(b_n - b) + b(a_n - a) + a(b_n - b)\}$$

is a null sequence; that is,

$$\{(a_n b_n - a_n b - a b_n + ab) + (b a_n - ab) + (a b_n - ab)\} = \{a_n b_n - ab\}$$

is a null sequence. Hence, (ii) holds.

Now, with $b \neq 0$, $\{1/b_n\}$ converges to $1/b$ by Lemma 3, so that

$$\lim_{n \to \infty} \frac{a_n}{b_n} = \lim_{n \to \infty} \left(a_n \cdot \frac{1}{b_n} \right) = \left(\lim_{n \to \infty} a_n \right) \left(\lim_{n \to \infty} \frac{1}{b_n} \right) \quad \text{by (ii)}$$

$$= a \cdot \frac{1}{b} = \frac{a}{b},$$

so that (iii) holds.

DEFINITION 13-2.3. *A sequence $\{a_n\}$ is **tending to infinity** (or increasing **without bound**) and the notation*

$$\lim_{n \to \infty} a_n = +\infty$$

is used if corresponding to each number G (no matter how large) there is an N such that,

$$\text{whenever} \quad n \geq N, \quad \text{then} \quad a_n > G.$$

There is a similar definition of $\lim_{n \to \infty} a_n = -\infty$, obtained by replacing $a_n > G$ with $a_n < G$, with G thought of as negative with large absolute value. Even though the limit notation is used, it should be understood that:

If $\{a_n\}$ tends to $+\infty$ or to $-\infty$, then the sequence is divergent.

Note, however, that the sequence (3) of positive terms (on p. 494) is divergent, although it does not tend to $+\infty$. There are terms of

$$-1, +2, -3, +4, \ldots, (-1)^n n, \ldots$$

greater than any preassigned number, but this sequence does not tend to $+\infty$ or to $-\infty$ and it does not have a limit.

The verbosity "$\{a_n\}$ is a convergent sequence converging to a" is often simplified to

$$a_n \to a.$$

Also, $a_n \to +\infty$ will be understood as meaning that the sequence under consideration satisfies Definition 13-2.3.

A ready extension of Theorem 13-2.1 may now be stated (for reference later).

THEOREM 13-2.4. *A nondecreasing sequence converges if it is bounded above, but diverges to $+\infty$ if it is not bounded above.*

In examining the limit of a sequence, any finite number of terms at the beginning may be neglected. Hence, if either of the sequences $a_1, a_2, \ldots, a_n, \ldots$ or $a_m, a_{m+1}, a_{m+2}, \ldots, a_{m+1}, \ldots$ converges, then so does the other, and

(8) $$\lim_{n \to \infty} a_{m+n} = \lim_{m \to \infty} a_m.$$

For example,

$$\lim_{n \to \infty} \frac{1}{10 + n} = \lim_{n \to \infty} \frac{1}{n}.$$

Problem 1. Prove the theorems symbolized by:

a. If $a_n \to a$, then $\{a_n\}$ is bounded.

b. If $a_n \to a$ and $a_n \to b$, then $a = b$. [This justifies speaking of *the* limit of a convergent sequence.]

c. If $a_n > 0$ and $a_n \to 0$, then $1/a_n \to +\infty$.

d. If $a_n \to a \neq 0$, $b_n \neq 0$ but $b_n \to 0$, then $|a_n/b_n| \to +\infty$.

e. If $a_n \leq c_n \leq b_n$, with both $a_n \to a$ and $b_n \to a$, then $c_n \to a$.

f. If $a_n \leq b$ and $a_n \to a$, then $a \leq b$.

g. If $a_n \to a$ and $\{b_n\}$ is defined by $b_n = a_{n+3}$, then $b_n \to a$. [This is usually shortened to:

$$\text{If } a_n \to a, \text{ then } a_{n+3} \to a.]$$

h. If $a_n \to +\infty$ and k is a positive integer, then $a_{n+k} \to +\infty$.

i. A nonincreasing sequence is either convergent or tends to $-\infty$.

Problem 2. Let $a_1 = \sqrt{2}$, $a_2 = \sqrt{2 + \sqrt{2}}$, ..., $a_{n+1} = \sqrt{2 + a_n}$, ... Prove:

a. $a_1 < a_2 < a_3 < \cdots < a_n < \cdots$.

b. $a_n < 2$, $n = 1, 2, 3, \ldots$.

c. $a_n \to 2$. [Hint: a_n and a_{n+1} both approach a, $0 < a \le 2$ and $a_{n+1}^2 = 2 + a_n$.]

Problem 3. Prove:

a. $\displaystyle\lim_{n \to \infty} \left(\frac{1}{n+1} + \frac{1}{n+2} + \cdots + \frac{1}{n+n} \right) = \ln 2.$ $\left[\text{Hint: } \displaystyle\int_1^2 \frac{dx}{x} = \lim_{n \to \infty} \sum_{k=1}^{n} (?). \right]$

b. $\displaystyle\lim_{n \to \infty} \left(\frac{1}{n+1} + \frac{1}{n+2} + \cdots + \frac{1}{3n} \right)$

$\qquad = 2 \displaystyle\lim_{n \to \infty} \left(\frac{1}{n+2} + \frac{1}{n+4} + \frac{1}{n+6} + \cdots + \frac{1}{3n} \right).$

$\qquad \left[\text{Hint: } \displaystyle\int_1^2 \frac{dx}{x} + \int_2^3 \frac{dx}{x} = \int_1^3 \frac{dx}{x}. \right]$

c. $\displaystyle\lim_{n \to \infty} \left(\frac{n}{n^2 + 1^2} + \frac{n}{n^2 + 2^2} + \cdots + \frac{n}{n^2 + n^2} \right) = \frac{\pi}{4}.$

Problem 4. By extending Fig. 13-2.4, show that

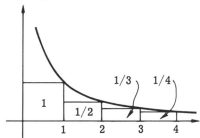

1/3   1/4

1

1/2

1   2   3   4

Fig. 13-2.4

$$s_n = 1 + \frac{1}{2} + \frac{1}{3} + \cdots + \frac{1}{n} < 1 + \ln n.$$

Then check that $s_{10} < 3.31$, $s_{100} < 5.61$, $s_{1000} < 7.91$, $s_{10000} < 10.22$.

Problem 5. Show in succession:

a. By using the binomial theorem:

$$\text{If } a_n > 0, \text{ then } (1 + a_n)^n > 1 + na_n.$$

b. If $p > 1$ and $a_n = \sqrt[n]{p} - 1$, then

$$0 < a_n \le \frac{p-1}{n} \quad \text{and} \quad \lim_{n \to \infty} a_n = 0.$$

c. If $p > 1$, then $\lim_{n \to \infty} \sqrt[n]{p} = 1$.

d. If $0 < p$, then $\lim_{n \to \infty} \sqrt[n]{p} = 1$.

Problem 6. Show in succession:

a. By using the binomial theorem:

$$\text{If} \quad a_n > 0, \quad \text{then} \quad (1 + a_n)^n > \frac{n(n-1)}{2} a_n^2 \quad \text{for} \quad n > 2.$$

b. If $a_n = \sqrt[n]{n} - 1$, then $0 < a_n < \sqrt{2/(n-1)}$ for $n > 2$ and

$$\lim_{n \to \infty} a_n = 0.$$

c. $\lim_{n \to \infty} \sqrt[n]{n} = 1$.

Problem 7. Given $0 < r < 1$, let $a_n = r^n$ for $n = 0, 1, 2, \ldots$. Show that:

a. $a_n > 0$ and $1 > a_1 > a_2 > \cdots$.

b. $\lim_{n \to \infty} a_n = a$ exists, with $0 \le a < 1$.

c. $\lim_{n \to \infty} r_n = 0$. [Hint: For any convergent sequence $\lim_{n \to \infty} a_{n+1} = \lim_{n \to \infty} a_n$.]

d. If $|r| < 1$, then $\lim_{n \to \infty} r^n = 0$.

e. If $|r| > 1$, then $\lim_{n \to \infty} r^n$ does not exist.

Problem 8. In case $\lim_{h \to c} F(h) = 0$, the function $F(h)$ is said to be a **null function at** $h = c$:

a. Show that $\lim_{h \to c} f(h) = a$ if and only if $f(h) - a$ is a null function at $h = c$.

b. Prove parts (ii) and (iii) of Theorem 2, p. 56.

Problem 9. Prove, or check, the following, in which n is a positive integer:

a. If $r > -1$, then $(1 + r)^n \ge 1 + nr$, for $n > 1$.

b. $\left(1 - \dfrac{1}{n^2}\right)^n > 1 - \dfrac{1}{n} = \dfrac{n-1}{n}$, for $n > 1$.

c. Given $u_n = \left(1 + \dfrac{1}{n}\right)^n$, then $u_{n-1} < u_n$; that is,

$$u_1 < u_2 < \cdots < u_n < \cdots.$$

$$\left[\text{Hint:} \frac{u_n}{u_{n-1}} = \frac{n}{n-1}\left(1 - \frac{1}{n^2}\right)^n, \text{ then use b.}\right]$$

d. Given $v_n = \left(1 + \dfrac{1}{n}\right)^{n+1}$, then $v_{n-1} > v_n$; that is,

$$v_1 > v_2 > \cdots > v_n > \cdots.$$

$$\left[\text{Hint:} \frac{v_{n-1}}{v_n} = \frac{n-1}{n}\left(1 + \frac{1}{n^2-1}\right)^{n+1}, \text{ then use a with } r = 1/(n^2-1)\right.$$

and the exponent n replaced by $n + 1$.$\Big]$

e. $u_n < v_n$.

f. If m is also a positive integer, then $u_n < v_m$. [Hint: If $n \le m$, then $u_n \le u_m < v_m$; if $m < n$, then $\cdots$.]

g. For each positive integer m,

$$\lim_{n \to \infty} u_n \le v_m.$$

h. Set $e = \lim_{n\to\infty} u_n = \lim_{n\to\infty}\left(1 + \dfrac{1}{n}\right)^n$. Then also

$$e = \lim_{n\to\infty} v_n = \lim_{n\to\infty}\left(1 + \frac{1}{n}\right)^{n+1}.$$

i. $2 \leq u_n \leq e \leq v_m \leq 4$. In particular, $u_n \leq e \leq v_{n-1}$ and

$$1 + \frac{1}{n} \leq e^{1/n} \leq 1 + \frac{1}{n-1}.$$

j. Let h be a number such that $0 < h < \frac{1}{2}$ and then let n be the positive integer such that $n \leq (1/h) < n + 1$. Then (since $e > 1$),

$$1 + \frac{1}{n+1} \leq e^{1/(n+1)} < e^h \leq e^{1/n} < 1 + \frac{1}{n-1},$$

$$\frac{1}{n+1} < e^h - 1 \leq \frac{1}{n-1}.$$

k. $\dfrac{h}{1+h} \leq \dfrac{1}{n+1}$, $\quad \dfrac{1}{n-1} < \dfrac{h}{1-2h}$, and $\quad \dfrac{h}{1+h} < e^h - 1 < \dfrac{h}{1-2h}$.

l. $\lim_{h\to 0+} \dfrac{e^h - 1}{h} = 1$.

m. $\lim_{k\to 0-} \dfrac{e^k - 1}{k} = 1$. [Hint: With $k < 0$, set $h = -k$ and use l.]

[Note: Recall that $\lim_{h\to 0} (e^h - 1)/h = 1$ was used in Sec. 6-4 as the basis of all derivative formulas for exponential and logarithmic functions. No circular reasoning is involved since none of these formulas was used in this problem.]

13-3. l'Hospital's Rules

The early terms of the sequence

$$\frac{1.1}{1}, \frac{1.21}{2}, \frac{1.331}{3}, \dots, \frac{(1.1)^n}{n}, \dots$$

get progressively smaller. Should this decreasing continue, then the limit of the sequence would exist and be less than 1.1. This, however, is not the case. Later in this section it will follow easily that

$$(0) \qquad\qquad \lim_{n\to\infty} \frac{(1.1)^n}{n} = \infty.$$

The purpose of this section (and the next) is to develop techniques for finding limits. Although the interest at the moment is to determine limits of sequences as the discrete variable n tends to infinity, the methods developed apply also to a continuous variable x either tending to a finite value or to $\pm\infty$. Everything will depend on Rolle's Theorem (p. 88).

With $f(x)$ and $g(x)$ continuous on $a \leq x \leq b$, $f'(x)$ and $g'(x)$ existing, and $g'(x) \neq 0$ on $a < x < b$, then there are numbers ξ_1 and ξ_2 between a and b, such that (by the Mean Value Theorem)

$$f(b) - f(a) = f'(\xi_1)(b - a), \quad g(b) - g(a) = g'(\xi_2)(b - a) \neq 0, \quad \text{and}$$

(1)
$$\frac{f(b) - f(a)}{g(b) - g(a)} = \frac{f'(\xi_1)}{g'(\xi_2)}.$$

The ξ_1 and ξ_2 may very well have different values.

The following theorem states a relation which agrees with (1) except for having a single ξ.

SECOND MEAN VALUE THEOREM. *Given $f(x)$ and $g(x)$ continuous on $a \leq x \leq b$ having $f'(x)$ and $g'(x) \neq 0$ existing on $a < x < b$, then there is a number ξ such that $a < \xi < b$ and*

(2)
$$\frac{f(b) - f(a)}{g(b) - g(a)} = \frac{f'(\xi)}{g'(\xi)}.$$

PROOF. Start with the function $F(x)$ defined on $a \leq x \leq b$ by

$$F(x) = [f(x) - f(a)] [g(b) - g(a)] - [f(b) - f(a)] [g(x) - g(a)].$$

Then $F'(x) = f'(x) [g(b) - g(a)] - [f(b) - f(a)] g'(x)$ for $a < x < b$. Also, $F(a) = F(b) = 0$. Hence, there is a number ξ such that $a < \xi < b$ and $F'(\xi) = 0$ (by Rolle's Theorem). Hence,

$$0 = f'(\xi) [g(b) - g(a)] - [f(b) - f(a)] g'(\xi),$$

which may be put in the form (2) since $g(b) - g(a) \neq 0$, as just noted above equation (1).

The slight difference between (1) and (2) might seem trivial, but notice all the following consequences of equation (2) that could not be drawn from equation (1).

With a fixed x such that $a < x \leq b$, the above reasoning shows the existence of a ξ_x for which

(3)
$$\frac{f(x) - f(a)}{g(x) - g(a)} = \frac{f'(\xi_x)}{g'(\xi_x)}, \quad a < \xi_x < x.$$

The indeterminate form $0/0$ is obtained in trying to take

$$\lim_{x \to a+} \frac{f(x) - f(a)}{g(x) - g(a)}$$

by the continuity of $f(x)$ and $g(x)$ at $x = a$. If, however,

$$\lim_{x \to a+} \frac{f'(x)}{g'(x)} \quad \text{exists and equals } L, \quad \text{then} \quad \lim_{x \to a+} \frac{f'(\xi_x)}{g'(\xi_x)} = L,$$

since ξ_x is even closer to a than x is and the *same ξ_x appears in both numerator and denominator.* Hence, from (3),

(4)
$$\lim_{x \to a+} \frac{f(x) - f(a)}{g(x) - g(a)} = \lim_{x \to a+} \frac{f'(x)}{g'(x)} = L.$$

Example 1. Find

$$\lim_{x \to 0+} \frac{x + \sin 2x}{x - \sin 3x}.$$

Solution. Since both numerator and denominator approach 0, the formula for the limit of a quotient is not applicable. However, by using $f(x) = x + \sin 2x$, $g(x) = x - \sin 3x$, and $a = 0$ in (4), then $f(a) = g(a) = 0$ and

$$\lim_{x \to 0+} \frac{x + \sin 2x}{x - \sin 3x} = \lim_{x \to 0+} \frac{D_x(x + \sin 2x)}{D_x(x - \sin 3x)}$$

$$= \lim_{x \to 0+} \frac{1 + 2 \cos 2x}{1 - 3 \cos 3x} = \frac{1 + 2}{1 - 3} = -\frac{3}{2}.$$

The first of l'Hospital's Rules contains the above result.

RULE 1. *Let $f'(x)$ and $g'(x)$ exist with $g'(x) \neq 0$ on some open interval $a < x < b$. Then:*

(i) *If* $\lim\limits_{x \to a+} f(x) = \lim\limits_{x \to a+} g(x) = 0$ *and*

(ii) *If* $\lim\limits_{x \to a+} \dfrac{f'(x)}{g'(x)} = L,$ *or is* $+\infty$, *or is* $-\infty$;

it follows that

$$\lim_{x \to a+} \frac{f(x)}{g(x)} = \lim_{x \to a+} \frac{f'(x)}{g'(x)}$$

(meaning that both limits exist and are equal, or both ratios tend to $+\infty$, or both to $-\infty$, as $x \to a+$).

PROOF FOR $+\infty$. Corresponding to an arbitrary number G, let $\delta > 0$ be such that,

$$\text{whenever} \quad a < x < a + \delta, \quad \text{then} \quad \frac{f'(x)}{g'(x)} > G.$$

Just in case $f(a)$ is undefined or has a value other than 0, let $\bar{f}(x) = f(x)$ for $x \neq a$ and $\bar{f}(a) = 0$. Then $\bar{f}(x)$ has right-hand continuity at $x = a$ [from (i)] and $\bar{f}'(x) = f'(x)$ for $x \neq a$. In the same way, introduce $\bar{g}(x)$ if necessary. Then, for each x such that $a < x < a + \delta$, there is a ξ_x, $a < \xi_x < x$, for which

$$\frac{\bar{f}(x)}{\bar{g}(x)} = \frac{\bar{f}(x) - \bar{f}(a)}{\bar{g}(x) - \bar{g}(a)} = \frac{\bar{f}'(\xi_x)}{\bar{g}'(\xi_x)}; \quad \text{that is,}$$

$$\frac{f(x)}{g(x)} = \frac{f'(\xi_x)}{g'(\xi_x)} > G, \quad \text{since} \quad a < \xi_x < a + \delta.$$

This means that

$$\lim_{x \to a+} \frac{f(x)}{g(x)} = +\infty.$$

By changing each $>$ to $<$, a proof for $-\infty$ is obtained.

In case the conditions hold to the left of $x = a$, then $x \to a-$ replaces

$x \to a+$. Also, $x \to a$ may be used if the conditions hold on both sides of $x = a$.

Example 2.

$$\lim_{x \to 0\pm} \frac{x + \sin x}{\sin^2 x} = \lim_{x \to 0\pm} \frac{1 + \cos x}{2 \sin x \cos x} = \pm\infty,$$

$$\lim_{x \to 0} \frac{x + \sin x}{\sin^3 x} = \lim_{x \to 0} \frac{1 + \cos x}{3 \sin^2 x \cos x} = +\infty.$$

Should it happen that also $\lim_{x \to a} f'(x) = \lim_{x \to a} g'(x) = 0$, then check whether

$$\lim_{x \to a} \frac{f''(x)}{g''(x)} = L, \quad \text{or } +\infty, \text{ or } -\infty.$$

If so, then

$$\lim_{x \to u} \frac{f(x)}{g(x)} = \lim_{x \to u} \frac{f'(x)}{g'(x)} = \lim_{x \to a} \frac{f''(x)}{g''(x)},$$

by applying Rule 1 with f' in place of f and g' in place of g for the second equality and then the rule itself for the first equality.

Example 3.

$$\lim_{x \to 0} \frac{x^2 + x \sin x}{1 - \cos x} = \lim_{x \to 0} \frac{2x + x \cos x + \sin x}{\sin x} \quad \left(\frac{0}{0}\right)$$

$$= \lim_{x \to 0} \frac{2 + 2 \cos x - x \sin x}{\cos x} = 4.$$

The second rule is essentially Rule 1 with $x \to a\pm$ replaced by $x \to \pm\infty$.

RULE 2. *If* $\lim_{x \to \pm\infty} f(x) = \lim_{x \to \pm\infty} g(x) = 0$, *if* $f'(x)$ *and* $g'(x)$ *exist and* $g'(x) \neq 0$ *for all sufficiently large* x (*or sufficiently negative* x), *and if*

$$\lim_{x \to \pm\infty} \frac{f'(x)}{g'(x)} = L, \quad \text{or } +\infty, \text{ or } -\infty,$$

then

$$\lim_{x \to \pm\infty} \frac{f(x)}{g(x)} = \lim_{x \to \pm\infty} \frac{f'(x)}{g'(x)}.$$

PROOF FOR $x \to \infty$. If $x = 1/y$, then $y \to 0+$ as $x \to +\infty$ and $dx/dy = -1/y^2$. Define

$$F(y) = \begin{cases} f(1/y) & \text{if } y > 0 \\ 0 & \text{if } y = 0 \end{cases} \quad \text{and} \quad G(y) = \begin{cases} g(1/y) & \text{if } y > 0 \\ 0 & \text{if } y = 0 \end{cases}.$$

Then $\lim_{y \to 0+} F(y) = \lim_{y \to 0+} f(1/y) = \lim_{x \to +\infty} f(x) = 0$ and $\lim_{y \to 0+} G(y) = 0$. Thus, $F(y)$ and $G(y)$ are continuous on some interval $0 \leq y \leq b$. Also, by the Chain Rule,

$$F'(y) = f'\left(\frac{1}{y}\right)\left(-\frac{1}{y^2}\right) \quad \text{and} \quad G'(y) = g'\left(\frac{1}{y}\right)\left(-\frac{1}{y^2}\right) \quad \text{if} \quad y > 0.$$

Thus,

$$\lim_{x \to +\infty} \frac{f(x)}{g(x)} = \lim_{y \to 0+} \frac{f(1/y)}{g(1/y)}$$

$$= \lim_{y \to 0+} \frac{F(y)}{G(y)} = \lim_{y \to 0+} \frac{F'(y)}{G'(y)} \quad \text{by Rule 1}$$

$$= \lim_{y \to 0+} \frac{f'(1/y)}{g'(1/y)} \quad \text{since } -1/y^2 \text{ cancels}$$

$$= \lim_{x \to +\infty} \frac{f'(x)}{g'(x)}.$$

Hence, Rule 2 is established for $x \to +\infty$.

RULE 3. *If $f'(x)$ and $g'(x)$ exist on appropriate domains and if, as $x \to a\pm$ or $x \to \pm\infty$, both*

$$\lim |g(x)| = \infty \quad \text{and} \quad \lim \frac{f'(x)}{g'(x)} = L, \quad \text{or} +\infty, \text{ or } -\infty,$$

then

$$\lim \frac{f(x)}{g(x)} = \lim \frac{f'(x)}{g'(x)}.$$

Some ideas on how this could be proved will be given for the case in which L exists as $x \to a+$. Let $\epsilon > 0$ be arbitrary and determine b such that,

whenever $\quad a < x < b, \quad$ then $\quad L - \dfrac{\epsilon}{2} < \dfrac{f'(x)}{g'(x)} < L + \dfrac{\epsilon}{2}.$

For each such x there is a ξ_x such that

$$\frac{f(x) - f(b)}{g(x) - g(b)} = \frac{f'(\xi_x)}{g'(\xi_x)}, \quad x < \xi_x < b.$$

Hence, whenever $a < x < b$, then also $a < \xi_x < b$, and thus

$$L - \frac{\epsilon}{2} < \frac{f(x) - f(b)}{g(x) - g(b)} < L + \frac{\epsilon}{2}.$$

By dividing both numerator and denominator by $g(x)$, then

$$L - \frac{\epsilon}{2} < \frac{f(x)/g(x) - f(b)/g(x)}{1 - g(b)/g(x)} < L + \frac{\epsilon}{2}.$$

But

$$\lim_{x \to a+} \frac{f(b)}{g(x)} = \lim_{x \to a+} \frac{g(b)}{g(x)} = 0, \quad \text{since} \quad \lim_{x \to a+} |g(x)| = \infty$$

and b is a constant. Thus, by relaxing $\epsilon/2$ to ϵ, to allow for $f(b)/g(x)$ and $g(b)/g(x)$ not being actually zero, then

$$L - \epsilon < \frac{f(x)}{g(x)} < L + \epsilon$$

for $x > a$ and sufficiently close to a. This means that

$$\lim_{x \to a+} \frac{f(x)}{g(x)} = L.$$

Example 4.

$$\lim_{x \to \infty} \frac{\ln x}{x} = \lim_{x \to \infty} \frac{D_x \ln x}{D_x x} = \lim_{x \to \infty} \frac{1/x}{1} = 0.$$

Note that none of the l'Hospital Rules applies to

$$\lim_{x \to 0+} \frac{\ln x}{x} = -\infty.$$

This brings up the warning:

Never apply a l'Hospital rule unless either:
(1) *Both numerator and denominator approach zero, or*
(2) *The absolute value of the denominator approaches infinity.*

For example, the careless setting of

$$\lim_{x \to 0+} \frac{\ln x}{x} = \lim_{x \to 0+} \frac{D_x \ln x}{D_x x} = \lim_{x \to 0+} \frac{1/x}{1} = \infty$$

would give a result that could not be farther off.

Example 5. Show that if $r > 1$ then $\lim_{n \to \infty} (r^n/n) = \infty$. [In equation (0) at the beginning of this section, $r = 1.1$.]

Solution. Upon replacing the discrete variable n by the continuous variable x, then

$$\lim_{x \to \infty} \frac{r^x}{x} = \lim_{x \to \infty} \frac{D_x r^x}{D_x x} = \lim_{x \to \infty} \frac{r^x \ln r}{1} = +\infty \quad \text{for} \quad r > 1.$$

Hence, for G arbitrary, there is an H such that,

$$\text{whenever} \quad x > H, \quad \text{then} \quad \frac{r^x}{x} > G.$$

Thus, whenever $n > H$, then $r^n/n > G$, which says that

$$\lim_{n \to \infty} \frac{r^x}{n} = \infty.$$

By generalizing the above change from continuous to discrete variable, it follows that:

If $\lim_{x \to \infty} F(x)$ exists, or is $+\infty$, or is $-\infty$, then the same is true of $\lim_{n \to \infty} F(n)$.

The converse, however, is not so. For example, $\lim_{x \to \infty} \sin(\pi x)$ does not exist even though $\lim_{n \to \infty} \sin(\pi n) = 0$.

Although n is usually assigned integer values,

$$\lim_{n \to \infty} \frac{r^n}{n} = \lim_{n \to \infty} \frac{D_n r^n}{D_n n} = \lim_{n \to \infty} \frac{r^n \ln r}{1} = \infty, \quad \text{for} \quad r > 1$$

should be easily interpreted.

Problem 1. Establish each of the following both by using a l'Hospital Rule and without using any of these rules:

a. $\lim\limits_{x \to 2\pm} \dfrac{x^2 - x - 2}{2 - x} = -3.$

c. $\lim\limits_{x \to \pm\infty} \dfrac{x^2 - x - 2}{2 - x} = \mp\infty.$

b. $\lim\limits_{x \to 0\pm} \dfrac{2x - \sin x}{x^2} = \pm\infty.$

d. $\lim\limits_{x \to \pm\infty} \dfrac{2x - \sin x}{x^2} = 0.$

Problem 2. Show that:

a. $\lim\limits_{x \to 0} \dfrac{\tan x}{x} = 0.$

e. $\lim\limits_{x \to \pi/2} \dfrac{1 + \cos 2x}{1 - \sin x} = 4.$

b. $\lim\limits_{x \to \pi+} \dfrac{\sin x}{\sqrt{x - \pi}} = 0.$

f. $\lim\limits_{x \to \infty} \dfrac{\ln (1 + x^{-1})}{x^{-1}} = 1.$

c. $\lim\limits_{x \to 0} \dfrac{1 - \cos 2x}{x^2} = 2.$

g. $\lim\limits_{x \to 2} \dfrac{x^2 - 5}{x + 1} = -\dfrac{1}{3}.$

d. $\lim\limits_{x \to \infty} \dfrac{\ln (e^{2x} + x)}{x} = 2.$

h. $\lim\limits_{x \to \pi/4} \dfrac{\sqrt{2} - \tan x}{1 - \sec x} = -1.$

Problem 3. Find the limit of both expressions

$$\frac{e^x - 1 - x - x^2}{x^3} \quad \text{and} \quad \frac{e^x - 1 - x - \frac{1}{2}x^2}{x^3}$$

as $x \to 0\pm$ and again as $x \to \pm\infty$. [Answer: $\mp\infty$, $1/3!$; ∞, 0.]

Problem 4. Show that l'Hospital's Rules lead nowhere for

a. $\lim\limits_{x \to \infty} \dfrac{\sqrt{10 + x^2}}{x}.$

b. $\lim\limits_{x \to 0} \dfrac{e^{-1/x^2}}{x}.$

Then evaluate the limits. [Hint for b: set $x = 1/y$.]

Problem 5. Show that:

a. $\lim\limits_{x \to 0+} \dfrac{1 - e^{\sqrt{x}}}{\sqrt{x}} = -1,$ then do it again after setting $\sqrt{x} = t.$

b. $\lim\limits_{x \to 0\pm} \dfrac{e^{ax} - e^x - x}{x^2} = \begin{cases} \frac{3}{2} & \text{if } a = 2, \\ \pm\infty & \text{if } a > 2, \\ \mp\infty & \text{if } a < 2. \end{cases}$

c. $\lim\limits_{x \to 1} \dfrac{n - \sum\limits_{k=0}^{n-1} x^k}{1 - x} = \dfrac{n(n - 1)}{2}.$

d. $\lim\limits_{x \to 0} \dfrac{(2 + x)^n - 2^n}{x} = n2^{n-1}.$

Problem 6. Find:

a. $\lim\limits_{x\to 0} \dfrac{\sin x}{x}$.

b. $\lim\limits_{x\to 0} \dfrac{1-\cos x}{x^2}$.

c. $\lim\limits_{x\to 0} \dfrac{\sin^{-1} x}{x}$.

d. $\lim\limits_{x\to 0} \dfrac{(\pi/2)-\cos^{-1} x}{x^2}$.

Problem 7. In Fig. 13-3.1, the circle with center C has constant radius r, but the radius h of the other circle will approach 0. A is the point $(0, h)$, B is the intersection of the circles, and the line through A and B cuts the x-axis at the point having abscissa called $P(h)$.

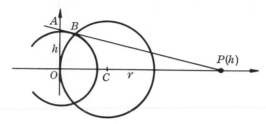

Fig.13-3.1

a. Show that $\lim_{h\to 0} P(h) = 4r$.

b. With A as before, relocate B so arc $(OB) = h$ and show that the limit is $3r$.

[Hint: Set up in terms of $\theta = $ angle OCB.]

Problem 8. Show that each denominator $\to \infty$ as $x \to \infty$, but that Rule 3 may not be applied; then find the limit by some other means:

a. $\lim\limits_{x\to\infty} \dfrac{x+\sin x}{x-\sin 2x} = 1$.

b. $\lim\limits_{x\to\infty} \dfrac{x\sin x}{x^2+1} = 0$.

13-4. Reduction to l'Hospital's Rules

None of l'Hospital's Rules applies directly to

$$\lim_{x\to 0+} x\ln x$$

since, as it stands, there is no quotient. A quotient may be formed (with denominator $\to \infty$) and the limit determined as follows:

(1) $$\lim_{x\to 0+} x\ln x = \lim_{x\to 0+} \frac{\ln x}{1/x} = \lim_{x\to 0+} \frac{D_x\ln x}{D_x(1/x)}$$

$$= \lim_{x\to 0+} \frac{1/x}{-1/x^2} = \lim_{x\to 0+}(-x) = 0.$$

Even though $\lim_{x\to 0+} \ln x = -\infty$, the tending of $\ln x$ toward $-\infty$ is so slow that $x \ln x$ approaches zero as $x \to 0+$.

This is an illustration of the third in the list of indeterminate forms

(2) $$\frac{0}{0}, \quad \frac{\infty}{\infty}, \quad 0\cdot\infty, \quad 0^0, \quad \infty^0, \quad 1^\infty, \quad \infty-\infty,$$

the first two of which fall under l'Hospital's Rules. The following examples illustrate methods by which the remaining forms may sometimes be reduced to one of the first two. The three having exponents are attacked via the formula

$$(3') \qquad\qquad a^p = e^{p \ln a}.$$

Example 1. Find $\lim_{x \to 0+} x^x$.

Solution. By using (3') and the result (1),

$$\lim_{x \to 0+} x^x = \lim_{x \to 0+} e^{x \ln x} = e^{\lim_{x \to 0+} x \ln x} = e^0 = 1.$$

A standard notation, introduced to avoid complicated exponents, is to define $\exp(x)$ by setting

$$\exp(x) = e^x.$$

Then a formula equivalent to (3') is

$$(3'') \qquad\qquad a^p = \exp(p \ln a).$$

Also, $\exp(x)$ is a continuous function. Hence, if $f(x)$ is continuous at $x = c$, then

$$\lim_{x \to c} \exp[f(x)] = \exp[\lim_{x \to c} f(x)].$$

Example 2.

$$\lim_{x \to \pi/4} (\tan x)^{\tan 2x} = \lim_{x \to \pi/4} \exp[\tan 2x \ln(\tan x)] \quad (\text{form } 1^\infty)$$

$$= \exp[\lim_{x \to \pi/4} \tan 2x \ln(\tan x)] \quad (\infty \cdot 0 \text{ inside})$$

$$= \exp\left[\lim_{x \to \pi/4} \frac{\ln(\tan x)}{\cot 2x}\right] \quad (0/0 \text{ inside})$$

$$= \exp\left(\lim_{x \to \pi/4} \frac{\sec^2 x/\tan x}{-2 \csc^2 2x}\right) \quad (\text{Rule 1})$$

$$= \exp[\lim_{x \to \pi/4} (-2 \sin x \cos x)] \quad (\text{trigonometry})$$

$$= \exp(-1) = e^{-1}.$$

The following example illustrates $\infty - \infty$ if $x \to 0+$ or $-\infty + \infty$ if $x \to 0-$.

Example 3.

$$\lim_{x \to 0} \left(\frac{1}{x} - \cot x\right) = \lim_{x \to 0} \frac{1 - x \cot x}{x} = \lim_{x \to 0} \frac{\sin x - x \cos x}{x \sin x} \quad \left(\frac{0}{0}\right)$$

$$= \lim_{x \to 0} \frac{x \sin x}{x \cos x + \sin x} = \lim_{x \to 0} \frac{\sin x}{\cos x + \dfrac{\sin x}{x}}$$

$$= \frac{0}{1 + 1} = 0 \text{ from the basic formula } \lim_{x \to 0} \frac{\sin x}{x} = 1.$$

Problem 1. Establish each of the following:

a. $\lim\limits_{x \to 0+} x^{\sin x} = 1.$

b. $\lim\limits_{x \to 0+} x(\ln x)^2 = 0.$

c. $\lim\limits_{x \to 0} (\cos x)^x = 1.$

d. $\lim\limits_{x \to \infty} \left(1 - \dfrac{1}{e^x}\right)^{e^x} = \dfrac{1}{e}.$

e. $\lim\limits_{x \to -\infty} x^2 e^x = 0.$

f. $\lim\limits_{x \to 0} \left[\dfrac{1}{x} - \dfrac{x}{\tan^{-1} x}\right] = 0.$

g. $\lim\limits_{x \to 1} \left[\dfrac{1}{\ln x} - \dfrac{x}{x - 1}\right] = -\dfrac{1}{2}.$

h. $\lim\limits_{x \to \infty} \left[\dfrac{\ln x}{x} - \dfrac{1}{\sqrt{x}}\right] = 0.$

Problem 2. The following are for additional practice:

a. $\lim\limits_{x \to 0} (e^x + 3x)^{1/x} = e^4.$

b. $\lim\limits_{x \to \pi/2} (\sin x - \cos x)^{\tan x} = \dfrac{1}{e}.$

c. $\lim\limits_{x \to 0} \dfrac{8^x - 2^x}{x} = \ln 4.$

d. $\lim\limits_{x \to 0} (\csc x - \cot x) = 0.$

e. $\lim\limits_{x \to \infty} (x - \ln x) = \infty.$

f. $\lim\limits_{x \to \infty} \left[\dfrac{x}{x - 2}\right]^x = e^2.$

g. $\lim\limits_{x \to \infty} \left[1 - \dfrac{1}{x^3}\right]^x = 1.$

h. $\lim\limits_{x \to \infty} \cos^{x^2} \dfrac{2}{x} = e^{-2}.$

i. $\lim\limits_{x \to 0} (1 + x)^{\ln x} = 1.$

j. $\lim\limits_{x \to 0} (1 + \tan x)^{1/x} = e.$

[Hint for e: Set $x = 1/y$.]

Problem 3. It is given that a function $f(x)$ has $f''(c)$ existing [but it is not assumed that $f''(x)$ exists for any $x \neq c$]. Show that

$$\lim_{h \to 0} \frac{f(c - h) - 2f(c) + f(c + h)}{h^2} = f''(c).$$

Problem 4. Show that $\lim_{x \to 0} x(\ln x)^{100} = 0$. [Note: As a matter of interest, $0.1(\ln 0.1)^{100}$ is greater than

$$16{,}650{,}000{,}000{,}000{,}000{,}000{,}000{,}000{,}000{,}000{,}000.$$

An elementary check will show that the maximum value of $f(x) = x(\ln x)^{100}$, $0 < x < 1$, is $f(e^{-100})$, having 256 digits before the decimal point. Also, e^{-100} has 434 zeros after the decimal point.]

13-5. Series Convergence and Divergence

Associated with an infinite series

(1) $$a_1 + a_2 + a_3 + \cdots + a_n + \cdots$$

is its sequence of **partial sums** $\{s_n\}$ defined by

(2) $$s_1 = a_1,$$
$$s_2 = a_1 + a_2,$$
$$s_3 = a_1 + a_2 + a_3,$$
$$\cdots \cdots$$

$$s_n = a_1 + a_2 + \cdots + a_n = \sum_{k=1}^{n} a_k$$

$$\cdots\cdots$$

For example, the geometric series

(3) $\qquad a + ar + ar^2 + \cdots + ar^{n-1} + \cdots,$ with $a \neq 0,$

has nth partial sum

$$s_n = \begin{cases} a \sum_{k=1}^{n} r^{k-1} = \dfrac{a}{1-r}(1 - r^n) & \text{if } r \neq 1, \\ na & \text{if } r = 1. \end{cases}$$

For $r \neq 1$, this follows from the identity

$$(1 - r^n) = (1 - r)(1 + r + r^2 + \cdots + r^{n-1}),$$

and for $r = 1$, by adding a exactly n times. Consequently,

(4) $\qquad \lim_{n \to \infty} s_n \begin{cases} = \dfrac{a}{1-r}(1 - \lim_{n \to \infty} r^n) = \dfrac{a}{1-r} & \text{if } |r| < 1. \\ \text{does not exist if } |r| \geq 1. \end{cases}$

DEFINITION. *The infinite series* (1) *with partial sums* (2) *is said to be convergent and to have sum* **s** *if* $\{s_n\}$ *converges to s; that is,* $\lim_{n \to \infty} s_n$ *exists and*

(5) $$\lim_{n \to \infty} s_n = \lim_{n \to \infty} \sum_{k=1}^{n} a_k = s.$$

If the series is convergent and has sum s, then

$$\sum_{k=1}^{\infty} a_k = s$$

is written. If the series is not convergent, it is said to be divergent (*and does not have a sum*).

Thus, the geometric series (3) converges if and only if $|r| < 1$, and if $|r| < 1$, then

$$a + ar + ar^2 + \cdots + ar^{n-1} + \cdots = \frac{a}{1-r}.$$

For example,

$$.3 + .03. + .003 + \cdots + \frac{3}{10^n} + \cdots = \frac{.3}{1 - .1} = \frac{.3}{.9} = \frac{1}{3}.$$

For this reason, 0.333... is called the **infinite decimal** representation of $\frac{1}{3}$. Even though the notation

$$\sum_{k=1}^{\infty} a_k = s$$

is used for convergent series, it should be understood that:

1. s is **not** found by an infinite number of additions; instead the sequence $\{s_n\}$ is formed and its limit determined.

2. There is no last term, k is never set $= \infty$, the symbolism a_∞ is not assigned a meaning.

Rather than writing out (1) each time, it is convenient to abbreviate (1) to $\sum\limits_{n=1}^{\infty} a_n$ whether the series converges or not. Also, $\sum a_k$ may be used.

If s_n is the nth partial sum of a convergent series $\sum a_n$, then $\lim_{n\to\infty} s_n$ exists. Hence, also [see (8) of p. 498]

$$\lim s_{n-1} = \lim s_n.$$

But $a_n = s_n - s_{n-1}$, so that

$$\lim_{n\to\infty} a_n = \lim_{n\to\infty} (s_n - s_{n-1}) = \lim_{n\to\infty} s_n - \lim_{n\to\infty} s_{n-1} = 0.$$

This proves the following result.

THEOREM 13-5.1. *If an infinite series* $\sum a_n$ *converges, then*

$$\lim_{n\to\infty} a_n = 0.$$

By convention, $\lim_{n\to\infty} a_n \neq a$ means that either the sequence $\{a_n\}$ does not converge or that it converges to a value different from a. Thus logical deduction from the above theorem is:

TEST 1 (FOR DIVERGENCE).

$$\text{If} \quad \lim_{n\to\infty} a_n \neq 0, \quad \text{then} \quad \sum a_n \quad \text{diverges.}$$

In convergence-divergence terminology, a result of Sec. 13-1 may now be stated as:

$$\text{The series} \quad 1 + \frac{1}{2} + \frac{1}{3} + \cdots + \frac{1}{n} + \cdots \quad \text{diverges.}$$

Thus, $\lim_{n\to\infty} 1/n = 0$, but $\sum 1/n$ diverges. The reason for mentioning this is to emphasize that

$$\lim_{n\to\infty} a_n = 0 \quad \text{does } \textbf{not} \text{ ensure convergence of} \quad \sum a_n$$

the way

$$\lim_{n\to\infty} a_n \neq 0 \quad \text{ensures divergence of} \quad \sum a_n.$$

Example 1. $\sum n/(n + 1)$ diverges since

$$\lim_{n\to\infty} \frac{n}{n + 1} = \lim_{n\to\infty} \frac{1}{1 + 1/n} = 1 \neq 0.$$

TEST 2 (FOR CONVERGENCE). *If* $a_1 \geq a_2 \geq \cdots \geq a_n \geq \cdots$, *if* $a_n \geq 0$ *for* $n = 1, 2, 3, \ldots$, *and if* $\lim_{n\to\infty} a_n = 0$, *then*

$$a_1 - a_2 + a_3 - a_4 + \cdots + (-1)^{n+1} a_n + \cdots$$

is a convergent series.

PROOF. The even partial sums are bounded above by a_1 since

$$s_2 = a_1 - a_2 \leq a_1,$$

$$s_4 = a_1 - (a_2 - a_3) - a_4 \leq a_1,$$

$$\cdots \cdots$$

$$s_{2n} = a_1 - (a_2 - a_3) - \cdots - (a_{2n-2} - a_{2n-1}) - a_{2n} \leq a_1.$$

Also,

$$s_{2n} \leq s_{2n} + (a_{2n+1} - a_{2n}) = s_{2n+2}.$$

Hence, the even partial sums form a nondecreasing sequence bounded above (by a_1), and hence this sequence of even partial sums converges. Since $s_{2n+1} = s_{2n} + a_{2n+1}$ and $a_{2n+1} \to 0$, then

$$\lim_{n \to \infty} s_{2n+1} = \lim_{n \to \infty} s_{2n} + \lim_{n \to \infty} a_{2n+1} = \lim_{n \to \infty} s_{2n}.$$

Thus, the sequence of all partial sums converges; that is, the series converges.

Example 2.

$$1 - \frac{1}{\sqrt{2}} + \frac{1}{\sqrt{3}} - \frac{1}{\sqrt{4}} + \cdots + (-1)^{n+1} \frac{1}{\sqrt{n}} + \cdots \quad \text{converges.}$$

THEOREM 13–5.2. *If $\sum a_n$ and $\sum b_n$ are convergent series and c is a constant, then $\sum(a_n + b_n)$ and $\sum(ca_n)$ are convergent, with*

(6)
$$\sum_{n=1}^{\infty} (a_n + b_n) = \sum_{n=1}^{\infty} a_n + \sum_{n+1}^{\infty} b_n \quad \text{and}$$

(7)
$$\sum_{n=1}^{\infty} (ca_n) = c \sum_{n+1}^{\infty} a_n.$$

PROOF. Let s_n and t_n be the nth partial sums of $\sum a_k$ and $\sum b_k$, respectively. Then $s_n + t_n$ is the nth partial sum of $\sum(a_k + b_k)$, and (6) follows since

$$\lim_{n \to \infty} (s_n + t_n) = \lim_{n \to \infty} s_n + \lim_{n \to \infty} t_n.$$

Similarly, (7) follows since cs_n is the nth partial sum of $\sum(ca_k)$.

Note that the theorem omits any statement about whether $\sum(a_n b_n)$ converges or not. To see that it need not converge, set

$$a_n = b_n = (-1)^{n+1} \frac{1}{\sqrt{n}}.$$

Then $\sum a_n$ and $\sum b_n$ both converge (see Example 2). However, $a_n b_n = 1/n$, so that $\sum(a_n b_n)$ is the divergent series $1 + \frac{1}{2} + \frac{1}{3} + \cdots$.

The following two related corollaries indicate the importance of close attention to hypotheses and conclusions.

COROLLARY 1. *If $\sum a_n$ and $\sum b_n$ converge, then $\sum(a_n - b_n)$ converges and*

$$\sum_{n+1}^{\infty} (a_n - b_n) = \sum_{n=1}^{\infty} a_n - \sum_{n=1}^{\infty} b_n.$$

COROLLARY 2. *If* $\sum a_n$ *converges but* $\sum b_n$ *diverges, then* $\sum (a_n + b_n)$ *diverges.*

PROOF. Assume $\sum (a_n + b_n)$ converges. Then $\sum [(a_n + b_n) - a_n]$ converges by Corollary 1; that is, $\sum b_n$ converges. This contradiction to hypotheses proves Corollary 2.

Note, however, that $\sum 1/n$ and $\sum -1/n$ both diverge, but

$$\sum \left(\frac{1}{n} + \frac{-1}{n}\right) \quad \text{converges.}$$

Problem 1. Prove the theorems below, assuming that each $a_n \neq 0$, although some of the theorems hold without this restriction:

a. If $\sum a_n$ diverges and $c \neq 0$, then $\sum (ca_n)$ diverges.

b. If $\sum a_n$ converges, then $\sum (1/a_n)$ diverges.

c. If $\lim_{n \to \infty} a_n$ exists and is $\neq 0$, then $\sum a_n$ and $\sum (1/a_n)$ both diverge. Also, give an example of a series $\sum a_n$ which diverges but $\sum (1/a_n)$ converges.

d. If $\lim_{n \to \infty} a_n$ exists, then $\sum (1/a_n)$ diverges.

Problem 2. Prove Test 2 again by first showing that the odd partial sums form a nonincreasing sequence bounded below by zero.

Problem 3. a. Recall that change of variable of integration yields

$$\int_1^4 (x + 2)^2\, dx = \int_3^6 t^2\, dt = \int_3^6 x^2\, dx.$$

Change the index of summation to justify

$$\sum_{k=1}^{n} a_k = \sum_{l=3}^{n+2} a_{l-2} = \sum_{k=3}^{n+2} a_{k-2}.$$

b. Use such change of index of summation to obtain

$$\sum_{k=1}^{n} \left(\frac{1}{k} - \frac{1}{k+2}\right) = \sum_{k=1}^{n} \frac{1}{k} - \sum_{k=3}^{n+2} \frac{1}{k} = 1 + \frac{1}{2} - \frac{1}{n+1} - \frac{1}{n+2}.$$

c. Use partial fractions to obtain

$$\frac{1}{k(k+2)} = \frac{1}{2}\left(\frac{1}{k} - \frac{1}{k+2}\right).$$

d. Show that

$$\sum_{n=1}^{\infty} \frac{1}{n(n+2)} = \frac{3}{4}.$$

Problem 4. Use the techniques of Prob. 3 to show that:

a. $\displaystyle\sum_{n=1}^{\infty} \frac{1}{n(n+3)} = \frac{11}{18}.$

b. $\displaystyle\sum_{n=1}^{\infty} \frac{1}{n(n+1)} = 1.$

c. $\displaystyle\sum_{n=1}^{\infty} \frac{1}{(2n-1)(2n+1)} = \frac{1}{2}.$

d. $\displaystyle\sum_{n=1}^{\infty} \frac{1}{n(n+1)(n+2)} = \frac{1}{4}.$

e. $\displaystyle\sum_{n=1}^{\infty} \frac{n}{(n+1)!} = 1.$

f. $\displaystyle\sum_{n=0}^{\infty} \frac{1}{(n+1)(n+4)} = \ ?.$

g. $\sum\limits_{n=1}^{\infty} \ln \dfrac{(n+1)^2}{n^2+2n} = \ln 2.$ $\left[\text{Hint for g: } \dfrac{(k+1)^2}{k^2+2k} = \left(1+\dfrac{1}{k}\right)\Big/\left(1+\dfrac{1}{k+1}\right).\right]$

Problem 5. Show that each of the series diverges:

a. $\sum \dfrac{2n-5}{2n}.$

b. $\sum \dfrac{1}{\sqrt{n+1}+\sqrt{n}}.$

c. $\sum \ln\left(\dfrac{n}{n+1}\right).$

d. $\sum \sin\left(\dfrac{n}{n+1}\right).$

Problem 6. Establish convergence or divergence:

a. $\sum \dfrac{n}{n^2+1}(-1)^n.$

b. $\sum \dfrac{n}{n+1}(-1)^n.$

c. $\sum \sin\left(n\dfrac{\pi}{2}\right).$

d. $\sum \dfrac{n}{100n+1}.$

e. $\sum e^{-n}.$

f. $\sum \left(\dfrac{1}{n} - \dfrac{1}{n+10}\right).$

[Answer: a, e, and f converge.]

Problem 7. Establish each part in turn:

a. If $n > 1$, then $\dfrac{n+1}{2^{n+1}} < \dfrac{n}{2^n}.$ Hence, $\dfrac{n}{2^n} \to a,\ 0 \le a < \dfrac{1}{2}.$

b. $\lim\limits_{n\to\infty} \dfrac{n}{2^n} = 0.$ [Hint: l'Hospital's Rule.]

c. $\dfrac{k-1}{2^{k+1}} = \dfrac{k}{2^k} - \dfrac{k+1}{2^{k+1}}.$

d. $\sum\limits_{n=1}^{\infty} \dfrac{n-1}{2^{n+1}} = \dfrac{1}{2}.$

e. $\sum\limits_{n=1}^{\infty} \dfrac{n+1}{2^n} = 3.$

f. $\sum\limits_{n=1}^{\infty} \dfrac{n}{2^n} = 2.$

Problem 8. Let x be a number such that $0 < x < 1$. Hence, from the geometric series,

$$\sum_{k=0}^{n-1} x^k = \dfrac{1}{1-x} - \dfrac{x^n}{1-x},$$

a. Is it permissible to take the derivative of both sides to obtain

$$\sum_{k=0}^{n-1} kx^k = \dfrac{1}{(1-x)^2} - \dfrac{(1-x)nx^{n-1}+x^n}{(1-x)^2}?$$

b. Prove that $\lim_{n\to\infty} nx^{n-1} = 0.$

c. Show that all this justifies taking

$$\dfrac{d}{dx} \sum_{k=0}^{\infty} x^k = \sum_{k=0}^{\infty} \dfrac{d}{dx} x^k \text{ if } 0 < x < 1.$$

Problem 9. It is usual to show infinitely repeating decimals by writing, for example, $0.4\overline{25}$ instead of

$$0.4252525.\ldots$$

Show that:

a. $0.4\overline{25} = \dfrac{421}{990}.$

b. $0.4\overline{9} = \dfrac{1}{2}.$

c. $0.\overline{2} = \dfrac{2}{9}.$

d. $0.\overline{20} = \dfrac{20}{99}.$

e. $0.\overline{123456789} = \dfrac{123456789}{999999999}.$

f. $0.\overline{285714} = \dfrac{2(142857)}{7(142857)} = \dfrac{2}{7}.$

13-6.   Improper Integrals

The region R between the x-axis and the curve $y = 1/x^2$, $x \geq 1$, is of infinite extent. In a sense, however, R has a finite area. For if t is any number > 1, then the portion of R above the closed interval $1 \leq x \leq t$ has area

$$A(t) = \int_1^t \frac{1}{x^2}\, dx = -\frac{1}{x}\bigg]_1^t = 1 - \frac{1}{t}.$$

Since $\lim_{t \to \infty} A(t) = 1$, the region R is assigned area 1.

Provided $\int_a^t f(x)\, dx$ exists for each $t \geq a$, then, by definition,

(1) $$\int_a^\infty f(x)\, dx = \lim_{t \to \infty} \int_a^t dx, \quad \text{if this limit exists.}$$

In a similar way,

(2) $$\int_{-\infty}^b f(x)\, dx = \lim_{s \to -\infty} \int_s^b f(x)\, dx, \quad \text{if this limit exists.}$$

The integral was originally defined for a finite closed interval $[a, b]$. The above extensions to half-lines are called **improper integrals** of the first kind.

Although the symbolism

(3) $$\int_1^\infty \frac{1}{x}\, dx$$

is used, it will be said that this integral does not exist. For an attempt to evaluate (3) by using (1) leads to

(4) $$\lim_{t \to \infty} \int_1^t \frac{1}{x} = \lim_{t \to \infty} \left[\ln x\right]_1^t = \lim_{t \to \infty} \ln t = \infty.$$

In agreement with series terminology, the integral

$$\int_a^\infty f(x)\, dx$$

is said to **converge** if the limit in (1) exists, but otherwise is said to **diverge**.

The following example may at first seem to state an anomaly.

Example 1. The region under $y = 1/x$ and above the x-axis for $x \geq 1$ is revolved about the x-axis. Show that this region of infinite area generates a solid of finite volume.

Solution. By (4) the region has infinite area. The formula for the volume of revolution for $1 \leq x \leq t$ yields

$$\text{volume} = \int_1^\infty \pi \left(\frac{1}{x}\right)^2 dx = \lim_{t \to \infty} \pi \int_1^t \frac{1}{x^2}\, dx = \pi \lim_{t \to \infty} \left[-\frac{1}{t} + 1\right] = \pi.$$

On several previous occasions it was shown how improper integrals arise in practice. Improper integrals will be used again in the next section in connection with tests for convergence or divergence of series. The result needed there is:

Given a constant p, then

(5) $\int_1^\infty \frac{1}{x^p} dx \begin{cases} \text{converges if } p > 1, \\ \text{diverges if } p \leq 1. \end{cases}$

PROOF. If $p = 1$, this integral is (3), already known to be divergent. Hence, take $p \neq 1$. Then

$$\int_1^\infty \frac{1}{x^p} dx = \lim_{t \to \infty} \int_1^t x^{-p} dx = \lim_{t \to \infty} \left[\frac{x^{-p+1}}{-p+1} \right]_1^t$$

$$= \frac{1}{1-p} \lim_{t \to \infty} [t^{1-p} - 1] = \begin{cases} \dfrac{-1}{1-p} & \text{if } 1 - p < 0; \text{ that is, } p > 1; \\ \infty & \text{if } 1 - p > 0; \text{ that is } p < 1. \end{cases}$$

Recall that integrals were defined originally not only on a finite closed interval $a \leq x \leq b$, but also only for the integrand defined and bounded on the interval. Improper integrals of a **second kind** arise when the integrand is defined except at one of the endpoints of the interval. For example, $f(x) = x^{-1/2}$, $0 < x \leq 1$, is unbounded near the origin, but

$$\lim_{t \to 0+} \int_t^1 x^{-1/2} dx = \lim_{t \to 0+} \left[2\sqrt{x} \right]_t^1 = \lim_{t \to 0+} [2 - 2\sqrt{t}] = 2.$$

Assuming that $f(x)$ is defined for $a < x \leq b$ and $\int_t^b f(x) dx$ exists for each t such that $a < t < b$, then, by definition,

(6) $\int_a^b f(x) dx = \lim_{t \to a+} \int_t^b f(x) dx,$ if this limit exists.

Similarly for $a \leq x < b$,

(7) $\int_a^b f(x) dx = \lim_{s \to b-} \int_a^s f(x) dx,$ if this limit exists.

A further situation arises when $a < c < b$ and c is the only bothersome point. Then, by definition,

$$\int_a^b f(x) dx = \int_a^c f(x) dx + \int_c^b f(x) dx,$$

if both integrals on the right exist according to (6) and (7), respectively.

Example 2. Show that $\int_{-1}^2 \frac{1}{x} dx$ does not exist.

Solution. Since $1/x$ is defined except for $x = 0$, then

(8) $\int_{-1}^0 \frac{1}{x} dx$ and $\int_0^2 \frac{1}{x} dx$

are to be examined separately. First, write

$$\int_{-1}^{0} \frac{1}{x}\,dx = \lim_{t \to 0-} \int_{-1}^{t} \frac{1}{x}\,dx = \lim_{t \to 0-} \ln|x| \Big]_{-1}^{t} = \lim_{t \to 0-} [\ln|t| - \ln|-1|]$$

$$= \lim_{t \to 0-} \ln|t| = -\infty.$$

The first integral in (8), therefore, does not exist. Hence, the given integral does not exist [there being no need to examine the second integral of (8)].

Example 3. $\int_{0}^{\infty} (1/x^2)e^{-1/x}\,dx$ is improper of the first kind (upper limit ∞) but also of the second kind (integrand undefined at $x = 0$). Since $d(-1/x) = (1/x^2)\,dx$, write

$$\lim_{s \to 0+} \lim_{t \to \infty} \int_{s}^{t} e^{-1/x}\,d\left(-\frac{1}{x}\right) = \lim_{s \to 0+} \lim_{t \to \infty} \left[e^{-1/x} \right]_{s}^{t}$$

$$= \lim_{s \to 0+} \lim_{t \to \infty} \left[\frac{1}{e^{1/t}} - \frac{1}{e^{1/s}} \right] = \lim_{s \to 0+} \left[\frac{1}{1} - \frac{1}{e^{1/s}} \right] = 1 - 0 = 1.$$

Hence, the integral exists.

Problem 1. Establish convergence or divergence and evaluate if convergent:

a. $\int_{1}^{\infty} \frac{dx}{x\sqrt{x}}$.   e. $\int_{-\infty}^{3} \frac{dx}{(4-x)^2}$.   i. $\int_{0}^{2} \frac{dx}{\sqrt{4-x^2}}$.

b. $\int_{0}^{1} \frac{dx}{x\sqrt{x}}$.   f. $\int_{3}^{5} \frac{dx}{(4-x)^2}$.   j. $\int_{0}^{\pi/2} \frac{\cos x\,dx}{\sqrt{1-\sin x}}$.

c. $\int_{-\infty}^{2} \frac{dx}{\sqrt{6-x}}$.   g. $\int_{0}^{\infty} \frac{dx}{1+x^2}$.   k. $\int_{0}^{\infty} \cos x\,dx$.

d. $\int_{0}^{\infty} \frac{dx}{(6+x)^{3/2}}$.   h. $\int_{0}^{\infty} \frac{x\,dx}{1+x^2}$.   l. $\int_{-\infty}^{0} e^{2x}\,dx$.

Problem 2. Show that:

a. $\int_{-2}^{\infty} \frac{dx}{x^2 + 4x + 4}$ does not exist, but $\int_{-2}^{\infty} \frac{dx}{x^2 + 4} = \frac{3}{8}\pi$.

b. $\int_{-\infty}^{-1} \frac{dx}{1 - x^2}$ does not exist, but $\int_{-\infty}^{-1} \frac{dx}{1 + x^2} = \frac{\pi}{4}$.

c. $\int_{1}^{\infty} \frac{dx}{x} - \int_{1}^{\infty} \frac{dx}{1+x}$ does not exist, but $\int_{1}^{\infty} \left(\frac{1}{x} - \frac{1}{1+x} \right) dx = \ln 2$.

d. $\int_{-1}^{3} \frac{dx}{x}$ does not exist, but $\lim_{t \to 0+} \left\{ \int_{-1}^{-t} \frac{dx}{x} + \int_{t}^{3} \frac{dx}{x} \right\} = \ln 3$.

Problem 3. Assuming $f(x)$ continuous for all x, then, by definition,

$$\int_{-\infty}^{\infty} f(x)\,dx = \int_{-\infty}^{0} f(x)\,dx + \int_{0}^{\infty} f(x)\,dx,$$

provided both integrals on the right exist. Show that:

a. $\int_{-\infty}^{\infty} \frac{dx}{1 + x^2} = \pi$.   b. $\int_{-\infty}^{\infty} \frac{dx}{e^x + e^{-x}} = \pi$.

c. $\int_{-\infty}^{\infty} \sin x\,dx$ does not exist, but $\lim_{t \to \infty} \int_{-t}^{t} \sin x\,dx = 0$.

d. $\int_{-\infty}^{\infty} \frac{dx}{x^3}$ does not exist, but $\lim_{t \to 0+} \left\{ \int_{-\infty}^{-t} \frac{dx}{x^3} + \int_{t}^{\infty} \frac{dx}{x^3} \right\} = 0$.

13-7. Series of Nonnegative Terms

Convergent series are useful for many purposes, even though the sum may not be known or readily obtainable. It is well, therefore, to have tests for determining convergence or divergence of series. Tests 1 and 2 were given in Sec. 13-5.

TEST 3 (INTEGRAL TEST). *Given a series* $\sum a_n$, *with* $a_n \geq 0$, *if there is a continuous decreasing function* $f(x)$, $x \geq 1$, *such that* $f(n) = a_n$, *then*

$$(1) \qquad\qquad \sum a_n \quad and \quad \int_1^\infty f(x)\,dx$$

either both converge or both diverge.

PROOF. Let $s_n = \sum_{k=1}^{n} a_k$. Then $\{s_n\}$ is a nondecreasing sequence (since $a_n \geq 0$) and thus converges if and only if it is bounded above (see Theorem 13-2.4). Since $f(x)$ is a decreasing function, then, as indicated in Fig. 13-7.1,

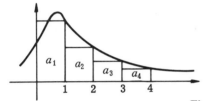 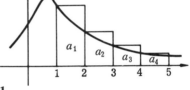

Fig. 13-7.1

$$(2) \qquad\qquad s_n \leq a_1 + \int_1^n f(x)\,dx \quad and \quad s_n \geq \int_1^{n+1} f(x)\,dx.$$

Hence, $\{s_n\}$ is bounded above if and only if $\int_1^\infty f(x)\,dx$ converges. Test 3 is thus established, since, by definition, convergence or divergence of $\sum a_n$ is the same as that of $\{s_n\}$.

A little extra work shows that this test may be applied if $a_n \geq 0$ for $n \geq N$, provided the function has the stated properties for $x \geq N$.

Example 1. Show that $\sum_{n=2}^{\infty} \dfrac{1}{n \ln n}$ diverges.

Solution. Set $f(x) = 1/(x \ln x)$, $x > 1$. Then

$$f'(x) = -\frac{1}{(x \ln x)^2}(1 + \ln x)$$

is negative, and $f(x)$ is decreasing, for $x \geq 2$. Since

$$\int_2^t \frac{dx}{x \ln x} = \ln(\ln x)\Big]_2^t = \ln(\ln t) - \ln(\ln 2),$$

this integral tends to ∞ with t. Hence, divergence of the series follows by Test 3.

TEST 4 (*p*-TEST). For *p* a number,

$$\sum \frac{1}{n^p} \begin{cases} converges \ if \ \ p > 1, \\ diverges \ if \ \ p \leq 1. \end{cases}$$

PROOF. If $p > 0$, this test is a corollary of Test 3 and (5) of Sec. 13–6. If $p \leq 0$, then $\lim_{n \to \infty} (1/n^p) = \infty \neq 0$, and divergence follows by Test 1.

TEST 5 (COMPARISON TEST). *Given $\sum a_n$ and $\sum b_n$ such that there is a number $c > 0$ and an integer N for which*

$$0 \leq a_n \leq c b_n \ \ for \ n \geq N,$$

then $\sum a_n$ and $\sum b_n$ either both converge or both diverge.

PROOF. Let s_n and t_n be the *n*th partial sums of $\sum a_n$ and $\sum b_n$, respectively. Then for $n \geq N$

$$\sum_{k=N}^{n} a_k \leq c \sum_{k=N}^{n} b_k; \ \ \text{that is,} \ \ s_n - s_{N-1} \leq c (t_n - t_{N-1}).$$

Let $\sum b_n$ be convergent with sum t. Since, for $n \geq N$, both $\{s_n\}$ and $\{t_n\}$ are nondecreasing sequences, then first $t_n \leq t$ and after this

$$s_n \leq c(t - t_{N-1}) + s_{N-1}, \ \ \text{for} \ \ n \geq N.$$

Thus, $\{s_n\}$ is bounded above and hence converges; that is, $\sum a_n$ converges.

To prove the rest of the theorem, let $\sum a_n$ diverge and assume $\sum b_n$ converges. Then, by the first part of this proof, $\sum a_n$ converges. This contradiction shows that $\sum b_n$ diverges whenever $\sum a_n$ diverges.

Example 2. Given a number $\lambda > 0$, show that

$$\sum \frac{1}{n^{3/2}} \sin \frac{\lambda}{n} \ \ \text{converges.}$$

Solution. Let N be an integer such that $N > \lambda/\pi$. Then

$$0 \leq \frac{1}{n^{3/2}} \sin \frac{\lambda}{n} \leq \frac{1}{n^{3/2}} \ \ \text{for} \ \ n \geq N.$$

Since $\sum 1/n^{3/2}$ converges by the *p*-test, the given series converges by the comparison test.

As soon as a series, with terms eventually positive, is shown to be convergent or divergent, it immediately becomes a candidate for checking other series by the comparison test. If there were only a "most slowly diverging series" of positive terms, it would be a useful comparison for other series. That there is no such series may be deduced from the following example.

Example 3. Show that if $a_n > 0$ and $\sum a_n$ diverges, then

$$\sum \frac{a_n}{1 + a_n} \ \ \text{also diverges.}$$

Solution. Assume there is a divergent series $\sum a_n$, $a_n > 0$, for which the series $\sum (a_n)/(1 + a_n)$ converges. Because of this convergence,

$$\lim_{n \to \infty} \frac{a_n}{1 + a_n} = 0.$$

Corresponding to $\epsilon = \frac{1}{2}$, let N be such that,

$$\text{whenever} \quad n \geq N, \quad \text{then} \quad \frac{a_n}{1 + a_n} < \frac{1}{2}.$$

Hence, whenever $n \geq N$, then $2a_n < 1 + a_n$, $a_n < 1$, $1 + a_n < 2$, and

$$a_n < 2\frac{a_n}{1 + a_n} \quad \text{for} \quad n \geq N.$$

By the comparison test, $\sum a_n$ would have to converge. This contradiction to the assumption shows that there is no divergent series $\sum a_n$, $a_n > 0$, for which $\sum (a_n)/(1 + a_n)$ converges.

The following test is probably used more than any other.

TEST 6 (RATIO TEST). *Let $\sum a_n$, having $a_n > 0$, be such that*

$$\lim_{n \to \infty} \frac{a_{n+1}}{a_n} = \rho.$$

Then

(3) $$\sum a_n \begin{cases} \text{converges if} \quad \rho < 1, \\ \text{diverges} \quad \text{if} \quad \rho > 1, \end{cases}$$

and there is no conclusion as to convergence or divergence if $\rho = 1$.

PROOF FOR $\rho < 1$. Let r be a number such that

$$\rho < r < 1.$$

Then $r - \rho > 0$. Corresponding to $\epsilon = r - \rho$, let N be such that,

$$\text{whenever} \quad n \geq N, \quad \text{then} \quad -(r - \rho) < \frac{a_{n+1}}{a_n} - \rho < r - \rho.$$

It follows (from the right inequality) that whenever $n \geq N$, then

$$\frac{a_{n+1}}{a_n} < r = \frac{r^{n+1}}{r^n}, \quad \text{so that} \quad \frac{a_{n+1}}{r^{n+1}} < \frac{a_n}{r^n}.$$

Hence, so long as the subscripts stay $\geq N$,

$$\frac{a_{n+1}}{r^{n+1}} < \frac{a_n}{r^n} < \frac{a_{n-1}}{r^{n-1}} < \cdots < \frac{a_N}{r^N}.$$

Out of this is separated the fact that

$$a_n \leq \frac{a_N}{r^N} r^n \quad \text{for} \quad n \geq N.$$

But $\sum r^n$ converges, since $0 < r < 1$. Thus, $\sum a_n$ converges, by the comparison Test 5 with $c = a_N/r^N$. Hence, the upper portion of (3) has been established.

PROOF FOR $\rho > 1$. By using $\epsilon = \rho - 1 > 0$, check that there is an N such that,

$$\text{whenever} \quad n \geq N \quad \text{then} \quad \frac{a_{n+1}}{a_n} > 1; \quad \text{that is,} \quad a_{n+1} > a_n.$$

Thus, whenever $n \geq N$, then $a_n \geq a_N > 0$, so that $\lim_{n \to \infty} a_n \neq 0$ and $\sum a_n$ diverges, by Test 1.

PROOF FOR $\rho = 1$. With p a constant, let $a_n = 1/n^p$. Then

$$\rho = \lim_{n \to \infty} \frac{a_{n+1}}{a_n} = \lim_{n \to \infty} \frac{n^p}{(n+1)^p} = \lim_{n \to \infty} \left(\frac{n}{n+1}\right)^p = 1^p = 1.$$

Since $\sum 1/n^p$ converges if $p > 1$ but diverges if $p \leq 1$, this shows that $\rho = 1$ gives no information about the convergence or divergence of the series being tested.

Example 4. Let $f_n(x) = nx^n$. Show that

$$\sum f_n\left(\frac{9}{10}\right) \quad \text{converges and} \quad \sum f_n\left(\frac{10}{9}\right) \quad \text{diverges.}$$

Solution. Consider x fixed but $x > 0$, so all terms will be positive. Then the ρ of Test 6 is a function of x:

$$\rho(x) = \lim_{n \to \infty} \frac{(n+1)x^{n+1}}{nx^n} = \lim_{n \to \infty} \frac{n+1}{n} x = x.$$

Hence, $\rho(9/10) = 9/10 < 1$ and the first series converges, but $\rho(10/9) = 10/9 > 1$ and the second series diverges.

Example 5. Show that* $\displaystyle\sum_{n=1} \frac{(n-1)!}{1 \cdot 3 \cdot 5 \cdot \,\cdots\, (2n-1)}$ converges.

Solution. Set $a_n = \dfrac{(n-1)!}{1 \cdot 3 \cdot \,\cdots\, (2n-1)}$ so that

$$a_{n+1} = \frac{n!}{1 \cdot 3 \cdot \,\cdots\, (2n-1)(2n+1)}.$$

Thus, $\displaystyle\lim_{n \to \infty} \frac{a_{n+1}}{a_n} = \lim_{n \to \infty} \left[\frac{n!}{1 \cdot 3 \cdot \,\cdots\, (2n-1)(2n+1)} \cdot \frac{1 \cdot 3 \cdot \,\cdots\, (2n-1)}{(n-1)!}\right]$

$$= \lim_{n \to \infty} \frac{n}{2n+1} = \frac{1}{2} < 1.$$

Hence, the series converges.

At the end of Sec. 13–1 an example was given of a particular convergent series and a rearrangement of it converging to half the original value. Series of nonnegative terms may, however, be rearranged, as the next theorem shows.

THEOREM 13-7.1. *If $a_n \geq 0$, and $\sum a_n$ converges with sum s, then any rearrangement of this series converges and to the same sum s.*

*Recall that $n! = 1 \cdot 2 \cdot \,\cdots\, \cdot n$ if n is a positive integer and $0! = 1$.

PROOF. Let $\sum b_m$ be a rearrangement of $\sum a_n$. This means that each a_n is one and only one b_m and every b_m is some a_n. Let $\{s_n\}$ and $\{t_m\}$ be the sequences of partial sums of $\sum a_n$ and $\sum b_m$, respectively. Then both these sequences are nondecreasing and $s_n \leq s$, with $s_n \to s$.

Select a positive integer m. Then there is a positive integer n such that each of

$$b_1, b_2, \ldots, b_m \quad \text{is one of} \quad a_1, a_2, \ldots, a_n$$

(and there may be some extra a's). With m and n so related,

$$t_m \leq s_n \leq s.$$

Thus, s is an upper bound of $\{t_m\}$ which therefore converges to a number t such that

$$t \leq s.$$

Hence, $\sum b_m$ is now known to be convergent to $t \leq s$.

The whole argument may now be repeated but starting with $\sum b_m$ converging with sum t and considering $\sum a_n$ a rearrangement of $\sum b_m$. The conclusion reached is $s \leq t$.

Thus, $t = s$ and the theorem is proved.

Problem 1. Use the integral test to determine convergence or divergence (even though some are already known):

a. $\sum \dfrac{1}{n}$.

b. $\sum \dfrac{100}{n(n+1)}$.

c. $\sum \dfrac{10}{\sqrt{n}(\sqrt{n}+1)}$.

d. $\sum \dfrac{n}{n^2+1}$.

e. $\sum \dfrac{n}{e^n}$.

f. $\sum \dfrac{1}{n^2} \cos \dfrac{2}{n}$.

Problem 2. Determine convergence or divergence by using the comparison test and/or the p-test:

a. $\sum \dfrac{1}{n\sqrt{n}-6}$.

b. $\sum \dfrac{n-6}{n^3}$.

c. $\sum \dfrac{1}{3^n+1}$.

d. $\sum \dfrac{n}{n^2-5}$.

e. $\sum \dfrac{n^5+5}{n^6}$.

f. $\sum \dfrac{1+\sin n}{n^2}$.

Problem 3. The ratio test may be applied to each of the following:

a. $\sum \dfrac{200^n}{n!}$.

b. $\sum \dfrac{3^n}{n^2+n}$.

c. $\sum \dfrac{(n+1)2^n}{n!}$.

d. $\sum \dfrac{(n-10)2^n}{n(n-1)(n-2)}$.

e. $\sum n^{10}(\ln 2)^n$.

f. $\sum \dfrac{(\ln 3)^n}{n^{10}}$.

Problem 4. Determine convergence or divergence of:

a. $\sum \dfrac{n!}{2 \cdot 4 \cdot \ldots \cdot (2n)}$.

b. $\sum \dfrac{n!+1}{2^n n!}$.

e. $\sum \dfrac{n+1}{n\sqrt{3n-2}}$.

f. $\sum \dfrac{10n}{(n+1)(n+3)(n+5)}$.

c. $\sum \dfrac{n!}{2 \cdot 5 \cdot 8 \cdots (3n-1)}$.

g. $\sum \sqrt[3]{1 - \dfrac{1}{n}}$.

d. $\sum \dfrac{1}{1 + \ln n}$.

h. $\sum (\sin 150°)^n$.

i. $\sum \left(1 + \dfrac{1}{n}\right)^{-n}$. [Hint: Recall the definition of e.]

Problem 5. Prove: Given $a_n \geq 0$ and $\lim_{n \to \infty} \sqrt[n]{a^n} = \lambda$, then

$$\sum a_n \quad \begin{cases} \text{converges if} & \lambda < 1, \\ \text{diverges} & \text{if} \quad \lambda > 1. \end{cases}$$

Also show that $\lambda = 1$ for both the convergent series $\sum 1/n^2$ and the divergent series $\sum 1/n$. [Hint: l'Hospital's Rules for $\lim_{n \to \infty} \sqrt[n]{n}$.] This is called the **Root Test**. Use this test on:

a. $\sum \dfrac{1}{n^n}$.

c. $\sum \left(\dfrac{n}{n+1}\right)^n$. $\left[\text{Hint: } \lambda = 1, \text{ but } \lim_{n \to \infty} \left(1 + \dfrac{1}{n}\right)^n = e.\right]$

b. $\sum \dfrac{n^3}{2^n}$.

d. $\sum \left(\dfrac{n}{n+1}\right)^{n^2}$.

Problem 6. Prove: If $a_n \geq 0$, $b_n > 0$, and $\lim_{n \to \infty} (a_n/b_n) = \lambda > 0$, then $\sum a_n$ and $\sum b_n$ either both converge or both diverge. [Hint: Show that $\frac{1}{2}\lambda < a_n/b_n < \frac{3}{2}\lambda$ for n sufficiently large.] Also prove: If $\lambda = 0$ and $\sum b_n$ converges, then $\sum a_n$ converges. Use this test on:

a. $\sum \dfrac{\sqrt{n}}{n^2 + 6}$. $\left[\text{Hint: Try } b_n = \dfrac{1}{n^{3/2}}.\right]$

b. $\sum \dfrac{1}{\sqrt{n^2 + 1}}$.

d. $\sum \dfrac{1 + \sin n}{1 + n^2}$. $\left[\text{Hint: } b_n = \dfrac{1}{n^p}, \ 1 < p < 2.\right]$

c. $\sum \dfrac{n + 10}{n \cdot 2^n}$.

e. $\sum \dfrac{1}{n^2 \ln n}$.

Problem 7. Prove that if $a_n > 0$ and $\lim_{n \to \infty} \dfrac{a_{n+1}}{a_n} < 1$, then $\lim_{n \to \infty} a_n = 0$.

Problem 8. a. Show that if $p > 1$ and $\{a_n\}$ is any sequence of nonnegative terms, then

$$\sum \dfrac{a_n}{1 + n^p a_n} \quad \text{converges.}$$

b. Find a sequence $\{a_n\}$ of positive terms for which

$$\sum \dfrac{a_n}{1 + n a_n}$$

diverges and a different sequence for which it converges.

13-8. Absolute Convergence

This section is concerned with properties of series that may have infinitely many negative and infinitely many positive terms.

DEFINITION. *A series $\sum a_n$ is said to be **absolutely convergent** if $\sum |a_n|$ converges.*

For example, the convergent (by Test 3) series

$$1 - \frac{1}{2} + \frac{1}{3} - \frac{1}{4} + \cdots + (-1)^{n+1}\frac{1}{n} + \cdots$$

is not absolutely convergent, since $\sum 1/n$ diverges.

Note that the definition does not say that an absolutely convergent series converges, but the following theorem does.

THEOREM 13-8.1. *Every absolutely convergent series* $\sum a_n$ *converges and*

(1)
$$\left| \sum_{n=1}^{\infty} a^n \right| \leq \sum_{n=1}^{\infty} |a_n|.$$

PROOF. From the properties of absolute values

(2)
$$-|a_n| \leq a_n \leq |a_n|.$$

Hence, $0 \leq a_n + |a_n| \leq 2|a_n|$. Since $\sum |a_n|$ converges, then, by the comparison test, the series $\sum(a_n + |a_n|)$ of nonnegative terms also converges. Therefore, the convergence of

$$\sum [(a_n + |a_n|) - |a_n|] = \sum a_n$$

follows (by Theorem 13-5.2).

Now that $\sum a_n$ and $\sum |a_n|$ are both known to be convergent, it follows from (2) that

$$-\sum_{n=1}^{\infty} |a_n| \leq \sum_{n=1}^{\infty} a_n \leq \sum_{n=1}^{\infty} |a_n|.$$

From properties of absolute values this is equivalent to (1).

All of the tests for convergence of series with nonnegative terms may be used as tests for absolute convergence merely by using $|a_n|$ instead of a_n.

Example 1. $\sum (1/n^2) \sin n$ converges absolutely by the comparison test:

$$\left| \frac{1}{n^2} \sin n \right| = \frac{1}{n^2} |\sin n| \leq \frac{1}{n^2}.$$

Example 2.

$$\frac{1}{3} - \frac{2}{3^2} + \frac{3}{3^3} - \frac{4}{3^4} + \cdots + (-1)^{n+1}\frac{n}{3^n} + \cdots$$

converges absolutely by the ratio test:

$$\lim_{n\to\infty} \frac{|(-1)^{n+2}(n+1)/3^{n+1}|}{|(-1)^{n+1}n/3^n|} = \lim_{n\to\infty} \frac{n+1}{n}\frac{1}{3} = \frac{1}{3} < 1.$$

Example 3.

$$1 - \frac{1}{\sqrt{2}} + \frac{1}{\sqrt{3}} + \frac{1}{\sqrt{4}} + \cdots + (-1)^{n+1}\frac{1}{n} + \cdots$$

converges by Test 2, but $\sum [(-1)^{n+1}(1/\sqrt{n})]^2 = \sum 1/n$ diverges.

The series in Example 3 shows that it is possible for $\sum a_n$ to converge but $\sum a_n^2$ to diverge. However:

(3)   *If $\sum a_n$ converges absolutely, then $\sum a_n^2$ converges.*

PROOF. Since $\sum |a_n|$ converges, then $|a_n| \to 0$. Hence, corresponding to $\epsilon = 1$ there is an N such that whenever $n > N$ then $|a_n| < 1$, and therefore $|a_n||a_n| < |a_n|$. Hence,

$$0 \le a_n^2 < |a_n| \quad \text{if } n \ge N,$$

and thus $\sum a_n^2$ converges, by the comparison test.

As shown earlier, if $\sum a_n$ and $\sum b_n$ converge, then $\sum (a_n \pm b_n)$ and $\sum (c a_n)$ converge, but $\sum (a_n b_n)$ might diverge (Theorem 13–5.2 and immediately following material). Similarities and a difference are given in the following theorem.

THEOREM 13–8.2. *If $\sum a_n$ and $\sum b_n$ are absolutely convergent, then $\sum (a_n \pm b_n)$, $\sum (c a_n)$, and $\sum (a_n b_n)$ are all absolutely convergent, and*

(4)
$$\sum_{n=1}^{\infty} |a_n b_n| \le \frac{1}{2} \left\{ \sum_{n=1}^{\infty} a_n^2 + \sum_{n=1}^{\infty} b_n^2 \right\}.$$

PROOF. Since $|a_k \pm b_k| \le |a_k| + |b_k|$ and $|c a_k| = |c||a_k|$, summing to n and then letting $n \to \infty$ establishes the first parts.

From $0 \le [|a_k| - |b_k|]^2 = |a_k|^2 - 2|a_k||b_k| + |b_k|^2$, it follows that the inequality $|a_k b_k| \le \frac{1}{2}[a_k^2 + b_k^2]$ holds. Thus,

$$\sum_{k=1}^{n} |a_k b_k| \le \frac{1}{2} \left\{ \sum_{k=1}^{n} a_k^2 + \sum_{k=1}^{n} b_k^2 \right\} \le \frac{1}{2} \left\{ \sum_{k=1}^{\infty} a_k^2 + \sum_{k=1}^{\infty} b_k^2 \right\},$$

in which (3) was used. By letting $n \to \infty$, the absolute convergence of $\sum (a_k b_k)$ and the inequality (4) are obtained.

If $\sum a_n$ has only nonnegative terms and converges, then any rearrangement converges and to the same value (Theorem 13–7.1). The notation

$$a^+ = \frac{a + |a|}{2} = \begin{cases} a & \text{if } a \ge 0, \\ 0 & \text{if } a < 0, \end{cases} \quad \text{and} \quad a^- = \frac{a - |a|}{2} = \begin{cases} 0 & \text{if } a \ge 0, \\ a & \text{if } a < 0, \end{cases}$$

is used in the proof of the following extension of Theorem 13–7.1. Note that

$$a^+ + a^- = a \quad \text{and} \quad a^+ - a^- = |a|.$$

THEOREM 13-8.3. *If $\sum a_n$ converges absolutely, with $\sum a_n = s$, then any rearrangement $\sum b_n$ also converges absolutely, with $\sum b_n = s$.*

PROOF. Since $\sum a_n$ and $\sum |a_n|$ both converge, then the convergences and equalities

$$\sum a_n^+ = \tfrac{1}{2} [\sum a_n + \sum |a_n|] \quad \text{and} \quad \sum a_n^- = \tfrac{1}{2} [\sum a_n - \sum |a_n|]$$

follow. As $\sum b_n$ is a rearrangement of $\sum a_n$, so are $\sum b_n^+$ and $\sum b_n^-$ corresponding rearrangements of $\sum a_n^+$ and $\sum a_n^-$. Since $a_n^+ \ge 0$ and $-a_n^- \ge 0$, then convergences, as well as equalities, in

$$\Sigma b_n^+ = \Sigma a_n^+, \quad \Sigma(-b_n^-) = \Sigma(-a_n^-), \quad \Sigma b_n^- = \Sigma a_n^-$$

are justified by Theorem 13–7.1. Hence,

$$\left.\begin{matrix} \Sigma b_n \\ \Sigma |b_n| \end{matrix}\right\} = \Sigma(b_n^+ \pm b_n^-) = \Sigma b_n^+ \pm \Sigma b_n^-$$

$$= \Sigma a_n^+ \pm \Sigma a_n^- = \begin{cases} \Sigma a_n, \\ \Sigma |a_n|. \end{cases}$$

COROLLARY. *If* Σa_n *converges but* $\Sigma |a_n|$ *diverges, then*

$$a_n \to 0, \quad \Sigma a_n^+ = +\infty, \quad \text{and} \quad \Sigma a_n^- = -\infty.$$

PROOF. $a_n \to 0$ since Σa_n converges. Since $|a_n| = 2a_n^+ - a_n$, the assumption of convergence of Σa_n^+ would lead to convergence of $\Sigma |a_n|$. Thus, Σa_n^+ diverges, and to $+\infty$ because it has no negative terms. In a similar way, $\Sigma a_n^- = -\infty$.

With Σa_n convergent but $\Sigma |a_n|$ divergent and λ any number:
1. Add enough a_n^+ terms to just overstep λ,
2. Add to these enough a_n^- terms to understep λ,
3. Add new a_n^+ terms to again overstep λ,
4. Use new a_n^- terms to again understep λ, etc.

This sketchily described procedure indicates how a rearrangement Σb_n of Σa_n could be made to converge to λ.

A series Σa_n which converges but $\Sigma |a_n|$ diverges is said to be **conditionally convergent.**

Problem 1. Test for absolute convergence:

a. $\Sigma \dfrac{\cos n}{n^2}$.

b. $\Sigma(-1)^n \dfrac{n(n+1)}{2^n}$.

c. $\Sigma(-1)^n \left(1 + \dfrac{1}{n}\right)^{-n}$.

d. $\Sigma(-1)^n \dfrac{n^n}{n!}$.

Problem 2. Test for conditional convergence:

a. $\Sigma(-1)^n \dfrac{1 \cdot 3 \cdot 5 \cdots (2n-1)}{4 \cdot 8 \cdot 12 \cdots (4n)}$.

b. $\Sigma \dfrac{(-1)^n n}{\sqrt{n^2+1}}$.

c. $\Sigma \dfrac{(-n)^n}{n!}$.

d. $\Sigma(-1)^n \dfrac{(n+2)}{n(n+1)}$.

e. $\Sigma(-1)^{[n/2]} \dfrac{1}{n}$, where $[x]$ = greatest integer in x.

Problem 3. a. Let $a_1, a_2, a_3, \ldots$ be a sequence with each $a_n \geq 0$ such that Σa_n converges. Prove that the series of terms with odd subscripts and the series of terms with even subscripts both converge and that

$$\sum_{n=1}^{\infty} a_n = \sum_{n=1}^{\infty} a_{2n-1} + \sum_{n=1}^{\infty} a_{2n}.$$

b. Show that

$$\sum_{n=1}^{\infty} \frac{1}{n^2} = \frac{4}{3} \sum_{n=1}^{\infty} \frac{1}{(2n-1)^2} = 4 \sum_{n=1}^{\infty} \frac{1}{(2n)^2}.$$

c. Show that the result of part a holds if $\sum a_n$ is given to be absolutely convergent.

Problem 4. Let $\sum a_n$ and $\sum b_n$ converge absolutely (so that $\sum a_n^2$ and $\sum b_n^2$ converge and $\sum (a_n b_n)$ converges absolutely).

a. Give reasons why

$$f(x) = \sum_{n=1}^{\infty} (xa_n - b_n)^2 = x^2 \sum_{n=1}^{\infty} a_n^2 - 2x \sum_{n=1}^{\infty} (a_n b_n) + \sum_{n=1}^{\infty} b_n^2$$

is defined for each number x and the equality holds.

b. Show that the **Schwarz Inequality,**

$$\left\{ \sum_{n=1}^{\infty} (a_n b_n) \right\}^2 \le \left\{ \sum_{n=1}^{\infty} a_n^2 \right\} \left\{ \sum_{n=1}^{\infty} b_n^2 \right\},$$

holds. [Hint: $f(x) \ge 0$. Find the minimum value of $f(x)$ (which must be greater than or equal to zero).]

c. With all sums from $n = 1$ to ∞, show that the **Minkowski Inequality**

$$\sum (a_n + b_n)^2 \le [\sqrt{\sum a_n^2} + \sqrt{\sum b_n^2}]^2$$

holds. [Hint: $\sum (a_n + b_n)^2 = \sum a_n^2 + 2 \sum (a_n b_n) + \sum b_n^2$. Use the Schwarz Inequality after taking square roots.]

13-9. Power Series

In contrast to the numerical sequences and series discussed so far, a particularly useful type of series of functions will be considered in this section.

DEFINITION. *Given a numerical sequence* $a_0, a_1, a_2, \ldots$, *then*

$$(1) \qquad \sum_{n=0}^{\infty} a_n x^n = a_0 + a_1 x + a_2 x^2 + \cdots + a_n x^n + \cdots$$

*is called a **power series** in x. Also, with c any constant* $\sum a_n (x - c)^n$ *is a power series in* $(x - c)$.

If x is assigned a numerical value, the power series becomes a numerical series that may converge, but a different assignment may yield a divergent series. For some x, the power series may converge absolutely, while for other x only conditionally.

Example 1. The power series

$$(2) \qquad 1 + \frac{x}{1 \cdot 2} + \frac{x^2}{2 \cdot 2^2} + \frac{x^3}{3 \cdot 2^3} + \cdots + \frac{x^n}{n \cdot 2^n} + \cdots$$

has $a_0 = 1$ and $a_n = 1/(n2^n)$ for $n \ge 1$. Show that

$$(3) \qquad \begin{cases} \text{If } -2 \le x < 2, \text{ the series converges, and} \\ \text{If } \qquad x \ge 2, \text{ the series diverges.} \end{cases}$$

Solution. If $x = 0$, the series has a single nonzero term and converges to 1. Hence, consider $x \neq 0$. Then the ratio test may be applied to investigate absolute convergence:

$$(4) \qquad \lim_{n \to \infty} \frac{|x^{n+1}/(n+1)2^{n+1}|}{|x^n/n2^n|} = \lim_{n \to \infty} \frac{n}{n+1} \frac{|x|}{2} = \frac{|x|}{2}.$$

If $|x| = 2$, the ratio test tells nothing about whether the absolute value series converges or diverges. However, if

$$x = 2, \quad \text{the series becomes} \quad 1 + 1 + \tfrac{1}{2} + \tfrac{1}{3} + \cdots,$$

which diverges and if

$$x = -2, \quad \text{the series becomes} \quad 1 - 1 + \tfrac{1}{2} - \tfrac{1}{3} + \tfrac{1}{4} - \tfrac{1}{5} + \cdots,$$

which converges conditionally.

Returning to (4), if $|x| < 2$, then $|x|/2 < 1$ and the series converges absolutely, and hence converges. So far it is known that, for any x satisfying

$$(5) \qquad\qquad -2 \leq x < 2, \text{ the series converges,}$$

but diverges if $x = 2$.

Again, from (4), if $|x| > 2$, the absolute value series diverges. In case $x > 2$, the series and the absolute value series are the same. Hence, the series diverges if $x > 2$ and both parts of (3) have been established.

The above discussion leaves open the question:

Is there any $x < -2$ for which the series (2) converges conditionally?
(Maybe because signs alternate if $x < -2$.)

This question may be answered on the basis of the next theorem. Note the use of a_n/a_{n+1} in the theorem instead of the usual ratio a_{n+1}/a_n.

THEOREM 13–9.1. If $a_n \neq 0$ and

$$(6) \qquad\qquad \lim_{n \to \infty} \left| \frac{a_n}{a_{n+1}} \right| \text{ exists and } = r > 0,$$

then

$$(7) \qquad \begin{cases} \sum |a_n x^n| & \text{converges if } -r < x < r, \\ \sum a_n x^n & \text{diverges if } |x| > r. \end{cases}$$

[Note: Each specific series must be examined by some other method to determine convergence or divergence when $x = r$ or $x = -r$.]

PROOF. If $x = 0$, then $\sum a_n x^n$ converges, so consider $x \neq 0$. Then

$$\lim_{n \to \infty} \frac{|a_{n+1}/x^{n+1}|}{|a_n/x^n|} = |x| \bigg/ \lim_{n \to \infty} \left| \frac{a_n}{a_{n+1}} \right| = \frac{|x|}{r}.$$

Hence, if $|x| < r$, the series $\sum |a_n x^n|$ converges, and the top line of (7) is therefore established. Also,

$$\text{if } |x| > r, \quad \text{then} \quad \sum |a_n x^n| \text{ diverges.}$$

This alone, however, does not preclude the possibility of conditional convergence at some x_1 with $|x_1| > r$.

Assume (which will lead to a contradiction) that

$$|x_1| > r \quad \text{and} \quad \sum a_n x_1^n \quad \text{converges.}$$

Select any number x_2 such that $r < |x_2| < |x_1|$ and note, from $|x_2| > r$, that

(8) $$\sum |a_n x_2^n| \quad \text{diverges.}$$

Since $\sum a_n x_1^n$ converges (by assumption), the sequence $\{a_n x_1^n\}$ of its terms is a null sequence and thus is a bounded sequence (recall Lemma 1, p.495). Let $c > 0$ be such that

$$|a_n x_1^n| < c, \quad n = 0,1,2,3, \ldots.$$

Then

$$|a_n x_2^n| = \left| a_n x_1^n \left(\frac{x_2}{x_1} \right)^n \right| = |a_n x_1^n| \left| \frac{x_2}{x_1} \right|^n < c \left| \frac{x_2}{x_1} \right|^n.$$

Since $\sum |x_2/x_1|^n$ converges (because $|x_2/x_1| < 1$), the series $\sum |a_n x_2^n|$ converges by the comparison test. But $\sum |a_n x_2^n|$ diverges, as noted in (8).

This contradiction shows that if $|x| > r$, then not only does $\sum |a_n x^n|$ diverge, but also $\sum a_n x^n$ itself diverges. Thus, the bottom line of (7) is established and the theorem is proved.

In some cases, the following theorem (with no reference to r) is useful.

THEOREM 13-9.2. *If $0 < |x_2| < |x_1|$ and if $\sum |a_n x_2^n|$ diverges, then $\sum a_n x_1^n$ diverges.*

To prove this theorem, assume that $\sum a_n x_1^n$ converges. With this start it is left as an exercise to establish the theorem by following the above proof from (8) on.

Example 2. Find all values of x for which each of the series

(9) $$1 + x + \frac{x^2}{2!} + \frac{x^3}{3!} + \cdots + \frac{x^n}{n!} + \cdots \quad \text{and}$$

(10) $$1 + x + 2!x^2 + 3!x^3 + \cdots + n!x^n + \cdots$$

converges.

Solution. They both converge if $x = 0$; thus, take $x \neq 0$.
For (9),

(11) $$\lim_{n \to \infty} \frac{|x^{n+1}/(n+1)!|}{|x^n/n!|} = |x| \lim_{n \to \infty} \frac{1}{n+1} = 0.$$

Since $0 < 1$, the first series converges absolutely (hence converges) for all x. It is usual to say that (9) converges for $-\infty < x < \infty$.
For (10),

(12) $$\lim_{n \to \infty} \frac{|(n+1)!x^{n+1}|}{|n!x^n|} = |x| \lim_{n \to \infty} (n+1) = \infty \quad \text{(since } |x| \neq 0).$$

This says that $\sum |n!x^n|$ diverges if $x \neq 0$. Now take any $x \neq 0$ and think of it as the fixed x_1 of Theorem 13-9.2. Since $|x| > 0$, take x_2 such that $0 < |x_2| < |x|$.

Then $\sum |a_n x_2^n|$ diverges, and thus $\sum a_n x^n$ diverges. Hence, (11) converges if and only if $x = 0$.

In (11) and (12) turn each of the ratios over and note that the results 0 and ∞ are interchanged. This is typical of the general situation expressed by:

$$\text{If} \quad \lim_{n \to \infty} \left| \frac{a_n}{a_{n+1}} \right| = \left\{ \begin{matrix} \infty \\ 0 \end{matrix} \right\}, \quad \text{then} \quad \sum a_n x^n \quad \text{converges} \quad \left\{ \begin{matrix} \text{for } -\infty < x < \infty, \\ \text{if and only if } x = 0. \end{matrix} \right.$$

DEFINITION. *A power series $\sum a_n x^n$ is said to have* **radius of convergence** *r, provided*

$$\left\{ \begin{matrix} r = 0 \\ 0 < r < \infty \\ r = \infty \end{matrix} \right\} \quad \text{and} \quad \sum a_n x^n \text{ converges} \quad \left\{ \begin{matrix} \text{if and only if } x = 0, \\ \text{if } -r < x < r, \text{ diverges if } |x| > r, \\ \text{if } -\infty < x < \infty. \end{matrix} \right.$$

The set of all points of convergence is called the **interval of convergence**.

The series (9) has infinite interval $-\infty < x < \infty$ of convergence.
Series (2) has half-open interval $-2 \le x < 2$ of convergence.
For those series for which the limit in (6) exists, the radius of convergence is determined by (6), but there are series for which this limit does not exist. By slight modifications of the above proofs, the following theorem can be shown.

THEOREM 13-9.3. *Every power series $\sum a_n x^n$ has a radius of convergence r such that:*

(i) *If* $-r < x < r$, *then* $\sum |a_n x^n|$ *converges.*

(ii) *If* $|x| > r$, *then* $\sum a_n x^n$ *diverges.*

Problem 1. Check the interval of convergence, that is, determine the radius of convergence, and in case $0 < r < \infty$ establish convergence or divergence when $x = r$ and $x = -r$:

a. $1 - x + \dfrac{1}{2} x^2 - \dfrac{1}{3} x^3 + \cdots; \quad -1 < x \le 1.$

b. $1 - x + 2x^2 - 3x^3 + \cdots; \quad -1 < x < 1.$

c. $1 - x + \dfrac{x^2}{2} - \dfrac{x^3}{3!} + \dfrac{x^4}{4!} - \cdots; \quad -\infty < x < \infty.$

d. $1 + 100x + 200x^2 + 300x^3 + \cdots; \quad -1 < x < 1.$

e. $1 + x + \dfrac{x^2}{3} + \dfrac{x^3}{5} + \cdots + \dfrac{x^n}{2n - 1} + \cdots; \quad -1 \le x < 1.$

f. $1 + 2x + 2x^2 + \dfrac{2^3 x^3}{3} + \cdots + \dfrac{2^n x^n}{n} + \cdots; \quad -\dfrac{1}{2} \le x < \dfrac{1}{2}.$

g. $3 + \dfrac{x}{2} + \dfrac{x^2}{5} + \dfrac{x^3}{10} + \dfrac{x^4}{17} + \cdots + \dfrac{x^n}{1 + n^2} + \cdots; \quad -1 \le x \le 1.$

h. $5 - \dfrac{x}{2} + x^2 + \dfrac{x^3}{6} + \dfrac{x^4}{13} + \cdots + \dfrac{x^n}{n^2 - 3} + \cdots; \quad -1 \le x \le 1.$

Problem 2. A series of the form

$$a_0 + a_1(x - a) + a_2(x - a)^2 + \cdots + a_n(x - a)^n + \cdots$$

is a power series in $x - a$. Series of this form may be brought under the above theory by making the translation $X = x - a$.

Check the interval of convergence for each of the following.

a. $5 + \dfrac{(x - 1)}{2} + \dfrac{(x - 1)^2}{4} + \dfrac{(x - 1)^3}{9} + \cdots + \dfrac{(x - 1)^n}{n^2} + \cdots; \quad 0 \le x \le 2.$

b. $3 + \dfrac{(x + 2)}{2} + \dfrac{(x + 2)^2}{4} + \cdots + \dfrac{(x + 2)^n}{n^2} + \cdots; \quad -3 \le x \le -1.$

c. $2 + (x - 10) + \dfrac{(x - 10)^2}{2} + \dfrac{(x - 10)^3}{3} + \cdots; \quad 9 \le x < 11.$

d. $1 + (x + 10) + \dfrac{(x + 10)^2}{2!} + \dfrac{(x + 10)^3}{3!} + \cdots; \quad -\infty < x < \infty.$

e. $0 + \dfrac{2x - 5}{5} + \dfrac{(2x - 3)^2}{5^2} + \dfrac{(2x - 3)^3}{5^3} + \cdots; \quad -1 < x < 4.$

f. $1 + (2x - 3) + \dfrac{(2x - 3)^2}{2} + \dfrac{(2x - 3)^3}{3} + \cdots; \quad 1 \le x < 2.$

Problem 3. Each of the following may be brought under the above theory by making an appropriate substitution. In each case, check the set of convergence:

a. $1 + x^2 + x^4 + x^6 + \cdots; \quad -1 < x < 1.$ [Hint: $x^2 = t$.]

b. $\displaystyle\sum_{n=1}^{\infty} \frac{1}{n}\left(\frac{x}{2}\right)^{2n}; \quad -2 < x < 2.$

c. $\displaystyle\sum_{n=1}^{\infty} \frac{1}{n}\left(\frac{x}{2}\right)^{3n}; \quad -2 \le x < 2.$

d. $\displaystyle\sum_{n=1}^{\infty} \frac{1}{n}\left(\frac{1}{x}\right)^{n}; \quad x \le -1 \quad \text{or} \quad x > 1.$

e. $\displaystyle\sum_{n=1}^{\infty} \frac{1}{n}\left(\frac{x}{2x - 3}\right)^{n}; \quad x \le 1 \quad \text{or} \quad x > 3.$

f. $\displaystyle\sum_{n=1}^{\infty} \frac{1}{n}\left(\frac{2x - 3}{x}\right)^{n}; \quad 1 \le x < 3.$

g. $\displaystyle\sum_{n=1}^{\infty} \frac{1}{n!}\left(\frac{2x - 3}{x}\right)^{n}; \quad x \ne 0.$

h. $\displaystyle\sum_{n=1}^{\infty} \cos^n x; \quad x \ne m\pi, \quad m = 0, \pm 1, \pm 2, \cdots.$

Problem 4. For each of the definitions of $f_n(x)$, check the intervals of convergence of

$$\sum f_n(x), \quad \sum \frac{d}{dx} f_n(x), \quad \text{and} \quad \sum \int_0^x f_n(t)\, dt.$$

a. $f_n(x) = x^n; \quad -1 < x < 1, \quad -1 < x < 1, \quad -1 \le x < 1.$

b. $f_n(x) = \dfrac{1}{n}\left(\dfrac{x}{3}\right)^{n}; \quad -3 \le x < 3, \quad -3 < x < 3, \quad -3 \le x \le 3.$

c. $f_n(x) = \dfrac{1}{n!}\left(\dfrac{x}{3}\right)^{n}; \quad -\infty < x < \infty.$

d. $f_n(x) = \dfrac{(x - 1)^n}{\sqrt{n}}; \quad 0 \le x < 2, \quad 0 < x < 2, \quad 0 \le x \le 2.$

Problem 5. Show that the series (2) diverges for $|x| > 2$ without using Theorem 13-9.1. [Hint: Find $\lim_{n \to \infty} (1/n)(|x|/2)^n$.]

Problem 6. Define $f(x)$ by setting

$$f(x) = \sum_{n=0}^{\infty} x(1 - x)^n \quad \text{for} \quad 0 \leq x < 2.$$

a. Check that $0 \leq x < 2$ is the domain of convergence of the series.

b. Show that $f(x) = \begin{cases} 0 & \text{if } x = 0 \quad \text{or} \quad x = 1, \\ 1 & \text{if } 0 < x < 1 \quad \text{or} \quad 1 < x < 2. \end{cases}$

[Note: This shows that a series of continuous functions need not converge to a continuous function.]

13-10. Natural Logarithms

A power series converging to $\ln (1 + b)$ for $-1 < b \leq 1$ is obtained in this section and error estimates are determined for how well the partial sums approximate $\ln (1 + b)$.

By ordinary long division,

$$\frac{1}{1 + x} = 1 - x + x^2 - x^3 + \cdots + (-1)^{n-1} x^{n-1} + (-1)^n \frac{x^n}{1 + x}$$

for $x \neq -1$, and $n = 0, 1, 2, \ldots$. Hence, for any constant $b > -1$,

$$\ln (1 + b) = \int_0^b \frac{dx}{1 + x} = \left[x - \frac{x^2}{2} + \frac{x^3}{3} - \cdots + (-1)^{n-1} \frac{x^n}{n} \right]_0^b + \int_0^b \frac{(-1)^n x^n}{1 + x} dx$$

(1) $$= b - \frac{b^2}{2} + \frac{b^3}{3} - \cdots + (-1)^{n-1} \frac{b^n}{n} + R_n \quad \text{where}$$

(2) $$R_n = \int_0^b \frac{(-x)^n}{1 + x} dx.$$

This holds for all $b > -1$, but R_n may be large for some values of b. It will be shown, however, that

(3) $$\lim_{n \to \infty} R_n = 0 \quad \text{for} \quad -1 < b \leq 1.$$

Hence, with n sufficiently large, the polynomial portion of (1) will approximate $\ln (1 + b)$ to within a preassigned accuracy, provided $-1 < b \leq 1$.

Separate proofs of (3) are given according to whether b is positive or negative.

Case 1. $0 \leq b \leq 1$. Then, in (2), the dummy variable of integration x always satisfies $0 \leq x \leq b$, so that

$$|-x| = x, \quad 1 \leq 1 + x, \quad \text{and} \quad 0 \leq \frac{x^n}{1 + x} \leq x^n.$$

Hence, from the Law of the Mean for Integrals,

(4) $$|R_n| \leq \int_0^b \frac{|-x|^n}{1 + x} dx = \int_0^b \frac{x^n}{1 + x} dx \leq \int_0^b x^n \, dx = \frac{b^{n+1}}{n + 1}.$$

Thus, (3) holds at least for $0 \leq b \leq 1$.

Case 2. $-1 < b < 0$. A little extra precaution needs to be taken, since in (2) the lower limit of integration is greater than the upper limit of integration. Now $-1 < b \leq x \leq 0$, so that $0 \leq -x$ and $0 < 1 + x$. Hence, the integrand in (2) is never negative for any n, and

$$0 \leq \frac{(-x)^n}{1+x} \leq \frac{(-x)^n}{1+b} \quad \text{since} \quad \frac{1}{1+x} \leq \frac{1}{1+b}.$$

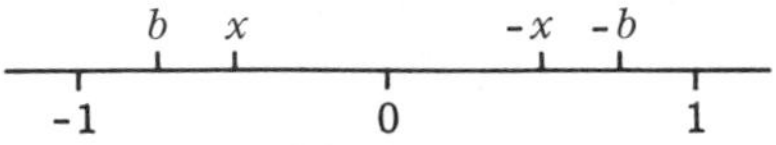

Fig. 13-10.1

Thus, by reversing the order of integration,

$$|R_n| = \int_b^0 \frac{(-x)^n}{1+x}\,dx \leq \int_b^0 \frac{(-x)^n}{1+b}\,dx = \frac{-1}{1+b}\left[\frac{(-x)^{n+1}}{n+1}\right]_b^0$$

$$= \frac{1}{1+b}\frac{(-b)^{n+1}}{n+1} < \frac{1}{(1+b)(n+1)} \quad \text{since} \quad 0 < -b < 1.$$

Thus, (3) holds for $-1 < b < 0$.

Hence, (3) holds for each constant b such that $-1 < b \leq 1$.

Also, notice from (1) that

(5) $$\left|\ln(1+b) - \left[b - \frac{b^2}{2} + \frac{b^3}{3} - \frac{b^4}{4} + \cdots + (-1)^n \frac{b^n}{n}\right]\right| = |R_n|.$$

Hence, the fact that (3) holds for $-1 < b \leq 1$ establishes the convergence of the series and the equality

$$\ln(1+b) = b - \frac{b^2}{2} + \frac{b^3}{3} - \cdots + (-1)^n \frac{b^n}{n} + \cdots \quad \text{for} \quad -1 < b \leq 1.$$

In particular, then

$$\ln 2 = 1 - \tfrac{1}{2} + \tfrac{1}{3} - \tfrac{1}{4} + \cdots,$$

a fact that was promised in Sec. 13-1. Convergence, however, is so slow that, from (4) with $b = 1$, it takes $n \geq 19{,}999$ to ensure that $|R_n| < 5 \times 10^{-5}$.

On the other hand, if $b = 0.1$, then $|R_n|$ decreases rapidly with increasing n and

$$\left|\ln 1.1 - \left(0.1 + \frac{0.01}{2} + \frac{0.001}{3} + \frac{0.0001}{4}\right)\right| < 5 \times 10^{-5}.$$

13-11. Taylor's Theorem

In the previous section, $\ln(1+b)$ with $-1 < b \leq 1$ was approximated, with error estimate, by a polynomial in b. The following theorem leads to polynomial approximations of more general functions. For the sake of generality and ease of application, the theorem leaves indefinite whether a is less than or greater than b.

TAYLOR'S THEOREM. *If a function $f(x)$ has its nth derivative $f^n(x)$ continuous on a closed interval with endpoints a and b, then*

(1)
$$f(b) = f(a) + f'(a)(b-a) + \frac{f''(a)}{2!}(b-a)^2$$

$$+ \frac{f'''(a)}{3!}(b-a)^3 + \cdots + \frac{f^{n-1}(a)}{(n-1)!}(b-a)^{n-1} + R_n,$$

where

(2)
$$R_n = \frac{1}{(n-1)!}\int_a^b (b-x)^{n-1} f^n(x)\, dx.$$

Note: The continuity of $f^n(x)$ means that $f(x)$ and $f^k(x)$, $k = 1, 2, \ldots,$ $n-1$ are also continuous on the same closed interval. In case the functions are not defined outside this interval, then one-sided existence and continuity at the endpoints a and b are intended.

PROOF. The earlier proofs of Taylor's Theorem (with a different form of R_n) were long and involved, but a clearer proof starting with the definition of constants

(3)
$$I_k = \int_a^b \frac{(b-x)^{k-1}}{(k-1)!} f^k(x)\, dx \quad \text{for} \quad k = 1, 2, \ldots, n$$

was discovered. In particular, for $k = 1$,

$$\int_a^b \frac{(b-x)^0}{0!} f'(x)\, dx = \int_a^b f'(x)\, dx = f(x)\Big]_a^b; \quad \text{that is,}$$

(4)
$$I_1 = f(b) - f(a).$$

Integration by parts is next used in (3) with

$$u = f^k(x) \quad \text{and} \quad dv = \frac{(b-x)^{k-1}}{(k-1)!} dx, \quad \text{so that}$$

$$du = f^{k+1}(x)\, dx \quad \text{and} \quad v = -\frac{(b-x)^k}{k!}.$$

Hence,

$$I_k = -f^k(x)\frac{(b-x)^k}{k!}\Big]_a^b - \int_a^b -\frac{(b-x)^k}{k!} f^{k+1}(x)\, dx$$

$$= f^k(a)\frac{(b-a)^k}{k!} + \int_a^b \frac{(b-x)^k}{k!} f^{k+1}(x)\, dx, \quad k = 1, 2, \ldots, n-1.$$

But this last integral is the same as the integral in (3) with k replaced by $k + 1$, so that

$$I_k = \frac{f^k(a)}{k!}(b-a)^k + I_{k+1} \quad \text{for} \quad k = 1, 2, \ldots, n-1.$$

By summing from $k = 1$ to $n - 1$, then

$$\sum_{k=1}^{n-1} I_k = \sum_{k=1}^{n-1} \frac{f^k(a)}{k!}(b-a)^k + \sum_{k=1}^{n-1} I_{k+1}.$$

Cancellation of like terms from both sides then yields

$$I_1 = \sum_{k=1}^{n-1} \frac{f^k(a)}{k!}(b-a)^k + I_n.$$

Finally, by using (4), and (3) with $k = n$, the result may be written as

$$f(b) = f(a) + \sum_{k=1}^{n-1} \frac{f^k(a)}{k!}(b-a)^k + I_n,$$

$$I_n = \frac{1}{(n-1)!}\int_a^b (b-x)^{n-1} f^n(x)\, dx.$$

But this is merely another form of writing (1) and (2); hence, the theorem is proved.

The equation (1), with R_n as given in (2), is called **Taylor's Formula** with remainder in **integral form.** In the special case in which $a = 0$, (1) is called **Maclaurin's Formula.**

The computation of values of a function to within a prescribed error is basic in many applications, especially since the advent of electronic computers. As used here, an "error" does not mean a "blunder," but rather a "tolerance" within which values are acceptable for the problem at hand. One of the principal uses of the Taylor and Maclaurin Formulas is for computing within a prescribed error.

Example 1. Use Taylor's Formula with $a = \pi/4$ and find an expression whose value is within 5×10^{-5} of $\sin 40°$.

Solution. Set $f(x) = \sin x$ and, since radians must be used,

$$b = \frac{40\pi}{180} = \frac{2}{9}\pi \quad \text{and} \quad b - a = \frac{-\pi}{36}.$$

Then $f^n(x)$ is either $\pm\sin x$ or $\pm\cos x$, so that $|f^n(x)| \leq 1$. Also, since $b < a$, then $b - x \leq 0$ for $b \leq x \leq a$. Hence,

$$|R_n| \leq \frac{1}{(n-1)!}\left|\int_a^b (b-x)^{n-1} f^n(x)\, dx\right| \leq \frac{1}{(n-1)!}\int_b^a |b-x|^{n-1} |f^n(x)|\, dx$$

$$\leq \frac{1}{(n-1)!}\int_b^a (x-b)^{n-1} dx = \frac{1}{n!}(a-b)^n = \frac{1}{n!}\left(\frac{\pi}{36}\right)^n.$$

Since $\pi/36 < 0.1$, it is safe to use any n for which

$$\frac{1}{n!}(0.1)^n \leq 5 \times 10^{-5}.$$

A check will show that $n = 4$ is the smallest such n. Thus, only $4 - 1 = 3$ derivatives of $\sin x$ are used to obtain

(5)
$$\sin 40° = \sin \frac{\pi}{4} + \left(\cos \frac{\pi}{4}\right)\left(\frac{-\pi}{36}\right) + \frac{1}{2!}\left(-\sin \frac{\pi}{4}\right)\left(\frac{-\pi}{36}\right)^2$$
$$+ \frac{1}{3!}\left(-\cos \frac{\pi}{4}\right)\left(\frac{-\pi}{36}\right)^3 \pm 5 \times 10^{-5}$$
$$= \frac{1}{\sqrt{2}}\left[1 - \frac{\pi}{36} - \frac{1}{2}\left(\frac{\pi}{36}\right)^2 + \frac{1}{6}\left(\frac{\pi}{36}\right)^3\right] \pm 5 \times 10^{-5}.$$

The usual way of indicating approximations is used here; it means that

$$-5 \times 10^{-5} \le \sin 40° - \frac{1}{\sqrt{2}}[\cdots] \le 5 \times 10^{-5}.$$

In addition to the integral form of R_n, there are several derivative forms. The simplest and most used derivative form is given in the following restatement of Taylor's Formula. Also, for the sake of a compact formula, the "0th derivative" of $f(x)$ is interpreted as $f(x)$ itself and the notation

$$f^0(x) = f(x)$$

is used. Then under the assumptions of Taylor's Theorem:

There is a number ξ_n on the open interval with endpoints a and b such that

(6)
$$f(b) = \sum_{k=0}^{n-1} \frac{f^k(x)}{k!}(b-a)^k + R_n, \quad \text{where}$$
$$R_n = \frac{f^n(\xi_n)}{n!}(b-a)^n.$$

Note: This is called the **Lagrange form** of the remainder.

PROOF FOR $a < b$. Let m be the minimum value and M the maximum value of $f^n(x)$ on $a \le x \le b$. Then $m \le f^n(x) \le M$ and

$$m(b-x)^{n-1} \le f^n(x)(b-x)^{n-1} \le M(b-x)^{n-1},$$

since $0 \le b - x$. Hence,

$$m\frac{(b-a)^n}{n} = m\int_a^b (b-x)^{n-1} dx \le \int_a^b (b-x)^{n-1} f^n(x)\, dx \le M\frac{(b-a)^n}{n},$$

and thus

$$m \le \frac{n}{(b-a)^n}\int_a^b (b-x)^{n-1} f^n(x)\, dx \le M.$$

By the intermediate value property of continuous functions, there is a ξ_n such that $a < \xi_n < b$ and $f^n(\xi_n)$ is equal to the middle term. This equality and the integral form of R_n show that

$$f^n(\xi_n) = \frac{n}{(b-a)^n} \cdot (n-1)! R_n,$$

and hence (6) holds for $a < b$. A little care with inequalities when $b < a$ will establish the result in this case as well.

For convenience in estimating remainders, Table 3 lists values of $1/n!$ and $\log_{10}(1/n!)$, each rounded off to the higher value for safety.

Example 2. Approximate sin 40° to within 5×10^{-5} by Maclaurin's expansion.

Solution. Now $a = 0$ and $b = \frac{2}{9}\pi$, but again $f(x) = \sin x$. Hence, the Lagrange form of the remainder gives

$$|R_n| = \frac{1}{n!}|f^{(n)}(\xi_n)|\left(\frac{2\pi}{9} - 0\right)^n < \frac{1}{n!}\left(\frac{2\pi}{9}\right)^n < \frac{1}{n!}(0.699)^n.$$

From Table 3, $1/8! = 2.481 \times 10^{-5} < 5 \times 10^{-5}$, so that an n less than 8 will likely work because of the factor $(0.699)^n$. Since

$$\log(5 \times 10^{-5}) = -5 + \log 5 < -5 + 0.6991 = -4.3009,$$

the smallest n is desired for which $\log|R_n| < -4.3009$. From

$$\log|R_7| \leq \log\frac{1}{7!} + 7\log(0.699) < -3.7024 + 7(-1 + 0.8445)$$

$$= -3.7024 + 7(-0.1555) = -3.7024 - 1.0885$$

$$= -4.7909 < -4.3009,$$

then $n = 7$ may be used. Furthermore,

$$\log|R_6| \leq \log\frac{1}{6!} + 6\log(0.699) < -2.8593 + 6(-0.1555)$$

$$= -2.8593 - 0.9333 = -3.7932 > -4.3009,$$

and it is not safe to use $n = 6$.

Since $a = 0$, then $\sin a = 0$ and $\cos a = 1$, so that, for $n = 7$,

$$\sin 40° = 0 + \frac{2\pi}{9} + 0 - \frac{1}{3!}\left(\frac{2\pi}{9}\right)^3 + 0 + \frac{1}{5!}\left(\frac{2\pi}{9}\right)^5 + 0 \pm 5 \times 10^{-5}$$

(7)
$$= \frac{2\pi}{9} - \frac{1}{6}\left(\frac{2\pi}{9}\right)^3 + \frac{1}{120}\left(\frac{2\pi}{9}\right)^5 \pm 5 \times 10^{-5}.$$

Note that (7) has one less term than (5).

With $\pi = 3.14159$ to an extra decimal place and

$$s = 2\frac{\pi}{9} = 2(0.34907) = 0.69814, \quad \text{then} \quad s^2 = 0.48740.$$

Then a convenient way to arrange the essential part of (7) for computation is

$$\left[\left(\frac{s^2}{5\cdot4} - 1\right)\frac{s^2}{3\cdot2} + 1\right]s = 0.64283.$$

Hence, sin 40° = 0.6428, accurate within 5×10^{-5}.

After obtaining Taylor's Formula with a and b constants, then with b replaced by x the result is

$$f(x) = \sum_{k=0}^{n-1}\frac{f^k(a)}{k!}(x - a)^k + R_n,$$

where R_n is in either

integral form　　$R_n = \dfrac{1}{(n-1)!} \displaystyle\int_a^x (x-t)^{n-1} f^n(t)\, dt$　　or

Lagrange form　　$R_n = \dfrac{f^n(\xi_n)}{n!} (x-a)^n,$　　ξ_n　between *a* and *x*.

Note that in the integral form the dummy variable of integration had to be changed to a letter other than *x*.

Problem 1. a. Start by dividing 1 by $1 + t^2$ and proceed as with the logarithm to obtain

$$\tan^{-1} x = x - \frac{x^3}{3} + \frac{x^5}{5} - \cdots + (-1)^{n-1}\frac{x^{2n-1}}{2n-1} + R_{2n},$$

where

$$R_{2n} = (-1)^n \int_0^x \frac{t^{2n}}{1+t^2}\, dt.$$

Prove that

$$\lim_{n\to\infty} R_{2n} = 0 \quad \text{for} \quad -1 \le x \le 1.$$

b. Show that $\frac{1}{4}\pi = \tan^{-1}\frac{1}{2} + \tan^{-1}\frac{1}{3}$ and show how this equation can be used to approximate π.

c. Check that $\dfrac{1}{4}\pi = 4\tan^{-1}\dfrac{1}{5} - \tan^{-1}\dfrac{1}{239}.$

Problem 2. Obtain the following Maclaurin expansions:

a. $e^x = 1 + x + \dfrac{x^2}{2!} + \dfrac{x^3}{3!} + \cdots + \dfrac{x^{n-1}}{(n-1)!} + \dfrac{e^{\xi_n}}{n!} x^n.$

b. $e^{-x} = 1 - x + \dfrac{x^2}{2!} - \dfrac{x^3}{3!} + \cdots + (-1)^{n-1}\dfrac{x^{n-1}}{(n-1)!} + (-1)^n \dfrac{e^{-\xi_n}}{n!} x^n.$

c. $\sin x = x - \dfrac{x^3}{3!} + \dfrac{x^5}{5!} + \cdots + (-1)^{n+1}\dfrac{x^{2n-1}}{(2n-1)!} + R_{2n}, \quad n = 1, 2, 3, \ldots,$

$$\text{with} \quad |R_{2n}| = \frac{|\cos\xi_n|}{(2n+1)!} |x|^{2n+1}.$$

d. $\cos x = 1 - \dfrac{x^2}{2!} + \dfrac{x^4}{4!} - \cdots (-1)^n\dfrac{x^{2n}}{(2n)!} + R_{2n+1}, \quad n = 0, 1, 2, 3, \ldots,$

$$\text{with} \quad |R_{2n+1}| = \frac{|\cos\xi_n|}{(2n+2)!} |x|^{2n+2}.$$

e. $\ln(1 + x) = x - \dfrac{x^2}{2} + \dfrac{x^3}{3} - \cdots \dfrac{(-1)^n}{n-1} x^{n-1} + R_n, \quad n = 2, 3, \cdots,$

$$\text{with} \quad R_n = \frac{(-1)^{n+1}}{n}\left(\frac{x}{1+\xi_n}\right)^n, \quad x > -1, \quad \xi_n \text{ between 0 and } x.$$

Problem 3. Obtain Taylor's Formula for the given function, *a*, and *n*:
a. $f(x) = \cos x; \quad a = \pi/4, \quad n = 5.$
d. $f(x) = \sin^{-1} x; \quad a = 0, \quad n = 4.$
c. $f(x) = \tan x; \quad a = \pi/4, \quad n = 4.$
d. $f(x) = \ln x, \quad x > 0; \quad a = 1, \quad \text{general } n.$

Problem 4. Find Taylor's Formula with $a = 1$ that will give $\ln (1.2)$ with error $\leq 5 \times 10^{-4}$.

Problem 5. Write a formula which will give $\sin 255°$ with error $< 5 \times 10^{-8}$.

Problem 6. The theorem in part a is Prob. 13 of Sec. 3-12. Try to prove the theorem without looking back.

a. Prove: If $F(x)$ and $G(x)$ are continuous, with $G(x) \geq 0$ on $a \leq x \leq b$, then there is a number ξ such that $a < \xi < b$ and

$$\int_a^b F(x)G(x)\, dx = F(\xi)\int_a^b G(x)\, dx.$$

b. Obtain the same result if $G(x) \leq 0$ on $a \leq x \leq b$.

c. Use $F(x) = f^n(x)$ and $G(x) = (b - x)^{n-1}$ in the integral form of R_n and again obtain the Lagrange form of R_n. What adjustments need to be made if $b < a$?

d. Show that there is a ξ between a and b such that

$$R_n = \frac{1}{(n-1)!}(b - \xi_n)^{n-1} f^n(\xi_n)(b - a).$$

[Note: This is called the **Cauchy form** of the remainder.]

13-12. Taylor's Series

If $f(x)$ possesses derivatives of all orders at $x = a$, then

$$(1) \qquad f(a) + f'(a)(x - a) + \frac{f''(a)}{2!}(x - a)^2 + \cdots + \frac{f^n(a)}{n!}(x - a)^n + \cdots$$

is called **Taylor's series** for $f(x)$ at $x = a$. Another phraseology is to say that (1) is the **Taylor expansion** of $f(x)$ about $x = a$, or the **Maclaurin expansion** if $a = 0$. For some values of x, the series may diverge, for others, it may converge. Since Taylor's Formula may be written as

$$(2) \qquad \left| f(x) - \sum_{k=0}^{n-1} \frac{f^k(a)}{k!}(x - a)^k \right| = |R_n|,$$

it follows that, if $\lim_{n \to \infty} |R_n| = 0$, then the series not only converges, but converges to $f(x)$. *This is a most fundamental condition for series representation.*

Example. The Maclaurin expansion of e^x is

$$(3) \qquad 1 + x + \frac{x^2}{2!} + \cdots + \frac{x^n}{n!} + \cdots.$$

By the ratio test, this series converges for all x. But does it converge to e^x?

Before answering this question, note [since (3) converges] that

$$(4) \qquad \lim_{n \to \infty} \frac{x^n}{n!} = 0 \quad \text{for all } x.$$

The question is attacked by recalling that there is a number ξ_n between 0 and x for which (see Prob. 2a of Sec. 13-11)

$$\left| e^x - \left(1 + x + \frac{x^2}{2!} + \cdots + \frac{x^{n-1}}{(n-1)!}\right) \right| = \frac{e^{\xi_n}}{n!} |x|^n.$$

If $0 < x$, then $0 < \xi_n < x$ and $0 < e^{\xi_n} < e^x$. If $x < 0$, then $x < \xi_n < 0$ and $0 < e^{\xi_n} < e^0 = 1$. Hence, in either case,

$$\lim_{n \to \infty} \frac{e^{\xi_n} |x|^n}{n!} = 0$$

from (4). Consequently,

(5) $$e^x = 1 + x + \frac{x^2}{2} + \cdots + \frac{x^n}{n!} + \cdots \quad \text{for all } x.$$

There are functions $f(x)$ such that $f(0) = 0$ and $f^n(0) = 0$ for all n. The Maclaurin expansion of such a function is therefore

$$0 + 0x + \frac{0}{2!}x^2 + \cdots + \frac{0}{n!}x^n + \cdots,$$

which converges to 0 for all x. One such function is

(6) $$f(x) = \begin{cases} e^{-1/x^2} & \text{for } x \neq 0, \\ 0 & \text{for } x = 0. \end{cases}$$

[Anyone who wants to check that this $f(x)$ has the above stated properties and needs hints to do so will find them in the following Prob. 12.] Hence, the Maclaurin expansion of this function converges for all x, but does not converge to $f(x)$ if $x \neq 0$. Now if $g(x)$ is a function [different from $-f(x)$] whose Maclaurin series converges to it, say, on $-r < x < r$, then

$$F(x) = g(x) + f(x)$$

has a Maclaurin series that converges on $-r < x < r$ but does not converge to $F(x)$ at all points of this range.

13-13. Binomial Theorem and Series

In order to avoid interrupting the main discussion, two facts are noted. *Fact 1*:

(1) $$\left| \frac{x-t}{1+t} \right| \leq |x| \quad \text{if either} \quad \begin{cases} 0 \leq t \leq x < 1 \quad \text{or} \\ -1 < x \leq t \leq 0. \end{cases}$$

The more bothersome case in which $-1 < x \leq t \leq 0$ will be established. Then $|x| = -x$, $0 \leq t - x$, $0 < 1 + t$, and it is to be shown that

$$0 \leq \frac{t-x}{1+t} \leq -x.$$

This is true if $t - x \leq -x - xt$, hence, if $t \leq -xt$, and, finally (since $t \leq 0$), if $1 \geq -x$. But in this case, 1 is greater than $-x$ and, by retracing the steps, the desired inequality holds in this case. [See also Prob. 10 at the end of this section.]

Fact 2. For a constant value of x such that $0 < |x| < 1$ and any constant α, then

(2) $$\lim_{n \to \infty} \frac{\alpha(\alpha - 1)(\alpha - 2) \cdots (\alpha - n + 1)}{(n - 1)!} |x|^{n-1} = 0.$$

A term is zero for some n if and only if α is a positive integer, and then all succeeding terms are zero. Hence, consider α not a positive integer. Then the terms are not equal to zero and are the terms of an absolutely convergent series by the ratio test:

(3) $$\lim_{n \to \infty} \left| \frac{\alpha(\alpha - 1) \cdots (\alpha - n)|x|^n}{n!} \cdot \frac{(n - 1)!}{\alpha(\alpha - 1) \cdots (\alpha - n + 1)|x|^{n-1}} \right|$$

$$= \lim_{n \to \infty} \frac{|\alpha - n|}{n} |x| = |x| < 1.$$

Hence, the terms approach zero; that is, (2) holds.

Note that (3) also may be interpreted as *the series*

$$1 + \sum_{n=1}^{\infty} \frac{\alpha(\alpha - 1) \cdots (\alpha - n + 1)}{n!} x^n$$

has radius of convergence $r = 1$.

With α a constant ($\alpha \neq 0$ to avoid triviality), let $f(x)$ be the function defined by

$$f(x) = (1 + x)^\alpha, \quad x > -1.$$

Then $f'(x) = \alpha(1 + x)^{\alpha-1}$, $f''(x) = \alpha(\alpha - 1)(1 + x)^{\alpha-2}$, etc.,

$$f^k(x) = \alpha(\alpha - 1) \cdots (\alpha - k + 1)(1 + x)^{\alpha-k}.$$

Hence, from the Maclaurin expansion with remainder in integral form,

$$f(x) = 1 + \sum_{k=1}^{n-1} \frac{\alpha(\alpha - 1) \cdots (\alpha - k + 1)}{k!} x^k + R_n(x), \quad \text{where}$$

$$R_n(x) = \frac{\alpha(\alpha - 1) \cdots (\alpha - n + 1)}{(n - 1)!} \int_0^x (x - t)^{n-1}(1 + t)^{\alpha-n} \, dt.$$

If $\alpha = m$ is a positive integer, then $R_n = 0$ for $n \geq m + 1$ and

$$(1 + x)^m = 1 + mx + \frac{m(m - 1)}{2!} x^2 + \cdots + \frac{m(m - 1) \cdots (2)(1)}{m!} x^m$$

(4) $$= \sum_{k=0}^{m} \binom{m}{k} x^k, \quad \text{where} \quad \binom{m}{k} = \frac{m!}{k!(m - k)!}.$$

Thus, the ordinary binomial expansion

$$(a + b)^m = a^m \left(1 + \frac{b}{a} \right)^m = a^m + m a^{m-1} b + \frac{m(m - 1)}{2!} a^{m-2} b^2 + \cdots + b^m$$

(5) $$= \sum_{k=0}^{m} \binom{m}{k} a^{m-k} b^k$$

is obtained. The binomial coefficients $\binom{m}{k}$ occur frequently in probability theory.

Further considerations are under the assumption that

(6) $\qquad\qquad\qquad\qquad \alpha$ *is not a positive integer.*

The integral in R_n may be written in the form

$$I_n(x) = \int_0^x \left[\frac{x-t}{1+t}\right]^{n-1} (1+t)^{\alpha-1} dt.$$

Hence, by using Fact 1:

$\qquad$ if $\quad 0 \le x < 1, \quad$ then $\quad |I_n(x)| \le |x|^{n-1} \int_0^x (1+t)^{\alpha-1} dt, \quad$ and

$\qquad$ if $\quad -1 < x \le 0, \quad$ then $\quad |I_n(x)| \le |x|^{n-1} \int_x^0 (1+t)^{\alpha-1} dt.$

Let c be the value of whichever of these last integrals is involved. Then $c \ge 0$ is independent of n and

$$|R_n(x)| \le \frac{|\alpha(\alpha-1)(\alpha-2)\cdots(\alpha-n+1)|}{(n-1)!} |x|^{n-1} c.$$

Thus, for $-1 < x < 1$, $R_n(x) \to 0$ as $n \to \infty$ by Fact 2.

The following theorem contains these results by stating that (7) holds under condition (i).

THEOREM 13-13.1. *Let α be a constant not zero and not a positive integer. Then the following series (called the **binomial** series) does not terminate, is convergent, and the equality*

(7) $\qquad (1+x)^\alpha = 1 + \sum_{n=1}^{\infty} \frac{\alpha(\alpha-1)(\alpha-2)\cdots(\alpha-n+1)}{n!} x^n$

holds under the conditions:

$\qquad$ (i) $-1 < x < 1, \quad \alpha$ *only restricted as above;*
$\qquad$ (ii) $x = 1, \quad \alpha > -1;$
$\qquad$ (iii) $x = -1, \quad \alpha > 0.$
The binomial series diverges in all other cases.

The binomial series has already been shown to have radius of convergence $r = 1$ and hence diverges if $|x| > 1$. Thus, convergence under condition (i) and divergence if $|x| > 1$ have been established. The remaining parts of the theorem are included for the sake of completeness, but will not be proved here. It is only occasionally, in very precise work, that convergence under conditions (ii) or (iii) is used, and the proofs under these conditions are long and involved.

Example 1. For $-1 < t < 1$, then

$$\frac{1}{\sqrt{1-t^2}} = (1-t^2)^{-1/2} = 1 + \sum_{n=1}^{\infty} \frac{(-\frac{1}{2})(-\frac{3}{2})\cdots(-\frac{1}{2}-n+1)}{n!}(-t^2)^n$$

$$= 1 + \sum_{n=1}^{\infty} \frac{1\cdot 3\cdot 5\cdots(2n-1)}{2^n n!} t^{2n}$$

$$= 1 + \frac{1}{2}t^2 + \frac{1\cdot 3}{2^2\cdot 2!}t^4 + \frac{1\cdot 3\cdot 5}{2^3\cdot 3!}t^6 + \cdots.$$

This series may be written in more compact form. For with n a positive integer, then

$$\frac{1\cdot 3\cdots(2n-1)}{2^n n!} = \frac{1\cdot 2\cdot 3\cdot 4\cdots(2n-1)2n}{2^n n!(2\cdot 4\cdot 6\cdots 2n)} = \frac{(2n)!}{2^n n!\, 2^n n!}.$$

But this expression is equal to 1 when $n = 0$, so that

(8) $$\frac{1}{\sqrt{1-t^2}} = \sum_{n=0}^{\infty} \binom{2n}{n}\left(\frac{t}{2}\right)^{2n}.$$

Example 2. The formal substitution of $x = 1$ and $\alpha = -1$ in (7) leads to

$$(1+1)^{-1} = 1 + \sum_{n=1}^{\infty} \frac{(-1)(-2)\cdots(-n)}{n!} 1^n = 1 + \sum_{n=1}^{\infty}(-1)^n; \quad \text{that is,}$$

$$\tfrac{1}{2} = 1 - 1 + 1 - 1 + \cdots.$$

According to Theorem 13-13.1 (ii), divergence of the series will occur for $x = 1$ and $\alpha = -1$, so that (7) should not be used with these values.

Problem 1. Show that the Maclaurin expansions of both $\sin x$ and $\cos x$ converge to the proper values for all x.

Problem 2. Use any previously established properties to show that:

a. $e^{ax} = \sum_{n=0}^{\infty} \frac{a^n x^n}{n!}$, $\quad -\infty < x < \infty$.

b. For $a > 0$, $a^x = \sum_{n=0}^{\infty} \frac{(\ln a)^n}{n!} x^n$, $\quad -\infty < x < \infty$. [Hint: $a^x = e^{x \ln a}$].

c. $\sinh x = \sum_{n=0}^{\infty} \frac{x^{2n+1}}{(2n+1)!}$, $\quad -\infty < x < \infty$.

d. $\sin x^2 = \sum_{n=0}^{\infty} \frac{(-1)^n}{(2n+1)!} x^{4n+2}$, $\quad -\infty < x < \infty$.

e. $\sin^2 x = \sum_{n=1}^{\infty} \frac{(-1)^{n+1} 2^{2n-1}}{(2n)!} x^{2n}$, $\quad -\infty < x < \infty$. [Hint: $\cos 2x = 1 - 2\sin^2 x$.]

f. $\sin^3 x = \frac{3}{4} \sum_{n=1}^{\infty} \frac{(-1)^n(1-3^{2n})}{(2n+1)!} x^{2n+1}$, $\quad -\infty < x < \infty$. [Hint: Prob. 5c, Sec. 1-5.]

g. $e^{-1/x^2} = \sum_{n=0}^{\infty} \frac{(-1)^n}{n!} \frac{1}{x^{2n}}$, $\quad x \neq 0$.

h. $\dfrac{1}{2x+1} = \sum\limits_{n=0}^{\infty}(-1)^n 2^n x^n, \quad |x| < \dfrac{1}{2}.$

i. $\dfrac{3x+2}{2x^2+3x+1} = \sum\limits_{n=0}^{\infty}(-1)^n(1+2^n)x^n, \quad |x| < \dfrac{1}{2}.$ [Hint: Partial fractions.]

Problem 3. In the Maclaurin expansion of $\cos x$, replace x by x^2 and obtain

$$\cos x^2 = 1 - \frac{x^4}{2!} + \frac{x^8}{4!} - \frac{x^{12}}{6!} + \cdots.$$

Next, set $f(x) = \cos x^2$, find $f'(x)$, $f''(x)$, etc., to start the Maclaurin expansion of this function to see how much more involved it is than the above procedure.

Problem 4. a. Given that $-\frac{1}{2}\pi \le x \le \frac{3}{2}\pi$, obtain the expansion

$$\sqrt{1+\sin x} = 1 + \frac{x}{2} - \frac{x^2}{2^2 \cdot 2!} - \frac{x^3}{2^3 \cdot 3!} + \frac{x^4}{2^4 \cdot 4!} + \frac{x^5}{2^5 \cdot 5!} - \cdots.$$

[Hint: $1 + \sin x = (\sin \frac{1}{2}x + \cos \frac{1}{2}x)^2$.]
   b. What modification must be made in the expression if $\frac{3}{2}\pi \le x \le \frac{7}{2}\pi$? [Hint: $\sqrt{a^2} = |a|$.]

Problem 5. The formal Taylor's series may be written as

$$f(b) = f(a) + f'(a)(b-a) + \frac{f''(a)}{2!}(b-a)^2 + \frac{f'''(a)}{3!}(b-a)^3 + \cdots.$$

Without being concerned about convergence, think through the substitutions and possible interpretations of each of the following:

$$f(b) = f(x) + f'(x)(b-x) + \frac{f''(x)}{2!}(b-x)^2 + \frac{f'''(x)}{3!}(b-x)^3 + \cdots.$$

$$f(x+h) = f(x) + f'(x)h + \frac{f''(x)}{2!}h^2 + \frac{f'''(x)}{3!}h^3 + \cdots.$$

$$f(x+\Delta x) = f(x) + f'(x)\,\Delta x + \frac{f''(x)}{2!}(\Delta x)^2 + \frac{f'''(x)}{3!}(\Delta x)^3 + \cdots.$$

$$f(x+dx) = f(x) + f'(x)\,dx + \frac{f''(x)(dx)^2}{2!} + \frac{f'''(x)(dx)^3}{3!} + \cdots$$

$$= f(x) + df(x) + \frac{d^2 f(x)}{2!} + \frac{d^3 f(x)}{3!} + \cdots$$

$$= \left[1 + d + \frac{d^2}{2!} + \frac{d^3}{3!} + \cdots\right]f(x).$$

$$f(x+dx) = e^d f(x).$$

Problem 6. Arbitrarily replace x by ix in (5) of Sec. 13-12, and from $i^2 = -1$ obtain another motivation* for the definition

$$e^{ix} = \cos x + i \sin x.$$

*See p. 334 for a motivation given earlier.

Problem 7. Use (4) and show that:

a. $2^m = 1 + \binom{m}{1} + \binom{m}{2} + \cdots + \binom{m}{m}$.

b. $0 = 1 - \binom{m}{1} + \binom{m}{2} - \binom{m}{3} + \cdots + (-1)^m$.

c. $m2^{m-1} = \binom{m}{1} + 2\binom{m}{2} + 3\binom{m}{3} + \cdots + m$. [Hint: Derivative.]

d. $\dfrac{2^{m+1}}{m+1} = \left[1 + \dfrac{1}{2}\binom{m}{1} + \dfrac{1}{3}\binom{m}{2} + \cdots + \dfrac{1}{m+1}\right] + \dfrac{1}{m+1}$.

e. $(-1)^n = 1 - 2\binom{n}{1} + 4\binom{n}{2} - 8\binom{n}{3} + \cdots + (-2)^n$.

Problem 8. In (5) replace b by x, take the derivative with respect to x, then set $x = b$ and show the result leads to

$$mb(a + b)^{m-1} = \sum_{k=0}^{m} k \binom{m}{k} a^{m-k} b^k.$$

Obtain the formula

$$m(m - 1)b^2(a + b)^{m-2} = \sum_{k=0}^{m} k(k - 1)\binom{m}{k} a^{m-k} b^k.$$

Problem 9. a. Use the formula for the sum of a (finite) geometric series, then use (4) to obtain

$$\sum_{k=0}^{n-1} (1 - x)^k = \frac{1 - (1 - x)^n}{x} = \sum_{k=1}^{n} (-1)^{k+1} \binom{n}{k} x^{k-1}.$$

b. Integrate from $x = 0$ to $x = 1$ and obtain

$$1 + \frac{1}{2} + \frac{1}{3} + \cdots + \frac{1}{n} = \binom{n}{1} - \frac{1}{2}\binom{n}{2} + \frac{1}{3}\binom{n}{3} - \cdots \frac{(-1)^{n+1}}{n}.$$

Problem 10. For a fixed value of $x \neq 0$ and $|x| < 1$, let

$$F(t) = \frac{x - t}{1 + t}$$

be the function of t on the closed interval with endpoints $t = 0$ and $t = x$. Show that $F'(t) < 0$. Use this to reestablish Fact 1. [Hint: Sketch one figure for $x > 0$ and another for $x < 0$.]

Problem 11. Let $f(x)$ have $f^4(x)$ existing on $a < x < b$ and $f^3(x)$ continuous on $a \leq x \leq b$, and let $p > 0$ be a constant. Define S_4 as the number satisfying

$$f(b) = f(a) + f'(a)(b - a) + \frac{f''(a)}{2}(b - a)^2 + \frac{f'''(a)}{3!}(b - a)^3 + S_4 \cdot (b - a)^p.$$

Define $F(x)$ on $a \leq x \leq b$ by setting

$$F(x) = -f(b) + \sum_{k=0}^{3} \frac{f^k(x)}{k!}(b - x)^k + S_4 \cdot (b - x)^p.$$

a. Find $F'(x)$, $a < x < b$, and simplify.

b. Show that $F(x)$ satisfies Rolle's Theorem on $a \leq x \leq b$.

c. Show that there is a number ξ such that $a < \xi < b$ and

$$S_4 = \frac{f^4(\xi)}{p \cdot 3!}(b - \xi)^{4-p}.$$

d. Generalize this result to obtain Taylor's Formula with

$$R_n = \frac{f^n(\xi_n)}{p(n-1)!}(b - \xi_n)^{n-p}(b - a)^p.$$

[Note: This is called the **Schlömilch form** of the remainder.]

Problem 12. A succession of statements or formulas is given below without reasons. If the reader supplies each reason, he will see why $f(x)$ of (6) in Sec. 13-12 has the properties attributed to it there.

Formula (5) yields, for $x \neq 0$,

$$e^{1/x^2} = 1 + \frac{1}{x^2} + \frac{1}{2x^4} + \cdots + \frac{1}{n!x^{2n}} + \cdots > \frac{1}{n!x^{2n}}, \quad n = 1, 2, 3, \ldots.$$

With λ any number and n such that $2n > \lambda$, then

$$\lim_{x \to 0} |x|^\lambda e^{1/x^2} \geq \lim_{x \to 0} \frac{1}{n!\,|x|^{2n-\lambda}} = \infty.$$

$$\lim_{x \to 0} \frac{e^{-1/x^2}}{|x|^\lambda} = 0.$$

With m and n any nonnegative integers,

$$\lim_{x \to 0} \frac{x^n e^{-1/x^2}}{x^m} = 0,$$

$$\lim_{x \to 0} \frac{P(x)e^{-1/x^2}}{x^m} = 0 \quad \text{for any polynomial } P(x) \text{ in } x.$$

For the function $f(x)$ defined in (6) of Sec. 13-12,

$$f'(0) = \lim_{x \to 0} \frac{f(x) - f(0)}{x - 0} = 0 \quad \text{and}$$

$$f'(x) = \frac{2e^{-1/x^2}}{x^3} \quad \text{for} \quad x \neq 0.$$

Let n be a positive integer for which it is known that $f^n(0) = 0$ and

$$f^n(x) = \frac{P_n(x)e^{-1/x^2}}{x^{3n}}, \quad x \neq 0, \text{ with } P_n(x) \text{ a polynomial.}$$

Then $f^{n+1}(0) = 0$, and there is a polynomial $P_{n+1}(x)$ such that

$$f^{n+1}(x) = \frac{P_{n+1}(x)e^{-1/x^2}}{x^{3(n+1)}}, \quad x \neq 0.$$

Hence, $f(0) = f'(0) = \cdots = f^n(0) = \cdots = 0$.

Problem 13. a. With $s_n = 1 + 1/1! + 1/2! + \cdots + 1/n!$ a partial sum of the e series (5), show that

$$0 < e - s_n < \frac{1}{n!n}.$$

$$\left[\text{Hint: } \frac{1}{(n+1)!} + \frac{1}{(n+2)!} + \cdots < \frac{1}{(n+1)!}\left(1 + \frac{1}{n+1} + \frac{1}{(n+1)^2} + \cdots\right) = \frac{1}{n!n}.\right]$$

b. Show that e is an irrational number.

[Hint: Assume $e = m/n$, with m and n positive integers. Show how this leads to the contradiction that $en! - s_n n!$ is a positive integer less than $(1/n) \leq 1$.]

13-14. Calculus of Power Series

Recall that every power series has a radius of convergence that may be 0, a positive constant, or $+\infty$. Consider a power series

$$(1) \qquad \sum a_n x^n \quad \text{with radius of convergence} \quad r_1 > 0.$$

Hence, if $-r_1 < x_1 < r_1$, not only does $\sum a_n x_1^n$ converge, but also the absolute value series $\sum |a_n x_1^n|$ converges (Theorem 13-9.3).

Two series related to (1) are

$$(2) \qquad \sum n a_n x^{n-1} \quad \text{with radius of convergence} \quad r_2, \quad \text{and}$$

$$(3) \qquad \sum \frac{a_n}{n+1} x^{n+1} \quad \text{with radius of convergence} \quad r_3.$$

A result to be used in the next proof is:

If $0 < \rho < 1$, then

$$(4) \qquad \sum n \rho^n, \quad \sum \frac{1}{n(n+1)} \rho^n, \quad \text{and} \quad \sum \frac{1}{n+1} \rho^n \quad \text{all converge.}$$

The ratio test shows this; for example, for $\sum n \rho^n$,

$$\lim_{n \to \infty} \frac{(n+1)\rho^{n+1}}{n\rho^n} = \rho \lim_{n \to \infty} \frac{n+1}{n} = \rho < 1.$$

The following theorem states an important result.

THEOREM 13-14.1. *The three series* (1), (2), *and* (3) *all have the same radius of convergence; that is,* $r_1 = r_2 = r_3$.

PROOF. Let x be fixed such that $0 < |x| < r_1$. Select an x_1 such that

$$|x| < |x_1| < r_1.$$

Then $\sum |a_n x_1^n|$ converges [as mentioned under (1) above]. Hence, the sequence $\{|a_n x_1^n|\}$ is a null sequence and as such is bounded above by some number c_1 (see Lemma 1, Sec. 13-2). Since $|a_n x_1^n| < c_1$ for all n, then

$$|n a_n x^{n-1}| = n \left| \frac{1}{x} a_n x_1^n \left(\frac{x}{x_1} \right)^n \right| = \frac{|a_n x_1^n|}{|x|} n \left| \frac{x}{x_1} \right|^n \leq \frac{c_1}{|x|} n \left| \frac{x}{x_1} \right|^n.$$

But $\sum n |x/x_1|^n$ converges by (4), since $|x/x_1| < 1$. Thus, $\sum |n a_n x^n|$ converges by the comparison test, since $c_1/|x|$ is independent of n. From this absolute convergence, convergence itself follows:

$$\sum n a_n x^n \quad \text{converges on} \quad -r_1 < x < r_1 \quad \text{at least.}$$

This shows that r_2 is if anything larger than r_1; that is,

$$r_1 \leq r_2.$$

Next take x such that $0 < |x| < r_2$, and then x_2 such that $|x| < |x_2| < r_2$. Hence, $\sum |na_n x_2^{n-1}|$ converges and there is a c_2 such that $|na_n x_2^{n-1}| \leq c_2$. Thus,

$$\left| \frac{a_n}{n+1} x^{n+1} \right| = \frac{|x|}{n(n+1)} |na_n x_2^n| \left| \frac{x}{x_2} \right|^n \leq |x| \, c_2 \frac{1}{n(n+1)} \left| \frac{x}{x_2} \right|^n.$$

First from (4) and then the comparison test, $\sum \left| \frac{a_n}{n+1} x^{n+1} \right|$ converges. Hence,

$$\sum \frac{a_n}{n+1} x^{n+1} \quad \text{converges for} \quad -r_2 < x < r_2 \quad \text{so that} \quad r_2 \leq r_3.$$

It is left as an exercise to use the same procedure and show that $r_3 \leq r_1$.

Thus, $r_1 \leq r_2 \leq r_3 \leq r_1$, so the equalities hold and the theorem is proved.

The following corollary is obtained by applying the theorem to the series (2).

COROLLARY. *Both of the series*

$$\sum n(n-1)a_n x^{n-2} \quad and \quad \sum a_n x^n$$

have the same radius of convergence.

The radius of convergence of (1), (2), (3) and $\sum n(n-1)a_n x^n$ will now be denoted by r.

Thus, there is a function $f(x)$ defined by

(1')
$$f(x) = \sum_{n=0}^{\infty} a_n x^n, \quad -r < x < r.$$

Even though each term of (2) or (3) is the derivative or integral of a corresponding term of (1), it is still necessary to prove the following most important theorem. In the course of the proof, Taylor's Formula (with Lagrange remainder after two terms) in the form

$$g(x + \Delta x) = g(x) + g'(x)\, \Delta x + \frac{g''(\xi_2)}{2} \overline{\Delta x}^2$$

will be used with $g(x) = x^n$. Hence, for each n there is an η_n between x and $x + \Delta x$ such that

(5)
$$(x + \Delta x)^n = x^n + nx^{n-1}\, \Delta x + \frac{n(n-1)}{2} (\eta_n)^{n-2} \overline{\Delta x}^2.$$

THEOREM 13-14.2. *With $f(x)$ defined by (1'), then*

(2')
$$\frac{df(x)}{dx} = \sum_{n=0}^{\infty} \frac{d}{dx}(a_n x^n), \quad -r < x < r, \text{ and}$$

(3')
$$\int_a^x f(t)\, dt = \sum_{n=0}^{\infty} \left[\int_a^x a_n t^n\, dt \right], \quad -r < a < r \quad and \quad -r < x < r.$$

"A power series may be differentiated or integrated term by term on the interior of its interval of convergence," is a way of paraphrasing the theorem.

PROOF OF (2'). Fix x such that $|x| < r$. Select a constant c such that $|x| < c < r$ and set

$$d = \sum_{n=2}^{\infty} n(n-1)\,|a_n|\,c^{n-2}.$$

This definition of the constant d is valid, since $0 < c < r$ is in the interval of convergence (hence, absolute convergence) of the series in the above corollary.

Because of the actual inequality $|x| < c$, then $\Delta x \neq 0$ may be selected such that also $|x + \Delta x| < c < r$. Convergence of the series and the following equalities are then assured:

$$f(x + \Delta x) - f(x) = \sum_{n=0}^{\infty} a_n(x + \Delta x)^n - \sum_{n=0}^{\infty} a_n x^n$$

$$= \sum_{n=0}^{\infty} a_n\,[(x + \Delta x)^n - x^n]$$

$$= a_o \cdot 0 + a_1\,\Delta x + \sum_{n=2}^{\infty} a_n\,[(x + \Delta x)^n - x^n]$$

$$= a_1\,\Delta x + \sum_{n=2}^{\infty} a_n\left[nx^{n-1}\,\Delta x + \frac{n(n-1)}{2}(\eta_n)^{n-2}\,\overline{\Delta x^2}\right] \quad \text{from (5)}$$

(6) $$= \Delta x \sum_{n=1}^{\infty} na_n\,x^{n-1} + \frac{\overline{\Delta x^2}}{2}\sum_{n=2}^{\infty} n(n-1)\,a_n(\eta_n)^{n-2},$$

with η_n between x and $x + \Delta x$ for $n = 2, 3, \ldots$. Even though the η_n vary with n, the last series converges. In fact, it converges absolutely, since $|\eta_n| < |c|$, so that each term is in absolute value less than or equal to the corresponding term in the series defining d. Then the absolute value of the series is $\leq d$, as seen by letting $N \to \infty$ in

$$\left|\sum_{n=2}^{N} n(n-1)\,a_n\,(\eta_n)^{n-2}\right| \leq \sum_{n=2}^{N} n(n-1)\,|a_n|\,c^{n-2} \leq d.$$

In (6) divide by $\Delta x \neq 0$, transpose $\sum na_n x^{n-1}$, and take absolute values to see that

$$\left|\frac{f(x + \Delta x) - f(x)}{\Delta x} - \sum_{n=1}^{\infty} na_n x^n\right| \leq \frac{|\Delta x|}{2} d.$$

Hence, by letting $\Delta x \to 0$, not only is the existence of $f'(x)$ established but the equality (2') as well [since the $(n = 0)$ term is zero].

PROOF OF (3'). Let $g(x)$ be the function defined by

$$g(x) = \sum_{n=0}^{\infty} \frac{a_n}{n+1} x^{n+1} \quad \text{for } -r < x < r.$$

With a and b any constants such that $-r < a < r$ and $-r < b < r$, then convergence justifies setting

$$g(x)\Big]_a^b = g(b) - g(a) = \sum_{n=0}^{\infty} \frac{a_n}{n+1} b^{n+1} - \sum_{n=0}^{\infty} \frac{a_n}{n+1} a^{n+1}$$

$$= \sum_{n=0}^{\infty} \left[a_n \frac{b^{n+1} - a^{n+1}}{n+1} \right] = \sum_{n=0}^{\infty} \left[\int_a^b a_n x^n \, dx \right].$$

By applying the derivative portion of this theorem (already established) to $g(x)$ instead of to $f(x)$, then

$$\frac{dg(x)}{dx} = \sum_{n=0}^{\infty} \frac{d}{dx} \left[\frac{a_n}{n+1} x^{n+1} \right] = \sum_{n=0}^{\infty} a_n x^n = f(x).$$

Thus, by the Fundamental Theorem of Calculus,

$$\int_a^b f(x) \, dx = g(x)\Big]_a^b = \sum_{n=0}^{\infty} \left[\int_a^b a_n x^n \, dx \right].$$

The result (3′) then follows upon replacing b by any x such that $-r < x < r$ (which forces the use of a dummy variable of integration other than x).

This completes the proof of the theorem.

In particular: *The sum of a power series is a continuous function on the interior of the interval of convergence.*

Example. The Maclaurin expansion of $f(x) = \sin^{-1} x$ directly from the definition requires obtaining $f'(x), f''(x), \ldots,$ and these soon become involved. The general law for $f^n(x)$ is not at all clear. However, by integrating the binomial series for $(1 - t^2)^{-1/2}$, as given in the example of Sec. 13-13, then

$$\sin^{-1} x = \int_0^x \frac{1}{\sqrt{1 - t^2}} \, dt = \sum_{n=0}^{\infty} \binom{2n}{n} \frac{1}{2^{2n}} \int_0^x t^{2n} \, dt = \sum_{n=0}^{\infty} \binom{2n}{n} \frac{1}{2^{2n}} \frac{x^{2n+1}}{2n+1}$$

$$= x + \sum_{n=1}^{\infty} \frac{1 \cdot 3 \cdot 5 \cdots (2n-1)}{2^n n! \, (2n+1)} x^{2n+1}$$

$$= x + \frac{1}{2 \cdot 3} x^3 + \frac{1 \cdot 3}{2^2 \cdot 2! 5} x^5 + \frac{1 \cdot 3 \cdot 5}{2^3 \cdot 3! 7} x^7 + \cdots \quad \text{for } -1 < x < 1.$$

Problem 1. Differentiate the sine series and obtain the cosine series. Try integrating the sine series.

Problem 2. Assume that the function e^x is known but its Maclaurin series is not known. Let $E(x)$ be the function defined by

$$E(x) = 1 + x + \frac{x^2}{2} + \frac{x^3}{3!} + \cdots.$$

Show that

$$\frac{dE(x)}{dx} = E(x) \quad \text{and} \quad E(0) = 1.$$

Use this differential equation (and initial condition) to show that $E(x) = e^x$.

Problem 3. Find the Maclaurin series for:

a. $\int_0^x e^{-t^2}\,dt.$

c. $\int_0^x \dfrac{\sin t}{t}\,dt$ (improper).

b. $\int_0^x \sin t^2\,dt.$

d. $x^2 + (4x+1)^3 + (6x-1)^4.$

Problem 4. Start with

$$\frac{1}{1-x} = \sum_{n=0}^{\infty} x^n, \quad -1 < x < 1,$$

and obtain:

a. $\dfrac{1}{(1-x)^2} = \sum_{n=1}^{\infty} nx^{n-1} = \sum_{n=0}^{\infty}(n+1)x^n, \quad -1 < x < 1.$

b. $\dfrac{1}{(1-x)^{m+1}} = \sum_{n=0}^{\infty} \binom{n+m}{n} x^n, \quad -1 < x < 1$ for $m = 0, 1, 2, \ldots.$

Problem 5. a. Obtain the compact form

$$\sqrt{1+x} = 1 + \frac{x}{2}\sum_{n=0}^{\infty}\frac{(-1)^n}{2^{2n}(n+1)}\binom{2n}{n}x^n.$$

b. Use this to obtain:

(i) $\dfrac{1}{\sqrt{1+x}} = \sum_{n=0}^{\infty}\dfrac{(-1)^n}{2^{2n}}\binom{2n}{n}x^n.$

(ii) $(1+x)^{3/2} = 1 + \dfrac{3}{2}x + \dfrac{3}{4}x^2\sum_{n=0}^{\infty}\dfrac{(-1)^n}{2^{2n}(n+1)(n+2)}\binom{2n}{n}x^n.$

(iii) $\dfrac{1}{\sqrt{1+x}+1} = \dfrac{1}{2} + \dfrac{1}{2}\sum_{n=1}^{\infty}\dfrac{(-1)^n}{2^{2n}(n+1)}\binom{2n}{n}x^n.$

Problem 6. Show that the circumference C of the ellipse $x = a\cos\theta$, $y = b\sin\theta$, $0 < a < b$, is

$$C = b\int_0^{2\pi}\sqrt{1 - e^2\sin^2\theta}\,d\theta, \quad \text{where } e = (\sqrt{b^2 - a^2})/b \text{ is the eccentricity,}$$

$$= b\left\{2\pi - \frac{e^2}{2}\sum_{n=0}^{\infty}\binom{2n}{n}\frac{1}{n+1}\left(\frac{e}{2}\right)^{2n}\int_0^{2\pi}\sin^{2n+2}\theta\,d\theta\right\}.$$

[Note:

$$\int_0^x \frac{dt}{\sqrt{1 - k^2\sin^2 t}} \quad \text{and} \quad \int_0^x \sqrt{1 - k^2\sin^2 t}\,dt$$

are called **elliptic integrals** of the first and second kind, respectively. Approximations are tabulated in B. O. Peirce, *A Short Table of Integrals* (Boston: Ginn and Company, 1929) and P. R. E. Jahnke and F. Emde, *Tables of Functions with Formulas and Curves* (New York: Dover Publications, 1945).]

Problem 7. Given sequences of constants $\{a_n\}$ and $\{b_n\}$, such that the series converge and the equality holds,

$$\sum_{n=0}^{\infty} a_n x^n = \sum_{n=0}^{\infty} b_n x^n,$$

on some interval $-r < x < r$, show that

$$a_n = b_n \quad \text{for } n = 0, 1, 2, \ldots.$$

Problem 8. Let $f(x)$ be a function and assume there are constants $a_0, a_1, a_2, \ldots$ such that

$$f(x) = a_0 + a_1 x + a_2 x^2 + \cdots$$

on some interval $-r < x < r$. Prove that

$$a_n = \frac{f^n(0)}{n!}, \quad n = 0, 1, 2, \ldots.$$

Problem 9. The series in the following definition of $f(x)$,

$$f(x) = \sum_{n=0}^{\infty} x(1 - x)^n, \quad 0 \le x < 2,$$

may look like a power series but it is not. For if it were a power series, then $f(x)$ would have a derivative at $x = 1$, but Prob. 6, Sec. 13-9, shows otherwise. Show, however, that

$$g(x) = \sum_{n=0}^{\infty} \left[\frac{d}{dx} x(1 - x)^n \right]$$

agrees with $f'(x)$ wherever $g(x)$ is defined; namely, if $0 < x < 1$ or $1 < x < 2$. [Hint: In the proof of the statement about $g(x)$, it is necessary to know what

$$\sum_{n=1}^{\infty} n(1 - x)^{n-1}$$

converges to. This may be found from

$$\frac{1}{x} = \frac{1}{1 - (1 - x)} = \sum_{n=0}^{\infty} (1 - x)^n, \quad 0 < x < 2.]$$

13-15. Computation

If $\sin x$, for a given x, is desired to accuracy 5×10^{-5} in a problem to be put on an electronic computer, then a sine subroutine is incorporated into the program. The subroutine first reduces the argument to a value between $-\frac{1}{2}\pi$ and $\frac{1}{2}\pi$ by repeated use of

$$\sin x = -\sin (x - \pi) \quad \text{in case} \quad x > \tfrac{1}{2}\pi \quad \text{or}$$
$$\sin x = -\sin (x + \pi) \quad \text{in case} \quad x < -\tfrac{1}{2}\pi.$$

Now with an argument x such that $-\frac{1}{2}\pi \le x \le \frac{1}{2}\pi$, Taylor's Formula is used. As a term is computed, it is both added to a previously accumulated sum and stored temporarily. Since

$$\left| \sin x - \sum_{k=1}^{n-1} \frac{(-1)^{k+1}}{(2k - 1)!} x^{2k-1} \right| \le \frac{|x^{2n+1}|}{(2n + 1)!} < 5 \times 10^{-5}$$

is desired, 0.00005 is subtracted from the absolute value of the stored term. As soon as this difference is negative, a "return to main program" order is executed. In case the difference is not negative, then $-x^2$ (previously computed) is divided by $(2n)(2n + 1)$ and the result multiplied by the term temporarily stored to produce the next term of the series. Also, $2n + 1$ is stored just in case still another term is needed.

A computing machine has memory locations $L_1, L_2, L_3, \ldots$ at which numbers can be stored. If the order "store 0.00005 in L_2" is given, the machine erases whatever number is in L_2 before storing 0.00005 there. The parenthesis notation (L_2) means "the present contents of L_2." Hence, after the above order, then $(L_2) = 0.00005$ until a subsequent order is given to store some other number in L_2. The order "$(L_1) + (L_3)$ in L_1" means "add the present contents of L_1 and L_3 and put this sum in L_1." Then L_1 gets a new number, but the number in L_3 remains there. If a number x is stored in L_1, then "copy (L_1) in L_3" not only stores x in L_3 but also leaves x stored in L_1.

Given $-\frac{1}{2}\pi \leq x \leq \frac{1}{2}\pi$ with x stored in L_1 and the comparison constant 0.00005 stored in L_2, the machine can be programmed to execute the following succession of orders. Steps 4, 5, ... , 9 will be done over and over, the first time putting $x - x^3/3!$ in L_1, the next time $x - x^3/3! + x^5/5!$ in L_1, etc.

Step	Order	Explanation
1	Copy (L_1) in L_3	Place to store x, then $-x^3/3!$, then $x^5/5!$, etc.
2	Store 1 in L_4	Place to store 1, then 3, then 5, etc.
3	$-(L_1)(L_1)$ in L_5	$-x^2$ kept in L_5.
$\overline{4}$	$(L_4) + 1$ in L_6	$2n$ in L_6; 2 first time, 4 second time, etc.
5	$(L_6) + 1$ in L_4	$2n + 1$ in L_4.
6	$(L_5)/[(L_6)(L_4)]$ in L_6	$-x^2/(2n)(2n + 1)$ in L_6 (previous contents erased).
7	$(L_3)(L_6)$ in L_3	New term in L_3 (after erasing old term).
8	$(L_1) + (L_3)$ in L_1	Previous sum plus new term.
$\underline{9}$	Is $|(L_3)| - (L_2) < 0$?	$\begin{cases}\text{Yes, return to main program.}\\ \text{No, go back to step 4 and repeat.}\end{cases}$

Since actual computation of $\sin x$ is done only if $-\frac{1}{2}\pi \leq x \leq \frac{1}{2}\pi$ and

$$\frac{(\pi/2)^{11}}{11!} < 0.00005,$$

then five or fewer terms will be computed. A term takes at most 0.01 sec on a slow computer. Hence, less than 0.1 sec will be used for preliminary bookkeeping and computation of $\sin x$.

If $\cos x$ is desired, then x is replaced by $x - \frac{1}{2}\pi$, and the sine subroutine is used.

Computation of values of the natural logarithm is not done by using

$$(1) \quad \ln (1 + x) = x - \frac{x^2}{2} + \frac{x^3}{3} - \frac{x^4}{4} + \cdots (-1)^{n+1}\frac{x^n}{n} + \cdots, \quad -1 < x \leq 1$$

directly, both because x is limited and the series converges slowly for some x. For example, with $x = 0.9$, the series converges to $\ln (1.9)$, but the fifty-sixth term is the first with absolute value less than 5×10^{-5}. This is not too bad from the standpoint of time, but roundoff error could be significant.

In (1) replace x by $-x$ to obtain

$$\ln (1 - x) = -x - \frac{x^2}{2} - \frac{x^3}{3} - \cdots - \frac{x^n}{n} - \cdots, \quad -1 \leq x < 1.$$

Then by subtracting corresponding terms of (1),

$$(2) \quad \ln \frac{1 - x}{1 + x} = -2 \left[x + \frac{x^3}{3} + \frac{x^5}{5} + \cdots + \frac{x^{2n-1}}{2n - 1} + \cdots \right], \quad -1 < x < 1.$$

Upon setting

$$\frac{1 - x}{1 + x} = 1.9, \quad \text{then} \quad x = -\frac{9}{29}$$

is between -1 and 1, and this value of x in (2) yields a series converging to $\ln 1.9$. Moreover, $n = 4$ is the first n for which

$$\frac{(9/29)^{2n-1}}{2n - 1} < 0.00005.$$

Also, (2) may be used to compute $\ln y$ for any positive y by setting

$$\frac{1 - x}{1 + x} = y \quad \text{since then} \quad x = \frac{1 - y}{1 + y} \quad \text{and} \quad -1 < x < 1 \quad \text{for} \quad y > 0.$$

A graph will aid in seeing this. Also, on the graph, if $1/e \leq y \leq e$; that is,

$$\frac{1}{e} \leq \frac{1 - x}{1 + x} \leq e, \quad \text{then} \quad |x| \leq \frac{e - 1}{e + 1} < \frac{1}{2},$$

and $\ln y$ can be computed by a series with terms approaching zero rapidly. In fact,

$$\frac{(0.5)^{2n-1}}{2n - 1} < 5 \times 10^{-5} \quad \text{first for} \quad n = 6.$$

If y is not in the range from e^{-1} to e, then the argument may be reduced to this range by repeated use of

$$\ln y = \ln (ee^{-1}y) = 1 + \ln (y/e) \text{ if } y > e$$
$$= -1 + \ln (ey) \text{ if } 0 < y < e^{-1}.$$

Just because the sixth term is less than 5×10^{-5} does not in itself, however, ensure that the remainder after six terms will be less than 5×10^{-5}, but it is as the following analysis shows. Division of 1 by $1 + t$ and integration from $t = 0$ to $t = x$ gives

$$\left| \ln (1 + x) - \sum_{k=1}^{2n} (-1)^{k+1} \frac{x^k}{k} \right| = \left| \int_0^x \frac{t^{2n}}{1 + t} dt \right|.$$

If $-\frac{1}{2} \leq x \leq 0$, then for $x \leq t \leq 0$ both $t^{2n} \geq 0$ and $0 < (1 + t)^{-1} \leq 2$. Hence,

$$\left| \int_0^x \frac{t^{2n}}{1+t} dt \right| = \int_x^0 \frac{t^{2n}}{1+t} \le -2 \frac{x^{2n+1}}{2n+1} = 2 \frac{|x|^{2n+1}}{2n+1}.$$

If $0 \le x \le \frac{1}{2}$, the factor 2 is missing. A similar analysis for $\ln(1-x)$, $-\frac{1}{2} \le x \le \frac{1}{2}$, combines with the above to give

$$\left| \ln \frac{1-x}{1+x} - \left[-2 \sum_{k=1}^n \frac{x^{2k-1}}{2k-1} \right] \right| < \frac{4|x|^{2n+1}}{2n+1}.$$

Hence, in using (2) with $|x| < \frac{1}{2}$ for computing a logarithm to within a prescribed error E, it is safe to stop with the first term such that 4 times it is less than E. In particular, with

$$\frac{1}{e} \le y = \frac{1-x}{1+x} \le e \quad \text{and hence} \quad |x| < \frac{1}{2},$$

at most 6 terms will be used to obtain $\ln y$ to within 5×10^{-5}, since

$$\frac{4(\frac{1}{2})^{13}}{13} < 5 \times 10^{-5}.$$

If $\log_{10} y$ is desired, then the constant

$$\frac{1}{\ln 10} = 0.43429\ 44819$$

is stored, $\ln y$ computed, and $\log_{10} y$ obtained from

$$\log_{10} y = \frac{\ln y}{\ln 10}.$$

If e^x is desired, then

(3) $$e^x = 1 + x + \frac{x^2}{2} + \frac{x^3}{3!} + \cdots$$

is used. By storing $e = 2.7182\ 81829$, then the argument may be reduced to $|x| < 1$ by repeated use of

$$e^x = e \cdot e^{x+1} \quad \text{or} \quad e^x = \frac{1}{e} e^{x+1}.$$

It is easy to find 3^4, but $(3.016894172)^{4.571870123}$ is a tedious logarithmic computation by hand. On an electronic computer, $\ln(3.016894172)$ is computed by (2), the result multiplied by 4.571870123, and this product used as x in (3), since

$$a^p = e^{p \ln a}.$$

Little, if any, more machine time would be used than for a human to decide what the value of 3^4 is.

Taylor's Formula may also be used to approximate definite integrals with error estimates. Note that

$$\int_0^{1/2} x \sin x^2\, dx = -\frac{1}{2} \cos x^2 \Big]_0^{1/2} = \frac{1}{2} - \frac{1}{2} \cos \frac{1}{4}, \quad \text{but}$$

(4)
$$\int_0^{1/2} \sin x^2 \, dx$$

is a different matter. Algebraic, trigonometric, logarithmic, and exponential functions are collectively called the **elementary functions**. Most definite integrals met so far have had integrands that are derivatives of elementary functions. Thus,

$$x \sin x^2 = f'(x), \quad \text{where} \quad f(x) = -\tfrac{1}{2} \cos x^2,$$

but, try as one may, he will never find an elementary function $f(x)$ having $f'(x) = \sin x^2$. Nevertheless, the integrand in (4) is continuous, so the integral exists, but it cannot be expressed in terms of values of elementary functions or "cannot be expressed in closed form."

To approximate (4) within 5×10^{-10}, start with the formula

$$\left| \sin t - \sum_{k=1}^n \frac{(-1)^{k+1} t^{2k-1}}{(2k-1)!} \right| \le \frac{t^{2n+1}}{(2n+1)!} \quad \text{for} \quad t \ge 0.$$

Then

$$\sin x^2 = \sum_{k=1}^n \frac{(-1)^{k+1}(x^2)^{2k-1}}{(2k-1)!} \pm \frac{(x^2)^{2n+1}}{(2n+1)!}.$$

Hence,

$$\int_0^{1/2} \sin x^2 \, dx = \sum_{k=1}^n \frac{(-1)^{k+1}}{(2k+1)!} \int_0^{1/2} x^{4k-2} \, dx \pm \frac{1}{(2n+1)!} \int_0^{1/2} x^{4n+2} \, dx$$

$$= \sum_{k=1}^n \frac{(-1)^{k+1}}{(2k+1)!} \left[\frac{x^{4k-1}}{4k-1} \right]_0^{1/2} \pm \frac{1}{(2n+1)!} \frac{1}{4n+3} \left(\frac{1}{2} \right)^{4n+3}$$

Now the first n is desired for which

$$\frac{1}{(2n+1)!(4n+3)2^{4n+3}} < 5 \times 10^{-10}; \quad \text{that is,}$$

$$-\log(2n+1)! - \log(4n+3) - (4n+3)\log 2 < -10 + \log 5 = -9.3010.$$

From Table 3, $-\log(13!) = -9.7942$ is itself less than -9.3010, so that $n = 6$ is sufficiently small, but $n = 4$ or even 3 might work. The left side with $n = 3$ is

$$-3.7024 - 1.1761 - 15(0.3010) = -9.3935,$$

which is less than -9.3010 but not enough less to try $n = 2$. Hence, with $n = 3$,

$$\int_0^{1/2} \sin x^2 \, dx = \left[\frac{x^3}{3} - \frac{x^7}{7 \cdot 3!} + \frac{x^{11}}{11 \cdot 5!} \right]_0^{1/2}$$

may be evaluated with full confidence that the result will be within 5×10^{-10} of being correct.

Problem 1. Find an expression that will evaluate to within 5×10^{-5} of:

a. $\int_0^1 \sin x^2 \, dx.$

b. $\int_0^1 \sin \sqrt{x} \, dx.$

c. $\int_0^{1/2} e^{x^2} \, dx.$

d. $\int_0^{1/2} e^{-x^2} \, dx.$

e. $\int_0^{1/2} \sqrt{1 + x^3} \, dx.$ [Start with $\sqrt{1 + t}.$]

f. $\int_0^{1/2} \frac{1}{\sqrt{1 - x^3}} \, dx.$

g. $\int_{1/2}^1 \frac{e^x}{x} \, dx.$

h. $\int_0^1 \sin e^x \, dx.$

Problem 2. Show that none of the following functions has a Maclaurin expansion:

$$\ln x, \quad x^{3/2}, \quad \csc x, \quad \sqrt{x - 1}, \quad e^{\sqrt{x}}.$$

Problem 3. a. Use integration by parts to obtain

$$\left| \int_0^1 x^9 \sin \sqrt{x} \, dx - \frac{\sin 1}{10} - \frac{\cos 1}{210} \right| < \frac{1}{4620}.$$

b. Extend the process two more steps and see that the approximation is within 5×10^{-6} of the integral.

13-16.   Simpson's Rule

Taylor's Formula is used to obtain another way of approximating definite integrals to any desired accuracy. This method is easier than the one of the previous section in many problems, especially those to be programmed for an electronic computer.

With $g(t)$ having fourth derivative $g^4(t)$ continuous on $-h \leq t \leq h$, let M be the maximum value of $|g^4(t)|$ on this interval. Then, from Maclaurin's Formula with Lagrange remainder,

(1) $$g(t) = g(0) + g'(0)t + \frac{g''(0)}{2}t^2 + \frac{g'''(0)}{3!}t^3 \pm \frac{M}{4!}t^4,$$

since $|g^4(\xi)| \leq M$ for $-h < \xi < h.$ Hence,

$$\int_{-h}^h g(t) \, dt = \left[g(0)t + \frac{g'(0)}{2}t^2 + \frac{g''(0)}{6}t^3 + \frac{g'''(0)}{4!}t^4 \pm \frac{M}{5!}t^5 \right]_{-h}^h$$

(2) $$= g(0)2h + \frac{g''(0)}{3}h^3 \pm \frac{M}{5!}2h^5.$$

The next step will seem mysterious at this time, but the following problems give some indication why the particular expression was thought of. From (1),

$$\frac{h}{3}\left\{ g(-h) + 4g(0) + g(h) \right\}$$

$$= \frac{h}{3}\left\{ \left[g(0) - g'(0)h + \frac{g''(0)}{2}h^2 - \frac{g'''(0)}{3!}h^3 \pm \frac{M}{4!}h^4 \right] + 4g(0) + \right.$$

$$+\left[g(0) + g'(0)h + \frac{g''(0)}{2}h^2 + \frac{g'''(0)}{3!}h^3 \pm \frac{M}{4!}h^4\right]\Big\}$$

$$= \frac{h}{3}\left\{6g(0) + g''(0)h^2 \pm 2\frac{M}{4!}h^4\right\}$$

$$= g(0)2h + \frac{g''(0)}{3}h^3 \pm \frac{2}{3}\frac{M}{4!}h^5.$$

By solving this equation for $g(0)2h + \frac{1}{3}g''(0)h^3$ and substituting into (2), the result is

$$\int_{-h}^{h} g(t)\,dt = \frac{h}{3}\left\{g(-h) + 4g(0) + g(h)\right\} \pm 2Mh^5\left[\frac{1}{5!} + \frac{1}{3\cdot4!}\right].$$

The most pessimistic view was taken regarding the error term. Even so, after simplifying the error term, it is certain that

$$-\frac{2}{45}h^5 M \le \int_{-h}^{h} g(t)\,dt - \frac{h}{3}\left\{g(-h) + 4g(0) + g(h)\right\} < \frac{2}{45}h^5 M.$$

There is a much better error estimate, as the following theorem states.

THEOREM 13-16.1. *If $g^4(t)$ is continuous on $-h \le t \le h$, then there is a number η such that*

$$(3) \quad \int_{-h}^{h} g(t)\,dt = \frac{h}{3}\left\{g(-h) + 4g(0) + g(h)\right\} - \frac{h^5}{90}g^4(\eta), \quad -h < \eta < h.$$

Note that the error term has a minus sign (not $\pm$), a fact most useful in some phases of numerical analysis, although not for the following applications. Prob. 1 contains suggestions for proving this theorem.

Next, with a point x_0 given, and with $h > 0$, set

$$x_1 = x_0 + h \quad \text{and} \quad x_2 = x_0 + 2h.$$

If a function $f(x)$ has fourth derivative $f^4(x)$ continuous on $x_0 \le x \le x_2$, then, for some ξ_1,

$$(4) \quad \int_{x_0}^{x_2} f(x)\,dx = \frac{h}{3}\left[f(x_0) + 4f(x_1) + f(x_2)\right] - \frac{h^5}{90}f^4(\xi_1), \quad x_0 < \xi_1 < x_2.$$

To see this, make the transformation of variables from x to t by setting

$$x = t + x_1, \quad \text{that is,} \quad t = x - x_1,$$

and define the function $g(t) = f(t + x_1)$. Hence, $t = -h$ when $x = x_0$, $t = 0$ when $x = x_1$, $t = h$ when $x = x_2$, and

$$\int_{x_0}^{x_2} f(x)\,dx = \int_{-h}^{h} f(t + x_1)\,d(t + x_1) = \int_{-h}^{h} g(t)\,dt$$

$$= \frac{h}{3}\left[g(-h) + 4g(0) + g(h)\right] - \frac{h^5}{90}g^4(\eta), \quad -h < \eta < h.$$

It therefore follows that

$$\int_{x_0}^{x_2} f(x)\, dx = \frac{h}{3}\left[f(x_0) + 4f(x_1) + f(x_2) \right] - \frac{h^5}{90} f^4(\eta + x_1).$$

Since $-h + x_1 < \eta + x_1 < h + x_1$, then, upon setting $\xi_1 = \eta + x_1$, the equation (4) follows.

For convenience, set $y_0 = f(x_0)$, $y_1 = f(x_1)$, $y_2 = f(x_2)$, and rewrite (4) as

$$\int_{x_0}^{x_2} f(t)\, dt = \frac{h}{3}\left[y_0 + 4y_1 + y_2 \right] - \frac{h^5}{90} f^4(\xi_1).$$

In the same way, if $x_3 = x_0 + 3h$, and $x_4 = x_0 + 4h$, then, for the interval $x_2 \le x \le x_4$,

$$\int_{x_2}^{x_4} f(x)\, dx = \frac{h}{3}\left[y_2 + 4y_3 + y_4 \right] - \frac{h^5}{90}(\xi_2), \quad x_2 < \xi_2 < x_4.$$

Hence,

(5) $$\int_{x_0}^{x_4} f(x)\, dx = \frac{h}{3}\left[y_0 + 4y_1 + 2y_2 + 4y_3 + y_4 \right] - \frac{h^5}{90}\left[f^4(\xi_1) + f^4(\xi_2) \right].$$

This procedure may be continued to intervals

$$x_0 \le x \le x_6, \, x_0 \le x \le x_8, \, \ldots, \, x_0 \le x \le x_{2n},$$

for any integer n, and leads to the following result, which is used a great deal.

SIMPSON'S RULE. *Given* $f(x)$ *with fourth derivative* $f^4(x)$ *continuous on* $a \le x \le b$, *let* M *be the maximum value of* $|f^4(x)|$ *on this interval. With* n *a positive integer, let*

$$h = \frac{b - a}{2n}, \quad x_k = a + kh, \quad and \quad y_k = f(x_k) \quad or \quad k = 0, 1, 2, \ldots, 2n.$$

Then

(6) $$\left| \int_a^b f(x)\, dx - \frac{b - a}{6n}\left[y_0 + 4y_1 + 2y_2 + \cdots + 2y_{2n-2} + 4y_{2n-1} + y_{2n} \right] \right|$$

$$\le \frac{(b - a)^5}{2880n^4} M.$$

PROOF. Extend (5) to have upper limit $x_{2n} = b$. Then transpose all except the error terms to the left side. The absolute value of this difference is then less than or equal to

$$\left| -\frac{h^5}{90}\left[f^4(\xi_1) + f^4(\xi_2) + \cdots + f^4(\xi_n) \right] \right| \le \frac{h^5}{90}\left[\left| f^4(\xi_1) \right| + \cdots + \left| f^4(\xi_n) \right| \right]$$

$$\le \frac{h^5}{90} nM = \frac{1}{90}\left(\frac{b - a}{2n} \right)^5 nM.$$

In any given problem, $(b - a)^5$ and M are constants. Since n^4 occurs in the denominator, then the error term in (6) may be made as small as desired by choosing n large enough.

For some integrands $f(x)$, it may be difficult to determine the maximum value of $|f^4(x)|$. Note, however, that any number greater than this maximum value may be used for M in (6). For example, functions of the form

$$f(x) = \sin(2\sin x - 3\cos x)$$

and their integrals arise in the study of molecular structures. Then $f^1(x)$ is quite an expression, but each term has products of sines, cosines, and constants, so its absolute value can be bounded above. The sum of the bounds of absolute values of all terms is an upper bound of $|f^4(x)|$. Even though this bound may be much larger than actually necessary, n can be determined to ensure the desired accuracy. This is an argument for having mathematicians around a computing center.

It should now be clear that actual calculation using Simpson's Rule should be preceded by the determination of an n to guarantee the desired accuracy of the final result. Without the aid of at least a desk calculator, the numerical work itself would be tedious and not very informative. Thus, the following problems are more on the theoretical than the numerical side. It is hoped that these problems and notes will indicate that knowledge of formulas is a necessary, **but not a sufficient**, condition for modern applications of mathematics. Actually, about the only human computing done around a modern computing center is in the determination of error estimates.

The following example is the simplest possible illustration of the techniques used in determining an expression for the error term in a method of approximating a definite integral.

Example. Given that $g''(x)$ is continuous on $0 \le x \le 1$, show there is a number η such that $0 < \eta < 1$ and

(7) $$\int_0^1 g(x)\,dx = \frac{1}{2}[g(0) + g(1)] - \frac{1}{12} g''(\eta).$$

Solution. In Fig. 13-16.1, the area of the trapezoid misses the area under the curve by an amount E; that is,

(8) $$\int_0^1 g(x)\,dx = \frac{1}{2}[g(0) + g(1)] + E.$$

In case $g(x) = mx + b$, the formula is exact ($E = 0$) and $g''(x) = 0$. Hence, it is natural to expect that for a general $g(x)$ the error E will be in terms of $g''(x)$. From Taylor's Formula with $n = 2$, and R_2 in integral form,

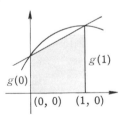

Fig. 13-16.1

(9) $$g(x) = g(0) + g'(0)\,x + \int_0^x (x - t)\,g''(t)\,dt.$$

Set $x = 1$ and substitute the result for $g(1)$ into the right-hand side of (8) to obtain

(10) $\int_0^1 g(x)\,dx = \frac{1}{2}\left[g(0) + g(0) + g'(0) + \int_0^1 (1-t)\,g''(t)\,dt\right] + E$

$$= g(0) + \frac{1}{2}g'(0) + \frac{1}{2}\int_0^1 (1-t)\,g''(t)\,dt + E.$$

Also, integrate (9) from $x = 0$ to $x = 1$ to obtain

$$\int_0^1 g(x)\,dx = g(0) + g'(0)\frac{1}{2} + \int_0^1\left[\int_0^x (x-t)\,g''(t)\,dt\right]dx.$$

Equating this expression and the one in (10) for the integral gives

$$E = -\frac{1}{2}\int_0^1 (1-t)\,g''(t)\,dt + \int_0^1\int_0^x (x-t)\,g''(t)\,dt\,dx.$$

From Example 1, Sec. 12-8, it follows there is a number η such that $0 < \eta < 1$ and

$$E = -\frac{1}{12}g''(\eta).$$

This expression substituted into (8) gives the desired result (7). Note that the curve of Fig. 13-16.1 is concave downward, and hence $g''(\eta) < 0$. The area of the trapezoid is too small, and (7) adjusts this approximation upward, as it should.

Then there is a ξ such that $a < \xi < b$ and

$$\int_a^b f(x)\,dx = \frac{b-a}{2}\left[f(a) + f(b)\right] - \frac{(b-a)^3}{12}f''(\xi).$$

To see this, change the variable of integration in (7) to t, then make the transformation

$$x = (b-a)t + a, \quad \text{and set} \quad g(t) = f[(b-a)t + a].$$

Problem 1. **a.** With $q(t) = b_0 + b_1 t + b_2 t^2 + b_3 t^3$ a third-degree polynomial, determine constants w_{-1}, w_0, w_1 (usually called "weights") such that

$$\int_{-1}^1 q(t)\,dt = w_{-1}q(-1) + w_0 q(0) + w_1 q(1).$$

[Hint: Integrate the left side, write out the expression for the right side, and then equate coefficients of the b's with like subscripts. Answer: $w_{-1} = w_1 = \frac{1}{3}$, $w_0 = \frac{4}{3}$.]

b. Let $p(x)$ be a third-degree polynomial. Transform the interval $-1 \leq t \leq 1$ to the interval $a \leq x \leq b$ by setting

$$x = \frac{b-a}{2}t + \frac{a+b}{2}$$

and use the formula of part a to obtain the so-called **midpoint rule**

$$\int_a^b p(x)\,dx = \frac{b-a}{6}\left[p(a) + 4p\left(\frac{a+b}{2}\right) + p(b)\right].$$

[Note: A third-degree polynomial can be determined so its graph passes through four given points. (Why?) Hence, with $f(x)$ given, many third-degree polynomials have graphs agreeing with $y = f(x)$ at the endpoints and midpoint of $a \leq x \leq b$. Some such polynomial $p(x)$ may thus have $y = p(x)$ close to $y = f(x)$ over $a \leq x \leq b$, and therefore have

$$\int_a^b p(x)\,dx \quad \text{close to} \quad \int_a^b f(x)\,dx.$$

But the actual coefficients of $p(x)$ need not be determined, since

$$p(a) = f(a), \quad p(b) = f(b), \quad \text{and} \quad p\!\left(\frac{a+b}{2}\right) = f\!\left(\frac{a+b}{2}\right).$$

Thus, nearness of

$$\frac{b-a}{6}\left[f(a) + 4f\!\left(\frac{a+b}{2}\right) + f(b) \right] \quad \text{to} \quad \int_a^b f(x)\,dx$$

is expected. The question "how near?" started research to obtain expressions for error terms such as in Theorem 13-16.1 and the example. All equipment is now in hand to prove Theorem 13-16.1 with $h = 1$ by merely modifying the above example to use the midpoint rule instead of the trapezoidal rule. Actually, the biggest hurdle has already been jumped if Prob. 3, Sec. 12-8, was worked.]

c. Without working out either integral, show that

$$\int_{-1}^1 (3 - 500t + t^2 + 1000t^3)\,dt = \int_{-1}^1 (3 + t^2)\,dt.$$

Problem 2. a. With $q(t)$ a third-degree polynomial, determine weights w_{-1}, w_0, and w_1 such that

$$\int_{-2}^2 q(t)\,dt = w_{+1}q(-1) + w_0 q(0) + w_1 q(1).$$

[Answer: $w_{-1} = w_1 = \frac{8}{3}$, $w_0 = -\frac{4}{3}$.]

b. With x_0 a given point and $h > 0$, set $x_k = x_0 + kh$ for $k = -2, -1, 0, 1, 2$. Obtain the following formula for any third-degree polynomial $p(x)$:

$$\int_{x_{-2}}^{x_2} p(x)\,dx = \frac{4}{3}h\,[2p(x_{-1}) - p(x_0) + 2p(x_1)].$$

[Note: Similar to the development in the text, the formula with $f(x)$ in place of $p(x)$ has the error term $+(14/45)\,h^5 f^4(\xi)$. The error terms here and in following problems are included for reference only.]

Problem 3. With x_0 given, $h > 0$, $x_k = x_0 + kh$ for $k = -2, -1, 0, 1$, and $p(x)$ a third-degree polynomial, show that

$$\int_{x_{-2}}^{x_{-1}} p(x)\,dx = \frac{3}{8}h\,[p(x_{-2}) + 3p(x_{-1}) + 3p(x_0) + p(x_1)].$$

$[-(3/80)\,h^5 f^4(\xi)$ is the error term if $p(x)$ is replaced by $f(x)$.]

Problem 4. With $q(t)$ a fifth-degree polynomial, determine weights w_0 and w_1 and a constant c such that

$$\int_{-1}^1 q(t)\,dt = w_1 q(-c) + w_0 q(0) + w_1 q(c).$$

[Answer: $w_0 = \frac{8}{9}$, $w_1 = \frac{5}{9}$, $c = \sqrt{\frac{3}{5}}$.] [Note: This is the basis of the famous Gauss' Quadrature Formula

$$\int_a^b f(x)\,dx = \frac{b-a}{18}[5f(c_{-1}) + 8f(c_0) + 5f(c_1)] + \frac{(b-a)^7 f^6(\xi)}{2{,}016{,}000},$$

where
$$c_0 = \frac{a+b}{2} \quad \text{and} \quad c_{\pm 1} = \frac{a+b}{2} \pm \frac{b-a}{2}\sqrt{\frac{3}{5}}.$$

The constant $\sqrt{\frac{3}{5}}$ is bothersome in hand computing but means little to an electronic computer. This formula is particularly useful in experiments that can be designed to take data at the three designated points of the interval. Fifth-degree approximation is unexpected from only three observations, especially with such phenomenal accuracy.]

Problem 5. Establish each of the following for a third-degree polynomial.

a. $\displaystyle\int_{-1}^{1} q(t)\,dt = q\left(-\frac{1}{\sqrt{3}}\right) + q\left(\frac{1}{\sqrt{3}}\right)$. [Hint: Set integral $= w_1 q(c_1) +$ $w_2 q(c_2)$.]

b. $\displaystyle\int_{0}^{1} q(t)\,dt = \frac{1}{2}[q(0) + q(1)] + \frac{1}{12}[q'(0) - q'(1)]$. $[(1/720) f^4(\xi)$ is error term if f is in place of q.]

Problem 6. For any fifth-degree polynomial, show that

$$\int_{0}^{2h} q(t)\,dt = \frac{h}{15}[7q(0) + 16q(h) + 7q(2h)] + \frac{h^2}{15}[q'(0) - q'(2h)].$$

$[(h^7 f^6(\xi)/4725)$ is the error term when f is in place of q. Note that specifying three points and derivatives at two of them makes five conditions, which leaves one degree of freedom for a fifth-degree polynomial.]

Problem 7. Show that there is a ξ, $a < \xi < b$, such that the formula in Simpson's Rule could be replaced by the equality

$$\int_{a}^{b} f(x)\,dx = \frac{b-a}{6n}[y_0 + 4y_1 + 2y_2 + \cdots + 2y_{2n-2} + 4y_{2n-1} + y_{2n}] - \frac{(b-a)^5}{2880n^4} f^4(\xi).$$

[Hint: Intermediate Value Theorem for Continuous Functions.]

13-17. Extrema for Functions of Two Variables

Taylor's Formula, with $n = 2$ and Lagrange remainder, is

$$f(x) = f(a) + f'(a)(x - a) + \frac{f''(\xi)}{2}(x - a)^2, \quad \xi \text{ between } a \text{ and } x.$$

If $f'(a) = 0$, then

$$f(x) = f(a) + \frac{f''(\xi)}{2}(x - a)^2.$$

Thus, if $f''(x)$ is continuous and $f''(a) \neq 0$, then, for all x in some interval centered at a,

$$f(x) < f(a) \text{ if } f''(a) < 0, \quad \text{but} \quad f(x) > f(a) \text{ if } f''(a) > 0.$$

This is a proof of the intuitively presented second-derivative test for local maxima or minima (that is, extreme) values of functions of one variable.

If $f'(a) = 0$, the curve $y = f(x)$ has a horizontal tangent at $(a, f(a))$ which is a relative high, a relative low, or an inflection point. The situation is not as simple for functions of two variables. For example, in a mountain pass, the highway may reach its greatest elevation at the lowest point of one trail, another trail may have an inflection at this point, and a third trail may stay level for some distance on both sides (such as the origin on $z = x^2 - y^2$ of Fig. 10-10.3). Criteria similar to the second derivative test will, however, be established for functions of two variables.

First recall that the tangent plane to a surface $z = F(x, y)$ at a point $(a, b, F(a, b))$ has equation

$$z = F(a, b) + F_x(a, b)(x - a) + F_y(a, b)(y - b),$$

provided the partials are continuous. If this point is a relative high or low point of the surface, the tangent plane is horizontal and has equation $z = F(a, b)$. Hence:

If $F(a, b)$ is a local extremum of $F(x, y)$ and the first partials are continuous at (a, b), then

(1) $$F_x(a, b) = F_y(a, b) = 0.$$

Under this necessary condition, sufficient conditions will be obtained for determining whether

$$F(x, y) < F(a, b) \quad \text{(local maximum) or}$$

$$F(x, y) > F(a, b) \quad \text{(local minimum)}$$

for all (x, y) sufficiently close to (a, b).

A surface $z = F(x, y)$ is said to have $(a, b, F(a, b))$ as a **saddle point**, or a **minimax** point, if $F(x, y) > F(a, b)$ for some (x, y) close to (a, b) but $F(x, y) < F(a, b)$ for others. Sufficient conditions for a saddle point where the tangent plane is horizontal will also be obtained.

Further development is under the assumption that:

Equation (1) holds and all second partials of $F(x, y)$ exist and are continuous at (a, b).

Let h and k be any consatnts not both zero. An h and k may be chosen so that $(a + h, b + k)$ is in any previously designated direction from (a, b). Then

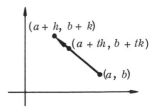

Fig. 13-17.1

$$F(a + th, b + tk), \quad |t| < 1$$

is a function of one variable and $\lim_{t \to 0} F(a + th, b + tk) = F(a, b)$. Thus, l'Hospital's Rules may be applied to evaluate

$$\lim_{t \to 0} \frac{F(a + th, b + tk) - F(a, b)}{t^2}.$$

The derivatives with respect to t of the function $F(a + th, b + tk)$ is then expressed in terms of the partials F_x and F_y to yield

$$\lim_{t \to 0} \frac{F(a + th, b + tk) - F(a, b)}{t^2}$$

$$= \lim_{t \to 0} \frac{F_x(a + th, b + tk)h + F_y(a + th, b + tk)k}{2t} \qquad \left[\frac{0}{0} \text{ by (1)}\right]$$

$$= \lim_{t \to 0} \frac{F_{xx}(a+th, b+tk)h^2 + 2F_{xy}(a+th, b+tk)hk + F_{yy}(a+th, b+tk)k^2}{2}$$

$$(2) \qquad = \frac{1}{2}\left[F_{xx}(a, b)h^2 + 2F_{xy}(a, b)hk + F_{yy}(a, b)k^2\right],$$

from the continuity of the second partials.

Hence, if (2) is not zero, then (since $t^2 > 0$)

(3) $F(a + th, b + tk) - F(a, b)$ and (2) *have the same sign for all sufficiently small t.*

As shown below, there are conditions under which (2) is negative for all (h, k) not both zero. Then, under these conditions,

$$F(a + th, b + tk) < F(a, b)$$

for sufficiently small t. This says that, in any direction from (a, b) all (x, y) sufficiently close to (a, b) are such that

$$F(x, y) < F(a, b).$$

Hence, $F(a, b)$ is a local maximum (under these conditions).

The relevance of the following algebraic results will then be seen. $A, B,$ and C are constants.

RESULT 1. *If $AC - B^2 > 0$, then, for any h and k not both zero,*

$$[Ah^2 + 2Bhk + Ck^2], \quad A, \quad \text{and} \quad C$$

are all positive or else all three are negative.

PROOF. Since $AC > B^2 \geq 0$, then A and C have the same sign (and, in particular, neither is zero). Then

$$(4) \qquad A[Ah^2 + 2Bhk + Ck^2] = A^2h^2 + 2ABhk + ACk^2$$

$$= \{A^2h^2 + 2ABhk + B^2k^2\} + ACk^2 - B^2k^2$$

$$= \{Ah + Bk\}^2 + (AC - B^2)k^2.$$

In case $k = 0$, then $h \neq 0$ and $\{Ah\}^2 > 0$. In case $k \neq 0$, then the second term is positive and the first term is nonnegative. Hence, in either case the product is positive. Thus, A and $[Ah^2 + 2Bhk + Ck^2]$ have the same sign.

RESULT 2. *If $AC - B^2 < 0$, then*

$$(5) \qquad [Ah^2 + 2Bhk + Ck^2]$$

is positive for some pairs (h, k) and negative for other pairs.

PROOF. *Case 1: $A \neq 0$ or $C \neq 0$.* If $A \neq 0$, again write the product of A

and (5) in the form (4). Take $k \neq 0$ and $h = -(B/A)k$. Then (4) reduces to

$$(AC - B^2)k^2 < 0.$$

Next, take $k = 0$. Then (4) reduces to $\{Ah\}^2 > 0$, since $h \neq 0$. In the first choice, (5) has sign opposite to A, but in the second, (5) has the sign of A. Hence, (5) is positive for some (h, k), negative for others. If $C \neq 0$, a similar proof can be made.

Case 2: $A = C = 0$. $B^2 \neq 0$ and (5) reduces to

$$2Bhk,$$

which has one sign for $h > 0$ and $k > 0$, but the opposite sign if $h > 0$ and $k < 0$.

The proof of the following theorem uses these algebraic results.

THEOREM 13-17.1. *Let $F(x, y)$ be defined and have continuous second partials in a circle with center at (a, b), where*

$$F_x(a, b) = F_y(a, b) = 0.$$

If, in addition,

(i) $$F_{xx}(a, b)F_{yy}(a, b) - F_{xy}^2(a, b) > 0,$$

then $F_{xx}(a, b) \neq 0$ and $F(x, y)$ has $F(a, b)$ as a local

$$\begin{Bmatrix} maximum \\ minimum \end{Bmatrix} \quad in \ case \quad F_{xx}(a, b) \quad is \quad \begin{Bmatrix} < 0 \\ > 0 \end{Bmatrix}.$$

If, however,

(ii) $$F_{xx}(a, b)F_{yy}(a, b) - F_{xy}^2(a, b) < 0,$$

then $(a, b, F(a, b))$ is a saddle point of the surface $z = F(x, y)$.
If

(iii) $$F_{xx}(a, b)F_{yy}(a, b) - F_{xy}^2(a, b) = 0,$$

then no conclusion can be drawn from this about extreme values or saddle points.

PROOF UNDER CONDITION (i). Consider $F_{xx}(a, b) < 0$. Then, by the first algebraic result, (2) is also negative for all (h, k) not both zero. It was shown just below (3) how this means that $F(a, b)$ is a local maximum of $F(x, y)$. In a similar way, $F(a, b)$ is a local minimum if $F_{xx}(a, b) > 0$.

PROOF UNDER CONDITION (ii). Then, by the second algebraic result, there is a pair (h_1, k_1) making (2) negative and another pair (h_2, k_2) making (2) positive. Hence, for all sufficiently small t,

$$F(a + th_1, b + tk_1) < F(a, b) \quad and$$
$$F(a + th_2, b + tk_2) > F(a, b).$$

Thus, $(a, b, F(a, b))$ is a saddle point of the surface $z = F(x, y)$.

PROOF UNDER CONDITION (iii). Consider

$$F(x, y) = x^4 + y^4 \quad \text{and} \quad G(x, y) = -(x^4 + y^4).$$

Clearly, $F(0, 0)$ is the minimum of $F(x, y)$, while $G(0, 0)$ is the maximum of $G(x, y)$, and it is easy to check that (iii) holds for both functions when $x = y = 0$.

For $z = x^4 - y^4$, all first and second partials are zero when $x = y = 0$, so the conditions under (iii) hold. However, the origin is a saddle point of the surface since the plane $y = 0$ cuts the surface in $z = x^4$ with points above the (x, y)-plane, while in the plane $x = 0$ there are points below this level.

It is convenient to set

(6) $$D(x, y) = F_{xx}(x, y)F_{yy}(x, y) - F_{xy}^2(x, y).$$

$D(a, b)$ is called the **discriminant** of the quadratic form appearing in (2).

Example 1. Examine $z = F(x, y) = x^3 - 12xy + 8y^3$ for extreme values and saddlepoints.

Solution. Since

$$z_x = 3x^2 - 12y \quad \text{and} \quad z_y = -12x + 24y^2,$$

the critical values are obtained by solving

$$3x^2 - 12y = 0 \quad \text{and} \quad -12x + 24y^2 = 0$$

simultaneously. These are $(0, 0)$ and $(2, 1)$.

Then $D(x, y) = (6x)(48y) - (-12)^2 = (12)^2(2xy - 1)$, so that

$$D(0, 0) = -(12)^2 \quad \text{and} \quad D(2, 1) = (12)^2 \cdot 3.$$

Since $D(0, 0) < 0$, the point $(0, 0, 0)$ is a saddle point of the surface. Since $D(2,1) > 0$ and $F_{xx}(2, 1) = 6(2) > 0$, the value $F(2, 1) = 2^3 - 12 \cdot 2 + 8 = -8$ is a local minimum for the function.

Example 2. Find the smallest distance between points on the lines having parametric equations

$$L_1: x = 5 + 2s, \quad y = 8 + 2s, \quad z = 6 - 2s;$$
$$L_2: x = -1 + t, \quad y = 6 - 2t, \quad z = t.$$

Solution. Let $F(s, t)$ be the square of the distance between the points of L_1 and L_2 determined by s and t, respectively:

$$F(s, t) = (6 + 2s - t)^2 + (2 + 2s + 2t)^2 + (6 - 2s - t)^2.$$

Then

$$F_s(s, t) = 4(6 + 2s - t) + 4(2 + 2s + 2t) - 4(6 - 2s - t)$$
$$= 8(1 + 3s + t) \quad \text{and}$$
$$F_t(s, t) = 4(-4 + 2s + 3t).$$

Hence, $3s + t = -1$ and $2s + 3t = 4$ are solved simultaneously to obtain the critical values

$$s = -1, \quad t = 2.$$

Since $F_{ss} = 24 > 0$ and $F_{ss}F_{tt} - F_{st}^2 = (24)(12) - 8^2 > 0$ [for all (s, t)], then the minimum distance is

$$\sqrt{F(-1, 2)} = \sqrt{2^2 + 4^2 + 6^2} = 2\sqrt{14}.$$

Note that the points giving this minimum distance are $(3, 6, 8)$ on L_1 and $(1, 2, 2)$ on L_2. The line joining these points has direction numbers 2, 4, 6. Hence, this line is perpendicular to both L_1 and L_2, as a mental check, using the direction numbers of L_1 and L_2, shows.

A function of two variables may assume an extreme value at a boundary point of its domain of definition. In much the same way that a function of one variable defined on an interval requires examination at the endpoints, boundaries of domains of functions of two variables may require attention. In Theorem 13-17.1, the phrase "let $F(x, y)$ be defined... in a circle with center (a, b)" is an essential part of the hypotheses. Hence, this theorem gives criteria for determining extrema and saddle points that occur at interior points of the domain of definition.

Example 3. Find the shortest distance from the origin to the surface.

(7) $$z^2 = xy - 1.$$

Solution. Let $F(x, y)$ be the square of the distance from the origin to a point (x, y, z) on the surface. Hence, the function

(8) $$F(x, y) = x^2 + y^2 + z^2 = x^2 + y^2 + xy - 1$$

is continuous, as are its first partials

$$F_x(x, y) = 2x + y \quad \text{and} \quad F_y(x, y) = 2y + x.$$

Then $2x + y = 0$ and $2y + x = 0$ have $x = 0, y = 0$ as the only simultaneous solution. These values substituted into (7) give the "points"

$$(0, 0, \pm\sqrt{-1}).$$

What is wrong?

Actually, (7) should carry the restriction $xy - 1 \geq 0$. Thus, (8) is pertinent to this problem if and only if $xy - 1 \geq 0$. The above shows that $F_x(x, y) = 0, F_y(x, y) = 0$ has no simultaneous solution in the domain

$$\{(x, y) \,|\, xy \geq 1\}$$

of definition. Hence, if $F(x, y)$ has a minimum, it must occur on the boundary of this domain. The boundary is the curve

$$xy = 1 \quad \text{of the } (x, y)\text{-plane.}$$

With x and y so related, the square of the distance is

$$f(x) = F\left(x, \frac{1}{x}\right) = x^2 + \frac{1}{x^2} + x\left(\frac{1}{x}\right) - 1 = x^2 + \frac{1}{x^2}$$

(since no point on the boundary curve has $x = 0$). Now

$$f'(x) = 2x - \frac{2}{x^3} = 0 \quad \text{for} \quad x = \pm 1 \quad \text{and}$$

$$f''(x) = 2 + \frac{6}{x^4} > 0 \quad \text{for all} \quad x \neq 0.$$

Hence, the minimum distance is

$$\sqrt{f(\pm 1)} = \sqrt{2},$$

and occurs at the points $(1, 1, 0)$ and $(-1, -1, 0)$ of the surface (7).

Problem 1. Examine each of the following for extrema and saddle points:

a. $z = x + y + 2$.
b. $z = x^2 + y^2 + 2$.
c. $z = x^2 - y^2 + 2$.
d. $z = x^2 + y^2 + 2x + 2y$.
e. $z = x^2 + 2xy + y^2$.
f. $z = x^2 + 3xy + y^2$.

g. $z = x^3 + y^3 + 2$.
h. $z = x^3 - y^3 + 2$.
i. $z = x^3 - y^3 - 3x^2 + 3x + 1$.
j. $z = x^3 - y^4$.
k. $z = x^3 - 3x - y^4 + 4y$.
l. $z = x^3 - y^3 - 3xy$.

Problem 2. a. Find the point on the plane $x + y + z = 18$ where the function xyz of three variables takes its maximum value.

b. Find the volume of the largest box that can be made having the sum of its three dimensions equal to 18.

c. Find the volume of the largest box without a lid that can be made having outside surface area 108.

Problem 3. Find the shortest distance from the origin to the surface:

a. $ax + by + cz = d$.
b. $z^2 = xy + 1$.

c. $z^2 = (1 - x)(3 + y)$.
d. $x^2 + y^2 + z^2 = 4$.

Problem 4. A thin metal disk over $x^2 + y^2 \leq 1$ has (hypothetical) temperature at (x, y) given by $T = 16x^2 + 24x + 40y^2$. Find the hottest and coldest points of the disk. Also, find the coldest point on the edge.

13-18. Taylor's Expansion in Two Variables

Maclaurin's expansion of a function $f(t)$ of one variable is

$$f(t) = f(0) + f'(0)t + \frac{f''(0)}{2!}t^2 + \frac{f'''(0)}{3!}t^3 + \cdots.$$

In particular,

(1) $$f(1) = f(0) + f'(0) + \frac{f''(0)}{2!} + \frac{f'''(0)}{3!} + \cdots.$$

This formula is used to obtain Taylor's expansion of a function $F(x, y)$ about a point (a, b), assuming continuity of the partials. With h and k constants, set

$$f(t) = F(a + th, b + tk).$$

First, $f'(t) = F_x(a + th, b + tk)h + F_y(a + th, b + tk)k$ and

$$f'(0) = F_x(a, b)h + F_y(a, b)k.$$

Then, with partials evaluated at $(a + th, b + tk)$,

$$f''(t) = (F_{xx}h + F_{xy}k)h + (F_{yx}h + F_{yy}k)k$$
$$= F_{xx}h^2 + 2F_{xy}hk + F_{yy}k^2 \quad \text{and}$$
$$f''(0) = F_{xx}(a, b)h^2 + 2F_{xy}(a, b)hk + F_{yy}(a, b)k^2.$$

In a similar way, it should be checked that

$$f'''(0) = F_{xxx}(a, b)h^3 + 3F_{xxy}(a, b)h^2k + 3F_{xyy}(a, b)hk^2 + F_{yyy}(a, b)k^3$$

The similarity with the binomial expansion continues for higher derivatives $f^n(0)$. In fact, the notation

$$\left(h\frac{\partial}{\partial x} + k\frac{\partial}{\partial y} \right)^n F(x, y)$$

is used with the agreement that, after a formal binomial expansion, the interpretation

$$\left(h\frac{\partial}{\partial x} \right)^{n-i} \left(k\frac{\partial}{\partial y} \right)^i F(x, y) = \frac{\partial^n F(x, y)}{\partial^{n-i}x\, \partial^i y} h^{n-i} k^i$$

is made.

Since $f(1) = F(a + h, b + k)$, substitution into (1) yields

(2) $$F(a + h, b + k) = F(a, b) + [F_x h + F_y k]_{(a, b)}$$

$$+ \frac{1}{2!}\left[F_{xx}h^2 + 2F_{xy}hk + F_{yy}k^2 \right]_{(a, b)} + \cdots$$

$$= F(a, b) + \left[\sum_{n=1}^{\infty} \left(h\frac{\partial}{\partial x} + k\frac{\partial}{\partial y} \right)^n \frac{F(x, y)}{n!} \right]_{(a, b)}$$

If the expansion in (1) is stopped, the Lagrange remainder is

$$\frac{f^n(\tau_n)}{n!}, \quad 0 < \tau_n < 1.$$

Then upon setting $\xi_n = a + \tau_n h$ and $\eta_n = b + \tau_n k$, the expansion (2) may be stopped by using the remainder

$$R_n = \frac{1}{n!}\left[\left(h\frac{\partial}{\partial x} + k\frac{\partial}{\partial y} \right)^n F(x, y) \right]_{(\xi_n, \eta_n)}.$$

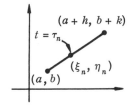

Fig. 13-18.1

Example. a. Given $F(x, y) = e^x \cos y$, find the Maclaurin expansion of $F(h, k)$ through second-order terms. b. Find the Maclaurin expansions of e^h and $\cos k$ through second-order terms, multiply the results, and compare with the result of part a.

Solution a. $F_x(0, 0) = e^0 \cos 0 = 1$, $F_y(0, 0) = -e^0 \sin 0 = 0$, $F_{xx} = e^0 \cos 0 = 1$, $F_{xy} = -e^0 \sin 0 = 0$, $F_{yy} = -e^0 \cos 0 = -1$. Hence, the requested portion of the expansion is

$$1 + h + 0k + \tfrac{1}{2}(h^2 + 2 \cdot 0hk - k^2) = 1 + h + \tfrac{1}{2}(h^2 - k^2).$$

Solution b.

$$(1 + h + \tfrac{1}{2}h^2)(1 - \tfrac{1}{2}k^2) = 1 + h + \tfrac{1}{2}h^2 - \tfrac{1}{2}k^2 - \tfrac{1}{2}hk^2 - \tfrac{1}{4}h^2 k^2.$$

The two agree through second-order terms.

Problem 1. a. Show that

$$\sin (a + h) \cos (b + k) = \sin a \cos b + [h \cos a \cos b - k \sin a \sin b]$$
$$+ \tfrac{1}{2} [-h^2 \sin a \cos b - 2hk \cos a \sin b - k^2 \sin a \cos b]$$
$$+ \cdots.$$

b. Start multiplying the Taylor expansions of $\sin (a + h)$ and $\cos (b + k)$ and compare with part a.

Problem 2. a. Use (2) to find the first two nonzero terms in the Maclaurin expansion of $\sin (hk)$.

b. Substitute $t = hk$ in the Maclaurin expansion of $\sin t$.

Problem 3. Approximate $\sqrt{(3.1)^2 + (3.8)^2}$ by using $F(x, y) = \sqrt{x^2 + y^2}$, $a = 3$, $b = 4$, $h = 0.1$, and $k = -0.2$, and going through second-order h, k terms.

Problem 4. Compare the second-order approximations of the two expressions $e^h \sin k$ and $e^h \ln (1 + k)$.

Problem 5. Show that

$$F(x + dx, y + dy) = F(x, y) + dF(x, y) + \frac{1}{2} d^2 F(x, y) + \cdots + \frac{d^{n-1} F(x, y)}{(n - 1)!} + R_n,$$

where

$$R_n = \frac{1}{n!} [d^n F(x, y)]_{(\xi_n, \eta_n)}.$$

Chapter 14

Differential Equations

14-1. Review and Terminology

In Sec. 3-3, it was shown how to solve a differential equation if the variables could be separated. The following example reviews the method.

Example 1. $x(3y - 2)^{-1} dx + (x^2 + 1) dy = 0.$

Solution. First write the equation as

$$\frac{x}{x^2 + 1} dx = -(3y - 2) dy$$

and then integrate both sides:

$$\int \frac{x}{x^2 + 1} dx = -\int (3y - 2) dy,$$

$$\tfrac{1}{2} \ln (x^2 + 1) = -\tfrac{1}{6}(3y - 2)^2 + c.$$

The variables may not be separable, but the expression might be an exact differential. In Sec. 11-9, it was shown that

(1) $$M(x, y) dx + N(x, y) dy$$

is an exact differential if and only if

(2) $$\frac{\partial M}{\partial y} = \frac{\partial N}{\partial x}.$$

Hence, if (1) is given and (2) holds, there is a function $f(x, y)$ such that

$$df = M dx + N dy$$

and the solution of $M dx + N dy = 0$ is $f(x, y) = c.$

Example 2. $e^x(y - x) dx + (1 + e^x) dy = 0.$

Solution. The variables cannot be separated, but

$$\frac{\partial e^x(y - x)}{\partial y} = e^x, \quad \frac{\partial}{\partial x}(1 + e^x) = e^x,$$

and hence the expression is the exact differential of the function $f(x, y)$ such that

$$\frac{\partial f}{\partial x} = e^x(y - x) \quad \text{and} \quad \frac{\partial f}{\partial y} = (1 + e^x).$$

From the first of these,

$$f(x, y) = ye^x - xe^x + e^x + c_1(y)$$

for some function $c_1(y)$ of y alone; whereas, from the second,

$$f(x, y) = y + ye^x + c_2(x).$$

Hence, both expressions are the same upon choosing

$$c_1(y) = y \quad \text{and} \quad c_2(x) = -xe^x + e^x.$$

The solution is therefore

$$f(x, y) = ye^x - xe^x + e^x + y = c.$$

Unfortunately, differential equations arise which fit neither of the above criteria. Before taking up additional methods, however, some standard terminology will be introduced.

An equation that involves only two variables and their differentials (or the derivatives of one variable with respect to the other) is called an **ordinary differential equation.** Partial differential equations involve more than two variables and partial derivatives, but such equations will not be considered in this book.

Examples of ordinary differential equations are:

(1) $$x^2\,dy + (2xy - 1)\,dx = 0,$$

(2) $$\frac{d^2y}{dx^2} - 3\frac{dy}{dx} + 2y = x^3 + e^x \quad \text{or} \quad y'' - 3y' + 2y = x^3 + e^x,$$

(3) $$y = x\frac{dy}{dx} - \frac{1}{4}\left(\frac{dy}{dx}\right)^2 \quad \text{or} \quad y = xy' - \frac{1}{4}(y')^2,$$

(4) $$s'' + (1 + t^2)\sqrt{s} = 0, \quad \text{where} \quad s'' = \frac{d^2s}{dt^2}.$$

The **order** of a differential equation is the order of the highest derivatives appearing. Thus, (1) and (3) are of order one, while (2) and (4) are of order two.

A differential equation is said to be **linear** if the dependent variable and its derivatives occur to the first degree and no term involves the product of any of these. Thus, (1) and (2) are linear, but (3) is not linear because one occurrence of dy/dx is squared, and (4) is not linear because of $\sqrt{s}$. Also,

(5) $$\tfrac{1}{2}y'y'' = x^2 + 1$$

is not linear because of the product $y'y''$.

If the dependent variable, and whichever of its derivatives are present, occurs in separate terms and all are raised to integer powers, then the equation is assigned a **degree**; namely, the exponent of the highest order derivative. Thus, (1) and (2) have degree one, (3) has degree two, but no degree is assigned to (4). Some books would start with (4) written as

$$s'' = -(1 + t^2)\sqrt{s},$$

square to obtain

$$(s'')^2 = (1 + t^2)^2 s$$

and, even though this is not the same equation as (4), assign the degree two to (4).

Notice that a linear equation is of first degree, but a first-degree equation need not be linear. For example,

$$y'' + 2(y')^2 - y = 0$$

is of first degree since the highest derivative y'' is raised to the first power, but the equation is not linear because of $(y')^2$.

A one-parameter family of functions of two variables x and y,

$$f(x, y, c) = 0,$$

with parameter c, also has its differential

$$df(x, y, c) = \frac{\partial f(x, y, c)}{\partial x} dx + \frac{\partial f(x, y, c)}{\partial y} dy = 0.$$

The elimination of the parameter c between the two equations

$$f(x, y, c) = 0 \quad \text{and} \quad df(x, y, c) = 0$$

gives rise to a first-order differential equation called the **differential equation of the family.**

Example 3. Find the differential equation of the family

$$xy - cy^2 - 4 = 0.$$

Solution. The differential expression is

(6) $y\, dx + (x - 2cy)\, dy = 0.$

The given equation solved for c is

(7) $c = \dfrac{xy - 4}{y^2},$

and this substituted into (6) gives

$$y\, dx + \left(x - 2y\, \frac{xy - 4}{y^2}\right) dy = 0,$$

which is the differential equation of the family and may be simpified to

(8) $y^2\, dx + (8 - xy)\, dy = 0.$

This same differential equation may be obtained from (7) by noting that

$$0 = dc = \frac{y^2\,d(xy-4) - (xy-4)\,dy^2}{y^4}$$

$$= \frac{1}{y^4}[y^2(x\,dy + y\,dx) - (xy-4)2y\,dy]$$

$$= \frac{y}{y^4}[xy\,dy + y^2\,dx - 2xy\,dy + 8\,dy],$$

and this simplifies to (8).

A one-parameter family

(9) $f(x, y, c) = 0$

thus has its differential equation of the form

(10) $M(x, y)\,dx + N(x, y)\,dy = 0,$

and (9) is said to be the **primitive** of (10).

In a regular course on differential equations, it is shown that, under slight restrictions, a first-order differential equation of the form (10) has a unique primitive which is then called the **general solution** of the differential equation. Similarly, an *n* parameter family

$$F(x, y, c_1, c_2, \ldots, c_n) = 0$$

has its differential equation of *n*th order, and conversely an *n*th-order differential equation has a unique *n* parameter family as its general solution. A **specific solution** is obtained from the general solution by assigning specific constants to each of the parameters $c_1, c_2, \ldots, c_n$.

Example 4. Find the differential equation of the two-parameter family

(11) $y = c_1 e^x + c_2 \sin x.$

Solution. Take two derivatives:

$$y' = c_1 e^x + c_2 \cos x,$$
$$y'' = c_1 e^x - c_2 \sin x.$$

The first minus the second and third give, respectively,

$$y - y' = c_2(\sin x - \cos x) \quad \bigg| \quad 2 \sin x$$
$$y - y'' = 2c_2 \sin x \quad\quad\;\; \bigg| \quad -(\sin x - \cos x)$$

The bar on the right (with the expressions after it) means to multiply through by $2 \sin x$ and $-(\sin x - \cos x)$, respectively, and then add to obtain

(12) $(\sin x - \cos x)y'' - 2(\sin x)y' + (\sin x + \cos x)y = 0,$

which is the second-order differential equation of the given family (11).

It is much more difficult to start with the differential equation (12), not knowing where it came from, and obtain the primitive (11) as the solution. The remainder of this chapter is concerned mainly with solving differential equations.

Problem 1. Each of the differential equations may be solved by separating the variables:

a. $\dfrac{dy}{dx} = \dfrac{xy}{x-1}.$

b. $xy\,dy = (x+1)(y+1)\,dx.$

c. $xy\,dx = (x+1)(y+1)\,dy.$

d. $e^{x+y}\,dy = x\,dx.$

e. $e^{x+y}\,dx = y\,dy.$

f. $x^2 y \dfrac{dy}{dx} = (1+x)\sec y.$

g. $x(1+\cos y)\,dx + (x+1)\,dy = 0.$

h. $x\sec y\,dx + y\,dy = 0.$

i. $2^{x+y}\,dx + 3^{x+y}\,dy = 0.$

j. $y e^{2x}\,dx + (e^x + 1)\,dy = 0.$

Problem 2. Solve each of the following differential equations:

a. $(y - x^2)\,dx + (x + y^2)\,dy = 0.$

b. $\dfrac{xy+1}{y}\,dx + \left(\dfrac{y-x}{y^2}\right)dy = 0.$

c. $(\cos x + \sin y)\,dx + x\cos y\,dy = 0.$

d. $\sin y\,dx - x\cos y\,dy = 0.$

e. $e^{x+y}\,dx + (e^x e^y + y)\,dy = 0.$

f. $e^{x+y}\,dx + y\,dy = 0.$

g. $2\cos 3t\cos 2\theta\,d\theta - 3\sin 3t\sin 2\theta\,dt = 0.$

h. $3\cos 3t\cos 2\theta\,d\theta - 2\sin 3t\sin 2\theta\,dt = 0.$

Problem 3. Find the particular solution that not only satisfies the differential equation but also the side condition.

a. $y^2(1+x)\,dx - x^3\,dy = 0; \quad y = 2$ when $x = 1.$

b. $(y^2 + x)\,dx + 2xy\,dy = 0; \quad y = 2$ when $x = 1.$

c. $x^2 y\,dy - dx = x^2\,dx; \quad y = 1$ when $x = 2.$

d. $\dfrac{dy}{dx} = \dfrac{x-3}{y-2}; \quad y = 3$ when $x = 2.$

e. $x^2 y \dfrac{dy}{dx} = (1+x)\csc y; \quad y = \pi$ when $x = -1.$

14-2. Homogeneous Functions

If a differential equation does not have its variables separable and is not an exact differential, then see if the equation can be written so that y and x occur only in the form y/x or x/y.

Example 1. $(x^2 + y^2)\,dx - 2xy\,dy = 0.$

Solution. Upon dividing through by x^2, the equation becomes

$$\left[1 + \left(\frac{y}{x}\right)^2\right]dx - 2\frac{y}{x}\,dy = 0.$$

Make the substitution

(1) $$\frac{y}{x} = u, \quad \text{so} \quad y = ux \quad \text{and} \quad dy = u\,dx + x\,du.$$

The result is

$$(1 + u^2)\,dx - 2u(u\,dx + x\,du) = 0$$

or, upon collecting terms,

$$(1 - u^2)\, dx - 2ux\, du = 0.$$

Now the variables x and u are separable:

$$\frac{dx}{x} = \frac{2u}{1 - u^2}\, du.$$

Hence, by integration,

$$\ln|x| = -\ln|1 - u^2| + c,$$

$$\ln|x(1 - u^2)| = c,$$

$$|x(1 - u^2)| = e^c.$$

Even though c is arbitrary, e^c is positive. The absolute values may be removed by replacing $\pm e^c$ by C to obtain

$$x(1 - u^2) = C.$$

By resubstitution to the original variables, the family

$$x^2 - y^2 = Cx$$

is obtained as the solution of the given differential equation.

Let a differential equation

$$M(x, y)\, dx + N(x, y)\, dy = 0$$

be such that division by x to some constant power (which need not be an integer, nor need it be positive) yields an equation in which x and y appear only in the combination y/x. Then the equation has the form

$$f\left(\frac{y}{x}\right) dx + g\left(\frac{y}{x}\right) dy = 0.$$

The substitution (1) now gives

$$f(u)\, dx + g(u)(u\, dx + x\, du) = 0,$$

and the variables x and u are separable:

$$\frac{dx}{x} = -\frac{g(u)}{f(u) + ug(u)}\, du.$$

Example 2. Find the solution of the differential equation which also satisfies the side condition.

$$(\sqrt{x^2 + y^2} - y)\, dx + x\, dy = 0; \quad y = 3 \text{ when } x = -4.$$

Solution. Since $x = -4$ is to be used, it must be considered that $x < 0$. Then

$$\sqrt{x^2 + y^2} = |x|\sqrt{1 + (y/x)^2} = -x\sqrt{1 + (y/x)^2}, \quad \text{since} \quad x < 0.$$

Thus, upon dividing the given differential equation by $-x > 0$, the result is

$$[\sqrt{1 + (y/x)^2} + y/x]\, dx - dy = 0.$$

The substitution (1) gives

$$(\sqrt{1 + u^2} + u)\, dx - (u\, dx + x\, du) = 0,$$

which may be written, with the variables separated, as

$$\frac{dx}{x} = \frac{du}{\sqrt{1+u^2}}.$$

Thus, $\ln|x| = \ln(u + \sqrt{1+u^2}) + c$. In terms of x and y,

$$\ln|x| = \ln[y/x + \sqrt{1+(y/x)^2}] + c.$$

The side condition, $y = 3$ when $x = -4$, gives

$$\ln|-4| = \ln[-\tfrac{3}{4} + \sqrt{1+(\tfrac{3}{4})^2}] + c,$$

$$c = \ln 4 - \ln(-\tfrac{3}{4} + \tfrac{5}{4}) = \ln 8.$$

Hence, the solution may be written first as

$$\ln|x| = \ln 8\,[y/x + \sqrt{1+(y/x)^2}]$$

and then without logarithms (remembering that $|x| = -x$) as

$$-x = 8\,[y/x + \sqrt{1+(y/x)^2}], \quad x < 0.$$

This solution looks rather cumbersome, but by a little algebraic manipulation it simplifies to half of a parabola:

$$x^2 = -16(y - 4), \quad x < 0.$$

The following example illustrates how a translation of axes may help.

Example 3. Solve $(x - 3y - 5)\,dx + (3x - y + 1)\,dy = 0$.

Solution. Were it not for the constant terms in each set of parentheses, a division by x would yield an equation in y/x. Hence, make the substitution

$$x = X + h, \quad y = Y + k, \quad dx = dX, \quad dy = dY$$

to obtain

$$(X - 3Y + h - 3k - 5)\,dX + (3X - Y + 3h - k + 1)\,dY = 0.$$

The constant terms will be removed by choosing h and k such that simultaneously

$$h - 3k = 5,$$

$$3h - k = -1.$$

Thus, $h = -1$, $k = -2$ reduces the (X, Y)-differential equation to

$$(X - 3Y)\,dX + (3X - Y)\,dY = 0,$$

or

$$\left(1 - \frac{3Y}{X}\right)dX + \left(3 - \frac{Y}{X}\right)dY = 0.$$

Hence, set $Y = UX$, $dY = U\,dX + X\,dU$, and obtain

$$(1 - 3U)\,dX + (3 - U)(U\,dX + X\,dU) = 0,$$

$$(1 - 3U + 3U - U^2)\,dX = (U - 3)\,X\,dU,$$

$$\frac{dX}{X} = -\frac{U - 3}{U^2 - 1}\,dU$$

$$= \left(\frac{1}{U - 1} - \frac{2}{U + 1}\right)dU,$$

where the last equation was obtained by using partial fractions. Thus,

$$\ln |X| = \ln |U - 1| - 2 \ln |U + 1| + \ln |c|,$$

where c is arbitrary except that $c \neq 0$, and hence

$$X(U + 1)^2 = c(U - 1).$$

But $U = Y/X$, and thus

$$(Y + X)^2 = c(Y - X).$$

Finally, $X = x - h = x + 1$ and $Y = y - k = y + 2$, so that

$$(x + y + 3)^2 = c(-x + y + 1)$$

is the solution of the given differential equation.

Example 4. $(2x - y + 5) \, dx + (4x - 2y + 5) \, dy = 0.$

Solution. The substitution $x = X + h, y = Y + k$ leads to

$$2h - k = -5 \quad \text{and}$$

$$4h - 2k = -5,$$

which have no simultaneous solution but point to the fact that x and y appear in both parentheses as $2x - y$. Thus, try setting

$$2x - y = u \quad \text{so} \quad y = 2x - u \quad \text{and} \quad dy = 2dx - du.$$

The result is

$$(u + 5) \, dx + (2u + 5)(2dx - du) = 0,$$

which collects, with variables x and u separated,

$$dx = \frac{2u + 5}{5u + 15} \, du$$

$$= \frac{2}{5} \frac{u + \frac{5}{2}}{u + 3} \, du$$

$$= \frac{2}{5} \left[1 - \frac{1}{2} \frac{1}{u + 3} \right] du.$$

Thus, the solution is

$$x = \tfrac{2}{5} u - \tfrac{1}{5} \ln |u + 3| + C$$

$$= \tfrac{2}{5} (2x - y) - \tfrac{1}{5} \ln |2x - y + 3| + C,$$

$$x + 2y + \ln |2x - y + 3| = c.$$

A function $F(x, y)$ that has the property

(2) $$F(tx, ty) = t^p F(x, y),$$

with p constant, is said to be **homogeneous of degree p**. For example,

$$\sqrt[3]{(tx)^2 + (ty)^2} = t^{3/2} \sqrt[3]{x^2 + y^2}, \quad t > 0,$$

shows that $\sqrt[3]{x^2 + y^2}$ is homogeneous of degree $\frac{3}{2}$.

If $M(x, y)$ and $N(x, y)$ are both homogeneous and of the same degree, then

$$M(x, y)\, dx + N(x, y)\, dy = 0$$

may be written so that x and y appear only in the combination y/x. This follows since

$$M(tx, ty)\, dx + N(tx, ty)\, dy = t^p [M(x, y)\, dx + N(x, y)\, dy]$$
$$= t^p \cdot 0 = 0,$$

and the choice $t = 1/x$ yields

$$M\left(1, \frac{y}{x}\right) dx + N\left(1, \frac{y}{x}\right) dy = 0,$$

with x and y appearing only in the combination y/x. Thus the following rule obtains.

RULE. *If $M(x, y)$ and $N(x, y)$ are homogeneous and of the same degree, then the substitution $y = ux$ will change*

$$M(x, y)\, dx + N(x, y)\, dy = 0$$

into a differential equation in x and u with these variables separable.

Problem 1. Solve the differential equation of Example 2 but subject to the side condition:
   a. $y = 3$ when $x = 4$.
   b. $y = -3$ when $x = -4$.
   c. $y = -3$ when $x = 4$.

Problem 2. Let $M(x, y)\, dx + N(x, y)\, dy = 0$ be such that x and y appear only in the combination $ax + by$, so the equation may be written in the form

$$\frac{dy}{dx} = f(ax + by).$$

[Note: The equation of Example 4 is of this type.] Show that the substitution

$$ax + by = u, \quad \text{so that} \quad y = \frac{1}{b}(u - ax),$$

yields a differential equation in x and u with these variables separable.

Problem 3. Use the result of Prob. 2 to solve each of the equations:

a. $\dfrac{dy}{dx} = \dfrac{x + y}{x + y + 2}$.

b. $\dfrac{dy}{dx} = (y - x)^2$.

c. $\dfrac{dy}{dx} = \cos(x + y)$.

d. $\dfrac{dy}{dx} = 2 + \dfrac{e^x}{e^y}$.

   e. $(2x - y + 2)\, dx + (4x - 2y + 1)\, dy = 0$.
   f. $(2x - y + 2)\, dx + (4x - 2y + 4)\, dy = 0$.

Problem 4. Solve each of the differential equations:

a. $(x^3 + y^3)\, dx - xy^2\, dy = 0.$
b. $(x^3 + y^3)\, dx + xy^2\, dy = 0.$
c. $(x^3 + y^3)\, dx + 3xy^2\, dy = 0.$
d. $\left[y + x \sin \left(\dfrac{y}{x} \right) \right] dx - x\, dy = 0.$
e. $\dfrac{dy}{dx} = \dfrac{x^2 e^{y/x} + y^2}{xy}.$

14-3. Integrating Factors

None of the previous methods is applicable to

(1) $$(2x^3 y - 1)\, dx + x^4\, dy = 0.$$

One method of solving this equation is to write it as

(2) $$x^4\, dy + 2x^3 y\, dx = dx$$

and then to multiply both sides by x^{-2}:

$$x^2\, dy + 2xy\, dx = x^{-2}\, dx.$$

Now the left side equals $d(x^2 y)$ and the right equals $d(-x^{-1})$:

$$d(x^2 y) = d(-x^{-1}).$$

Consequently, (1) has solution $x^2 y = -x^{-1} + c$, which is preferably written as

$$y = -x^{-3} + cx^{-2}.$$

In this illustration, x^{-2} is said to be an integrating factor of (1), or the equivalent equation (2).

If the left side of

$$M(x, y)\, dx + N(x, y)\, dy = 0$$

is not an exact differential, then a function $u(x, y)$ is said to be an **integrating factor** if the left side of

$$u(x, y)M(x, y)\, dx + u(x, y)N(x, y)\, dy = 0$$

is an exact differential. An integrating factor $u(x, y)$ need not depend explicitly upon both x and y; in fact, $u(x, y) = x^{-2}$ in the above illustration did not depend on y.

There is no straightforward method applicable in all cases for determining integrating factors, but a few suggestions should help. For example, if an equation involves the combination

$$x\, dy - y\, dx,$$

then it would be worthwhile trying $u(x, y) = x^{-2}$ or $u(x, y) = y^{-2}$, since

$$d\left(\frac{y}{x} \right) = \frac{x\, dy - y\, dx}{x^2} \quad \text{and} \quad d\left(\frac{x}{y} \right) = \frac{y\, dx - x\, dy}{y^2} = -\frac{x\, dy - y\, dx}{y^2}.$$

Example 1. $(xy^2 - y) \, dx + (x + y^3) \, dy = 0.$

Solution. Write this equation as

$$x \, dy - y \, dx = -xy^2 \, dx - y^3 \, dy.$$

Upon trying $u(x, y) = x^{-2}$ as an integrating factor,

$$\frac{x \, dy - y \, dx}{x^2} = -\frac{y^2}{x} \, dx - \frac{y^3}{x^2} \, dy.$$

Although the left side is $d(y/x)$, the right side is not an exact differential. Thus, try y^{-2} or, even better, $-y^{-2}$:

$$\frac{y \, dx - x \, dy}{y^2} = x \, dx + y \, dy.$$

Consequently,

$$d\left(\frac{x}{y}\right) = d \, \frac{1}{2} x^2 + d \, \frac{1}{2} y^2,$$

and the solution is

$$\frac{x}{y} = \frac{1}{2}(x^2 + y^2) + c.$$

Whenever $x \, dy - y \, dx$ appears, then, in addition to x^{-2} and y^{-2}, a third possible integrating factor is

$$\frac{1}{x^2 + y^2},$$

which might not be thought of until it is recalled that

$$d \tan^{-1} \frac{y}{x} = \frac{d(y/x)}{1 + (y/x)^2} = \frac{(x \, dy - y \, dx)/x^2}{(x^2 + y^2)/x^2} = \frac{x \, dy - y \, dx}{x^2 + y^2}.$$

Other combinations to be on the alert for are the right sides (or portions thereof) in

$$d(xy) = x \, dy + y \, dx,$$

$$d \ln (xy) = \frac{x \, dy + y \, dx}{xy}$$

$$= \frac{dy}{y} + \frac{dx}{x},$$

$$d \ln\left(\frac{y}{x}\right) = \frac{dy}{y} - \frac{dx}{x}$$

$$= \frac{x \, dy - y \, dx}{xy},$$

$$d \ln\sqrt{x^2 + y^2} = \frac{x \, dx + y \, dy}{x^2 + y^2},$$

$$d(x^n y) = x^n \, dy + nx^{n-1} y \, dx.$$

Sometimes a previous method is applicable, but the use of an integrating factor is easier.

Example 2. $(y^2 - y)\,dx + x\,dy = 0$.

Solution. The variables are separable:

$$\frac{dx}{x} + \frac{dy}{y^2 - y} = 0,$$

but this would involve using partial fractions, etc. The equation may be written

$$y\,dx - x\,dy = y^2\,dx,$$

$$\frac{y\,dx - x\,dy}{y^2} = dx, \quad d\!\left(\frac{x}{y}\right) = dx,$$

$$\frac{x}{y} = x + c.$$

Example 3. Show that

$$(-6y + x^2 y^2)\,dx + (8x + 6x^3 y)\,dy = 0$$

has an integrating factor in the form $x^m y^n$, and then solve the equation.

Solution. Multiply by $x^m y^n$:

(3) $\qquad (-6x^m y^{n+1} + x^{m+2} y^{n+2})\,dx + (8x^{m+1} y^n + 6x^{m+3} y^{n+1})\,dy = 0.$

For this to be an exact differential, the partial with respect to y of the coefficient of dx must equal the partial with respect to x of the coefficient of dy:

$$-6(n + 1)x^m y^n + (n + 2)x^{m+2} y^{n+1} = 8(m + 1)x^m y^n + 6(m + 3)x^{m+2} y^{n+1}.$$

This holds if coefficients of like terms on both sides are equal:

$$-6(n + 1) = 8(m + 1), \quad (n + 2) = 6(m + 3).$$

These equations are

$$4m + 3n = -7 \quad \text{and}$$
$$6m - n = -16,$$

with simultaneous solutions

$$m = -\tfrac{5}{2}, \quad n = 1.$$

These values substituted into (3) yield

$$(-6x^{-5/2} y^2 + x^{-1/2} y^3)\,dy + (8x^{-3/2} y + 6x^{1/2} y^2)\,dy = 0,$$

which is known to be an exact differential, and a check shows it to be

$$d(4x^{-3/2} y^2 + 2x^{1/2} y^3) = 0.$$

Hence, the solution of the given equation is

$$2x^{-3/2} y^2 + x^{1/2} y^3 = c,$$

where a division by 2 was made.

Example 4. Show that $(y + 1)\,dx + x^2\,dy = 0$ does not have an integrating factor of the form $x^m y^n$. Solve the equation.

Solution. If there were such an integrating factor, then

$$(x^m y^{n+1} + x^m y^n)\, dx + x^{m+2} y^n\, dy = 0$$

would be an exact differential. This would mean

$$(n+1)x^m y^n + nx^m y^{n-1} = (m+2)x^{m+1} y^n$$

should hold, which requires the impossible equations

$$n+1 = 0, \quad n = 0, \quad \text{and} \quad m+2 = 0.$$

The variables are, however, separable. Another way of thinking of it is that $x^{-2}(y+1)^{-1}$ is an integrating factor, since multiplication by this expression yields

$$\frac{dx}{x^2} + \frac{dy}{y+1} = 0, \quad d(-x^{-1} + \ln|y+1|) = 0,$$

having solution $y = ce^{1/x} - 1$.

Problem 1. It is strongly suggested that each part of this problem be worked:

a. $x\, dy - y\, dx = 0.$

b. $x\, dy - y\, dx = x\, dx.$

c. $x\, dy - y\, dx = y\, dx.$

d. $x\, dy - y\, dx = xy\, dx.$

e. $x\, dy - y\, dx = x^2 y^2\, dx.$

f. $x\, dy - y\, dx = (x^2 + y^2)\, dx.$

g. $x\, dy - y\, dx = x^2 y^3\, dx.$

h. $x\, dy + y\, dx = 0.$

i. $x\, dy + y\, dx = x\, dx.$

j. $x\, dy + y\, dx = y\, dx.$

k. $x\, dy + y\, dx = xy\, dx.$

l. $x\, dy + y\, dx = x^2 y^2\, dx.$

m. $y\, dy + x\, dx = (x^2 + y^2)\, dx.$

n. $x\, dy + y\, dx = x^2 y^3\, dx.$

Problem 2. Solve each of the following by finding an integrating factor:

a. $y\, dx + (x + x^3 y^2)\, dy = 0.$

b. $y\, dx - x(2xy + 1)\, dy = 0.$

c. $y(y^3 - x)\, dx + x(y^3 + x)\, dy = 0.$

d. $(x^2 + y^2 + y)\, dx - x\, dy = 0.$

e. $xy' - y + x^2 y^4(xy' + y) = 0.$

f. $x^2(yy' + x) = \sqrt{x^2 + y^2}\,(y - xy').$

Problem 3. Solve each of the following by determining m and n such that $x^m y^n$ is an integrating factor:

a. $y(x^3 - y)\, dx - x(x^3 + y)\, dy = 0.$

b. $3x\, dy - 2y\, dx = 5x^3 y^2\, dy.$

c. $2x^3\, dy + x^2 y\, dx = 3y^3\, dy.$

d. $(2y - 3xy^2)\, dx + (3x - 4x^2 y)\, dy = 0.$

14-4. Linear Equations of First Degree

If $p = p(x)$ and $q = q(x)$ are functions of x alone, then

$$\text{(1)} \qquad \frac{dy}{dx} + py = q$$

is a linear differential equation of first degree. For such an equation there is a definite procedure for determining an integration factor. In fact,

$$\text{(2)} \qquad e^{\int p\, dx}$$

is an integrating factor. First notice that

$$\frac{d}{dx} e^{\int p\, dx} = e^{\int p\, dx} \frac{d}{dx} \int p\, dx = e^{\int p\, dx} p.$$

Thus, upon multiplying (1) through by (2),

$$e^{\int p\, dx} \frac{dy}{dx} + e^{\int p\, dx} py = e^{\int p\, dx} q;$$

the left side is the derivative shown on the left in the equation

$$\frac{d}{dx}(e^{\int p\, dx} y) = e^{\int p\, dx} q;$$

and now an integration with respect to x gives

(3)
$$e^{\int p\, dx} y = \int e^{\int p\, dx} q\, dx + c,$$

from which y may be obtained by a division.

Example 1. $(2x^3 y - 1)\, dx + x^4\, dy = 0$.

Solution. This equation may be written as

(4)
$$\frac{dy}{dx} + \frac{2}{x}\, y = \frac{1}{x^4},$$

which is in the form (1) with $p = 2/x$ and $q = 1/x^4$. Hence,

(5)
$$\int p\, dx = \int \frac{2}{x}\, dx = 2\ln|x| + a = a + \ln x^2,$$

where the additive constant of integration is denoted by a. Hence, according to (2), an integrating factor is

$$e^{\int p\, dx} = e^{a + \ln x^2} = e^a e^{\ln x^2} = e^a x^2.$$

Upon multiplying both sides of (4) by $e^a x^2$, the result is

$$e^a x^2 \frac{dy}{dx} + e^a 2xy = e^a \frac{1}{x^2}.$$

Now the factor $e^a \neq 0$ cancels and the equation may be written

$$\frac{d}{dx}(x^2 y) = \frac{1}{x^2}.$$

Hence, by an integration, $x^2 y = -x^{-1} + c$, and the solution expressing y explicitly as a function of x is

$$y = -x^{-3} + cx^{-2}.$$

In the above example an additive constant of integration was used in (5) to show that it always cancels out. Hence:

In obtaining an integrating factor (2), the simplest integral of $p\, dx$ may be used.

The final integration in (3) must, however, have the additive constant of integration.

Probably the way (2) was discovered was in an attempt to answer the question "Does (1) have an integrating factor $u = u(x)$ depending on x alone?" If it does, then u must be such that

$$u \frac{dy}{dx} + upy = uq$$

has its left side the exact derivative with respect to x of uy:

$$u\frac{dy}{dx} + upy = \frac{d(uy)}{dx}$$

$$= u\frac{dy}{dx} + y\frac{du}{dx}.$$

If this holds, then by cancellation, u must be such that

$$up = \frac{du}{dx},$$

which may be written

$$\frac{du}{u} = p\,dx.$$

But there are functions satisfying this equation, namely, any function u such that

$$\ln u = \int p\,dx + a.$$

Hence, (1) has

$$u = e^a e^{\int p\,dx}$$

as an integrating factor for any constant a, and the simplest such integrating factor is obtained by setting $a = 0$ to obtain (2).

The differential equation

$$\frac{ds}{dt} + \frac{2}{t}s = \frac{1}{t^4}$$

is a linear differential equation of first degree, with s the dependent variable and t the independent variable. This comment is made to emphasize that the letters used in (1) are immaterial; the relative positions of the dependent and independent variables are all important.

Example 2. $(x - y - xy)\,dy + y\,dx = y^2\,dx.$

Solution. An attempt to put this in the form (1) is

$$\frac{dy}{dx} + \frac{1}{x - y - xy}y = \frac{y^2}{x - y - xy},$$

in which it would be necessary to have

$$p(x) \quad \text{equal to} \quad \frac{1}{x - y - xy},$$

but this is not permissible since then $p(x)$ would not depend on x alone.

Thus, try putting the given equation in the form (1), with x and y interchanged:

(6) $$\frac{dx}{dy} + \frac{1}{y}x = \frac{1}{1 - y}.$$

This is all right with

$$p(y) = \frac{1}{y} \quad \text{and} \quad q(y) = \frac{1}{1 - y}.$$

By integrating with respect to y (instead of x), an integrating factor is

$$e^{\int p \, dy} = e^{\int (1/y) \, dy} = e^{\ln y} = y.$$

Hence, multiply (6) through by y to obtain

$$y \frac{dx}{dy} + x = \frac{y}{1 - y} \quad \text{and then} \quad \frac{d(yx)}{dy} = \frac{y}{1 - y}.$$

Consequently,

$$yx = \int \frac{y}{1 - y} \, dy = -y - \ln |1 - y| + c.$$

The type of equation in Prob. 4 occurs frequently.

Problem 1. First write each of the following equations in the form (1) and then solve:

a. $dy + 2y \, dx = e^{-x} \, dx.$
b. $(2x^3 y - 1) \, dx + x^4 \, dy = 0.$
c. $dy = (1 - y \cot x) \, dx.$

d. $x^2 \, dy = (\ln x - yx) \, dx.$
e. $x \, dy + (y - \sin x) \, dx = 0.$
f. $(x^2 + 1) \, dy + (3xy + 1) \, dx = 0.$

Problem. 2. Each of the following may be put in the form (1) except for different names for the variables:

a. $du + 2(u - 4v) \, dv = 0.$
b. $e^y (dx + 2x \, dy) = dy.$
c. $e^{3y} [dx + (3x + 6) \, dy] = 2y \, dy.$

d. $d\rho + \rho \cos \theta \, d\theta = \sin 2\theta \, d\theta.$
e. $d\theta - d\rho = \rho \cot \theta \, d\theta.$
f. $t \, ds = 2(t^4 + s) \, dt.$

Problem 3. Find the particular solution satisfying the differential equation and the side condition:

a. $x^2 \, dy + (3xy - 1) \, dx = 0; \quad y = 1$ when $x = 2.$
b. $y' = 2x + y; \quad y = 0$ when $x = 0.$
c. $dy + (y - \sin x) \cos x \, dx = 0; \quad y = 0$ when $x = 0.$
d. $dx - dy = y \cot x \, dx; \quad y = 1$ when $x = \pi/2.$

Problem 4. The equation

$$\frac{dy}{dx} + py = qy^a \quad \text{with} \quad a \neq 0, \quad a \neq 1,$$

with p and q functions of x, is known as the **Bernoulli Equation.** Multiply through by $(1 - a)y^{-a}$ and show that the result may be written as

$$\frac{d}{dx} y^{1-a} + (1 - a)py^{1-a} = (1 - a)q.$$

The substitution $u = y^{1-a}$ now yields

$$\frac{du}{dx} + (1 - a)pu = (1 - a)q,$$

and since $(1 - a)p$ and $(1 - a)q$ are functions of x alone, this equation is in the form (1). Show that each of the following is a Bernoulli Equation and then solve:

a. $x\,dy = y(y^2 + 1)\,dx.$

c. $y\,dy + (2 + x^2 - y^2)\,dx = 0.$

b. $x\dfrac{dy}{dx} = y - x^3 y^3.$

d. $\dfrac{dx}{dt} - 2x = 4x^{3/2}\sin t.$

14-5. Mixtures, Decay, Reflection

This section shows how some practical situations lead to differential equations.

Example 1. A 10-gal tank is full of water. Brine containing 3 lb of salt per gallon starts flowing in at the rate of 2 gal/min. The solution is kept uniform by stirring. The diluted solution flows out at the same rate of 2 gal/min. Find the number of pounds of salt in the tank 20 min after the process starts.

Solution. Let x be the number of pounds of salt in the tank at the end of t min. Then x is a function of t such that

$$\frac{dx}{dt}$$

is the time rate of change of the amount of salt. Hence,

(1) $$\frac{dx}{dt} = \text{rate of increase} - \text{rate of decrease},$$

where these rates must have the same dimension. The increase is

$$\frac{2\text{ gal}}{\text{min}} \cdot \frac{3\text{ lb}}{\text{gal}} = 6\,\frac{\text{lb}}{\text{min}}.$$

 Brine

At time t there are x lb of salt in 10 gal of solution flowing out at 2 gal/min, so that the rate of decrease is

(2) $$\frac{x\text{ lb}}{10\text{ gal}} \cdot \frac{2\text{ gal}}{\text{min}} = \frac{x}{5}\,\frac{\text{lb}}{\text{min}}.$$

In both cases, the dimension is lb/min, and hence

$$\frac{dx}{dt} = \left(6 - \frac{x}{5}\right)\frac{\text{lb}}{\text{min}}, \quad \text{where} \quad x = 0 \text{ when } t = 0.$$

Fig. 14-5.1

The side condition means "no salt was in the tank when the process started." By the method of the previous section (or by separating the variables), the differential equation has the general solution

$$x = 30 + ce^{-0.2t}.$$

The side condition now yields $c = -30$, so that

(3) $$x = 30(1 - e^{-0.2t})$$

is the expression for the number of pounds of salt in the tank t min after the process started (at time $t = 0$). Hence, the desired answer is

$$x(20) = 30(1 - e^{-(0.2)20}) = 30(1 - e^{-4})$$

$$= 30(1 - 0.018) = 29.46 = 29.5\text{ lb}.$$

Example 2. The output of the tank of Example 1 flows into a second 10-gal tank initially full of pure water. The contents of this tank are also kept uniform by stirring, and the outflow is at 2 gal/min. Find the number of pounds of salt in the second tank t min after the process starts.

Solution. Let y be the function of t giving the number of pounds of salt in the second tank. Then

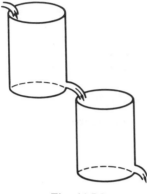

Fig. 14-5.2

$$\frac{2}{10}y \text{ lb/min} = \text{output rate of salt.}$$

Since input rate of salt to the second tank is the same as the output rate of salt from the first tank, it follows from (2) and (3) that

$$\tfrac{1}{5}x = \tfrac{1}{5}\cdot 30(1 - e^{-0.2t}) = 6(1 - e^{-0.2t}) \text{ lb/min}$$

is the input rate of salt to the second tank. Thus, the rate of change of y with respect to t is

$$\frac{dy}{dt} = 6(1 - e^{-0.2t}) - 0.2y, \text{ where } y = 0 \text{ when } t = 0.$$

Again, by the method of the previous section, the differential equation has the general solution

$$y = 30 - 6te^{-0.2t} + ce^{-0.2t}.$$

From the side condition, $c = -30$, and therefore

(4) $$y = 30 - 6(t + 5)e^{-0.2t}$$

is the desired solution.

Note that when $t = 20$ there are

$$30 - 6(20 + 5)e^{-4} = 30 - 150(0.018)$$
$$= 30 - 27 = 3 \text{ lb}$$

of salt in the second tank.

Example 3. Water is heated to the boiling point, $100°$ C, and is then removed from the stove and put in a room of constant temperature $70°$ C. After 3 min, the temperature of the water dropped to $92°$. a. Find the temperature after 10 min. b. When will the temperature be $75°$ C?

Solution. It is confirmed by experiment that the rate of change of temperature of a hot body is proportional to the difference of the temperatures of the body and its surroundings. With x the temperature t min after removal from the stove,

$$\frac{dx}{dt} = k(x - 70).$$

Thus, for the general solution,

(5) $$x = 70 + ce^{kt}.$$

Note that there are two undetermined constants, c and k, but there are two side conditions; namely,

$$x = 100 \text{ when } t = 0, \quad \text{and}$$

$$x = 92 \text{ when } t = 3.$$

From the first of these, $100 = 70 + c$, so that $c = 30$. Now from the second,

$$92 = 70 + 30e^{k3}, \quad e^{k3} = \frac{22}{30} = \frac{11}{15},$$

$$3k \log e = \log 11 - \log 15,$$

so that

$$k = \frac{\log 11 - \log 15}{3 \log e} = \frac{1.0414 - 1.1761}{3(0.4343)} = -0.1034.$$

Thus, the particular solution is

(6) $$x = 70 + 30e^{-0.1034t}.$$

Upon substituting $t = 10$ in this equation, the answer to part a is

$$x = 70 + 30e^{-1.034} = 80.66$$

by logarithmic computation.

The answer to part b is the solution for t of

$$75 = 70 + 30e^{-0.1034t}.$$

Thus,

$$t = \frac{\log 6}{(0.1034) \log e} = \frac{0.7782}{(0.1034)(0.4343)} = 17.33 \text{ min.}$$

Example 4. For certain chemicals A and B, 2 g of A combine with 1 g of B to form 3 g of a chemical C. The Law of Mass Action (see a chemistry text) states that the rate at which C is formed is proportionad to the product of the amounts of A and B present at the time. Given that 10 g of A and 15 g of B are present initially and that 6 g of C is formed in 20 min, find the amount of C at any time.

Solution. Let x be the function giving the number of grams of C formed in t min. Hence, $2x/3$ g of A and $x/3$ g of B are used to form x g of C in t min. At time t, there are thus $10 - 2x/3$ g of A, $15 - x/3$ g of B, and

$$\frac{dx}{dt} = k\left(10 - \frac{2}{3}x\right)\left(15 - \frac{1}{3}x\right)\frac{g}{min},$$

where $x = 0$ when $t = 0$ and $x = 6$ when $t = 20$.

In the differential equation, the variables are separable and hence

$$\int \frac{3^2\, dx}{2(15 - x)(45 - x)} = \int k\, dt.$$

Integration by the use of partial fractions yields

(7) $$\ln\left(\frac{45 - x}{15 - x}\right) = \frac{20}{3}kt + c.$$

The first side condition now gives

$$c = \ln 3.$$

Upon substituting $c = \ln 3$ into (7) and then using the second side condition,

$$\frac{20}{3}k = \frac{1}{20}\ln\frac{39}{27} = 0.01846.$$

Hence, (7) becomes

$$\ln\left(\frac{45-x}{45-3x}\right) = 0.01846t,$$

and this equation solved for x gives

$$x = 45\,\frac{1 - e^{0.01846t}}{1 - 3e^{0.01846t}}\ \text{g}$$

of chemical C, t min after the process starts.

Note that the limiting amount of C is 15 g.

Example 5. A parachutist plus his parachute and other equipment weighs W lb. Assume that when his parachute opens he is falling straight down at a ft/sec. When the parachute is open, the upward force is a constant b times the velocity v (speed downward). Find the velocity v as a function of t from the time $t = 0$ when the parachute opens.

Solution. Consider a linear x coordinate system (unit 1 ft) positive downward, with origin at the point where the parachute opens. The downward force is then W, the upward force is (as given) bv, so that the force is

Fig. 14-5.3

$$W - bv.$$

But, by Newton's Law, force is mass times acceleration, so that

$$\frac{W}{g}\frac{dv}{dt} = W - bv, \quad v = a \text{ when } t = 0.$$

The differential equation may be written as

$$\frac{dv}{dt} = g - \frac{bg}{W}v,$$

so that

$$v = \frac{W}{b} + ce^{-(bg/W)t}.$$

The determination of c thus yields

$$v = \frac{W}{b} + \left(a - \frac{W}{b}\right)e^{-(bg/W)t}.$$

Note that the limiting velocity is W/b ft/sec regardless of how large the initial velocity a is.

Example 6. Find the shape of a reflector such that a bundle of parallel light rays that hit it will all be focused on a single point F. [Note: In Example 3 of Sec. 4-5 it was checked that a parabolic reflector has this property; the present example shows that all reflectors having this property are parabolic.]

Solution. By considerations of symmetry, the reflector will be a surface of revolution about the line of one of the rays in the bundle of parallel light rays, this line passing through F and intersecting the reflector at a point V. Establish this line as the x-axis with origin at F. Consider a ray not along the x-axis hitting the reflector at point P. Establish the plane determined by the x-axis and FP as the (x, y)-plane.

Whatever the curve of intersection of the reflector and the (x, y)-plane is, consider a segment of the tangent to the curve at $P(x, y)$ as the intersection of a plane mirror. By the incidence-reflection optical principle, the two angles labeled α in Fig. 14-5.4 are of equal size. Also,

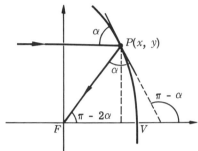

Fig. 14-5.4

$$y' = \frac{dy}{dx} = \tan(\pi - \alpha) = -\tan \alpha \quad \text{and}$$

$$\frac{y}{x} = \tan(\pi - 2\alpha) = -\tan 2\alpha.$$

These equations and the formula from trigonometry

$$\frac{2 \tan \alpha}{1 - \tan^2 \alpha} = \tan 2\alpha,$$

lead to the differential equation

$$\frac{2y'}{1 - y'^2} = \frac{y}{x}.$$

This is a quadratic equation in y' whose solution for y' is

(8) $$y' = \frac{-x \pm \sqrt{x^2 + y^2}}{y}.$$

Finally, this equation may be put in the differential form

$$\frac{x\,dx + y\,dy}{\sqrt{x^2 + y^2}} = \pm dx.$$

Consequently, $d\sqrt{x^2 + y^2} = \pm dx$, so that

$$\sqrt{x^2 + y^2} = \pm x + c$$

are equations of possible curves which, revolved about the x-axis, generate reflectors having the desired property. These curves may not be recognized as being parabolas, but squaring yields $x^2 + y^2 = x^2 \pm 2cx + c^2$, so that

$$y^2 = \pm 2cx + c^2,$$

and these have parabolic graphs for $c \neq 0$.

Problem 1. In Examples 1 and 2, it follows from physical considerations that neither tank will ever have as much as 30 lb of salt. This is borne out by equations (3) and (4) each having right side 30 minus a positive quantity (for $t > 0$). Also, for $t > 0$, each tank contains some salt. Clearly, x in (3) is positive, since

$$0 < e^{-0.2t} < 1 \quad \text{because} \quad 1 < e^{0.2t} \quad \text{for} \quad t > 0.$$

It may not be clear, however, that y in (4) is positive for $t > 0$. a. Show this to be the case. b. Also show that

$$\lim_{t \to \infty} x = 30 \quad \text{and} \quad \lim_{t \to \infty} y = 30.$$

Problem 2. a. A 10-gal tank is full of brine of concentration 3 lb of salt per gallon. Pure water starts flowing in at 2 gal/min. The solution is kept uniform by stirring. The diluted solution flows out at the same rate of 2 gal/min. Find the number of pounds of salt in the tank 20 min after the process starts.

b. The output of the tank in part a flows into a second 10-gal tank initially full of pure water. The contents of this tank are also kept uniform by stirring and the outflow is at 2 gal/min. Find the number of pounds of salt in the second tank t min after the process starts.

c. When will both tanks have the same concentration and what is this concentration?

Problem 3. For Example 5, find the distance fallen (from the time the parachute opens) as a function of t.

Problem 4. In Example 4, keep all of the given conditions except that the amount of B initially present is 5 g.

Problem 5. A radioactive substance disintegrates at a rate proportional to the amount present. A quantity A_0 of such a substance was observed to diminish by 0.5 % in 15 years:

a. What percentage will be lost in 1000 years?

b. How many years will it take for half the substance to disappear? (This time is called the **half-life** of the substance.)

c. A mummy is tested and found to have one-fifth as much of this substance as a living man. Estimate the age of the mummy.

Problem 6. Note that equation (8) in Example 6 is homogeneous. Use the method of Sec. 14-2 to find the solution.

Problem 7. Let P be invested at the annual rate of r so that at the end of one year the new principal is

$$P_1 = P + \frac{r}{100} P = P \left(1 + \frac{r}{100}\right).$$

Show that the principal after one year is:

a. $P_2 = P[1 + (r/200)]^2$ if interest is compounded semiannually.

b. $P_3 = P[1 + (r/300)]^3$ if interest is compounded three times a year.

c. $P_n = P[1 + (r/100n)]^n$ if interest is compounded n times a year.

d. Also show that

$$\lim_{n \to \infty} P_n = Pe^{r/100}.$$

Problem 8. Two 10-gal tanks stand side by side. The first tank is full of brine containing 3 lb salt per gallon, while the second tank is full of pure water. Pumps now start circulating liquid between the tanks at the rate of 2 gal/min.

a. Find the numbers x and y of lb of salt in the first and second tanks, respectively, t min after the process starts.

b. When will the first tank contain twice as much salt as the second tank?

Problem 9. Work Example 6 using polar coordinates.

14-6. Algebra of Operators

If $y(x)$ is a differentiable function of x, then

$$D_x y(x), \quad \frac{dy(x)}{dx}, \quad \text{and} \quad y'(x)$$

all indicate the operation of taking the derivative of $y(x)$ with respect to x. In spite of the earlier admonition not to omit the subscript x in $D_x y(x)$, the practice in operator theory is to omit this subscript. For example,

$$D \sin wx = w \cos wx$$

for w constant. Also, with a and b either constants or functions of x, then

$$(1) \qquad\qquad\qquad aD + b$$

is considered an operator, which juxtaposed to the left of a function of x produces a new function, for example,

$$(2D + x) \sin wx = 2w \cos wx + x \sin wx.$$

An expression such as $(2D + x)D$ is an operator in which D operates first and then $2D + x$ operates on the result:

$$(2) \qquad (2D + x)D \sin wx = (2D + x)w \cos wx$$
$$= -2w^2 \sin wx + xw \cos wx.$$

Note, however, that with $2D + x$ and D reversed, then

$$(3) \qquad D(2D + x) \sin wx = D(2w \cos wx + x \sin wx)$$
$$= -2w^2 \sin wx + xw \cos wx + \sin wx.$$

Since the results in (2) and (3) are different, the operators $(2D + x)D$ and $D(2D + x)$ are said to be unequal:

$$(2D + x)D \neq D(2D + x).$$

Another way of expressing this nonequality is "the operators $2D + x$ and D do not commute."

Consider, however, the operators $(2D + 3)D$ and $D(2D + 3)$, in which the coefficients are constants. For $y(x)$ a twice differentiable function of x,

(4) $$(2D + 3)D\ y(x) = (2D + 3)y'(x)$$
$$= 2y''(x) + 3y'(x)\quad \text{and}$$

(5) $$D(2D + 3)\ y(x) = D[2y'(x) + 3y(x)]$$
$$= 2y''(x) + 3y'(x).$$

Both results are the same. The operators $2D + 3$ and D are said to **commute**, and this is expressed by

$$(2D + 3)D = D(2D + 3).$$

The analogy with ordinary algebra is fostered further by defining D^2, $D^3, \ldots$ for positive integer "powers" by

$$D^2 = DD, \quad D^3 = D^2D, \text{ etc.}$$

Moreover, the fact that in both (4) and (5) the result is twice the second derivative plus three times the derivative leads to setting

$$(2D + 3)D = D(2D + 3) = 2D^2 + 3D.$$

It should now be checked that, for a_1, b_1, a_2, b_2, all constants, then

$$(a_1D + b_1)(a_2D + b_2) = (a_2D + b_2)(a_1D + b_1)$$
$$= a_1a_2D^2 + (a_1b_2 + a_2b_1)D + b_1b_2.$$

This merely means that any of these three operators, when operating on a twice differentiable function $y(x)$, will produce the result

$$a_1a_2y''(x) + (a_1b_2 + a_2b_1)y'(x) + b_1b_2y(x).$$

Hence, ordinary algebraic expansion by using the distributive law (that is, removing parentheses) may be used for differential operators *so long as the coefficients are constant.*

Since factoring is merely the reverse of expanding, then factoring of differential operators may be used *so long as the coefficients are constants.*

Example 1. Solve the differential equation

(6) $$\frac{d^2y}{dx^2} + \frac{dy}{dx} - 12y = \sin x.$$

Solution. In operator notation this equation is

$$(D^2 + D - 12)y = \sin x.$$

In ordinary algebra, $r^2 + r - 12 = (r + 4)(r - 3)$, so that

(7) $$(D + 4)(D - 3)y = \sin x.$$

Make the substitution

(8) $$(D - 3)y = u,$$

so that (7) takes the form $(D + 4)u = \sin x$, which, in differential notation, is

$$\frac{du}{dx} + 4u = \sin x.$$

This is a linear equation of first degree in u and (see Sec. 14-4) has integrating factor e^{4x}, so that

$$\frac{d(ue^{4x})}{dx} = e^{4x} \sin x.$$

Consequently, $ue^{4x} = \int e^{4x} \sin x \, dx$. Upon carrying out this integration [see formula 61 of the Table of Integrals], the result is

$$ue^{4x} = \frac{e^{4x}}{17} (4 \sin x - \cos x) + C_1.$$

Upon multiplying by e^{-4x}, then

$$u = \frac{1}{17} (4 \sin x - \cos x) + C_1 e^{-4x}.$$

Now substitute this expression for u in the right side of (8) and write the result as

$$\frac{dy}{dx} - 3y = \frac{1}{17} (4 \sin x - \cos x) + C_1 e^{-4x}.$$

Again a linear equation of first degree results, this time having integrating factor e^{-3x}. Hence,

$$\frac{d(ye^{-3x})}{dx} = \frac{e^{-3x}}{17} (4 \sin x - \cos x) + C_1 e^{-7x}.$$

Thus,

$$ye^{-3x} = \frac{4}{17} \int e^{-3x} \sin x \, dx - \frac{1}{17} \int e^{-3x} \cos x \, dx + C_1 \int e^{-7x} \, dx$$

$$= \frac{4}{17} \frac{e^{-3x}}{10} (-3 \sin x - \cos x) - \frac{1}{17} \frac{e^{-3x}}{10} (\sin x - 3 \cos x) - \frac{C_1}{7} e^{-7x} + c_2.$$

Since $-C_1/7$ is an arbitrary constant, replace it by c_1. Now collection of terms and multiplication by e^{3x} yield

(9) $$y = \frac{-1}{170} (13 \sin x + \cos x) + c_1 e^{-4x} + c_2 e^{3x}$$

as the general solution of (6).

     Example 2. Solve the differential equation

(10) $$(D^2 - 4D + 4)y = \sin x.$$

     Solution. $D^2 - 4D + 4$ is the "perfect square" $(D - 2)^2$, but write

$$(D - 2)(D - 2)y = \sin x.$$

Set $(D - 2)y = u$ so that $(D - 2)u = \sin x$, and hence (this should be checked)

$$u = -\tfrac{1}{5} (2 \sin x + \cos x) + c_1 e^{2x}.$$

Therefore, $(D - 2)y = u$ becomes

$$(D - 2)y = -\tfrac{1}{5} (2 \sin x + \cos x) + c_1 e^{2x}.$$

Again the integrating factor is e^{-2x}, so that

$$D(ye^{-2x}) = -\frac{e^{-2x}}{5} (2 \sin x + \cos x) + c_1.$$

Hence (again the integration should be checked),

$$ye^{-2x} = \frac{e^{-2x}}{25}(3 \sin x + 4 \cos x) + c_1 x + c_2.$$

Therefore,

(11) $$y = \frac{1}{25}(3 \sin x + 4 \cos x) + (c_1 x + c_2)e^{2x}.$$

The above two examples illustrate that if a differential equation can be written in the form

(12) $$(D - r_1)(D - r_2)y = f(x),$$

with r_1 and r_2 constants, then a procedure is to set

(13) $$(D - r_2)y = u,$$

so that (12) is first written as

$$(D - r_1)u = f(x).$$

An integrating factor is $e^{-r_1 x}$, so that

$$ue^{-r x} = \int e^{-r_1 x} f(x)\, dx + C_1,$$

$$u = e^{r_1 x} \int e^{-r_1 x} f(x)\, dx + C_1 e^{r_1 x}.$$

This expression for u substituted into (13) yields

$$(D - r_2)y = e^{r_1 x} \int e^{-r_1 x} f(x)\, dx + C_1 e^{r_1 x},$$

whose solution for y is also the solution (12). Now the integrating factor is $e^{-r_2 x}$, so that

$$ye^{-r_2 x} = \int e^{-r_2 x} \left[e^{r_1 x} \int e^{-r_1 x} f(x)\, dx + C_1 e^{r_1 x} \right] dx + c_2$$

$$= \int e^{(r_1 - r_2) x} \left[\int e^{-r_1 x} f(x)\, dx \right] dx + C_1 \int e^{(r_1 - r_2) x}\, dx + c_2.$$

Hence,

$$y = e^{r_2 x} \int e^{(r - r_2) x} \left[\int e^{-r_1 x} f(x)\, dx \right] dx + C_1 e^{r_2 x} \int e^{(r_1 - r_2) x}\, dx + c_2 e^{r_2 x}.$$

It now becomes necessary to distinguish between whether $r_2 \neq r_1$ or $r_2 = r_1$, since

$$\int e^{(r_1 - r_2) x}\, dx = \begin{cases} \dfrac{1}{r_1 - r_2} e^{(r_1 - r_2) x} & \text{if } r_1 \neq r_2, \\ x & \text{if } r_1 = r_2. \end{cases}$$

Hence,

$$C_1 e^{r_2 x} \int e^{(r_1 - r_2) x}\, dx = \begin{cases} \dfrac{C_1}{r_1 - r_2} e^{r_1 x} & \text{if } r_2 \neq r_1, \\ C_1 x & \text{if } r_2 = r_1. \end{cases}$$

It is customary to set $C_1/(r_1 - r_2) = c_1$ or $C_1 = c_1$, as the case may be, and to define $y_P(x)$ and $y_H(x)$ by setting

(15)
$$y_P(x) = e^{r_2 x} \int e^{(r_1 - r_2) x} \left[\int e^{-r_1 x} f(x) \, dx \right] dx,$$

(16)
$$y_H(x) = \begin{cases} c_1 e^{r_1 x} + c_2 e^{r_2 x} & \text{if } r_2 \neq r_1, \\ (c_1 x + c_2) e^{r_1 x} & \text{if } r_2 = r_1. \end{cases}$$

These results are collected as: *If*

(17)
$$(D - r_1)(D - r_2)y = f(x),$$

with r_1 and r_2 constants, then this differential equation has general solution

(18)
$$y = y_P(x) + y_H(x).$$

Notice that $y_H(x)$ is independent of $f(x)$ and, in fact, is the general solution of the simpler differential equation

$$(D - r_1)(D - r_2)y = 0.$$

This equation is called the **homogeneous equation** associated with (17)—hence the subscript H in $y_H(x)$.

The subscript P is because $y_P(x)$ is called the **particular solution;** depending on the particular function $f(x)$ and the constants r_1 and r_2 but not containing the arbitrary constants c_1 and c_2.

In the two previous examples, a quadratic operator with real constant coefficients was factored into two real linear factors:

$$D^2 + D - 12 = (D - 3)(D + 4) \quad \text{in Example 1,}$$
$$D^2 - 4D + 4 = (D - 2)(D - 2) \quad \text{in Example 2.}$$

Even an algebraic quadratic expression with real coefficients need not have real factors; for example,

$$r^2 - 6r + 13 = [r - (3 + 2i)][r - (3 - 2i)].$$

The usual way of finding these factors is to set

$$r^2 - 6r + 13 = 0$$

and then use the quadratic factor formula

$$r = \frac{-(-6) \pm \sqrt{(-6)^2 - 4 \cdot 13}}{2 \cdot 1} = \frac{6 \pm \sqrt{-16}}{2} = 3 \pm 2i.$$

Recall that, as defined in Sec. 9-14,

$$e^{(a+ib)x} = e^{ax} e^{ibx}$$
$$= e^{ax}(\cos bx + i \sin bx).$$

Also recall that the formal rules for differentiation may be applied as if i were any constant to yield

$$\frac{d}{dx} e^{(a+ib)x} = (a + ib)e^{(a+ib)x} \quad \text{and}$$

$$\int e^{(a+ib)x} \, dx = \frac{1}{a + ib} e^{(a+ib)x} + c.$$

In the previous discussion of the quadratic differential equation (17), it was tacitly assumed that r_1 and r_2 were real. The same formal manipulations may be carried through if r_1 and r_2 are imaginary constants (and the student should make at least a cursory check to see that this is so). If, however, $b \neq 0$ and

$$r_1 = a + ib, \quad \text{then} \quad r_2 = a - ib.$$

Hence, these cannot be equal, so that only the first form of $y_H(x)$ in (16) is used. This form may be (and usually is) changed as follows:

$$
\begin{aligned}
(19) \qquad y_H(x) &= C_1 e^{(a+ib)x} + C_2 e^{(a-ib)x} \\
&= e^{ax}[C_1(\cos bx + i \sin bx) + C_2(\cos bx - i \sin bx)] \\
&= e^{ax}[(C_1 + C_2) \cos bx + i(C_1 - C_2) \sin bx] \\
&= e^{ax}(c_1 \cos bx + c_2 \sin bx),
\end{aligned}
$$

where $c_1 = C_1 + C_2$ and $c_2 = i(C_1 - C_2)$.

Example 3. Solve the differential equation

$$(20) \qquad\qquad (D^2 - 6D + 13)y = \sin x.$$

Solution. This equation may be written as

$$[D - (3 + 2i)][D - (3 - 2i)]y = \sin x.$$

Hence, $r_1 = 3 + 2i$, $r_2 = 3 - 2i$, so that $a = 3$, $b = 2$, and

$$y_H(x) = e^{3x}(c_1 \cos 2x + c_2 \sin 2x).$$

Also, $r_1 - r_2 = 4i$, so that $y_P(x)$, as given by (15), becomes

$$(21) \qquad y_P(x) = e^{(3-2i)x} \int e^{4ix} \left[\int e^{-(3+2i)x} \sin x \, dx \right] dx.$$

The student who wants additional practice may now use formulas 61 and 62 of the Table of Integrals to carry out these integrations to see that

$$(22) \qquad\qquad y_P(x) = \frac{1}{30}(2 \sin x + \cos x).$$

Thus, the general solution of (20) is

$$y = \frac{1}{30}(2 \sin x + \cos x) + e^{3x}(c_1 \cos 2x + c_2 \sin 2x).$$

Anyone who has successfully carried through all the complicated manipulations to go from (21) to (22) will be in a better position to appreciate the ingenious methods for finding $y_P(x)$ as developed in succeeding sections.

Problem 1. Perform each of the indicated operations:

a. $(2D^2 + 3D - 4)\sin x.$

b. $(aD^2 + bD + c)\sin x.$

c. $(D + 1)(D - x)e^x.$

d. $(D - x)(D + 1)e^x.$

e. $(D - x)(D + x)e^x.$

f. $(D + x)(D - x)e^x.$

g. $(D^2 - x^2)e^x.$

h. $\left(D + \dfrac{1}{x}\right)\left(D - \dfrac{1}{x}\right)(2 + 3x).$

i. $\left(D - \dfrac{1}{x}\right)\left(D + \dfrac{1}{x}\right)(2 + 3x).$

j. $\left(D^2 - \dfrac{1}{x^2}\right)(2 + 3x).$

Problem 2. Show that the pair of operators do not commute:

a. $D, \quad D - 2x.$

b. $xD + 1, \quad D - 1.$

c. $D, \quad D + \sin x.$

d. $e^x D + 1, \quad D - 1.$

Problem 3. In each case, let y be a twice differentiable function of x and solve the given equation for y:

    a. $(D - x)(D + x)y = (D + x)(D - x)y.$

    b. $(xD + 1)Dy = D(xD + 1)y.$

    c. $(xD + x + 1)Dy = D(xD + x + 1)y.$

    d. $[(x + 1)D + 1](D + x)y = (D + x)[(x + 1)D + 1]y.$

Problem 4. Each of the following quadratic differential equations has constant coefficients. Solve each of these equations:

a. $2\dfrac{d^2 y}{dx^2} + 3\dfrac{dy}{dx} - 2y = e^x.$

b. $4\dfrac{d^2 y}{dx^2} - 4\dfrac{dy}{dx} + y = e^x.$

c. $2\dfrac{d^2 y}{dx^2} + 3\dfrac{dy}{dx} = \cos x.$

d. $\dfrac{d^2 y}{dx^2} - 4y = 2^x.$

Problem 5. Write each of the following equations in differential form. Then use the given factored form and the method of the present section to solve:

a. $(D - 1)(D - 2)(D - 3)y = e^x.$ b. $(2D + 1)(D - 2)(3D + 4)y = 6.$

14-7.   Variation of Parameters

This method will be illustrated by using it to solve

(1) $$y'' + y = \tan x.$$

First solve the simpler differential equation

(2) $$y'' + y = 0; \quad \text{that is,} \quad (D^2 + 1)y = 0.$$

Since $r^2 + 1 = 0$ has solutions $r = \pm i = 0 \pm 1 \cdot i$, it follows from the previous section that the general solution of equation (2) may be put in the form $y = e^{0 \cdot x}(c_1 \cos x + c_2 \sin x)$; that is,

(3) $$y = c_1 \cos x + c_2 \sin x.$$

As illustrated below, there are functions $A(x)$ and $B(x)$ such that

(4) $$y = A(x) \cos x + B(x) \sin x$$

is a solution of the given equation (1). To find these functions, first differentiate (4):

(5)$\qquad y' = -A(x) \sin x + B(x) \cos x + A'(x) \cos x + B'(x) \sin x.$

Simplify this expression for y' by setting

(6)$\qquad\qquad\qquad A'(x) \cos x + B'(x) \sin x = 0,$

so that (5) becomes

(5')$\qquad\qquad\qquad y' = -A(x) \sin x + B(x) \cos x.$

Now

(7)$\qquad y'' = -A(x) \cos x - B(x) \sin x - A'(x) \sin x + B'(x) \cos x.$

The y as given by (4) and y'' as given by (7) substituted into (1) yield

$$[-A(x) \cos x - B(x) \sin x - A'(x) \sin x + B'(x) \cos x]$$
$$+ A(x) \cos x + B(x) \sin x = \tan x;$$

that is,

(8)$\qquad\qquad -A'(x) \sin x + B'(x) \cos x = \tan x.$

But (8) and (6) are linear equations in $A'(x)$ and $B'(x)$ whose simultaneous solution for these derivatives is

$$A'(x) = -\frac{\sin^2 x}{\cos x}, \quad B'(x) = \sin x.$$

Integrations now give the desired functions $A(x)$ and $B(x)$ themselves:

$$A(x) = -\int \frac{\sin^2 x}{\cos x}\, dx = -\int \frac{1 - \cos^2 x}{\cos x}\, dx = -\int (\sec x - \cos x)\, dx$$
$$= -\ln (\sec x + \tan x) + \sin x + c_1,$$

$$B(x) = \int \sin x\, dx = -\cos x + c_2.$$

These expressions for $A(x)$ and $B(x)$ substituted into (4) yield

$$y = [-\ln (\sec x + \tan x) + \sin x + c_1] \cos x$$
$$+ (-\cos x + c_2) \sin x,$$
$$= -\cos x \ln (\sec x + \tan x) + c_1 \cos x + c_2 \sin x,$$

which is the general solution of (1).

It is usual to associate two equations with a given differential equation

(9)$\qquad\qquad \dfrac{d^2 y}{dx^2} + a_1 \dfrac{dy}{dx} + a_2 y = f(x), \quad a_1 \text{ and } a_2 \text{ constants.}$

The first of these associated equations is called the **homogeneous differential equation**, obtained by replacing $f(x)$ by 0:

(10)
$$\frac{d^2 y}{dx^2} + a_1 \frac{dy}{dx} + a_2 y = 0.$$

The second associated equation is the algebraic equation

(11)
$$r^2 + a_1 r + a_2 = 0,$$

and is called the **characteristic equation.**

The characteristic equation is always solvable for roots $r = r_1$, $r = r_2$. From these roots, the homogeneous equation has solution (according to the previous section) of the form

(12)
$$y = \begin{cases} c_1 e^{r_1 x} + c_2 e^{r_2 x} & \text{if } r_1 \neq r_2 \\ (c_1 + c_2 x) e^{r_1 x} & \text{if } r_1 = r_2, \\ e^{ax}(c_1 \cos bx + c_2 \sin bx) & \text{if } \begin{cases} r_1 = a + ib, \\ r_2 = a - ib, \quad b \neq 0. \end{cases} \end{cases}$$

Hence, regardless of the given function $f(x)$ in (9), the homogeneous equation (10) is always solvable as

(13)
$$y = c_1 Q_1(x) + c_2 Q_2(x),$$

with $Q_1(x)$ and $Q_2(x)$ appropriately selected from (12). Note, therefore, that

(14)
$$Q_1''(x) + a_1 Q_1'(x) + a_2 Q_1(x) = 0 \quad \text{and}$$
$$Q_2''(x) + a_1 Q_2'(x) + a_2 Q_2(x) = 0.$$

The method of **variation of parameters** uses these functions $Q_1(x)$ and $Q_2(x)$, together with $f(x)$, to obtain the general solution of (9).

First: Replace the parameters c_1 and c_2 in (13) by functions $A(x)$ and $B(x)$:

(15)
$$y = A(x)Q_1(x) + B(x)Q_2(x).$$

(In order to save space, the variable x will not be written.)

Second: Differentiate:

$$y' = AQ_1' + BQ_2' + A'Q_1 + B'Q_2.$$

Third: Simplify by setting

(16)
$$A'Q_1 + B'Q_2 = 0$$

to obtain

(17)
$$y' = AQ_1' + BQ_2'.$$

Fourth: Differentiate again:

$$y'' = AQ_1'' + BQ_2'' + A'Q_1' + B'Q_2'.$$

Fifth: Substitute these expressions for y'', y' from (17), and y into (9), and collect terms:

$$A[Q_1'' + a_1 Q_1' + a_2 Q_1] + B[Q_2'' + a_1 Q_2' + a_2 Q_2] + A'Q_1' + B'Q_2' = f(x).$$

This expression simplifies, by using (14), to

(18) $$A'Q_1' + B'Q_2' = f(x).$$

Sixth: Solve (18) and (16) simultaneously for A' and B':

(19) $$A' = -\frac{fQ_2}{Q_1Q_2' - Q_2Q_1'}, \quad B' = \frac{fQ_1}{Q_1Q_2' - Q_2Q_1'}.$$

Seventh: Integrate to find $A(x)$ and $B(x)$. Finally, substitute these expressions for $A(x)$ and $B(x)$ into (15) to obtain the general solution of the given differential equation (9).

The method of variation of parameters is also applicable to linear differential equations with constant coefficients, even if the order is greater than 2.

Example. Solve the differential equation

(20) $$(D^3 + 2D^2 - D - 2)y = e^x \sin x.$$

Solution. The characteristic equation is

$$r^3 + 2r^2 - r - 2 = 0.$$

Since this equation may be factored as

$$(r - 1)(r + 1)(r + 2) = 0,$$

the roots are $1, -1, -2$. The homogeneous equation

$$(D^3 + 2D^2 - D - 2)y = 0,$$

therefore, has solution

$$y = c_1 e^x + c_2 e^{-x} + c_3 e^{-2x}.$$

Next, let A, B, and C be functions of x and write

(21) $$y = Ae^x + Be^{-x} + Ce^{-2x}.$$

Find y', but set the portion containing A', B', and C' equal to zero:

$$y' = Ae^x - Be^{-x} - 2Ce^{-2x}, \quad A'e^x + B'e^{-x} + C'e^{-2x} = 0.$$

Also set the portion of y'' containing A', B' and C' equal to zero:

$$y'' = Ae^x + Be^{-x} + 4Ce^{-2x}, \quad A'e^x - B'e^{-x} - 2C'e^{-2x} = 0.$$

Hence,

$$y''' = Ae^x - Be^{-x} - 8Ce^{-2x} + A'e^x + B'e^{-x} + 4C'e^{-2x}.$$

Now multiply y''' by 1, y'' by 2, y' by -1, and y by -2. Add the resulting expressions and set equal to $e^x \sin x$. After cancellation, the result is

$$A'e^x + B'e^{-x} + 4C'e^{-2x} = e^x \sin x.$$

This equation and the two equations above in A', B', C' solved simultaneously for A', B', and C' yield

$$A' = \tfrac{1}{6} \sin x, \quad B' = -\tfrac{1}{2} e^{2x} \sin x, \quad C' = \tfrac{1}{3} e^{3x} \sin x.$$

(It would be a good review of determinants to solve simultaneously by using Cramer's Rule as learned in high school algebra.)

Hence, by integration,

$$A = -\tfrac{1}{6}\cos x + c_1,$$

$$B = -\frac{e^{2x}}{10}(2\sin x - \cos x) + c_2 \quad \text{(see Table formula 61),}$$

$$C = \frac{e^{3x}}{30}(3\sin x - \cos x) + c_3.$$

Now, according to (21), multiply A by e^x, B by e^{-x}, and C by e^{-2x} to obtain, after collection of terms,

$$y = -\frac{e^x}{10}(\sin x + \cos x) + c_1 e^x + c_2 e^{-x} + c_3 e^{-2x}.$$

It would be good practice to check that this is the general solution of (20).

Problem 1. Show that the denominator in (19) is never zero.

Problem 2. Solve $y'' + y = f(x)$, with:
a. $f(x) = \sec x.$ c. $f(x) = \tan^2 x.$
b. $f(x) = \sec^2 x.$ d. $f(x) = \sec^2 x \csc x.$

Problem 3. Solve:
a. $y'' + 4y' + 4y = e^{-2x}x^{-2}.$
b. $y'' - 2y' + 2y = 2e^x \csc 2x.$
c. $y'' - 3y' + 2y = e^x(1 + e^x)^{-1}.$
d. $y'' - 5y' + 6y = 10\sin x.$

14-8. Annihilators

The operator D^2 is an annihilator of the function $f(x) = x$ in the sense that

$$D^2 f(x) = D^2 x = \frac{d^2 x}{dx^2} = 0.$$

A differential operator is said to be an **annihilator** of a function $f(x)$ if the operation produces zero.

Thus, D^3 is an annihilator of x^2, x, and any constant function.

The function $f(x) = e^{rx}$ has $D - r$ as an annihilator, since

(1) $(D - r)e^{rx} = De^{rx} - re^{rx}$

$$= re^{rx} - re^{rx} = 0.$$

But $f(x) = xe^{rx}$ has $(D - r)^2$ as an annihilator:

(2) $(D - r)^2 xe^{rx} = (D - r)(D - r)xe^{rx}$

$$= (D - r)(Dxe^{rx} - rxe^{rx}) =$$

$$= (D - r)(rxe^{rx} + e^{rx} - rxe^{rx})$$
$$= (D - r)e^{rx} = 0 \quad \text{by (1)}.$$

Also, $(D - r)^3 xe^{rx} = (D - r)(D - r)^2 xe^{rx} = (D - r)0 = 0$, and

$$(D - r)^3 x^2 e^{rx} = (D - r)^2 (rx^2 e^{rx} + 2xe^{rx} - rx^2 e^{rx})$$
$$= 2(D - r)^2 xe^{rx} = 0 \quad \text{by (2)}.$$

It may be shown, by mathematical induction, that $(D - r)^k$ is an annihilator of each of the functions

$$e^{rx}, xe^{rx}, \ldots, x^{k-1} e^{rx}.$$

Hence, $(D - r)^k$ is an annihilator of

$$(c_1 + c_2 x + \cdots + c_k x^{k-1}) e^{rx}$$

for any constants $c_1, c_2, \ldots, c_k$.

The homogeneous differential equation

$$(3) \qquad (D^2 + a_1 D + a_2) y = 0$$

has characteristic equation $r^2 + a_1 r + a_2 = 0$. As pointed out in Sec. 14-6, if this characteristic equation has $r_1 = a + ib$, $b \neq 0$, as one root, then $r_2 = a - ib$ is the other root, while

$$y = e^{ax} \sin bx \quad \text{and} \quad y = e^{ax} \cos bx$$

are both solutions of (3). This last statement may now be expressed as:

$$[D - (a + ib)][D - (a - ib)] = D^2 - 2aD + a^2 + b^2$$

is an annihilator of both $e^{ax} \sin bx$ and $e^{ax} \cos bx$.

For example, if $f(x) = e^{-2x} \sin 3x$, then

$$[D - (-2 + 3i)][D - (-2 - 3i)]e^{-2x} \sin 3x$$
$$= (D^2 + 4D + 13)e^{-2x} \sin 3x$$
$$= D(3e^{-2x} \cos 3x - 2e^{-2x} \sin 3x)$$
$$\qquad + 4(3e^{-2x} \cos 3x - 2e^{-2x} \sin 3x) + 13e^{-2x} \sin x$$
$$= (-9e^{-2x} \sin 3x - 12e^{-2x} \cos 3x + 4e^{-2x} \sin 3x)$$
$$\qquad + 12e^{-2x} \cos 3x + 5e^{-2x} \sin 3x = 0.$$

Consider the nth-order homogeneous differential equation with constant coefficients

$$(4) \qquad (D^n + a_1 D^{n-1} + a_2 D^{n-2} + \cdots + a_{n-1} D + a_n) y = 0.$$

Under what conditions will $y = e^{rx}$ be a solution of (4)? Since $D^k e^{rx} = r^k e^{rx}$, it follows, upon substituting $y = e^{rx}$ into (4), that r must satisfy

$$(r^n + a_1 r^{n-1} + a_2 r^{n-2} + \cdots + a_{n-1} r + a_n) e^{rx} = 0.$$

Since $e^{rx} \neq 0$, then $y = e^{rx}$ is a solution of the diffential equation (4) if r is any root of the polynomial equation

(5) $$r^n + a_1 r^{n-1} + a_2 r^{n-2} + \cdots + a_{n-1} r + a_n = 0.$$

Moreover, if $r_1, r_2, \ldots, r_n$ are the roots of (5), then

(6) $$y = c_1 e^{r_1 x} + c_2 e^{r_2 x} + \cdots + c_n e^{r_n x}$$

is a solution of (4) but, as discussed below, may not be the general solution of (4). Also, (4) may be written

(7) $$(D - r_1)(D - r_2) \cdots (D - r_n)y = 0.$$

If k of the roots are equal, say $r_1 = r_2 = \cdots = r_k$, then (7) may be written

$$(D - r_1)^k (D - r_{k+1}) \cdots (D - r_n)y = 0.$$

Since $(D - r_1)^k$ is an annihilator of

$$(c_1 + c_2 x + c_3 x^2 + \cdots + c_k x^{k-1})e^{r_1 x},$$

then this expression must be used instead of the first k terms of (6) in the general solution of (4).

Moreover, if one root of (5) is $a + ib$ then another root* is $a - ib$ and two of the factors in (7) may be combined as

$$D^2 - 2aD + a^2 + b^2.$$

Since this annihilates both

(8) $$e^{ax} \sin bx \quad \text{and} \quad e^{ax} \cos bx,$$

these terms multiplied by arbitrary constants appear in the general solution of (4).

Also, $(D^2 - 2aD + a^2 + b^2)^2$ is an annihilator of both

(9) $$xe^{ax} \cos bx \quad \text{and} \quad xe^{ax} \sin bx$$

(see Prob. 1). Thus, if $a + ib$ is a double root of (5), then the general solution of (4) contains the four terms of (8) and (9), each multiplied by an arbitrary constant. By mathematical induction it can be proved that

$$(D^2 - 2aD + a^2 + b^2)^k$$

is an annihilator of both

$$x^{k-1} e^{ax} \sin bx \quad \text{and} \quad x^{k-1} e^{ax} \cos bx.$$

From the above discussion, it follows that a function $f(x)$ has an annihilator of the form

$$D^k + a_1 D^{k-1} + a_2 D^{k-2} + \cdots + a_{k-1} D + a_k,$$

with each a_i a real constant, if $f(x)$ is:

1. A constant.
2. x raised to a positive integer power. (Continue to p. 608.)

---

*From algebra, if a polynomial with real coefficients has $a + ib$ as a root, then $a - ib$ is also a root.

3. e^{rx}.

4. $\sin bx$ or $\cos bx$.

5. Products of terms in 1, 2, 3, 4.

6. Sums of such products.

Hence, x^{-1}, $\sqrt{x}$, $\tan x$, and $\ln x$ are examples of functions that do not have annihilators of the above form, but $\sin^2 x$ does since

$$\sin^2 x = \tfrac{1}{2} + \tfrac{1}{2}\cos 2x.$$

14-9. Undetermined Coefficients

The use of annihilators in solving nonhomogeneous differential equations will be given in this section.

Example 1. Solve

(1) $$(D^2 - 4D + 4)y = x + 3 - 4e^{2x}.$$

Solution. The associated homogeneous and the characteristic equations are

$$(D^2 - 4D + 4)y = 0 \quad \text{and} \quad r^2 - 4r + 4 = 0.$$

Since $r^2 - 4r + 4 = (r - 2)^2 = 0$, then (1) has homogeneous solution

(2) $$y_H = (c_1 + c_2 x)e^{2x}.$$

Also, (1) may be written as

(1′) $$(D - 2)^2 y = x + 3 - 4e^{2x}.$$

Now D^2 is an annihilator of $x + 3$, while $D - 2$ is an annihilator of e^{2x}. Operate on both sides of (1′) by $(D - 2)D^2$:

$$(D - 2)D^2[(D - 2)^2 y] = (D - 2)D^2[x + 3 - 4e^{2x}]$$
$$= (D - 2)[-16e^{2x}] = 0.$$

Hence, a new homogeneous equation,

$$D^2(D - 2)^3 y = 0,$$

is obtained. According to Sec. 14-8, this homogeneous equation has general solution

$$
\begin{aligned}
y &= (c_1 + c_2 x + c_3 x^2)e^{2x} + c_4 + c_5 x \\
&= c_3 x^2 e^{2x} + c_4 + c_5 x + (c_1 + c_2 x)e^{2x} \\
&= c_3 x^2 e^{2x} + c_4 + c_5 x + y_H \quad \text{by (2)} \\
&= y_P + y_H.
\end{aligned}
$$

The object is now to determine c_3, c_4, and c_5 so that

(3) $$y_P = c_3 x^2 e^{2x} + c_4 + c_5 x$$

will be the particular solution of (1). The following schematic array indicates the substitution of this y_P into (1):

$$4 \qquad y_P = c_3 x^2 e^{2x} + c_1 + c_5 x,$$

$$-4 \qquad y'_P = 2c_3 x^2 e^{2x} + 2c_3 x e^{2x} + c_5,$$

$$1 \qquad y''_P = 4c_3 x^2 e^{2x} + 8c_3 x e^{2x} + 2c_3 e^{2x},$$

$$(4 - 8 + 4)c_3 x^2 e^{2x} + (8 - 8)c_3 x e^{2x} + 2c_3 e^{2x} - 4c_5 + 4c_1 + 4c_5 x$$
$$\equiv x + 3 - 4e^{2x}.$$

The terms with zero coefficients drop out, and hence

$$2c_3 e^{2x} - 4c_5 + 4c_1 + 4c_5 x \equiv x + 3 - 4e^{2x}.$$

Equality of coefficients of like terms yields

$$2c_3 = -4, \quad -4c_5 + 4c_1 = 3, \quad 4c_5 = 1.$$

The simultaneous solution is $c_3 = -2$, $c_1 = 1$, $c_5 = \frac{1}{4}$. Substitute these values into (3). The general solution of (1) is, therefore,

$$y = y_P + y_H$$
$$= -2x^2 e^{2x} + 1 + \frac{1}{4}x + (c_1 + c_2 x)e^{2x}.$$

This method of **undetermined coefficients** may be applied if the given differential equation with constant coefficients

$$(4) \qquad D^n + a_1 D^{n-1} + a_2 D^{n-2} + \cdots + a_{n-1} D + a_n)y = f(x)$$

is such that the function $f(x)$ on the right is in the class of functions given at the end of Sec. 14-8. The method is as follows:

First: Find y_H, which will involve n arbitrary constants $c_1, c_2, \ldots, c_n$.

Second: Determine a polynomial operator that will annihilate $f(x)$, and apply this operator to both sides of (4). The result is a homogeneous differential equation.

Third: Find the general solution of the homogeneous equation obtained in the second step. Write this solution as

$$y = y_P + y_H,$$

where the terms involving the above constant $c_1, c_2, \ldots, c_n$ are collected as y_H, while y_P contains all new constants.

Fourth: Substitute y_P into the given equation (4) and determine these new constants.

Example 2. Solve

$$(D^3 + D^2 - 2)y = \cos 3x.$$

Solution. First: $r^3 + r^2 - 2 = 0$ has $r = 1$ as a root by inspection. Hence, $r - 1$ is a factor and by division

$$r^3 + r^2 - 2 = (r - 1)(r^2 + 2r + 2) = 0.$$

The roots are therefore 1 and $-1 \pm i$. Thus,

$$y_H = c_1 e^x + e^{-x}(c_2 \cos x + c_3 \sin x).$$

Second: Since $D^2 - 2aD + a^2 + b^2$ is an annihilator of $e^{ax} \cos bx$, it follows that $D^2 + 3^2$ is an annihilator of $e^{0x} \cos 3x = \cos 3x$. Hence,

$$(D^2 + 3^2)(D^3 + D^2 - 2)y = (D^2 + 3^2)\cos 3x = 0.$$

Third: This homogeneous equation has solution

$$y = c_1 e^x + e^{-x}(c_2 \cos x + c_3 \sin x) + c_4 \cos 3x + c_5 \sin 3x$$
$$= c_4 \cos 3x + c_5 \sin 3x + y_{II}.$$

Fourth: Therefore,

$$
\begin{array}{r|l}
-2 & y_P = c_4 \cos 3x + c_5 \sin 3x, \\
0 & y_P' = -3c_4 \sin 3x + 3c_5 \cos 3x, \\
1 & y_P'' = -9c_4 \cos 3x - 9c_5 \sin 3x, \\
1 & y_P''' = 27c_4 \sin 3x - 27c_5 \cos 3x,
\end{array}
$$

$$(-27c_5 - 9c_4 - 2c_4)\cos 3x + (27c_4 - 9c_5 - 2c_5)\sin 3x = \cos 3x,$$

$$-11c_4 - 27c_5 = 1,$$

$$27c_4 - 11c_5 = 0.$$

Hence, $c_4 = -11/850$, $c_5 = -27/850$, and the general solution is

$$y = -\frac{1}{850}(11 \cos 3x + 27 \sin 3x) + c_1 e^x + e^{-x}(c_2 \cos x + c_3 \sin x).$$

Problem 1. Show that the operator $(D^2 - 2aD + a^2 + b^2)^2$ is an annihilator of both $xe^{ax} \cos bx$ and $xe^{ax} \sin bx$.

Problem 2. Solve $(D^2 - 2D - 3)y = f(x)$ with:
a. $f(x) = 3x - 5$.
b. $f(x) = 5 \cos 2x$.
c. $f(x) = 3e^{-x}$.
d. $f(x) = 3x - 5 + 5 \cos 2x + 3e^{-x}$.
e. $f(x) = e^x$.
f. $f(x) = e^{-x} \cos 2x$.

Problem 3. Replace the differential equations of Prob. 2 by

$$(D^2 - 3D + 2)y = f(x).$$

Problem 4. Solve each of the differential equations by the method of undetermined coefficients:
a. $(D^2 + 4D + 5)y = e^{-x} + 15x$.
b. $(D^2 + 2D + 1)y = e^{-x}$.
c. $(D^2 - 2D + 2)y = e^x(2 \cos x - \sin x)$.
d. $(D^3 + 4D)y = e^x \sin 2x$.

Problem 5. Solve each of the following both by the method of undetermined coefficients and by the method of variation of parameters:
a. $(D^2 - 5D + 6)y = 10 \sin x$.
b. $(D^2 - 2D + 5)y = 5x^2$.

14-10. Variables Missing

If the dependent variable y does not appear explicitly in a differential equation, then set

(1)
$$\frac{dy}{dx} = u, \quad \frac{d^2 y}{dx^2} = \frac{du}{dx}, \quad \text{etc.}$$

and the result will be a differential equation (in x and u) of one lower order than the given equation.

Example 1. Solve the second-order differential equation

(2)
$$x\frac{d^2 y}{dx^2} - \frac{dy}{dx} = \left(\frac{dy}{dx}\right)^2.$$

Solution. The substitutions (1) yield the first-order equation

$$x\frac{du}{dx} - u = u^2.$$

The variables are separable:

$$\frac{du}{u^2 + u} = \frac{dx}{x}.$$

Hence,

$$\ln\left|\frac{u}{u+1}\right| = \ln|c_1 x| \quad \text{and} \quad \frac{u}{u+1} = c_1 x.$$

Solve this equation for u:

$$u = \frac{c_1 x}{1 - c_1 x}.$$

But $u = dy/dx$, and thus an integration gives the solution of (2) as

$$y = -\frac{1}{c_1} \ln|1 - c_1 x| - x + c_2.$$

Example 2. A cable with uniformly distributed weight w lb/ft is suspended from two points A and B, as shown in Fig. 14-10.1. The coordinate system (unit 1

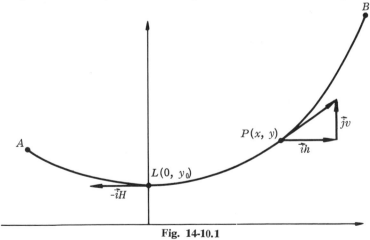

Fig. 14-10.1

ft) has been chosen with x-axis horizontal and $L(0, y_0)$ the lowest point of the curve. Find the equation of the curve.

Solution. Think of cutting the cable at L and attaching the tangential force with proper magnitude to retain the first quadrant portion of the curve. Then at a variable point $P(x, y)$, cut the cable and insert the tangential force to retain the cable between L and P. Since the tangent to the curve is horizontal at L, the first force has no vertical component, and thus there is a constant H such that

$$-\vec{i}H = \text{total force at } L.$$

At P there will be both a vertical component $\vec{j}v$ and a horizontal component $\vec{i}h$, where

$$\frac{v}{h} = (\text{slope of tangent at } P) = \frac{dy}{dx}.$$

The physical principle to be relied upon is: *For a static body, the sum of horizontal forces is zero and the sum of vertical forces is zero.*

Hence, $-\vec{i}H + \vec{i}h = 0$, so that $h = H$.

The only downward force is $-\vec{j}(ws)$, where s is the length (in feet) of the cable between L and P. Hence,

$$-\vec{j}(ws) + \vec{j}v = 0 \quad \text{and} \quad v = ws.$$

Thus,

(3)
$$\frac{dy}{dx} = \frac{v}{h} = \frac{ws}{H},$$

in which w and H are constants. Simplify by setting

$$a = \frac{w}{H}.$$

There are three variables x, y, and s which, however, are related by the differential of arc length formula

$$\frac{ds}{dx} = \sqrt{1 + \left(\frac{dy}{dx}\right)^2}.$$

First substitute $a = w/H$ into (3) and then take the derivative of both sides:

(4)
$$\frac{d^2y}{dx^2} = a\frac{ds}{dx} = a\sqrt{1 + \left(\frac{dy}{dx}\right)^2}.$$

This result is the differential equation (in x and y) of the curve. In addition, the side conditions (at the point L) are

$$y = y_0 \quad \text{and} \quad \frac{dy}{dx} = 0 \quad \text{when} \quad x = 0.$$

Note that y does not appear explicitly in (4), so make the substitutions (1) and obtain

$$\frac{du}{dx} = a\sqrt{1 + u^2}; \quad u = 0 \text{ when } x = 0.$$

The variables x and u are separable,

$$\frac{du}{1 + u^2} = dx,$$

so that $\ln (u + \sqrt{1 + u^2}) = ax + c_1$. But $u = 0$ when $x = 0$, and hence

$$\ln (u + \sqrt{1 + u^2}) = ax.$$

Solve this equation for u:

$$u + \sqrt{1 + u^2} = e^{ax}, \quad \sqrt{1 + u^2} = e^{ax} - u, \quad 1 + u^2 = e^{2ax} - 2ue^{ax} + u^2,$$

$$u = \frac{e^{2ax} - 1}{2e^{ax}} = \frac{1}{2}(e^{ax} - e^{-ax})$$

Since $u = dy/dx$, an integration gives

$$y = \frac{1}{2}\left(\frac{e^{ax}}{a} - \frac{e^{-ax}}{-a}\right) + c_2$$

$$= \frac{1}{2a}(e^{ax} + e^{-ax}) + c_2.$$

The side condition $y = y_0$ when $x = 0$ shows that $c_2 = y_0 - (1/a)$. Hence, the equation of the curve is

$$y = \frac{1}{2a}(e^{ax} + e^{-ax}) + y_0 - \frac{1}{a}.$$

It is judicious to use hindsight and at the very beginning choose the coordinate system so that

$$y_0 = \frac{1}{a} = \frac{1}{w/H} = \frac{H}{w}$$

and thus obtain the simpler equation

$$y = \frac{1}{2a}(e^{ax} + e^{-ax}).$$

Warning: Instead of choosing $a = w/H$ as above, some books choose $a = H/w$ and thus obtain

$$y = \frac{a}{2}(e^{x/a} + e^{-x/a}).$$

The curve of a hanging cable is called a **catenary**.

If the independent variable x does not appear explicitly in a differential equation, then again set

$$\frac{dy}{dx} = u.$$

Now, however, it is better to obtain a differential equation in y and u (instead of x and u) by using

(5) $$\frac{d^2 y}{dx^2} = \frac{du}{dx} = \frac{du}{dy}\frac{dy}{dx} = \frac{du}{dy}u.$$

Example 3. Solve

$$y\frac{d^2 y}{dx^2} + \left(\frac{dy}{dx}\right)^2 + 1 = 0.$$

Solution. The above substitutions yield

$$y \frac{du}{dy} u + u^2 + 1 = 0,$$

in which the variables y and u are separable:

$$\frac{u \, du}{u^2 + 1} = -\frac{dy}{y}.$$

Hence, $\frac{1}{2} \ln (u^2 + 1) = -\ln |c_1 y|$, so that $(u^2 + 1)(c_1 y)^2 = 1$. Thus,

$$u = \pm \frac{1}{c_1 y} \sqrt{1 - c_1^2 y^2}.$$

But $u = dy/dx$, so that

$$\frac{c_1 y}{\sqrt{1 - c_1^2 y^2}} \, dy = \pm 1 \, dx.$$

By an integration,

$$(1 - c_1^2 y^2)^{1/2} = \pm c_1 x + c_2.$$

Problem 1. Solve the differential equations in which the dependent variable does not appear explicitly:

a. $\dfrac{d^2 y}{dx^2} = x \left(\dfrac{dy}{dx}\right)^2.$

c. $(1 + x^2) \dfrac{d^2 y}{dx^2} + 2x \left(\dfrac{dy}{dx} + 1\right) = 0.$

b. $x \dfrac{d^2 y}{dx^2} + 1 = \left(\dfrac{dy}{dx}\right)^2.$

d. $\dfrac{d^2 x}{dt^2} + t \dfrac{dx}{dt} = t^3.$

Problem 2. Solve the differential equations in which the independent variable does not appear explicitly:

a. $\dfrac{d^2 y}{dx^2} + y \dfrac{dy}{dx} = 0.$

c. $y y'' + (y')^2 = yy'.$

b. $y \dfrac{d^2 y}{dx^2} - 1 = \left(\dfrac{dy}{dx}\right)^2.$

d. $y \dfrac{d^2 y}{dx^2} = \left(\dfrac{dy}{dx}\right)^2 + y^2 \dfrac{dy}{dx}.$

Problem 3. A suspension bridge is designed with supports 60 ft high, 200 ft apart, and lowest point L of the cable 20 ft above the level, horizontal roadbed. The uniform roadbed is so heavy that the weight of the cable may be neglected. The vertical rods from the roadbed to the cable are so close together they may be considered as forming a continuous sheet. With the x-axis along the roadbed and the y-axis through L, find the equation of the curve the cable hangs in.

Problem 4. Solve (4) by using the fact that x does not appear explicitly.

Problem 5. Show that if

$$\frac{dy}{dx} = u, \quad \text{then} \quad \frac{d^3 y}{dx^2} = \frac{d^2 u}{dy^2} u^2 + \left(\frac{du}{dy}\right)^2 u, \quad \text{and}$$

$$\frac{d^4 y}{dx^4} = \frac{d^3 u}{dy^3} u^3 + 4 \frac{d^2 u}{dy^2} \frac{du}{dy} u^2 + \left(\frac{du}{dy}\right)^3 u.$$

14-11.   Numerical Methods

With $f(x, y)$ a given function of two variables, then

(1) $\dfrac{dy}{dx} = f(x, y), \quad y = y_0 \text{ when } x = x_0,$

is a type of differential equation (with initial condition) often met. The solution $y = y(x)$, assumed to exist, has its graph passing through the point (x_0, y_0), and at each point (x, y) on the curve the tangent to the curve has slope $m = f(x, y)$.

A crude way of approximating this curve is to compute the slope $m_0 = f(x_0, y_0)$. Then go along the tangent to a point having abscissa given by $x_1 = x_0 + h$. The ordinate y_1 of this point on the tangent is such that

$$\frac{y_1 - y_0}{h} = f(x_0, y_0), \quad \text{so that} \quad y_1 = y_0 + hf(x_0, y_0).$$

Probably the point (x_1, y_1) is not on the curve, but $f(x_1, y_1)$ should be close to the slope of the tangent at the point on the curve having $x = x_1$, if h is

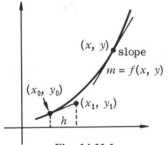

Fig. 14-11.1

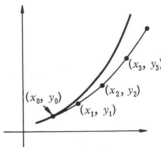

Fig. 14-11.2

small. Thus, by using $f(x_1, y_1)$ as a slope at (x_1, y_1), then a second point (x_2, y_2), with $x_2 = x_1 + h$ and $y_2 = y_1 + hf(x_1, y_1)$, is obtained. Points $(x_1, y_1), (x_2, y_2), \ldots, (x_k, y_k)$ are determined and then (x_{k+1}, y_{k+1}) where

$$x_{k+1} = x_k + h, \quad y_{k+1} = y_k + hf(x_k, y_k).$$

Figure 14-11.2 indicates that these approximating points may get farther and farther away from the solution curve.

As another method, consider $(x_1, y_1), (x_2, y_2), \ldots, (x_k, y_k)$, already obtained, with $x_k = x_0 + kh$. Proceed as follows:

1. Compute the slope $m_k = f(x_k, y_k)$, but
2. Go back to (x_{k-1}, y_{k-1}) to draw the line of slope m_k.
3. Advance along this line to the point with abscissa $x_{k+1} = x_{k-1} + 2h$. The ordinate y_{k+1} of this point is such that

$$\frac{y_{k+1} - y_{k-1}}{2h} = f(x_k, y_k), \quad \text{and hence}$$

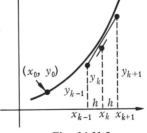

Fig. 14-11.3

(2) $\qquad y_{k+1} = y_{k-1} + 2hf(x_k, y_k)$

$\qquad\qquad = y_{k-1} + 2hy'(x_k) \quad$ from (1).

Figure 14-11.3 indicates how this point has possibilities of being close to the curve.

An analytic way of seeing that (x_{k+1}, y_{k+1}) is likely to be close to the curve follows from two Taylor expansions of $y(x)$ about $x = x_k$. These are

$$y(x_k + h) = y(x_k) + y'(x_k)h + \frac{y''(x_k)}{2!} h^2 + \frac{y'''(\xi_1)}{3!} h^3 \quad \text{and}$$

$$y(x_k - h) = y(x_k) + y'(x_k)(-h) + \frac{y''(x_k)}{2!}(-h)^2 + \frac{y'''(\xi_2)}{3!}(-h)^3.$$

Hence, by subtraction,

$$y(x_k + h) - y(x_k - h) = 2hy'(x_k) + \frac{1}{3!} [y'''(\xi_1) + y'''(\xi_2)]h^3.$$

Since $y_{k+1} = y(x_k + h)$ and $y_{k-1} = y(x_k - h)$, then this formula agrees with (2) except for the h^3 term. Thus, (2) is said to be accurate to **second order.**

Since two known points are necessary in (2) and only the one point (x_0, y_0) is initially given, some other method is required to find (x_1, y_1) accurate to second order. One way is to start with (1) written in the form $y'(x) = f(x, y(x))$ and take a derivative:

$$y''(x) = f_x(x, y(x)) + f_y(x, y(x))y'(x).$$

Thus, since $x_1 = x_0 + h$,

$$y_1 = y(x_1) = y(x_0) + y'(x_0)h + \frac{y''(x_0)}{2} h^2$$

$$= y_0 + y'(x_0)h + \tfrac{1}{2}[f_x(x_0, y_0) + f_y(x_0, y_0)y'(x_0)]h^2$$

is accurate to second order.

Example. Use the second method to approximate the solution for $0 \le x \le 1$ of

$$(3) \qquad\qquad \frac{dy}{dx} = \frac{-y}{1 + x}; \quad y = 1 \text{ when } x = 0,$$

by using $h = 0.2$.

Solution. First set $y' = -y(1 + x)^{-1}$ and obtain

$$y'' = -[-y(1 + x)^{-2} + (1 + x)^{-1}y'] = \frac{y}{(1 + x)^2} - \frac{y'}{1 + x}.$$

Since $y'(0) = -y(0)/(1 + 0) = -1$, then

$$y''(0) = \frac{y(0)}{(1 + 0)^2} - \frac{y'(0)}{1 + 0} = 1 - (-1) = 2.$$

Thus, to second-order accuracy,

$$y_1 = y(0.2) = y(0) + y'(0)(0.2) + \frac{y''(0)}{2!} (0.2)^2$$

$$= 1 - 1(0.2) + \frac{2}{2!} (0.2)^2 = 0.84.$$

With the initial conditions and this value $y_1 = 0.84$, the remaining entries of the table are filled in to slide-rule accuracy by using

$$y'_k = \frac{-y_k}{1 + x_k} \quad \text{and} \quad y_{k+1} = y_{k-1} + 2(0.2)y'_k.$$

k	x_k	y_k	y'_k	y_k
0	0	1	−1	1
1	0.2	0.84	−0.7	0.833
2	0.4	0.72	−0.514	0.714
3	0.6	0.634	−0.396	0.625
4	0.8	0.562	−0.312	0.556
5	1	0.509		0.5

Note that $y = 1/(1 + x)$ is the solution of (3). The isolated column gives the values of y_k from this equation.

There are a variety of methods for obtaining greater accuracy than the above scheme. Also, by employing remainder terms in a judicious way, a computing machine can be programmed to decide upon, and execute, a change to a smaller value of h if the desired accuracy is not being maintained or to a larger h if unjustified accuracy is prolonging the computation. More research is necessary in this field, especially for partial differential equations.

Tables

Table 1. Four-Place Logarithms

	Mantissas										Proportional Parts								
N	0	1	2	3	4	5	6	7	8	9	1 2 3			4 5 6			7 8 9		
10	0000	0043	0086	0128	0170	0212	0253	0294	0334	0374	4 8 12			17 21 25			29 33 37		
11	0414	0453	0492	0531	0569	0607	0645	0682	0719	0755	4 8 11			15 19 23			26 30 34		
12	0792	0828	0864	0899	0934	0969	1004	1038	1072	1106	3 7 10			14 17 21			24 28 31		
13	1139	1173	1206	1239	1271	1303	1335	1367	1399	1430	3 6 10			13 16 19			23 26 29		
14	1461	1492	1523	1553	1584	1614	1644	1673	1703	1732	3 6 9			12 15 18			21 24 27		
15	1761	1790	1818	1847	1875	1903	1931	1959	1987	2014	3 6 8			11 14 17			20 22 25		
16	2041	2068	2095	2122	2148	2175	2201	2227	2253	2279	3 5 8			11 13 16			18 21 24		
17	2304	2330	2355	2380	2405	2430	2455	2480	2504	2529	2 5 7			10 12 15			17 10 22		
18	2553	2577	2601	2625	2648	2672	2695	2718	2742	2765	2 5 7			9 12 14			16 19 21		
19	2788	2810	2833	2856	2878	2900	2923	2945	2967	2989	2 4 7			9 11 13			16 18 20		
20	3010	3032	3054	3075	3096	3118	3139	3160	3181	3201	2 4 6			8 11 13			15 17 19		
21	3222	3243	3263	3284	3304	3324	3345	3365	3385	3404	2 4 6			8 10 12			14 16 18		
22	3424	3444	3464	3483	3502	3522	3541	3560	3579	3598	2 4 6			8 10 12			14 16 17		
23	3617	3636	3655	3674	3692	3711	3729	3747	3766	3784	2 4 6			7 9 11			13 15 17		
24	3802	3820	3838	3856	3874	3892	3909	3927	3945	3962	2 4 5			7 9 11			12 14 16		
25	3979	3997	4014	4031	4048	4065	4082	4099	4116	4133	2 4 5			7 9 10			12 14 16		
26	4150	4166	4183	4200	4216	4232	4249	4265	4281	4298	2 3 5			7 8 10			11 13 15		
27	4314	4330	4346	4362	4378	4393	4409	4425	4440	4456	2 3 5			6 8 9			11 12 14		
28	4472	4487	4502	4518	4533	4548	4564	4579	4594	4609	2 3 5			6 8 9			11 12 14		
29	4624	4639	4654	4669	4683	4698	4713	4728	4742	4757	1 3 4			6 7 9			10 12 13		
30	4771	4786	4800	4814	4829	4843	4857	4871	4886	4900	1 3 4			6 7 9			10 11 13		
31	4914	4928	4942	4955	4969	4983	4997	5011	5024	5038	1 3 4			5 7 8			10 11 12		
32	5051	5065	5079	5092	5105	5119	5132	5145	5159	5172	1 3 4			5 7 8			9 11 12		
33	5185	5198	5211	5224	5237	5250	5263	5276	5289	5302	1 3 4			5 7 8			9 11 12		
34	5315	5328	5340	5353	5366	5378	5391	5403	5416	5428	1 2 4			5 6 8			9 10 11		
35	5441	5453	5465	5478	5490	5502	5514	5527	5539	5551	1 2 4			5 6 7			9 10 11		
36	5563	5575	5587	5599	5611	5623	5635	5647	5658	5670	1 2 4			5 6 7			8 10 11		
37	5682	5694	5705	5717	5729	5740	5752	5763	5775	5786	1 2 4			5 6 7			8 9 11		
38	5798	5809	5821	5832	5843	5855	5866	5877	5888	5899	1 2 3			5 6 7			8 9 10		
39	5911	5922	5933	5944	5955	5966	5977	5988	5999	6010	1 2 3			4 5 7			8 9 10		
40	6021	6031	6042	6053	6064	6075	6085	6096	6107	6117	1 2 3			4 5 6			8 9 10		
41	6128	6138	6149	6160	6170	6180	6191	6201	6212	6222	1 2 3			4 5 6			7 8 9		
42	6232	6243	6253	6263	6274	6284	6294	6304	6314	6325	1 2 3			4 5 6			7 8 9		
43	6335	6345	6355	6365	6375	6385	6395	6405	6415	6425	1 2 3			4 5 6			7 8 9		
44	6435	6444	6454	6464	6474	6484	6493	6503	6513	6522	1 2 3			4 5 6			7 8 9		
45	6532	6542	6551	6561	6571	6580	6590	6599	6609	6618	1 2 3			4 5 6			7 8 9		
46	6628	6637	6646	6656	6665	6675	6684	6693	6702	6712	1 2 3			4 5 6			7 7 8		
47	6721	6730	6739	6749	6758	6767	6776	6785	6794	6803	1 2 3			4 5 6			7 7 8		
48	6812	6821	6830	6839	6848	6857	6866	6875	6884	6893	1 2 3			4 5 6			7 7 8		
49	6902	6911	6920	6928	6937	6946	6955	6964	6972	6981	1 2 3			4 4 5			6 7 8		
50	6990	6998	7007	7016	7024	7033	7042	7050	7059	7067	1 2 3			3 4 5			6 7 8		
51	7076	7084	7093	7101	7110	7118	7126	7135	7143	7152	1 2 3			3 4 5			6 7 8		
52	7160	7168	7177	7185	7193	7202	7210	7218	7226	7235	1 2 3			3 4 5			6 7 7		
53	7243	7251	7259	7267	7275	7284	7292	7300	7308	7316	1 2 3			3 4 5			6 6 7		
54	7324	7332	7340	7348	7356	7364	7372	7380	7388	7396	1 2 3			3 4 5			6 6 7		
N	0	1	2	3	4	5	6	7	8	9	1 2 3			4 5 6			7 8 9		

Table 1. Four-Place Logarithms

N	0	1	2	3	4	5	6	7	8	9	1	2	3	4	5	6	7	8	9
				Mantissas										Proportional Parts					
55	7404	7412	7419	7427	7435	7443	7451	7459	7466	7474	1	2	2	3	4	5	5	6	7
56	7482	7490	7497	7505	7513	7520	7528	7536	7543	7551	1	2	2	3	4	5	5	6	7
57	7559	7566	7574	7582	7589	7597	7604	7612	7619	7627	1	1	2	3	4	5	5	6	7
58	7634	7642	7649	7657	7664	7672	7679	7686	7694	7701	1	1	2	3	4	4	5	6	7
59	7709	7716	7723	7731	7738	7745	7752	7760	7767	7774	1	1	2	3	4	4	5	6	7
60	7782	7789	7796	7803	7810	7818	7825	7832	7839	7846	1	1	2	3	4	4	5	6	6
61	7853	7860	7868	7875	7882	7889	7896	7903	7910	7917	1	1	2	3	3	4	5	6	6
62	7924	7931	7938	7945	7952	7959	7966	7973	7980	7987	1	1	2	3	3	4	5	5	6
63	7993	8000	8007	8014	8021	8028	8035	8041	8048	8055	1	1	2	3	3	4	5	5	6
64	8062	8069	8075	8082	8089	8096	8102	8109	8116	8122	1	1	2	3	3	4	5	5	6
65	8129	8136	8142	8149	8156	8162	8169	8176	8182	8189	1	1	2	3	3	4	5	5	6
66	8195	8202	8209	8215	8222	8228	8235	8241	8248	8254	1	1	2	3	3	4	5	5	6
67	8261	8267	8274	8280	8287	8293	8299	8306	8312	8319	1	1	2	3	3	4	5	5	6
68	8325	8331	8338	8344	8351	8357	8363	8370	8376	8382	1	1	2	3	3	4	4	5	6
69	8388	8395	8401	8407	8414	8420	8426	8432	8439	8445	1	1	2	3	3	4	4	5	6
70	8451	8457	8463	8470	8476	8482	8488	8494	8500	8506	1	1	2	3	3	4	4	5	6
71	8513	8519	8525	8531	8537	8543	8549	8555	8561	8567	1	1	2	3	3	4	4	5	6
72	8573	8579	8585	8591	8597	8603	8609	8615	8621	8627	1	1	2	3	3	4	4	5	6
73	8633	8639	8645	8651	8657	8663	8669	8675	8681	8686	1	1	2	3	3	4	4	5	5
74	8692	8698	8704	8710	8716	8722	8727	8733	8739	8745	1	1	2	2	3	4	4	5	5
75	8751	8756	8762	8768	8774	8779	8785	8791	8797	8802	1	1	2	2	3	3	4	5	5
76	8808	8814	8820	8825	8831	8837	8842	8848	8854	8859	1	1	2	2	3	3	4	4	5
77	8865	8871	8876	8882	8887	8893	8899	8904	8910	8915	1	1	2	2	3	3	4	4	5
78	8921	8927	8932	8938	8943	8949	8954	8960	8965	8971	1	1	2	2	3	3	4	4	5
79	8976	8982	8987	8993	8998	9004	9009	9015	9020	9025	1	1	2	2	3	3	4	4	5
80	9031	9036	9042	9047	9053	9058	9063	9069	9074	9079	1	1	2	2	3	3	4	4	5
81	9085	9090	9096	9101	9106	9112	9117	9122	9128	9133	1	1	2	2	3	3	4	4	5
82	9138	9143	9149	9154	9159	9165	9170	9175	9180	9186	1	1	2	2	3	3	4	4	5
83	9191	9196	9201	9206	9212	9217	9222	9227	9232	9238	1	1	2	2	3	3	4	4	5
84	9243	9248	9253	9258	9263	9269	9274	9279	9284	9289	1	1	2	2	3	3	4	4	5
85	9294	9299	9304	9309	9315	9320	9325	9330	9335	9340	1	1	2	2	3	3	4	4	5
86	9345	9350	9355	9360	9365	9370	9375	9380	9385	9390	1	1	2	2	3	3	4	4	5
87	9395	9400	9405	9410	9415	9420	9425	9430	9435	9440	1	1	2	2	3	3	4	4	5
88	9445	9450	9455	9460	9465	9469	9474	9479	9484	9489	0	1	1	2	2	3	3	4	4
89	9494	9499	9504	9509	9513	9518	9523	9528	9533	9538	0	1	1	2	2	3	3	4	4
90	9542	9547	9552	9557	9562	9566	9571	9576	9581	9586	0	1	1	2	2	3	3	4	4
91	9590	9595	9600	9605	9609	9614	9619	9624	9628	9633	0	1	1	2	2	3	3	4	4
92	9638	9643	9647	9652	9657	9661	9666	9671	9675	9680	0	1	1	2	2	3	3	4	4
93	9685	9689	9694	9699	9703	9708	9713	9717	9722	9727	0	1	1	2	2	3	3	4	4
94	9731	9736	9741	9745	9750	9754	9759	9763	9768	9773	0	1	1	2	2	3	3	4	4
95	9777	9782	9786	9791	9795	9800	9805	9809	9814	9818	0	1	1	2	2	3	3	4	4
96	9823	9827	9832	9836	9841	9845	9850	9854	9859	9863	0	1	1	2	2	3	3	4	4
97	9868	9872	9877	9881	9886	9890	9894	9899	9903	9908	0	1	1	2	2	3	3	4	4
98	9912	9917	9921	9926	9930	9934	9939	9943	9948	9952	0	1	1	2	2	3	3	3	4
99	9956	9961	9965	9969	9974	9978	9983	9987	9991	9996	0	1	1	2	2	3	3	3	4
N	0	1	2	3	4	5	6	7	8	9	1	2	3	4	5	6	7	8	9

Table 2. Trig and Log Trig
[Subtract 10 from logs = n.xxxx if n = 7, 8, or 9]

Ra-dians	De-grees	Sine Value	Sine Log	Tangent Value	Tangent Log	Cotangent Value	Cotangent Log	Cosine Value	Cosine Log		
.0000	0°00′	.0000	—	.0000	—	—	—	1.0000	0.0000	90°00′	1.5708
.0029	10	.0029	7.4637	.0029	7.4637	343.77	2.5363	1.0000	.0000	50	1.5679
.0058	20	.0058	.7648	.0058	.7648	171.89	.2352	1.0000	.0000	40	1.5650
.0087	30	.0087	7.9408	.0087	7.9409	114.59	2.0591	1.0000	.0000	30	1.5621
.0116	40	.0116	8.0658	.0116	8.0658	85.940	1.9342	.9999	.0000	20	1.5592
.0145	50	.0145	.1627	.0145	.1627	68.750	.8373	.9999	0.0000	10	1.5563
.0175	1°00′	.0175	8.2419	.0175	8.2419	57.290	1.7581	.9998	9.9999	89°00′	1.5533
.0204	10	.0204	.3088	.0204	.3089	49.104	.6911	.9998	.9999	50	1.5504
.0233	20	.0233	.3668	.0233	.3669	42.964	.6331	.9997	.9999	40	1.5475
.0262	30	.0262	.4179	.0262	.4181	38.188	.5819	.9997	.9999	30	1.5446
.0291	40	.0291	.4637	.0291	.4638	34.368	.5362	.9996	.9998	20	1.5417
.0320	50	.0320	.5050	.0320	.5053	31.242	.4947	.9995	.9998	10	1.5388
.0349	2°00′	.0349	8.5428	.0349	8.5431	28.636	1.4569	.9994	9.9997	88°00′	1.5359
.0378	10	.0378	.5776	.0378	.5779	26.432	.4221	.9993	.9997	50	1.5330
.0407	20	.0407	.6097	.0407	.6101	24.542	.3899	.9992	.9996	40	1.5301
.0436	30	.0436	.6397	.0437	.6401	22.904	.3599	.9990	.9996	30	1.5272
.0465	40	.0465	.6677	.0466	.6682	21.470	.3318	.9989	.9995	20	1.5243
.0495	50	.0494	.6940	.0495	.6945	20.206	.3055	.9988	9.9995	10	1.5213
.0524	3°00′	.0523	8.7188	.0524	8.7194	19.081	1.2806	.9986	.9994	87°00′	1.5184
.0553	10	.0552	.7423	.0553	.7429	18.075	.2571	.9985	.9993	50	1.5155
.0582	20	.0581	.7645	.0582	.7652	17.169	.2348	.9983	.9993	40	1.5126
.0611	30	.0610	.7857	.0612	.7865	16.350	.2135	.9981	.9992	30	1.5097
.0640	40	.0640	.8059	.0641	.8067	15.605	.1933	.9980	.9991	20	1.5068
.0669	50	.0669	.8251	.0670	.8261	14.924	.1739	.9978	.9990	10	1.5039
.0698	4°00′	.0698	8.8436	.0699	8.8446	14.301	1.1554	.9976	9.9989	86°00′	1.5010
.0727	10	.0727	.8613	.0729	.8624	13.727	.1376	.9974	.9989	50	1.4981
.0756	20	.0756	.8783	.0758	.8795	13.197	.1205	.9971	.9988	40	1.4952
.0785	30	.0785	.8946	.0787	.8960	12.706	.1040	.9969	.9987	30	1.4923
.0814	40	.0814	.9104	.0816	.9118	12.251	.0882	.9967	.9986	20	1.4893
.0844	50	.0843	.9256	.0846	.9272	11.826	.0728	.9964	.9985	10	1.4864
.0873	5°00′	.0872	8.9403	.0875	8.9420	11.430	1.0580	.9962	9.9983	85°00′	1.4835
.0902	10	.0901	.9545	.0904	.9563	11.059	.0437	.9959	.9982	50	1.4806
.0931	20	.0929	.9682	.0934	.9701	10.712	.0299	.9957	.9981	40	1.4777
.0960	30	.0958	.9816	.0963	.9836	10.385	.0164	.9954	.9980	30	1.4748
.0989	40	.0987	8.9945	.0992	8.9966	10.078	1.0034	.9951	.9979	20	1.4719
.1018	50	.1016	9.0070	.1022	9.0093	9.7882	0.9907	.9948	.9977	10	1.4690
.1047	6°00′	.1045	9.0192	.1051	9.0216	9.5144	0.9784	.9945	9.9976	84°00′	1.4661
.1076	10	.1074	.0311	.1080	.0336	9.2553	.9664	.9942	.9975	50	1.4632
.1105	20	.1103	.0426	.1110	.0453	9.0098	.9547	.9939	.9973	40	1.4603
.1134	30	.1132	.0539	.1139	.0567	8.7769	.9433	.9936	.9972	30	1.4573
.1164	40	.1161	.0648	.1169	.0678	8.5555	.9322	.9932	.9971	20	1.4544
.1193	50	.1190	.0755	.1198	.0786	8.3450	.9214	.9929	.9969	10	1.4515
.1222	7°00′	.1219	9.0859	.1228	9.0891	8.1443	0.9109	.9925	9.9968	83°00′	1.4486
.1251	10	.1248	.0961	.1257	.0995	7.9530	.9005	.9922	.9966	50	1.4457
.1280	20	.1276	.1060	.1287	.1096	7.7704	.8904	.9918	.9964	40	1.4428
.1309	30	.1305	.1157	.1317	.1194	7.5958	.8806	.9914	.9963	30	1.4399
.1338	40	.1334	.1252	.1346	.1291	7.4287	.8709	.9911	.9961	20	1.4370
.1367	50	.1363	.1345	.1376	.1385	7.2687	.8615	.9907	.9959	10	1.4341
.1396	8°00′	.1392	9.1436	.1405	9.1478	7.1154	0.8522	.9903	9.9958	82°00′	1.4312
.1425	10	.1421	.1525	.1435	.1569	6.9682	.8431	.9899	.9956	50	1.4283
.1454	20	.1449	.1612	.1465	.1658	6.8269	.8342	.9894	.9954	40	1.4254
.1484	30	.1478	.1697	.1495	.1745	6.6912	.8255	.9890	.9952	30	1.4224
.1513	40	.1507	.1781	.1524	.1831	6.5606	.8169	.9886	.9950	20	1.4195
.1542	50	.1536	.1863	.1554	.1915	6.4348	.8085	.9881	.9948	10	1.4166
.1571	9°00′	.1564	9.1943	.1584	9.1997	6.3138	0.8003	.9877	9.9946	81°00′	1.4137

Value	Log	Value	Log	Value	Log	Value	Log	De-	Ra-
	Cosine		Cotangent		Tangent		Sine	grees	dians

Table 2. Trig and Log Trig
[Subtract 10 from logs = *n.xxxx* if *n* = 7, 8, or 9]

Ra-dians	De-grees	Sine Value	Sine Log	Tangent Value	Tangent Log	Cotangent Value	Cotangent Log	Cosine Value	Cosine Log		
0.1571	9°00′	.1564	9.1943	.1584	9.1997	6.3138	0.8003	.9877	9.9946	81°00′	1.4137
0.1600	10	.1593	.2022	.1614	.2078	6.1970	.7922	.9872	.9944	50	1.4108
0.1629	20	.1622	.2100	.1644	.2158	6.0844	.7842	.9868	.9942	40	1.4079
0.1658	30	.1650	.2176	.1673	.2236	5.9758	.7764	.9863	.9940	30	1.4050
0.1687	40	.1679	.2251	.1703	.2313	5.8708	.7687	.9858	.9938	20	1.4021
0.1716	50	.1708	.2324	.1733	.2389	5.7694	.7611	.9853	.9936	10	1.3992
0.1745	10°00′	.1736	9.2397	.1763	9.2463	5.6713	0.7537	.9848	9.9934	80°00′	1.3963
0.1774	10	.1765	.2468	.1793	.2536	5.5764	.7464	.9843	.9931	50	1.3934
0.1804	20	.1794	.2538	.1823	.2609	5.4845	.7391	.9838	.9929	40	1.3904
0.1833	30	.1822	.2606	.1853	.2680	5.3955	.7320	.9833	.9927	30	1.3875
0.1862	40	.1851	.2674	.1883	.2750	5.3093	.7250	.9827	.9924	20	1.3846
0.1891	50	.1880	.2740	.1914	.2819	5.2257	.7181	.9822	.9922	10	1.3817
0.1920	11°00′	.1908	9.2806	.1944	9.2887	5.1446	0.7113	.9816	9.9919	79°00′	1.3788
0.1949	10	.1937	.2870	.1974	.2953	5.0658	.7047	.9911	.9917	50	1.3759
0.1978	20	.1965	.2934	.2004	.3020	4.9894	.6980	.9805	.9914	40	1.3730
0.2007	30	.1994	.2997	.2035	.3085	4.9152	.6915	.9799	.9912	30	1.3701
0.2036	40	.2022	.3058	.2065	.3149	4.8430	.6851	.9793	.9909	20	1.3672
0.2065	50	.2051	.3119	.2095	.3212	4.7729	.6788	.9787	.9907	10	1.3643
0.2094	12°00′	.2079	9.3179	.2126	9.3275	4.7046	0.6725	.9781	9.9904	78°00′	1.3614
0.2123	10	.2108	.3238	.2156	.3336	4.6382	.6664	.9775	.9901	50	1.3584
0.2153	20	.2136	.3296	.2186	.3397	4.5736	.6603	.9769	.9899	40	1.3555
0.2182	30	.2164	.3353	.2217	.3458	4.5107	.6542	.9763	.9896	30	1.3526
0.2211	40	.2193	.3410	.2247	.3517	4.4494	.6483	.9757	.9893	20	1.3497
0.2240	50	.2221	.3466	.2278	.3576	4.3897	.6424	.9750	.9890	10	1.3468
0.2269	13°00′	.2250	9.3521	.2309	9.3634	4.3315	0.6366	.9744	9.9887	77°00′	1.3439
0.2298	10	.2278	.3575	.2339	.3691	4.2747	.6309	.9737	.9884	50	1.3410
0.2327	20	.2306	.3629	.2370	.3748	4.2193	.6252	.9730	.9881	40	1.3381
0.2356	30	.2334	.3682	.2401	.3804	4.1653	.6196	.9724	.9878	30	1.3352
0.2385	40	.2363	.3734	.2432	.3859	4.1126	.6141	.9717	.9875	20	1.3323
0.2414	50	.2391	.3786	.2462	.3914	4.0611	.6086	.9710	.9872	10	1.3294
0.2443	14°00′	.2419	9.3837	.2493	9.3968	4.0108	0.6032	.9703	9.9869	76°00′	1.3265
0.2473	10	.2447	.3887	.2524	.4021	3.9617	.5979	.9696	.9866	50	1.3235
0.2502	20	.2476	.3937	.2555	.4074	3.9136	.5926	.9689	.9863	40	1.3206
0.2531	30	.2504	.3986	.2586	.4127	3.8667	.5873	.9681	.9859	30	1.3177
0.2560	40	.2532	.4035	.2617	.4178	3.8208	.5822	.9674	.9856	20	1.3148
0.2589	50	.2560	.4083	.2648	.4230	3.7760	.5770	.9667	.9853	10	1.3119
0.2618	15°00′	.2588	9.4130	.2679	9.4281	3.7321	0.5719	.9659	9.9849	75°00′	1.3090
0.2647	10	.2616	.4177	.2711	.4331	3.6891	.5669	.9652	.9846	50	1.3061
0.2676	20	.2644	.4223	.2742	.4381	3.6470	.5619	.9644	.9843	40	1.3032
0.2705	30	.2672	.4269	.2773	.4430	3.6059	.5570	.9636	.9839	30	1.3003
0.2734	40	.2700	.4314	.2805	.4479	3.5656	.5521	.9628	.9836	20	1.2974
0.2763	50	.2728	.4359	.2836	.4527	3.5261	.5473	.9621	.9832	10	1.2945
0.2793	16°00′	.2756	9.4403	.2867	9.4575	3.4874	0.5425	.9613	9.9828	74°00′	1.2915
0.2822	10	.2784	.4447	.2899	.4622	3.4495	.5378	.9605	.9825	50	1.2886
0.2851	20	.2812	.4491	.2931	.4669	3.4124	.5331	.9596	.9821	40	1.2857
0.2880	30	.2840	.4533	.2962	.4716	3.3759	.5284	.9588	.9817	30	1.2828
0.2909	40	.2868	.4576	.2994	.4762	3.3402	.5238	.9580	.9814	20	1.2799
0.2938	50	.2896	.4618	.3026	.4808	3.3052	.5192	.9572	.9810	10	1.2770
0.2967	17°00′	.2924	9.4659	.3057	9.4853	3.2709	0.5147	.9563	9.9806	73°00′	1.2741
0.2996	10	.2952	.4700	.3089	.4898	3.2371	.5102	.9555	.9802	50	1.2712
0.3025	20	.2979	.4741	.3121	.4943	3.2041	.5057	.9546	.9798	40	1.2683
0.3054	30	.3007	.4781	.3153	.4987	3.1716	.5013	.9537	.9794	30	1.2654
0.3083	40	.3035	.4821	.3185	.5031	3.1397	.4969	.9528	.9790	20	1.2625
0.3113	50	.3062	.4861	.3217	.5075	3.1084	.4925	.9520	.9786	10	1.2595
0.3142	18°00′	.3090	9.4900	.3249	9.5118	3.0777	0.4882	.9511	9.9782	72°00′	1.2566
		Value	Log	Value	Log	Value	Log	Value	Log	De-	Ra-
		Cosine		Cotangent		Tangent		Sine		grees	dians

Table 2. Trig and Log Trig

[Subtract 10 from logs = n.xxxx if n = 7, 8, or 9]

Ra-dians	De-grees	Sine Value	Sine Log	Tangent Value	Tangent Log	Cotangent Value	Cotangent Log	Cosine Value	Cosine Log		
0.3142	18°00'	.3090	9.4900	.3249	9.5118	3.0777	0.4882	.9511	9.9782	72°00'	1.2566
0.3171	10	.3118	.4939	.3281	.5161	3.0475	.4839	.9502	.9778	50	1.2537
0.3200	20	.3145	.4977	.3314	.5203	3.0178	.4797	.9492	.9774	40	1.2508
0.3229	30	.3173	.5015	.3346	.5245	2.9887	.4755	.9483	.9770	30	1.2479
0.3258	40	.3201	.5052	.3378	.5287	2.9600	.4713	.9474	.9765	20	1.2450
0.3287	50	.3228	.5090	.3411	.5329	2.9319	.4671	.9465	.9761	10	1.2421
0.3316	19°00'	.3256	9.5126	.3443	9.5370	2.9042	0.4630	.9455	9.9757	71°00'	1.2392
0.3345	10	.3283	.5163	.3476	.5411	2.8770	.4589	.9446	.9752	50	1.2363
0.3374	20	.3311	.5199	.3508	.5451	2.8502	.4549	.9436	.9748	40	1.2334
0.3403	30	.3338	.5235	.3541	.5491	2.8239	.4509	.9426	.9743	30	1.2305
0.3432	40	.3365	.5270	.3574	.5531	2.7980	.4469	.9417	.9739	20	1.2275
0.3462	50	.3393	.5306	.3607	'5571	2.7725	.4429	.9407	.9734	10	1.2246
0.3491	20°00'	.3420	9.5341	.3640	9.5611	2.7475	0.4389	.9397	9.9730	70°00'	1.2217
0.3520	10	.3448	.5375	.3673	.5650	2.7228	.4350	.9387	.9725	50	1.2188
0.3549	20	.3475	.5409	.3706	.5689	2.6985	.4311	.9377	.9721	40	1.2159
0.3578	30	.3502	.5443	.3739	.5727	2.6746	.4273	.9367	.9716	30	1.2130
0.3607	40	.3529	.5477	.3772	.5766	2.6511	.4234	.9356	.9711	20	1.2101
0.3636	50	.3557	.5510	.3805	.5804	2.6279	.4196	.9346	.9706	10	1.2072
0.3665	21°00'	.3584	9.5543	.3839	9.5842	2.6051	0.4158	.9336	9.9702	69°00'	1.2043
0.3694	10	.3611	.5576	.3872	.5879	2.5826	.4121	.9325	.9697	50	1.2014
0.3723	20	.3638	.5609	.3906	.5917	2.5605	.4083	.9315	.9692	40	1.1985
0.3752	30	.3665	.5641	.3939	.5954	2.5386	.4046	.9304	.9687	30	1.1956
0.3782	40	.3692	.5673	.3973	.5991	2.5172	.4009	.9293	.9682	20	1.1926
0.3811	50	.3719	.5704	.4006	.6028	2.4960	.3972	.9283	.9677	10	1.1897
0.3840	22°00'	.3746	9.5736	.4040	9.6064	2.4751	0.3936	.9272	9.9672	68°00'	1.1868
0.3869	10	.3773	.5767	.4074	.6100	2.4545	.3900	.9261	.9667	50	1.1839
0.3898	20	.3800	.5798	.4108	.6136	2.4342	.3864	.9250	.9661	40	1.1810
0.3927	30	.3827	.5828	.4142	.6172	2.4142	.3828	.9239	.9656	30	1.1781
0.3956	40	.3854	.5859	.4176	.6208	2.3945	.3792	.9228	.9651	20	1.1752
0.3985	50	.3881	.5889	.4210	.6243	2.3750	.3757	.9216	.9646	10	1.1723
0.4014	23°00'	.3907	9.5919	.4245	9.6279	2.3559	0.3721	.9205	9.9640	67°00'	1.1694
0.4043	10	.3934	.5948	.4279	.6314	2.3369	.3686	.9194	.9635	50	1.1665
0.4072	20	.3961	.5978	.4314	.6348	2.3183	.3652	.9182	.9629	40	1.1636
0.4102	30	.3987	.6007	.4348	.6383	2.2998	.3617	.9171	.9624	30	1.1606
0.4131	40	.4014	.6036	.4383	.6417	2.2817	.3583	.9159	.9618	20	1.1577
0.4160	50	.4041	.6065	.4417	.6452	·2.2637	.3548	.9147	.9613	10	1.1548
0.4189	24°00'	.4067	9.6093	.4452	9.6486	2.2460	0.3514	.9135	9.9607	66°00'	1.1519
0.4218	10	.4094	.6121	.4487	.6520	2.2286	.3480	.9124	.9602	50	1.1490
0.4247	20	.4120	.6149	.4522	.6553	2.2113	.3447	.9112	.9596	40	1.1461
0.4276	30	.4147	.6177	.4557	.6587	2.1943	.3413	.9100	.9590	30	1.1432
0.4305	40	.4173	.6205	.4592	.6620	2.1775	.3380	.9088	.9584	20	1.1403
0.4334	50	.4200	.6232	.4628	.6654	2.1609	.3346	.9075	.9579	10	1.1374
0.4363	25°00'	.4226	9.6259	.4663	9.6687	2.1445	0.3313	.9063	9.9573	65°00'	1.1345
0.4392	10	.4253	.6286	.4699	.6720	2.1283	.3280	.9051	.9567	50	1.1316
0.4422	20	.4279	.6313	.4734	.6752	2.1123	.3248	.9038	.9561	40	1.1286
0.4451	30	.4305	.6340	.4770	.6985	2.0965	.3215	.9026	.9555	30	1.1257
0.4480	40	.4331	.6366	.4806	.6817	2.0809	.3183	.9013	.9549	20	1.1228
0.4509	50	.4358	.6392	.4841	.6850	2.0655	.3150	.9001	.9543	10	1.1199
0·4538	26°00'	.4384	9.6418	.4877	9.6882	2.0503	0.3118	.8988	9.9537	64°00'	1.1170
0.4567	10	.4410	.6444	.4913	.6914	2.0353	.3086	.8975	.9530	50	1.1141
0.4596	20	.4436	.6470	.4950	.6946	2.0204	.3054	.8962	.9524	40	1.1112
0.4625	30	.4462	.6495	.4986	.6977	2.0057	.3023	.8949	.9518	30	1.1083
0.4654	40	.4488	.6521	.5022	.7009	1.9912	.2991	.8936	.9512	20	1.1054
0.4683	50	.4514	.6546	.5059	.7040	1.9768	.2960	.8923	.9505	10	1.1025
0.4712	27°00'	.4540	9.6570	.5095	9.7072	1.9626	0.2928	.8910	9.9499	63°00'	1.0996

Value	Log	Value	Log	Value	Log	Value	Log	De-	Ra-
	Cosine		Cotangent		Tangent		Sine	grees	dians

Table 2. Trig and Log Trig
[Subtract 10 from logs = *n.xxxx* if *n* = 7, 8, or 9]

Ra-dians	De-grees	Sine Value	Sine Log	Tangent Value	Tangent Log	Cotangent Value	Cotangent Log	Cosine Value	Cosine Log		
0.4712	27°00′	.4540	9.6570	.5095	9.7072	1.9626	0.2928	.8910	9.9499	63°00′	1.0996
0.4741	10	.4566	.6595	.5132	.7103	1.9486	.2897	.8897	.9492	50	1.0966
0.4771	20	.4592	.6620	.5169	.7134	1.9347	.2866	.8884	.9486	40	1.0937
0.4800	30	.4617	.6644	.5206	.7165	1.9210	.2835	.8870	.9479	30	1.0908
0.4829	40	.4643	.6668	.5243	.7196	1.9074	.2804	.8857	.9473	20	1.0879
0.4858	50	.4669	.6692	.5280	.7226	1.8940	.2774	.8843	.9466	10	1.0850
0.4887	28°00′	.4695	9.6716	.5317	9.7257	1.8807	0.2743	.8829	9.9459	62°00′	1.0821
0.4916	10	.4720	.6740	.5354	.7287	1.8676	.2713	.8816	.9453	50	1.0792
0.4945	20	.4746	.6763	.5392	.7317	1.8546	.2683	.8802	.9446	40	1.0763
0.4974	30	.4772	.6787	.5430	.7348	1.8418	.2652	.8788	.9439	30	1.0734
0.5003	40	.4797	.6810	.5467	.7378	1.8291	.2622	.8774	.9432	20	1.0705
0.5032	50	.4823	.6833	.5505	.7408	1.8165	.2592	.8760	.9425	10	1.0676
0.5061	29°00′	.4848	9.6856	.5543	9.7438	1.8040	0.2562	.8746	9.9418	61°00′	1.0647
0.5091	10	.4874	.6878	.5581	.7467	1.7917	.2533	.8732	.9411	50	1.0617
0.5120	20	.4899	.6901	.5619	.7497	1.7796	.2503	.8718	.9404	40	1.0588
0.5149	30	.4924	.6923	.5658	.7526	1.7675	.2474	.8704	.9397	30	1.0559
0.5178	40	.4950	.6946	.5696	.7556	1.7556	.2444	.8689	.9390	20	1.0530
0.5207	50	.4975	.6968	.5735	.7585	1.7437	.2415	.8675	.9383	10	1.0501
0.5236	30°00′	.5000	9.6990	.5774	9.7614	1.7321	0.2386	.8660	9.9375	60°00′	1.0472
0.5265	10	.5025	.7012	.5812	.7644	1.7205	.2356	.8646	.9368	50	1.0443
0.5294	20	.5050	.7033	.5851	.7673	1.7090	.2327	.8631	.9361	40	1.0414
0.5323	30	.5075	.7055	.5890	.7701	1.6977	.2299	.8616	.9353	30	1.0385
0.5352	40	.5100	.7076	.5930	.7730	1.6864	.2270	.8601	.9346	20	1.0356
0.5381	50	.5125	.7097	.5969	.7759	1.6753	.2241	.8587	.9338	10	1.0327
0.5411	31°00′	.5150	9.7118	.6009	9.7788	1.6643	0.2212	.8572	9.9331	59°00′	1.0297
0.5440	10	.5175	.7139	.6048	.7816	1.6534	.2184	.8557	.9323	50	1.0268
0.5469	20	.5200	.7160	.6088	.7845	1.6426	.2155	.8542	.9315	40	1.0239
0.5498	30	.5225	.7181	.6128	.7873	1.6319	.2127	.8526	.9308	30	1.0210
0.5527	40	.5250	.7201	.6168	.7902	1.6212	.2098	.8511	.9300	20	1.0181
0.5556	50	.5275	.7222	.6208	.7930	1.6107	.2070	.8496	.9292	10	1.0152
0.5585	32°00′	.5299	9.7242	.6249	9.7958	1.6003	0.2042	.8480	9.9284	58°00′	1.0123
0.5614	10	.5324	.7262	.6289	.7986	1.5900	.2014	.8465	.9276	50	1.0094
0.5643	20	.5348	.7282	.6330	.8014	1.5798	.1986	.8450	.9268	40	1.0065
0.5672	30	.5373	.7302	.6371	.8042	1.5697	.1958	.8434	.9260	36	1.0036
0.5701	40	.5398	.7322	.6412	.8070	1.5597	·1930	.8418	.9252	20	1.0007
0.5730	50	.5422	.7342	.6453	.8097	1.5497	.1903	.8403	.9244	10	0.9977
0.5760	33°00′	.5446	9.7361	.6494	9.8125	1.5399	0.1875	.8387	9.9236	57°00′	0.9948
0.5789	10	.5471	.7380	.6536	.8153	1.5301	.1847	.8371	.9228	50	0.9919
0.5818	20	.5495	.7400	.6577	.8180	1.5204	.1820	.8355	.9219	40	0.9890
0.5847	30	.5519	.7419	.6619	.8208	1.5108	.1792	.8339	.9211	30	0.9861
0.5876	40	.5544	.7438	.6661	.8235	1.5013	.1765	.8323	.9203	20	0.9832
0.5905	50	.5568	.7457	.6703	.8263	1.4919	.1737	.8307	.9194	10	0.9803
0.5934	34°00′	.5592	9.7476	.6745	9.8290	1.4826	0.1710	.8290	9.9186	56°00′	0.9774
0.5963	10	.5616	.7494	.6787	.8317	1.4733	.1683	.8274	.9177	50	0.9745
0.5992	20	.5640	.7513	.6830	.8344	1.4641	.1656	.8258	.9169	40	0.9916
0.6021	30	.5664	.7531	.6873	.8371	1.4550	.1629	.8241	.9160	30	0.9687
0.6050	40	.5688	.7550	.6916	.8398	1.4460	.1602	.8225	.9151	20	0.9657
0.6080	50	.5712	.7568	.6959	.8425	1.4370	.1575	.8208	.9142	10	0.9628
0.6109	35°00′	.5736	9.7586	.7002	9.8452	1.4281	0.1548	.8192	9.9134	55°00′	0.9599
0.6138	10	.5760	.7604	.7046	.8479	1.4193	.1521	.8175	.9125	50	0.9570
0.6167	20	.5783	.7622	.7089	.8506	1.4106	.1494	.8158	.9116	40	0.9541
0.6196	30	.5807	.7640	.7133	.8533	1.4019	.1467	.8141	.9107	30	0.9512
0.6225	40	.5831	.7657	.7177	.8559	1.3934	.1441	.8124	.9098	20	0.9483
0.6254	50	.5854	.7675	.7221	.8586	1.3848	.1414	.8107	.9089	10	0.9454
0.6283	36°00′	.5878	9.7692	.7265	9.8613	1.3764	0.1387	.8090	9.9080	54°00′	0.9425

		Value	Log	Value	Log	Value	Log	Value	Log	De-	Ra-
			Cosine		Cotangent		Tangent		Sine	grees	dians

Table 2. Trig and Log Trig
[Subtract 10 from logs = n.xxxx if n = 7, 8, or 9]

Ra-dians	De-grees	Sine Value	Sine Log	Tangent Value	Tangent Log	Cotangent Value	Cotangent Log	Cosine Value	Cosine Log		
0.6283	36°00′	.5878	9.7692	.7265	9.8613	1.3764	0.1387	.8090	9.9080	54°00′	0.9425
0.6312	10	.5901	.7710	.7310	.8639	1.3680	.1361	.8073	.9070	50	0.9396
0.6341	20	.5925	.7727	.7355	.8666	1.3597	.1334	.8056	.9061	40	0.9367
0.6370	30	.5948	.7744	.7400	.8692	1.3514	.1308	.8039	.9052	30	0.9338
0.6400	40	.5972	.7761	.7445	.8718	1.3432	.1282	.8021	.9042	20	0.9308
0.6429	50	.5995	.7778	.7490	.8745	1.3351	.1255	.8004	.9033	10	0.9279
0.6458	37°00′	.6018	9.7795	.7536	9.8771	1.3270	0.1229	.7986	9.9023	53°00′	0.9250
0.6487	10	.6041	.7811	.7581	.8797	1.3190	.1203	.7969	.9014	50	0.9221
0.6516	20	.6065	.7828	.7627	.8824	1.3111	.1176	.7951	.9004	40	0.9192
0.6545	30	.6088	.7844	.7673	.8850	1.3032	.1150	.7934	.8995	30	0.9163
0.6574	40	.6111	.7861	.7720	.8876	1.2954	.1124	.7916	.8985	20	0.9134
0.6603	50	.6134	.7877	.7766	.8902	1.2876	.1098	.7898	.8975	10	0.9105
0.6632	38°00′	.6157	9.7893	.7813	9.8928	1.2799	0.1072	.7880	9.8965	52°00′	0.9076
0.6661	10	.6180	.7910	.7860	.8954	1.2723	.1046	.7862	.8955	50	0.9047
0.6690	20	.6202	.7926	.7907	.8980	1.2647	.1020	.7844	.8945	40	0.9018
0.6720	30	.6225	.7941	.7954	.9006	1.2572	.0994	.7826	.8935	30	0.8988
0.6749	40	.6248	.7957	.8002	.9032	1.2497	.0968	.7808	.8925	20	0.8959
0.6778	50	.6271	.7973	.8050	.9058	1.2423	.0942	.7790	.8915	10	0.8930
0.6807	39°00′	.6293	9.7989	.8098	9.9084	1.2349	0.0916	.7771	9.8905	51°00′	0.8901
0.6836	10	.6316	.8004	.8146	.9110	1.2276	.0890	.7753	.8895	50	0.8872
0.6865	20	.6338	.8020	.8195	.9135	1.2203	.0865	.7735	.8884	40	0.8843
0.6894	30	.6361	.8035	.8243	.9161	1.2131	.0839	.7716	.8874	30	0.8814
0.6923	40	.6383	.8050	.8292	.9187	1.2059	.0813	.7698	.8864	20	0.8785
0.6952	50	.6406	.8066	.8342	.9212	1.1988	.0788	.7679	.8853	10	0.8756
0.6981	40°00′	.6428	9.8081	.8391	9.9238	1.1918	0.0762	.7660	9.8843	50°00′	0.8727
0.7010	10	.6450	.8096	.8441	.9264	1.1847	.0736	.7642	.8832	50	0.8698
0.7039	20	.6472	.8111	.8491	.9289	1.1778	.0711	.7623	.8821	40	0.8668
0.7069	30	.6494	.8125	.8541	.9315	1.1708	.0685	.7604	.8810	30	0.8639
0.7098	40	.6517	.8140	.8591	.9341	1.1640	.0659	.7585	.8800	20	0.8610
0.7127	50	.6539	.8155	.8642	.9366	1.1571	.0634	.7566	.8789	10	0.8581
0.7156	41°00′	.6561	9.8169	.8693	9.9392	1.1504	0.0608	.7547	9.8778	49°00′	0.8552
0.7185	10	.6583	.8184	.8744	.9417	1.1436	.0583	.7528	.8767	50	0.8523
0.7214	20	.6604	.8198	.8796	.9443	1.1369	.0557	.7509	.8756	40	0.8494
0.7243	30	.6626	.8213	.8847	.9468	1.1303	.0532	.7490	.8745	30	0.8465
0.7272	40	.6648	.8227	.8899	.9494	1.1237	.0506	.7470	.8733	20	0.8436
0.7301	50	.6670	.8241	.8952	.9159	1.1171	.0481	.7451	.8722	10	0.8407
0.7330	42°00′	.6691	9.8255	.9004	9.9544	1.1106	0.0456	.7431	9.8711	48°00′	0.8378
0.7359	10	.6713	.8269	.9057	.9570	1.1041	.0430	.7412	.8699	50	0.8348
0.7389	20	.6734	.8283	.9110	.9595	1.0977	.0405	.7392	.8688	40	0.8319
0.7418	30	.6756	.8297	.9163	.9621	1.0913	.0379	.7373	.8676	30	0.8290
0.7447	40	.6777	.8311	.9217	.9646	1.0850	.0354	.7353	.8665	20	0.8261
0.7476	50	.6799	.8324	.9271	.9671	1.0786	.0329	.7333	.8653	10	0.8232
0.7505	43°00′	.6820	9.8338	.9325	9.9697	1.0724	0.0303	.7314	9.8641	47°00′	0.8203
0.7534	10	.6841	.8351	.9380	.9722	1.0661	.0278	.7294	.8629	50	0.8174
0.7563	20	.6862	.8365	.9435	.9747	1.0599	.0253	.7274	.8618	40	0.8145
0.7592	30	.6884	.8378	.9490	.9772	1.0538	.0228	.7254	.8606	30	0.8116
0.7621	40	.6905	.8391	.9545	.9798	1.0477	.0202	.7234	.8594	20	0.8087
0.7650	50	.6926	.8405	.9601	.9823	1.0416	.0177	.7214	.8582	10	0.8058
0.7679	44°00′	.6947	9.8418	.9657	9.9848	1.0355	0.0152	.7193	9.8569	46°00′	0.8029
0.7709	10	.6967	.8431	.9713	.9874	1.0295	.0126	.7173	.8557	50	0.7999
0.7738	20	.6988	.8444	.9770	.9899	1.0235	.0101	.7153	.8545	40	0.7970
0.7767	30	.7009	.8457	.9827	.9924	1.0176	.0076	.7133	.8532	30	0.7941
0.7796	40	.7030	.8469	.9884	.9949	1.0117	.0051	.7112	.8520	20	0.7912
0.7825	50	.7050	.8482	.9942	9.9975	1.0058	0.0025	.7092	.8507	10	0.7883
0.7854	45°00′	.7071	9.8495	1.0000	0.0000	1.0000	0.0000	.7071	9.8495	45°00′	0.7854

		Value Cosine	Log	Value Cotangent	Log	Value Tangent	Log	Value Sine	Log	De-grees	Ra-dians

Table 3.

n	$\dfrac{1}{n!}$	$\log\left(\dfrac{1}{n!}\right)$
1	1	0
2	5×10^{-1}	-0.3010
3	1.667×10^{-1}	-0.7780
4	4.167×10^{-2}	-1.3802
5	8.334×10^{-3}	-2.0791
6	1.389×10^{-3}	-2.8593
7	1.985×10^{-4}	-3.7024
8	2.481×10^{-5}	-4.6055
9	2.756×10^{-6}	-5.5597
10	2.756×10^{-7}	-6.5597
11	2.506×10^{-8}	-7.6010
12	2.088×10^{-9}	-8.6803
13	1.606×10^{-10}	-9.7942
14	1.148×10^{-11}	-10.9403
15	7.648×10^{-12}	-12.1164
16	4.780×10^{-14}	-13.3206
17	2.812×10^{-15}	-14.5510
18	1.562×10^{-16}	-15.8063
19	8.211×10^{-18}	-17.0850
20	4.111×10^{-19}	-18.3861

Constants

$\pi = 3.14159$	26535	89793	23846	26433	83280
$e = 2.71828$	18284	59045	23536	02874	71353
$\log e = 0.43429$	44819	03251	82765	11289	18917
$\ln 10 = 2.30258$	50929	94045	68401	79914	54684
$\log \pi = 0.49714$	98726	94133	85435	12682	88291
$\log \log e = 9.63778$	43113	00536	78912	-10	

Table 4. Integrals

The additive constant is omitted

I. Minimum Memorization List.

1. $\int x^p \, dx = \dfrac{x^{p+1}}{p+1}$ if $p \neq -1$

2. $\int \dfrac{dx}{x} = \ln|x|$

3. $\int \sin x \, dx = -\cos x$

4. $\int \cos x \, dx = \sin x$

5. $\int \tan x \, dx = -\ln|\cos x|$

6. $\int \cot x \, dx = \ln|\sin x|$

7. $\int \sec^2 x \, dx = \tan x$

8. $\int \csc^2 x \, dx = -\cot x$

9. $\int \sec x \tan x \, dx = \sec x$

10. $\int \csc x \cot x \, dx = -\csc x$

11. $\int \dfrac{dx}{\sqrt{a^2 - x^2}} = \begin{cases} \sin^{-1}\dfrac{x}{a} \\ -\cos^{-1}\dfrac{x}{a} \end{cases}$

12. $\int \dfrac{dx}{a^2 + x^2} = \begin{cases} \dfrac{1}{a}\tan^{-1}\dfrac{x}{a} \\ -\dfrac{1}{a}\cot^{-1}\dfrac{x}{a} \end{cases}$

13. $\int a^x \, dx = \dfrac{a^x}{\ln a}$

14. $\int e^x \, dx = e^x$

15. $\int \sec x \, dx = \ln|\sec x + \tan x|$

16. $\int \csc x \, dx = \ln|\csc x - \cot x|$

II. Recommended for Memorization

17. $\int \dfrac{dx}{x(ax+b)} = \dfrac{1}{b}\ln\left|\dfrac{x}{ax+b}\right|$

18. $\int \dfrac{dx}{x^2 - a^2} = \dfrac{1}{2a}\ln\left|\dfrac{x-a}{x+a}\right|$

19. $\int \dfrac{dx}{\sqrt{x^2 \pm a^2}} = \ln|x + \sqrt{x^2 \pm a^2}|$

20. $\int \dfrac{x \, dx}{ax^2 + b} = \dfrac{1}{2a}\ln|ax^2 + b|$

21. $\int \sqrt{a^2 - x^2} \, dx = \dfrac{1}{2}\left(x\sqrt{a^2 - x^2} + a^2 \sin^{-1}\dfrac{x}{a}\right)$

22. $\int \sqrt{x^2 \pm a^2} \, dx = \dfrac{1}{2}(x\sqrt{x^2 \pm a^2} \pm a^2 \ln|x + \sqrt{x^2 \pm a^2}|)$

23. $\int \sin^2 ax \, dx = \dfrac{x}{2} - \dfrac{1}{4a}\sin 2ax$

24. $\int \cos^2 ax \, dx = \dfrac{x}{2} + \dfrac{1}{4a}\sin 2ax$

III. Integrals Involving $ax + b$

[Also see 17, 77, and 78]

25. $\int \dfrac{dx}{x^2(ax+b)} = -\dfrac{1}{bx} + \dfrac{a}{b^2}\ln\left|\dfrac{ax+b}{x}\right|$

26. $\int \dfrac{dx}{x(ax+b)^2} = \dfrac{1}{b(ax+b)} - \dfrac{1}{b^2}\ln\left|\dfrac{ax+b}{x}\right|$

27. $\int x\sqrt{ax+b} \, dx = \dfrac{2}{15a^2}(3ax - 2b)(ax+b)^{3/2}$

28. $\int \dfrac{x \, dx}{\sqrt{ax+b}} = \dfrac{2}{3a^2}(ax - 2b)\sqrt{ax+b}$

29. $\int x^2\sqrt{ax+b} \, dx = \dfrac{2}{105a^3}(15a^2 x^2 - 2abx + 8b^2)(ax+b)^{3/2}$

30. $\int \frac{x^2 \, dx}{\sqrt{ax+b}} = \frac{2}{15a^3}(3a^2 x^2 - 4abx + 8b^2)\sqrt{ax+b}$

31. $\int \frac{dx}{x\sqrt{ax+b}} = \begin{cases} \dfrac{1}{\sqrt{b}} \ln \left| \dfrac{\sqrt{ax+b} - \sqrt{b}}{\sqrt{ax+b} + \sqrt{b}} \right| & \text{if } b > 0 \\ \dfrac{2}{\sqrt{-b}} \tan^{-1} \sqrt{\dfrac{ax+b}{-b}} & \text{if } b < 0 \end{cases}$

IV. Integrals Involving $\sqrt{a^2 - x^2}$

[Also see 21]

32. $\int \frac{\sqrt{a^2 - x^2}}{x} \, dx = \sqrt{a^2 - x^2} - a \ln \frac{a + \sqrt{a^2 - x^2}}{|x|}$

33. $\int \frac{dx}{x\sqrt{a^2 - x^2}} = \frac{1}{a} \ln \frac{a - \sqrt{a^2 - x^2}}{|x|}$

34. $\int x^2 \sqrt{a^2 - x^2} \, dx = \frac{x}{8}(2x^2 - a^2)\sqrt{a^2 - x^2} + \frac{a^4}{8} \sin^{-1} \frac{x}{a}$

35. $\int \frac{\sqrt{a^2 - x^2}}{x^2} \, dx = -\frac{\sqrt{a^2 - x^2}}{x} - \sin^{-1} \frac{x}{a}$

36. $\int \frac{x^2 \, dx}{\sqrt{a^2 - x^2}} = -\frac{x}{2}\sqrt{a^2 - x^2} + \frac{a^2}{2} \sin^{-1} \frac{x}{a}$

37. $\int \frac{dx}{x^2 \sqrt{a^2 - x^2}} = -\frac{\sqrt{a^2 - x^2}}{a^2 x}$

38. $\int \frac{dx}{x^3 \sqrt{a^2 - x^2}} = -\frac{\sqrt{a^2 - x^2}}{2a^2 x^2} + \frac{1}{2a^3} \ln \frac{a - \sqrt{a^2 - x^2}}{|x|}$

39. $\int (a^2 - x^2)^{3/2} \, dx = \frac{x}{8}(5a^2 - 2x^2)\sqrt{a^2 - x^2} + \frac{3}{8} a^4 \sin^{-1} \frac{x}{a}$

40. $\int \frac{dx}{(a^2 - x^2)^{3/2}} = \frac{x}{a^2 \sqrt{a^2 - x^2}}$

41. $\int \frac{x^2 \, dx}{(a^2 - x^2)^{3/2}} = \frac{x}{\sqrt{a^2 - x^2}} - \sin^{-1} \frac{x}{a}$

V. Integrals Involving $\sqrt{x^2 \pm a^2}$

[Also see 19 and 22]

42. $\int \frac{\sqrt{x^2 - a^2}}{x} \, dx = \sqrt{x^2 - a^2} - a \cos^{-1} \frac{a}{|x|}$

43. $\int \frac{\sqrt{x^2 + a^2}}{x} \, dx = \sqrt{x^2 + a^2} - a \ln \frac{a + \sqrt{x^2 + a^2}}{|x|}$

44. $\int \frac{dx}{x\sqrt{x^2 - a^2}} = \frac{1}{a} \cos^{-1} \frac{a}{|x|}$

45. $\int \frac{dx}{x\sqrt{x^2 + a^2}} = -\frac{1}{a} \ln \frac{a + \sqrt{x^2 + a^2}}{|x|}$

46. $\int x^2 \sqrt{x^2 \pm a^2} \, dx = \frac{x}{8}(2x^2 \pm a^2)\sqrt{x^2 \pm a^2} - \frac{a^4}{8} \ln|x + \sqrt{x^2 \pm a^2}|$

47. $\int \frac{\sqrt{x^2 \pm a^2}}{x^2} \, dx = -\frac{\sqrt{x^2 \pm a^2}}{x} + \ln|x + \sqrt{x^2 \pm a^2}|$

48. $\int \frac{x^2 \, dx}{\sqrt{x^2 \pm a^2}} = \frac{x}{2}\sqrt{x^2 \pm a^2} \mp \frac{a^2}{2} \ln|x + \sqrt{x^2 \pm a^2}|$

49. $\int \dfrac{dx}{x^2\sqrt{x^2 \pm a^2}} = \mp\dfrac{\sqrt{x^2 \pm a^2}}{a^2 x}$

50. $\int \dfrac{dx}{x^3\sqrt{x^2 - a^2}} = \dfrac{\sqrt{x^2 - a^2}}{2a^2 x^2} + \dfrac{1}{2a^3} \cos^{-1}\dfrac{a}{|x|}$

51. $\int \dfrac{dx}{x^3\sqrt{x^2 + a^2}} = -\dfrac{\sqrt{x^2 + a^2}}{2a^2 x^2} + \dfrac{1}{2a^3} \ln \dfrac{a + \sqrt{x^2 + a^2}}{|x|}$

52. $\int (x^2 \pm a^2)^{3/2}\, dx = \dfrac{x}{8} (2x^2 \pm 5a^2) \sqrt{x^2 \pm a^2} + \dfrac{3}{8} a^4 \ln |x + \sqrt{x^2 \pm a^2}|$

53. $\int \dfrac{dx}{(x^2 \pm a^2)^{3/2}} = \dfrac{\pm x}{a^2\sqrt{x^2 \pm a^2}}$

54. $\int \dfrac{x^2\, dx}{(x^2 \pm a^2)^{3/2}} = \dfrac{-x}{\sqrt{x^2 \pm a^2}} + \ln |x + \sqrt{x^2 \pm a^2}|$

VI. Integrals Involving $X = ax^2 + bx + c$, $(q = b^2 - 4ac)$

[Also see 79-84]

55. $\int \dfrac{dx}{X} = \begin{cases} \dfrac{1}{\sqrt{q}} \ln \left|\dfrac{2ax + b - \sqrt{q}}{2ax + b + \sqrt{q}}\right| & \text{if } q > 0 \\[3mm] \dfrac{2}{\sqrt{-q}} \tan^{-1}\dfrac{2ax + b}{\sqrt{-q}} & \text{if } q < 0 \end{cases}$

56. $\int \dfrac{dx}{\sqrt{X}} = \begin{cases} \dfrac{1}{\sqrt{a}} \ln |2ax + b + 2\sqrt{aX}| & \text{if } a > 0 \\[3mm] -\dfrac{1}{\sqrt{-a}} \sin^{-1}\dfrac{2ax + b}{\sqrt{q}} & \text{if } a < 0 \text{ and } q > 0 \end{cases}$

57. $\int \dfrac{dx}{x\sqrt{X}} = \begin{cases} -\dfrac{1}{\sqrt{c}} \ln \left|\dfrac{\sqrt{X} + \sqrt{c}}{x} + \dfrac{b}{2\sqrt{c}}\right| & \text{if } c > 0 \\[3mm] \dfrac{1}{\sqrt{-c}} \sin^{-1}\dfrac{bx + 2c}{x\sqrt{q}} & \text{if } c < 0 \text{ and } q > 0 \\[3mm] -\dfrac{2}{b} \dfrac{\sqrt{X}}{x} & \text{if } c = 0 \end{cases}$

58. $\int \dfrac{dx}{X^{3/2}} = \dfrac{-2(2ax + b)}{q\sqrt{X}}$ 59. $\int \dfrac{x\, dx}{X^{3/2}} = \dfrac{2(bx + 2c)}{q\sqrt{X}}$

VII. Transcendental Integrals

60. $\int x^n \ln ax\, dx = x^{n+1}\left[\dfrac{\ln ax}{n + 1} - \dfrac{1}{(n + 1)^2}\right]$

61. $\int e^{ax} \sin bx\, dx = \dfrac{e^{ax}}{a^2 + b^2} (a \sin bx - b \cos bx)$

62. $\int e^{ax} \cos bx\, dx = \dfrac{e^{ax}}{a^2 + b^2} (b \sin bx + a \cos bx)$

63. $\int \sin (\ln x)\, dx = \dfrac{x}{2} [\sin (\ln x) - \cos (\ln x)]$

64. $\int \cos (\ln x)\, dx = \dfrac{x}{2} [\sin (\ln x) + \cos (\ln x)]$

65. $\int \sin ax \sin bx\, dx = \dfrac{\sin (a - b) x}{2(a - b)} - \dfrac{\sin (a + b) x}{2(a + b)}$

66. $\int \sin ax \cos bx\, dx = -\dfrac{\cos (a - b) x}{2(a - b)} - \dfrac{\cos (a + b) x}{2(a + b)}$

67. $\int \cos ax \cos bx \, dx = \dfrac{\sin (a - b) x}{2(a - b)} + \dfrac{\sin (a + b) x}{2(a + b)}$

68. $\int \dfrac{dx}{a + b \cos x} = \begin{cases} \dfrac{2}{\sqrt{a^2 - b^2}} \tan^{-1} \dfrac{(a - b) \tan (x/2)}{\sqrt{a^2 - b^2}} & \text{if } a^2 > b^2 \\[3mm] \dfrac{1}{\sqrt{b^2 - a^2}} \ln \left| \dfrac{(a - b) \tan (x/2) - \sqrt{b^2 - a^2}}{(a - b) \tan (x/2) + \sqrt{b^2 - a^2}} \right| & \text{if } b^2 > a^2 \end{cases}$

69. $\int \dfrac{dx}{a + b \sin x} = \begin{cases} \dfrac{2}{\sqrt{a^2 - b^2}} \tan^{-1} \dfrac{b + a \tan (x/2)}{\sqrt{a^2 - b^2}} & \text{if } a^2 > b^2 \\[3mm] \dfrac{1}{\sqrt{b^2 - a^2}} \ln \left| \dfrac{b + a \tan (x/2) - \sqrt{b^2 - a^2}}{b + a \tan (x/2) + \sqrt{b^2 - a^2}} \right| & \text{if } b^2 > a^2 \end{cases}$

70. $\int \dfrac{dx}{a^2 \cos^2 x + b^2 \sin^2 x} = \dfrac{1}{ab} \tan^{-1} \dfrac{b \tan x}{a}$

71. $\int \sin^{-1} \dfrac{x}{a} \, dx = x \sin^{-1} \dfrac{x}{a} + \sqrt{a^2 - x^2}$

72. $\int \cos^{-1} \dfrac{x}{a} \, dx = x \cos^{-1} \dfrac{x}{a} - \sqrt{a^2 - x^2}$

73. $\int \tan^{-1} \dfrac{x}{a} \, dx = x \tan^{-1} \dfrac{x}{a} - \dfrac{a}{2} \ln (a^2 + x^2)$

74. $\int x \sin^{-1} \dfrac{x}{a} \, dx = \dfrac{1}{4} (2x^2 - a^2) \sin^{-1} \dfrac{x}{a} + \dfrac{x}{4} \sqrt{a^2 - x^2}$

75. $\int x \cos^{-1} \dfrac{x}{a} \, dx = \dfrac{1}{4} (2x^2 - a^2) \cos^{-1} \dfrac{x}{a} - \dfrac{x}{4} \sqrt{a^2 - x^2}$

76. $\int x \tan^{-1} \dfrac{x}{a} \, dx = \dfrac{1}{2} (x^2 + a^2) \tan^{-1} \dfrac{x}{a} - \dfrac{ax}{2}$

VIII. Reduction Formulas

77. $\int \dfrac{\sqrt{ax + b}}{x} \, dx = 2\sqrt{ax + b} + b \int \dfrac{dx}{x\sqrt{ax + b}}$

78. $\int \dfrac{dx}{x^2 \sqrt{ax + b}} = -\dfrac{\sqrt{ax + b}}{bx} - \dfrac{a}{2b} \int \dfrac{dx}{x\sqrt{ax + b}}$

79. $\int \dfrac{x}{X} \, dx = \dfrac{1}{2a} \ln |X| - \dfrac{b}{2a} \int \dfrac{dx}{X}$

80. $\int \sqrt{X} \, dx = \dfrac{(2ax + b)}{4a} \sqrt{X} - \dfrac{q}{8a} \int \dfrac{dx}{\sqrt{X}}$

81. $\int \dfrac{x \, dx}{\sqrt{X}} = \dfrac{\sqrt{X}}{a} - \dfrac{b}{2a} \int \dfrac{dx}{\sqrt{X}}$

82. $\int X^{3/2} \, dx = \dfrac{2ax + b}{8a} \left[X - \dfrac{3q}{8a} \right] \sqrt{X} + \dfrac{3q^2}{128a^2} \int \dfrac{dx}{\sqrt{X}}$

83. $\int \dfrac{dx}{X^2} = -\dfrac{2ax + b}{qX} - \dfrac{2a}{q} \int \dfrac{dx}{X}$

84. $\int \dfrac{x \, dx}{X^2} = -\dfrac{1}{aX} - \dfrac{b}{a} \int \dfrac{dx}{X^2}$

85. $\int x^n e^{ax} \, dx = \dfrac{x^n e^{ax}}{a} - \dfrac{n}{a} \int x^{n-1} e^{ax} \, dx$

86. $\int x^n (\ln ax)^m \, dx = \dfrac{x^{n+1}}{n + 1} (\ln ax)^m - \dfrac{m}{n + 1} \int x^n (\ln ax)^{m-1} \, dx$

87. $\int x^n \sin ax \, dx = -\dfrac{1}{a} x^n \cos ax + \dfrac{n}{a} \int x^{n-1} \cos ax \, dx$

88. $\int x^n \cos ax \, dx = \dfrac{1}{a} x^n \sin ax - \dfrac{n}{a} \int x^{n-1} \sin ax \, dx$

89. $\int \sin^n x \, dx = -\dfrac{\sin^{n-1} x \cos x}{n} + \dfrac{n-1}{n} \int \sin^{n-2} x \, dx$

90. $\int \cos^n x \, dx = \dfrac{\cos^{n-1} x \sin x}{n} + \dfrac{n-1}{n} \int \cos^{n-2} x \, dx$

91. $\int \tan^n x \, dx = \dfrac{\tan^{n-1} x}{n-1} - \int \tan^{n-2} x \, dx$

92. $\int \cot^n x \, dx = -\dfrac{\cot^{n-1} x}{n-1} - \int \cot^{n-2} x \, dx$

93. $\int \sec^n x \, dx = \dfrac{\tan x \sec^{n-2} x}{n-1} + \dfrac{n-2}{n-1} \int \sec^{n-2} x \, dx$

94. $\int \csc^n x \, dx = -\dfrac{\cot x \csc^{n-2} x}{n-1} + \dfrac{n-2}{n-1} \int \csc^{n-2} x \, dx$

95. $\int \cos^m x \sin^n x \, dx = \begin{cases} \dfrac{\cos^{m-1} x \sin^{n+1} x}{m+n} + \dfrac{m-1}{m+n} \int \cos^{m-2} x \sin^n x \, dx \\[2ex] \dfrac{-\cos^{m+1} x \sin^{n-1} x}{m+n} + \dfrac{n-1}{m+n} \int \cos^m x \sin^{n-2} x \, dx \end{cases}$

96. $\int \dfrac{\cos^m x}{\sin^n x} \, dx = \dfrac{-\cos^{m+1} x}{(n-1)\sin^{n-1} x} - \dfrac{m+2-n}{n-1} \int \dfrac{\cos^m x}{\sin^{n-2} x} \, dx$

97. $\int \dfrac{\sin^m x}{\cos^n x} \, dx = \dfrac{-\sin^{m+1} x}{(n-1)\cos^{n-1} x} - \dfrac{m+2-n}{n-1} \int \dfrac{\sin^m x}{\cos^{n-2} x} \, dx$

98. $\int x^m (ax^n + b)^p \, dx = \begin{cases} \dfrac{x^{m-n+1}(ax^n+b)^{p+1}}{a(m+np+1)} - \dfrac{b(m-n+1)}{a(m+np+1)} \int x^{m-n}(ax^n+b)^p \, dx \\[2ex] \dfrac{x^{m+1}(ax^n+b)^p}{m+np+1} + \dfrac{bnp}{m+np+1} \int x^m (ax^n+b)^{p-1} \, dx \end{cases}$

99. $\int \dfrac{(ax^n+b)^p}{x^m} \, dx = \dfrac{-(ax^n+b)^{p+1}}{b(m-1)x^{m-1}} - \dfrac{a(m-np-n-1)}{b(m-1)} \int \dfrac{(ax^n+b)^p}{x^{m-n}} \, dx$

100. $\int \dfrac{x^m}{(ax^n+b)^p} \, dx = \dfrac{x^{m+1}}{bn(p-1)(ax^n+b)^{p-1}} - \dfrac{m-np+n+1}{bn(p-1)} \int \dfrac{x^m \, dx}{(ax^n+b)^{p-1}}$

Answers

to

Problems

1. a. $\dfrac{3}{4} + \dfrac{1}{4} = 1$.   **c.** $\dfrac{1}{2} + \dfrac{1}{2} = 1$.   **d.** $\dfrac{25}{169} + \dfrac{144}{169} = 1$.

2. a. 5.   **c.** $3\sqrt{2}$.   **e.** $\sqrt{2}$.

3. With $\vec{u} = \vec{i}x + \vec{j}y$, $\dfrac{1}{|\vec{u}|}\vec{u} = \dfrac{x}{\sqrt{x^2+y^2}}\vec{i} + \dfrac{y}{\sqrt{x^2+y^2}}\vec{j}$

with norm $\sqrt{\dfrac{x^2}{x^2+y^2} + \dfrac{y^2}{x^2+y^2}} = 1$.

5. a. 5.   **c.** $\sqrt{109}$.   **e.** 5.   **g.** $4\sqrt{2}$.   **i.** 1.3.

7. $(0, 2)$, $(1, 4)$, $(2, 6)$, $(3, 8)$.

9. a. $(2.5, 3.5)$.   **c.** $(10, -9)$.   **e.** $(0.5, 3)$.

10. $\vec{u}_1 + \vec{u}_2 + \vec{u}_3 = (-3\vec{i} + \vec{j}) + (4\vec{i} + 2\vec{j}) + (\vec{i} + 8\vec{j}) = 2\vec{i} + 11\vec{j}$,

$\vec{v}_1 + \vec{v}_2 + \vec{v}_3 = (0.5\vec{i} + 1.5\vec{j}) + (-\vec{i} + 4.5\vec{j}) + (2.5\vec{i} + 5\vec{j}) = 2\vec{i} + 11\vec{j}$.

11. a. $-4\vec{i} - 3\vec{j}$.   **c.** $3\vec{i} - 4\vec{j}$.   **e.** $-3\vec{i} - 4\vec{j}$.

1. a. $4.526, 2.126$.   **c.** $0.6124, 1.904$.   **e.** $-2.525, 1.619$.

2. a. $-1.5\vec{i} - 3.7\vec{j}$.   **c.** $3.7\vec{i} - 1.5\vec{j}$.   **e.** $1.5\vec{i} - 3.7\vec{j}$.   **g.** Same as **a.**

3. a. $5.6\vec{i} - 1.2\vec{j}$.   **c.** $1.2\vec{i} + 5.6\vec{j}$.   **e.** $-5.6\vec{i} - 1.2\vec{j}$.   **g.** Same as **a.**

4. a. $\sqrt{2}(\vec{i} + \vec{j})$.   **c.** and   **e.** $\sqrt{2}(-\vec{i} + \vec{j})$.   **g.** Same as **a.**

5. a. $126° 50'$.   **c.** $338°$.   **e.** $248°$.

Sec. 1-4, p. 11.

2. a. $2 \tan \theta$.   **c.** 0.   **e.** $\csc \theta$.   **g.** $\tan \theta$.   **i.** 1.   **k.** $\cos^2 \theta$.

3. a. Since $a > 0$ and $b > 0$, there is an angle θ such that $0° < \theta < 90°$ and $\tan \theta = b/a$. Then

$$\sqrt{a^2 + b^2} = a \sqrt{1 + \left(\frac{b}{a}\right)^2} = a\sqrt{1 + \tan^2 \theta} = a\sqrt{\sec^2 \theta} = a \sec \theta = \frac{a}{\cos \theta}.$$

Sec. 1-5, p. 14.

1. a. $\sin [2n \cdot 90° + \alpha] \equiv \sin (n \cdot 180°) \cos \alpha + \cos (n \cdot 180°) \sin \alpha$
$$\equiv 0 \cdot \cos \alpha + (-1)^n \sin \alpha.$$

c. $\sin [n \cdot 180° + (90° + \alpha)] \equiv \sin (n \cdot 180°) \cos (90° + \alpha)$
$$+ \cos (n \cdot 180°) \sin (90° + \alpha)$$
$$\equiv 0 + (-1)^n (\sin 90° \cos \alpha + \cos 90° \sin \alpha)$$
$$\equiv (-1)^n (1 \cdot \cos \alpha + 0 \cdot \sin \alpha) = (-1)^n \cos \alpha.$$

2. a. $\tan (\alpha + \beta) \equiv \dfrac{\sin(\alpha + \beta)}{\cos(\alpha + \beta)} \equiv \dfrac{\sin \alpha \cos \beta + \cos \alpha \sin \beta}{\cos \alpha \cos \beta - \sin \alpha \sin \beta}$

$$\equiv \dfrac{\dfrac{\sin \alpha \cos \beta}{\cos \alpha \cos \beta} + \dfrac{\cos \alpha \sin \beta}{\cos \alpha \cos \beta}}{\dfrac{\cos \alpha \cos \beta}{\cos \alpha \cos \beta} + \dfrac{\sin \alpha \sin \beta}{\cos \alpha \cos \beta}} \equiv \dfrac{\tan \alpha + \tan \beta}{1 - \tan \alpha \tan \beta}.$$

Sec. 1-6, p. 16.

1. a. $\theta = 14°50'$, $|\vec{v}| = 35.2$.   **b.** $8°43'$, 18.13.   **c.** $139°18'$, 217.8.   **d.** $8°16'$, 76.31.

2. a. 9.02, $56°19'$.   **b.** 51.27, $126°55'$.   **c.** 27.6, $48°58'$.   **d.** 37.92, $19°46'$.

Sec. 1-7, p. 19.

1. a. -2.   **c.** 0.   **e.** 1.

2. a. $\cos \theta = \dfrac{1 \cdot 1 + \sqrt{3} \cdot 0}{1\sqrt{1 + 3}} = \dfrac{1}{2}$, $\theta = 60°$.   **c.** $30°$.   **e.** $180°$.

3. a. $105°15'$, $40°30'$, $34°30'$.   **c.** $56°13'$, $71°34'$, $52°13'$.   **e.** $90°$, $45°$, $45°$.

5. a. $x = 13/3$.   **c.** $y = -11/3$.

Sec. 1-8, p. 23.

1. a. $1(x - 2) - 3(y - 4) = 0$, or $x - 3y + 10 = 0$.   **c.** $x = 4$.   **e.** $3x + 4y = 4$.

2. a. $3x - y = 5$.   **c.** $x + y = 1$.   **e.** $x = 3$.

3. a. $y = 2x + 3$.   **c.** $x = 3$.

4. a. $3x - 7y = -34$.   **c.** $2x + 3y = 11$.   **e.** $4x - 3y = 25$.

Sec. 1-10, p. 25.

1. **a.** $3x + 2y = -3$. **c.** $y = -4$. **e.** $2x + y = -12$.
3. **a.** 1. **c.** 3/13. **4. a.** 1.7. **c.** $1/\sqrt{10}$. **5.** 2.

Sec. 2-2, p. 37.

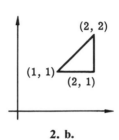

2. a.

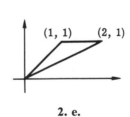

2. b.

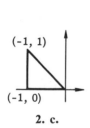

2. c.

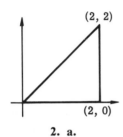

2. d.

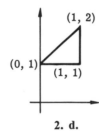

2. e.

3. **a.** $\{x \mid \frac{1}{2} < x \leq 3\}$. **c.** $\{x \mid 2 < x < 3\}$.

4. **a.** The set of all real numbers. **c.** $\{x \mid x > 2\}$.

5. **a.** $-1 < x < 1$. **c.** $-\frac{3}{4} < x < \frac{3}{4}$ **e.** $x < -2$ or $x > 1$.
   g. $-2 < x < -1$.

Sec. 2-4, p. 45.

1. **a.** $4, 8, 0.31, (3 + h)h$. **c.** $1, \dfrac{\sqrt{3}}{2}, \dfrac{\sqrt{3}}{2}, \dfrac{-\sqrt{3}}{2}, \dfrac{2 - \sqrt{3}}{2} = 0.134$.

2. **a.** $2a + h$. **c.** $a^2 + ah + \dfrac{h^2}{3}$. **e.** $1 - \dfrac{1}{a(a + h)}$.

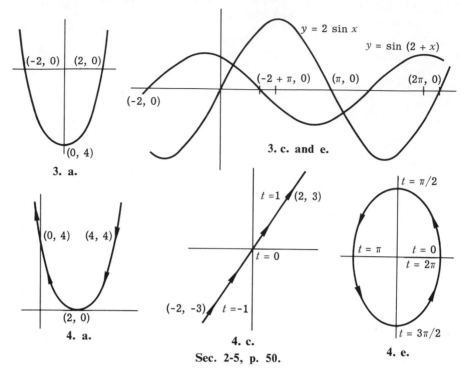

3. a.

3. c. and e.

4. a.

4. c.

4. e.

Sec. 2-5, p. 50.

1. a. $m_P = 4$. c. $m_P = 3$. e. $m_P = -1$.

2. a. $1 - 4x_1$. c. $3x_1^2 - 2x_1$.

5. a. $\vec{V}(t_1) = -2t_1\vec{i} + \vec{j}$, $\vec{F}(0) = \vec{j}$, $\vec{F}(1) = -2\vec{i} + \vec{j}$, $\vec{F}(2) = -4\vec{i} + \vec{j}$,
   $\vec{F}(3) = -6\vec{i} + \vec{j}$.

   c. $\vec{V}(t_1) = 2t_1(\vec{i} - \vec{j})$.

Sec. 2-6, p. 53.

1. a. $\dfrac{-1}{(x + 1)^2}$. c. $\dfrac{-6x}{(x^2 + 1)^2}$. e. $\dfrac{x}{\sqrt{x^2 + 1}}$. g. $2x - \dfrac{1}{x^2}$. i. $\dfrac{1}{(x + 1)^2}$.

3. a. $2x - 1$. c. $\dfrac{2x - 1}{2\sqrt{x^2 - x + 1}}$. e. $\dfrac{3}{2(\sqrt{10 - t})^3}$.

   g. $2s - 3$. i. $2v + \dfrac{1}{2\sqrt{v}}$.

4. a. $D_t\vec{u} = \left[2t - \dfrac{1}{t^2}\right]\vec{i} + 2t\vec{j}$. c. $t\left[\dfrac{1}{\sqrt{t^2 + 1}}\vec{i} + \dfrac{1}{\sqrt{t^2 + 5}}\vec{j}\right]$.

Sec. 2-7, p. 58.

1. a. $\dfrac{1}{5}$. c. $-\dfrac{13}{2}$. e. $\dfrac{1}{2\sqrt{3}}$.   2. a and c. $-\dfrac{1}{15}, -\dfrac{1}{9}$.

3. a. 2. c. $\frac{1}{2}$. e. 8. g. -1

Sec. 2-8, p. 62.

1. a. $20x^4 - 6x$. **c.** $3\sqrt{x} - 4$. **e.** $5x^4 + 8x^3 - 27x^2 - 20x + 22$.

g. $\dfrac{-5}{(x-3)^2}$. **i.** $\dfrac{-(x^2+5)}{(x^2+4x-5)^2}$. **k.** $-\dfrac{16}{x^2} - \dfrac{50x}{(x^2+1)^2}$.

2. a. $3x^2 - 8x + 45$. **c.** $1/(2\sqrt{x}) - 1$. **e.** $32.2t$.

3. a. 4. **c.** -1. **e.** $1/18$. **g.** 0.8.

4. a. $15x - 4y = 12$. **c.** $5x + 27y = 16$. **e.** $x - 37y = 6$.

5. a. $D_t \vec{u} = 6t\vec{i} + (3t^2 - 6)\vec{j}$. **c.** $10t\vec{i} - (6t^2 + 2)\vec{j}$.

Sec. 2-9, p. 66.

1. a. $8x(x^2+1)^3$. **c.** $\dfrac{x^2+3}{3(x^2+1)^{4/3}}$. **e.** $\dfrac{3(x+\sqrt{x^2+1})^3}{\sqrt{x^2+1}}$.

g. $4\{x + [1 + (2+x)^2]^3\}^3\{1 + 3[1 + (2+x)^2]^2\}\,2(2+x)$.

2. a. $12x^2(x^3+1)^3$. **c.** $\dfrac{1}{2\sqrt{x}\,(1+\sqrt{x})^2}$. **e.** $2(x+1)$.

3. a. $4x - 5y = -9$. **c.** $x - 320y = -1344$.

Sec. 2-10, p. 69.

1. a. $10(5x - 3)$. **c.** $\dfrac{3x^2+6}{2\sqrt{x^3+6x}}$.

2. a. $\dfrac{-x}{\sqrt{20-x^2}}$. **c.** $\dfrac{x}{\sqrt{x^2-16}}$. **e.** $\dfrac{8}{(x^2+2)^{3/2}}$.

3. a. $\dfrac{3x^2 - y^2 + 4}{2xy}$. **c.** $-\sqrt{\dfrac{y}{x}}$. **e.** $\dfrac{x+6y}{2x-y}$.

4. a. $D_x y = \dfrac{1-2y}{2x+2y-1}$, $D_y x = \dfrac{2x+2y-1}{1-2y}$.

c. $D_x y = \dfrac{15x^4 - 12x^2 y}{3y^2 + 4x^3}$, $D_y x = \dfrac{3y^2 + 4x^3}{15x^4 - 12x^2 y}$.

5. a. $x + 7y = 15$. **c.** $3x + 2y = 30$.

Sec. 2-11, p. 75.

1. a. 2. **c.** 1. **e.** 0. **g.** $\frac{1}{2}$.

2. a. $2\cos(2x - 3)$. **c.** $\dfrac{x\cos x - \sin x}{x^2}$. **e.** $\cos x - x\sin x$.

g. $2x + 3\cos 3x$. **i.** $\dfrac{3\sin 3x}{2\sqrt{3 - \cos 3x}}$.

3. a. $\vec{V}(t) = (-6\pi \sin 2\pi t)\,\vec{i} + (8\pi \cos 2\pi t)\vec{j}$,
$S(t) = \sqrt{36\pi^2 \sin^2 2\pi t + 64\pi^2 \cos^2 2\pi t} = 2\pi\sqrt{9 + 7\cos^2 2\pi t}$.

c. $\vec{V}(t) = \vec{i}(-3\sin 3t) + \vec{j}(3\cos 3t)$, $S(t) = 3$.

Sec. 2-12, p. 77.

1. a. $dy = -2x\sin x^2\,dx$. **c.** $3x^2\cos x^3\,dx$. **e.** $-3x^{-4}\cos(x^{-3})\,dx$.

2. a. $(2x - 3)\,dx$.   **c.** $(2x - 3)\cos(x^2 - 3x + 4)\,dx$.   **e.** $3x^2\,dx$.

g. $3x^2\,dx$.   **i.** $\dfrac{2x^3}{\sqrt{x^4 + 5}}\,dx$.   **k.** $6x^3\sqrt{x^4 + 5}\,dx$.

3. a. $4x^3\,dx - x^2\,dy - 2xy\,dx + 3y^2\,dy = 0$, $D_x y = \dfrac{dy}{dx} = \dfrac{2xy - 4x^3}{3y^2 - x^2}$.

c. $-\dfrac{\sin y}{1 + x\cos y}$.

Sec. 2-13, p. 80.

1. a. $f'(x) = 2(x - 2)$.   **c.** $2\sin x(\cos x\cos 2x - \sin x\sin 2x) = 2\sin x\cos 3x$.

e. $\dfrac{\sin x - x\cos x}{\sin^2 x}$.

2. a. $D_x f\!\left(\dfrac{\pi}{4}\right) = D_x\,2\sin\dfrac{\pi}{4} = D_x\sqrt{2} = 0, \dfrac{df(\pi/4)}{dx} = 0$,

$f'(x) = 2\cos x,$ $f'(\pi/4) = 2\cos(\pi/4) = \sqrt{2}$.

c. $D_x f(1) = D_x(1 + \sqrt{1 - 1}) = D_x\,1 = 0$,

$f'(x) = x + (1/\sqrt{x - 1})$, $f'(1)$ is undefined.

3. a. $2x - y = 1, y = 2x^2 - 2x + 1$.   **c.** $y - \tfrac{1}{2} = (\sqrt{3}/2)(x - \tfrac{1}{6}\pi)$.

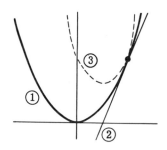

3. a.

4. a. $f'(x) = \cos x$, $f'(2t) = \cos 2t$, $D_t f(2t) = D_t\sin 2t = 2\cos 2t$.

c. $f'(2t) = \dfrac{1}{4t^2}$, $D_t f(2t) = \dfrac{1}{2t^2}$.

5. a. $x = 3$.   **c.** $x = \pm 4$.

6. a. $f'(x) = \dfrac{x\cos x - \sin x}{x^2}$,

$D_x[f'(x)] = \dfrac{x^2(-x\sin x + \cos x - \cos x) - (x\cos x - \sin x)\,2x}{x^4}$

$= \dfrac{2\sin x - 2x\cos x - x^2\sin x}{x^3}$.

c. $6x + 10$.

7. a. $\vec{F}(t) = \vec{i}\cos t - \vec{j}\,2\sin 2t$.

Sec. 2-14, p. 84.

1. a. $-4 \sin 2x$.   **c.** $12x^2 + 2$.   **e.** $-(3/16)\, x^{-7/4} - \frac{1}{4} x^{-3/2}$.

2. a. $y'' = -12 \cos 2x - 20 \sin 2x = -4(3 \cos 2x + 5 \sin 2x) = -4y$.

3. $\vec{u} = 2(\vec{i} \cos \frac{1}{2}t + \vec{j} \sin \frac{1}{2}t),\ \vec{v} = -\vec{i} \sin \frac{1}{2}t + \vec{j} \cos \frac{1}{2}t$,

$\vec{u} \cdot \vec{v} = 2\,(-\cos \frac{1}{2}t \sin \frac{1}{2}t + \sin \frac{1}{2}t \cos \frac{1}{2}t) = 0$. For this motion, the position and velocity vectors are always perpendicular.

4. a. $\vec{u}(t) = t^2\vec{i} + \frac{1}{3}t^3\vec{j},\ \vec{v}(t) = 2t\vec{i} + t^2\vec{j},\ \vec{\alpha}(t) = 2\,(\vec{i} + t\vec{j})$,

t	$\vec{u}(t)$	$\vec{v}(t)$	$\vec{\alpha}(t)$
0	$\vec{0}$	$\vec{0}$	$2\vec{i}$
1	$\vec{i} + \frac{1}{3}\vec{j}$	$2\vec{i} + \vec{j}$	$2(\vec{i} + \vec{j})$
2	$4\vec{i} + (8/3)\vec{j}$	$4(\vec{i} + \vec{j})$	$2(\vec{i} + 2\vec{j})$
3	$9(\vec{i} + \vec{j})$	$6\vec{i} + 9\vec{j}$	$2(\vec{i} + 3\vec{j})$

c. $\vec{u}(t) = t\vec{i} + \vec{j} \sin \frac{1}{4}\pi t,\ \vec{v}(t) = \vec{i} + \vec{j}\frac{1}{4}\pi \cos \frac{1}{4}\pi t,\ \vec{\alpha}(t) = -\vec{j}(\pi^2/16) \sin \frac{1}{4}\pi t$,

t	$\vec{u}(t)$	$\vec{v}(t)$	$\vec{\alpha}(t)$
0	$\vec{0}$	$\vec{i} + \dfrac{\pi}{4}\vec{j}$	$\vec{0}$
1	$\vec{i} + \dfrac{1}{\sqrt{2}}\vec{j}$	$\vec{i} + \dfrac{\pi}{4\sqrt{2}}\vec{j}$	$-\dfrac{\pi^2}{16\sqrt{2}}\vec{j}$
2	$2\vec{i} + \vec{j}$	$\vec{i}$	$-\dfrac{\pi^2}{16}\vec{j}$
3	$3\vec{i} + \dfrac{1}{\sqrt{2}}\vec{j}$	$\vec{i} - \dfrac{\pi}{4\sqrt{2}}\vec{j}$	$-\dfrac{\pi^2}{16\sqrt{2}}\vec{j}$

Sec. 3-1, p. 96.

2. a. $x^{5/2} - \frac{1}{2}x^2 + c$.   **c.** $\frac{1}{3}x^3 + \cos x + c$.   **e.** $\frac{1}{5}x^5 + \frac{4}{3}x^3 + 4x + c$.

3. a. $(9/2)\sqrt{x^3 + 1}\, x^2,\ (2/9)(x^3 + 1)^{3/2} + c$.   **c.** $3 \sin^2 x \cos x,\ \frac{1}{3} \sin^3 x + c$.

e. $\dfrac{4}{(x^2 + 4)^{3/2}},\ \dfrac{1}{4}\dfrac{x}{\sqrt{x^2 + 4}} + c$.   **g.** $x \cos x,\ x \sin x + \cos x + c$.

Sec. 3-2, p. 98.

1. a. $\frac{1}{8}(x^2 + 1)^4 + c$.   **c.** $(1/15)(x^3 + 3x + 5)^5 + c$.   **e.** $\frac{2}{3}\sqrt{4 + x^3} + c$.

g. $\frac{1}{2} \sin^2 x + c,\ -\frac{1}{2} \cos^2 x + c,\ -\frac{1}{4} \cos 2x + c$.

2. a. $\frac{1}{6}(4 + x^4)^{3/2} + c$.   **c.** $-\frac{1}{2} \cos (x^2 - 2x + 5) + c$.

e. $-\frac{2}{3}(2 + \cos x)^{3/2} + c$.   **g.** $4 \sin x + \frac{1}{4} \sin^4 x + c$.

3. a. $x + c$.   **c.** $x^4 \sin^3 x^2 + c$.   **e.** $x^2 - 2x \sin x + \cos^2 x$.

Sec. 3-3, p. 101.

1. a. $1/y = \frac{9}{4} - \frac{1}{2}(x + 1)^2$.   **c.** $y = x$.   **e.** $y = 1 + (1/\sqrt{2}) - \cos x$.

2. a. $4\sqrt{y + 1} = (x + 1)^2 + c$.   **c.** $\sin y = x - \frac{1}{3}x^3 + c$.

3. a. $\sqrt{y} = \frac{1}{3}x^{3/2} + c$.   **c.** $y = -(2/x) + 6$.

Sec. 3-4, p. 105.

1. a. 32 sec, 28,377 ft, 4096 ft. **c.** 55.4 sec, 28,377 ft, 12,288 ft.
2. a. 32.1 sec, 28,484 ft, 4160 ft. **c.** 55.5 sec, 28,416 ft, 12,352 ft.
3. Initial velocity $44\sqrt{2}/3$ ft/sec. First distance 44 ft, second distance $110\sqrt{2}/3$ or almost 52 ft.
4. Nearly 188 ft farther than the first.

Sec. 3-5, p. 109.

1. a. $52/3$. **c.** $\frac{4}{3}$. **e.** 4.
2. a. $dA(x) = (b/h)\,x$, $A(0) = 0$; $A(x) = (b/h)\,\frac{1}{2}x^2 + c, c = 0$;
$A(h) = (b/h)\,\frac{1}{2}h^2 = \frac{1}{2}bh$.
3. a and **c.** 0, as much area below as above the x-axis.
e. 2, same as area below $y = \sin x, 0 \le x \le \pi$ since $y = \cos x, 0 \le x \le \pi$, is as much below as above the x-axis on $0 \le x \le \pi$.

Sec. 3-6, p. 114.

3. a. $1875\,\pi$ ft·lb. **c.** With $x = 0$ at the center and $x = 5$ at the bottom of the bowl, $d\,W(x) = 62.5\,\pi\,(25 - x^2)(8 + x)\,dx$ subject to $W(0) = 0$. Therefore, $W(5) = 62.5(9875/12)$ ft·lb. **e.** $62.5\,(2060/3)$ ft·lb.
4. 1350 ft·lb.

Sec. 3-9, p. 122.

1. a. $28/3$. **c.** $61/3$. **e.** 1. **g.** -6. **i.** $-\frac{1}{3}$.

Sec. 3-10, p. 126.

2. $\dfrac{15}{4}, \dfrac{1}{2}, \dfrac{49}{20}, \dfrac{1}{8}; \dfrac{49}{20} \neq \dfrac{15}{4} \cdot \dfrac{1}{2}, \dfrac{1}{8} \neq \dfrac{1/2}{15/4} = \dfrac{2}{15}$.

Sec. 3-11, p. 130.

1. a. $\frac{1}{6}$. **c.** $125/6$. **e.** $16/3$. **g.** $4096/75$ (use horizontal strips).
i. $(\pi^2/2) - 2$. **k.** $\sqrt{2} - 1$. **m.** $32/3$.
2. a. $\frac{1}{4}, \frac{1}{4}$. **c.** $\frac{3}{4}, 32$. **e.** $53/60, 37/60, 124/15$.

Sec. 3-12, p. 132.

1. c. $\vec{u} = (-2\vec{i} + 5\vec{j}) + \frac{1}{2}(6\vec{i} - 6\vec{j}) = (-2\vec{i} + 5\vec{j}) + (3\vec{i} - 3\vec{j}) = \vec{i} + 2\vec{j}, (1, 2)$.
$\vec{v} = (4\vec{i} - \vec{j}) + \frac{1}{2}(-6\vec{i} + 6\vec{j}) = \vec{i} + 2\vec{j}, (1, 2)$.
e. $\vec{x} = (9\vec{i} - \vec{j}) - (3\vec{i} + 4\vec{j}) = 4\vec{i} - 5\vec{j}$.
3. a. $2x - y = 11$. **c.** $4x + 2y = 17$. **4.** $k = -p$.
5. a. $3, -3, -9, 3$.
c. $D_x f(x) = \lim\limits_{\Delta x \to 0} \dfrac{3 + (x + \Delta x) - (x + \Delta x)^2 - (3 + x - x^2)}{\Delta x}$
$= \lim\limits_{\Delta x \to 0} \dfrac{\Delta x - 2x\,\Delta x + \overline{\Delta x}^2}{\Delta x} = \lim\limits_{\Delta x \to 0}(1 - 2x - \Delta x) = 1 - 2x.$

7. a. $x + 2y = 7$.

10. Measuring x up from the bottom,

$$W = 50\pi \int_0^4 (2 + \tfrac{1}{2}x)^2(13 - x)\, dx = 59{,}200\, \frac{\pi}{3}.$$

11. a. $(x^2/2) + x - (1/x) + c$.   **c.** $-\tfrac{1}{3}\cos x^3 + c$.

12. a. $y^2 = \tfrac{2}{3}x^3 + 4x + c$.   **c.** $y = (1/x) + (3/2x^2) + c$.

13. Proof: Let m be the minimum and M the maximum of $f(x)$ on $a \le x \le b$. Then $m \le f(x) \le M$ for $a \le x \le b$. Since $g(x) > 0$, it follows that

$$mg(x) \le f(x)\, g(x) \le Mg(x) \text{ for } a \le x \le b.$$

Therefore,

$$\int_a^b mg(x)\, dx \le \int_a^b f(x)\, g(x)\, dx \le \int_a^b Mg(x)\, dx.$$

Since m and M are constants, it follows that

$$m \int_a^b g(x)\, dx \le \int_a^b f(x)\, g(x)\, dx \le M \int_a^b g(x)\, dx.$$

Division by the positive number $\int_a^b g(x)\, dx$ yields

$$m \le \frac{\int_a^b f(x)\, g(x)\, dx}{\int_a^b g(x)\, dx} \le M.$$

Since $f(x)$ is continuous, it assumes all values between its minimum and its maximum on $a \le x \le b$. Hence, there is a number ξ such that $a < \xi < b$ and

$$f(\xi) = \frac{\int_a^b f(x)\, g(x)\, dx}{\int_a^b g(x)\, dx}.$$

This equation may be written as

$$f(\xi) \int_a^b g(x)\, dx = \int_a^b f(x)\, g(x)\, dx,$$

which is the formula of the theorem.

Sec. 4-1, p. 139.

1. a. $(-x)^2\, y - 4 \equiv x^2\, y - 4$, symmetrical to y-axis. $x^2(-y) \ne x^2\, y - 4$, not symmetrical to x-axis. $(-x)^2(-y) - 4 \ne x^2\, y - 4$, not symmetrical to origin.

   c. Symmetrical to x-axis, y-axis, and hence also to the origin.

   e. $(-x)\, y - \sin(-x) \equiv -(xy - \sin x)$, so symmetrical to y-axis. Not symmetrical to x-axis or origin.

2. a. $-4 \le x \le 4$, $-2 \le y \le 2$.

   c. $-4 \le x - 2 \le 4$, so $-2 \le x \le 6$, $-2 \le y \le 2$.

   e. No restriction on x, but $-3 \le y \le 3$.

3. a. y-axis in both directions, $y = 1$ in both directions.

   c. No vertical asymptote (note y-restriction $-1 < y \le 3$), $y = 1$ horizontal asymptote in both directions.

   e. $x = 3$ and $y = -2$ in both directions.

4. a. Symmetrical to y-axis; extent $x \ne \pm 1$, $y > 0$ or $y \le -1$; asymptotes x-axis and $x = \pm 1$; passes through $(0, -1)$; since $D_x y = -2x/(x^2 - 1)$, tangent at $(0, -1)$ is horizontal.

c. Symmetrical to y-axis; extent $0 < y \le 1$; x-axis asymptote; passes through $(0, 1)$; since $D_x y = -2x/(x^2 + 1)^2$, the tangent at $(0, 1)$ is horizontal.

e. Symmetrical to x-axis, y-axis, and origin; extent $x \ge 1$ or $x \le -1$ and $-1 < y < 1$; asymptotes $y = \pm 1$; passes through $(\pm 1, 0)$; since $D_y x = \pm 2y/(1 - y^2)^2$, by substituting $y = 0$ the curve has vertical tangents at $(\pm 1, 0)$.

Sec. 4-2, p. 143.

2. a. $y = x + 1$ and $x = -1$, since $y = x + 1 + 1/(x + 1)$ is equation of curve.
   c. $y = -2x - 1$ and $x = 0$.

3. Asymptotes.   **a.** $y = \pm\frac{3}{2}x$.   **c.** $y = \pm\frac{2}{3}x$.

4. a.

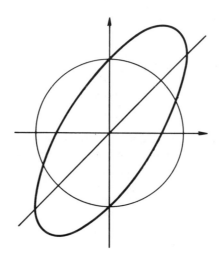

Sec. 4-3, p. 145.

1. a. $x - 3y = 1$.   **c.** $x^2 + y^2 = 4$.   **e.** $y^2 = -16x$.
   g. $x^2 + y^2 = 1$.   **i.** $(x^2/25) + (y^2/9) = 1$.
2. a. $x - 3y + 11 = 0$.   **c.** $3x + y = 7$.   **e.** $x^2 + y^2 = 4$.

Sec. 4-4, p. 148.

1. a. $x^2 + y^2 + 8x - 6y = 0$.   **c.** $x^2 + y^2 + 2x + 4y + 1 = 0$.
   e. $x^2 + y^2 - 2x + 4y - 4 = 0$.   **g.** $x^2 + y^2 - 18y + 56 = 0$.
   i. $x^2 + y^2 + 12x + 4y + 14 = 0$.
2. a. $(1, -2), r = 2$.   **c.** $(\frac{1}{2}, -1), r = \sqrt{2}$.   **e.** $(1, 1), r = 5$.
3. a. $\dfrac{y - 2}{x + 1}\dfrac{y - 4}{x - 5} = -1$, $x^2 + y^2 - 4x - 6y + 3 = 0$.
   c. $\vec{u} = (2 - x)\vec{i} + (3 - y)\vec{j}$, $\vec{v} = (-2 - x)\vec{i} + (1 - y)\vec{j}$, so $\vec{u} \cdot \vec{v} = 4$ and equation is $(2 - x)(-2 - x) + (3 - y)(1 - y) = 4$, $x^2 + y^2 - 4y - 5 = 0$.
   e. $2x^2 + 2y^2 - 6x - 8y + 23 = 0$.
4. a. $x^2 + y^2 - 2x - 4y + 6 = (x^2 - 2x + 1) + (y^2 - 4y + 4) - 1 - 4 + 6$
   $\qquad\qquad = (x - 1)^2 + (y - 2)^2 + 1 \ne 0$.

c. $[x^2 + y^2] + [x^2 + (y-1)^2] + [(x-1)^2 + y^2] + [(x-1)^2 + (y-1)^2]$
$= 4x^2 + 4y^2 - 4x - 4y + 4 = 4[(x-\frac{1}{2})^2 + (y-\frac{1}{2})^2] + 2 \geq 2 > 1.$

5. a. $(6-2)^2 + (-2-1)^2 = 4^2 + 3^2 = 25;$
$(x-2)(6-2) + (y-1)(-2-1) = 25, 4x - 3y = 30.$
$2(x-2) + 2(y-1) D_x y = 0; (6-2) + (-2-1) m = 0, m = \frac{4}{3};$
$y + 2 = \frac{4}{3}(x-6), 4x - 3y = 30.$

c. $y = -6.$

Sec. 4-5, p. 152.

1.

	Focus	Directrix	End of L. R.
a.	$(2, 0)$	$x = -2$	$(2, \pm 4)$
c.	$(0, -\frac{3}{4})$	$y = \frac{3}{4}$	$(\pm\frac{3}{2}, -\frac{3}{4})$
e.	$(0, -5/16)$	$y = 5/16$	$(\pm\frac{5}{8}, -5/16)$
g.	$(0, -\frac{1}{9})$	$y = \frac{1}{9}$	$(\pm\frac{2}{9}, -\frac{1}{9})$
i.	$(-\frac{6}{5}, 0)$	$x = \frac{6}{5}$	$(\frac{6}{5}, \pm 12/5)$

2. a. $y^2 = 20x.$ **c.** $x^2 = -24y.$ **e.** $5y^2 = x.$ **g.** $2x^2 = -5y.$

3. a. $(-3)^2 = 3(3). 2y\, dy = 3dx, m = 3/2(-3) = -\frac{1}{2}, x + 2y + 3 = 0.$

c. $x + 10y + 10 = 0.$

6. a. Terminal end of $\vec{F}(x) = \vec{i}x + \vec{j}x^2$ is on $y = x^2.$

c. Set $x = 2t, y = t^2,$ eliminate t to obtain $y = (x/2)^2.$

e. $x = y^2.$

7. For $y^2 = 4px, p > 0,$ area $= 2\int_0^p \sqrt{2px}\, dx = \frac{8}{3}p^2.$

Sec. 4-6, p. 156.

1.

	Vertices	Foci	Intercepts	Asymptotes
a.	$(\pm 5, 0)$	$(\pm 4, 0)$	$(\pm 5, 0), (0, \pm 3)$	
c.	$(0, \pm 3)$	$(0, \pm 5)$	$(0, \pm 3)$	$4y = \pm 3x.$
e.	$(\pm\frac{3}{2}, 0)$	$(\pm\frac{5}{2}, 0)$	$(\pm\frac{3}{2}, 0)$	$3y = \pm 4x.$
g.	$(\pm 5, 0)$	$(\pm 3, 0)$	$(\pm 5, 0), (0, \pm 4)$	
i.	$(\pm 1, 0)$	$(\pm\sqrt{2}, 0)$	$(\pm 1, 0)$	$y = \pm x.$
k.	$(\pm\frac{1}{3}, 0)$	$(\pm 5/12, 0)$	$(\pm\frac{1}{3}, 0)$	$4y = \pm 3x.$

2. a. $\frac{x^2}{36} + \frac{y^2}{20} = 1.$ **c.** $\frac{y^2}{9} - \frac{x^2}{40} = 1.$ **e.** $\frac{x^2}{4} - \frac{y^2}{9/4} = 1.$

g. $\frac{y^2}{45} + \frac{x^2}{9} = 1.$ **i.** $\frac{x^2}{25} - \frac{y^2}{16} = 1.$

3. a. Set $x = 5\cos t, y = 4\sin t$ so $(x/5)^2 + (y/4)^2 = \cos^2 t + \sin^2 t = 1.$

c. $x = \sin t \cos t = \frac{1}{2}\sin 2t, y = \cos 2t, (2x)^2 + y^2 = 1.$

e. $x = 2\sec t, y = 3\tan t; (x^2/4) - (y^2/9) = \sec^2 t - \tan^2 t = 1.$

4. a. $\frac{x^2}{16} + \frac{y^2}{12} = 1.$ **c.** $\frac{x^2}{16} - \frac{y^2}{20} = 1.$ **e.** $\frac{x^2}{16} + \frac{y^2}{25} = 1.$

Sec. 4-7, p. 161.

2. a. $(\pm 13, 0), 5/13, (\pm 5, 0), x = \pm 169/5, (0, \pm 12).$

c. $(\pm 4, 0), \sqrt{65}/4, (\pm\sqrt{65}, 0), y = 16/\sqrt{65}, (\pm 7, 0).$

e. $(0, \pm 2\sqrt{3})$, $1/\sqrt{3}$, $(0, \pm 2)$, $y = \pm 6$, $(\pm 2\sqrt{2}, 0)$.

3. a. $\dfrac{x^2}{25} + \dfrac{y^2}{9} = 1$. c. $\dfrac{y^2}{144} - \dfrac{x^2}{829.44} = 1$. e. $4x^2 + 5y^2 = 1$.

Sec. 4-8, p. 164.

1. a. Center $(-2, 1)$; vertices $(1, 1)$, $(-5, 1)$; foci $(3, 1)$, $(-7, 1)$; ends conj. axis$(-2, 5)$, $(-2, -3)$; asymptotes $4x - 3y + 11 = 0$, $4x + 3y + 5 = 0$.
   c. $(-1, 2)$; $(-1, 7)$, $(-1, -3)$; $(-1, 5)$, $(-1, -1)$; ends minor axis $(3, 2)$, $(-5, 2)$.
   e. Circle with center $(0, -4)$, radius $\sqrt{5}$.
   g. Parabola; vertex $(-3, 2)$, focus $(-2, 2)$; ends latus rectum $(-2, 4)$, $(-2, 0)$; directrix $x = -4$.
2. a. $9x^2 - 16y^2 + 18x + 64y - 199 = 0$.
   c. $16x^2 + 25y^2 - 64x - 50y - 311 = 0$.
   e. $x^2 - 8x - 6y + 37 = 0$.
3. a. $\left(x^2 - x + \dfrac{1}{4}\right) - \left(y^2 - 5y + \dfrac{25}{4}\right) = 6 + \dfrac{1}{4} - \dfrac{25}{4} = 0$,

   $\left(x - \dfrac{1}{2}\right)^2 = \left(y - \dfrac{5}{2}\right)^2$, $x - \dfrac{1}{2} = \pm\left(y - \dfrac{5}{2}\right)$,

   pair of lines $x - y = -2$ and $x + y = 3$.
   c. Point $(-2, 3)$. e. No graph.

Sec. 4-9, p. 166.

2. a. $X^2 + 3Y^2 = 1$, an ellipse.
   c. $XY = 0$, lines $y = \sqrt{3}\,x$ and $\sqrt{3}\,y + x = 0$.
   e. $2X^2 + Y^2 + 1 = 0$; hence, no graph.
   g. With θ in the second quadrant and $\cot \theta = -\frac{4}{3}$, then $\cos \theta = -\frac{4}{5}$, $\sin \theta = \frac{3}{5}$, and the resulting equation is $X^2 = 1$. Hence, the graph is two lines $4x - 4y = \pm 5$,
3. a. $-2XY = 1$, $2XY = 1$. c. $2X^2 = 1$, $2Y^2 = 1$.
   e. $X^2 + Y^2 = 4$ in both cases.

Sec. 4-10, p. 168.

1. a. $\cot 2\theta = -\frac{3}{4}$, $\cos 2\theta = -\frac{3}{5}$, $\sin 2\theta = \frac{4}{5}$, $\cos \theta = 1/\sqrt{5}$, $\sin \theta = 2/\sqrt{5}$.

   $$\dfrac{X^2}{9} + \dfrac{Y^2}{4} = 1.$$

   c. $\cot 2\theta = 0$, $2\theta = 90°$, $\theta = 45°$, $5Y^2 - X^2 = 10$.
   e. $\cot 2\theta = -5/12$, $\cos 2\theta = -5/13$, $\cos \theta = 2/\sqrt{13}$, $\sin \theta = 3/\sqrt{13}$,

   $$9X^2 - 4Y^2 = 1.$$

2. a. $\cot 2\theta = -7/24$, $\cos 2\theta = -7/25$, $\cos \theta = \frac{3}{5}$, $\sin \theta = \frac{4}{5}$,

   $$4X^2 - Y^2 - 2Y = 3,$$
   $$\mathscr{X} = X, \mathscr{Y} = Y + 1, 4\mathscr{X}^2 - \mathscr{Y}^2 = 2.$$

Sec. 5-1, p. 172.

1. a. $4x - y = 4$, $x + 4y = 18$.
   c. $3x + 2\sqrt{3}\,y = \sqrt{3} + \pi$, $12x - 6\sqrt{3}\,y = 4\pi - 3\sqrt{3}$.

2. a. (1) $-\sqrt{3} < x < 0$ or $x > \sqrt{3}$, (2) $x < -\sqrt{3}$ or $0 < x < \sqrt{3}$,
   (3) $x < -1$ or $x > 1$, (4) $-1 < x < 1$.
   c. (1) $x \neq -1$, (2) nowhere, (3) $x < -1$, (4) $x > -1$.
   e. (1) $x < -2$ or $x > 2$, (2) $-2 < x < 0$ or $0 < x < 2$, (3) $x > 0$, (4) $x < 0$.

4. a. $(1, -5)$ concave up. **c.** $(1, 2)$ concave up, $(-1, -2)$ concave down.
   e. $(-1, 11/6)$ concave up, $(2, 19/3)$ concave down.

6. b. $\dfrac{f(0 + \Delta x) - f(0)}{\Delta x} = \begin{cases} \dfrac{(\Delta x)^2}{\Delta x} = \Delta x \text{ if } \Delta x > 0 \\[2mm] \dfrac{(\Delta x)^3}{\Delta x} = (\Delta x)^2 \text{ if } \Delta x < 0. \end{cases} \qquad \lim\limits_{\Delta x \to 0} \dfrac{\Delta f(0)}{\Delta x} = 0$

Hence, the tangent exists at the origin (and is the x-axis).

c. $f'(x) = \begin{cases} 2x \text{ if } x > 0 \\ 3x^2 \text{ if } x < 0, \end{cases} \qquad f''(x) = \begin{cases} 2 \text{ if } x > 0, \\ 6x \text{ if } x < 0. \end{cases}$

Hence, $f''(x) > 0$, but $f''(x) < 0$ if $x < 0$. Thus, to the right of the origin the curve is concave upward, but to the left is concave downward. The origin (since the tangent exists there) is a point of inflection.

d. $\dfrac{\Delta f'(0)}{\Delta x} = \dfrac{f'(0 + \Delta x) - f'(0)}{\Delta x} = \begin{cases} 2 \text{ if } \Delta x > 0 \\ 3\Delta x \text{ if } \Delta x < 0. \end{cases}$

Hence, $\lim\limits_{\Delta x \to 0+} \dfrac{\Delta f'(0)}{\Delta x} = 2$, but $\lim\limits_{\Delta x \to 0-} \dfrac{\Delta f'(0)}{\Delta x} = 0$, so $f''(0)$ does not exist.

Sec. 5-2, p. 175.

1. Equilateral triangle of side 6 in.
3. $(5 - \sqrt{7})$ in. $\times$ $(8 + 2\sqrt{7})$ in. $\times$ $(2 + 2\sqrt{7})$ in., vol $8(10 + 7\sqrt{7})$ in³.
5. 2 in. $\times$ 5 in. $\times$ 10 in., vol 100 in³.
7. 4 in. $\times$ 4 in. $\times$ 4 in.
9. $r = 3/\sqrt[3]{\pi}$ in., $h = 6/\sqrt[3]{\pi}$ in.
11. 3 ft 11 in., 4 ft 1 in.
13. 3 in. $\times$ 3 in. $\times$ 6 in.
15. 50 ft parallel to existing fence, ends 25 ft.
16. a. 50 ft, ends $16\frac{2}{3}$ ft.
17. a. Base $4\sqrt{2}$, altitude $2\sqrt{2}$.
18. a. $r = 2$ in., $h = 4$ in.
19. a. Side of square $l/(4 + \pi)$, also diameter of circle.
20. Bases 5, 9; altitude 14.

Sec. 5-3, p. 179.

1. a. $\left(\dfrac{25}{9}, \pm \dfrac{8\sqrt{14}}{9}\right)$, $(-5, 0)$. **c.** $(0, 4)$, $\left(\pm \dfrac{5}{9}\sqrt{17}, -\dfrac{32}{9}\right)$.
2. a. $AC = 4$ mi. **c.** $C = B$.
3. a. $3, 5\sqrt{2}$. **c.** $\frac{5}{3}, 116/3$. **e.** $0, 5$.
4. a. $0, 3 + \sqrt{29}$. **c.** $5, 72$. **e.** $5, 7.5$.
5. a. $\frac{7}{3}, 1/12$. **c.** $2, 0$.
7. a. 6×12 revolved about side 6.
9. Radius $(2\sqrt{2}/3) r$, altitude $\frac{4}{3} r$.
11. a. $x = \frac{3}{2}$. **c.** $x = 1$. **e.** $x = 2$.

Sec. 5-4, p. 183.

1. **a.** $4/\sqrt{15}$ ft/sec.   **c.** 3 ft/sec.
2. **a.** $2/\pi$ ft/min.   **c.** $1/(8\pi)$ ft/min.
3. **a.** $20/(81\pi)$ ft/min.
5. $20/7$ in²./min.
7. $8/25$ in./min.
9. $\sqrt{15}/10$ ft/min.
10. **a** and **b.** $1/\pi$ in.   **c.** $1/\pi$ ft.
11. $1/(200\pi)$ ft/min, $\frac{2}{5}$ ft²/min.
12. **a.** $18/41$ ft/sec.   **b.** $(289/640)\cdot 25 = 9.73$ lb.
13. $2\sqrt{19}$ ft/sec, $-2\sqrt{19/3}$ ft/sec.

Sec. 5-6, p. 190.

1. **a.** $P(x) = 2(x - 3)^2 + 14(x - 3)^2 + 31(x - 3) + 16$.
   c. $P(x) = 2(x + 3)^2 - 22(x + 3) + 79(x + 3) - 98$.
3. **a.** 5.991.
4. **a.** 3.128.   **c.** 2.625.   **e.** 4.410.   **g.** 0.692.   **i.** 65.101.
5. **a.** 2.217 rounded to 2.22, or 0.83.   **c.** 52.51.

Sec. 5-7, p. 196.

1. **a.** $f(3) = 32, f'(3) = 36, f''(3) = 28, f'''(3) = 12$.
   c. $f(-4) = -220, f'(-4) = 134, f''(-4) = -56, f'''(-4) = 12$.
2. **a.** $6, 7; -7, -6$.   **c.** $0, 1; 1, 2; -2, -1$.
3. **a.** ± 6.403.   **c.** $0.519, 1.406, -2 + 0.452 = -1.548$.
4. **a.** 273.066. Note that the usual arithmetic method of extracting square roots is merely a further formalization of Horner's Method.
   c. 25.0228.
5. $(-3, 2), (-2, 1); -3.721$.
7. **b.** $x = 1.31$.   **c.** $x^3 - 6x^2 + 24 = 0, x = 2.69$.

Sec. 5-8, p. 201.

3. **a.** $x = 0$ by inspection, $x_0 = \pi/3, x_2 = 0.9479$,

$$x_3 = 0.9479 - \frac{0.0003}{1.6384}, \text{ so answer is } 0.948.$$

   c. $x = 0; x_0 = 70° = 1.2217$ radians.

$$x_1 = 1.2217 - \frac{0.9397 - 2(1.2217)(0.3420)}{2(1.2217)(0.9397) - (0.3420)}$$

$$= 1.2217 - \frac{0.1041}{1.9540} = 1.2217 - 0.0533 = 1.1684,$$

$$x_2 = 1.1684 - \frac{0.9201 - 2(1.1684)(0.3916)}{2(1.1684)(0.9201) - 0.3916} = 1.1655,$$

$$x_3 = 1.1655 - \frac{0.9190 - 2(1.1655)(0.3943)}{2(1.1655)(0.9190) - 0.3943} = 1.1655 + \frac{0.0002}{1.7479}.$$

   Answer; 1.166.

e. $60° = 1.0472$ radians from graph, but rough mental check from tables shows $x_0 = 59° = 1.0297$ radians is better.

$$x_1 = 1.0297 - \frac{2(0.5150) - (1.0297)^2}{-2(1.0297 + 0.8572)} = 1.0217,$$

$$x_2 = 1.0217 - \frac{2(0.5219) - (1.0217)^2}{-2(1.0217 + 0.8530)} = 1.0217 + \frac{-0.0001}{2(1.8747)}.$$

Answer: 1.0217.

6. $x_1 = 0.5625$, $x_2 = 0.57678$, $x_3 = 0.57735$, $x_4 = 0.57736$ [Note: $3x_4 = 1.73208$.]

Sec. 6-1, p. 206.

1. a. $4x \sec^2 (2x^2 + 1)$. c. $\cos x + \sec^2 x$. e. $-\frac{1}{x} \sec^2 \frac{1}{x} + \tan \frac{1}{x}$.

g. $2 \sec^3 x \tan x$. i. $\cot x - x \csc^2 x$.

3. a. $2 \tan x \sec^2 x$, $2 \sec^2 x(1 + 3 \tan^2 x)$.

c. $-\frac{1}{x^2} \sec \frac{1}{x} \tan \frac{1}{x}$, $\frac{1}{x^4} \sec \frac{1}{x} \left(\sec^2 \frac{1}{x} + \tan^2 \frac{1}{x} + 2x \tan \frac{1}{x} \right)$.

e. $2 \sin 2x$, $4 \cos 2x$.

g. $x^2 \sec^2 x + 2x \tan x$, $2 \tan x + 2x \sec^2 x(2 + x \tan x)$.

4. a. $-1 - \sin^2 (x + y)$. c. $-x \cot y \cos^2 y$.

7. $(5^{2/3} + 8^{2/3})^{3/2} = 18.22$ ft.

8. $\frac{1}{2}(4^{2/3} + 3^{2/3})^{3/2} = 4.93$ ft. [Note: $\theta = 45°$ gives 4.949.]

Sec. 6-2, p. 212.

1. a. $\frac{1}{\sqrt{4 - x^2}}$. c. $\sin^{-1}x$. e. $\frac{1}{\sqrt{2x - x^2}}$. g. $\frac{-1}{2\sqrt{x}(x +)}$.

2. a. $\frac{-x}{|x|\sqrt{1 - x^2}} = \begin{cases} -(1 - x^2)^{-1/2} & \text{if } 0 < x < 1 \\ (1 - x^2)^{-1/2} & \text{if } -1 < x < 0. \end{cases}$

c. $\frac{x}{|x|(1 + x^2)} = \begin{cases} 1/(1 + x^2) & \text{if } x > 0 \\ -1/(1 + x^2) & \text{if } x < 0. \end{cases}$

e. $\frac{1}{|x|\sqrt{x^2 - 4}} = \begin{cases} x^{-1}(x^2 - 4)^{-1/2} & \text{if } x > 2 \\ -x^{-1}(x^2 - 4)^{-1/2} & \text{if } x < -2. \end{cases}$

5. $2\sqrt{26} - 4 = 6.20$.

6. a. 4.8 rad/hr.

Sec. 6-3, p. 215.

2. a. 4. c. -4. e. -4. g. $\frac{3}{2}$.

3. c. 2.1080.

Sec. 6-4, p. 220.

1. a. $y' = \frac{10x}{x^2 + 4}$, $y'' = \frac{10(4 - x^2)}{(x^2 + 4)^2}$.

c. $y' = \frac{2x^2}{x^2 + 1} + \ln (x^2 + 1)$, $y'' = \frac{2x(x^2 + 3)}{(x^2 + 1)^2}$.

e. $y' = \frac{1}{\sqrt{x^2 - 4}}$, $y'' = \frac{-x}{(x^2 - 4)^{3/2}}$.

g. $y' = 6 \csc 6x$, $y'' = -36 \csc 6x \cot 6x$.

3. a. $y' = x(1 + 2 \ln|x|)$, $m = -3(1 + 2 \ln|-3|) = -3(1 + 2 \ln 3)$
$= -3[1 + 2(2.3026)(0.4771)] = -9.5914$.

c. $\frac{1}{4}(1 - \ln 2) = 0.0767$. **e.** $1/\sqrt{3}$.

Sec. 6-5, p. 223.

1. a. $\dfrac{1}{3x + 4} - \dfrac{1}{x - 1} - \dfrac{2x}{x^2 + 2}$. **c.** $\dfrac{\cos x}{1 + \sin x} - \dfrac{2x}{x^2 + 5}$.

e. $\dfrac{1}{x} - \dfrac{\sin x}{1 + \cos x} + \dfrac{\sin x}{2 + \cos x}$.

2. a. $(x - 1)(x - 2) + x(x - 2) + x(x - 1) = 3x^2 - 6x + 2$.

c. $\dfrac{x \cos x + \sin x}{1 + \sin x} - \dfrac{x \sin x \cos x}{(1 + \sin x)^2}$.

e. $\sqrt{\dfrac{x^2 \sin x}{x^2 + 4}} \left[\dfrac{1}{x} + \dfrac{1}{2} \cot x - \dfrac{x}{x^2 + 4} \right]$.

3. a. $(\ln 2) 2^{\sin x} \cos x$. **c.** $(\ln 3) 3^{x - \sin x}(1 - \cos x)$.

e. $(\sqrt{10})^x \ln \sqrt{10}$.

Sec. 6-6, p. 226.

1. a. $y' = x^{\sin x} \left(\dfrac{\sin x}{x} + \cos x \ln x \right)$.

$y'' = x^{\sin x} \left[\left(\dfrac{\sin x}{x} + \cos x \ln x \right)^2 + \dfrac{2 \cos x}{x} - \dfrac{\sin x}{x^2} - \sin x \ln x \right]$.

c. $y' = |x|^x(1 + \ln|x|)$, $y'' = |x|^x[(1 + \ln|x|)^2 + (1/x)]$.

e. $y' = \dfrac{x^{x/2}}{2}(1 + \ln x)$, $y'' = \dfrac{x^{x/2}}{2} \left[\dfrac{1}{2}(1 + \ln x)^2 + \dfrac{1}{x} \right]$.

g. $y' = 5 \sin^2 x \cos x$, $y'' = 5 \sin^3 x(4 \cos^2 x - \sin^2 x)$.

2. a. e^x, e^{-2x}. **c.** $e^{3x}, e^{x/2}$.

3. $r = \frac{1}{2}$.

Sec. 6-7, p. 228.

2. a. $\sinh(u - v)$.

5. a. $(6x - 4) \cosh(3x^2 - 4x)$. **c.** $(1/\sqrt{x}) \tanh \sqrt{x} \operatorname{sech}^2 \sqrt{x}$.

e. $-\dfrac{1 + y^2 \cosh x}{2y \sinh x}$. **g.** $\dfrac{1}{\sqrt{x^2 + a^2}}$ if $a < 0$.

Sec. 7-1, p. 232.

1. a. $\frac{1}{9}(x^3 + 4) + c$. **c.** $\ln|x^2 + x| + c$. **e.** $\frac{1}{2} \ln^2|x| + c$.

g. $\ln|\ln|x|| + c$. **i.** $2\sqrt{1 + \sec x} + c$.

2. a. $\frac{1}{4}(x^2 + x) - \frac{1}{8} \ln|2x + 1| + c$. **c.** $\frac{1}{3}x^3 + \frac{1}{2} \ln(x^2 + 1) + c$.

e. $t + 2 \ln|t| - (1/t) + c$.

3. a. $-\frac{1}{2} \cos x^2 + c$. **e.** $\frac{1}{2} e^{2x} + c$. **c.** $(16^x/\ln 16) + c$.

g. $\frac{1}{2} \sin^{-1} 2x + c$. **i.** $\frac{1}{8} \sec(2x)^2 + c$. **k.** $2 \ln|\csc\sqrt{x} - \cot\sqrt{x}| + c$.

Sec. 7-2, p. 234.

3. a. $\frac{1}{4}\left(2x\sqrt{9-4x^2}+9\sin^{-1}\frac{2x}{3}\right)+c, \frac{1}{2}\sin^{-1}\frac{2x}{3}+c, -\frac{1}{4}\sqrt{9-4x^2}+c.$

c. $-\frac{1}{8}\cos(4x^2)+c, \frac{x}{2}-\frac{1}{16}\sin 8x+c, \frac{1}{12}\sin^3 4x+c.$

e. $\frac{1}{2\sqrt{2}}(\sqrt{2}\,x\sqrt{2x^2-3}-3\ln|\sqrt{2}\,x+\sqrt{2x^2-3}|)+c.$

$\frac{1}{\sqrt{2}}\ln|\sqrt{2}\,x+\sqrt{2x^2-3}|+c, \frac{1}{6}(2x^2-3)^{3/2}+c.$

Sec. 7-3, p. 238.

1. a. $x\sin x+\cos x+c.$ **c.** $\frac{1}{4}e^{2x}(2x-1)+c.$

e. $\frac{2}{3}x^2(x+3)^{3/2}-(8/15)\,x\,(x+3)^{5/2}+(16/105)(x+3)^{7/2}+c.$

g. $\frac{1}{2}(\sec x\tan x+\ln|\sec x+\tan x|)+c.$ [Hint: Set $u=\sec x, dv=\sec^2 x\,dx,$

and obtain $\displaystyle\int\sec^3 x\,dx=\sec x\tan x-\int\sec^3 x\,dx+\int\sec x\,dx.$]

i. $x\tan x+\ln|\cos x|+c.$

k. $\sqrt{1+x^2}\tan^{-1}x-\ln(x+\sqrt{1+x^2})+c.$

4. a. $-\frac{1}{2}\cos x^2+c, (2-x^2)\cos x+2x\sin x,$

$\frac{1}{4}x^2-\frac{1}{4}x\sin 2x-\frac{1}{8}\cos 2x+c.$

c. $\sqrt{x^2+4}+c, \frac{1}{3}(x^2+4)^{3/2}+c,$

$\frac{2}{3}x^2(x+4)^{3/2}-(8/15)\,x(x+4)^{5/2}+(16/105)(x+4)^{7/2}+c.$

e. $x(1-\ln|x|)+c, \frac{1}{2}\ln^2|x|+c, \frac{1}{4}x^2(1-2\ln|x|)+c.$

Sec. 7-5, p. 242.

1. a. $\frac{1}{4}\tan^{-1}\left(x+\frac{3}{2}\right)+c, \frac{1}{8}\ln\left|\frac{2x+1}{2x+5}\right|+c, \frac{-1}{2}\frac{1}{2x+3}+c.$

c. $-\frac{1}{2}\ln\left|\frac{\sqrt{x^2+6x+4}+2}{x}+\frac{3}{2}\right|+c,$

$\frac{1}{\sqrt{7}}\sin^{-1}\frac{3x-7}{4x}+c, -\frac{\sqrt{x^2+6x}}{3x}+c.$

e. $\ln|2x+1+2\sqrt{x^2+x+1}|+c,$

$\sqrt{x^2+x+1}-\frac{1}{2}\ln|2x+1+2\sqrt{x^2+x+1}|+c,$

$\frac{1}{4}(2x+1)\sqrt{x^2+x+1}+\frac{3}{8}\ln|2x+1+2\sqrt{x^2+x+1}|+c.$

2. If $q<0$ then, by (2), $X=a\left[\left(x+\frac{b}{2a}\right)^2+\left(\frac{\sqrt{-q}}{2a}\right)^2\right].$ The terms in the brackets

are both squares. Thus, X is negative if both $a<0$ and $q<0.$

Sec. 7-6, p. 246.

1. a. $3\ln|x-1|-\frac{4}{x-1}+6\ln|x+2|+c.$

c. $\frac{13}{9}\ln|x-1|+\frac{4}{3}\frac{1}{x-1}-\frac{4}{9}\ln|x+2|+c.$

2. a. $\ln|(x^2-4)/(x+5)|+c.$

3. a. $\frac{1}{7}\ln|(2x-1)/(3x+2)| + c.$ **c.** $2x^3 + \frac{1}{2}x^2 - 2x + c.$
e. $\ln|x^3 + 2x^2 - x - 2| + c.$ **g.** $\frac{1}{4}\tan^{-1}(x - \frac{1}{2}) + c.$

Sec. 7-7, p. 250.

1. a. $\ln|x+1| + \ln\sqrt{x^2+2} + c.$
c. $\frac{1}{3}\{\ln[(x+1)(x^2+2)]^2 - (1/\sqrt{2})\tan^{-1}(x/\sqrt{2})\} + c.$
e. $-\dfrac{1}{2}\left[\dfrac{1}{x^2+1} + \dfrac{1}{x^2+2}\right] + c.$

3. a. $x + 6\ln|x-4| - 2\ln|x-3| + c.$ **c.** $\frac{1}{2}x^2 - (1/x) + c.$
e. $\ln|x| - \frac{1}{2}\ln|x^2-1| - \frac{1}{2}\dfrac{1}{x^2-1} + c.$ **g.** $\frac{1}{4}x^4 + x^2 + \ln|x| + c.$
i. $-\ln|\sin x| + \ln|\sin x - 1| + c.$
k. $\dfrac{ax}{c} + \dfrac{bc-ad}{c^2}\ln|cx+d| + C.$

Sec. 7-8, p. 251.

1. a. $-\dfrac{1}{9}\cos^5 x\left(\sin^4 x + \dfrac{4}{7}\sin^2 x + \dfrac{8}{35}\right) + c,$ by $95_2.$
c. $\frac{1}{4}\tan x\sec^3 x + \frac{3}{8}\tan x\sec x + \frac{3}{8}\ln|\sec x + \tan x| + c,$ by 93 and 15.
e. $\frac{1}{2}x^4\sin 2x + x^3\cos 2x - \frac{3}{2}x^2\sin 2x - \frac{3}{2}x\cos 2x + \frac{3}{4}\sin 2x + c,$ by 88.
g. $\dfrac{1}{10}\dfrac{x^5}{2x^2+5} - \dfrac{x^3}{20} + \dfrac{3}{8}x - \dfrac{15}{16}\sqrt{\dfrac{2}{5}}\tan^{-1}\sqrt{\dfrac{2}{5}}\,x + c,$ by 100 and 12.

2. a. $\frac{1}{6}\sin^6 x + c.$ **c.** $\frac{1}{5}\sec^5 x + c.$
e. $\dfrac{1}{10}\sin(2x^5) + c.$ **g.** $-\dfrac{1}{8}\dfrac{1}{2x^4+5} + c.$

Sec. 7-9, p. 254.

1. a. $2\sqrt{x+1} + 3\ln|x| + \ln\left|\dfrac{\sqrt{x+1}-1}{\sqrt{x+1}+1}\right| + c.$
c. $\frac{1}{8}[\frac{1}{3}(3+4x)^{3/2} - \frac{1}{2}(3+4x) - 2\sqrt{3+4x} + 2\ln(1+\sqrt{3+4x})] + c.$
e. $-\frac{2}{3}\ln(1+\sqrt{x+2}) + \frac{1}{3}\ln|3+x-\sqrt{x+2}|$
$\qquad +\dfrac{2}{\sqrt{3}}\tan^{-1}\dfrac{2\sqrt{2+x}-1}{\sqrt{3}} + c.$
g. $12\left[\displaystyle\sum_{k=0}^{25}\dfrac{(x^{1/12})^{k+1}}{k+1} + \ln|x^{1/12}-1|\right].$

Sec. 7-10, p. 254.

1. $(3/11)x^{11/3} + c.$ **3.** $-\frac{1}{8}\cos^4 2x + c.$ **5.** $-\frac{1}{6}\cot^3 2x + c.$
7. $-\frac{2}{3}e^{-3x} - \frac{1}{2}e^{-3x} + c.$ **9.** $\frac{1}{2}e^{2\sin x} + c.$
11. $\frac{1}{2}\ln(1+2e^x) + c.$ **13.** $-\frac{1}{2}\cot 2x + c.$
15. $\frac{1}{2}x - (1/12)\sin 6x + c.$ **17.** $\frac{1}{3}\sin^{-1}(3x/4) + c.$
19. $\dfrac{1}{18}\ln\left|\dfrac{x^3-3}{x^3+3}\right| + c.$ **21.** $\dfrac{3}{40}(2x+3)^{2/3}(4x-9) + c.$

23. $\frac{1}{5}\ln |5x +\sqrt{1 + 25x^2}| + c.$ **25.** $\frac{1}{14}\ln\left|\frac{9x - 5}{x + 1}\right| + c.$

27. $-2\sqrt{-x^2 + 6x +7} + 11\sin^{-1}(x - 3)/4 + c.$

29. $-\ln |x| + \frac{2}{3}\ln |x - 1| + \frac{1}{6}\ln (x^2 + x + 1) - \frac{1}{\sqrt{3}}\tan^{-1}\frac{2x + 1}{\sqrt{3}} + c.$

31. $\frac{1}{2}x^2 \ln |x| - \frac{1}{4}x^2 + c.$ **33.** $\ln\left|\frac{\sqrt{1 + 4x} - 1}{\sqrt{1 + 4x} + 1}\right| + c.$

35. $(2/35)(x - 2)^{5/2}(5x + 4) + c.$ **37.** $(1/15)(3x^2 + 1)^{3/2}(x^2 - \frac{2}{9}) + c.$

39. $(1/27)\sqrt{3x^2 + 1}\,(3x^2 - 2) + c.$

Sec. 8-1, p. 257.

1. a. $\pi.$ **c.** $2\pi^2 - 16.$ **e.** $3\sqrt{3} - 4.$

2. a. $\frac{1}{2}\ln 2.$ **c.** $\pi/4.$ **e.** $\frac{1}{2}(e^\pi + 1).$ **g.** $6 + \ln 2.$

3. a. $\displaystyle\int_0^{\pi/3}\left(x^2 \cos x - \frac{1}{2}x^2\right) dx = \left(\frac{\pi}{3}\right)^2\frac{\sqrt{3}}{2} + \frac{\pi}{3} - \sqrt{3} - \frac{1}{6}\left(\frac{\pi}{3}\right)^3.$

    c. $\pi - 3\ln\sqrt{3}.$

4. a. $\displaystyle\int_{1.445}^{2.802}\left(-x^2 + 4x - 3 - \frac{1}{x}\right) dx = -\frac{1}{3}x^3 + 2x^2 - 3x - \ln x\,\Big]_{1.445}^{2.802}$

$$= \left[\left(-\frac{2.802}{3} + 2\right) 2.802 - 3\right] 2.802$$

$$- \left[\left(-\frac{1.445}{3} + 2\right) 1.445 - 3\right] 1.445$$

$$-2.3026\,(\log 2.802 - \log 1.445).$$

5. a. $-1 + \ln 4.$ **c.** $2 - \ln 4.$

    e. $\displaystyle\int_0^1 x \cos^{-1} x\, dx = -\int_{\pi/2}^0 (\cos y)\, y \sin y\, dy = \frac{1}{2}\int_0^{\pi/2} y \sin 2y\, dy = \pi/8.$

Sec. 8-2, p. 262.

2. a. $(28/11, 2).$

3. a. $\left(\frac{3}{2}, \frac{6}{5}\right),$ **c.** $\left(\frac{1}{2}, \frac{8}{5}\right),$ **e.** $\left(\frac{\pi^2 - 4\pi + 8}{4\pi - 8}, \frac{\pi}{4\pi - 8}\right).$

    g. $\left(\frac{4}{3}\frac{a}{\pi}, \frac{4}{3}\frac{b}{\pi}\right).$ **i.** $\left(-\frac{12}{5}, -\frac{3}{2}\right).$

5. $\left(\frac{26}{7}, \frac{41}{28}\right), \left(\frac{91 + 30\pi}{30 + 6\pi}, 0\right), \left(\frac{42 + 62\sqrt{2}}{3 + 24\sqrt{2}}, \frac{24 + 13\sqrt{2}}{3 + 24\sqrt{2}}\right).$

6. a. $\left(\frac{50 - 3\pi}{20 - \pi}, \frac{80 - 3\pi}{40 - 2\pi}\right) = (2.41, 2.09).$

    c. $\left(\frac{5}{2}, \frac{125 - 8\pi}{50 - 4\pi}\right) = (2.5, 2.67).$

Sec. 8-3, p. 266.

1. a. 375 tons. **c.** 351.6 tons. **2. a.** 15 (62.5) lb.

3. Let s ft be the depth of the swivel. With y measured positively downward from the surface of the water, a strip of the rectangle y ft below the surface has turning moment $(s - y)(62.5)\, 2y\, dy.$ Thus, s must satisfy

(62.5) $2 \int_1^4 (s - y)\, y\, dy = 0$; that is, $s = \int_1^4 y^2\, dy \big/ \int_1^4 y\, dy = 2.8$.

5. 2 ft 2 in. below the vertex.

7. 27 (62.5) π lb, (20.25)(62.5) π lb.

Sec. 8-4, p. 269.

1. a. 37.5 in.-lb.   **c.** $37.5 + 25\,a$ in.-lb.   **e.** $(50/3)(ah + h^2)$.

2. a. 180 in.-lb.   **c.** $180 + 120\,a$ in.-lb.   **e.** $80\,h(a + h)$ in.-lb.

3. a. $7312.5\,\pi$ ft-lb.   **c.** $(62.5)(171)\,\pi$ ft-lb.

   e. $3.6 \times 10^4\,\pi$ ft-lb.   **g.** 8.5×10^3 ft-lb.   **i.** $62.5(11 + 45\pi)$ ft-lb.

4. b. $62.5\,\pi\,ab^2\,(25 + \tfrac{1}{4}a)$.

   d. $62.5\,\pi \int_0^3 (78 - h)(9 - h^2)\, dh = 62.5\,\pi\,(5535/4)$.

   f. $62.5\,\pi\,[(5535/4) + 5904]$ ft-lb.   **h.** $(62.5)\,18\,(39\pi - 1)$ ft-lb.

5. a. 1200 ft-lb.   **c.** $\tfrac{1}{3}(3500)$ ft-lb.

6. a. $(75)^2(13/2)$ ft-lb.   **c.** $(75)^2(31/8)$ ft-lb.

Sec. 8-5, p. 275.

1. a. $(32/5)\pi$.   **c.** $(40/3)\pi$.

2. a. $\tfrac{4}{3}\pi ab^2$.   **c.** $\tfrac{1}{2}\pi(e^2 - 1)$.   **e.** $\tfrac{1}{4}\pi(4 + e^2 - e^{-2})$.   **g.** $(162/35)\pi$.

3. a. 216π.   **c.** $(1656/5)\pi$.

4. a. $8\pi \ln \tfrac{5}{2}$.   **c.** $\pi \int_2^4 \left\{ \left[\frac{8}{4 + x^2} + 1 \right]^2 - 1 \right\} dx = \pi \left(-\dfrac{2}{5} - 3\pi + 12 \tan^{-1}2 \right)$.

   [Hint: Use Table formula 83.]

5. Hint: In a circle with center at the origin and radius $r > 3$, a chord parallel to the x-axis cuts the circle at $(\pm 3, \sqrt{r^2 - 9})$.

   Volume $= \pi \int_{-3}^3 [(\sqrt{r^2 - x^2})^2 - (\sqrt{r^2 - 9})^2]\, dx$.

Sec. 8-6, p. 276.

1. a. $2 \sinh 1 = e - e^{-1}$.   **c.** 14/3.

   e. $\int_0^1 \sqrt{1 + e^{2x}}\, dx = \sqrt{1 + e^2} - \sqrt{2} + \ln \dfrac{e(1 + \sqrt{2})}{1 + \sqrt{1 + e^2}}$ by using $u = e^x$.

   g. $2\sqrt{6} - \sqrt{3}$.

2. $4/\sqrt{3}$.

3. a. $2\,(10\sqrt{10} - 1)$.

   c. $3\,|a| \int_0^\pi \sqrt{\sin^2 t \cos^2 t}\, dt = 3\,|a| \left\{ \int_0^{\pi/2} \sin t \cos t\, dt - \int_{\pi/2}^\pi \sin t \cos t\, dt \right\} = 3|a|$.

   e. 8π.

Sec. 8-7, p. 278.

1. a. $(208/3)\pi$.   **c.** $(\pi/27)(10\sqrt{10} - 1)$.   **e.** $(56/3)\pi$.

   g. $\pi\,[2\sqrt{2} + \ln(3 + 2\sqrt{2})]$.

2. a. $(19/3)\pi$.   **c.** $(\pi/27)(730\sqrt{730} - 1)$.   **e.** $(12/5)\pi a^2$.

4. $4\pi^2 ab$.

Sec. 9-1, p. 283.

2. a. $(x/a)^2 - (y/b)^2 = \sec^2\theta - \tan^2\theta = 1$. Conversely, given that x and y satisfy (11), construct the vector $\vec{i} + \vec{j}\,|y|/b$, let α be its amplitude, note its length

$$\sqrt{1 + \frac{y^2}{b^2}} = \sqrt{\frac{x^2}{a^2}} = \frac{|x|}{a},$$

and hence obtain $\tan\alpha = |y|/b$ and $\sec\alpha = |x|/a$. Thus, one of the angles $\pm\alpha$, $180° \pm \alpha$ has both its tan equal to y/b and its sec equal to x/a, so this angle may be used for θ in (10).

b. $\cosh^2 t - \sinh^2 t = 1$, but $x \geq a$ since $\cosh t \geq 1$.

c. $x = OA = OT\dfrac{OA}{OT} = a\sec\theta$, $y = SB = OS\dfrac{SB}{OS} = b\tan\theta$.

3. a. $y = 1 + \cos 2\theta = 2\cos^2\theta = 2x^2$, but $|x| \leq 1$.

c. $y = 2(1/t)^2 = 2x^2$. All of parabola except $(0, 0)$.

e. $y = 1 + (2\cosh^2 t - 1) = 2x^2$. Above and to the right of $(1, 2)$.

4. a. $y = 3x + 1$, $x \geq 0$. **c.** $x = 3y - 7$, $-4 \leq x \leq 2$. **e.** $x + y = 1$, $x \geq 1$.

5. a. The angles θ and ϕ are both measured positively counterclockwise. Since arc AT (with central angle θ) must equal arc TP (with central angle $\phi - \theta$), then $a\theta = b(\phi - \theta)$. $\vec{CP}$ has amplitude $180° + \phi$. Hence,

$$\vec{OP} = \vec{OC} + \vec{CP} = (a + b)[\vec{i}\cos\theta + \vec{j}\sin\theta]$$
$$+ b[\vec{i}\cos(180° + \phi) + \vec{j}\sin(180° + \phi)].$$

These yield

$$x = (a + b)\cos\theta - b\cos\frac{a+b}{b}\theta, \quad y = (a + b)\sin\theta - b\sin\frac{a+b}{b}\theta.$$

6. a. $x = a(\cos\theta + \theta\sin\theta)$, $y = a(\sin\theta - \theta\cos\theta)$.

7. a. Starts at $(2, 0)$, goes into fourth quadrant on $y = (x - 2)/(x - 1)$.

c. Starts at vertex $(1, 0)$ of the parabola, goes on this parabola to $(-1, 1)$, $(1, 0)$, $(-1, -1)$, $(1, 0)$.

Sec. 9-2, p. 287.

1. a. $D_x y = \frac{3}{2}t^2 = \frac{3}{2}(\frac{1}{2}x)^2 = \frac{3}{8}x^2$; $y = (\frac{1}{2}x)^3 = \frac{1}{8}x^3$, $D_x y = \frac{3}{8}x^2$.

c. $(2/x)\ln x$. **e.** $e = -x/\sqrt{1 - x^2}$.

2. a. $-\frac{1}{3}\tan t$, $-\frac{1}{9}\sec^3 t$. **c.** $1 - \tan t$, $-\sec^3 t$.

3. $D_x^2 y = -\sec^3 t$, $D_y^2 x = -\csc^3 t \neq -1/\sec^3 t$.

5. a. $y = 2\sqrt{2}x - 1$, up. **c.** $y = 32x + 28$, down.

Sec. 9-4, p. 293.

2. a. $(14, -17)$, $10\sqrt{5}$. **c.** $(-2, -\frac{3}{4})$, $\frac{5}{4}\sqrt{5}$.

3. a. $(0, \frac{1}{2})$, $\frac{1}{2}$. **c.** $(-4, \frac{8}{3})$, $\frac{5}{3}\sqrt{10}$.

e. $(\frac{1}{4}\pi - \frac{3}{2}, -\sqrt{2})$, $\frac{3}{2}\sqrt{3}$. **g.** $(-1, 2)$, $\sqrt{2}$.

Sec. 9-5, p. 297.

1. a. $-1/(10\sqrt{5})$. **c.** $2/(17\sqrt{17})$. **e.** 1.

2. a. Both have $m = 1$ and $\kappa = 1/\sqrt{2}$.

3. b. Not unless

$$\frac{\frac{1}{2}[f_1''(x_0) + f_2''(x_0)]}{\{1 + \frac{1}{4}[f_1'(x_0) + f_2'(x_0)]^2\}^{3/2}} = \frac{1}{2}\left\{\frac{f_1''(x_0)}{[1 + f_1'^2(x_0)]^{3/2}} + \frac{f_2''(x_0)}{[1 + f_2'^2(x_0)]^{3/2}}\right\}.$$

This does not hold, for example, if $f_1(x) = x$, $f_2(x) = x^2$.

5. a. For $y = \sqrt{x^2 - 1}$, $\kappa = -(2x^2 + 1)^{-3/2} < 0$.

For $y = -\sqrt{x^2 - 1}$, $\kappa = (2x^2 + 1)^{-3/2} > 0$.

b. If $\tan t$ is defined, then

$$\kappa = \frac{-\sec^3 t}{|\sec^3 t| (\tan^2 t + \sec^2 t)^{3/2}}.$$

For $-\pi/2 < t < \pi/2$, $\kappa < 0$ and $(\sec t, \tan t)$ has positive abscissa. For $\pi/2 < t < 3\pi/2$, $\kappa > 0$ and $(\sec t, \tan t)$ is on the left-hand branch.

c. As t increases over $-\pi/2 < t < \pi/2$, the point comes along the fourth quadrant branch to $(1, 0)$ and then along the first quadrant branch, with the tangent rotating clockwise throughout. As t increases over $\pi/2 < t < 3\pi/2$, the point comes in the third quadrant to $(-1, 0)$ and then out the second quadrant, with the tangent rotating counterclockwise.

6.
$$-\csc^2\phi \frac{d\phi}{ds} = \frac{d}{ds}\left(\frac{x'}{y'}\right),$$

$$\kappa = \frac{d\phi}{ds} = -\frac{1}{\csc^2\phi} \frac{d}{dt}\left(\frac{x'}{y'}\right) \frac{dt}{ds}$$

$$= \frac{-1}{1 + \cot^2\phi} \frac{y'x'' - x'y''}{y'^2} \frac{1}{\sqrt{x'^2 + y'^2}}$$

$$= \text{etc.} = \frac{x'y'' - y'x''}{(x'^2 + y'^2)^{3/2}}.$$

7. a. $\kappa = 4/(17\sqrt{17})$.

b. $y = 1 - (1 - 2\sin^2 t) = 2x^2$. The point $(\sin\frac{1}{2}\pi, 1 - \cos^2\pi)$ is $(1, 2)$.

$$\kappa(t) = \frac{4\cos t \cos 2t + 2\sin 2t \sin t}{[\cos^2 t + 4\sin^2 2t]^{3/2}}$$

is defined unless the denominator is zero, which it is if $t = \pi/2$.

c. By trigonometric identities,

$$\kappa(t) = \frac{4\cos^3 t}{|\cos^3 t| (1 + 16\sin^2 t)^{3/2}}.$$

For t slightly less than $\pi/2$, $\kappa(t)$ is close to $4/(17\sqrt{17})$.

For t slightly more than $\pi/2$, $\kappa(t)$ is close to $-4/(17\sqrt{17})$.

Since $r(t) = 1/|\kappa(t)|$,

$$r(t) = \frac{|\cos^3 t| (1 + 16\sin^2 t)^{3/2}}{4|\cos^3 t|} = \frac{1}{4}(1 + 16\sin^2 t)^{3/2}, t \neq \frac{\pi}{2} + m\pi,$$

and $\lim_{t \to \pi/2} r(t) = 17\sqrt{17}/4$.

Sec. 9-6, p. 303.

1. From (7) of Sec. 9-5, $x'y'' - y'x'' = \kappa(x'^2 + y'^2)^{3/2}$, and this substituted into (5) of Sec. 9-6 yields

$$\vec{a}_N = \frac{\kappa(x'^2 + y'^2)^{3/2}}{x'^2 + y'^2}(-\vec{i}y' + \vec{j}x')$$

$$= \kappa(x'^2 + y'^2)\frac{-\vec{i}y' + \vec{j}x'}{\sqrt{x'^2 + y'^2}} = \kappa\left(\frac{ds}{dt}\right)^2\vec{\eta},$$

since $(ds/dt)^2 = x'^2 + y'^2$ and $(-\vec{i}y' + \vec{j}x')/\sqrt{x'^2 + y'^2}$ is a unit normal vector.

2. From (3),

$$\vec{a}_M = \frac{\vec{M}\cdot\vec{a}}{\vec{M}\cdot\vec{M}}\,\vec{M} = \frac{(\vec{i}y' - \vec{j}x')\cdot(\vec{i}x'' + \vec{j}y'')}{(\vec{i}y' - \vec{j}x')\cdot(\vec{i}y' - \vec{j}x')}\,(\vec{i}y' - \vec{j}x')$$

$$= \frac{y'x'' - x'y''}{y'^2 + (-x')(-x')}\,(\vec{i}y' - \vec{j}x') = \frac{x'y'' - y'x''}{x'^2 + y'^2}\,(-\vec{i}y' + \vec{j}x') = \vec{a}_N.$$

The answer is yes.

3. If $|\vec{a}_N| = 0$, then from (11), either $\kappa = 0$ or $ds/dt = 0$ since $|\vec{\eta}| = 1$. If $ds/dt \neq 0$, at least for some times, then there is motion but $\kappa = 0$, which means the path is a straight line. If, however, $ds/dt = 0$ at all times, then there is no motion at all.

4. $ds/dt = $ constant is given. Hence $d^2s/dt^2 = 0$ so $\vec{a}_T = 0$ from (10). Hence force $= m \times \vec{a} = m \times (\vec{a}_T + \vec{a}_N) = m \times \vec{a}_N.$

Sec. 9-7, p. 306.

1. **a.** $y = c^2(3x - 2c).$ **c.** $x + 3c^2y = 3c^5 + c.$
   e. $x^2 + y^2 - 6(x\cos\theta + y\sin\theta) + 5 = 0.$
   g. $y^2 = 4(2 - c)(x - c), c \neq 2.$ Vertex at $(c, 0).$
   i. $x^2/a^2 + y^2/(a^2 - 4) = 1, a \neq 0, a \neq \pm 2.$
2. **a.** $2xy\,(dy/dx) + x^2 - y^2 = 0.$ **c.** $(x + y^2)(dy/dx) = y.$
   e. $4xy^3(dy/dx) + 2x^3 - y^4 + 5 = 0.$
3. **a.** $(dy/dx)^2 - 4x(dy/dx) + 4y = 0.$
   c. $(x^2 - 2xy - y^2)(dy/dx) = x^2 + 2xy - y^2.$

Sec. 9-8, p. 310.

1. **a.** A four-leaf clover with a leaf in each quadrant.
   c. Circle tangent to initial ray at the pole and below the ray.
   e. Eight leaves.   **g.** Same as **f.**
2. **c.** $\theta = \pi/2, \theta = 5\pi/2.$ The points $(\sin\frac{1}{2}\theta, \theta)$ and $(\cos\frac{1}{2}\theta, \theta)$ trace out the same curve but are at different places except for $\theta = \pi/2$ or $\theta = 5\pi/2, 0 \leq \theta \leq 4\pi.$
3. **a.** A loop through $(3, 0°), (2, 90°), (1, 180°), (2, 270°), (3, 360°).$
   c. A loop within a loop.   **e.** Circle.
4. **a.** $2 + \cos 90° = 2 \neq -2.$ However, the point $(-2, 90°)$ is also the point $(2, 270°)$ and $2 + \cos 270° = 2.$
   c. $(\sqrt{3}/2, 60°)$ is also $(-\sqrt{3}/2, -120°),$ which satisfy $\rho = \sin(\theta/2).$
   e. $(1, 3\pi)$ is also $(1, \pi),$ which satisfy $\pi\rho = \theta.$
   g. $(0, 0°)$ is also $(0, 90°),$ which satisfy $\rho = \cos\theta.$

Sec. 9-9, p. 316.

1. **a.** $\rho(4\cos\theta + 3\sin\theta) = 6.$ This may be written as
   $$\rho\sin(\theta + \alpha) = \tfrac{6}{5}, \text{ where } \sin\alpha = \tfrac{4}{5} \text{ and } \cos\alpha = \tfrac{3}{5}, \text{ or as}$$
   $$\rho\cos(\theta - \beta) = \tfrac{6}{5}, \text{ where } \cos\beta = \tfrac{4}{5} \text{ and } \sin\beta = \tfrac{3}{5}.$$

c. $\rho = 4 \cos \alpha$. **e.** $\rho = \sqrt{2^{3/2} \sin (\theta + \frac{1}{4}\pi)}$, $-\frac{1}{4}\pi \le \theta \le \frac{3}{4}\pi$.

g. $\rho = 2a/(1 - \cos \theta)$ or $\rho = -2a/(1 + \cos \theta)$.

2. a. $(x + 2)^2/16 + y^2/12 = 1$. **c.** $x^2 + (y - 2)^2 = 4$.

e. $(x^2 + y^2)^3 = 16(x^2 - y^2)^2$.

3. a. The graph of the first equation also has equation

$$\rho = -\sin \frac{\theta + \pi}{2} = -\sin \left(\frac{\theta}{2} + \frac{\pi}{2}\right) = -\cos \frac{\theta}{2}, \text{ then also}$$

$$\rho = +\cos \left(\frac{\theta}{2} + \frac{\pi}{2}\right) = -\sin \frac{\theta}{2} \text{ and finally also}$$

$$\rho = +\sin \left(\frac{\theta}{2} + \frac{\pi}{2}\right) = \cos \frac{\theta}{2}.$$

c. The graph of the first equation in the answer of **1. g** also has equation

$$\rho = -\frac{2a}{1 - \cos (\theta + \pi)} = \frac{-2a}{1 + \cos \theta}.$$

4. a. $(\frac{1}{2}, \pm 120°), (2, 0°)$, pole. **c.** $(\frac{1}{2}, \pm 60°)$, pole.

e. $(1, \pm 45°), (1, \pm 135°)$, pole.

Sec. 9-10, p. 321.

1. a. $\rho^2 = \dfrac{a^2(1 - e^2)}{1 - e^2 \cos^2\theta}$. **c.** $\rho = \dfrac{-a(1 - e^2)}{1 + e \cos \theta}$ or $\rho = \dfrac{a(1 - e^2)}{1 - e \cos \theta}$.

2. a. $e = \frac{3}{5}, -eq = -16/5, q = 16/3, a = 5, c = 3, b = 4,$

$F_1(0, 0°), F_2(6, 0°), C(3, 0°), V_1(2, 180°), V_2(8, 0)$. Ellipse.

c. $e = \frac{1}{2}, q = -3, a = 2, c = 1, b = \sqrt{3}, F_1(0, 0°), F_2(2, 180°), C(1, 180°),$

$V_1(1, 0°), V_2(3, 180°)$. Ellipse.

4. In the equations of conics in the text replace θ by $\theta + 90°$ and obtain

$$\rho = \frac{eq}{1 - e \sin \theta} \quad \text{or} \quad \rho = \frac{-eq}{1 + e \sin \theta}.$$

5. a. $(1, \pm 90°)$. **b.** $(\frac{3}{2}, \pm 60°)$. Note that when the given expressions are set equal, the result is $\cos \theta = -1$, which is not permissible in either case.

Sec. 9-11, p. 325.

1. c. Subtract angles at which the curves pass through the pole.

2. a. $46°6'$. **c.** $90°$. **3. a.** $60°$. **c.** $71°34'$.

4. a. $46°6', 46°6', 0°, 90°$. **c.** $79°6', 0°$.

Sec. 9-13, p. 331.

1. $\frac{1}{4}(e^{2\pi} - e^{-2\pi}), e^\pi - e^{-\pi}$.

2. a. $\pi\sqrt{1 + \pi^2} + \ln (\pi + \sqrt{1 + \pi^2}), \frac{1}{3}\pi^3$.

b. $8, \frac{3}{2}\pi$. **d.** $\pi\sqrt{a^2 + b^2}, \frac{1}{4}\pi(a^2 + b^2)$.

3. a. $2 |a|$. **b.** The graph has rectangular equation $x = a$.

c. $4 |a|/\sqrt{3}$. **d.** $2a^2/\sqrt{3}$.

4. c. $a^2 \pi/4n$.

6. No. Since $q < 0$, the numerator of ρ is positive, and since $0 < e < 1$, the denominator of ρ is also positive. Hence, $\vec{r}$ is directed away from the pole. Also, since $q < 0$, c^2/eq is negative so $\vec{a}$ is opposite to $\vec{r}$.

7. With $b = \sqrt{a^2 - (ae)^2}$, the area of the ellipse is πab. Hence,

$$\pi ab = \int_{t=0}^{t=T} \tfrac{1}{2} \rho^2 \, d\theta = \int_0^T \tfrac{1}{2} c_1 \, dt = \tfrac{1}{2} c_1 T,$$

$$T = \frac{2\pi}{c_1} ab, \quad T^2 = \frac{4\pi^2}{c_1^2}(1 - e^2) a^4.$$

Sec. 9-14, p. 337.

1. **a.** $-1, \tfrac{1}{2}(1 \pm i\sqrt{3})$. **c.** $\pm 2, \pm 2i$.
3. **c.** Since $2 = 2 + i \cdot 0$, it follows from part b that

$$(\sin x)\frac{e^y + e^{-y}}{2} = 2, (\cos x)\frac{e^y - e^{-y}}{2} = 0.$$

From the second equation, $\cos x = 0$. For if $e^y - e^{-y} = 0$, then $y = 0$ and the first equation would be $\sin x = 2$, which is impossible with x real. Hence, a possible value of x is $x = \pi/2$. For $x = \pi/2$, the first equation may be written

$$e^y + e^{-y} = 4, e^{2y} - 4e^y + 1 = 0, e^y = \frac{4 \pm \sqrt{16 - 4}}{2} = 2 \pm \sqrt{3}.$$

Thus, possible solutions of $\sin z = 2$ are $z = \tfrac{1}{2}\pi + i \ln (2 \pm \sqrt{3})$. It should be checked that these are both solutions.

Sec. 9-15, p. 341.

1. Since r is greatest and least when $\theta = 0$ and $\theta = \pi$, respectively,

$$2a = r_0 + r_\pi = \frac{c_1^2}{k}\left[\frac{1}{1 - (c_1 c_2/k)} + \frac{1}{1 + (c_1 c_2/k)}\right], a = \frac{c_1^2 k}{k^2 - c_1^2 c_2^2};$$

$$b = a\sqrt{1 - e^2} = a\sqrt{1 - \left(\frac{c_1 c_2}{k}\right)^2} = \frac{c_1^2}{\sqrt{k^2 - c_1^2 c_2^2}}.$$

2. **b.** $\theta = \pi$ and $\theta = 0$, respectively.

Sec. 9-16, p. 347.

1. $$\frac{r_0^2 \omega_0^2}{2gR^2 - r_0^3 \omega_0^2} = r_0 + 200, \frac{r_0^3 \omega_0^2}{gR^2} = \frac{r_0 + 200}{r_0 + 100} = \frac{R + 300}{R + 200},$$

$$e = \frac{R + 300}{R + 200} - 1 = \frac{100}{R + 200}.$$

$$v_0 = r_0 \omega_0 = \sqrt{\frac{gR^2(R + 300)}{r_0(R + 200)}} = \sqrt{\frac{gR^2(R + 300)}{(R + 100)(R + 200)}},$$

$$(R + 300)^2 \theta'(\pi) = r_0^2 \omega_0 = \sqrt{\frac{gR^2(R + 300)(R + 100)}{R + 200}}.$$

$$v_\pi = (R + 300) \theta'(\pi) = \sqrt{\frac{gR^2(R + 100)}{(R + 300)(R + 200)}}.$$

2. With m the distance to the moon, (19) yields

$$r_0^4 \omega_0^2 = m(2gR^2 - r_0^3 \omega_0^2), r_0^3 \omega_0^2(r_0 + m) = 2gmR^2,$$

$$r_0 \omega_0 = \sqrt{\frac{2gmR^2}{r_0(r_0 + m)}} = \sqrt{\frac{2(32.2)(237,000)(3930)^2(5280)}{(4030)(241,030)}} \text{ ft/sec} = 6.771 \text{ mi/sec}.$$

3. **a.** 6.699 mi/sec. **b.** 6.924 mi/sec. **c.** 6.717 mi/sec. **d.** 6.784 mi/sec.
   e. 7.011 mi/sec.

Sec. 10-2, p. 354.

1. a. $(2, 1, -4)$.   **c.** $(3, -1, -7)$.   **e.** $(5, -7, 4)$.   **g.** $(-2, 2, -3)$.

2. a. $27°, 63°, 3\sqrt{21}$.

4. a. $AC = BC = \sqrt{14}, 44°26', 2\sqrt{6}$.

5. a. $\left(5 \pm \dfrac{10}{\sqrt{77}}, -4 \mp \dfrac{8}{\sqrt{77}}, 6 \pm \dfrac{12}{\sqrt{77}}\right)$.

6. a. The line from the first center to the second center has parametric equations
$$x = -1 + 4t, y = 1 + 8t, z = -5 + 4t.$$
This line pierces the first sphere when $t = \pm\frac{1}{4}$ and the second sphere when $t = \frac{1}{2}$ and $t = \frac{3}{2}$. The desired points are $(0, 3, -4)$ and $(1, 5, -3)$ obtained from $t = \frac{1}{4}$ and $t = \frac{1}{2}$.

7. a. No.

Sec. 10-3, p. 358.

1. a. Direction numbers are $6 - 2 = 4, 1 - 1 = 0, 0 - (-3) = 3$. Hence, direction cosines are $\cos \alpha = 4/\sqrt{4^2 + 0^2 + 3^2} = \frac{4}{5}, \cos \beta = 0, \cos \gamma = \frac{3}{5}$.

2. a. From (2), $\cos^2 \alpha + \cos^2 \beta + \cos^2 \gamma = (a^2 + b^2 + c^2)/(a^2 + b^2 + c^2) = 1$.

   c. If $0 < \alpha < 90°, 0 < \beta < 90°$ and $\alpha + \beta < 90°$, then $0 < \alpha < 90° - \beta$,
   $\cos \alpha > \cos (90° - \beta) = \sin \beta > 0$, so that
   $\cos^2 \alpha > \sin^2 \beta = 1 - \cos^2 \beta$ and $\cos^2 \alpha + \cos^2 \beta > 1$.

   e. $\cos^2 \gamma = 1 - \cos^2 \alpha - \cos^2 \beta = \sin^2 \alpha - \cos^2 \beta$
   $= (\sin \alpha - \cos \beta)(\sin \alpha + \cos \beta)$.

3. a. $\cos^2 \gamma = 1 - (\frac{1}{4} + \frac{1}{2}) = \frac{1}{4}; \gamma_1 = 60°, \gamma_2 = 120°, \theta = 60°$.

   c. $\cos^2 \gamma = 1 - [(0.5736)^2 + (0.7431)^2] = 1 - 0.8812 = 0.1188$;
   $\log \cos^2 \gamma = 19.0749 - 20, \log \cos \gamma = 9.5375 - 10$;
   $\gamma_1 = 69°50', \gamma_2 = 110°10', \theta = 40°20'$.

4. a. Let $f(t)$ be the square of the distance from P_0 to a general point on the line:
   $f(t) = (2t - 1 + 2)^2 + (4t - 6 - 1)^2 + (-7t + 10 + 6)^2$,
   $f'(t) = 2[2(2t + 1) + 4(4t - 7) - 7(-7t + 16)]$
   $= 2[69t - 138] = 0$ for $t = 2, f''(t) > 0$.
   Hence, minimum distance $= \sqrt{f(2)} = \sqrt{30}$.
   Also, point where minimum occurs is $(3, 2, -4)$.

5. a. $(6, 5, -1), (-2, 1, 3)$.   **6. a.** $x = 1 + 5t, y = -2 + 3t, z = 3 + 6t$.

Sec. 10-4, p. 364.

1. a, 2. a, and **3. a.** $3x + 5y - z = 18$.   **4. a.** $3x + 5y - z = 14$.

5. a. $2x - 3y + z = 18$.   **c.** $x = 2$.   **6. a.** $2, -1, 3$.   **c.** $3, -1, 2$.

7. The line pierces the plane when t satisfies
   $A(x_0 + At) + B(y_0 + Bt) + C(z_0 + Bt) = D$ and thus when
   $$t = t_0 = [D - (Ax_0 + By_0 + Cz_0)]/(A^2 + B^2 + C^2).$$
   The pierce point (x_1, y_1, z_1) has $x_1 = x_0 + At_0, y_1 = y_0 + Bt_0$, and $z_1 = z_0 + Ct_0$.
   Hence,
   distance $= \sqrt{(x_1 - x_0)^2 + (y_1 - y_0)^2 + (z_1 - z_0)^2} = \sqrt{(At_0)^2 + (Bt_0)^2 + (Ct_0)^2}$
   $=$ etc.

Sec. 10-5, p. 367.

1. a. -27. **b.** -13. **c.** 1. **d.** -1. **e.** 34. **f.** -7. **g.** -14.

Sec. 10-6, p. 373.

1. a. Vectors from $(3, 2, 1)$ to the other points are $\vec{u} = 2\vec{i} - \vec{j} + \vec{k}$ and $\vec{v} = -\vec{i} + \vec{j} + 2\vec{k}$. Hence, $\vec{u} \times \vec{v} = -3\vec{i} - 5\vec{j} + \vec{k}$, being perpendicular to the plane, furnish the coefficients $-3, -5, 1$. Hence the plane, using $(3, 2, 1)$ as one of its points, has equation
$$-3(x - 3) - 5(y - 2) + 1(z - 1) = 0, \quad 3x + 5y - z = 18,$$
without finding a single simultaneous solution.

2. a. The coefficients of t give one vector $\vec{u} = 2\vec{i} - \vec{j} + \vec{k}$. The points $(3, 2, 1)$ (by putting $t = 0$) and $(4, 1, -1)$ furnish another vector in the plane.

4, 5. Cross products are no help here.

6. Same technique as the first part of Example 2.

7. a. $T = \frac{1}{2}\sqrt{7^2 + 1^2 + 4^2} = \frac{1}{2}\sqrt{66}$. The points projected onto the (x, y) - plane are $(1, 2, 0), (0, 5, 0), (2, 3, 0)$ or, better yet, $\vec{u} = \overrightarrow{AB}$ and $\vec{v} = \overrightarrow{AC}$ projected onto the (x, y)-plane are $-\vec{i} + 3\vec{j} + 0\vec{k}$ and $\vec{i} + \vec{j} + 0\vec{k}$, so that
$T_1 = \frac{1}{2}|(-\vec{i} + 3\vec{j}) \times (\vec{i} + \vec{j})| = 2, T_2 = \frac{1}{2}, T_3 = \frac{7}{2}$.

8. a. $\frac{1}{6}$.

9. a. $5x + 3y + 9z = 43$. [Hint: From the coefficients of t, the plane is parallel to both $\vec{u} = 3\vec{i} + \vec{j} - 2\vec{k}$ and $\vec{v} = -6\vec{i} + \vec{j} + 3\vec{k}$. Hence the plane is perpendicular to $\vec{u} \times \vec{v}$. The plane contains the point $(2, -1, 4)$.]

10. a. $5x + 4y - 3z = 3$. [Hint: With $\vec{u}_1$ and $\vec{u}_2$ normals to the plane, $\vec{u}_1 \times \vec{u}_2$ is parallel to the intersection. Since $\overrightarrow{P_1 P_2}$ is in the plane, it follows that $\overrightarrow{P_1 P_2} \times (\vec{u}_1 \times \vec{u}_2)$ is normal to the plane.]

Sec. 10-7, p. 377.

1. a.
$$(2\vec{i} - 3\vec{j} + \vec{k}) \times \begin{vmatrix} \vec{i} & \vec{j} & \vec{k} \\ 1 & 4 & -2 \\ 3 & -1 & 1 \end{vmatrix} = \begin{vmatrix} \vec{i} & \vec{j} & \vec{k} \\ 2 & -3 & 1 \\ 2 & -7 & -13 \end{vmatrix} = 46\vec{i} + 28\vec{j} - 8\vec{k},$$

$(6 + 3 + 1)(\vec{i} + 4\vec{j} - 2\vec{k}) - (2 - 12 - 2)(3\vec{i} - \vec{j} + \vec{k}) = 46\vec{i} + 28\vec{j} - 8\vec{k}$.

c. $-2\vec{i} + 4\vec{j} + 19\vec{k}$.

2. $(\vec{A} \vec{B} \vec{D})\vec{C} - (\vec{A} \vec{B} \vec{C})\vec{D}$, which therefore means that
$$(\vec{A} \vec{C} \vec{D})\vec{B} - (\vec{B} \vec{C} \vec{D})\vec{A} = (\vec{A} \vec{B} \vec{D})\vec{C} - (\vec{A} \vec{B} \vec{C})\vec{D}.$$

3. a. $(\vec{B} \vec{B} \vec{C}) = (\vec{B} \times \vec{B}) \cdot \vec{C} = \vec{0} \cdot \vec{C} = 0$.

c. $(\vec{A} \vec{B} \vec{C}) = \begin{vmatrix} 1 & 2 & 3 \\ 2 & -1 & 0 \\ -4 & 1 & 1 \end{vmatrix} = -11, (\vec{D} \vec{B} \vec{C}) = \begin{vmatrix} -12 & 7 & -3 \\ 2 & -1 & 0 \\ -4 & 1 & 1 \end{vmatrix} = 4,$

$x = 4/(-11)$. Similarly, $y = 106/(11), z = 21/(11)$.

4. a. $= \vec{A} \cdot (\vec{C} \times \vec{D}) + \vec{B} \cdot (\vec{C} \times \vec{D}) = (\vec{A}\,\vec{C}\,\vec{D}) + (\vec{B}\,\vec{C}\,\vec{D}).$

c. Use mean-minus-last law.

Sec. 10-8, p. 381.

4. d. $\vec{u} \times \vec{u}' = -2\omega\,\vec{a} \times \vec{b},\ \vec{u}'' = \omega^2 \vec{u},$

$(\vec{u}\,\vec{u}'\,\vec{u}'') = (\vec{u}\,\vec{u}'\,\omega^2\vec{u}) = \omega^2(\vec{u}\,\vec{u}'\,\vec{u}) = 0.$

Sec. 10-9, p. 389.

1. From the expression for $\vec{n}$ in (20),

$$\frac{d\vec{n}}{ds} = \frac{d\vec{n}}{dt}\frac{dt}{ds} = \frac{1}{\sqrt{2}}\{\vec{i}(-\cos t + \sin t) + \vec{j}(-\sin t - \cos t)\}\frac{1}{\sqrt{3}\,e^t}.$$

The right-hand side of (12) is

$$-\kappa\vec{t} - \tau\vec{b} = -\frac{\sqrt{2}}{3e^t}\frac{1}{\sqrt{3}}\{\vec{i}(\cos t - \sin t) + \vec{j}(\sin t + \cos t) + \vec{k}\}$$

$$-\left(\frac{-1}{3e^t}\right)\frac{1}{\sqrt{6}}\{\vec{i}(-\cos t + \sin t) + \vec{j}(-\sin t - \cos t) + 2\vec{k}\}$$

$$= \frac{1}{3\sqrt{6}\,e^t}\{-2\vec{i}(\cos t - \sin t) - 2\vec{j}(\sin t + \cos t) - 2\vec{k}$$

$$+ \vec{i}(-\cos t + \sin t) + \vec{j}(-\sin t - \cos t) + 2k\}$$

$$= \frac{1}{3\sqrt{6}\,e^t}\{\vec{i}(-3\cos t + 3\sin t) + \vec{j}(-3\sin t - 3\cos t)\}$$

$$= \frac{1}{\sqrt{6}\,e^t}\{\vec{i}(-\cos t + \sin t) \mp j(-\sin t - \cos t)\},$$

which is equivalent to the above expression for $d\vec{n}/ds$.

2. a. The distance between $(a\cos t, a\sin t, ct)$ and $(0, 0, ct)$ is equal to a for all t.

b. $\dfrac{ds}{dt} = \{(-a\sin t)^2 + (a\cos t)^2 + c\}^{1/2} = \sqrt{a^2 + c^2}$, so that

$$\int_0^{2\pi}\left(\frac{ds}{dt}\right)dt = \int_0^{2\pi}\sqrt{a^2 + c^2}\ dt = 2\pi\sqrt{a^2 + c^2}.$$

c. $\vec{t} = \dfrac{d\vec{u}}{ds} = \dfrac{d\vec{u}}{dt}\dfrac{dt}{ds} = \{\vec{i}(-a\sin t) + \vec{j}a\cos t + \vec{k}c\}\dfrac{1}{\sqrt{a^2 + c^2}},$

$\dfrac{d\vec{t}}{ds} = \dfrac{d\vec{t}}{dt}\dfrac{dt}{ds} = -\{\vec{i}a\cos t + \vec{j}a\sin t\}\dfrac{1}{a^2 + c^2},$

$\kappa = \left|\dfrac{d\vec{t}}{ds}\right| = \dfrac{a}{a^2 + c^2},\ \vec{n} = \dfrac{1}{\kappa}\dfrac{d\vec{t}}{ds} = -\vec{i}\cos t - \vec{j}\sin t,$

$\vec{b} = \vec{t} \times \vec{n} = \dfrac{1}{\sqrt{a^2 + c^2}}(\vec{i}c\sin t - \vec{j}c\cos t + \vec{k}a),$

$\dfrac{d\vec{b}}{ds} = \dfrac{1}{\sqrt{a^2 + c^2}}(\vec{i}c\cos t + \vec{j}c\sin t)\dfrac{1}{\sqrt{a^2 + c^2}}$

$\qquad = \dfrac{c}{a^2 + c^2}(-\vec{n}),\ \tau = \dfrac{-c}{a^2 + c^2}.$

d. It is a circle in which κ is known to be $1/a$ and $\tau = 0$.

3. **a.** $\dfrac{ds}{dt} = 2\sqrt{2}\,\cosh 2t,\ \vec{t} = \dfrac{1}{\sqrt{2}}\,(\vec{i}\,\tanh 2t + \vec{j} + \vec{k}\,\mathrm{sech}\,2t),$

$\kappa = \tfrac{1}{2}\,\mathrm{sech}^2\,2t,\ \vec{n} = \vec{i}\,\mathrm{sech}\,2t - \vec{k}\,\tanh 2t.$

b. $\dfrac{ds}{dt} = 13,\ \vec{t} = \dfrac{1}{13}\,(-12\vec{i}\,\sin 3t + 12\vec{j}\,\cos 3t + 5\vec{k}),$

$\kappa = 36/(169),\ \vec{n} = -(\vec{i}\,\cos 3t + \vec{j}\,\sin 3t).$

c. $\dfrac{ds}{dt} = 3\sqrt{2}\,(1 + t^2),\ \vec{t} = \dfrac{1}{\sqrt{2}\,(1 + t^2)}\,[\vec{i}(1 - t^2) + \vec{j}\,2t + \vec{k}(1 + t^2)],$

$\kappa = \dfrac{1}{3(t^2 + 1)^2},\ \vec{n} = \dfrac{1}{(1 + t^2)}\,[-2\vec{i}t + \vec{j}(1 - t^2)].$

4. Work out $\vec{t}_1(t),\ \kappa_1(t),\ \vec{n}_1(t),\ \vec{t}_2(t),\ \kappa_2(t),$ and $\vec{n}_2(t)$. Then check that

$$\vec{t}_2(\ln t) = \vec{t}_1(t),\ \kappa_2(\ln t) = \kappa_1(t),\ \text{and}\ \vec{n}_2(\ln t) = \vec{n}_1(t).$$

5. From the second formula in (8),

$$\frac{d^3 u}{ds^3} = \frac{d}{ds}\,(\kappa\vec{n}) = \text{etc., using (12).}$$

Sec. 10-10, p. 396.

1. **a.** A parabola in the (x, y)-plane, no third dimension.
   A parabola in the (x, y)-plane of (x, y, z)-space.
   A parabolic cylinder.
   c. Hyperbola in an (x, z)-plane (no y-axis), asymptotic to the axes. Same shape hyperbola in (x, y, z)-space, but in the plane perpendicular to the y-axis at $(0, 2, 0)$. Hyperbolic cylinder.

2. **a.** Circular hyperboloid of one sheet with axis of symmetry the line perpendicular to the (x, y)-plane at $(1, 0, 0)$.
   c. Circular cone with vertex $(1, -2, -3)$ and axis through this point parallel to the z-axis.

3. **a.** With (x_0, y_0, z_0) on the surface, the lines
   $$L_1\colon x = x_0 + t,\, y = y_0 + t,\, z = z_0 + 2(y_0 - x_0)\,t$$
   $$L_2\colon x = x_0 - t,\, y = y_0 + t,\, z = z_0 + 2(y_0 + x_0)\,t$$
   are completely on the surface.

4. Any line with equations
   $x = At,\, y = \pm\sqrt{1 - A^2}\,t,\, z = t,$ with $|A| < 1,$ passes through the origin and lies on the cone.

   Through (x_0, y_0, z_0) on the cone, with $z_0 \neq 0$, the only line on the cone is
   $$x = x_0 + \frac{x_0}{z_0}\,t,\, y = y_0 + \frac{y_0}{z_0}\,t,\, z = z_0 + t.$$
   Upon changing the parameter by setting $t = z_0 s - z_0$, this line has equations
   $$x = x_0 s,\quad y = y_0 s,\quad z = z_0 s.$$

5. **b.** $L_1\colon x = x_0,\, y = y_0 + t,\, z = z_0 + x_0 t$
   $L_2\colon x = x_0 + t,\, y = y_0,\, z = z_0 + y_0 t.$
   c. Hint: In the (x, y)-plane rotate the axes $45°$.

6. **a.** If the (x, y)-axes are rotated $45°$, the result is
   $$X^2 + 2Y^2 - z^2 = 0;\ \text{if} - 45°,\ \text{then}\ 2X^2 + Y^2 - z^2 = 0.$$
   c. Set $x = X + h,\, y = Y + k,\, z = Z + l$ and determine $h, k,$ and l to eliminate

first-degree terms. The result is $X^2 + YZ = 0$, known by part b to be an elliptic cone.

7. a. Two planes $x + y + z = 1$ and $x - y + z = 1$.
   c. Hyperbolic cylinder $xY = 2\sqrt{2}$.

Sec. 10-11, p. 399.

1. a. $(\sqrt{2}, 45°, 1), (\sqrt{3}, 45°, 54°44'); \alpha = \beta = \gamma = 54°44'$.
   c. $(\sqrt{5}, 26°34', -2), (3, 26°34', 131°49'); 48°11', 70°32', 131°49'$.
   e. $(2, 120°, 2), (2\sqrt{2}, 120°, 45°); 110°42', 52°14', 45°$.
2. a. $(2, 210°, 150°)$.   **c.** $(2, 330°, 150°)$.
3. a. Reflections in x-, y-, z-axes, (x, y)-, (x, z)-, and (y, z)-planes:
   $(2, 30°, -60°), (2, 30°, 60°), (2, -30°, 120°),$
   $(2, 150°, 60°), (2, 210°120°), (2, 30°, 120°)$.
4. a. $\frac{5}{2}\sqrt{3}\,h$.   **c.** $5h$.

Sec. 11-2, p. 404.

1. a. $2xy^3 + y^2, 3x^2 y^2 + 2xy$.   **c.** $yx^{y-1}, x^y \ln x$.

2. a. $\dfrac{-y}{x^2 + y^2}, \dfrac{x}{x^2 + y^2}$.   **c.** $\dfrac{-y}{|x|}\dfrac{1}{\sqrt{x^2 - y^2}}, \dfrac{|x|}{x}\dfrac{1}{\sqrt{x^2 - y^2}}$.

3. a. $2xy(x^2 + 1)^{y-1}, (x^2 + 1)^y \ln(x^2 + 1)$.   **c.** $-2y(x - y)^{-2}, 2x(x - y)^{-2}$.

4. a. $-xy \sin(xy) + \cos(xy)$ first two parts,
   $-x^2 \sin(xy)$ last two parts.
   c. $\cos(3x) - 3x \sin(3x), -x^2 \sin(3x); \cos(3x) - 3x \sin(3x), 0$.

5. a. $2xy^3 \sec^2(x^2 y)$ first two parts,
   $x^2 y^2 \sec^2(x^2 y) + 2y \tan(x^2 y)$ last two parts.
   c. $54x \sec^2(3x^2), 9x^2 \sec^2(3x^2) + 6 \tan(3x^2); 54x \sec^2(3x^2), 0$.

6. c. First part,

$$\lim_{\Delta x \to 0} \frac{(x + \Delta x) \sin[y(x + \Delta x)] - x \sin(xy)}{\Delta x}$$

$$= \lim_{\Delta x \to 0} \left\{ \frac{x[\sin(xy + y\Delta x) - \sin(xy)]}{\Delta x} + \sin(xy + y\,\Delta x) \right\}$$

$$= x \lim_{\Delta x \to 0} \left\{ \frac{\sin(xy)\cos(y\,\Delta x) + \cos(xy)\sin(y\,\Delta x) - \sin(xy)}{\Delta x} \right\} + \sin(xy)$$

$$= -x \sin(xy) \lim_{\Delta x \to 0} \frac{1 - \cos(y\,\Delta x)}{\Delta x}$$

$$+ x \cos(xy) \lim_{\Delta x \to 0} \frac{\sin(y\,\Delta x)}{\Delta x} + \sin(xy)$$

$$= -xy \sin(xy) \lim_{\Delta x \to 0} \frac{1 - \cos(y\,\Delta x)}{y\,\Delta x}$$

$$+ xy \cos(xy) \lim_{\Delta x \to 0} \frac{\sin(y\,\Delta x)}{y\,\Delta x} + \sin(xy)$$

$$= [-xy \sin(xy)] \cdot 0 + [xy \cos(xy)] \cdot 1 + \sin(xy)$$

$$= xy \cos(xy) + \sin(xy).$$

Sec. 11-4, p. 413.

2. a. $6x - 8y + z = -25; x = -3 + 6t, y = 4 - 8t, z = 25 + t$.

c. $4x - 2y + 4z = \pi - 6; x = -1 + 2t, y = 1 - t, z = \frac{1}{4}\pi + 2t.$

e. $2x - z = 2; x = 1 + 2t, y = 0, z = -t.$

4. a. $\dfrac{\partial z}{\partial x} = -\dfrac{y + z}{x + y}, \dfrac{\partial z}{\partial y} = -\dfrac{x + z}{x + y}, \dfrac{\partial y}{\partial x} = -\dfrac{y + z}{x + z}.$ Therefore,

$$\frac{\partial z}{\partial y}\frac{\partial y}{\partial x} = \frac{y + z}{x + y} = -\frac{\partial z}{\partial x}.$$

5. a. $2x + 3y - 4z = 4.$

7. a. Since $f(h, h) = \frac{1}{2}$, the initial point of $\vec{N}(h, h)$ is $(h, h, \frac{1}{2})$, which does not approach $(0, 0, 0)$ as $h \to 0$. [Note: This shows that $f(x, y)$ is not continuous at the origin.]

b. $\vec{N}(h, 2h) = (6/25h)\vec{i} - (3/25h)\vec{j} + \vec{k}$, so that an angle θ between this normal and $\vec{N}(0, 0) = \vec{k}$ is such that

$$\cos\theta = \frac{25\,|h|}{\sqrt{45 + (25h)^2}},$$

which approaches 0 (so θ approaches $90°$) as $h \to 0$.

c. Yes. $6x - 3y - 25z = -10$. In fact, the surface has a tangent plane at each of its points except the origin.

Sec. 11-6, p. 421.

1. a. $dz/ds = 2x(-e^s \sin s + e^s \cos s) + 2y(e^s \cos s + e^s \sin s)$
$\qquad = 2e^s(\cos s)\,e^s(-\sin s + \cos s) + 2e^s(\sin s)\,e^s(\cos s + \sin s)$
$\qquad = 2e^{2s}(-\cos s \sin s + \cos^2 s + \sin s \cos s + \sin^2 s) = 2e^{2s}.$
$\qquad z = (e^s \cos s)^2 + (e^s \sin s)^2 = e^{2s}(\cos^2 s + \sin^2 s) = e^{2s},$
$\qquad dz/ds = 2e^{2s}.$

c. $dz/ds = (1 - y)(2s) - (1 + x)\,3s^2 = (1 - s^3)\,2s - (1 + s^2)\,3s^2$
$\qquad = -5s^4 - 3s^2 + 2s.$
$\qquad z = (1 + s^2)(1 - s^3) = 1 + s^2 - s^3 - s^5,$
$\qquad dz/ds = 2s - 3s^2 - 5s^4.$

2. a. $\partial z/\partial s = 0, \partial z/\partial t = 2e^t.$

c. $\partial z/\partial s = t - t^2 - 2st^3, \partial z/\partial t = s - 2st - 3s^2t^2.$

3. a. $\partial z/\partial x = 2xy\,f'(x^2 y), \partial z/\partial y = x^2 f'(x^2 y)$; therefore, $x(\partial z/\partial x) = 2y(\partial z/\partial y).$

c. $\partial z/\partial x = 2x\,f'(x^2 + y^2), \partial z/\partial y = 2y\,f'(x^2 + y^2)$; therefore, $y(\partial z/\partial x) = x(\partial z/\partial y).$

e. $\partial z/\partial x = 1 + y\,f'(x, y), \partial z/\partial y = x\,f'(xy)$; therefore,
$\qquad x(\partial z/\partial x) = x + xy\,f'(xy) = x + y(\partial z/\partial y).$

g. $\partial z/\partial x = y^n[mx^{m-1}f(y/x) + x^m f'(y/x)(-y/x^2)]$
$\qquad = x^{m-2}y^n[mxf(y/x) - yf'(y/x)],$
$\qquad \partial z/\partial y = x^m[ny^{n-1}f(y/x) + y^n f'(y/x)(1/x)]$
$\qquad = x^{m-1}y^{n-1}[nxf(y/x) + yf'(y/x)],$
$\qquad x(\partial z/\partial x) = x^{m-1}y^n[mxf(y/x) - yf'(y/x)],$
$\qquad y(\partial z/\partial y) = x^{m-1}y^n[nxf(y/x) + yf'(y/x)],$
$\qquad x(\partial z/\partial x) + y(\partial z/\partial y) = x^{m-1}y^n[(m + n)\,xf(y/x)]$
$\qquad = x^m y^n(m + n)\,z.$

Sec. 11-7, p. 428.

1. a. $\vec{\nabla} z = (2x - y)\vec{i} + (-x + 2y)\vec{j}, \vec{\theta} = \frac{1}{5}(3\vec{i} + 4\vec{j}),$

$D[z(1, 2), \vec{\theta}] = (0\vec{i} + 3\vec{j}) \cdot (3\vec{i} + 4\vec{j})\frac{1}{5} = 12/5$. **c.** 1.

2. a. $-2(x^2 + y^2)^{-1/2}$. **c.** 0.

3. a. $(c, -\frac{4}{5}c)$. [Hint: Find minimum of $z_x^2(c_1 y) + z_y^2(c, y)$.]

    b. At $(c, \pm\sqrt{1 - c^2})$ if $|c| \leq 1$; at $(c, 0)$ if $|c| > 1$.

    [Hint: Since the maximum directional derivative at (c, y) is equal to $2\sqrt{e^{-c^2}e^{-y^2}(c^2 + y^2)}$, it is necessary merely to find where the maximum value occurs for $g(y) = e^{-y^2}(c^2 + y^2)$. Since $g'(y) = 2ye^{-y^2}(1 - c^2 - y^2)$, two cases must be considered according to whether $1 - c^2 \geq 0$ or $1 - c^2 < 0$. In case $c^2 \leq 1$, show that

$$g''(\pm\sqrt{1 - c^2}) = 4e^{-(1-c^2)}(c^2 - 1) \leq 0.]$$

4. a. $x^2 + 3y^2 = c^2$. **c.** $xy^2 = c$. **e.** $\cos x = ce^{y^2}$.

5. Hint 1: Obtain the differential equation

$$y(y')^2 + 2xy' = y$$

of the family. In this equation, replace y' by $-1/y'$ and see that the same equation is obtained.

Hint 2: Show that two members

$$y = 4p(x + p) \text{ and } y = 4q(x + q)$$

intersect at the points $(-p - q, \pm\sqrt{-pq})$ if and only if p and q have opposite signs. Obtain the slopes of the curves at these points. Show that the product of the slopes at each point is equal to -1.

Sec. 11-8, p. 433.

1. a. $z_{xx} = -y^4 \sin(xy^2)$, $z_{xy} = 2y \cos(xy^2) - 2xy^3 \sin(xy^2) = z_{yx}$,
    $z_{yy} = 2x \cos(xy^2) - 4x^2 y^2 \sin(xy^2)$.

    c. $z_{xx} = 2y + 6xy^4$, $z_{xy} = 4y + 2x + 12x^2 y^2 = z_{yx}$,
    $z_{yy} = 4x + 12x^3 y$.

7. a. $\dfrac{\partial^2 u}{\partial x^2} = \dfrac{\partial}{\partial x}\left(\dfrac{\partial u}{\partial x}\right) = \dfrac{\partial}{\partial x}\left(\dfrac{\partial v}{\partial y}\right) = \dfrac{\partial}{\partial y}\left(\dfrac{\partial v}{\partial x}\right) = \dfrac{\partial}{\partial y}\left(-\dfrac{\partial u}{\partial y}\right) = -\dfrac{\partial^2 u}{\partial y^2}$.

    b. $\dfrac{\partial u}{\partial \rho} = \dfrac{\partial u}{\partial x}\dfrac{\partial x}{\partial \rho} + \dfrac{\partial u}{\partial y}\dfrac{\partial y}{\partial \rho} = \dfrac{\partial u}{\partial x}\cos\theta + \dfrac{\partial u}{\partial y}\sin\theta$,

    $\dfrac{\partial v}{\partial \theta} = \dfrac{\partial v}{\partial x}(-\rho\sin\theta) + \dfrac{\partial v}{\partial y}(\rho\cos\theta)$, and therefore

    $\dfrac{\partial u}{\partial \rho} - \dfrac{1}{\rho}\dfrac{\partial v}{\partial \theta} = \left(\dfrac{\partial u}{\partial x} - \dfrac{\partial v}{\partial y}\right)\cos\theta + \left(\dfrac{\partial u}{\partial y} + \dfrac{\partial v}{\partial x}\right)\sin\theta = 0$.

Sec. 11-9, p. 439

2. a. $f(x, y) = xy^2 + \frac{1}{3}(x^3 + y^3)$. **b.** Not exact.

    c. $f(x, y) = -e^{-x} \sin y$. **d.** Not exact.

    e. $f(x, y) = x^3 y + e^x + \ln|\cos y|$. **f.** Not exact.

3. a. $x^2 + y^2 - xy = c$. **c.** $x^2 + y^2 = c^2$. **e.** $x^3 y + x^2 - y = c$.

4. a. $xy^2 + \sin x + e^y = 2$.

Sec. 11-10, p. 445.

3. c. π. Circle of radius 1 with center $(1, 1)$ traced counterclockwise.

    d. 0. Circle of radius $\frac{1}{2}$ with center $(\frac{1}{2}, 0)$ traced clockwise.

4. First find that $\vec{F} = 2c(x^2 + y^2)^{-1}(-\vec{i}y + \vec{j}x)$.

    a. $2c(\frac{1}{4}\pi + \tan^{-1}7)$.   **b.** $4c\tan^{-1}2$. [Note: The answers in parts **a** and **b** are the same. Both $\tan^{-1}7$ and $\tan^{-1}2$ are in the first quadrant, but $\frac{1}{4}\pi + \tan^{-1}7$ and $2\tan^{-1}2$ are in the second quadrant. Check that
$$\tan(\tfrac{1}{4}\pi + \tan^{-1}7) = \tan(2\tan^{-1}2).]$$

    c. $2\pi c$. **d, e.** $4\pi c$. **f.** $2c\left[-\pi + 2(\tan^{-1}2 + \tan^{-1}\tfrac{1}{2})\right] = 0$.

Sec. 11-11, p. 451.

3. With the integrand $\vec{F} \cdot d\vec{r}$ omitted for easier writing, the integral around the polygon is equal to
$$\int_{C_1} + \int_{C_2} + \int_{C_3} + \int_{C_4} + \int_{C_5}.$$
With D_1' denoting D_1 traversed in the opposite direction,
$$\int_{D_1'} = -\int_{D_1}, \text{ so that } \int_{D_1'} + \int_{D_1} = 0.$$
The same is true of D_2. Hence, the integral around the polygon may be written
$$\left(\int_{C_1} + \int_{C_2} + \int_{D_1}\right) + \left(\int_{C_3} + \int_{C_4} + \int_{D_2}\right) + \left(\int_{D_1'} + \int_{D_2'} + \int_{C_5}\right),$$
with each parenthesis the integral around a triangle.

Sec. 12-2, p. 464.

1. a. $-3/20$. **c.** $\frac{1}{2}(1 - \cos 1)$. **e.** $\frac{2}{3}$.

2. a. $\dfrac{7}{12}$. **c.** $\displaystyle\int_0^1\int_x^1 (x^2 + xy)\,dy\,dx = \dfrac{5}{24}$ or $\displaystyle\int_0^1\int_0^y (x^2 + xy)\,dx\,dy$.

3. a. $\displaystyle\int_{-1}^1\int_{-\sqrt{1-x^2}}^{\sqrt{1-x^2}} (x + y + 3)\,dy\,dx = 3\pi$. **c.** $\dfrac{11}{6}$.

    e. $\dfrac{22}{3}$. **g.** $\displaystyle 16\int_0^a\int_0^x \sqrt{a^2 - x^2}\,dy\,dx = \dfrac{16}{3}a^3$.

Sec. 12-3, p. 467.

1. a. $\bar{x} = a/2,\ \bar{y} = b/2$.

    c. Mass $= k\dfrac{ab}{3}(a^2 + b^2)$, $M_y = k\dfrac{a^2 b}{12}(3a^2 + 4b^2)$,

$$\bar{x} = \frac{a}{4}\frac{3a^2 + 2b^2}{a^2 + b^2}, \quad \bar{y} = \frac{b}{4}\frac{2a^2 + 3b^2}{a^2 + b^2}.$$

2. a. $\bar{x} = \frac{1}{3}(a + b),\ \bar{y} = \frac{2}{3}h$.

    c. Mass $= k\left[\dfrac{b^3 - a^3}{3h^3} + \dfrac{b - a}{h}\right]\dfrac{h^4}{4}$,

$$\bar{x} = \tfrac{3}{4}(a + b)\frac{a^2 + b^2 + 2h^2}{a^2 + ab + b^2 + 3h^2}, \quad \bar{y} = \tfrac{4}{5}h.$$

3. a. Mass $= (16/3)k$, $\bar{x} = \frac{3}{4}$, $\bar{y} = \frac{8}{5}$.

    c. Mass $= k\,2^6(13/35)$, $\bar{x} = 35/52$, $\bar{y} = 280/117$.

4. a. $\bar{x} = \frac{1}{2}$, $\bar{y} = \frac{8}{5}$. **c.** $(\frac{1}{2}\pi, \frac{1}{8}\pi)$. **e.** $\bar{x} = \pi/4 - \ln\sqrt{2}$, $\bar{y} = \frac{2}{3}$.

5. a. $(13/7, 27/14)$. **c.** $\bar{x} = \frac{2}{7}[(64/3\pi) - 1]$, $\bar{y} = 124/21\pi$.

Sec. 12-5, p. 473.

1. a. $2\int_{3/4}^{3/2}\int_{0}^{\sqrt{9/4-x^2}} dy\,dx = \frac{3}{4}\pi - \frac{9}{16}\sqrt{3}$.

  b. $2\int_{0}^{\pi/3}\int_{(3/4)\,\sec\theta}^{3/2} \rho\,d\rho\,d\theta$. **c.** $\frac{27}{32}\sqrt{3}$.

2. a. $\bar{x} = \bar{\rho} = 128\sqrt{2}/105\pi,\ \bar{y} = \bar{\theta} = 0$.

  c. Area $= \left(\frac{\pi}{3} + \frac{\sqrt{3}}{2}\right)a^2,\ \bar{x} = \frac{8\pi + 3\sqrt{3}}{2(2\pi + 3\sqrt{3})}\,a,\ \bar{y} = 0$.

  [Hint: Check by method of Prob. 5, Sec. 12-3.]

3. a. $\theta = \pi/4,\ \bar{\rho} = (4\sqrt{2}/3\pi)r$. **c.** $\bar{x} = \frac{3}{8}r,\ \bar{y} = (3\pi/16)\,r$.

4. a. $\frac{4}{3}\pi$. **c.** $3\pi - (32/9)$. **e.** $\frac{1}{3}\pi r^2 h$.

Sec. 12-6, p. 476.

1. a. $I_x = h^3(b-a)/4,\ R_x = h/\sqrt{2},\ I_y = h(b^3 - a^3)/12,\ R_y = \sqrt{(a^2 + ab + b^2)/6}$.

  c. $I_x = h^3 b/12,\ R_x = h/\sqrt{6},\ I_y = hb^3/12,\ R_y = b/\sqrt{6}$.

  e. $I_x = \frac{1}{4}a^4\pi,\ R_x = \frac{1}{2}a,\ I_y = \frac{5}{4}\pi a^4,\ R_y = \frac{1}{2}\sqrt{5}\,a$.

  [Hint: Write the circle as $\rho = 2a\cos\theta$.]

  g. $I_x = \frac{128}{15},\ R_x = 2\sqrt{\frac{2}{5}},\ I_y = \frac{32}{5},\ R_y = \sqrt{\frac{6}{5}}$.

2. a. $\pi - 2$. **c.** $\int_{0}^{\pi/2}\int_{0}^{\cos x}\left(\frac{x-y}{\sqrt{2}}\right)^2 dy\,dx = \frac{3}{32}\pi^2 - \frac{55}{72}$. [Hint: Use the formula for

  the distance from a point to a line.]

3. a. Mass $= k\,\frac{2}{3}a^3,\ I = k\,\frac{4}{15}a^5,\ R = \sqrt{\frac{2}{5}}\,a$.

  c. $I = k\left(\frac{14}{15} - \frac{\pi}{4}\right)a^5,\ R = a\sqrt{\frac{7}{5} - \frac{3}{8}\pi}$.

5. $\frac{1}{6}(b^3 h^3)/(b^2 + h^2)$.

Sec. 12-7, p. 479.

1. b. $4\int_{0}^{2a}\int_{0}^{\sqrt{4a^2 - 2ax}} \frac{a}{\sqrt{2ax - x^2}}\,dy\,dx = 16a^2$.

2. a. $2\int_{0}^{\pi}\int_{0}^{a\sin\theta} \frac{a}{\sqrt{a^2 - \rho^2}}\,\rho\,d\rho\,d\theta = 2a^2(\pi - 2)$.

  c. $4a^2[\pi - \sqrt{2} - \ln(1 + \sqrt{2})]$.

3. $4a^2$. [Note: This is really Prob. 1 with a replaced by $a/2$.]

4. Spherical portion $= 2\pi a^2(2 - \sqrt{2})$; total $= 4a^2(4 - \sqrt{2})$.

6. a. $\frac{\sqrt{2}}{6}[(1 + 2b^2)^{3/2} - 1]$. **7. a.** $\frac{\sqrt{A^2 + B^2 + C^2}}{|C|}\,\pi a^2$. **9.** $16a^2$.

Sec. 12-8, p. 482.

2. a. $\int_{0}^{\pi/4}\int_{\tan y}^{1} x\,dx\,dy$. **c.** $\int_{0}^{\pi/2}\int_{0}^{\cos y} y\,dx\,dy$. **e.** $\int_{0}^{1}\int_{\sqrt{y}}^{2\sqrt{y}} x\,dx\,dy$.

Sec. 12-9, p. 486.

2. The integral appearing in the $\vec{i}$-component may be expressed in spherical coordinates as

$$\int_0^a \int_0^\pi \int_0^{2\pi} \frac{1}{r^2 + h^2 - 2hr\cos\phi} (\cos\theta)\, r^2 \sin\phi\, d\theta\, d\phi\, dr$$

$$= \int_0^a \int_0^\pi \left[\frac{r^2 \sin\phi}{r^2 + h^2 - 2hr\cos\phi} \int_0^{2\pi} \cos\theta\, d\theta \right] d\phi\, dr,$$

which has value zero since the inside integral does.

4. $\int_{-a}^a \frac{4}{3}\pi (\sqrt{a^2 - w^2})^3\, dw = \frac{1}{2}\pi^2 a^4.$

Sec. 13-2, p. 498.

1. a. The sequence $\{a_n - a\}$ is a null sequence and hence, by Lemma 1, is bounded. Let B be such that

$$|a_n - a| \le B, \qquad n = 1, 2, 3, \ldots.$$

Then $|a_n| = |(a_n - a) + a| \le |a_n - a| + |a| \le B + |a|$ and

$$-(B + |a|) \le a_n \le B + |a|, \qquad n = 1, 2, 3, \ldots.$$

This says that $\{a_n\}$ is bounded.

c. Let G be an arbitrarily large positive number. Corresponding to $\epsilon = 1/G$, let N be such that,

$$\text{whenever } n \ge N, \text{ then } 0 < a_n < \epsilon.$$

Hence, whenever $n \ge N$, then $1/a_n > 1/\epsilon = G$. This says that $1/a_n \to +\infty$.

e. Let $\epsilon > 0$ be arbitrary. Determine N_1 and N_2 such that,

$$\text{whenever } n \ge N_1, \text{ then } a - \epsilon < a_n < a + \epsilon, \text{ and}$$
$$\text{whenever } n \ge N_2, \text{ then } a - \epsilon < b_n < a + \epsilon.$$

Let N be the larger of N_1 and N_2. Hence,

$$\text{whenever } n \ge N, \text{ then } a - \epsilon < a_n \le c_n \le b_n < a + \epsilon;$$

that is, whenever $n \ge N$, then $a - \epsilon < c_n < a + \epsilon$. This says that $c_n \to a$.

g. Corresponding to $\epsilon > 0$ arbitray, let N be such that,

$$\text{whenever } n \ge N, \text{ then } |a_n - a| < \epsilon.$$

Hence, whenever $n \ge N$, then $|a_{n+3} - a| < \epsilon$; that is,

$$\text{whenever } n \ge N, \text{ then } |b_n - a| < \epsilon.$$

This says that $b_n \to a$.

i. Let $\{a_n\}$ be a nonincreasing sequence. Then $\{-a_n\}$ is a nondecreasing sequence. Then either $\{-a_n\}$ converges or else $-a_n \to +\infty$ by Theorem 13-2.4. If $-a_n \to b$, then $a_n \to -b$ and $\{a_n\}$ converges. If $-a_n \to +\infty$, then $a_n \to -\infty$.

2. a. First note that $0 < a_1 = \sqrt{2} < \sqrt{2 + \sqrt{2}} = a_2$. Next let n be a positive integer for which $0 < a_n < a_{n+1}$.
Then $2 + a_n < 2 + a_{n+1}$, $0 < \sqrt{2 + a_n} < \sqrt{2 + a_{n+1}}$. Hence, by the definition of the sequence, $0 < a_{n+1} < a_{n+2}$.
Now, from $a_1 < a_2$ it follows that $a_2 < a_3$, then that $a_3 < a_4$, etc.

c. From the hint, $a^2 = \lim_{n \to \infty} a_{n+1}^2 = \lim_{n \to \infty}(2 + a_n) = 2 + \lim_{n \to \infty} a_n = 2 + a.$

Hence, a must satisfy the equation $a^2 = a + 2$; that is,

$$a^2 - a - 2 = 0, (a - 2)(a + 1) = 0.$$

Since $a > 0$, the root $a = -1$ is extraneous. Thus, $a = 2$.

3. a. In (2) of Sec. 3-9 substitute $f(x) = 1/x$, $a = 1$, $b = 2$, $\Delta_k x = (b-a)/n = 1/n$, and $x_k^* = 1 + k\,\Delta_k x = 1 + k/n$. The result is

$$\int_1^2 \frac{dx}{x} = \lim_{n \to \infty} \sum_{k=1}^n \frac{1}{1 + k/n}\frac{1}{n} = \lim_{n \to \infty} \sum_{k=1}^n \frac{1}{n + k}$$

$$= \lim_{n \to \infty} \left[\frac{1}{n + 1} + \frac{1}{n + 2} + \cdots + \frac{1}{n + n}\right].$$

c. $\displaystyle \lim_{n \to \infty} \sum_{k=1}^n \frac{n}{n^2 + k^2} = \lim_{n \to \infty} \sum_{k=1}^n \frac{1}{1 + (k/n)^2}\frac{1}{n}$

$$= \int_0^1 \frac{1}{1 + x^2}dx = \tan^{-1} x \Big|_0^1 = \frac{\pi}{4}.$$

Sec. 13-3, p. 507.

6. a. 1.　**b.** 0.　**c.** 1.　**d.** Does not exist.

8. a. $\dfrac{D_x(x + \sin x)}{D_x(x - \sin 2x)} = \dfrac{1 + \cos x}{1 - 2\cos 2x}$, but this ratio does not approach a limit as $x \to \infty$. However,

$$\lim_{x \to \infty} \frac{x + \sin x}{x - \sin 2x} = \lim_{x \to \infty} \frac{1 + (\sin x)/x}{1 - 2\cos x\,(\sin x)/x} = \frac{1 + 0}{1 - 0} = 1.$$

Sec. 13-4, p. 510.

3. The derivative of the numerator and denominator with respect to h gives

$$\frac{-f'(c - h) + f'(c + h)}{2h}.$$

This may be written as

$$\frac{1}{2}\left[\frac{f'(c + h) - f'(c)}{h} + \frac{f'(c - h) - f'(c)}{-h}\right].$$

As $h \to 0$, this approaches $\frac{1}{2}[f''(c) + f''(c)] = f''(c)$.
Note that, if $f''(x)$ were given as continuous at $x = c$, then l'Hospital's Rules could have been used a second time.

Sec. 13-5, p. 514.

1. a. Assume $\sum (ca_n)$ converges. Then $(1/c) \sum (ca_n) = \sum a_n$ converges. This contradiction shows that $\sum (ca_n)$ diverges.

c. Let $\lim_{n \to \infty} a_n = a$. Since $a \neq 0$, $\sum a_n$ diverges, by Test 1. Also, $\lim (1/a_n)$
$= 1/a \neq 0$ and $\sum (1/a_n)$ also diverges by Test 1.
Example: $\sum 2^n$ diverges, but $\sum (1/2^n)$ converges.

5. a. $\lim_{n \to \infty} \dfrac{2n - 5}{2n} = 1 \neq 0$ and hence the series diverges, by Test 1.

c. $s_n = \sum_{k=1}^{\infty} [\ln k - \ln (k + 1)] = -\ln (n + 1)$, so $\lim_{n \to \infty} s_n$ does not exist.

Sec. 13-7, p. 523.

1. The series in b, e, and f converge, the others diverge.
2. a, b, c, f converge.　　**3.** a, c, e converge.
4. a, b, c, f, h converge.　**5.** a, b, d converge.

6. *a, c, d, e* are convergent.

8. a. Let $b_n = \dfrac{a_n}{1 + n^p a_n}$. If $a_n = 0$, then $b_n = 0$.

If $a_n \neq 0$, then $b_n = \dfrac{1}{(1/a_n) + n^p} < \dfrac{1}{n^p}$. Hence, $\Sigma\, b_n$ converges by the *P*-test.

b. $a_n = 1/n$, or $a_n = 1/n^2$.

Sec. 13-8, p. 527.

1. a. Abs. conv. by comparison test. **b.** Abs. conv. by ratio test.
c. Not abs. conv., since $\lim\limits_{n\to\infty} |a_n| = e^{-1} \neq 0$.

d. Not abs. conv., since $|a_{n+1}/a_n| \to e > 1$.

2. a. Abs. conv. **b.** Cond. conv. **c.** Div. **d.** Cond. conv. **e.** Cond. conv.

3. b. $\displaystyle\sum_{n=1}^{\infty} \frac{1}{n^2} = \sum_{n=1}^{\infty} \frac{1}{(2n-1)^2} + \sum_{n=1}^{\infty} \frac{1}{(2n)^2}$ (odd terms + even terms)

$$= \sum_{n=1}^{\infty} \frac{1}{(2n-1)^2} + \frac{1}{4} \sum_{n=1}^{\infty} \frac{1}{n^2}, \text{ so that}$$

$$\sum_{n=1}^{\infty} \frac{1}{(2n-1)^2} = \frac{3}{4} \sum_{n=1}^{\infty} \frac{1}{n^2}.$$

Sec. 13-11, p. 539.

3. a. $\dfrac{1}{\sqrt{2}}\left[1 - \left(x - \dfrac{\pi}{4}\right) - \dfrac{1}{2!}\left(x - \dfrac{\pi}{4}\right)^2 + \dfrac{1}{3!}\left(x - \dfrac{\pi}{4}\right)^3 + \dfrac{1}{4!}\left(x - \dfrac{\pi}{4}\right)^4 \right]$

$$- \frac{1}{5!} \sin\xi \left(x - \frac{\pi}{4}\right)^5.$$

b. $x + \dfrac{x^3}{3!} + \dfrac{\xi(6\xi^2 + 9)}{(1 - \xi^2)^{7/2}} \dfrac{x^4}{4!}.$

c. $1 + 2\left(x - \dfrac{\pi}{4}\right) + \dfrac{4}{2!}\left(x - \dfrac{\pi}{4}\right)^2 + \dfrac{16}{3!}\left(x - \dfrac{\pi}{4}\right)^3$

$$+ 2\sec^2\xi \tan\xi\,(2 + 3\tan^2\xi)\frac{1}{4!}\left(x - \frac{\pi}{4}\right)^4.$$

d. $(x - 1) - \dfrac{(x-1)^2}{2} + \dfrac{(x-1)^3}{3} - \cdots + \dfrac{(-1)^n}{n-1}(x - 1)^{n-1}$

$$+ \frac{(-1)^{n+1}}{n} \frac{1}{\xi_n^n}(x - 1)^n.$$

4. $|R_n| = \dfrac{1}{n} \dfrac{1}{\xi^n}(1.2 - 1)^n < \dfrac{1}{n}(0.2)^n$ since $1 < \xi < 1.2$.

$\frac{1}{4}(0.2)^4 = \frac{1}{4}(0.0016) = 0.0004 < 5 \times 10^{-4}.$

$\ln(1.2) = (0.2) - \frac{1}{2}(0.2)^2 + \frac{1}{3}(0.2)^3 \pm 5 \times 10^{-4}.$

5. $\sin 255° = -\cos 15°$

$$= -\left[1 - \frac{1}{2}\left(\frac{\pi}{12}\right)^2 + \frac{1}{4!}\left(\frac{\pi}{12}\right)^4 - \frac{1}{6!}\left(\frac{\pi}{12}\right)^6 \right] \pm 5 \times 10^{-8}.$$

Sec. 13-14, p. 551.

3. a. $\displaystyle\int_0^x e^{-t^2} dt = \int_0^x \sum_{n=0}^{\infty} \frac{(-1)^n}{n!} t^{2n}\, dt = \sum_{n=0}^{\infty} \frac{(-1)^n}{(2n+1)n!} x^{2n+1}.$

b. $\displaystyle\sum_{n=0}^{\infty} \frac{(-1)^n}{(4n+3)(2n+1)!} x^{4n+3}.$ **c.** $\displaystyle\sum_{n=0}^{\infty} \frac{(-1)^n}{(2n+1)(2n+1)!} x^{2n+1}.$

d. $\sum_{n=1}^{\infty} \dfrac{(-1)^{n+1}}{2(2n)!} x^{2n}.$

5. a. In (7) of Sec. 13-13, replace n by $n+1$ and start the summation with $n=0$:

$$(1+x)^{1/2} = 1 + \sum_{n=0}^{\infty} \frac{1}{(n+1)!}\left(\frac{1}{2}\right)\left(\frac{1}{2}-1\right)\left(\frac{1}{2}-2\right)\cdots\left(\frac{1}{2}-n\right)x^{n+1}$$

$$= 1 + \sum_{n=0}^{\infty} \frac{(-1)^n}{2^{n+1}} \frac{1\cdot 3\cdot 5\cdots(2n-1)}{(n+1)!} x^{n+1}$$

$$= 1 + \sum_{n=0}^{\infty} \frac{(-1)^n}{2^{n+1}} \frac{1\cdot 2\cdot 3\cdot 4\cdot 5\cdots(2n-1)(2n)}{2\cdot 4\cdots(2n)(n+1)!} x^{n+1}$$

$$= 1 + \sum_{n=0}^{\infty} \frac{(-1)^n}{2^{n+1}} \frac{(2n)!}{2^n n!n!(n+1)} x^{n+1}$$

$$= 1 + \frac{x}{2}\sum_{n=0}^{\infty} \frac{(-1)^n}{2^{2n}(n+1)}\binom{2n}{n} x^n.$$

Sec. 13-15, p. 558.

1. a. $\dfrac{x^3}{3} - \dfrac{x^7}{7(3!)} + \dfrac{x^{11}}{11(5!)}\Big|_0^1.$ **b.** $2\left[\dfrac{1}{3} - \dfrac{1}{5(3!)} + \dfrac{1}{7(5!)}\right].$

c. $\dfrac{1}{2} + \dfrac{1}{3}\left(\dfrac{1}{2}\right)^3 + \dfrac{1}{5(2!)}\left(\dfrac{1}{2}\right)^5 + \dfrac{1}{7(3!)}\left(\dfrac{1}{2}\right)^7,$ since $e^{\xi} < e^{1/4} < 1.3.$

d. $\dfrac{1}{2} - \dfrac{1}{3}\left(\dfrac{1}{2}\right)^3 + \dfrac{1}{5(2!)}\left(\dfrac{1}{2}\right)^5 - \dfrac{1}{7(3!)}\left(\dfrac{1}{2}\right)^7.$

e. $x + \dfrac{1}{8}x^4 - \dfrac{1}{56}x^7 + \dfrac{1}{160}x^{10}\Big|_0^{1/2}.$ **f.** $x + \dfrac{1}{8}x^4 + \dfrac{3}{56}x^7 + \dfrac{5}{160}x^{10}\Big|_0^{1/2}.$

g. $-\ln 2 + \left[\sum_{n=1}^{7} \dfrac{x^n}{n(n!)}\right]_{1/2}^1.$ **h.** $e^x - \dfrac{e^{3x}}{3(3!)} + \dfrac{e^{5x}}{5(5!)} - \dfrac{e^{7x}}{7(7!)} + \dfrac{e^{9x}}{9(9!)} - \dfrac{e^{11x}}{11(11!)}\Big|_0^1.$

Sec. 13-17, p. 570.

1. a. No extrema or saddle points.   **b.** Min. 2 at $(0,0).$ **c.** $(0,0,2)$ saddle point.
     d. Min. 2 at $(-1,-1).$ **e.** Min. 0 at any point on the line $x+y=0, z=0.$
     f, g, h. Saddle point at $(0,0,0).$ **i.** Translation of **h.**   **j.** Saddle point $(0,0,0).$
     k. Saddle point $(1,1,1),$ max. 5 at $(-1,1).$
     l. Saddle point $(0,0,0),$ max. 1 at $(-1,1).$
2. a. $(6,6,6).$ **b.** 216.   **c.** 108.
3. b. 1 at $(0,0,1).$ **c.** 1 at $(1,0,0).$ The lines $x=1$ and $y=-3$ form the bounda-
     ry. There is another relative minimum at $(0,-3,0).$
4. -9 at $\left(-\frac{3}{4},0\right),$ 46 at $\left(\frac{1}{2}, \pm\frac{1}{2}\sqrt{3}\right);$ -8 at $(-1,0).$

Sec. 14-1, p. 577.

1. a. $\ln|y| = x + \ln|x-1| + c.$ **c.** $x - \ln|x+1| = y + \ln|y| + c.$
     e. $e^x = -e^{-y}(y+1) + c.$ **g.** $x - \ln|1+x| + \tan\left(\frac{1}{2}y\right) = c.$
     i. $\left(\frac{2}{3}\right)^x - \left(\frac{3}{2}\right)^y = c.$
2. a. $xy - \frac{1}{3}x^3 + \frac{1}{3}y^3 = c.$ **c.** $\sin x + x\sin y = c.$ **e.** $e^x e^y + \frac{1}{2}y^2 = c.$
     g. $\cos 3t \sin 2\theta = c.$
3. a. $y = 2x^2/(1+2x-2x^2).$ **c.** $y^2 = 2(x-x^{-1}-1).$
     e. $-y\cos y + \sin y = -1/x + \ln|x| + \pi - 1.$

Sec. 14-2, p. 581.

1. **a.** $x^2 = -16(y - 4)$, $x > 0$. **b.** $x^2 = -4(y - 1)$, $x < 0$.
 c. $x^2 = -4(y - 1)$, $x > 0$.
2. Since $dy = (du - adx)/b$, the equation becomes

$$\frac{1}{b}du - \frac{a}{b}dx = f(u)\, dx, \quad [a + bf(u)]\, dx = du,$$

$$dx = \frac{1}{a + bf(u)}\, du, \quad x = \int \frac{du}{a + bf(u)} + c.$$

3. **a.** $x = y + \ln|x + y + 1| + c$. **b.** $y = x + (1 - ce^{2x})/(1 + ce^{2x})$.
 c. $x = \tan\frac{1}{2}(x + y) + c$. **d.** $e^x + e^y = ce^{2x}$, $c > 0$.
 e. $5x + 10y + 3\ln|10x - 5y + 4| = c$.
 f. Either $y = 2x + 2$ or $y = \frac{1}{2}x + c$.
4. **a.** $y^3 = x^3(\ln|x| + c)$. **b.** $2y^3 = cx^{-3} - x^3$. **c.** $x^4 + 4xy^3 = c$.
 d. $\csc(y/x) - \cot(y/x) = cx$. **e.** $x + y + xe^{y/x}\ln|cx| = 0$.

Sec. 14-3, p. 585.

1. **a.** $y = cx$. **b.** $y = cx^2$. **e.** $3x = y(c - x^3)$.
 g. $x^4 + 2x^2y^{-2} = c$. [Integrating factor of form $x^m y^n$.]
 i. $2xy = x^2 + c$. **k.** $xy = ce^x$. **m.** $x^2 + y^2 = ce^{2x}$, $c > 0$.
2. **a.** $2x^2y^2\ln|cy| = 1$. **c.** $2xy - (x/y)^2 = c$. **e.** $(x/y) + \frac{1}{3}(xy)^3 = c$.
3. **a.** $x^3 + 2y = cxy^2$. **c.** $x^3y^6 - y^9 = c$.

Sec. 14-4, p. 588.

1. **a.** $y = e^{-x} + ce^{-2x}$. **c.** $y = c\csc x - \cot x$. **e.** $xy = \cos x + c$.
2. **a.** $(du/dv) + 2u = 8v$, $u = 4v - 2 + ce^{-2v}$. **c.** $x = (y^2 + c)e^{-3y} - 2$.
 e. $\rho = c\csc\theta - \cot\theta$.
3. **a.** $y = \frac{1}{2}x^{-1} + 6x^{-3}$. **c.** $y = -1 + \sin x + e^{-\sin x}$.
4. **a.** $x^2 + x^2y^2 = cy^2$. **c.** $y^2 = x^2 + x + \frac{5}{2} + ce^{2x}$.

Sec. 14-5, p. 594.

1. **a.** On a (t, y)-coordinate system, the graph of $y = 30 - 6(t + s)e^{-0.2t}$ passes
 through the origin and $y' = 1.2te^{-0.2t}$ is positive for $t > 0$. Thus, the graph
 is above the t-axis for $t > 0$.
2. **a.** $x = 30e^{-(0.2)20} = 0.55$ approximately.
 c. $t = 5$. Concentration approximately 1.1 lb/gal.
3. $x = \dfrac{W}{bg}\left(a - \dfrac{W}{b}\right)(1 - e^{-bgt/W}) + \dfrac{W}{b}t$.
5. With A the quantity (in the same units used for A_0), then at time t years
 $$dA/dt = kA; \quad A = A_0 \text{ when } t = 0, \quad A = 0.995A_0 \text{ when } t = 15.$$
 a. 28.33%. **b.** Half-life close to 2050 years. **c.** Approximately 4765 years.
8. **a.** $x = 15(1 + e^{-0.4t})$, $y = 15(1 - e^{-0.4t})$. **b.** Approximately 2.75 min.
9. In Fig. 14-5.4 use $P(\rho, \theta)$, instead of $P(x, y)$, but keep all other notation. Recall
 from Sec. 9-11 that

$$d\rho/d\theta = \rho\cot(\tau - \theta),$$

with τ and θ as illustrated in Fig. 9-11.1. By comparing the meanings of angles in Fig. 9-11.1 and Fig. 14-5.4, see that

$$\theta = \pi - 2\alpha \text{ and } \tau = \pi - \alpha.$$

Use these facts to see that the differential equation of the optical problem is

$$d\rho/d\theta = \rho \tan \tfrac{1}{2}\theta.$$

Now show that the solution may be put in the form $\rho = c/(1 + \cos \theta)$, which is a polar equation of a parabola [see (1) of Sec. 9-10].

Sec. 14-6, p. 601.

1. a. $-6 \sin x + 3 \cos x.$ **c.** $(1 - 2x)e^x.$ **e.** $(2 - x^2)e^x.$ **g.** $(1 - x^2)e^x.$
   i. $-4/x^2 - 6/x.$
2. a. $D(D - 2x)f(x) = f''(x) - 2xf'(x) - 2f(x), (D - 2x)Df(x) = f''(x) - 2xf'(x).$
   c. $f''(x) + f'(x) \sin x + f(x) \cos x, f''(x) + f'(x) \sin x.$
3. a. $y = 0.$ **c.** $y = ce^{-x}.$
4. a. $y = \tfrac{1}{3}e^x + c_1 e^{x/2} + c_2 e^{-2x}.$ **c.** $y = (2/13)(\tfrac{3}{2} \sin x - \cos x) + c_1 + c_2 e^{-3x/2}.$
5. a. $y = \tfrac{1}{2}xe^x + c_1 e^x + c_2 e^{2x} + c_3 e^{3x}.$

Sec. 14-7, p. 605.

1. In case $r_1 \neq r_2$, then $Q_1 = e^{r_1 x}, Q_2 = e^{r_2 x}$, and
$$Q_1 Q_2' - Q_2 Q_1' = e^{r_1 x} r_2 e^{r_2 x} - e^{r_2 x} r_1 e^{r_1 x}$$
$$= (r_2 - r_1)e^{r_1 x} e^{r_2 x} \neq 0, \text{ since } r_1 \neq r_2.$$
In case $r_1 = r_2$, then $Q_1 = e^{rx}, Q_2 = xe^{rx}$, and
$$Q_1 Q_2' - Q_2 Q_1' = e^{rx}(xre^{rx} + e^{rx}) - xe^{rx} re^{rx} = e^{2rx} \neq 0.$$
2. a. $y = x \sin x + \cos x \ln |\cos x| + c_1 \cos x + c_2 \sin x.$
   c. $y = -2 + \sin x \ln |\sec x + \tan x| + c_1 \cos x + c_2 \sin x.$
3. a. $y = (c_1 + c_2 x - \ln |x|)e^{-2x}.$
   c. $y = [-x + \ln (e^x + 1)](e^x + e^{2x}) + c_1 e^x + c_2 e^{2x}.$

Sec. 14-9, p. 610.

1. Let $L = D^2 - 2aD + a^2 + b^2$. It is then known that
$L(e^{ax} \cos bx) = L(e^{ax} \sin bx) = 0.$
With u a twice-differentiable function of x, check that
$$L(xu) = (xu'' + 2u') - 2a(xu' + u) + (a^2 + b^2)xu$$
$$= x[u'' - 2au' + (a^2 + b^2)u] + 2u' - 2au$$
$$= xL(u) + 2(D - a)u.$$
Thus, $L(xe^{ax} \cos bx) = xL(e^{ax} \cos bx) + 2(D - a)e^{ax} \cos bx$
$$= x \cdot 0 - 2be^{ax} \sin bx.$$
Hence, $L^2(xe^{ax} \cos bx) = L(-2be^{ax} \sin bx)$
$$= -2bL(e^{ax} \sin bx) = 0.$$
Similarly, $L^2(xe^{ax} \sin bx) = 0.$
2. In each case, $y_{II} = c_1 e^{-x} + c_2 e^{3x}.$
   a. $y_P = \tfrac{7}{3} - x.$ **c.** $y_P = -\tfrac{3}{4}xe^{-x}.$ **e.** $y_P = -\tfrac{1}{4}e^x.$
3. In each case $y_{II} = c_1 e^x + c_2 e^{2x}.$
   b. $y_P = -\tfrac{1}{4}(\cos 2x + 3 \sin 2x).$ **d.** Sum of a, b, and c.
   f. $y_P = (1/52)e^{-x}(\cos 2x - 5 \sin 2x).$

4. a. $y = \frac{1}{2}e^{-x} + 3x - (12/5) + e^{-2x}(c_1 \cos x + c_2 \sin x)$.

c. $y = e^x[(c_1 + \frac{1}{2}x)\cos x + (c_2 + x)\sin x]$.

5. a. $y = \sin x + \cos x + c_1 e^{2x} + c_2 e^{3x}$.

Sec. 14-10, p. 614.

1. a. $y = \dfrac{1}{a} \ln \left| \dfrac{x+a}{x-a} \right| + b$ or $y = -\dfrac{2}{a} \tan^{-1} \dfrac{x}{a} + b$, where $\pm\frac{1}{2}a^2$ was used as the additive constant of the first integration.

b. $y = \begin{cases} -x - \dfrac{1}{a}\ln\left|\dfrac{ax-1}{ax+1}\right| + b \ \text{if} \ \dfrac{u-1}{u+1} = (ax)^2 \\[2mm] -x + \dfrac{2}{a}\tan^{-1}(ax) + b \ \text{if} \ \dfrac{u-1}{u+1} = -(ax)^2. \end{cases}$

c. $y = -x + c_1 \tan^{-1} x + c_2$.

d. $x = \frac{1}{3}t^3 - 2t + c_1 \int e^{-(1/2)t^2}\, dt + c_2$. The integral here is not expressible in closed form using only elementary functions. Some method of approximating the integral would be used in a practical problem in which a side condition were given.

2. a. $y = c$ and in addition, when the result of the first integration is expressed as $u = -(y^2 + a)/2$,

$$x = -\frac{2}{y} + b \ \text{if} \ a = 0, \quad x = \frac{-2}{\sqrt{a}} \tan^{-1} \frac{y}{\sqrt{a}} + b \ \text{if} \ a > 0,$$

$$y = \frac{1}{\sqrt{-a}} \ln \left| \frac{y + \sqrt{-a}}{y - \sqrt{-a}} \right| + b \ \text{if} \ a < 0.$$

b. $\pm x = (1/a) \ln |ay + \sqrt{a^2 y^2 - 1}| + b$.

c. $y = c$ or $x = \ln |y^2 + a| + b$, which may be put in the form $y = c_1 + c_2 e^x$.

d. $y = c$ or $x = (1/a) \ln |y/(y+a)| + b$, which also has the form $y = c_1 c_2 e^{c_1 x}/(1 - c_2 e^{c_1 x})$.

3. $y = (1/250)x^2 + 20$ [Hint: Use H, h, and v as in Example 2, but note that the downward force is $-\vec{j}(wx)$, where w is the weight per foot of the roadbed.]

Index